श्री BalaJi

Problems in

INORGANIC CHEMISTRY

for JEE

Main & Advanced

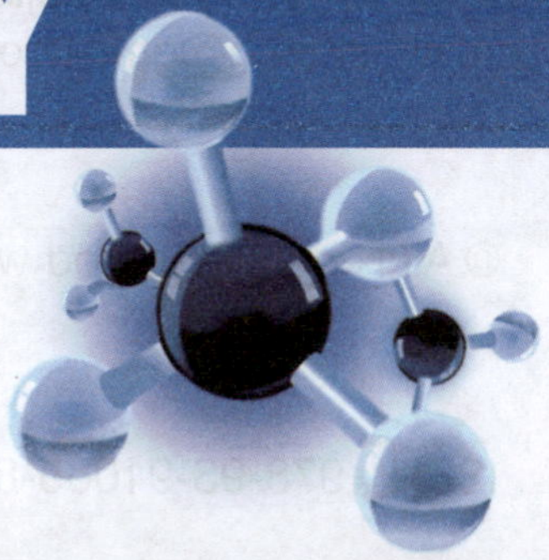

Free Worth Rs. 200/-

PYQ (Previous Year Questions)

INORGANIC CHEMISTRY

with Complete Solutions

[redacted]

by:

V.K. Jaiswal

Director

Vibrant Academy India (P) Ltd.

KOTA

SHRI BALAJI PUBLICATIONS

(EDUCATIONAL PUBLISHERS & DISTRIBUTORS)

AN ISO 9001-2008 CERTIFIED ORGANIZATION

Muzaffarnagar (U.P.) - 251001

Published by:
SHRI BALAJI PUBLICATIONS
(EDUCATIONAL PUBLISHERS & DISTRIBUTORS)
6, Gulshan Vihar, Gali No. 1,
Opp. Mahalaxmi Enclave,
Jansath Road, Muzaffarnagar (U.P.)
Phone : 0131-2660440 (O),
website : www.shribalajibooks.com
email : sbjpub@gmail.com

ISBN : 978-93-91065-88-1

First edition : 2008
Seventeenth edition : 2024

Price : [redacted]

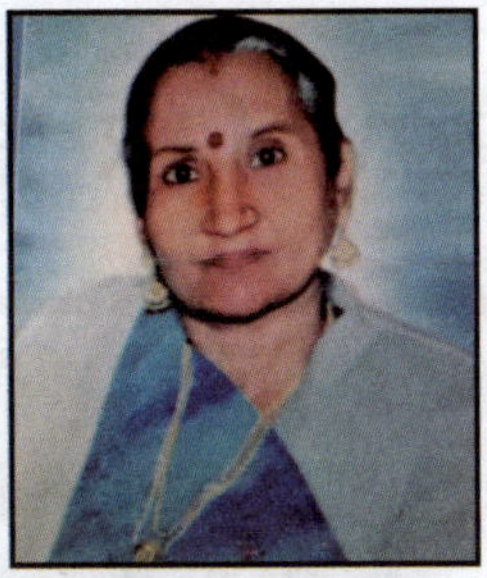

Dedicated to

my

Beloved Mother

for

their blessings and support

GROW GREEN

Save Nature

Preface

It is a matter of great pleasure for me to present the fully revised Seventeenth edition of **"Problems in Inorganic Chemistry"** for JEE aspirants. This book is an outcome of the experience gained during my interaction with the students going to appear in JEE. The hours spent with them raised an idea to present the concepts of Inorganic Chemistry through problematic approach. The major objective to write this book is to provide relevant part of concepts of this wide subject of Inorganic Chemistry. The problems are framed in such a manner that they touch the required depth.

Each chapter in this book is divided into three levels of problems. The level of problems given in this book is essentially required for JEE aspirants. The objective behind this division is that students may revise the different types of problems being asked in JEE in an organised and progressive way. The detail of each level are as under :

LEVEL-1: Problems based on basic concepts are useful for IIT-JEE (Mains) Exam.

LEVEL-2: Challenging problems based on twists and wide applications of topics are useful for IIT-JEE (Advanced) Exam.

LEVEL-3: Problems based on Comprehensions, Problems with One or More than one Correct Option, Matching Type Problems, Assertion – Reason Type Problems and Subjective Problems (Integer Type Problems) to make the students familiar with current IIT-JEE Pattern.

In the last, hints and solution have also been provided wherever necessary, to save precious time of students.

I hope that my effort will cater to the needs of JEE aspirants and they will enjoy the topics covered in this book. I would feel rewarded if they achieve their goal with the help of this book.

All attempts have been made to make it free from errors. In the last constructive criticism and valuable suggestion from the readers are most welcome to make this effort more useful.

V.K. Jaiswal
vimalj3@gmail.com

Acknowledgement

I wish to acknowledge my indebtedness to Mr. Nitin Jain, Mr. N.K. Sethia, Mr. M.S. Chouhan, Mr. N. Avasthi, Mr. Vikas Gupta and Mr. Pankaj Joshi for their enthusiastic support.

I would like to thank Mr. Dhirendra Singh, Mr. Nitesh Tiwari, Mr. Jitesh Pareek, Madam Tanmeet Sahany, Mr. Kumar Mannu and Dr. Prabhat Kumar for their comments and valuable suggestions towards the improvement of this book.

Finally, this part of book will remain incomplete without co-operation of co-author Mrs. Anjali Jaiswal, whose time was spent during this job. I admire for her patience, understanding and support.

I also pay my sincere thanks to all the esteemed members of **M/s Shri Balaji Publications** in bringing out this book in such a nice form.

There are undoubtedly many other who are learning their indelible mark on this book. Thanks to every one for their assistance.

V.K. Jaiswal

Contents

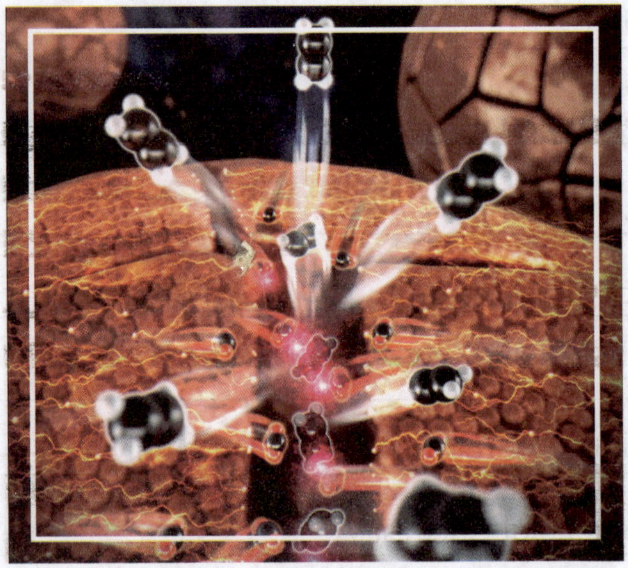

Inorganic Chemistry

1

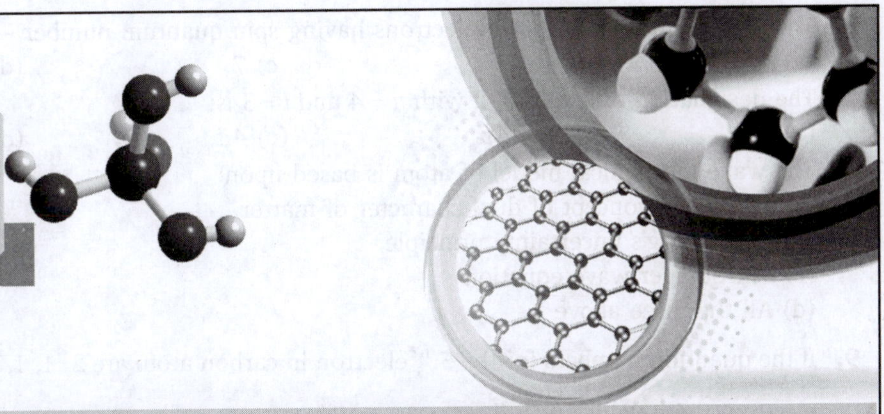

QUANTUM NUMBERS AND PERIODIC PROPERTIES

Part A

QUANTUM NUMBER

Level 1

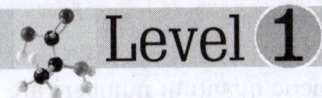

1. Which of the following set of quantum number is allowed ?

(a) $n = 2, l = 1, m = 0, s = +1/2$ (b) $n = 2, l = 2, m = -1, s = -1/2$

(c) $n = 3, l = 3, m = 1, s = +1/2$ (d) $n = 2, l = 1, m = 0, s = 0$

2. The lowest orbit (shell) having g sub-shell is:

(a) 4 (b) 5 (c) 6 (d) 7

3. For total number of m, the particular value of l is given by:

(a) $l + 1$ (b) $\frac{m+1}{2}$ (c) $\frac{m-1}{2}$ (d) $\frac{2m+1}{2}$

4. The wave function ψ in the Schrodinger wave equation represents :

(a) Probability of the electron (b) Amplitude of the electron wave

(c) Frequency of the electron wave (d) Speed of the electron wave

5. For an electron if the uncertainty in velocity is Δv, the uncertainty in its position Δx is given by:

(a) $\frac{hm}{4\pi\Delta v}$ (b) $\frac{4\pi}{hm\Delta v}$

(c) $\frac{h}{4\pi m\Delta v}$ (d) $\frac{4\pi m}{h\Delta v}$

6. The maximum number of $4f$-electrons having spin quantum number $-1/2$ is:
(a) 4 (b) 5 (c) 7 (d) 14

7. The designation of a sub-shell with $n = 4$ and $l = 3$ is:
(a) $4s$ (b) $4p$ (c) $4d$ (d) $4f$

8. The wave mechanical model of atom is based upon:
(a) de Broglie concept of dual character of matter
(b) Heisenberg's uncertainty principle
(c) Schrodinger wave equation
(d) All the three above

9. If the quantum numbers for the 5th electron in carbon atom are 2, 1, 1, $+\frac{1}{2}$, then for the 6th electron, these values would be:
(a) 2, 1, 0, $-\frac{1}{2}$ (b) 2, 0, 1, $+\frac{1}{2}$
(c) 2, 1, 1, $-\frac{1}{2}$ (d) 2, 1, −1, $+\frac{1}{2}$

10. The number of electrons having $m = -1$, in phosphorous atom is:
(a) 3 (b) 4 (c) 6 (d) 9

11. The set of quantum numbers for the 19th electron in Cr atom is:
(a) $n = 4, l = 0, m = 0, s = +\frac{1}{2}$ or $-\frac{1}{2}$ (b) $n = 3, l = 2, m = 1, s = +\frac{1}{2}$ or $-\frac{1}{2}$
(c) $n = 3, l = 2, m = -1, s = +\frac{1}{2}$ or $-\frac{1}{2}$ (d) $n = 4, l = 1, m = 0, s = +\frac{1}{2}$ or $-\frac{1}{2}$

12. The orbital angular momentum of an electron in $2s$ orbital is:
(a) $+\frac{1}{2} \cdot \frac{h}{2\pi}$ (b) Zero (c) $\frac{h}{2\pi}$ (d) $\sqrt{2}\frac{h}{2\pi}$

13. Principal, azimuthal and magnetic quantum numbers are respectively related to:
(a) size, orientation and shape (b) size, shape and orientation
(c) shape, size and orientation (d) none of these

14. The total number of subshells in N shell is:
(a) 3 (b) 4 (c) 5 (d) 7

15. Match List I with List II and select the correct answer:

List I	List II
(A) Number of values of (l) for an energy level	(1) 0, 1, 2,..........(n − 1)
(B) Actual values of (l) for an energy level	(2) $+l$, ...+2, +1, 0, −1, −2,......... $-l$
(C) Number of 'm' values for a particular type of orbital	(3) ($2l$ + 1)
(D) Actual values of 'm' for a particular type of orbital	(4) n

	A	B	C	D		A	B	C	D
(a)	4	1	2	3	(b)	4	1	3	2
(c)	1	4	2	3	(d)	1	4	3	2

16. The uncertainty principle and the concept of wave nature of matter was proposed by ______ and ______ respectively.
(a) Heisenberg, de Broglie (b) de Broglie, Heisenberg
(c) Heisenberg, Planck (d) Planck, Heisenberg

17. The angular momentum of an electron in an orbital is given as:
(a) $L = n\left(\frac{h}{2\pi}\right)$ (b) $L = l\left(\frac{h}{2\pi}\right)$ (c) $L = \sqrt{l(l+1)}\frac{h}{2\pi}$ (d) $L = m\left(\frac{h}{2\pi}\right)$

18. Which set of quantum numbers defines one electrons in an atomic orbitals with $n = 2$ and $l = 0$?
(a) $n = 2, l = 0, m_l = 1, m_s = +1$ (b) $n = 2, l = 0, m_l = 1, m_s = +1/2$
(c) $n = 2, l = 0, m_l = 0, m_s = +1/2$ (d) $n = 2, l = 0, m_l = 0, m_s = +1$

19. The probability of finding the electron (ψ^2) in p_x orbitals is zero:
(a) At two opposite sides of the nucleus along *x*-axis
(b) At the nucleus
(c) Around the nucleus
(d) None of these

20. Which of the following can be the quantum number for an orbital?
(a) $n = 4, l = 4, m = 3$ (b) $n = 2, l = 3, m = 1$
(c) $n = 3, l = 2, m = -1$ (d) $n = 3, l = 0, m = -3$

21. For a principal quantum number *n*, how many atomic orbitals are possible?
(a) n (b) $2n$ (c) $n + 1$ (d) n^2

22. Two electrons occupying the same orbital are distinguished by:
(a) Magnetic quantum number (b) Azimuthal quantum number
(c) Spin quantum number (d) Principal quantum number

23. How many electrons can fit in the orbital for which $n = 3$ and $l = 1$?
(a) 2 (b) 6 (c) 10 (d) 14

24. What is the maximum number of orbitals that can be identified with the following quantum number $n = 3, l = 1, m = 0$?
(a) 1 (b) 2 (c) 3 (d) 4

25. Choose the correct set of quantum number of last electron of Ag atom ($Z = 47$):
(a) $4, 1, 0, +\frac{1}{2}$ (b) $4, 2, -3, +\frac{1}{2}$ (c) $4, 2, -2, -\frac{1}{2}$ (d) None of these

26. Find the sum of maximum number of electrons having +1 and –1 value of '*m*' in Ca atom.
(a) 6 (b) 8 (c) 10 (d) 12

27. Find the correct set of quantum numbers for 30th electron entered into As (At. No. 33).

	n	*l*	*m*	*s*		*n*	*l*	*m*	*s*
(a)	4	1	0	$-\frac{1}{2}$	(b)	4	1	1	$+\frac{1}{2}$
(c)	3	2	–1	$+\frac{1}{2}$	(d)	4	0	0	$-\frac{1}{2}$

28. Which of the following quantum number gives the shape of atomic orbital of sub-shell ?
(a) n (b) l (c) m (d) s

Level 2

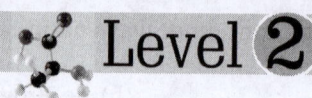

1. Electrons are filled in degenerate orbitals according to:
(a) $n + l$ rule (b) Hund's rule
(c) Pauli's exclusion principle (d) None of these

2. The number of unpaired electrons present in Cr^{2+}, Fe^{2+}, Co^{2+} and Ni^{2+} cations are respectively:
(a) 4, 2, 1 and 0 (b) 2, 4, 1 and 0
(c) 4, 4, 3 and 2 (d) 4, 2, 0 and 1

3. The correct set of quantum numbers for the unpaired electron of Cl-atom is:
(a) $2, 0, 0, +\frac{1}{2}$ (b) $2, 1, -1, +\frac{1}{2}$
(c) $3, 1, 1, \frac{1}{2}$ (d) $3, 0, 0, \pm\frac{1}{2}$

4. Which of the following sets of quantum numbers is not allowed ?
(a) $n = 3, l = 2, m = 0, s = -\frac{1}{2}$ (b) $n = 3, l = 2, m = -2, s = -\frac{1}{2}$
(c) $n = 3, l = 3, m = -3, s = -\frac{1}{2}$ (d) $n = 3, l = 0, m = 0, s = -\frac{1}{2}$

5. Which of the following configuration is not correct according to Hund's rule?
(a) [↑↓] [↑↓ | ↑ | ↑] (b) [↑↓] [↑ | ↑ |]
(c) [↑↓] [↑↓ | ↑↓ |] (d) [↑↓] [↑ | ↑ | ↑]

6. The energy of electron in Li^{2+} species depends on:
(a) principal quantum number
(b) principal and azimuthal quantum numbers
(c) principal, azimuthal and magnetic quantum numbers
(d) principal, azimuthal, magnetic and spin quantum numbers

7. Which of the following configuration has highest magnetic moment ?
(a) d^4 (b) d^2 (c) d^5 (d) d^7

8. The total spin of $3d^7$ electron in an atom is:
(a) 1/2 (b) 3/2 (c) 5/2 (d) 7/2

9. In the presence of magnetic field, *d*-sub-shell is:
(a) 5-fold non-degenerate (b) 3-fold non-degenerate
(c) 7-fold non-degenerate (d) degenerate

10. The number of *d*-electrons in Fe^{2+} $(Z = 26)$ is not equal to:
(a) *p*-electrons in Ne $(Z = 10)$ (b) *s*-electrons in Mg $(Z = 12)$
(c) *d*-electrons in Fe $(Z = 26)$ (d) *p*-electrons in Cl $(Z = 17)$

11. Which of the following arrangement of electrons is most likely to be unstable ?

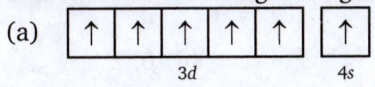

(a) 3d: [↑ | ↑ | ↑ | ↑ | ↑] 4s: [↑] (b) 3d: [↑↓ | ↑ | ↑ | ↑ | ↑] 4s: [↑]

(c) 3d: [↓ | ↓ | ↓ | ↓ | ↓] 4s: [↓] (d) 3d: [↑ | ↑ | ↑ | ↑ | ↑] 4s: [↑↓]

12. If Hund's rule is not followed, (maximum paired electron) magnetic moment of Fe^{2+}, Mn^{+}, and Cr, all having 24 electrons will be in the order of:

(a) $Fe^{2+} < Mn^{+} < Cr$ (b) $Fe^{2+} = Cr < Mn^{+}$

(c) $Fe^{2+} = Mn^{+} < Cr$ (d) $Mn^{+} = Cr < Fe^{2+}$

13. If there are three possible values (−1/2, 0, +1/2) for the spin quantum number '*s*', then electronic configuration of K (19) will be:

(a) $1s^3 2s^3 2p^9 3s^3 3p^1$ (b) $1s^2 2s^2 2p^6 3s^2 3p^6 4s^1$

(c) $1s^2 2s^2 2p^9 3p^4$ (d) none is correct

14. Which of the following pair of atomic numbers of elements, is showing same magnetic behaviour ?

(a) 33, 36 (b) 10, 12 (c) 28, 30 (d) 17, 18

15. Total number of orbitals in a shell having principal quantum number *n* is:

(a) $2n$ (b) n^2 (c) $2n^2$ (d) $(n+1)$

16. The maximum number of electrons having same value of spin quantum number in any subshell is:

(a) $l+1$ (b) $2l+1$ (c) $2(2l+1)$ (d) $\sqrt{l(l+1)}$

17. Find correct set of quantum numbers of n, l, m_l, m_s for last electron of element (atomic number 89).

(a) $4, 3, 0, +\frac{1}{2}$ (b) $5, 3, 0, +\frac{1}{2}$ (c) $6, 2, 0, +\frac{1}{2}$ (d) $7, 0, 0, +\frac{1}{2}$

18. For a *d*-electron, the orbital angular momentum is:

(a) $\frac{h}{2\pi}\sqrt{6}$ (b) $\frac{h}{2\pi}\sqrt{2}$ (c) $\frac{h}{2\pi}$ (d) $\frac{h}{2\pi}\sqrt{12}$

19. Which of the following statements is not correct for an electron that has the quantum numbers $n = 4$ and $m = 2$?

(a) The electron may have the quantum number $s = +1/2$

(b) The electron may have the quantum number $l = 2$

(c) The electron may have the quantum number $l = 3$

(d) The electron may have the quantum number $l = 0, 1, 2, 3$

20. The correct set of four quantum numbers for the valence electron of rubidium ($Z = 37$) is:

(a) $n = 5, l = 0, m = 0, s = +1/2$ (b) $n = 5, l = 1, m = 0, s = +1/2$

(c) $n = 5, l = 1, m = 1, s = +1/2$ (d) $n = 6, l = 0, m = 0, s = +1/2$

21. Magnetic moment of V ($Z = 23$), Cr ($Z = 24$) and Mn ($Z = 25$) and x, y and z respectively. Then:

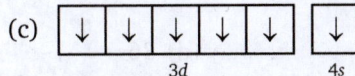

(a) $x = y = z$ (b) $x < y < z$ (c) $x < z < y$ (d) $z < y < x$

22. Magnetic moment of M^{x+} $(Z = 26)$ is $\sqrt{24}$ B.M. Hence the number of unpaired electrons and value of x respectively are:
(a) 4, 2 (b) 2, 4 (c) 3, 1 (d) 0, 2

23. If each orbital can hold a maximum of 3 electrons, number of elements in fourth period of periodic table is:
(a) 48 (b) 54 (c) 27 (d) 36

24. If aufbau rule is not followed, 19th electron in Fe $(Z = 26)$ will have:
(a) $n = 3, l = 0$ (b) $n = 3, l = 1$
(c) $n = 3, l = 2$ (d) $n = 4, l = 0$

25. Consider these ions : (1) Ni^{2+} (2) Co^{2+} (3) Cr^{2+} (4) Fe^{3+}
(Atomic numbers : Cr = 24, Fe = 26, Co = 27, Ni = 28)
The correct sequence of the increasing order of the number of unpaired electrons in these ions is:
(a) 1, 2, 3, 4 (b) 4, 2, 3, 1
(c) 1, 3, 2, 4 (d) 3, 4, 2, 1

26. In transition elements, the incoming electron occupies $(n - 1)$ d-subshell in preference to:
(a) np-subshell (b) ns-subshell (c) $(n - 1)$ p-subshell (d) $(n + 1)$ s-subshell

27. Which shape is associated with the orbital designated by $n = 2, l = 1$?
(a) Spherical (b) Tetrahedral (c) Dumbell (d) Pyramidal

28. Which of the following rule could explain the presence of three unpaired electrons in phosphorus atom?
(a) Hund's rule (b) Pauli's exclusion principle
(c) Heisenberg's uncertainty principle (d) None of these

29. The maximum energy is present in any electron at:
(a) Nucleus (b) Ground state
(c) First excited state (d) Infinite distance from the nucleus

30. Electrons represented by quantum numbers
(i) $n = 4, l = 1$ (ii) $n = 4, l = 0$ (iii) $n = 3, l = 2$ (iv) $n = 3, l = 1$
are placed in order of increasing energy level as:
(a) iv < ii < iii < i (b) ii < iv < i < iii
(c) i < iii < ii < iv (d) iii < i < iv < ii

31. The set of quantum number, $n = 3, l = 1, m = 0$:
(a) describes an electron in a $2s$-orbital
(b) describes an electron in one of the three degenerate orbitals
(c) describes an electron in one of the five degenerate orbitals
(d) it is not permissible

32. Which of the following statements is incorrect regarding probability of finding electron in p_x orbital ?
(a) It is zero at the nucleus
(b) It is zero on the z-axis
(c) It is same on all sides around the nucleus
(d) It is maximum on the two opposite sides of the nucleus along x-axis

33. The *d*-orbital which has maximum electron density of two *p*-orbitals:

(a) $d_{x^2-y^2}$ (b) d_{xy} (c) d_{z^2} (d) d_{zx}

34. The maximum probability of finding electrons in d_{xy} orbitals is:

(a) along with X and Y axis (b) along Y and Z axis

(c) along with Y and Z axis (d) at an angle of $\frac{\pi}{4}$ with X axis

35. What is the atomic number of the element with the maximum number of unpaired $4p$ electrons ?

(a) 33 (b) 26 (c) 23 (d) 15

36. Which of the given sub-shells will follow relationship $n + l = 7$?

(a) $7s, 6p, 5d, 4f$ (b) $7s, 6p, 3d, 4f$ (c) $7s, 5d, 5f, 5p$ (d) $6s, 4f, 3d, 7p$

37. The total number of subshells in terms of $(n + l)$ level between $7s$ and $8p$ orbitals are:

(a) 3 (b) 5 (c) 7 (d) None of these

38. Which of the following electronic configuration does not satisfy all given conditions?

(i) The principal quantum number for valence electron is 5.

(ii) The value of spin magnetic moment is 2.83 B.M.

(iii) One electron which has $n = 5, l = 0, m = 0$

(iv) Paramagnetic atom of element

(a) $[Kr]4d^2 5s^2$ (b) $[Kr]4d^8 5s^2$

(c) $[Kr]4d^{10} 5s^2 5p^2$ (d) $[Kr]4d^{10} 5s^2 5p^3$

39. The sum of all the quantum numbers of hydrogen atom is:

(a) -1 (b) 0 (c) $+\frac{1}{2}$ (d) $\frac{3}{2}$

40. If aufbau rule is not followed in filling of the sub-shells then which of the following element will change its sub-shell in the periodic table ?

(a) K (19) (b) Sc (21) (c) V (23) (d) Ni (28)

41. How many electrons in an atom with atomic number 105 can have $(n + l) = 8$?

(a) 30 (b) 17

(c) 15 (d) Can not be predicted

42. Consider the ground state of Cr $(Z = 24)$. The numbers of electrons with the azimuthal quantum numbers $l = 1$ and 2 respectively are:

(a) 16 and 4 (b) 12 and 5 (c) 12 and 4 (d) 16 and 5

43. The configuration $1s^2 2s^2 2p^5 3s^1$ is valid for:

(a) ground state of fluorine (b) excited state of fluorine

(c) excited state of neon (d) Excited state of O^- ion

44. Which of the following atom has highest magnetic moment?

(a) Fe (b) Mn (c) Cr (d) V

45. Calculate the maximum and minimum number of electrons. Which may have magnetic quantum number ?

$m = +1$ and spin quantum number $s = +\frac{1}{2}$ in Chromium (Cr).

(a) 3, 2 (b) 6, 4 (c) 4, 2 (d) 2, 1

46. Which of the following statements about quantum number is incorrect ?
(a) If the value of $l = 0$, the electron distribution is spherical
(b) The shape of the orbital is given by Azimuthal subsidiary quantum number
(c) The Zeeman's effect is explained by subsidiary quantum number
(d) The magnetic quantum number gives the orientations of electron cloud

47. Which of the following sets of quantum number is not possible ?
(a) $n = 2, l = 1, m = -1, s = \frac{1}{2}$
(b) $n = 2, l = 0, m = 0, s = +\frac{1}{2}$
(c) $n = 3, l = 2, m = -2, s = +\frac{1}{2}$
(d) $n = 3, l = 2, m = -3, s = +\frac{1}{2}$

48. In $2s$ and $2p$-orbitals of an element, five electrons a, b, x, y and z are filled such that the spins of a, x and z are same, whereas spins of y and z are opposite to the spin of b. Which sets of electrons will have three identical quantum numbers ?

$2s^2$	$2p^3$		
ab	x	y	z

(a) ax, by, byz
(b) ab, yz
(c) ab only
(d) ax, by, xz

Level 3

Passage 1

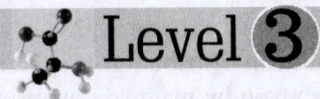

The four quantum numbers define completely the position of an electron in an atom. They give its position in major energy level (n), sub-energy level (l), orientation in the sub-energy level (m) and the direction of the spin (s). It is thus possible to identify an electron in an atom completely by stating the values of its four quantum numbers. They serve as an 'address' for the electron. According to "Pauli's exclusion principle" It is impossible for any two electrons in the same atom to have all the four quantum numbers identical.

1. Which of the following statement is incorrect?
(a) Azimuthal quantum number also known as angular momentum quantum number.
(b) The principal quantum number determines to a large extent of the energy of electron
(c) Orbitals in a given energy sublevel within a principal energy level is represented by azimuthal quantum number.
(d) The spin quantum number does not follow wave mechanical model treatment.

2. The value of four quantum numbers for any electron of element 'X' are 4, 3, – 2, –1/2 then incorrect statement regarding element 'X' is:
(a) Element 'X' may be belongs to Lanthanoids series.
(b) Element 'X' may be belongs to Actinoids series
(c) Element 'X' may be belongs to 2nd transition series.
(d) Element 'X' may be belongs to 3rd transition series.

3. Which quantum number(s) can same for 19th and 23th electrons of cadmium ($Z = 48$) ?
(a) l, m and s (b) s only (c) n, l, m and s (d) m and s

ONE OR MORE ANSWERS IS/ARE CORRECT

1. Choose the correct statement among the following:
(a) Number of orbitals in n^{th} shell $= n^2$
(b) Number of orbitals in l subshell $= (2l + 1)$
(c) Number of subshell in n^{th} shell $= n$
(d) Maximum number of electrons in l subshell $= 2(2l + 1)$

2. Which of the following set of quantum numbers is/are valid for electrons in ground state electronic configuration of Mn atom ($Z = 25$) ?

	n	l	m	s		n	l	m	s
(a)	3	2	0	$+\frac{1}{2}$	(b)	4	0	0	$+\frac{1}{2}$
(c)	4	3	0	$-\frac{1}{2}$	(d)	2	2	+1	$+\frac{1}{2}$

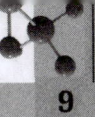

3. Which of the following statement(s) is/are wrong?
(a) If the value of $l = 0$, the electron distribution is spherical
(b) The shape of the orbital is given by magnetic quantum number
(c) Orbital angular momentum of $1s, 2s, 3s$ electrons are equal
(d) In an atom, all electrons travel with the same velocity

4. There are three elements A, B and C. Their atomic number are Z_1, Z_2 and Z_3 respectively. If $Z_1 - Z_2 = 2$ and $\frac{Z_1 + Z_2}{2} = Z_3 - 2$ and the electronic configuration of element A is $[Ar]3d^6\,4s^2$, then correct order of magnetic moment is/are:
(a) $B^+ > A^{2+} > C^{2+}$ (b) $A^{3+} > B^{2+} > C$
(c) $B > A > C^{2+}$ (d) $B = A^{3+} > C^{3+}$

5. The electronic configuration of an element is

$$1s^2 2s^2 2p^6 3s^2 3p^3$$

The atomic number of the element which is just below the given element in the vertical column in the periodic table is:
(a) 49 (b) 47 (c) 23 (d) 33

6. The number of '*d*' electrons in Fe^{2+} $(Z = 26)$ is equal to that of the:
(a) *p*-electrons in Ne (b) *s*-electrons in Mg
(c) *s*-electrons in O (d) *p*-electrons in Cl

7. In the following six electronic configuration (remaining inner orbitals are completely filled). Mark the correct option(s).

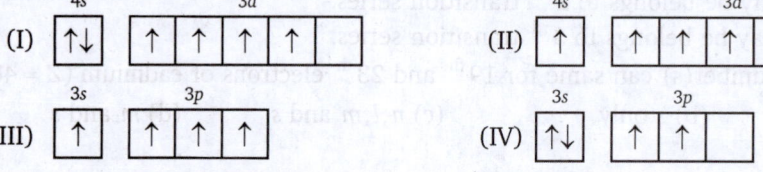

(I) 4s: [↑↓] 3d: [↑][↑][↑][↑][ ]
(II) 4s: [↑] 3d: [↑][↑][↑][↑][↑]
(III) 3s: [↑] 3p: [↑][↑][↑]
(IV) 3s: [↑↓] 3p: [↑][↑][ ]
(V) 4s: [↑↓] 3d: [↑][↑][ ][ ][ ]
(VI) 4s: [↑] 4p: [↑][↓][↑↑]

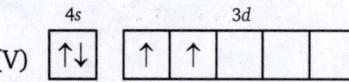

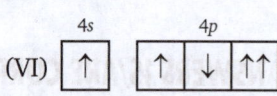

(a) Order of spin multiplicity : II > I = III > IV
(b) Stability order : II > I and IV > III
(c) If V represents element A then A^{2+} acts as diamagnetic.
(d) VI violates all the three rules of electronic configuration

MATCH THE COLUMN

1.

Column-I	Column-II
(A) No. of orbitals in the nth shell	(P) $2(2l+1)$
(B) Max. no. of electrons in a subshell	(Q) n
(C) No. of subshells in n^{th} shell	(R) $2l+1$
(D) No. of orbitals in a subshell	(S) n^2

2.

Column-I	Column-II
(A) Orbital angular momentum	(P) Unpaired electrons
(B) Stark and Zeeman effect	(Q) Azimuthal quantum number
(C) Magnetic moment	(R) Magnetic quantum number
	(S) Spin quantum number

3.

Column-I	Column-II
(A) p_x-orbital	(P) Orbital having no lobe and nodal plane
(B) d_{zx}-orbital	(Q) Orbital electronic distribution is maximum at an angle of 45° to the axial direction
(C) $d_{x^2-y^2}$-orbital	(R) Opposite lobes have same sign of wave function (ψ)
(D) *s*-orbital	(S) Opposite lobes have opposite sign of wave function (ψ)

4. Column I shows partial electronic configuration of an atom which may or may not be correct. Select the rule(s) they violate from column II.

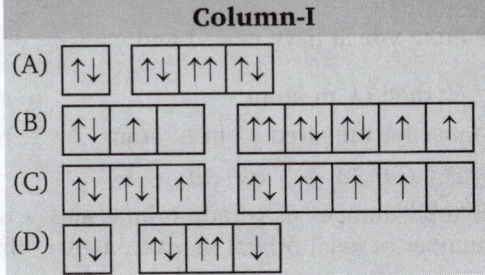

Column-I	Column-II
(A) [↑↓] [↑↓ | ↑↑ | ↑↓]	(P) Pauli's exclusion principle
(B) [↑↓ | ↑ |] [↑↑ | ↑↓ | ↑↓ | ↑ | ↑]	(Q) Hund's rule
(C) [↑↓ | ↑↓ | ↑] [↑↓ | ↑↑ | ↑ | ↑ |]	(R) $(n+l)$ rule
(D) [↑↓] [↑↓ | ↑↑ | ↓]	(S) None

5.

Column-I	Column-II
(A) *s*-orbital	(P) Zero nodal plane
(B) p_x-orbital	(Q) Two nodal plane
(C) $d_{x^2-y^2}$-orbital	(R) $\psi(g)$ [Gerade]
(D) d_{z^2}-orbital	(S) $\psi(u)$ [Ungerade]

ASSERTION-REASON TYPE QUESTIONS

These questions consist of two statements each, printed as assertion and reason, while answering these questions you are required to choose any one of the following responses.

(A) If both assertion and reason are true and the reason is the correct explanation of assertion

(B) If both assertion and reason are true but reason is not the correct explanation of assertion

(C) If assertion is true but the reason is false

(D) If assertion is false but the reason is true

1. **Assertion** : d_{z^2}-orbital is gerade orbital.
   Reason : d_{z^2}-orbital does not have four lobes like other *d*-orbitals.
2. **Assertion** : The number of electrons having magnetic quantum number '–1' in chromium atom in ground states are 5.
   Reason : The electronic configuration of chromium is $[Ar]\,4s^1\,3d^5$ and for a given '*p*' and '*d*' subshell "*m*" may have value '–1'.
3. **Assertion** : The *xy*-plane acts as nodal plane for d_{z^2} orbital.
   Reason : For a '*d*' orbital number of angular nodes are 2.

SUBJECTIVE PROBLEMS

1. How many orbitals are required for the electronic configuration of iron:
2. Find maximum number of electrons in 'Ca' $(Z = 20)$ atom for which $\frac{m}{n \times l} = 0$
3. Find the maximum number of electrons in P atom which have $m = -1$ and $s = +\frac{1}{2}$.
4. Find the total number of orbitals present in '*N*' shell of an atom.
5. What is the value of Azimuthal quantum number for unpaired e^- in Al atom $(Z = 13)$?
6. Consider the following orbitals (i) $3p_x$ (ii) $4d_{z^2}$ (iii) $3d_{x^2-y^2}$ (iv) $3d_{yz}$
   Then calculate value of "$x - y + z$" here x is total number of gerade orbital and y is total number of ungerade orbitals and z is total number of axial orbital in given above orbitals.
7. Atomic number of an element is 27.
   (a) How many electrons are there in its $3d$ subshell?
   (b) Number of unpaired electrons in its dipositive and tripositive ion respectively are?
8. How many unpaired electrons are there in each of the following in the ground state?
   (i) O, (ii) O^+, (iii) O^-, (iv) Fe, (v) Mn, (vi) S, (vii) F, (viii) Ar

Answers

Level-1

1.	(a)	**2.**	(b)	**3.**	(c)	**4.**	(b)	**5.**	(c)	**6.**	(c)	**7.**	(d)	**8.**	(d)	**9.**	(d)	**10.**	(a)
11.	(a)	**12.**	(b)	**13.**	(b)	**14.**	(b)	**15.**	(b)	**16.**	(a)	**17.**	(c)	**18.**	(c)	**19.**	(b)	**20.**	(c)
21.	(d)	**22.**	(c)	**23.**	(a)	**24.**	(a)	**25.**	(c)	**26.**	(b)	**27.**	(c)	**28.**	(b)				

Level-2

1.	(b)	**2.**	(c)	**3.**	(c)	**4.**	(c)	**5.**	(c)	**6.**	(a)	**7.**	(c)	**8.**	(b)	**9.**	(a)	**10.**	(d)
11.	(b)	**12.**	(b)	**13.**	(a)	**14.**	(b)	**15.**	(b)	**16.**	(b)	**17.**	(c)	**18.**	(a)	**19.**	(d)	**20.**	(a)
21.	(c)	**22.**	(a)	**23.**	(c)	**24.**	(c)	**25.**	(a)	**26.**	(a)	**27.**	(c)	**28.**	(a)	**29.**	(d)	**30.**	(a)
31.	(b)	**32.**	(c)	**33.**	(a)	**34.**	(d)	**35.**	(a)	**36.**	(a)	**37.**	(c)	**38.**	(d)	**39.**	(d)	**40.**	(a)
41.	(b)	**42.**	(b)	**43.**	(c)	**44.**	(c)	**45.**	(a)	**46.**	(c)	**47.**	(d)	**48.**	(b)				

Level-3

Passage-1	**1.**	(c)	**2.**	(c)	**3.**	(d)

One or More Answers is/are correct

1. (a,b,c,d) **2.** (a,b) **3.** (b,d) **4.** (a,b,c) **5.** (d) **6.** (a,b)
7. (a,b,d)

Match the Column

1. A → S; B → P; C → Q; D → R
2. A → Q; B → R; C → P
3. A → S; B → Q, R; C → R; D → P
4. A → P or P,Q (More appropriate will be PQ) ; B → P,Q,R ; C → P,Q,R; D → P,Q
5. A → P, R ; B → S; C → Q, R; D → P, R

Assertion-Reason Type Questions

1. (B) **2.** (A) **3.** (C)

Subjective Problems

1. (15) **2.** (4) **3.** (2) **4.** (16) **5.** (1) **6.** (5) **7.** **(a)** (7) **(b)** (3 & 4)
8. (i) 2, (ii) 3, (iii) 1, (iv) 4, (v) 5, (vi) 2, (vii) 1, (viii) 0

Hints and Solutions

Level 1

1. (a) $l \neq n$

$\therefore \; n = 2, \; l = 1, \; m = 0, \; s = +1/2$

2. (b) $n \Rightarrow$

n	1	2	3	4	5
	K	L	M	N	O

(n = no. of shell)

Value of $l = n - 1$

$\Rightarrow \; 5s, \; 5p, \; 5d, \; 5f, \; 5g$

$5g$ is possible for $n = 5$

3. (c) $m = 2l + 1$

$$\therefore \; l = \frac{m - 1}{2}$$

4. (b) Wave function (ψ) shows amplitude of wave.

5. (c) $\Delta x \times m\Delta v \geq \dfrac{h}{4\pi}$

or $\quad \Delta x \geq \dfrac{h}{4\pi m \Delta v}$

6. (c) Maximum electrons in $4f$ subshell are 14, seven having $+1/2$ and seven having $-1/2$ spin.

7. (d) $n = 4, \; l = 3$

then it shows $4f$ sub-shell.

8. (d) Wave mechanical model of atom is based upon de-Broglie concept of dual character, Heisenberg's uncertainty principle, Schrodinger wave equation.

9. (d) C = [↑↓] [↑][↑][ ]

$2s^2 \qquad 2p^2$

For 6th electron of carbon ;

$n = 2, \; l = 1, \; m = -1, \; s = +1/2$

10. (a) $P = 1s^2 2s^2 2p^6 3s^2 3p^3$

$l = 1, \; m = -1, \; 0, \; +1$ (three p-orbitals)

$\therefore$ Three electrons have $m = -1$ in phosphorus.

11. (a) $Cr = 1s^2 2s^2 2p^6 3s^2 3p^6 4s^1 3d^5$

$\Rightarrow$ 19th electron of chromium goes in $4s$-orbital.

$\therefore \; n = 4, \; l = 0, \; m = 0, \; s = +1/2$ or $-1/2$

12. (b) Orbital angular momentum for s-orbital is zero.

13. (b) Principal, azimuthal and magnetic quantum numbers respectively show size, shape and orientation.

14. (b)

	K	L	M	N
$n = 1$	1	2	3	4

(n = shell)

15. (b) ⇒ Number of values of (l) for an energy level is equal to n.

⇒ Actual values of (l) for an energy level are 0 to $(n-1)$

⇒ Number of 'm' value $= 2l+1$

⇒ Actual values of $m = -l$ to 0 to $+l$

16. (a) Uncertainty principle given by Heisenberg and wave nature of matter is given by de-Broglie.

17. (c) $L = \sqrt{l(l+1)}\dfrac{h}{2\pi}$

Level 2

1. (b) Electrons are filled in degenerate orbitals according to Hund's rule.

2. (c) Cr^{2+}, Fe^{2+}, Co^{2+} and Ni^{2+} have 4, 4, 3 and 2 unpaired electrons respectively.

3. (c) $Cl = 1s^2 2s^2 2p^6 3s^2 3p^5$

For unpaired electron of chlorine, $n=3$, $l=1$, $m=1$, $s=+1/2$

4. (c) $l \neq n$

5. (c) According to Hund; degenerate orbitals are singly occupied and then pairing of electrons occurs.

6. (a) For species having one electron like H, Li^{2+}, Be^{3+} etc; energy of electron depends upon principal quantum number.

7. (c) d^5 have 5 unpaired electrons.

Magnetic moment $\propto$ no. of unpaired electron.

8. (b) Multiplicity $= n/2$

$n =$ no. of unpaired electron.

for $3d^7$; $n=3$

$\therefore$ Multiplicity $= 3/2$

9. (a) d-subshell have 5-fold non-degenerate.

10. (d) $Fe^{2+} = 3d^6 4s^2$

$Cl = 1s^2 2s^2 2p^6 3s^2 3p^5$

Chlorine have 5 electron is p-orbital.

11. (b) Firstly electrons are filled in 4s-orbital then in 3d-orbital. $(n+l)$ rule.

12. (b) If Hund's rule is not followed, Fe^{2+}, Mn^{2+} and Cr have 0, 2 and 0 unpaired electrons.

13. (a) If three electron are filled in one orbital; electronic configuration of potassium is

$K = 1s^3 2s^3 2p^9 3s^3 3p^1$

14. (b) Atomic number $= 10$ (Neon) and atomic number $= 12$ (magnesium) are diamagnetic.

15. (b) Total no. of orbital $= n^2 (n = \text{shell})$

16. (b) Total electron in any subshell $= 2(2l+1)$

$\therefore$ with same spin $= 2l+1$

32. (c) Probability of finding electron in p_x-orbital is maximum on the two opposite sides of nucleus along x-axis.

33. (a) $d_{x^2-y^2}$ have electron density equal to two p-orbitals.

Level 3

MATCH THE COLUMN

1. No. of orbitals in n^{th} shell $= n^2$

Max. no. of electrons in a subshell $= 2(2l + 1)$

Number of subshells in n^{th} shell $= n$

Number of orbitals in a subshell $= 2l + 1$

SUBJECTIVE PROBLEMS

1. $Fe = 1s^2 2s^2 2p^6 3s^2 3p^6 3d^6 4s^2$

$\Rightarrow$ Total fifteen orbitals are required for electronic configuration of iron.

6. $4d_{z^2}$, $3d_{x^2-y^2}$, $3d_{yz}$ are gerade orbitals have even no. of nodal plane.

$3p_x$ = ungerade orbital (1 NP)

Axial orbital $= 3p_x, 4d_{z^2}, 3d_{x^2-y^2} = 3$

$\therefore \quad x - y + z = 3 - 1 + 3 = 2 + 3 = 5$

Part B
PERIODIC PROPERTIES

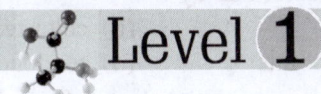

Level 1

Periodic Table

1. Which is not similar characteristic(s) about the electronic configuration of Be, Mg, Ca?
(a) All the atoms have a pair of *s*-electrons in their outermost energy level
(b) All the atoms contain a pair of *p*-electrons in their outermost energy level
(c) All are alkaline earth metals
(d) All are of second group of the periodic table

2. The elements with atomic number 117 and 120 are yet to be discovered. In which group would you place these elements when discovered ?
(a) 17 , 2 (b) 16 , 4 (c) 15 , 3 (d) 18 , 2

3. The most electropositive element possesses the electronic configuration :
(a) [He] $2s^1$ (b) [Ne] $3s^2$ (c) [Xe] $6s^1$ (d) [Xe] $6s^2$

4. Which one of the following elements shows both positive and negative oxidation states?
(a) Cesium (b) Fluorine (c) Iodine (d) Xenon

5. The number of elements present in fifth period is :
(a) 18 (b) 32 (c) 8 (d) 24

6. Which of the following arrangements shows the correct order of decreasing paramagnetism?
(a) N > Al > O > Ca (b) N > O > Al > Ca
(c) O > N > Al > Ca (d) O > N > Ca > Al

7. The outer electronic structure of lawrencium (atomic number 103) is :
(a) Rn $5f^{13}7s^2 7p^2$ (b) Rn $5f^{13}6d^1 7s^1 7p^2$
(c) Rn $5f^{14}7s^1 7p^2$ (d) Rn $5f^{14}6d^1 7s^2$

8. The elements with the lowest atomic number that has a ground state electronic configuration of $(n-1)\,d^6 ns^2$ is located in the :
(a) fifth period (b) sixth period (c) fourth period d) third period

9. Which of the following sets of atomic numbers corresponds to elements of group 16 ?
(a) 8, 16, 32, 54 (b) 16, 34, 54, 86
(c) 8, 16, 34, 52 (d) 10, 16, 32, 50

10. The atomic numbers of the metallic and non-metallic elements which are liquid at room temperature respectively are :
(a) 55, 87 (b) 33, 87 (c) 35, 80 (d) 80, 35

11. In the periodic table, metallic character of the elements shows one of the following trend :
(a) Decreases down the group and increases across the period
(b) Increases down the group and decreases across the period
(c) Increases across the period and also down the group
(d) Decreases across the period and also down the group

12. Nucleus of an element contains 9 protons. It's valency would be :
(a) 1 (b) 2 (c) 3 (d) 5

13. Transition metals are not characterized by :
(a) fixed valency (b) coloured compound
(c) high melting and boiling points (d) tendency to form complexes

14. Sodium generally does not shown oxidation state of +2, because of its :
(a) High first ionisation potential (b) High second ionization potential
(c) Large ionic radius (d) High electronegativity

15. The element with atomic number $Z = 118$ will be:
(a) Transition metal (b) Alkali metal
(c) Alkaline earth metal (d) Noble gas

16. According to modern periodic law the properties of elements repeat at regular intervals when the elements are arranged in order of :
(a) decreasing atomic number (b) increasing atomic weight
(c) increasing atomic number (d) decreasing atomic weights

17. Give the symbol of the elements of lowest atomic number that has three 2*p* electrons :
(a) Mg (b) P (c) N (d) Si

18. In the fourth period of the periodic table, how many elements have one or more 4*d* electrons?
(a) 2 (b) 18 (c) 0 (d) 6

19. What would be the atomic number of the alkaline earth metal of the eighth period?
(a) 113 (b) 120 (c) 119 (d) 106

20. Which of the following represents an excited state of an atom?
(a) [Ne] $3s^2 3p^6 3d^8 4s^2$ (b) [Ne] $3s^2 3p^6 3d^5 4s^1$
(c) [Ne] $3s^2 3p^6 3d^1 4s^2$ (d) $1s^2 2s^2 2p^5 3s^1$

21. Choose the correct statement regarding transition elements?
(a) Transition elements has low melting points
(b) Transition elements do not have catalytic activity
(c) Transition elements exhibit variable oxidation states
(d) Transition elements exhibit inert pair effect

22. Which one of the following is a different pair?
(a) Li, Na (b) Be, Ba
(c) N, As (d) O, At

23. The element having electronic configuration [Kr]$4d^{10} 4f^{14}, 5s^2 5p^6, 6s^2$ belongs to :
(a) *s*-block (b) *p*-block (c) *d*-block (d) *f*-block

24. Which element has symbol after the name of a planet ?
(a) Hg (b) Po (c) Pu (d) Ra

25. Zn and Cd metals do not show variable valency because :
(a) They have only two electrons in the outermost subshells
(b) Their *d*-subshells are completely filled
(c) Their *d*-subshells are partially filled
(d) They are relatively soft metals

26. An element whose IUPAC name is ununtrium (Uut) belongs to :
(a) *s*-block element (b) *p*-block element
(c) *d*-block element (d) Transition element

27. Which of the following is not representative element ?
(a) Tellurium (b) Tantalum
(c) Thallium (d) Astatine

28. The period number and group number of "Tantalum" ($Z = 73$) are respectively :
(a) 5, 7 (b) 6, 13
(c) 6, 5 (d) None of these

29. Which of the following pair of elements belong to the same period?
(a) Mg and Sb (b) Ca and Zn
(c) Na and Ca (d) Ca and Cl

30. Consider the following electronic configuration of an element(P) :

$$[Xe]4f^{14}5d^{1}6s^{2}$$

Then correct statement about element 'P' is :
(a) It belongs to 6th period and 1st group (b) It belongs to 6th period and 2nd group
(c) It belongs to 6th period and 3rd group (d) None of these

31. Which of the following metal is highest electropositive (metallic) in nature ?
(a) Be (b) Rb (c) Mn (d) Tl

32. Which of the following species must have maximum number of electrons in 'd_{xy}' orbital ?
(a) Cr (b) Fe^{3+} (c) Cu^{+} (d) Both (a) and (b)

33. Which of the following graph is correct representation between atomic number (Z) and magnetic moment of *d*-block elements? [Outer electronic configuration : $(n-1)d^{x}ns^{1 \text{ or } 2}$]

(a) 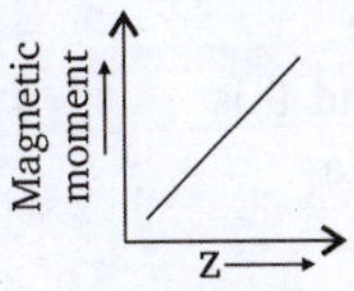

(b) 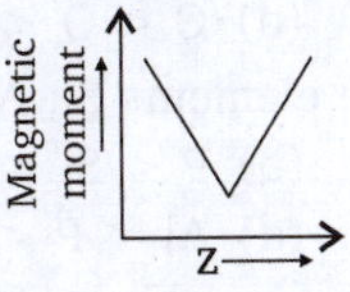

(c) 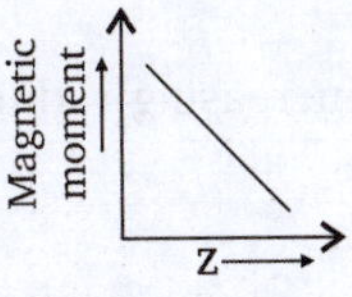

(d) 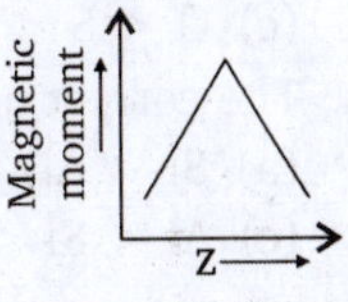

34. If IUPAC name of an element is "unununium" then correct statement regarding element is :
(a) It is a inner transition element (b) It belongs to 8th period in periodic table
(c) It is transition element (d) It is a non-transition element

35. Which property decreases from left to right across the periodic table and increases from top to bottom?
(i) Atomic radius (ii) Electronegativity (iii) Ionisation energy (iv) Metallic character
(a) (i) only (b) (i), (ii) and (iii)
(c) (i), (iii) and (iv) (d) (i) and (iv)

36. Consider the following information about element *P* and *Q* :

	Period number	Group number
P	2	15
Q	3	2

Then formula of the compound formed by *P* and *Q* element is :
(a) PQ (b) P_3Q_2 (c) P_2Q_3 (d) PQ_2

37. Which electronic configuration must represent an atom in an excited state?
(a) $1s^2, 2s^2 2p^1$ (b) $1s^2, 2s^2 2p^2$
(c) $1s^2, 2s^2 2p^2, 3s^1$ (d) $1s^2, 2s^2 2p^5$

Atomic/Ionic Radius

38. Which of the following anion has the smallest radius?
(a) H^- (b) F^- (c) Cl^- (d) Br^-

39. The ionic radii of Li^+, Be^{2+} and B^{3+} follow the order :
(a) $Be^{2+} > B^{3+} > Li^+$ (b) $Li^+ > B^{3+} > Be^{2+}$
(c) $B^{3+} > Be^{2+} > Li^+$ (d) $Li^+ > Be^{2+} > B^{3+}$

40. Largest in size out of Na^+, Ne and F^- is :
(a) Na^+ (b) Ne (c) F^- (d) all are equal

41. Which of the following atom or ions has the smallest size?
(a) F (b) F^- (c) O (d) N

42. The single covalent radius of P is 0.11 nm. The single covalent radius of Cl will be :
(a) smaller than P (b) greater than P (c) same as P (d) twice of P

43. Which of the following is arranged in decreasing order of size?
(a) $Mg^{2+} > Al^{3+} > O^{2-}$ (b) $O^{2-} > Mg^{2+} > Al^{3+}$
(c) $Al^{3+} > Mg^{2+} > O^{2-}$ (d) $Al^{3+} > O^{2-} > Mg^{2+}$

44. The correct order of increasing atomic radius of the following elements is :
(a) S < O < Se < C (b) O < C < S < Se
(c) O < S < Se < C (d) C < O < S < Se

45. The correct order of increasing radius of the elements Si, Al, Na and P is :
(a) Si < Al < P < Na (b) P < Si < Al < Na
(c) Al < Si < P < Na (d) Al < P < Si < Na

46. The size of the species, Pb, Pb^{2+}, Pb^{4+} decreases as :
(a) $Pb^{4+} > Pb^{2+} > Pb$ (b) $Pb > Pb^{2+} > Pb^{4+}$
(c) $Pb > Pb^{4+} > Pb^{2+}$ (d) $Pb^{4+} > Pb > Pb^{2+}$

47. Incorrect order of radius is :
(a) $Sr^{2+} < Rb^+ < Br^- < Se^{2-}$ (b) $Nb^{5+} < Zr^{4+} < Y^{3+}$
(c) $Co > Co^{2+} > Co^{3+} > Co^{4+}$ (d) None of these

48. The correct order of atomic/ionic radii is :
(a) Sc > Ti > V > Cr (b) Co > Ni > Cu > Zn
(c) $S^{2-} > Cl^- > O^{2-} > N^{3-}$ (d) None of these

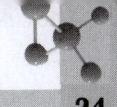

49. The radius of which ion is closest to that of Li^+ ion?
(a) Na^+ (b) Be^{2+} (c) Mg^{2+} (d) Al^{3+}

Ionisation Energy

50. The first, second and third ionisation energies (E_1, E_2 and E_3) for an element are 7 eV, 12.5 eV and 42.5 eV respectively. The most stable oxidation state of the element will be:
(a) +1 (b) +4 (c) +3 (d) +2

51. Element having highest I.P. value is:
(a) Ne (b) He (c) Be (d) N

52. The order of ionisation potential between He^+ ion and H-atom (both species are in gaseous state) is:
(a) I.P. (He^+) = I.P. (H) (b) I.P. (He^+) < I.P. (H)
(c) I.P. (He^+) > I. P. (H) (d) cannot be compared

53. Which of the following metal is expected to have the highest third ionization enthalpy?
(a) Cr ($Z=24$) (b) V ($Z=23$)
(c) Mn ($Z=25$) (d) Fe($Z=26$)

54. Second ionization potential of Li, Be and B is in the order :
(a) Li > Be > B (b) Li > B > Be
(c) Be > Li > B (d) B > Be > Li

55. The ionization energy of boron is less than that of beryllium because :
(a) beryllium has a higher nuclear charge than boron
(b) beryllium has a lower nuclear charge than boron
(c) the outermost electron in boron occupies a 2*p*-orbital
(d) the 2*s* and 2*p*-orbitals of boron are degenerate

56. The first four I.E. values of an element are 284, 412, 656 and 3210 kJ mol^{-1}. The number of valence electrons in the element are :
(a) one (b) two (c) three (d) four

57. The first I.E. of Na, Mg, Al and Si are in the order :
(a) Na < Mg < Al < Si (b) Na < Al < Mg < Si
(c) Na < Al < Si < Mg (d) Na > Mg > Al > Si

58. The ionization energy will be higher when the electron is removed from :
(a) *s*-orbital (b) *p*-orbital (c) *d*-orbital (d) *f*-orbital

59. Which of the following isoelectronic ion has the lowest ionization energy?
(a) K^+ (b) Cl^- (c) Ca^{2+} (d) S^{2-}

60. Amongst the following elements, the highest ionization energy is :
(a) $[Ne]3s^2 3p^1$ (b) $[Ne]3s^2 3p^3$
(c) $[Ne]3s^2 3p^2$ (d) $[Ar]3d^{10} 4s^2 4p^3$

61. The ionization potentials of Li and K are 5.4 and 4.3 eV respectively. The ionization potential of Na will be :
(a) 9.7 eV (b) 1.1 eV
(c) 4.9 eV (d) cannot be calculated

62. Which of the following electronic configuration is associated with the biggest jump between the second and third ionization energies?

(a) $1s^2 2s^2 2p^2$ (b) $1s^2 2s^2 2p^6 3s^1$
(c) $1s^2 2s^2 2p^6 3s^2$ (d) $1s^2 2s^2 2p^1$

63. The second ionization energy is maximum for :

(a) boron (b) beryllium
(c) magnesium (d) aluminium

64. A large difference between the fourth and fifth ionization energies indicates the presence of :

(a) 5 valence electrons in an atom (b) 6 valence electrons in an atom
(c) 4 valence electrons in an atom (d) 8 valence electrons in an atom

65. For which of the following reaction ΔH° value is equal to the first ionization energy of Ca is ?

(a) $Ca^+(g) \longrightarrow Ca^{2+}(g) + e$ (b) $Ca(g) \longrightarrow Ca^+(g) + e$
(c) $Ca(s) \longrightarrow Ca^+(g) + e$ (d) $Ca(g) \longrightarrow Ca^{2+}(g) + 2e$

66. Ionization enthalpy of an atom is equal to :

(a) Electron gain enthalpy of the cation (b) Electronegativity of the ion
(c) Ionization enthalpy of the cation (d) None of these

67. From the ground state electronic configuration of the elements given below, pick up the one with highest value of second ionization energy :

(a) $1s^2 2s^2 2p^6 3s^2$ (b) $1s^2 2s^2 2p^6 3s^1$
(c) $1s^2 2s^2 2p^6$ (d) $1s^2 2s^2 2p^5$

68. An element has successive ionization enthalpies as 940 (first), 2080, 3090, 4140, 7030, 7870, 16000 and 19500 kJ mol^{-1}. To which group of the periodic table does this element belong?

(a) 14 (b) 15 (c) 16 (d) 17

69. The second ionization potential of elements is invariable higher than first ionization potential because :

(a) The size of cation is smaller than its atom
(b) It is easier to remove electron from cation
(c) Ionization is an endothermic process
(d) None of above

70. The first, second and third ionisation energies (E_1, E_2 & E_3) for an element are 7eV, 12.5eV and 42.5eV respectively. The most stable oxidation state of the element will be :

(a) +1 (b) +4 (c) +3 (d) +2

71. Which of the following electronic configurations represents a sudden large gap between the values of second and third ionisation energies of an element?

(a) $1s^2, 2s^2 2p^3$ (b) $1s^2, 2s^2 2p^6, 3s^2 3p^3$
(c) $1s^2, 2s^2 2p^6, 3s^2 3p^1$ (d) $1s^2, 2s^2 2p^6, 3s^2$

72. Element having highest I.P. value is :

(a) Ne (b) He (c) Be (d) N

73. Which of the following anionic species has maximum ionisation energy?

(a) O^- (b) S^- (c) Se^- (d) Te^-

74. The correct order of $I.E._2$. is:

(a) Ne > F > O > N (b) O > F > Ne > N
(c) Ne > O > F > N (d) O > Ne > F > N

75. Which of the following transformation least energy is required?

(a) $F^-_{(g)} \longrightarrow F_{(g)} + e^-$
(b) $P^-_{(g)} \longrightarrow P_{(g)} + e^-$
(c) $S^-_{(g)} \longrightarrow S_{(g)} + e^-$
(d) $Cl^-_{(g)} \longrightarrow Cl_{(g)} + e^-$

Electron Affinity

76. The amount of energy released on the addition of an electron in outermost shell of an isolated atom is called :

(a) Ionization enthalpy
(b) Hydration enthalpy
(c) Electronegativity
(d) Electron gain enthalpy

77. To which of the following atom, the attachment of electron is most difficult?

(a) Radon
(b) Nitrogen
(c) Oxygen
(d) Radium

78. Which of the following processes involves absorption of energy?

(a) $S(g) + e^- \longrightarrow S^-(g)$
(b) $S^- + e^- \longrightarrow S^{2-}(g)$
(c) $Cl(g) + e^- \longrightarrow Cl^-(g)$
(d) None of these

79. Arrange N, O and S in order of decreasing electron affinity :

(a) S > O > N
(b) O > S > N
(c) N > O > S
(d) S > N > O

80. Among the following configurations, the element which has the highest electron affinity is :

(a) $[Ne]\,3s^1 3p^2$
(b) $[Ne]\,3s^2 3p^5$
(c) $[Ne]\,3s^2 3p^4$
(d) $[Ne]\,3s^2 3p^6 3d^5 4s^1$

81. The increasing order of electron affinity for the following electronic configurations of element is :

(I) $1s^2 2s^2 2p^6 3s^2 3p^5$
(II) $1s^2 2s^2 2p^3$
(III) $1s^2 2s^2 2p^5$
(IV) $1s^2 2s^2 2p^6 3s^1$

(a) II < IV < III < I
(b) I < II < III < IV
(c) I < III < II < IV
(d) IV < III < II < I

82. Second electron gain enthalpy :

(a) is always negative
(b) is always positive
(c) can be positive or negative
(d) is always zero

83. The element having very high ionization enthalpy but zero electron affinity is :

(a) H (b) F (c) He (d) Be

84. Which of the following represents correct order of electron affinity?

(a) Cl > F > S > O
(b) F > O > S > Cl
(c) F > Cl > S > O
(d) Cl > S > O > F

85. The process requiring absorption of energy is :

(a) $N \longrightarrow N^-$ (b) $F \longrightarrow F^-$ (c) $Cl \longrightarrow Cl^-$ (d) $H \longrightarrow H^-$

Electronegativity

86. The electronegativity of the following elements increases in the order :

(a) C < N < Si < P
(b) Si < P < C < N
(c) N < C < P < Si
(d) C < Si < N < P

87. Which of the following order is incorrect ?
(a) Electronegativity of central atom : $CF_4 > CH_4 > SiH_4$
(b) Hydration energy : $Al^{3+} > Be^{2+} > Mg^{2+} > Na^+$
(c) Electrical conductance : $F^-_{(aq.)} > Cl^-_{(aq.)} > S^{2-}_{(aq.)}$
(d) Magnetic moment : $Ni^{4+} > V^{3+} > Sr^{2+}$

88. Correct expression of "Allred and Rochow's" scale is :
(a) Electronegativity $= 0.744 \frac{Z_{eff.}}{r^2} + 0.359$
(b) Electronegativity $= 0.359 \frac{r^2}{Z_{eff.}} + 0.744$
(c) Electronegativity $= 0.359 \frac{Z_{eff.}}{r} + 0.744$
(d) Electronegativity $= 0.359 \frac{Z_{eff.}}{r^2} + 0.744$

Hydration Energy

89. The hydration energy of Mg^{2+} ions is lesser than that of :
(a) Al^{3+}
(b) Ba^{2+}
(c) Na^+
(d) None of these

90. Among the following, which has the maximum hydration energy?
(a) OH^-
(b) NH_4^+
(c) F^-
(d) H^+

91. Which of the following is arranged in order of increasing radius?
(a) $K^+(aq) < Na^+(aq) < Li^+(aq)$
(b) $Na^+(aq) < K^+(aq) < Li^+(aq)$
(c) $K^+(aq) < Li^+(aq) < Na^+(aq)$
(d) $Li^+(aq) < Na^+(aq) < K^+(aq)$

92. Which of the following compounds has more negative enthalpy of solution?
(a) KCl
(b) KBr
(c) KF
(d) KI

93. Which among the following factors is the most important in making fluorine, the strongest oxidising halogen ?
(a) Bond dissociation energy
(b) Ionisation enthalpy
(c) Hydration enthalpy
(d) Electron affinity

Lattice Energy

94. Amongst sodium halides (NaF, NaCl, NaBr and NaI), NaF has the highest melting point because of :
(a) High oxidising power
(b) Lowest polarity
(c) Maximum lattice energy
(d) Minimum ionic character

95. Among the following oxides, which has the maximum lattice energy?
(a) MgO
(b) CaO
(c) SrO
(d) BaO

96. Which of the following compounds has a positive enthalpy of solution?
(a) LiF
(b) LiCl
(c) LiBr
(d) LiI

97. Born-Haber cycle can be used to estimate :
(a) Lattice energy of ionic crystals
(b) Electron gain enthalpy
(c) Electronegativity
(d) Both (a) and (b)

Nature of Oxides

98. Which of the following is different from other three oxides?
(a) MgO
(b) SnO
(c) ZnO
(d) PbO

99. Select the amphoteric substance in the following :
(a) SO_3
(b) NaOH
(c) CO_2
(d) $Al(OH)_3$

100. Which of the following compound is most acidic?
(a) Cl_2O_7
(b) P_4O_{10}
(c) SO_3
(d) B_2O_3

Level 2

Periodic Table

1. A compound contains three elements *A*, *B* and *C*, if the oxidation number of $A = +2$, $B = +5$ and $C = -2$, the possible formula of the compound is :

(a) $A_3(B_4C)_2$ (b) $A_3(BC_4)_2$ (c) $A_2(BC_3)_2$ (d) ABC_2

2. Consider the following four elements, which are arranged according to long form of periodic table.

	Y	
W	X	Z

Here *W*, *Y* and *Z* are left, up and right elements with respect to the element 'X' and 'X' belongs to 16th group and 3rd period. Then according to given information the incorrect statement regarding given elements is :

(a) Maximum electronegativity : *Y*
(b) Maximum catenation property : *X*
(c) Maximum electron affinity : *Z*
(d) *Y* exhibits variable covalency

3. Which of the following sequence represents atomic number of only representative elements?

(a) 55, 12, 48, 53 (b) 13, 33, 54, 83 (c) 3, 33, 53, 87 (d) 22, 33, 55, 66

4. The ground state electronic configurations of the elements, *U*, *V*, *W*, *X*, and *Y* (these symbols do not have any chemical significance) are as follows :

U $1s^2 2s^2 2p^3$
V $1s^2 2s^2 2p^6 3s^1$
W $1s^2 2s^2 2p^6 3s^2 3p^2$
X $1s^2 2s^2 2p^6 3s^2 3p^6 3d^5 4s^2$
Y $1s^2 2s^2 2p^6 3s^2 3p^6 3d^{10} 4s^2 4p^6$

Determine which sequence of elements satisfy the following statements :

(i) Element forms a carbonate which is not decomposed on heating
(ii) Element is most likely to form coloured ionic compounds
(iii) Element has largest atomic radius
(iv) Element forms only acidic oxide

(a) *V W Y U*
(b) *V X Y W*
(c) *V W Y X*
(d) *V X W U*

5. When magnesium burns in air, compounds of magnesium formed are magnesium oxide and :

(a) Mg_3N_2
(b) $MgCO_3$
(c) $Mg(NO_3)_2$
(d) $MgSO_4$

6. Which of the following ions is most unlikely to exist?

(a) Li^-
(b) Be^-
(c) B^-
(d) F^-

7. A, B and C are hydroxy-compounds of the elements X, Y and Z respectively. X, Y and Z are in the same period of the periodic table. A gives an aqueous solution of pH less than seven. B reacts with both strong acids and strong alkalis. C gives an aqueous solution which is strongly alkaline.

Which of the following statements is/are true ?

I : The three elements are metals.

II : The electronegativities decrease from X to Y to Z.

III : The atomic radius decreases in the order X, Y and Z.

IV : X, Y and Z could be phosphorus, aluminium and sodium respectively.

(a) I, II and III are correct
(b) I and III are correct
(c) II and IV are correct
(d) II, III and IV are correct

8. La (lanthanum) having atomic number 57 is a member of :
(a) *s*-block elements
(b) *p*-block elements
(c) *d*-block elements
(d) *f*-block elements

9. If the aufbau principle had not been followed, Ca ($Z = 20$) would have been placed in the :
(a) *s*-block
(b) *p*-block
(c) *d*-block
(d) *f*-block

10. What is the atomic number of the element with the maximum number of unpaired $4p$ electrons?
(a) 33
(b) 26
(c) 23
(d) 15

11. The electronic configuration of four elements are :
(I) $[Kr]5s^1$
(II) $[Rn]5f^{14}6d^1 7s^2$
(III) $[Ar]3d^{10}4s^2 4p^5$
(IV) $[Ar]3d^6 4s^2$

Consider the following statements :
(i) I shows variable oxidation state
(ii) II is a *d*-block element
(iii) The compound formed between I and III is covalent
(iv) IV shows single oxidation state

Which statement is True (T) or False (F)?
(a) FTFF
(b) FTFT
(c) FFTF
(d) FFFF

12. If period number and group number of any representative element(s) are same then which of the following statement is incorrect regarding such type element(s) in their ground state? (Period number and group number are according to modern form of periodic table)
(a) The possible value of principal quantum number is 2
(b) The possible value of azimuthal quantum number is zero
(c) The possible value of magnetic quantum number is 1
(d) The species could be paramagnetic

13. How does the energy gap between successive energy levels in an atom vary from low to high n values?
(a) All energy gaps are the same
(b) The energy gap decreases as n increases
(c) The energy gap increases as n increases
(d) The energy gap changes unpredictably as n increases

14. Which of the following properties of the alkaline earth metals increase from Be to Ba?
(i) Atomic radius (ii) Ionisation energy (iii) Nuclear charge
(a) (i) and (ii) (b) (i) and (iii)
(c) (ii) and (iii) (d) (i), (ii) and (iii)

15. Which of the following is the incorrect match for atom of element ?
(a) $[Ar]3d^5 4s^1 \rightarrow 4^{th}$ period, 6th group
(b) $[Kr]4d^{10} \rightarrow 5^{th}$ period, 12th group
(c) $[Rn]6d^2 7s^2 \rightarrow 7^{th}$ period, 3th group
(d) $[Xe]4f^{14}5d^2 6s^2 \rightarrow 6^{th}$ period, 4th group

Atomic/Ionic Radius

16. The set representing the correct order of ionic radius is:
(a) $Na^+ > Mg^{2+} > Al^{3+} > Li^+ > Be^{2+}$ (b) $Na^+ > Li^+ > Mg^{2+} > Al^{3+} > Be^{2+}$
(c) $Na^+ > Mg^{2+} > Li^+ > Al^{3+} > Be^{2+}$ (d) $Na^+ > Mg^{2+} > Li^+ > Be^{2+}$

17. In which of the following pair, both the species are isoelectronic but the first one is large in size than the second?
(a) S^{2-}, O^{2-} (b) Cl^-, S^{2-} (c) F^-, Na^+ (d) N^{3-}, P^{3-}

18. The correct order of ionic size of $N^{3-}, Na^+, F^-, Mg^{2+}$ and O^{2-} is :
(a) $Mg^{2+} > Na^+ > F^- > O^{2-} < N^{3-}$ (b) $N^{3-} < F^- > O^{2-} > Na^+ > Mg^{2+}$
(c) $Mg^{2+} < Na^+ < F^- < O^{2-} < N^{3-}$ (d) $N^{3-} > O^{2-} > F^- > Na^+ < Mg^{2+}$

19. The order of increasing ionic radius of the following is :
(a) $K^+ < Li^+ < Mg^{2+} < Al^{3+}$ (b) $K^+ < Mg^{2+} < Li^+ < Al^{3+}$
(c) $Li^+ < K^+ < Mg^{2+} < Al^{3+}$ (d) $Al^{3+} < Mg^{2+} < Li^+ < K^+$

20. If the ionic radii of K^+ and F^- are nearly the same (*i.e.*, 1.34 Å), then the atomic radii of K and F respectively are :
(a) 1.34 Å, 1.34 Å (b) 0.72 Å, 1.96 Å (c) 1.96 Å, 0.72 Å (d) 1.96 Å, 1.34 Å

21. Incorrect order of ionic size is :
(a) $La^{3+} > Gd^{3+} > Eu^{3+} > Lu^{3+}$ (b) $V^{2+} > V^{3+} > V^{4+} > V^{5+}$
(c) $Tl^+ > In^+ > Sn^{2+} > Sb^{3+}$ (d) $K^+ > Sc^{3+} > V^{5+} > Mn^{7+}$

Ionisation Energy

22. $X_{(g)} \longrightarrow X^+_{(g)} + e^-$, $\Delta H = +720\,kJ\,mol^{-1}$

Calculate the amount of energy required to convert 110 mg of 'X' atom in gaseous state into X^+ ion. (Atomic wt. for $X = 7$ g/mol)
(a) 10.4 kJ (b) 12.3 kJ (c) 11.3 kJ (d) 14.5 kJ

23. Consider the following changes :

$$M(s) \longrightarrow M(g) \quad ...(1)$$
$$M(s) \longrightarrow M^{2+}(g) + 2e^- \quad ...(2)$$
$$M(g) \longrightarrow M^+(g) + e^- \quad ...(3)$$

$$M^+(g) \longrightarrow M^{2+}(g) + e^- \quad ...(4)$$

$$M(g) \longrightarrow M^{2+}(g) + 2e^- \quad ...(5)$$

The second ionization energy of M could be calculated from the energy values associated with :

(a) 1 + 3 + 4 (b) 2 − 1 + 3 (c) 1 + 5 (d) 5 − 3

24. The correct order of second I.E. of C, N, O and F are in the order :

(a) F > O > N > C (b) C > N > O > F

(c) O > N > F > C (d) O > F > N > C

25. Which is the correct order of ionization energies?

(a) $F^- > F > Cl^- > Cl$ (b) $F > Cl > Cl^- > F^-$

(c) $F^- > Cl^- > Cl > F$ (d) $F^- > Cl^- > F > Cl$

26. Which of the following statements is incorrect?

(a) The second ionization energy of sulphur is greater than that of chlorine

(b) The third ionization energy of aluminium is greater than that of phosphorus

(c) The first ionization energy of aluminium is approximately the same as that of gallium

(d) The second ionization energy of boron is greater than that of carbon

27. First ionization energy is the lowest with :

(a) Lead (b) Carbon (c) Silicon (d) Tin

28. The incorrect statement among the following is :

(a) The first ionization potential of Al is less than the first ionization potential of Mg

(b) The second ionization potential of Mg is greater than the second ionization potential of Na

(c) The first ionization potential of Na is less than the first ionization potential of Mg

(d) The third ionization potential of Mg is greater than the third ionization potential of Al

29. The correct values of ionization enthalpies (in kJ mol^{-1}) of Si, P, Cl and S respectively are :

(a) 786, 1012, 999, 1256 (b) 1012, 786, 999, 1256

(c) 786, 1012, 1256, 999 (d) 786, 999, 1012, 1256

30. The third ionization energy is maximum for :

(a) Nitrogen (b) Phosphorus (c) Aluminium (d) Boron

31. Consider the following ionisation reactions :

	I.E. (kJ mol^{-1})		I.E. (kJ mol^{-1})
$A_{(g)} \longrightarrow A^+_{(g)} + e^-$,	A_1	$B_{(g)} \longrightarrow B^+_{(g)} + e^-$,	B_1
$B^+_{(g)} \longrightarrow B^{2+}_{(g)} + e^-$,	B_2	$C_{(g)} \longrightarrow C^+_{(g)} + e^-$,	C_1
$C^+_{(g)} \longrightarrow C^{2+}_{(g)} + e^-$,	C_2	$C^{2+}_{(g)} \longrightarrow C^{3+}_{(g)} + e^-$,	C_3

If monovalent positive ion of A, divalent positive ion of B and trivalent positive ion of C have zero electron. Then incorrect order of corresponding I.E. is :

(a) $C_3 > B_2 > A_1$ (b) $B_1 > A_1 > C_1$

(c) $C_3 > C_2 > B_2$ (d) $B_2 > C_3 > A_1$

32. The incorrect statement is :

(a) The second ionisation energy of Se is greater than that of second ionisation energy of As

(b) The first ionisation energy of C^{2+} ion is greater than that of first ionisation energy of N^{2+} ion

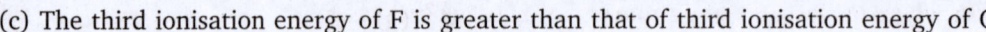

(c) The third ionisation energy of F is greater than that of third ionisation energy of O
(d) Helogens have highest I.E. in respective period

33. First three ionisation energies (in kJ/mol) of three representative elements are given below :

Element	IE_1	IE_2	IE_3
P	495.8	4562	6910
Q	737.7	1451	7733
R	577.5	1817	2745

Then incorrect option is :
(a) *Q*: Alkaline earth metal
(b) *P*: Alkali metal
(c) *R*: *s*-block element
(d) They belong to same period

Electron Affinity

34. Which of the following statement is correct regarding following process?
(i) $Cl \xrightarrow{E.A.} Cl^-$ (ii) $Cl^- \xrightarrow{I.E.} Cl$ (iii) $Cl \xrightarrow{I.E.} Cl^+$ (iv) $Cl^+ \xrightarrow{I.E.} Cl^{2+}$
(a) |I.E. of process (ii)| = |E.A. of process (i)|
(b) |I.E. of process (iii)| = |I.E. of process (ii)|
(c) |I.E. of process (iv)| = |E.A. of process (i)|
(d) |I.E. of process (iv)| = |I.E. of process (iii)|

35. The correct order of increasing electron affinity of the following elements is :
(a) O < S < F < Cl
(b) O < S < Cl < F
(c) S < O < F < Cl
(d) S < O < Cl < F

36. The second electron gain enthalpies (in kJ mol^{-1}) of oxygen and sulphur respectively are :
(a) –780, +590 (b) –590, +780 (c) +590, +780 (d) +780, +590

37. Which of the following statements is correct?
(a) The magnitude of the second electron affinity of sulphur is greater than that of oxygen
(b) The magnitude of the second electron affinity of sulphur is less than that of oxygen
(c) The first electron affinities of bromine and iodine are approximately the same
(d) The first electron affinity of fluorine is greater than that of chlorine

38. Which one of the following statements is incorrect?
(a) Greater is the nuclear charge, greater is magnitude of electron gain enthalpy
(b) Nitrogen has almost zero electron affinity
(c) Electron gain enthalpy decreases from fluorine to iodine in the group
(d) Chlorine has highest magnitude of electron gain enthalpy

39. The formation of the oxide ion $O^{2-}(g)$ requires first an exothermic and then an endothermic step as shown below :

$$O(g) + e^- \longrightarrow O^-(g); \quad \Delta H = -142 \text{ kJ mol}^{-1}$$
$$O^-(g) + e \longrightarrow O^{2-}(g); \quad \Delta H = 844 \text{ kJ mol}^{-1}$$

This is because :
(a) O^- ion has comparatively larger size than oxygen atom
(b) Oxygen has high electron affinity
(c) O^- ion will tend to resist the addition of another electron
(d) Oxygen is more electronegative

40. In which of the following processes energy is absorbed?

(a) $Cl + e^- \longrightarrow Cl^-$ (b) $O^- + e^- \longrightarrow O^{2-}$

(c) $O^{2-} - e^- \longrightarrow O^-$ (d) $Na^+ + e^- \longrightarrow Na$

41. The electron affinity of the following elements can be arranged :

(a) Cl > O > N > C (b) Cl > O > C > N (c) Cl > N > C > O (d) Cl > C > O > N

42. In which of the following arrangements, the order is not correct according to the property indicated against it?

(a) Increasing size : $Al^{3+} < Mg^{2+} < Na^+ < F^-$

(b) Increasing $I.E._1$: B < C < N < O

(c) Increasing $E.A._1$: I < Br < F < Cl

(d) Increasing metallic radius : Li < Na < K < Rb

43. Which of the following statements is/are wrong?

(a) van der Waals' radius of iodine is more than its covalent radius

(b) All isoelectronic ions belong to same period of the periodic table

(c) $I.E._1$ of N is higher than that of O while $I.E._2$ of O is higher than that of N

(d) The electron affinity N is almost zero while that of P is 74.3 kJ mol^{-1}

44. Consider the following conversions :

(i) $O_{(g)} + e^- \rightarrow O^-_{(g)}$, ΔH_1 (ii) $F_{(g)} + e^- \rightarrow F^-_{(g)}$, ΔH_2

(iii) $Cl_{(g)} + e^- \rightarrow Cl^-_{(g)}$, ΔH_3 (iv) $O^-_{(g)} + e^- \rightarrow O^{2-}_{(g)}$, ΔH_4

That according to given information the incorrect statement is :

(a) ΔH_3 is more negative than ΔH_1 and ΔH_2

(b) ΔH_1 is less negative than ΔH_2

(c) $\Delta H_1, \Delta H_2$ and ΔH_3 are negative whereas ΔH_4 is positive

(d) ΔH_1 and ΔH_3 are negative whereas ΔH_2 and ΔH_4 are positive

Electronegativity

45.

Element	Electronegative value
W	2.7
X	2.1
Y	0.8
Z	3.4

The incorrect statement regarding given information is :

(a) *WZ* does not conduct electricity in solid and fused state

(b) *YZ* conducts electricity in fused as well as solution state

(c) *XZ* conducts electricity only in solution state

(d) *WX* conducts electricity only in fused state

46. In the compound *M* — O — H, the *M* — O bond will be broken if:

(a) Δ (E.N.) of *M* and O < Δ (E.N.) of O and H

(b) Δ (E.N.) of *M* and O = Δ (E.N.) of O and H

(c) Δ (E.N.) of *M* and O > Δ (E.N.) of O and H

(d) Cannot be predicated according Δ (E.N.) data

47. Aqueous solutions of two compounds M_1-O-H and M_2-O-H are prepared in two different beakers. If, the electronegativity of $M_1=3.4, M_2=1.2, O=3.5$ and $H=2.1$, then the nature of two solutions will be respectively :
(a) acidic, basic (b) acidic, acidic (c) basic, acidic (d) basic, basic

48. If the ionization enthalpy and electron gain enthalpy of an element are 275 and 86 kcal mol^{-1} respectively, then the electronegativity of the element on the Pauling scale is :
(a) 2.8 (b) 0.0 (c) 4.0 (d) 2.6

49. Consider the following statements :
(I) The radius of an anion is larger than that of the parent atom.
(II) The ionization energy generally increases with increasing atomic number in a period.
(III) The electronegativity of an element is the tendency of an isolated atom to attract an electron.
Which of the above statements is/are correct?
(a) I alone (b) II alone
(c) I and II (d) II and III

50. Which of the following order is correct for the property mentioned in brackets ?
(a) $S^{2-} > Cl^- > K^+ > Ca^{2+}$ (Ionisation energy)
(b) $C < N < F < O$ (2nd Ionisation energy)
(c) $B > Al > Ga > In > Tl$ (Electronegativity)
(d) $Na^+ > Li^+ > Mg^{2+} > Be^{2+} > Al^{3+}$ (Ionic radius)

Level 3

Passage 1

The energy required to pull the most loosely bound electron form an isolated atom is known as ionization potential. It is expressed in electron volts. The value of ionization potential depends on three factors: (i) the charge on the nucleus (ii) the atomic radius and (iii) the screening effect of inner electron shells.

1. Ionization potential of Na would be numerically the same as:
(a) electron affinity of Na^+
(b) electronegativity of Na^+
(c) electron affinity of Na
(d) ionization potential of Mg

2. Which of the following elements has the least ionization potential?
(a) Lithium (b) Cesium (c) Magnesium (d) Calcium

3. Incorrect order of ionisation energy is :
(a) Pb (I.E.) > Sn (I.E.)
(b) Na^+ (I.E.) > Mg^+ (I.E.)
(c) Li^+ (I.E.) < O^+ (I.E.)
(d) Be^+ (I.E.) < C^+ (I.E.)

Passage 2

All the elements, on the basis of electronic configuration can be divided into four blocks, *s*, *p*, *d* and *f*. The ionization energies, electron affinities, electronegativities, atomic and ionic radii and other physical properties usually shown a regular pattern of change within a group or along period with some irregularities.

1. On moving from Li to F in the second period, there would be a decrease in:
(a) non-metallic property
(b) atomic radius
(c) ionization potential
(d) electronegativity

2. Which of the following element has the maximum value of electronegativity?
(a) Aluminium (b) Silicon (c) Phosphorus (d) Sulphur

3. Which of the following element has the maximum electron affinity?
(a) Nitrogen (b) Oxygen (c) Fluorine (d) Chlorine

Passage 3

The second ionisation energies are higher than the first ionisation energies. This is mainly due to the fact that after the removal of the first electron, the atom changes into monovalent positive ion. In the ion, the number of electrons decreases but the nuclear charge remains the same. As a result of this, the remaining electrons are held more tightly by the nucleus and it becomes difficult to remove the second electron. Therefore , the value of second ionisation energy. (IE_2), is greater than that of the first ionisation energy (IE_1). Similarly third ionisation energy (IE_3) is greater than that of second IE_2 .

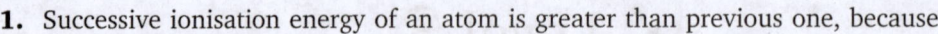

1. Successive ionisation energy of an atom is greater than previous one, because:

(a) $\frac{p}{e}$ ratio increases
(b) $\frac{p}{e}$ ratio decreases
(c) $\frac{p}{e}$ ratio remains constant
(d) none of these

2. Correct order of ionisation potential of coinage metals is:

(a) Au > Ag > Cu
(b) Cu > Ag > Au
(c) Au > Cu > Ag
(d) Ag > Cu > Au

3. IE_1 and IE_2 of Mg metal are 178 and 348 kcal/mol respectively. The energy required for the given reaction is:

$$Mg(g) \longrightarrow Mg^{+2}(g) + 2e^-$$

(a) +170 kcal/mol
(b) +526 kcal/mol
(c) –170 kcal/mol
(d) –526 kcal/mol

Passage 4

Nuclear charge actually experienced by an electron is termed as effective nuclear charge. The effective nuclear charge Z^* actually depends on type of shell and orbital in which electron is actually present. The relative extent to which the various orbitals penetrate the electron clouds of other orbitals is.

$$s > p > d > f \text{ (for the same value of } n)$$

The phenomenon in which penultimate shell electrons act as screen or shield in between nucleus and valence shell electrons and thereby reducing nuclear charge is known as shielding effect. The penultimate shell electrons repel the valence shell electron to keep them loosely held with nucleus. It is thus evident that more is the shielding effect, lesser is the effective nuclear charge and lesser is the ionization energy.

1. Which of the following valence electron experience maximum effective nuclear charge?

(a) $4s^1$
(b) $4p^1$
(c) $3d^1$
(d) $2p^3$

2. Which of the following is not concerned to effective nuclear charge?

(a) Higher ionization potential of carbon than boron
(b) Higher ionization potential of magnesium than aluminium
(c) Higher values of successive ionization energy
(d) Higher electronegativity of higher oxidation state

3. Ionization energy is not influenced by :

(a) Size of atom
(b) Effective nuclear charge
(c) Electrons present in inner shell
(d) Change in entropy

Passage 5

Ionization energies of five elements in kcal/mol are given below :

Atom	I	II	III
P	300	549	920
Q	99	734	1100
R	118	1091	1652
S	176	347	1848
T	497	947	1500

1. Which element is a noble gas ?
(a) *P* (b) *T* (c) *R* (d) *S*

2. Which element form stable unipositive ion ?
(a) *P* (b) *Q* (c) *S* (d) *T*

3. The element having most stable oxidation state +2 is ?
(a) *Q* (b) *R* (c) *S* (d) *T*

4. Which is a non-metal (excluding noble gas)?
(a) *P* (b) *Q* (c) *R* (d) *S*

5. If *Q* reacts with fluorine and oxygen, the molecular formula of fluoride and oxide will be respectively :
(a) QF_3, Q_2O_3 (b) QF, Q_2O (c) QF_2, QO (d) None of these

6. Which of the following pair represents elements of same group ?
(a) *Q, R* (b) *P, Q* (c) *P, S* (d) *Q, S*

Passage 6

The $I.E._1$, and the $I.E._2$ in kJ mol^{-1} of a few elements designated by *P, Q, R, S* are shown below:

Atom	$I.E._1$	$I.E._2$
P	2372	5251
Q	520	7300
R	900	1760
S	1680	3380

Based on the above information, answer the following questions :

1. Which of the element is likely to be reactive metal?
(a) *P* (b) *Q* (c) *R* (d) *S*

2. Which of the elements is likely to be reactive non-metal?
(a) *P* (b) *Q* (c) *R* (d) *S*

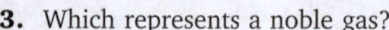

3. Which represents a noble gas?
(a) P (b) Q (c) R (d) S

4. Which of the above elements forms a stable binary halide of the formula MX_2?
(a) P (b) Q (c) R (d) S

Passage 7

Some elements along with their electronic configurations are given below :

I : $1s^2 2s^2$ II : $1s^2 2s^2 2p^6$ III : $1s^2 2s^2 2p^6 3s^2$ IV : $1s^2 2s^2 2p^3$ V : $1s^2 2s^2 2p^5$

Answer the following questions :

1. The element with highest I.E. is :
(a) I (b) III
(c) II (d) V

2. The most ionic compound will be formed between :
(a) I and IV (b) I and V
(c) III and IV (d) III and V

3. Which of the following is the correct order of increasing size?
(a) I < III < IV < V (b) V < IV < III < I
(c) I < IV < V < III (d) V < IV < I < III

Passage 8

J.C. Slater proposed an empirical constant that represents the cumulative extent to which the other electrons of an atom shield (or screen) any particular electron from the nuclear charge. Thus, Slater's screening constant σ is used as : $Z^* = Z - \sigma$

Here, Z is the atomic number of the atom, and hence is equal to the actual number of protons in the atom. The parameter Z^* is the effective nuclear charge, which is smaller than Z, since the electron in question is screened (shielded) from Z by an amount σ. We found that in cases for which screening is small, the effective nuclear charge Z^* is large. Conversely, an electron that is well shielded from the nuclear charge Z experiences a small effective nuclear charge Z^*.

The value of σ for any one electron in a given electron configuration (*i.e.*, in the presence of the other electrons of the atom in question) is calculated using a set of empirical rules developed by Slater. According to these rules, the value of σ for the electron in question is the cumulative total provided by the various other electrons of the atom.

1. The effective nuclear charge at the periphery of chromium atom [$Z = 24$]:
(a) 4.25
(b) 2.60
(c) 3.60
(d) 1.21

2. Which of the following statement is correct?
(a) A 4s-orbital is filled earlier than a 3d-orbital because, Z^* for $3d > Z^*$ for 4s.
(b) A 4s-orbital is filled earlier than a 3d-orbital because, Z^* for $4s > Z^*$ for 3d
(c) The effective nuclear charge for 3d-and 4s-orbitals are same, but energy of 3d-orbital becomes higher.
(d) The effective nuclear charge for 3d and 4s-orbitals are same, but energy of 4s-orbital becomes higher.

3. According to Slater's rule, order of effective nuclear charge (Z^*) for last electron in case of Li, Na and K.
(a) Li > Na > K
(b) K > Na > Li
(c) Na > Li > K
(d) K = Na > Li

Passage 9

Metals have few electrons in their valence shell while non-metals generally have more electrons in their valence shell. Metallic character is closely related to atomic radius and ionisation enthalpy. Metallic character increases from top to bottom in a group and decreases from left to right in a period of periodic table. Metallic character is inversely related to electronegativity of element.

1. The electronegativity of the following elements increase in the order :
(a) C, N, Si, P
(b) N, Si, C, P
(c) Si, P, C, N
(d) P, Si, N, C

2. Considering the elements B, Al, Mg and K, the correct order of their metallic character is :
(a) B > Al > Mg > K
(b) Al > K > B > Mg
(c) Mg > Al > K > B
(d) K > Mg > Al > B

3. 3 $N_0/2$ atoms of $X_{(g)}$ are converted in to $X^+_{(g)}$ by energy E_1, 2 $N_0/3$ atoms of $X_{(g)}$ are converted in to $X^-_{(g)}$ by energy E_2. Hence, ionisation potential and electron affinity of $X_{(g)}$ are:
(N_0 = Avogadro's number)
(a) $\frac{2E_1}{3N_0}, \frac{2E_2}{3N_0}$
(b) $\frac{2E_1}{3N_0}, \frac{3E_2}{2N_0}$
(c) $\frac{3E_1}{2N_0}, \frac{3E_2}{2N_0}$
(d) $\frac{3E_1}{2N_0}, \frac{2E_2}{3N_0}$

Passage 10

The value of four quantum number for the last electron of atom of element 'X' are $n = 7, l = 1, m = +1$ and $s = +1/2$ or $-1/2$ and value of spin magnetic momentum for element 'X' is zero. Element 'X' has two isotopes (I) ${}^{A}_{Z}X$ and, (II) ${}^{B}_{Z}X$.

(Given: "$B - A = B - 2Z = 18$", where A and B are atomic masses and Z is atomic number.)

1. The incorrect statement regarding element 'X' is :
(a) Element 'X' belongs to 18th group.
(b) Number of unpaired electrons in element 'X' is zero
(c) Atomic number of element 'X' is 118
(d) 'X' is representative element

2. The value of A and B respectively are :
(a) 118 and 136 (b) 218 and 236
(c) 236 and 254 (d) 226 and 244

3. The possible value of all four quantum numbers for 90th electron of atom of element 'X' is :

	n	l	m	s
(a)	6	2	0	$-1/2$
(b)	5	2	-1	$+1/2$
(c)	6	0	0	$+1/2$
(d)	5	3	-2	$-1/2$

Passage 11

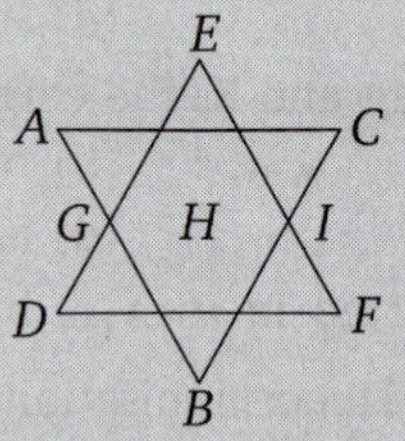

There are nine elements A to I. They belongs to p-block element other than halogen. If atomic number of B is average of atomic number of A and C and atomic number of E is average of atomic number of D and F and atomic number of H is average of atomic number of G and I. Atomic numbers of B, E and H are 7, 15 and 83 respectively and atomic numbers of C, I and F are greater than A, G and D respectively.

1. The incorrect order is :
(a) $F > E$: Second ionisation energy (b) $C > B$: Z_{eff} on valence shell
(c) $I > H$: First ionisation energy (d) $C > F > E$: Electronegativity

2. The correct statement is :
(a) +5 oxidation state of H is more stable than its +3 oxidation state.

(b) G^{2+} is better oxidising agent than G^{4+}
(c) +3 oxidation state of E is more stable than its +5 oxidation state
(d) Ionisation energy of G is greater than that of "Tin".

3. Which of the following statement is incorrect ?
(a) B_2C_5 is acidic in nature
(b) AC_2 is acidic in nature
(c) FC_3 is basic in nature
(d) GC_2 is amphoteric in nature

Passage 12

If P, Q, R and S are elements of 3rd period of p-block in Modern Periodic Table, among these one element is metal and rest are non-metals and their order of electronegativity is given as :

$$P < Q < R < S$$

1. In which of the following linkage release of H^+ is relatively more easier?
(a) P — O — H
(b) S — O — H
(c) Q — O — H
(d) R — O — H

2. Which element is expected to form amphoteric oxide?
(a) P (b) Q (c) R (d) S

3. Chloride compound of which element is hypovalent?
(a) S (b) Q (c) R (d) P

Passage 13

Consider the following representation based on long form of periodic table.

A		U	V	W
B		T		
C	D	X	S	R
		E		Q
H	G	F		P

Value of all four quantum number for last electron of element 'X' in their ground state is $n = 4$, $l = 1$, $m = 1$ and $s = -\frac{1}{2}$ and spin multiplicity of element 'X' in their ground state is 4.

1. Which of the following order is incorrect ?
(a) Magnetic moment : $U > V > A$
(b) Atomic radius : $E > X > T$
(c) Ionisation energy : $R > X > B$
(d) Stability : $F^{3+} < E^{3+} < X^{3+}$

2. The correct order is :
(a) Ionisation energy of V > ionisation energy of U
(b) Electron affinity of X > electron affinity of S
(c) Electron affinity of X > electron affinity of D
(d) $|\Delta H_{EG}|$ of $T > |\Delta H_{EG}|$ of U

3. Which of the following statement is incorrect?
(a) Element P is radioactive
(b) Elements B and C have their almost similar size
(c) Element G is more stable in +4 oxidation state
(d) Element G has electron with $n = 4, l = 3, m = 0$ and $s = +\frac{1}{2}$ quantum numbers

Passage 14

Consider the following elements with their electronegativity value.

Elements	A	B	C	D
Electronegativity (Pauling scale)	3.77	1.12	2.25	3.10

1. Incorrect statements is :
(a) AOH is more acidic than DOH
(b) BOH is more basic than COH
(c) 'AB' molecule is predominantly ionic
(d) 'D — OH' bond is more weaker than 'B — OH' bond in polar solvent

2. Select correct statement :
(a) Oxide of element D is more acidic than that of A
(b) Oxides of elements C and D are basic in nature
(c) Oxide of element B is acidic in nature
(d) BOH is more basic than H_2O

Passage 15

In the modern periodic table, elements are arranged in order of increasing atomic numbers which is related to the electronic configuration. Depending upon the type of orbitals receiving the last electron, the elements in the periodic table have been divided into four blocks, *viz.*, *s*, *p*, *d*, and *f*. The modern periodic table consists of 7 periods and 18 groups. Each period begins with the filling of a new energy shell. In accordance with the Aufbau principle, the seven periods (1 to 7) have 2, 8, 8, 18, 18, 32 and 32 elements respectively. To avoid the periodic table being too long, the two series of *f*-block elements, called lanthanoids and actinoids are placed at the bottom of the main body of the periodic table.

1. Which of the elements whose atomic numbers are given below, cannot be accommodated in the present set up of the long form of the periodic table?
(a) 107 (b) 118 (c) 126 (d) 102

2. The element with atomic number 57 belongs to :
(a) *s*-block (b) *p*-block (c) *d*-block (d) *f*-block

ONE OR MORE ANSWERS IS/ARE CORRECT

Periodic Table

1. Assign the position of the element having outer electronic configuration,

(A) ns^2np^2 $(n=6)$

(B) $(n-1)\ d^2ns^2$ $(n=4)$

(C) $(n-2)\ f^7\ (n-1)\ d^{-1}ns^2$ $(n=6)$

Which of the following statement(s) is/are correct?

(a) The element 'A' belong to 3rd period and 16th group.

(b) The element 'B' belong to 4th period and 4th group.

(c) The element 'C' belong to 6th period and 3rd group and is lanthanide element.

(d) All *A*, *B*, *C* elements are metals

2. Which of the following statement(s) regarding periodic properties is/ are incorrect?

(a) Alkali metals have highest I.E. in respective period

(b) Noble gas have highest I.E. in respective period

(c) First electron affinity of nitrogen is less than oxygen

(d) F atom has smallest radius in periodic table

3. Which of the following properties among halogens decrease(s) from fluorine to iodine?

(a) Electronegativity (b) Bond energy

(c) Ionisation energy (d) Electron affinity

4. In halogens, which of the following decreases from fluorine to iodine?

(a) Bond length (b) Electronegativity

(c) The ionization energy of the element (d) Oxidizing power

5. Mark the correct statements out of the following :

(a) He has the highest $I.E._1$ in the periodic table

(b) Cl has the highest E.A. out of all the elements in the periodic table

(c) Hg and Br are liquid at room temperature

(d) In any period, the atomic radius of the noble gas is lowest

6. *S*, *T* and *U* are the aqueous chlorides of the elements *X*, *Y* and *Z* respectively. *X*, *Y* and *Z* are in the same period of the periodic table. *U* gives a white precipitate with NaOH but this white precipitate dissolves as more NaOH is added. When NaOH is added to *T*, a white precipitate forms which does not dissolve when more base is added. *S* does not give precipitate with NaOH.

Which of the following statements are correct ?

(a) The three elements are metals

(b) The electronegativity decreases from *X* to *Y* to *Z*.

(c) *X*, *Y* and *Z* could be sodium, magnesium and aluminium respectively.

(d) The first ionization increases from *X* to *Y* to *Z*.

7. The diagram below shows part of the skeleton of the periodic table in which elements are indicated by letters which are not their usual symbols.

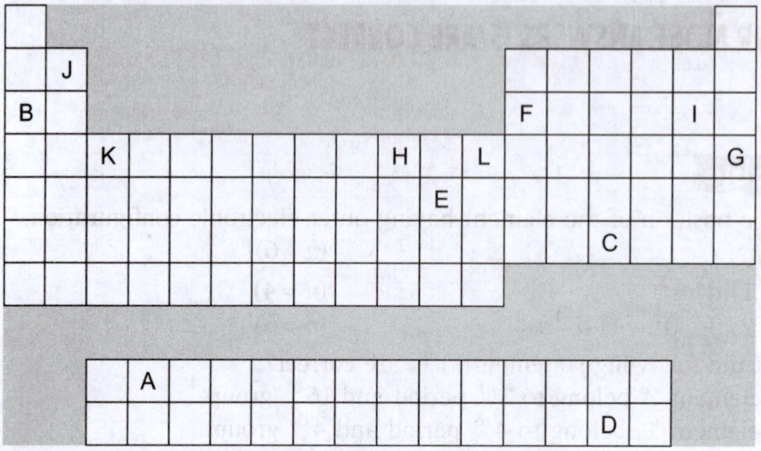

Answer the following on the basis of modern periodic table :

(I) Alkali metal(s)
(II) An elements with the outer configuration of d^8s^2
(III) Lanthanoids
(IV) Representative element(s)
(V) Elements with incomplete *f*-subshell
(VI) Halogen(s)
(VII) *s*-block element(s)
(VIII) Transition element(s)
(IX) Noble gase(s)
(X) Non-transition element(s)

8. The diagram below shows part of the skeleton of the periodic table in which elements are indicated by letters which are not their usual symbols.

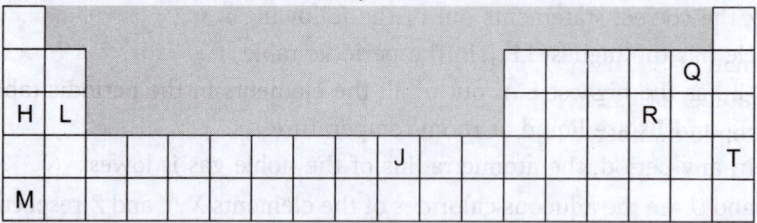

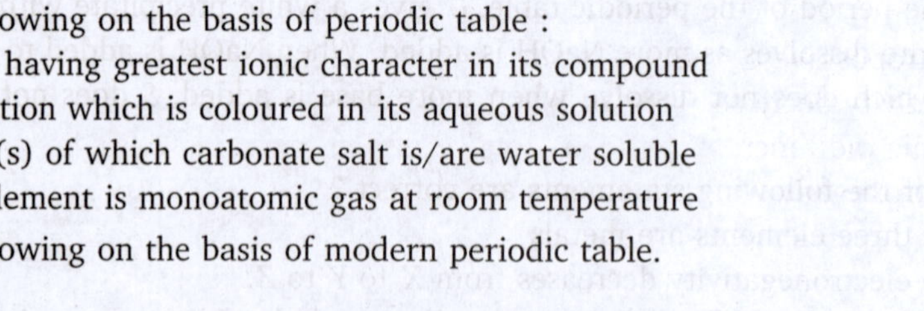

Answer the following on the basis of periodic table :

(I) Element having greatest ionic character in its compound
(II) Metal cation which is coloured in its aqueous solution
(III) Element(s) of which carbonate salt is/are water soluble
(IV) Which element is monoatomic gas at room temperature

9. Answer the following on the basis of modern periodic table.

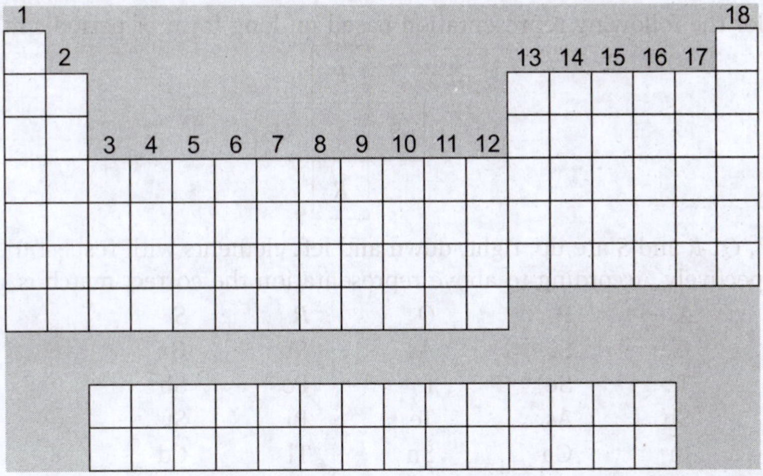

(I) Group no. of the elements with the valence shell ground state electron configuration ns^2np^5

(II) Group no. of the elements with the valence shell ground state electron configuration ns^2np^3

(III) Group no. of the elements that have only three unpaired *p* electron in ground state

(IV) Alkaline earth metals

(V) Group 3A elements

10. Which of the following statements concerning elements with atomic number 10 is true?

(a) It forms a covalent network solid

(b) Element is monoatomic

(c) It has a almost zero value of electron affinity

(d) It has extremely high value of ionization energy

11. Which of the following pairs of elements have same number of electrons in their outermost shell ?

(a) Mn, Fe (b) Na, Sr (c) As, Bi (d) Se, Te

12. A change of Zn to Zn^{2+} is a accompanied by a decrease in :

(a) number of valence electrons (b) atomic mass

(c) atomic number (d) number of shells

13. The elements which are radioactive and have been named after the names of planets are :

(a) Hg (b) Np (c) Pu (d) Ra

14. The properties which are common to both groups 1 and 17 elements in the periodic table are :

(a) Electropositive character increases down the groups

(b) Reactivity decreases from top to bottom in these groups

(c) Atomic radii increases as the atomic number increases

(d) Electronegativity decreases on moving down a group

15. There are three elements *A*, *B* and *C*. Their atomic number are Z_1, Z_2 and Z_3 respectively. If $Z_1 - Z_2 = 2$ and $\frac{Z_1 + Z_2}{2} = Z_3 - 2$ and the electronic configuration of element *A* is $[Ar]3d^6 4s^2$, then correct order of magnetic momentum is/are :

(a) $B^+ > A^{2+} > C^{2+}$ (b) $A^{3+} > B^{2+} > C$

(c) $B > A > C^{2+}$ (d) $B = A^{3+} > C^{3+}$

16. Consider the following representation based on long form of periodic table.

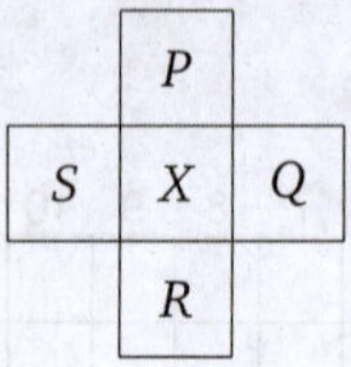

Here P, Q, R and S are up, right, down and left elements with respect to the central element 'X' respectively. According to above representation the correct match is/are :

	X	P	Q	R	S
(a)	Ge	Si	As	Sn	Ga
(b)	Te	Se	I	Po	Sb
(c)	Sb	As	Te	Bi	Sn
(d)	In	Ga	Sn	Tl	Cd

17. Which of the following match is/are correct regarding B, Al, C and S elements?
(a) The highest first ionisation enthalpy : C
(b) The largest atomic size : Al
(c) The most negative electron gain enthalpy : C
(d) The most metallic character : Al

18. Consider the value of all four quantum number for last electron and spin multiplicity $(2s + 1)$ for given two element 'X' and 'Y' in their ground state :

	n	l	m	s	$\|2s + 1\|$
X:	2	0	0	$+1/2$	1
Y:	2	1	-1	$-1/2$	4

The according to given information the correct statement is :
(a) The bond angle $(H - \hat{Y} - H)$ of possible hydride of element Y is less than $109°28'$
(b) The possible halide of 'X' has two vacant p-orbitals on its central atom.
(c) Magnetic moment of Y is greater than X
(d) X and Y element exhibits only single oxidation state

19. An element 'X' present in its ground state, the value of principal and azimuthal quantum number for last electron of element 'X' is $n = 3$ and $l = 1$ and spin multiplicity for given element is 4. Then according to given information correct statement(s) regarding given element 'X' is/are :
(a) Element 'X' is 3rd period and 15th group element
(b) In valence shell of element 'X' electron density is symmetrically distributed.
(c) Element 'X' has full filled valence shell.
(d) None of the above

Atomic/Ionic Radius

20. Which of the following pairs have approximately the same atomic radii?
(a) Zr and Hf (b) Al and Mg (c) Al and Ga (d) Na and Ne

21. The correct order of radii is/are :
(a) $Pb > Pb^{2+} > Pb^{4+}$
(b) $In^{+} > Sn^{2+} > Sb^{3+} > Te^{4+}$
(c) Co > Ni > Cu > Zn
(d) $K^{+} > Li^{+} > Mg^{2+} > Al^{3+}$

Ionisation Energy

22. The first ionisation energy of first atom is greater than that of second atom, whereas reverse order is true for their second ionisation energy. Which set of elements is in accordance to above statement ?
(a) C > B (b) P > S (c) Be > B (d) Mg > Na

23. Ionization energy of an element is :
(a) Equal in magnitude but opposite in sign to the electron gain enthalpy of the cation of the element
(b) Same as electron affinity of the element
(c) Energy required to remove one valence electron from an isolated gaseous atom in its ground state
(d) Equal in magnitude but opposite in sign to the electron gain enthalpy of the anion of the element

24. Consider the following ionization steps :

$$M(g) \longrightarrow M^+(g) + e^-; \quad \Delta H = +100 \text{ eV}$$

$$M(g) \longrightarrow M^{2+}(g) + 2e^-; \quad \Delta H = +250 \text{ eV}$$

Select correct statement(s) :
(a) $I.E._1$ of $M(g)$ is 100 eV (b) $I.E._1$ of $M^+(g)$ is 150 eV
(c) $I.E._2$ of $M(g)$ is 250 eV (d) $I.E._2$ of $M(g)$ is 150 eV

25. Select the correct order of periodic properties of species :
(a) $Fe^{2+} < Fe^{3+}$: ionic radii (b) N < O : second ionisation energy
(c) Cu < Zn : atomic radius (d) In < Tl : first ionisation energy

26. Select the incorrect statement(s)/order(s) :
(a) *d*-orbital can accommodate 10 electrons
(b) $\underset{2s^2 2p^6 3s^1}{Na} \xrightarrow{I.E._1} \underset{2s^2 2p^6}{Na^+} \xrightarrow{I.E._2} \underset{2s^2 2p^5}{Na^{2+}} \xrightarrow{I.E._3} \underset{2s^2 2p^4}{Na^{3+}}$, order of successive I.E. is $I.E._1 < I.E._2 > I.E._3$
(c) Number of unpaired electrons in Co^{2+} cation > Number of unpaired electrons in Co^{3+} cation
(d) First ionisation energy of Pt is greater than that of Pd

27. Consider the following values of I.E. (eV) for elements *W* and *X* :

Element	$I.E._1$	$I.E._2$	$I.E._3$	$I.E._4$
W	10.5	15.5	24.9	79.8
X	8	14.8	78.9	105.8

Other two element *Y* and *Z* have outer electronic configuration ns^2np^4 and ns^2np^5 respectively. Then according to given information which of the following compound(s) is/are not possible?
(a) W_2Y_3 (b) X_2Y_3 (c) WZ_2 (d) XZ_2

28. The sum of IE_1 and IE_2, IE_3 and IE_4 for element *P* and *Q* are given below :

	$IE_1 + IE_2$	$IE_3 + IE_4$
(*P*)	2.45	8.82
(*Q*)	2.85	6.11

Then according to the given information the correct statement(s) is/are :

(a) P^{2+} is more stable than Q^{2+}
(b) P^{2+} is less stable than Q^{2+}
(c) P^{4+} is more stable than Q^{4+}
(d) P^{4+} is less stable than Q^{4+}

29. Consider value of all four quantum number for last electrons and magnetic moment and valence electrons of elements *W*, *X*, *Y* and *Z* in their ground state :

Element	***n***	***l***	***m***	***s***	**Magnetic moment (μ)**	**Valence electrons**
W	3	0	0	$+\frac{1}{2}$	0	2
X	3	1	+1	$-\frac{1}{2}$	$\sqrt{3}$	3
Y	3	1	−1	$+\frac{1}{2}$	$\sqrt{15}$	5
Z	3	1	0	$-\frac{1}{2}$	$\sqrt{8}$	6

Then according to given information the correct statement(s) is/are :

(a) $I.E._1$ of element *W* is greater than $I.E._1$ of element *X*
(b) $I.E._1$ of element *Y* is greater than $I.E._1$ of element *Z*
(c) $I.E._2$ of element *X* is greater than $I.E._2$ of element *W*
(d) $I.E._2$ of element *Z* is greater than $I.E._2$ of element *Y*

30. Consider the successive ionisation energy for an element '*A*'.
IE_1, IE_2, IE_3, IE_4, IE_5 are 100 eV, 150 eV, 181 eV, 2000 eV, 2200 eV.
Select correct statement(s) for element '*A*' :

(a) Element '*A*' may be metal
(b) Element '*A*' may form trivalent cation
(c) Oxide of element '*A*' may be amphoteric
(d) Element '*A*' may be non-metal

31. According to Slater's rule, correct order of $Z_{eff.}$ on valence shell electron is :

(a) $Fe > Fe^{2+} > Fe^{3+}$
(b) $N^{3-} < O^{2-} < F^-$
(c) $Na^+ < Mg^{2+} < Al^{3+}$
(d) $Tl^{2+} < V^{3+} < Mn^{5+}$

Electron Affinity

32. Which of the following order is/are correct?

(a) Mg^{2+} (size) > Li^+ (size)
(b) S (E.A.) > O(E.A.)
(c) Hg (I.E.) > Cd(I.E.)
(d) P(I.E.) > S(I.E.)

33. Correct order of electron affinity is/are:

(a) S > O
(b) Al > B
(c) Mg > Na
(d) P > N

34. Which of the following statement(s) is/are correct?

(a) van der Waals' radius of iodine is more than its covalent radius.
(b) All isoelectronic ions of corresponding elements belong to the same period of the periodic table.
(c) IE of N-atom is higher than that of O-atom, while IE_2 of O-atom is higher than that of N-atom.
(d) The electron affinity of fluorine is greater than that of chlorine.

35. Which of the following statement regarding halogens is/are correct?
(a) Ionization energy decreases with increase in atomic number
(b) Electronegativity decreases with increase in atomic number
(c) Electron affinity decreases with increase in atomic number
(d) Enthalpy of fusion increases with increase in atomic number

36. Which of the following statements are correct?
(a) F is the most electronegative and Cs is the most electropositive element
(b) The ionization energy of halogens decreases from F to I
(c) The electron affinity of Cl is higher than that of F through their electronegativities are in the reverse order
(d) The electron affinity of noble gases is almost zero

37. Consider the order $O^{2-} < F^- < Na^+ < Mg^{2+}$. Then correct statement(s) is/are :
(a) Increasing order of Z_{eff} (b) Increasing order of size
(c) Increasing order of I.E. (d) Increasing order of E.A.

38. Consider the following reactions :
(i) $O_{(g)} + e^- \longrightarrow O^-_{(g)}$, ΔH_1 (ii) $F_{(g)} + e^- \longrightarrow F^-_{(g)}$, ΔH_2
(iii) $Cl_{(g)} + e^- \longrightarrow Cl^-_{(g)}$, ΔH_3 (iv) $O^-_{(g)} + e^- \longrightarrow O^{2-}_{(g)}$, ΔH_4
Then according to given information the correct statement is/are:
(a) ΔH_3 is more negative than ΔH_1 and ΔH_2
(b) ΔH_1 is less negative than ΔH_2
(c) $\Delta H_1, \Delta H_2$ and ΔH_3 are negative whereas ΔH_4 is positive.
(d) ΔH_1 and ΔH_3 are negative whereas ΔH_2 and ΔH_4 are positive.

39. Which of the following is incorrect order of property as indicated ?
(a) $Na^+ < F^- < O^{2-} < Ne < Ar$: Atomic size
(b) Br < Se < As < Ge : Metallic character
(c) Na < Al < Si < Mg : Ionisation energy
(d) I < Br < Cl < F : Electron affinity

40. Which of the following is/are correct order ?
(a) Atomic radius : $F < O < F^- < O^{2-}$
(b) 2nd ionisation energy : C < N < F < O
(c) Electron affinity : I < Br < F < Cl
(d) Z_{eff} (effective nuclear change) : $Al < Al^+ < Al^{3+} < Al^{2+}$

41. Consider the following sequence of reaction :

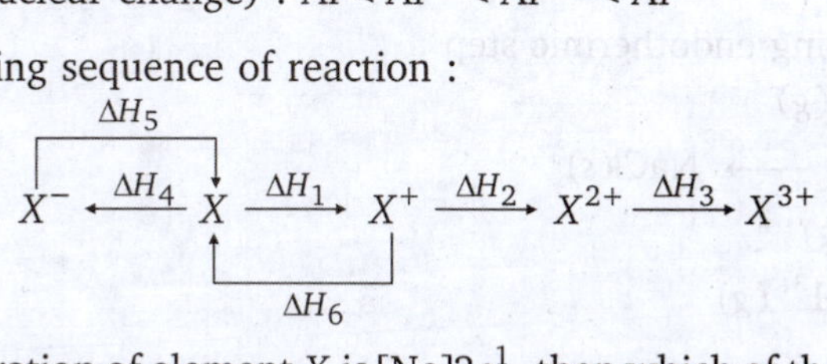

If electronic configuration of element X is $[Ne]3s^1$, then which of the following order is correct regarding given enthalpies?
(a) $|\Delta H_4| = |\Delta H_5|$ (b) $|\Delta H_2| > |\Delta H_1|$
(c) $|\Delta H_2| > |\Delta H_3|$ (d) $|\Delta H_1| = |\Delta H_6|$

Electronegativity

42. The correct statement is/are :
(a) Zirconium (Zr) and hafnium (Hf) have almost same size
(b) Correct order of ionisation energy of coinage metals is : Cu > Ag < Au
(c) Carbon atom in CCl_4 is more electronegative than carbon atom in CF_4
(d) Pb^{2+} is more stable than Pb^{4+}

43. Which of the following statements is true about electronegativity?
(a) Electronegativity of an element depends upon its effective nuclear charge
(b) Electronegativity of a cation is proportional to charge on the cation
(c) Electronegativity increases as the *s*-character in hybrid orbital increases
(d) Electronegativity of a anion is proportional to charge on the anion

44. Which of the following elements have the almost equal value of electronegativity?
(a) H (b) S
(c) Te (d) P

45. Which of the following parameters cannot be estimated by using Born-Haber cycle?
(a) Hydration energy of ion (b) Electron gain enthalpy
(c) Lattice energy (d) Electronegativity

46. Select correct order(s) of electronegativity of element is/are :
(a) Paulling scale (E.N. of F-atom) > Mulliken scale (E.N. of F-atom)
(b) Cl_2O_7 (E.N. of Cl-atom) > Cl_2O_5 (E.N. of Cl-atom)
(c) CH_4 (E.N. of C-atom) > CO_2 (E.N. of C-atom)
(d) Cu^{2+} (E.N.) > Cu^{+} (E.N.)

Hydration Energy

47. Choose the correct statement(s) :
(a) H^+ is the smallest size cation in the periodic table.
(b) van der Waals' radius of chlorine is more than covalent radius.
(c) Ionic mobility of hydrated Li^+ is greater than that of hydrated Na^+.
(d) He atom is having highest I.E. in the periodic table.

Lattice Energy

48. Select equations having endothermic step :
(a) $S^-(g) \longrightarrow S^{2-}(g)$
(b) $Na^+(g) + Cl^-(g) \longrightarrow NaCl(s)$
(c) $N(g) \longrightarrow N^-(g)$
(d) $Al^{2+}(g) \longrightarrow Al^{3+}(g)$

49. Consider the following Born-Haber's cycle :

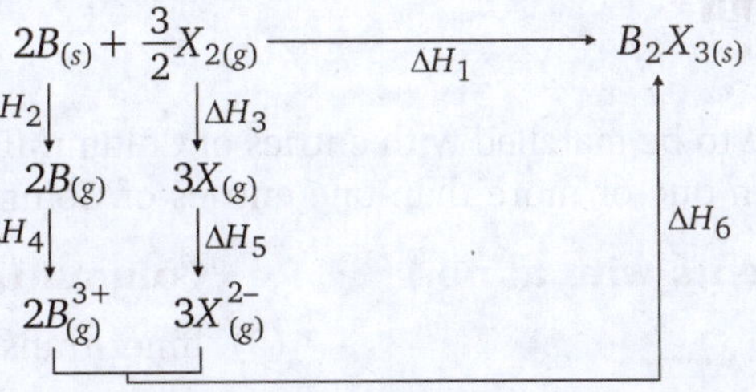

(Where ΔH_1, ΔH_2, ΔH_3, ΔH_4, ΔH_5 and ΔH_6 are in kJ/mol)
Then according to given information the correct statement is/are :

(a) ΔH_2 and ΔH_3 are always positive

(b) $\Delta H_1 = 2\Delta H_2 + \frac{3}{2}\Delta H_3 + 2\Delta H_4 + 3\Delta H_5 + \Delta H_6$

(c) Second electron gain enthalpy of X is negative

(d) ΔH_1 must be negative for formation of B_2X_3(s)

Nature of Oxides

50. Which of the following oxides is/are amphoteric?

(a) Na_2O (b) CaO (c) Al_2O_3 (d) SnO_2

51. Which of the following show amphoteric behaviour?

(a) $Zn(OH)_2$ (b) $Be(OH)_2$

(c) $Al(OH)_3$ (d) $Pb(OH)_2$

MATCH THE COLUMN

Entries of Column-I are to be matched with entries of Column-II. Each entry of Column-I may have the matching with one or more than one entries of Column-II.

1.

Column-I (elements with at no.)	Column-II (types of elements)
(A) X (at. no. = 52)	(P) Inner-transition element
(B) Y (at. no. = 57)	(Q) Representative element
(C) Z (at. no. = 48)	(R) Non-transition element
	(S) *d*-block element

2.

Column-I	Column-II
(A) Increasing order of I.E.	(P) F < O < S < Se
(B) Increasing order of electron affinity	(Q) O < N < F < Ne
(C) Increasing order of atomic size	(R) Na < Mg < Al< Si
	(S) $O^{2-} < O^- < O < O^+$

3.

Column-I	Column-II
(A) F > Cl > Br > I	(P) Ionisation energy
(B) $Fe^{3+} > Fe^{2+} > Fe$	(Q) Size
(C) $I^- > I > I^+$	(R) Magnitude of ΔH_{eg}
(D) O > C > B > N	(S) Effective nuclear charge

4.

Column-I	$(IE)_1$	$(IE)_2$	Column-II
(A)	2372	5251	(P) More reactive metal
(B)	520	7300	(Q) Reactive non-metal
(C)	900	1760	(R) Noble gas
(D)	1680	3380	(S) Metal forms a stable binary halide of the formula AX_2
			(T) Exhibit+2 electrovalency

5.

Column-I (atomic number of element)	Column-II (IUPAC name)
(A) 105	(P) Uun
(B) 107	(Q) Uns
(C) 109	(R) Unp
(D) 110	(S) Une

6.

Column-I (atomic number)	Column-II (position in the periodic table)
(A) 52	(P) *s*-block
(B) 56	(Q) *p*-block
(C) 57	(R) *d*-block
(D) 60	(S) *f*-block

7.

Column-I (type of elements)	Column-II (outer electronic configuration)
(A) Inert gas elements	(P) ns^{1-2} to ns^2np^5
(B) Representative elements	(Q) $1s^2$ and ns^2np^6
(C) Transition elements	(R) $(n-2)\, f^{1-14}\, (n-1)\, d^{1 \text{ or } 0}\, ns^2$
(D) Inner transition elements	(S) $(n-1)\, d^{1-10}\, ns^{1 \text{ or } 2}$

8.

Column-I (elements)	Column-II (periodic properties)
(A) F	(P) Maximum ionization energy
(B) Cl	(Q) Maximum electronegativity
(C) Fe	(R) Maximum electron affinity
(D) He	(S) Variable oxidation state

9.

Column-I	Column-II
(A) Fullerene	(P) Actinoids
(B) Promethium	(Q) Lewis base
(C) Water	(R) Allotrope
(D) Lawrencium	(S) Lanthanoids

10.

Column-I	Column-II
(A) $1s^2, 2s^2 2p^6, 3s^2 3p^1$	(P) Largest $(\text{I.E.})_1$
(B) $1s^2, 2s^2 2p^6, 3s^2 3p^5$	(Q) Largest $(\text{I.E.})_4$
(C) $1s^2, 2s^2 2p^6, 3s^2 3p^6, 4s^1$	(R) Largest $(\text{I.E.})_3$
(D) $1s^2, 2s^2 2p^6, 3s^2 3p^6$	(S) Lowest $(\text{I.E.})_1$
	(T) Largest $(\text{I.E.})_2$

11.

Column-I (Electronic configuration)	Column-II (Corresponding elements)
(A) $[Xe]4f^{14}5d^{10}6s^2$	(P) *s*-block element
(B) $[Rn]5f^{14}6d^1 7s^2$	(Q) Transition element
(C) $[Xe]4f^{14}5d^{10}6s^2 6p^6 7s^2$	(R) *d*-block element
(D) $[Xe]4f^{14}5d^2 6s^2$	(S) Representative element
	(T) Inner-transition element

12.

Column-I Elements (Electrons in K, L, M, N...)	Column-II Statements
(A) W (2,8,7)	(P) Paramagnetic
(B) X (2,8,18,8)	(Q) 3rd group element
(C) Y (2,8,14,2)	(R) Last electron does not enter to valence shell
(D) Z (2,8,18,25,8,2)	(S) Reactive non-metal
	(T) Diamagnetic

13.

Column-I (Outer electronic configuration of element in ground state)	Column-II (Characteristics/period and group number in long from of periodic table)
(A) $(n-1)d^5 ns^1$	(P) Highest spin magnetic moment
(B) $(n-1)d^1 ns^2$	(Q) 6th period element
(C) $ns^2 np^3$	(R) Period number and group number are same
(D) $(n-2)f^1 (n-1)d^1 ns^2$	(S) Period number is double than group number
	(T) Symmetrical distribution of electron density

14.

Column-I	Column-II
(A) $F^- > Cl^- > Br^- > I^-$	(P) Hydration energy
(B) $Na^+ < Mg^{2+} < Al^{3+}$	(Q) Hydrated size
(C) $Li^+ < Na^+ < K^+$	(R) Ionic mobility
(D) $Cr^{2+} < Cr^{3+} < Cr^{6+}$	(S) Electrical conductance
	(T) Ionic radius

ASSERTION-REASON TYPE QUESTIONS

These questions consist of two statements each, printed as assertion and reason, while answering these questions you are required to choose any one of the following responses.

(A) If both assertion and reason are true and the reason is the correct explanation of assertion

(B) If both assertion and reason are true but reason is not the correct explanation of assertion

(C) If assertion is true but the reason is false

(D) If assertion is false but the reason is true

1. **Assertion :** In CsF salt, size of Cs^+ is slight higher than size of F^-.
   Reason : Cs^+ is largest monoatomic cation and F^- is smallest anion.
2. **Assertion :** First electron affinity of all elements is positive.
   Reason : Successive electron affinity of all elements is negative.
3. **Assertion :** Helium atom has highest ionisation energy among all the elements.
   Reason : Helium is smallest atom among all the elements.
4. **Assertion :** F^- ion has highest hydrated radius among the other halide ions.
   Reason : Ionic radius of F^- is smallest among anion.
5. **Assertion :** Magnitude of electron gain enthalpy of oxygen is less than that of fluorine but greater than that of nitrogen.
   Reason : Ionisation enthalpy order is as follows : N>O<F.
6. **Assertion :** Formation of Cl^- ion is exothermic whereas O^{2-} ion formation is endothermic.
   Reason : EA_2 of oxygen is endothermic and greater than its exothermic EA_1 value of oxygen.
7. **Assertion :** The electron gain enthalpy of N is +ve while that of P is –ve.
   Reason : Smaller atomic size of N in which there is a considerable electron-electron repulsion and hence the additional electron is not accepted easily.
8. **Assertion :** The formation of $F^-_{(g)}$ from $F_{(g)}$ is exothermic, whereas that of $O^{2-}_{(g)}$ from $O_{(g)}$ is endothermic.
   Reason : The addition of second electron to a monovalent anion is difficult because both have the same charge and experience more repulsion.
9. **Assertion :** Na^+ and Al^{3+} are isoelectronic but ionic radius Al^{3+} is less than that of Na^+.
   Reason : The magnitude of effective nuclear charge on the outershell electrons in Al^{3+} is greater than that in Na^+.
10. **Assertion :** The third period contains only 8 elements and not 18 like 4th period.
    Reason : In III period filling starts from $3s^1$ and complete at $3p^6$ whereas in IV period it starts from $4s^1$ and complete after $3d^{10}$.
11. **Assertion :** Cs and F_2 combines violently to form CsF.
    Reason : Cs is most electropositive and F is most electronegative.

12. Assertion : Second E.A. for halogens is almost zero.
Reason : Fluorine has maximum value of electron affinity.

13. Assertion : F atom has less electron affinity than Cl atom.
Reason : Additional electrons are repelled more strongly by 3*p* electrons in Cl atom than by 2*p* electrons in F atom.

14. Assertion : Among the halogens bond energy of F_2 is minimum.
Reason : Among halogens F atom is smallest in size.

15. Assertion : The first ionization energy of Be is greater than that of B.
Reason : 2*p*-orbital is lower in energy than 2*s*-orbital.

16. Assertion : Noble gases have highest ionization enthalpies in their respective periods.
Reason : Noble gases have stable closed shell electronic configuration.

17. Assertion : Helium and beryllium have similar outer electronic configuration of the type ns^2.
Reason : Both are chemically inert.

18. Assertion : The first ionization enthalpy of aluminium is lower than that of magnesium.
Reason : Ionic radius of aluminium cation is smaller than that of magnesium cation.

SUBJECTIVE PROBLEMS

1. The number of electrons for Zn^{2+} cation that have the value of azimuthal quantum number = 0 is :

2. Calculate the electronegativity of silicon atom using Allred-Rochow's method. If covalent radius of silicon is 1.0Å. (rounded in nearest integer value)

3. If heat of solution for $AB(s)$ is -0.95×10^{x} kcal/mol and lattice energy for $AB(s)$ is 700 kcal/mol and hydration energy for $A^+(g)$ is –1000 kcal/mol and $B^-(g)$ is –650 kcal/mol then calculate value of x.

4. Consider the following Born-Haber's cycle for formation of $MX_3(s)$.

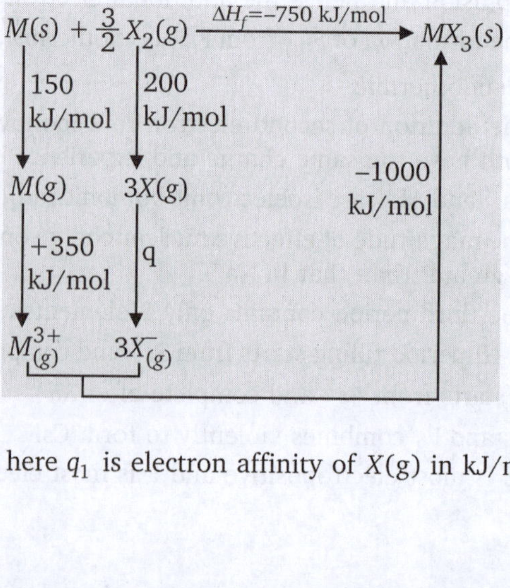

Then calculate value $\frac{q_1}{50}$, here q_1 is electron affinity of $X(g)$ in kJ/mol.

5. Calculate the value of $-U/100$, for $AB(s)$, from following data of Born-Haber's cycle. [where U is lattice energy in kJ/mol]

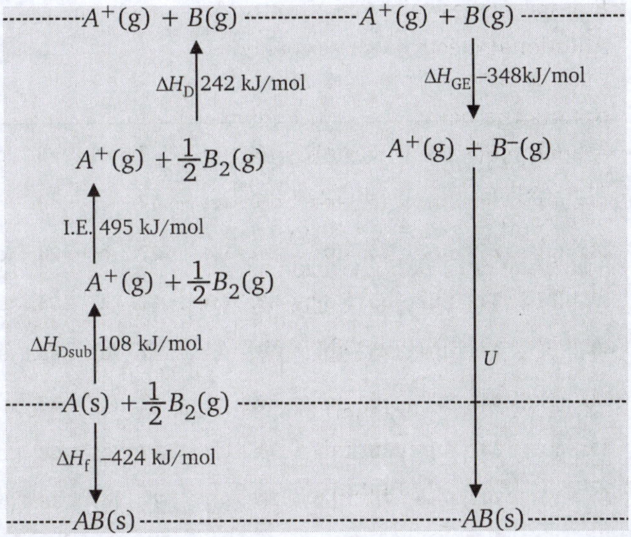

6. Consider the following orders :
(i) HF > HCl > HBr > HI : Lewis basic character
(ii) $CH_4 < CCl_4 < CF_4$: Electronegativity of central 'C'-atom
(iii) $Mg^{2+} < K^+ < S^{2-} < Se^{2-}$: Ionic radius
(iv) Ni > Pd > Pt : Ionisation energy
(v) $As^{5+} > Sb^{5+} > Bi^{5+}$: Stable oxidation state
(vi) LiF > NaF > KF > RbF: Lattice energy
(vii) $F^-_{(aq.)} > Cl^-_{(aq.)} > Br^-_{(aq.)} > I^-_{(aq.)}$: Electrical conductance
(viii) $Li^+ < Mg^{2+} < Al^{3+}$: Hydration energy
(ix) F > Cl > Br > I : Electron affinity
(x) $BeCl_2 < AlCl_3 < SiCl_4$: Lewis acidic character
Then calculate value of $|x-y|^2$, where x and y are correct and incorrect orders respectively.

7. Find out total number of representative elements among the given elements :
Cd, Nb, Ta, Te, Ra, Mo, Po, Pd, Tc

8. An element 'X' has its electronic configuration of 'K' shell is $(n-5)s^2$ and total number of electrons in its outermost, penultimate and antipenultimate shell are 2, 8 and 25 respectively, then find out total number of unpaired electrons in element 'X' in their ground state.

9. If value of spin quantum number(s) $= -1/2, 0, +1/2$ then calculate number of groups in the new form of periodic table if all other rules of electronic configurations are remain same.

10. How many pairs are, in which first species has lower ionisation energy than second species:
(i) N and O (ii) Br and K (iii) Be and B (iv) I and I^-
(v) Li and Li^+ (vi) O and S (vii) Ba and Sr

11. Total number of element(s) which have only single oxidation state (other than zero) in their corresponding stable compounds : Cs, Ba, F, Zn, Be, Al, Sr, Ga, Pb

Answers

Level-1

1.	(b)	2.	(a)	3.	(c)	4.	(c)	5.	(a)	6.	(b)	7.	(d)	8.	(c)	9.	(c)	10.	(d)
11.	(b)	12.	(a)	13.	(a)	14.	(b)	15.	(d)	16.	(c)	17.	(c)	18.	(c)	19.	(b)	20.	(d)
21.	(c)	22.	(d)	23.	(d)	24.	(c)	25.	(b)	26.	(b)	27.	(b)	28.	(c)	29.	(b)	30.	(c)
31.	(b)	32.	(c)	33.	(d)	34.	(c)	35.	(d)	36.	(c)	37.	(c)	38.	(b)	39.	(d)	40.	(b)
41.	(a)	42.	(a)	43.	(b)	44.	(b)	45.	(b)	46.	(b)	47.	(d)	48.	(a)	49.	(c)	50.	(d)
51.	(b)	52.	(c)	53.	(c)	54.	(b)	55.	(c)	56.	(c)	57.	(b)	58.	(a)	59.	(d)	60.	(b)
61.	(c)	62.	(c)	63.	(a)	64.	(c)	65.	(b)	66.	(a)	67.	(b)	68.	(c)	69.	(a)	70.	(d)
71.	(d)	72.	(b)	73.	(b)	74.	(c)	75.	(b)	76.	(d)	77.	(a)	78.	(b)	79.	(a)	80.	(b)
81.	(a)	82.	(b)	83.	(c)	84.	(a)	85.	(a)	86.	(b)	87.	(c)	88.	(d)	89.	(a)	90.	(d)
91.	(a)	92.	(c)	93.	(c)	94.	(c)	95.	(a)	96.	(a)	97.	(d)	98.	(a)	99.	(d)	100.	(a)

Level-2

1.	(b)	2.	(d)	3.	(c)	4.	(b)	5.	(a)	6.	(b)	7.	(c)	8.	(c)	9.	(c)	10.	(a)
11.	(d)	12.	(c)	13.	(b)	14.	(b)	15.	(b)	16.	(b)	17.	(c)	18.	(c)	19.	(d)	20.	(c)
21.	(a)	22.	(c)	23.	(d)	24.	(d)	25.	(b)	26.	(b)	27.	(d)	28.	(b)	29.	(c)	30.	(a)
31.	(d)	32.	(d)	33.	(c)	34.	(a)	35.	(a)	36.	(d)	37.	(b)	38.	(c)	39.	(c)	40.	(b)
41.	(b)	42.	(b)	43.	(b)	44.	(d)	45.	(d)	46.	(c)	47.	(a)	48.	(a)	49.	(c)	50.	(b)

Level-3

Passage-1	1.	(a)	2.	(b)	3.	(c)						
Passage-2	1.	(b)	2.	(d)	3.	(d)						
Passage-3	1.	(a)	2.	(c)	3.	(b)						
Passage–4	1.	(d)	2.	(b)	3.	(d)						
Passage–5	1.	(b)	2.	(b)	3.	(c)	4.	(a)	5.	(b)	6.	(a)
Passage–6	1.	(b)	2.	(d)	3.	(a)	4.	(c)				

Passage–7	1.	(c)	2.	(d)	3.	(d)
Passage–8	1.	(b)	2.	(b)	3.	(d)
Passage–9	1.	(c)	2.	(d)	3.	(b)
Passage–10	1.	(d)	2.	(c)	3.	(d)
Passage–11	1.	(c)	2.	(d)	3.	(c)
Passage–12	1.	(b)	2.	(a)	3.	(d)
Passage–13	1.	(d)	2.	(d)	3.	(c)
Passage–14	1.	(d)	2.	(d)		
Passage–15	1.	(c)	2.	(c)		

One or More Answers is/are correct

1. (b, c, d) **2.** (a, d) **3.** (a, c) **4.** (b, c, d) **5.** (a, b, c) **6.** (a, c)

7. (I) (B) (II) H (III) A (IV) B, C, F, J, I (V) A (VI) I (VII) B, J (VIII) E, H, K (IX) G (X) L

8. (I) M (II) J^{2+} (III) H, M (IV) T

9. (I) 17 (II) 15 (III) 15 (IV) 2 (V) 13

10.	(b, c, d)	**11.**	(a, c, d)	**12.**	(d)	**13.**	(b, c)	**14.**	(a, c, d)	**15.**	(a, b, c)
16.	(a, b, c, d)	**17.**	(a, b, d)	**18.**	(a, b, c)	**19.**	(a, b)	**20.**	(a, c)	**21.**	(a, b, d)
22.	(a, b, c, d)	**23.**	(a, c)	**24.**	(a, b, d)	**25.**	(b, c, d)	**26.**	(a, b, c)	**27.**	(b, c)
28.	(a, d)	**29.**	(a, b, c, d)	**30.**	(a, b, c, d)	**31.**	(b, c, d)	**32.**	(b, c, d)	**33.**	(a, b, d)
34.	(a, c)	**35.**	(a, b, d)	**36.**	(a, b, c, d)	**37.**	(a, c, d)	**38.**	(a, b, c)	**39.**	(c, d)
40.	(a, b, c)	**41.**	(a, b, d)	**42.**	(a, b, d)	**43.**	(a, b, c)	**44.**	(a, c, d)	**45.**	(d)
46.	(b, d)	**47.**	(a, b, d)	**48.**	(a, c, d)	**49.**	(a, b, d)	**50.**	(c, d)	**51.**	(a, b, c, d)

Match the Column

1. A→ Q;	B→ S;	C→ R, S	
2. A→ Q, S;	B→ S;	C→ P	
3. A→ P, S;	B→ P, R, S;	C→ Q;	D→ R
4. A→ R;	B→ P;	C→ S, T;	D→ Q
5. A→ R;	B→ Q;	C→ S;	D→ P
6. A→ Q;	B→ P;	C→ R;	D→ S
7. A→ Q;	B→ P;	C→ S;	D→ R

8. A→ Q;	B→ R, S;	C→ S;	D→ P
9. A→ R;	B→S;	C→ Q;	D→ P
10. A→ Q;	B→ R;	C→ S, T;	D→ P
11. A→ R;	B→ T;	C→ P, S;	D→ Q, R
12. A→ P, S;	B→ T;	C→ P, R;	D→ P, Q, R
13. A→ P, Q, R, T;	B→ Q, S;	C→ Q, T;	D→ Q, S
14. A → P, Q ;	B → P, Q, S ;	C → R, S, T ;	D → P, Q, S

Assertion-Reason Type Questions

1. (A) **2.** (D) **3.** (C) **4.** (A) **5.** (B) **6.** (A) **7.** (A) **8.** (A) **9.** (A) **10.** (A)
11. (A) **12.** (C) **13.** (C) **14.** (D) **15.** (C) **16.** (A) **17.** (C) **18.** (B)

Subjective Problems

1. (6) **2.** (2) **3.** (3) **4.** (4) **5.** (8) **6.** (16) **7.** (3) **8.** (7) **9.** (27) **10.** (2)
11. (7)

Hints and Solutions

Level 1

26. (b) Ununtrium for atomic number = 113; for $Z > 86$, pd. no. = 7

113 [Rn]$7s^2, 5f^{14}, 6d^{10}, 7p^1$

p-block

27. (b) Tantalum ($Z = 73$) is a transition element.

28. (c)

Period number	Group number	Element
5	7	Tc
6	13	Tl
6	5	Ta

30. (c) [Xe]$4f^{14}5d^1 6s^2$

Atomic number = 71 Period number = 6th Group number = 3rd

31. (b) Rubidium is most electropositive in nature.

32. (c) (a) Cr : $4s^1 3d^5$ (each *d*-orbital has $1e^-$)

(b) Fe^{3+} : $4s^0 3d^5$ (each *d*-orbital has $1e^-$)

(c) Cu^+: $4s^0 3d^{10}$ (each *d*-orbital has $2e^-$)

33. (d) Magnetic moment $= \sqrt{n(n+2)}$ BM

N : Number of unpaired e^-

As atomic number increases in *d*-block element number of unpaired e^- first increases upto middle then decreases.

34. (c) "Unununium" : At number = 111

It is a transition element. Period number = 7th; Group number = 11

35. (d) Atomic radius and metallic character decreases from left to right across the period and increases from top to bottom down the group.

36. (c) *P* is trivalent non-metal *Q* is divalent metal hence formula of compound is P_2Q_3.

37. (c) $1s^2, 2s^2 2p^2, 3s^1$ (Excited state)

47. (d) In (a) and (b) use (Z / e) concept for isoelectronic species.

In (c) size of neutral atom is greater than its cation.

48. (a) (a) Sc > Ti > V > Cr (size decrease initially in 3*d*-series)

(b) Correct order : Zn > Cu > CO ≈ Ni

(c) Correct order : $S^{2-} > Cl^- > N^{3-} > O^{2-}$

49. (c) Due to diagonal relationship radius of Li^+ is close to Mg^{2+} ion.

74. (c) The correct order of IE_2 is Ne > O > F > N

75. (b) If we consider the opposite process :

(a) $F_{(g)} + e^- \longrightarrow F^-_{(g)}$; ΔH_1

(b) $P_{(g)} + e^- \longrightarrow P^-_{(g)}$; ΔH_2

(c) $S_{(g)} + e^- \longrightarrow S^-_{(g)}$; ΔH_3

(d) $Cl_{(g)} + e^- \longrightarrow Cl^-_{(g)}$; ΔH_4

Order of energy released is : $\Delta H_4 > \Delta H_1 > \Delta H_3 > \Delta H_2$

So, $P^-_{(g)} \longrightarrow P_{(g)} + e^-$; Requires least energy.

84. (a) Correct order of electron affinity is : Cl > F > S > O

Electron affinity of 2nd period non-metals is less than that of respective 3rd period non-metals.

85. (a) Nitrogen has stable $2p^3$ configuration and also due to high e^- charge density at outermost orbital it requires energy to add one extra e^- in its outer most shell *i. e.*, its first electron gain enthalpy is positive.

88. (d) According to Allred and Rochow scale

(c) $EN_{(AR)} = 0.359 \frac{Z_{eff.}}{r} + 0.744$ (r : radius in Å)

95. (a) LiF is sparingly soluble at room temperature due to its high lattice energy.

99. (a) Oxidation state of non-metal increases acidic nature of oxide increase $\overset{+7}{Cl_2O_7}$ is most acidic.

Level 2

1. (b) Sum of oxidation numbers of all atoms in a neutral molecule is zero.

$\rightarrow A_3(B_4C)_2 : +2\times3+2\times[4\times5-2] = 42 \neq 0$

$\rightarrow A_3(BC_4)_2 : +2\times3+2\times[+5-8] = 0$

$\rightarrow A_2(BC_3)_2 : +2\times2+2\times[+5-6] = +2 \neq 0$

$\rightarrow ABC_2 : +2+5+(-2)\times2 = +3 \neq 0$

2. (d) W : Phosphorus Y : Oxygen X : Sulphur Z : Chlorine

Electronegativity : O > Cl > S > P Catenation : S > P > O > Cl

Electron Affinity : Cl > O > S > P Oxygen exhibits covalency of two only

4. (b) (i) Alkali metal carbonates do not decompose even at red hot → V

(ii) Transition metal ions having unpaired d-electrons are coloured in aq. sol./compounds → X

(iii) In case of Kr van der Waals' radius is considered, which is largest atomic radius → Y

(iv) Si atom has acidic oxide, $SiO_2 \rightarrow W$

11. (d) (I) $[Kr]5s^1$, shows only single oxidation state +1

(II) $[Rn]5f^{14}6d^17s^2$, it is f-block element (Z = 103)

(III) The compound formed between I and III is ionic.

(IV) $[Ar]3d^64s^2$, (Z = 26) Fe shows variable oxidation state.

12. (c)

	Possible elements	Period number	Group number	Electronic configuration
(i)	H	1	1	$1s^1$
(ii)	Be	2	2	$1s^22s^2$

13. (b) As value of n increases, energy gap decreases due to increasing $Z_{eff.}$ on valence shell.

14. (b) Atomic radius and nuclear charge increases from top to bottom because number of shell and atomic number increases down the group.

15. (d)

(a) $[Ar]3d^54s^1 \rightarrow$ Cr(24) → 4th period, 6th group

(b) $[Kr]4d^{10} \rightarrow$ Pd(46) → 5th period, 12th group

(c) $[Rn]6d^27s^2 \rightarrow$ Th(90) → 7th period, 3rd group

(d) $[Xe]4f^{14}5d^26s^2 \rightarrow$ Hf(72) → 6th period, 4th group

21. (a) Correct order : $La^{3+} > Eu^{3+} > Gd^{3+} > Lu^{3+}$

23. (d) Second ionization energy is amount of energy required to take out an electron from the monopositive cation.

Hence, $M(g) \longrightarrow M^{2+} + 2e^-$ ...(5)

$M(g) \longrightarrow M^+ + e^-$ ...(3)

31. (d) $A \Rightarrow H(1s^1)$
$B \Rightarrow He(1s^2)$
$C \Rightarrow Li(1s^2 2s^1)$

$A_1 = IE_1(A)$ $\quad B_2 = IE_2(B)$
$B_1 = IE_1(B)$ $\quad C_2 = IE_2(C)$
$C_1 = IE_1(C)$ $\quad C_3 = IE_3(C)$

$B_1 > A_1 > C_1$ $\quad C_3 > B_2 > A_1$ $\quad C_3 > C_2 > B_2$
$He > H > Li$ $\quad Li^{2+}\ He^+\ H$ $\quad Li^{2+}\ Li^+\ He^+$
$1s^2\ 1s^1\ 2s^1$ $\quad 1s^1\ 1s^1\ 1s^1$ $\quad 1s^2\ 1s^2\ 1s^1$

32. (d)

(a) $\underset{4p^4}{Se} \xrightarrow{I.E._1} \underset{4p^3}{Se^+} \xrightarrow{I.E._2} \underset{4p^2}{Se^{2+}}$ $\quad \underset{4p^3}{As} \xrightarrow{I.E._1} \underset{4p^2}{As^+} \xrightarrow{I.E._2} \underset{4p^1}{As^{2+}}$

(b) $\underset{2p^2}{C} \longrightarrow \underset{2p^1}{C^+} \longrightarrow \underset{2s^2}{C^{2+}}$ $\quad \underset{2p^3}{N} \longrightarrow \underset{2p^2}{N^+} \longrightarrow \underset{2p^1}{N^{2+}}$ $\quad \underset{2p^4}{O} \longrightarrow \underset{2p^3}{O^+} \longrightarrow \underset{2p^2}{O^{2+}}$

(c) $\underset{2p^5}{F} \xrightarrow{I.E._1} \underset{2p^4}{F^+} \xrightarrow{I.E._2} \underset{2p^3}{F^{2+}} \xrightarrow{I.E._3} F^{3+}$ $\quad \underset{2p^4}{O} \xrightarrow{I.E._1} \underset{2p^3}{O^+} \xrightarrow{I.E._2} \underset{2p^2}{O^{2+}} \xrightarrow{I.E._3} O^{3+}$

(d) In respective period, noble gases have highest I.E.

33. (c) R is p-block element, because difference between IE_2 and IE_3 is not very high as compared to between IE_1 and IE_2; hence stable oxidation state of R will be higher than +2.

43. (b) In the isoelectronic species, all isoelectronic anions belong to the same period and cations to the next period.

44. (d) Order of electron gain enthalpy : Cl > F > O

Second electron gain enthalpy for an element is always positive.

47. (a) The electronegativity difference between M_1 and O is 0.1, which indicates $M_1 - O$ bond will be covalent, since O—H bond having more ionic character thus bond will break and H^+ ions will release and acidic solution is formed. Whereas difference between electronegativity of $M_2 - O$ bond is 2.3, thus, M_2—OH bond will break. Hence, solution will be basic in nature.

48. (a) $I.E. + E.A. = 275 + 86 = 361\ kcal\ mol^{-1}$

$= 361 \times 4.184 = 1510.42\ kJ\ mol^{-1}$

$\therefore$ Electronegativity $= \dfrac{1510.42}{540} = 2.797 = 2.8$

50. (b)

(a) Correct order → $Ca^{2+} > K^+ > Cl^- > S^{2-}$ (Ionisation energy)

For isoelectronic species (I.E. $\propto Z_{eff}$)

(b) Correct order → C < N < F < O (2nd I.E.)

Second electron removal from oxygen requires more energy as it acquires stable $2s^2 2p^3$ configuration after removal of one electron.

(c) Correct order → B > Tl > In > Ga > Al (Electronegativity)

In general EN increases in boron family from top to bottom due to increase in Z_{eff} on valence shell while boron has highest E.N. due to its vary small size.

(d) Correct order → $Na^+ > Li^+ > Mg^{2+} > Al^{3+} > Be^{2+}$ (Ionic radius)

Ionic radius depends on Z_{eff} and number of shells.

Level 3

Passage-4

1. (d) Electrons closer to nucleus will experience higher effective nuclear charge.

$2p^3$ is closer to $4s^1$ as principal quantum number is concerned first.

2. (b) Magnesium having higher ionization potential due to more stable electronic arrangement [Ne] $3s^2$ in comparison to aluminium [Ne] $3s^2 3p^1$.

3. (d) Ionization enrgy is not affected by entropy.

Passage-5

1. (b) T has abnormally higher I.E.$_1$ value.

2. (b) There is sudden jump in I.E.$_2$ of Q, *i.e.*, unipositive has noble gas configuration.

3. (c) I.E.$_3$ of S is abnormally higher.

4. (a) High I.E. values show its non-metallic nature.

5. (b) Q is alkali metal as it shows jump in I.E.$_2$ value.

6. (a) Both Q and R shows jump in I.E.$_2$ values and belong to alkali metals.

Passage-8

1. (b) $_{24}Cr \Rightarrow 1s^2, 2s^2 2p^6, 3s^2 3p^6 3d^5, 4s^1$

So extra electron now coming in $4s^1$ orbital.

$\sigma = (1 \times 0.35) + (13 \times 0.85) + (10 \times 1.0) = 21.40$

$Z^* = Z - \sigma = 24.0 - 21.4 = 2.6$

3. (d) $_3Li \Rightarrow 3 - (0.85 \times 2) \Rightarrow 1.3$

$_{11}Na \Rightarrow 11 - (0.85 \times 8 + 1 \times 2) = 11 - 8.8 = 2.2$

$_{19}K \Rightarrow 19 - (0.85 \times 8 + 1 \times 10) = 19 - 16.8 = 2.2$

Passage-10

1. (d) For last e^- of element 'X' $\rightarrow \overset{n}{7}\quad \overset{l}{1}\quad \overset{m}{+1}\quad \overset{s}{+1/2}$ or $-1/2$ so last e^- present in "$7p$" subshell and spin magnetic momentum for element 'X' is zero so their is no unpaird e^- in element 'X' so outer electronic configuration of element 'X' will be $7p^6$.

(a) According to electronic configuration element 'X' belongs to 18th group.

(b) Spin magnetic momentum zero so their is no unpaired e^-.

(c) Element 'X' belongs to 7th period and 18th group so atomic number is 118.

(d) 'X' is noble gas not representative element according to Bohr's classification.

2. (c) $Z = 118$, $B - 2Z = 18$, so $B = 254$

and $B - A = 18$ so $A = 236$

3. (d) 90th e^- goes to $5f$ subshell so possible four quantum numbers are 5, 3, –2 and –1/2 or +1/2.

Passage-11

1. (c) The correct order of IE$_1$ $H_{(Bi)} > I_{(Po)}$

2. (d)

(a) +5 oxidation state of H(Bi) is more stable than its +3 oxidation state. (false)

(b) $G^{2+}(Pb)^{2+}$ is better oxidising agent than $G^{4+}(Pb)^{4+}$. (false)

(c) +3 oxidation state of E(P) is more stable than its +5 oxidation state. (false)

(d) Pb > Sn(Tin): IE$_1$ (true)

3. (c)

(a) $B_2C_5(N_2O_5)$ is acidic in nature

(b) $AC_2(CO_2)$ is acidic in nature

(c) $FC_3(SO_3)$ is acidic in nature

(d) $GC_2(PbO_2)$ is amphoteric in nature

Passage-12

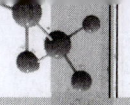

1. (b) In $X—O—H$, linkage as X is more electronegative the shared electron pair between $O—H$ shifts more towards oxygen atom and $O—H$ bond weakens which facilitates release of H^+.
2. (a) According to the given information, element P is aluminium which forms amphoteric oxide: Al_2O_3
3. (d) According to the given information, element P, belongs to 13th group and rest elements belong to higher groups, hence chloride of 13th group will only be hypovalent.

Passage-13

X is "As" $\Rightarrow$ $[Ar]3d^{10}4s^24p^3$ $2s+1=4$, $s=\frac{3}{2}$

B		N	O	F
Al		P		
Ga	Ge	As	Se	Br
		Sb		I
Tl	Pb	Bi		At

So unpaired electron in element X is 3.

Passage-14

1. (b) Bond energy is inversely proportional to difference of electronegativity in polar solvent. Hence, '$B—OH$' is more basic '$D—OH$'.
2. (d) Due to more difference of electronegativity in $B—O$ bond, $B—OH$ is more basic than water.

Passage-15

1. (c) In present set up of long form of periodic table element with atomic number > 118 can not be accommodated.
2. (c) $[Xe]^{54}6s^25d^1$ (last e^- enters to d-orbitals)

ONE OR MORE ANSWERS IS/ARE CORRECT

5. Statements (a), (b) and (c) are correct. Statement (d) is incorrect as in any period, the atomic radius of the noble gas is largest.

13. Np, Pu and Ra are radioactive but Np and Pu have been named after the names of the planets Neptune and Pluto.

14. Statements (a), (c) and (d) are common to both the groups 1 and 17. Statement (b) is true only for group 17 elements.

15. A is Fe ($Z_1=26$), according to their electronic configuration.

$Z_1-Z_2=2$, $Z_1=26$ (Fe $=A$)

$26-Z_2=2$, $Z_2=24$ (Cr $=B$)

$\frac{26+24}{2}=Z_3-2$, $Z_3=27$ (Co $=C$)

(Here, n is unpaired electrons)

(a) $B^+(n=5)>A^{2+}(n=4)>C^{2+}(n=3)$

(b) $A^{3+}(n=5)>B^{2+}(n=4)>C\ (n=3)$

(c) $B\ (n=6)>A\ (n=4)>C^{2+}(n=3)$

(d) $B\ (n=6)\neq A^{3+}(n=5)>C^{3+}(n=4)$

18. According to given information $X\Rightarrow$ Be and $Y\Rightarrow$ N

(a) Possible hydride of N is NH_3 ($H—\hat{N}—H$ bond angle is less than 109°28')

(b) In BeX_2, Be has two vacant p-orbitals

(c) Magnetic moment of N > Be. (Number of unpaired e^- in N > Be)

(d) N can exhibit variable oxidation states.

21. The correct order of radii is : $Co \approx Ni < Cu < Zn$

25. (a) $\frac{p}{e} = \overset{Fe^{2+}}{\frac{26}{24}}, \overset{Fe^{3+}}{\frac{26}{23}}$, due to high p/e ratio, (high Z_{eff}) in Fe^{3+}, ionic radii of $Fe^{2+} > Fe^{3+}$

(b) In case of second I.E. for 'O' e^- is removed from stable configuration $(1s^2, 2s^2 2p^3)$ so $N(IE_2) < O(IE_2)$

(c) Due to high shielding effect atomic radius of Zn > Cu.

(d) Due to high $Z_{eff.}$ I.E. of Tl > In (due to poor shielding effect of $4f$ subshell)

26. (a) Any orbital can accommodate max. 2 electrons

(b) For same Z, successive I.E. increases due to increase in $\left(\frac{Z}{e}\right)$

(c) $_{27}Co$ $[Ar]3d^7 4s^2$

Co^{2+} $[Ar]3d^7 4s^0$, unpaired $e^- = 3$

Co^{3+} $[Ar]3d^6 4s^0$, unpaired $e^- = 4$

(d) I.E. of Pt (6 period) > I.E. of Pd (5 period) due to poor shielding effect of $4f$ subshell in 6 period elements.

27. W show +3 oxidation state and X show +2 oxidation state.

$Y = ns^2np^4$, Y show –2 oxidation state

$Z = ns^2np^5$, Z show –1 oxidation state Formed compounds :

(a) $W^{3+}Y^{2-} = W_2Y_3$ (d) $X^{2+}Z^{1-} = XZ_2$

28. (a) Sum of IE_1 and IE_2 is lower for element P

(d) Sum of first four IE is lower for element Q

30. According to the values of I.E. given it can be concluded that

* $IE_1 < IE_2 < IE_3 <<< IE_4 < IE_5$
* This shows that it achieved stable noble gas configuration after removing three e^-.
* It belongs to 13th group of periodic table
* It could be metal or non-metal or metalloid.
* It form stable trivalent cation.

31. (a) $Fe < Fe^{2+} < Fe^{3+}$ [$Z_{eff.} \propto$ charge on cation] (b) $N^{3-} < O^{2-} < F^-$ [$Z_{eff.} \propto \frac{1}{\text{Charge on anion}}$]

(c) $Na^+ < Mg^+ < Al^{3+}$ (d) $Tl^{2+} < V^{3+} < Mn^{5+}$

37. Increasing order of size : $Mg^{2+} < Na^+ < F^- < O^{2-}$

38. $\Delta H_1, \Delta H_2$ and ΔH_3 are negative whereas ΔH_4 is positive.

39. Correct order is :

(b) Ge > Se > As > Br : Metallic character

(c) Si > Mg > Al > Na : Ionisation energy

(d) Cl > F > Br > I : Electron affinity

40. (a) The radius of isoelectronic species $\propto \frac{1}{\frac{Z}{e}\text{ ratio}}$

(b) Ionisation energy $\propto \frac{1}{\text{size}} \propto$ Effective nuclear charge

(c) Normally the electron affinity $(E_A) \propto \frac{1}{\text{Size of atom}}$

41. (a) $|\Delta H_4| = |\Delta H_5|$ $[(\Delta H_{eg.})_X = (\Delta H_{IE})_{X^-}]$

(b), (c) $\rightarrow \Delta H_3 > \Delta H_2 > \Delta H_1$ [Successive IE always higher than previous IE]

(c) $|\Delta H_1| = |\Delta H_6|$ $[(\Delta H_{IE})_X = (\Delta H_{eg.})_{X^+}]$

42. 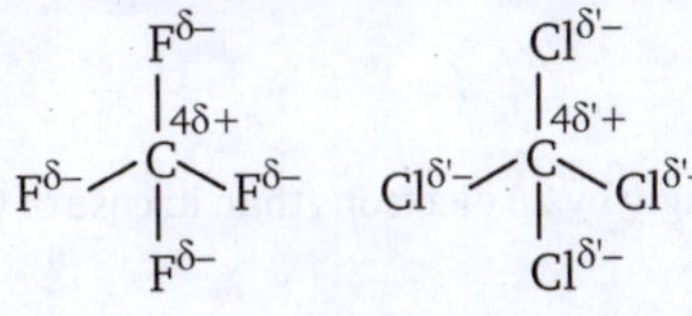

Since $\delta > \delta'$, hence C-atom in CF_4 is more electronegative than in CCl_4.

44. On Pauling's scale electronegativities of H (2.1), Te (2.1) and P (2.1) are similar but the electronegativity of S (2.5) is different from the other three elements.

45. Electronegativity and hydration energy cannot be estimated by using Born-Haber cycle.

46. Electronegativity of central atom is directly proportional to oxidation state.

48. (a) $S^-(g) \longrightarrow S^{2-}(g)$; $\Delta H_{e.g.} = (+)ve$

(b) $Na^+(g) + Cl^-(g) \longrightarrow Na^+Cl^-(s)$; $\Delta H_{L.E.} = (-)ve$

(c) $N(g) \longrightarrow N^-(g)$; $\Delta H_{e.g.} = (+)ve$

(d) $Al^{2+}(g) \longrightarrow Al^{3+}(g)$; $\Delta H_{I.E.} = (+)ve$

49. $\Rightarrow \Delta H_1 = 2\Delta H_2 + \frac{3}{2}\Delta H_3 + 2\Delta H_4 - 3\Delta H_5 \Rightarrow$ second electron gain enthalpy of X will be positive.

MATCH THE COLUMN

6. 52 $[Kr]^{36} 4d^{10}5s^25p^4$
$\Rightarrow$ *p*-block

56 $[Xe]^{54}6s^2$ $\Rightarrow$ *s*-block

57 $[Xe]^{54}5d^16s^2$ $\Rightarrow$ *d*-block

60 $[Xe]^{54}4f^46s^2$ $\Rightarrow$ *f*-block

11. (A) $[Xe]4f^{14}5d^{10}6s^2$, last e^- goes to $5d$ subshell so it is a *d*-block element and $5d$ subshell is fulfilled so it is not considered as transition element $(A \rightarrow R)$

(B) $[Rn]5f^{14}6d^17s^2$, last e^- goes to $5f$ subshell so it is *f*-block or inner-transition element $(B \rightarrow T)$

(C) $[Xe]4f^{14}5d^{10}6s^26p^67s^2$, last e^- goes to $7s$ subshell so it is a *s*-block or representative element $(C \rightarrow P, S)$.

(D) $[Xe]4f^{14}5d^26s^2$, last e^- goes to $5d$ subshell so it is a *d*-block element and $5d$ subshell is partially field so it is also considered as transition element $(D \rightarrow Q, R)$.

12. (a) $W(2,8,7)$ Cl $(Z=17)$ → (P) Paramagnetic (one unpaired e^-)
→ (S) Reactive non-metal

(b) $X(2,8,18,8)$ Kr $(Z=36)$ → (T) Diamagnetic (zero unpaired e^-)

(c) $Y(2,8,14,2)$ Fe $(Z=26)$ → (P) Paramagnetic (4 unpaired e^-)
→ (R) Last e^- does not enter to valence shell (last e^- enter to $(n-1)$ shell)

(d) $Z(2,8,18,25,8,2)$ Eu $(Z=63)$ → (P) Paramagnetic (7 unpaired e^-)
→ (Q) 3rd group element
→ (R) Last e^- does not enter to valence shell (last e^- enter to $(n-2)$ shell)

ASSERTION-REASON TYPE QUESTIONS

13. Due to small size of F atom added electron is repelled more strongly by $2p$ electrons than in case of Cl atom.

SUBJECTIVE PROBLEMS

1. Electronic configuration of Zn^{2+}: $\underline{1s^2}, \underline{2s^2}, 2p^6, \underline{3s^2}, 3p^6, 3d^6, 4s^0$

3.
$$-0.95\times10^x = 700-1000-650$$
$$-0.95\times10^x = -950$$
$$x = \mathbf{3}$$

4.
$$-750 = 150+\frac{3}{2}\times200+350+q-1000$$
$$q = 3\times\Delta H_{EG} = -550;$$
$$q_1 = \frac{550}{3} = 183,\ \frac{q_1}{50} = 3.66 \approx 4.0$$

5.
$$-424 = 108+495+\frac{242}{2}-348+U$$
$$-424 = +376+U$$
$$U = -424-376 = -800\ \text{kJ/mol}$$
$$-\frac{(-800)}{100} = 8$$

6. Correct orders

(i) HF > HCl > HBr > HI : Lewis basic character	(T)
(ii) $CH_4 < CCl_4 < CF_4$: Electronegativity of central 'C'-atom	(T)
(iii) $Mg^{2+} < K^+ < S^{2-} < Se^{2-}$: Ionic radius	(T)
(iv) Ni > Pd > Pt : Ionisation energy	(F)
(v) $As^{5+} > Sb^{5+} > Bi^{5+}$: Stable oxidation state	(T)
(vi) LiF > NaF > KF > RbF: Lattice energy	(T)
(vii) $F^-_{(aq.)} > Cl^-_{(aq.)} > Br^-_{(aq.)} > I^-_{(aq.)}$: Electrical conductance	(F)
(viii) $Li^+ < Mg^{2+} < Al^{3+}$: Hydration energy	(T)
(ix) Cl > Br > F > I : Electron affinity	(F)
(x) $BeCl_2 < AlCl_3 < SiCl_4$: Lewis acidic character	(T)

$$x = 7,\quad y = 3$$
$$|x-y|^2 = |7-3|^2 = 16$$

7. Te, Po, Ra

8. $X \Rightarrow \frac{1s^2}{K}$ so value of n is '6'

Electronic configuration of 'X' $\Rightarrow$ $\frac{1s^2}{K} \; \frac{}{L} \; \frac{}{M} \; \frac{25}{N} \; \frac{8}{O} \; \frac{2}{P}$ (K, L, M, N, O, P = 1, 2, 3, 4, 5, 6)

$$1s^2 \ldots\ldots\ldots \underbrace{4s^2 4p^6 4d^{10} 4f^7}_{25}\ \underbrace{5s^2 5p^6 5d^0}_{8}\ \underbrace{6s^2}_{2}$$

Unpaired electron is 7.

10. (v) $Li < Li^+$ (vii) Ba < Sr

11.

Cs → (+1)	Zn → (+2)	Sr → (+2)
Ba → (+2)	Be → (+2)	Ga → (+1, +3)
F → (−1)	Al → (+3)	Pb → (+2, +4)

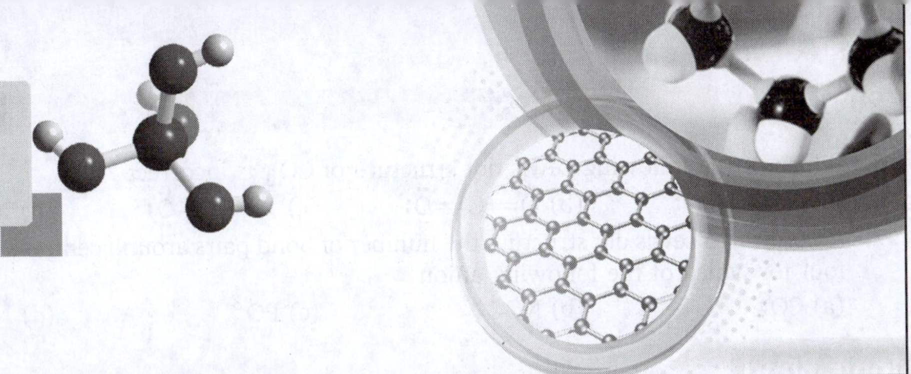

2

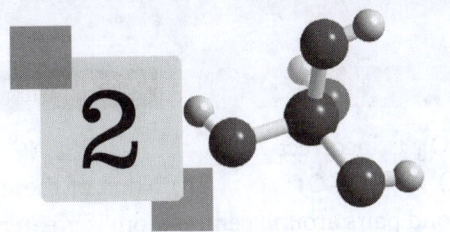

CHEMICAL BONDING (BASIC)

Level 1

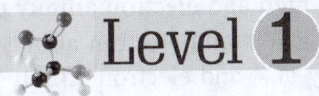

Introductory Questions

1. The combination of atoms take place so that :
(a) They can gain two electrons in the outermost shell
(b) They get eight electrons in the outermost shell
(c) They acquire stability by lowering of energy
(d) They get eighteen electrons in the outermost shell.

Lewis Dot Structure

2. N_2O has a linear, unsymmetrical structure that may be thought of as a hybrid of two resonance forms. If a resonance form must have a satisfactory Lewis structure, which two of the five structures shown below are the two resonance forms of N_2O ?
(a) $:N\equiv N=\ddot{O}:$ (b) $:\ddot{N}=\overset{+}{N}=\ddot{O}:$ (c) $:\ddot{N}=\ddot{N}-\ddot{O}:$ (d) $:N\equiv\overset{+}{N}=\underset{..}{\ddot{O}}:$

3. Which of the following molecular species/compound is not hypovalent ?
(a) CH_3^+ (b) B_2H_6 (c) NH_2^+ (d) AlF_3

4. N_2CO has three possible structures ;
ONCN (nitrosyl cyanide), ONNC (nitrosyl isocyanide) NOCN (isonitrosyl cyanide).
Which of the following structure has lowest potential energy ?
(a) ONCN (b) ONNC
(c) NOCN (d) All have same energy

5. Which of the following statement is correct for NO_3^- ion ?
(a) Sum of all formal charges = +1
(b) Formal charge on one of the oxygen atom = –2
(c) Formal charge on nitrogen atom = +1
(d) Average formal charge on oxygen atom $= -\frac{1}{3}$

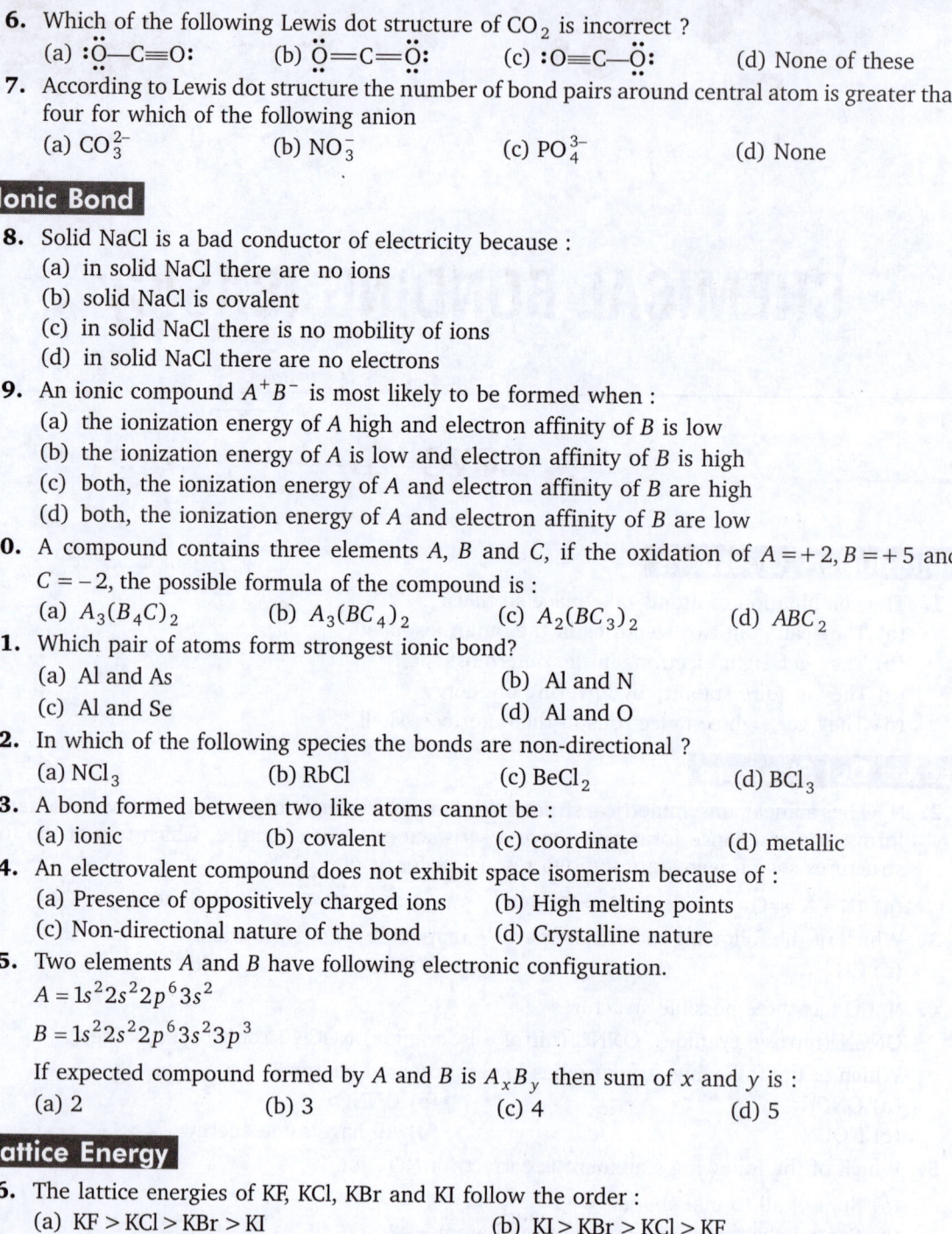

6. Which of the following Lewis dot structure of CO_2 is incorrect ?

(a) :Ö—C≡O: (b) Ö=C=Ö: (c) :O≡C—Ö: (d) None of these

7. According to Lewis dot structure the number of bond pairs around central atom is greater than four for which of the following anion

(a) CO_3^{2-} (b) NO_3^- (c) PO_4^{3-} (d) None

Ionic Bond

8. Solid NaCl is a bad conductor of electricity because :

(a) in solid NaCl there are no ions

(b) solid NaCl is covalent

(c) in solid NaCl there is no mobility of ions

(d) in solid NaCl there are no electrons

9. An ionic compound A^+B^- is most likely to be formed when :

(a) the ionization energy of A high and electron affinity of B is low

(b) the ionization energy of A is low and electron affinity of B is high

(c) both, the ionization energy of A and electron affinity of B are high

(d) both, the ionization energy of A and electron affinity of B are low

10. A compound contains three elements A, B and C, if the oxidation of $A = +2, B = +5$ and $C = -2$, the possible formula of the compound is :

(a) $A_3(B_4C)_2$ (b) $A_3(BC_4)_2$ (c) $A_2(BC_3)_2$ (d) ABC_2

11. Which pair of atoms form strongest ionic bond?

(a) Al and As (b) Al and N

(c) Al and Se (d) Al and O

12. In which of the following species the bonds are non-directional ?

(a) NCl_3 (b) RbCl (c) $BeCl_2$ (d) BCl_3

13. A bond formed between two like atoms cannot be :

(a) ionic (b) covalent (c) coordinate (d) metallic

14. An electrovalent compound does not exhibit space isomerism because of :

(a) Presence of oppositively charged ions (b) High melting points

(c) Non-directional nature of the bond (d) Crystalline nature

15. Two elements A and B have following electronic configuration.

$A = 1s^2 2s^2 2p^6 3s^2$

$B = 1s^2 2s^2 2p^6 3s^2 3p^3$

If expected compound formed by A and B is A_xB_y then sum of x and y is :

(a) 2 (b) 3 (c) 4 (d) 5

Lattice Energy

16. The lattice energies of KF, KCl, KBr and KI follow the order :

(a) KF > KCl > KBr > KI (b) KI > KBr > KCl > KF

(c) KF > KCl > KI > KBr (d) KI > KBr > KF > KCl

17. Which set of compounds in the following pair of ionic compounds has the higher lattice energy?

(i) KCl or MgO (ii) LiF or LiBr (iii) Mg_3N_2 or NaCl
(a) KCl, LiBr, Mg_2N_2 (b) MgO, LiBr, Mg_3N_2
(c) MgO, LiF, NaCl (d) MgO, LiF, Mg_3N_2

18. The incorrect order of lattice energy is :
(a) $AlF_3 > MgF_2$ (b) $Li_3N > Li_2O$
(c) $NaCl > LiF$ (d) $TiC > ScN$

19. Which ionic compound has the largest amount of lattice energy?
(a) NaF (b) AlF_3 (c) AlN (d) MgF_2

20. The order of increasing lattice energy of the following salt is :
(a) NaCl < CaO < NaBr < BaO (b) NaBr < NaCl < BaO < CaO
(c) NaCl < NaBr < BaO < CaO (d) NaBr < NaCl < CaO < BaO

21. Which combination will give strongest ionic bond ?
(a) Na^+ and Cl^- (b) Mg^{2+} and Cl^- (c) Na^+ and O^{2-} (d) Mg^{2+} and O^{2-}

22. Among the following isostructural compounds, identify the compound, which has the highest lattice energy :
(a) LiF (b) LiCl (c) NaCl (d) MgO

23. In which of the following ionic compounds, ΔH_f is negative only due to lattice energy ?
(i) NaF (ii) MgO (iii) Li_3N (iv) Na_2S
(a) Only (iv) (b) Only (iii), (iv)
(c) Only (ii), (iii), (iv) (d) All of these

24. Select the correct reason for given statement "Flouride of Al is ionic while chloride of Al is covalent".
(a) IE of Al in $AlF_3 > AlCl_3$ (b) EA of Flourine > Chlorine
(c) Lattice energy of $AlF_3 > AlCl_3$ (d) EA of Flourine < Chlorine

Covalent Bond

25. Which pair of elements can form multiple bond with itself and oxygen?
(a) F, N (b) N, Cl (c) N, P (d) N, C

26. Which of the following is a covalent compound?
(a) Al_2O_3 (b) AlF_3 (c) $AlCl_3$ (d) $Al_2(SO_4)_3$

27. Which of the following is an example of super octet molecule?
(a) ClF_3 (b) PCl_5 (c) IF_7 (d) All the three

28. Which of the following molecule is theoretically not possible?
(a) SF_4 (b) OF_2 (c) OF_4 (d) O_2F_2

29. The phosphate of a metal has the formula $MHPO_4$. The formula of its chloride would be :
(a) MCl (b) MCl_2 (c) MCl_3 (d) M_2Cl_3

30. The compound that has the highest ionic character associated with the X — Cl bond is :
(a) PCl_5 (b) BCl_3 (c) CCl_4 (d) $SiCl_4$

31. The bond having the highest bond energy is :
(a) C=C (b) C=S (c) C=O (d) P=N

32. Which of the following species is neither hypervalent nor hypovalent ?
(a) ClO_4^- (b) BF_3 (c) SO_4^{2-} (d) CO_3^{2-}

33. In which of the following species central atom is NOT surrounded by exactly 8 valence electrons?
(a) BF_4^- (b) NCl_3 (c) PCl_4^+ (d) SF_4

34. Which atom can have more than eight valence electrons when it is forming covalent bonds?
(a) H (b) N (c) F (d) Cl

35. Which bond is expected to be the least polar?
(a) O—F (b) P—F (c) Si—N (d) B—F

36. Which set contains only covalently bonded molecules?
(a) BCl_3, $SiCl_4$, PCl_3 (b) NH_4Br, N_2H_4, HBr
(c) I_2, H_2S, NaI (d) Al, O_3, As_4

37. Which molecule does not exist?
(a) OF_2 (b) OF_4 (c) SF_2 (d) SF_4

38. Which of the following does not contain any coordinate bond ?
(a) NH_4Cl (b) $Na^+[BF_4]^-$ (c) H_3O^+ (d) CO_3^{2-}

39. A : tetracyanomethane B : carbondioxide
C : benzene D : 1, 3-buta-di-ene
Ratio of σ and π bonds is in order :
(a) $A = B < C < D$ (b) $A = B < D < C$
(c) $A = B = C = D$ (d) $C < D < A < B$

40. In a compound

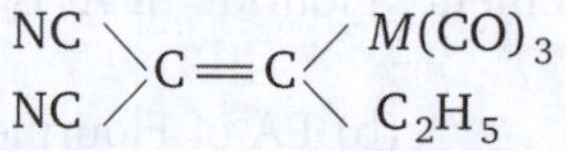

(M : d - block metal)

the number of sigma and pi bonds respectively are :
(a) 19, 11 (b) 19, 5 (c) 13, 11 (d) 7, 3

41. Which of the following does not contain any co-ordinate bond?
(a) H_3O^+ (b) BF_4^- (c) HF_2^- (d) NH_4^+

42. Which of the following molecules does not have co-ordinate bonds?
(a) PH_4^+ (b) NO_2 (c) O_3 (d) CO_3^{2-}

43. Which of the following bonds have lowest bond energy?
(a) C—C (b) N—N (c) H—H (d) O—O

44. The bond having the minimum bond energy is :
(a) C — C (b) O — O (c) S — S (d) P — P

Valence Bond Theory

45. The fluorine molecules is formed by :
(a) *p-p* orbitals (sideways overlap) (b) *p-p* orbitals (end-to-end overlap)
(c) *sp-sp* orbitals (d) *s-s* orbitals

46. Which of the following leads to bonding?

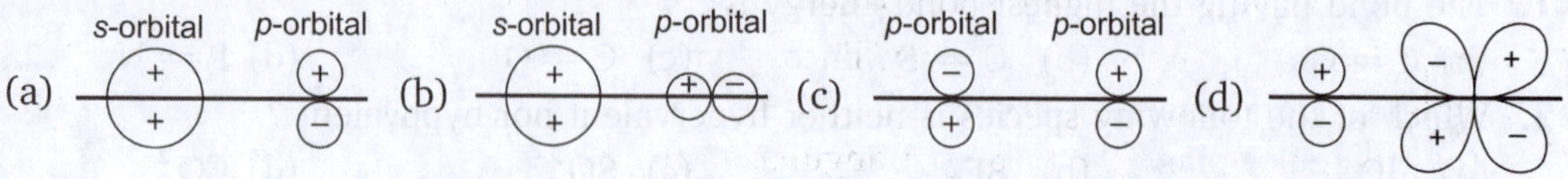

47. Which of the following overlaps is incorrect (assuming Z-axis is internuclear axis) ?

(A) $2p_y + 2p_y \longrightarrow \pi$-Bond formation
(B) $2p_x + 2p_x \longrightarrow \sigma$-Bond formation
(C) $3d_{xy} + 3d_{xy} \longrightarrow \pi$-Bond formation
(D) $2s + 2p_y \longrightarrow \pi$-Bond formation
(E) $3d_{xy} + 3d_{xy} \longrightarrow \delta$-Bond formation
(F) $2p_z + 2p_z \longrightarrow \sigma$-Bond formation

(a) A, B, C (b) C, F (c) B, E (d) B, C, D

48. Which of the following overlapping is not present in XeO_3 molecule ?

(a) $sp^3 + p_x$ (b) $sp^3 + p_y$ (c) $d_{xz} + p_x$ (d) $sp^3 + s$

49. How many sigma bonds are in a molecule of diethyl ether, $C_2H_5OC_2H_5$?

(a) 14 (b) 12 (c) 8 (d) 16

50. Which combination of orbitals will form π-bond, if internuclear axis is x-axis ?

(a) $p_x + p_x$ (b) $d_{xy} + d_{xy}$ (c) $d_{x^2-y^2} + d_{x^2-y^2}$ (d) $d_{yz} + d_{yz}$

51. If d_{xz} orbital of atom A and p_x orbital of atom B form π-bond along a particular molecular axis, then which bond will be formed along same molecular axis by combination of $(d_{xy} + d_{xy})$ orbitals of (A) and (B) atom :

(a) σ-bond (b) π-bond (c) δ-bond (d) Can't be predicted

52. Which of the following is correct order of σ-bond strength ?

(I) $2s-2s$ (II) $2s-2p$ (III) $2p-2p$ (IV) $3s-3s$

(a) I > II > III > IV (b) III > II > I > IV (c) IV > I > II > III (d) III > I > II > IV

53. Which of the following overlaps gives σ-bond along x-axis as internuclear axis ?

(a) p_z and p_z (b) s and p_z (c) s and p_y (d) $d_{x^2-y^2}$ and $d_{x^2-y^2}$

54. Which of the following orbital combination can not form π-bond ?

(a) $p_x + p_x$ sideways overlapping
(b) $d_{x^2-y^2} + p_y$ sideways overlapping
(c) $d_{xy} + d_{xy}$ sideways overlapping
(d) $d_{yz} + p_y$ sideways overlapping

55. Which of the following overlaps gives σ-bond along x-axis as internuclear axis ?

(a) p_z and p_z (b) s and p_z (c) s and p_y (d) $d_{x^2-y^2}$ and $d_{x^2-y^2}$

56. Which of the following orbital combination can not form π-bond ?

(a) $p_x + p_x$ sideways overlapping
(b) $d_{x^2-y^2} + p_y$ sideways overlapping
(c) $d_{xy} + d_{xy}$ sideways overlapping
(d) $d_{yz} + p_y$ sideways overlapping

VSEPR Theory

57. In which of the following species maximum atom can lie in same plane?

(a) XeF_2O_2 (b) PCl_5 (c) AsH_4^+ (d) XeF_4

58. Correct statement regarding molecules SF_4, CF_4 and XeF_4 are:

(a) 2, 0 and 1 lone pairs of central atom respectively
(b) 1, 0 and 1 lone pairs of central atom respectively
(c) 0, 0 and 2 lone pairs of central atom respectively
(d) 1, 0 and 2 lone pairs of central atom respectively

59. The geometrical arrangement of orbitals and shape of I_3^- are respectively :

(a) trigonal bipyramidal geometry, linear shape
(b) hexagonal geometry, T-shape
(c) triangular planar geometry, triangular shape
(d) tetrahedral geometry, pyramidal shape

60. Which of the following statements is incorrect for PCl_5?
(a) Its three P—Cl bond lengths are equal (b) It involves sp^3d hybridization
(c) It has an regular geometry (d) Its shape is trigonal bipyramidal

61. Molecular shapes of SF_4, CF_4 and XeF_4 are :
(a) the same with 2,0 and 1 lone pair of electrons respectively
(b) the same, with 1,1 and 1 lone pair of electrons, respectively
(c) different, with 0,1 and 2 lone pair of electrons, respectively
(d) different with 1,0 and 2 lone pair of electrons, respectively

62. The structure of the noble gas compound XeF_4 is :
(a) square planar (b) distorted tetrahedral
(c) tetrahedral (d) octahedral

63. The molecule exhibiting maximum number of non-bonding electron pairs (l.p.) around the central atom is :
(a) $XeOF_4$ (b) XeO_2F_2 (c) XeF_3^+ (d) XeO_3

64. Which is the following pairs of species have identical shapes?
(a) NO_2^+ and NO_2^- (b) PCl_5 and BrF_5 (c) XeF_4 and ICl_4^- (d) $TeCl_4$ and XeO_4

65. The shapes of XeF_4, XeF_5^- and $SnCl_2$ are :
(a) octahedral, trigonal bipyramidal and bent
(b) square pyramidal, pentagonal planar and linear
(c) square planar, pentagonal planar and angular
(d) see-saw, T-shaped and linear

66. Which is not correctly matched?
(a) XeO_3—Trigonal bipyramidal (b) ClF_3—bent T-shape
(c) $XeOF_4$—Square pyramidal (d) XeF_2—Linear shape

67. Amongst NO_3^-, AsO_3^{3-}, CO_3^{2-}, ClO_3^- and SO_3^{2-}, the non-planar species are :
(a) CO_3^{2-}, SO_3^{2-} (b) AsO_3^{3-}, ClO_3^-, SO_3^{2-}
(c) NO_3^-, CO_3^{2-} (d) SO_3^{2-}, NO_3^-

68. The geometry of ammonia molecule can be best described as :
(a) Nitrogen at one vertex of a regular tetrahedron, the other three vertices being occupied by three hydrogens
(b) Nitrogen at the centre of the tetrahedron, three of the vertices being occupied by three hydrogens
(c) Nitrogen at the centre of an equilateral triangle, three corners being occupied by three hydrogens
(d) Nitrogen at the junction of a T, three open ends being occupied by three hydrogens

69. Which molecular geometry is least likely to result from a trigonal bipyramidal electron geometry?
(a) Trigonal planar (b) See-saw (c) Linear (d) Bent T-shaped

70. Give the correct order of initials **T** or **F** for following statements. Use **T** if statement is true and **F** if it is false :
(I) The order of repulsion between different pair of electrons is $l_p - l_p > l_p - b_p > b_p - b_p$

(II) In general, as the number of lone pair of electrons on central atom increases, value of bond angle from normal bond angle also increases

(III) The number of lone pair on O in H_2O is 2 while on N in NH_3 is 1

(IV) The structures of xenon fluorides and xenon oxyfluorides could not be explained on the basis of VSEPR theory

(a) TTTF (b) TFTF (c) TFTT (d) TFFF

71. Which species is planar?

(a) CO_3^{2-} (b) SO_3^{2-} (c) ClO_3^- (d) BF_4^-

72. What is the geometry of the IBr_2^- ion?

(a) Linear
(b) Bent shape with bond angle of about 90°
(c) Bent shape with bond angle of about 109°
(d) Bent shape with bond angle of about 120°

73. What is the shape of the ClF_3 molecule?

(a) Trigonal planar (b) Trigonal pyramidal
(c) T-shaped (d) Tetrahedral

74. Which species has the same shape as NH_3?

(a) SO_3^{2-} (b) CO_3^{2-}
(c) NO_3^- (d) SO_3

75. According to VSEPR theory, in which species do all the atoms lie in the same plane? 1. CH_3^+ 2. CH_3^-

(a) 1 only (b) 2 only
(c) both 1 and 2 (d) neither 1 nor 2

76. Which of the following species/molecules does not have same number of bond pairs and lone pairs?

(a) OCN^- (b) H_2O (c) $C_2H_2Cl_2$ (d) O_3

Hybridisation

77. How many sp^2 and *sp*-hybridised carbon atoms are present respectively in the following compound ?

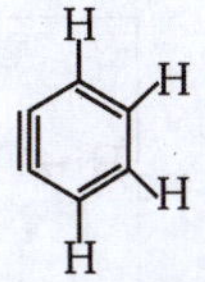

(a) 4, 2 (b) 6, 0 (c) 3, 3 (d) 5, 1

78. Which one of the following is the correct set with respect to molecule, hybridization and shape?

(a) $BeCl_2, sp^2$, linear (b) $BeCl_2, sp^2$, triangular planar
(c) BCl_3, sp^2, triangular planar (d) BCl_3, sp^3, tetrahedral

79. The hybridization of the central atom in ICl_2^+ is :

(a) dsp^2 (b) sp (c) sp^2 (d) sp^3

80. The state of hybridization of the central atom is not the same as in the others :

(a) B in BF_3 (b) O in H_3O^+ (c) N in NH_3 (d) P in PCl_3

81. The number of $sp^2 - s$ sigma bonds in benzene are :

(a) 3 (b) 6 (c) 12 (d) none of these

82. The hybridization of the central atom will change when :

(a) NH_3 combines with H^+ (b) H_3BO_3 combines with OH^-

(c) NH_3 forms NH_2^- (d) H_2O combines with H^+

83. $CH_3—CH_2—CH{=}CH_2$ has hybridisation:

(a) sp, sp, sp^2, sp^2 (b) sp^3, sp^3, sp^2, sp

(c) sp^3, sp^3, sp^2, sp^2 (d) sp^3, sp^2, sp^2, sp

84. What is the state of hybridisation of Xe in cationic part of solid XeF_6?

(a) sp^3d^3 (b) sp^3d^2 (c) sp^3d (d) sp^3

85. During the complete combustion of methane CH_4, what change in hybridisation does the carbon atom undergo?

(a) sp^3 to sp (b) sp^3 to sp^2 (c) sp^2 to sp (d) sp^2 to sp^3

86. The hybridisation of central iodine atom in IF_5, I_3^- and I_3^+ are respectively :

(a) sp^3d^2, sp^3d, sp^3 (b) sp^3d, sp^3d, sp^3 (c) sp^3d^2, sp^3d^2, sp^3 (d) sp^3d, sp^3d^2, sp^3

87. In which of the following combination hybridisation of central atom (*) does not change?

(a) $H_2O + \overset{*}{C}O_2$ (b) $H_3\overset{*}{B}O_3 + OH^-$ (c) $BF_3 + \overset{*}{N}H_3$ (d) None of these

88. Which of the following species used both axial set of *d*-orbitals in hybridisation of central atom?

(a) PBr_4^+ (b) PCl_4^- (c) ICl_4^- (d) None of these

89. Which bonds are formed by a carbon atom with sp^2-hybridisation?

(a) 4π-bonds (b) 2π-bonds and 2σ-bonds

(c) 1π-bonds and 3σ-bonds (d) 4σ-bonds

90. What are the hybridisation of the carbon atoms labeled C_1 and C_2, respectively in glycine?

	C_1	C_2
(a)	sp^2	sp^2
(b)	sp^2	sp^3
(c)	sp^3	sp^2
(d)	sp^3	sp^3

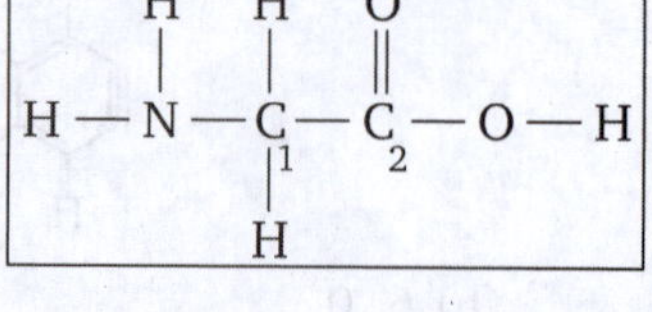

91. The H—O—H bond angles in H_3O^+ are approximately 107°. The orbitals used by oxygen in these bonds are best described as :

(a) *p*-orbitals (b) *sp*-hybrid orbitals

(c) sp^2-hybrid orbital (d) sp^3-hybrid orbital

Molecular Geometry/Shape

92. Among given species identify the isostructural pairs :
(a) [NF_3 and BF_3] (b) [BF_4^- and NH_4^+] (c) [BCl_3 and $BrCl_3$] (d) [NH_3 and NO_3^-]

93. 0.01 mole of H_3PO_x is completely neutralised by 0.56 gram of KOH hence :
(a) $x = 3$ and given acid is dibasic
(b) $x = 2$ and given acid is monobasic
(c) $x = 3$ and given acid is monobasic
(d) $x = 4$ and given acid forms three series of salt

94. Phosphorus pentachloride in the solid exists as :
(a) PCl_5 (b) $PCl_4^+Cl^-$ (c) $PCl_4^+PCl_6^-$ (d) $PCl_5 \cdot Cl_2$

95. The ratio of σ-bond and π-bond in tetracyano ethylene is :
(a) 2 : 1 (b) 1 : 1 (c) 1 : 2 (d) None of these

96. Bonds present in N_2O_5 (nitrogen pentaoxide) are :
(a) only ionic (b) only covalent
(c) covalent and co-ordinate (d) covalent and ionic

97. The pair of species with similar shape is :
(a) PCl_3, NH_3 (b) CF_4, SF_4 (c) $PbCl_2, CO_2$ (d) PF_5, IF_5

98. Which of the following statements is correct in the context of the allene molecule, C_3H_4?
(a) The central carbon is *sp* hybridized
(b) The terminal carbon atoms are sp^2 hybridized
(c) The planes containing the CH_2 groups are mutually perpendicular to permit the formations two separate π-bonds
(d) All are correct

99. Number of S — S bond is $H_2S_nO_6$:
(a) *n* (b) $(n-1)$ (c) $(n-2)$ (d) $(n+1)$

100. How many S — S bonds, S — O — S bonds, σ-bonds, π-bonds are present in trimer of sulphur trioxide?
(a) 0, 3, 16, 2 (b) 0, 3, 12, 6 (c) 0, 6, 12, 16 (d) 0, 4, 12, 6

101. Number of identical Cr—O bonds in dichromate ion $Cr_2O_7^{2-}$ is :
(a) 4 (b) 6 (c) 7 (d) 8

102. The nodal plane in the π-bond of ethene is located in :
(a) the molecular plane
(b) a plane parallel to the molecular plane
(c) a plane perpendicular to the molecular plane which bisects the carbon-carbon σ bond at right angle
(d) a plane perpendicular to the molecular plane which contains the carbon-carbon bond

103. Which of the following are isoelectronic and isostructural?

$$NO_3^-,\ CO_3^{2-},\ ClO_3^-,\ SO_3$$

(a) NO_3^-, CO_3^{2-} (b) SO_3, NO_3^- (c) ClO_3^-, CO_3^{2-} (d) CO_3^{2-}, ClO_3^-

104. In the electronic structure of H_2SO_4, the total number of unshared electrons is :
(a) 20 (b) 16 (c) 12 (d) 8

105. Which of the following xenon compound has the same number of lone pairs as in I_3^-?

(a) XeO_4 (b) XeF_4 (c) XeF_2 (d) XeO_3

106. The shape of XeF_3^+ is :

(a) Trigonal planar (b) Pyramidal
(c) Bent T-shape (d) See-saw

107. Which of the following shape are not possible for possible value of 'n' in XeF_n molecule ?

(a) Linear (b) Square planar
(c) Trigonal planar (d) Capped octahedral

108. $BeCl_2$ is not isostructural with :

(a) ICl_2^- (b) C_2H_2 (c) XeF_2 (d) $GeCl_2$

109. Which statement is true about the most stable Lewis structure for CS_2?

(a) There are no lone pairs in molecule
(b) All bonds are double bonds
(c) The central atom does not have an octet of electrons
(d) A sulfur atom must be the central atom for the structure to be stable

110. SbF_5 reacts with XeF_4 and XeF_6 to form ionic compounds $[XeF_3^+][SbF_6^-]$ and $[XeF_5^+][SbF_6^-]$ then molecular shape of $[XeF_3^+]$ ion and $[XeF_5^+]$ ion respectively :

(a) Square pyramidal, T-shaped (b) Bent-T-shape, square pyramidal
(c) See-saw, square pyramidal (d) Square pyramidal, see-saw

Dipole Moment

111. BF_3 and NF_3 both are covalent compounds but NF_3 is polar whereas BF_3 is non-polar. This is because :

(a) Nitrogen atom is smaller than boron atom
(b) N—F bond is more polar than B—F bond
(c) NF_3 is pyramidal whereas BF_3 is planar triangular
(d) BF_3 is electron deficient whereas NF_3 is not

112. Dipole moment of NF_3 is smaller than :

(a) NH_3 (b) CO_2 (c) BF_3 (d) CCl_4

113. Which of the following molecules will have polar bonds but zero dipole moment?

(a) O_2 (b) $CHCl_3$ (c) CF_4 (d) none of these

114. Which has maximum dipole moment?

(a) 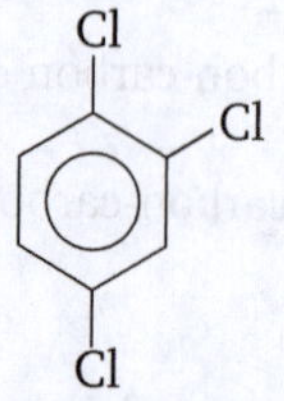

(b) 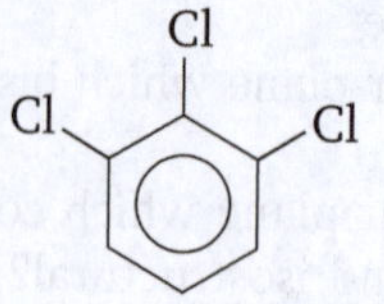

(c) 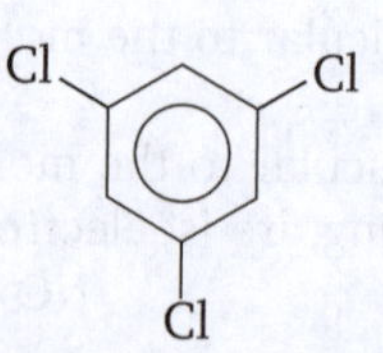

(d) 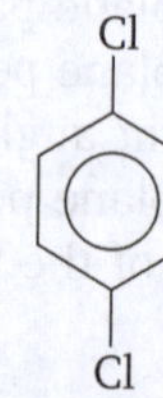

115. Which of the following compound is planar and non-polar ?

(a) XeO_4 (b) SF_4
(c) XeF_4 (d) CF_4

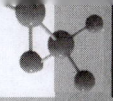

116. H_2O has a net dipole moment while BeF_2 has zero dipole moment because :

(a) F is more electronegativity than oxygen
(b) Be is more electronegativity than oxygen
(c) H_2O molecule is linear and BeF_2 is bent
(d) BeF_2 molecule is linear and H_2O is bent

117. Correct set of species with zero dipole moment is :

(i) CO_2 (ii) $COCl_2$ (iii) CH_2Cl_2 (iv) BCl_3
(a) (i) and (iv) (b) (ii) and (iv)
(c) (iii) and (iv) (d) (i), (iii) and (iv)

118. Which pair of molecules are polar species?

(a) CO_2 and H_2O (b) BF_3 and PCl_3
(c) SO_2 and SCl_2 (d) CS_2 and SO_3

119. In which molecule does the chlorine atom has positive partial charge?

(a) HCl (b) BrCl (c) OCl_2 (d) SCl_2

Bond Parameters

120. Least stable hydride is :

(a) stannane (b) silane (c) plumbane (d) germane

121. The lowest O — O bond length in the following molecule is :

(a) O_2F_2 (b) O_2 (c) H_2O_2 (d) O_3

122. Which one of the following compounds has the smallest bond angle?

(a) OH_2 (b) SH_2 (c) NH_3 (d) SO_2

123. Maximum bond angle is present in :

(a) BBr_3 (b) BCl_3 (c) BF_3 (d) none of these

124. The correct order of H — *M* — H bonds angle is :

(a) $NH_3 < PH_3 < SbH_3 < BiH_3$ (b) $AsH_3 < SbH_3 < PH_3 < NH_3$
(c) $NH_3 < PH_3 < BiH_3 < SbH_3$ (d) $BiH_3 < SbH_3 < AsH_3 < PH_3$

125. The correct increasing order of adjacent bond angle among BF_3, PF_3 and ClF_3 :

(a) $BF_3 < PF_3 < ClF_3$ (b) $PF_3 < BF_3 < ClF_3$
(c) $ClF_3 < PF_3 < BF_3$ (d) $BF_3 = PF_3 = ClF_3$

126. Among the following species, the least angle around the central atom is in :

(a) O_3 (b) I_3^- (c) NO_2^- (d) PH_3

127. The bond angles of NH_3, NH_4^+ and NH_2^- are in the order :

(a) $NH_2^- > NH_3 > NH_4^+$ (b) $NH_4^+ > NH_3 > NH_2^-$
(c) $NH_3 > NH_2^- > NH_4^+$ (d) $NH_3 > NH_4^+ > NH_2^-$

128. The H—C—H bond angle in CH_4 is 109.5°, due to lone pair repulsion, the H—O—H angle in H_2O will :

(a) remain the same (b) increase
(c) decrease (d) become 180°

129. The molecule having the largest bond angle is :

(a) H_2O (b) H_2S (c) H_2Se (d) H_2Te

130. The compound MX_4 is tetrahedral. The number of $\angle XMX$ angles in the compound is :

(a) three (b) four
(c) five (d) six

131. The "O — N̂ — O" bond angle is maximum in :

(a) N_2O (b) NO_2^+ (c) NO_2^- (d) NO_3^-

132. Which of the following is the correct order for increasing bond angle ?

(a) $NH_3 < PH_3 < AsH_3 < SbH_3$ (b) $H_2O < OF_2 < Cl_2O$
(c) $H_3Te^+ < H_3Se^+ < H_3S^+ < H_3O^+$ (d) $BF_3 < BCl_3 < BBr_3 < BI_3$

Molecular Forces

133. Which of the following attraction is strongest ?

(a) Cl^- ⋯⋯ H—Cl (b) $CHCl_3$ ⋯⋯ $CHCl_3$
(c) CCl_4 ⋯⋯ H_2O (d) Cl^- ⋯⋯ H_2O

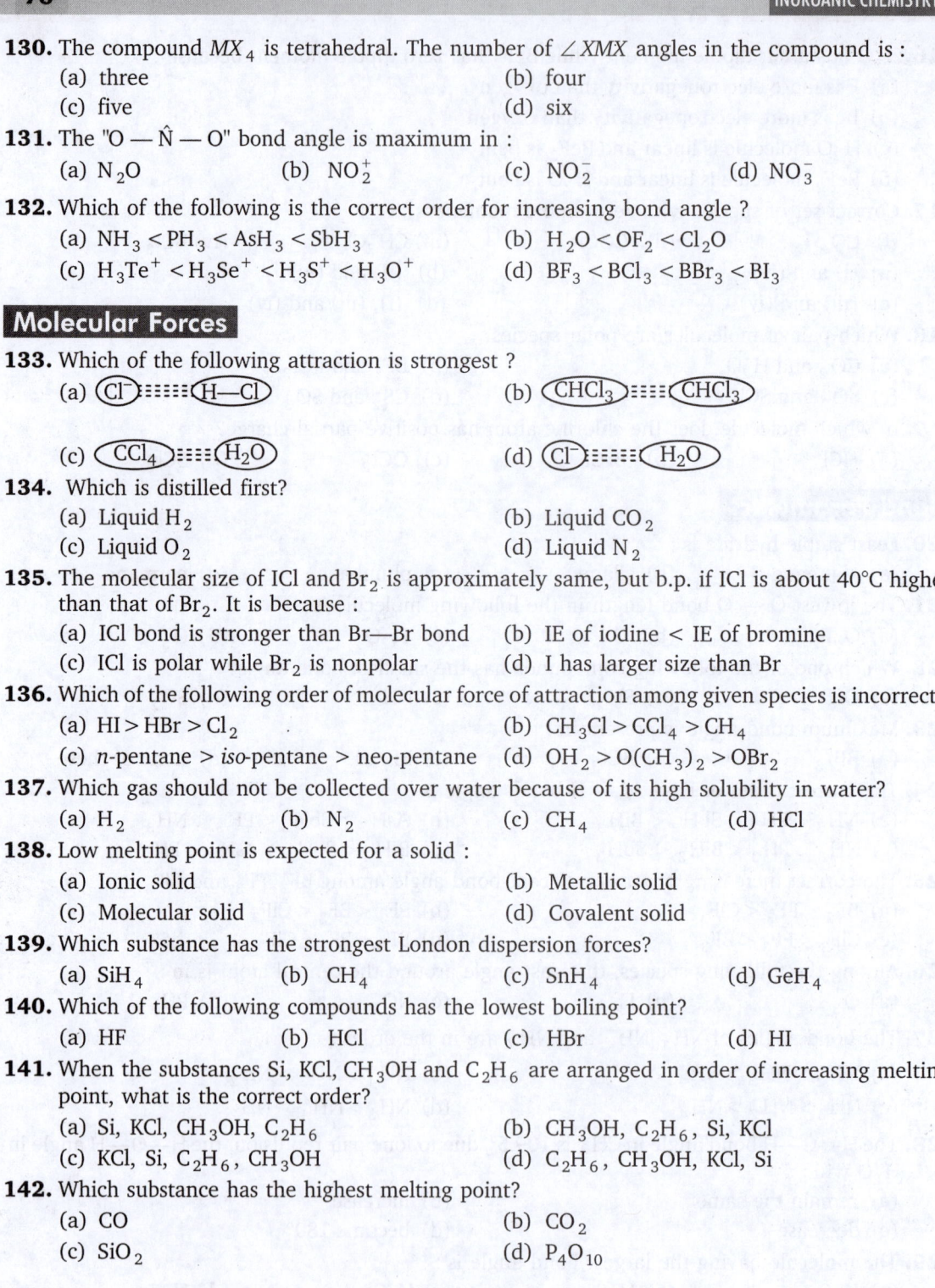

134. Which is distilled first?

(a) Liquid H_2 (b) Liquid CO_2
(c) Liquid O_2 (d) Liquid N_2

135. The molecular size of ICl and Br_2 is approximately same, but b.p. if ICl is about 40°C higher than that of Br_2. It is because :

(a) ICl bond is stronger than Br—Br bond (b) IE of iodine < IE of bromine
(c) ICl is polar while Br_2 is nonpolar (d) I has larger size than Br

136. Which of the following order of molecular force of attraction among given species is incorrect?

(a) $HI > HBr > Cl_2$ (b) $CH_3Cl > CCl_4 > CH_4$
(c) *n*-pentane > *iso*-pentane > neo-pentane (d) $OH_2 > O(CH_3)_2 > OBr_2$

137. Which gas should not be collected over water because of its high solubility in water?

(a) H_2 (b) N_2 (c) CH_4 (d) HCl

138. Low melting point is expected for a solid :

(a) Ionic solid (b) Metallic solid
(c) Molecular solid (d) Covalent solid

139. Which substance has the strongest London dispersion forces?

(a) SiH_4 (b) CH_4 (c) SnH_4 (d) GeH_4

140. Which of the following compounds has the lowest boiling point?

(a) HF (b) HCl (c) HBr (d) HI

141. When the substances Si, KCl, CH_3OH and C_2H_6 are arranged in order of increasing melting point, what is the correct order?

(a) Si, KCl, CH_3OH, C_2H_6 (b) CH_3OH, C_2H_6, Si, KCl
(c) KCl, Si, C_2H_6, CH_3OH (d) C_2H_6, CH_3OH, KCl, Si

142. Which substance has the highest melting point?

(a) CO (b) CO_2
(c) SiO_2 (d) P_4O_{10}

Hydrogen Bond

143. The correct order of boiling point is :

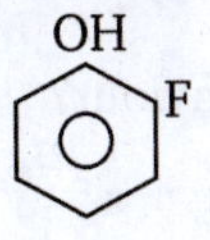
(I)

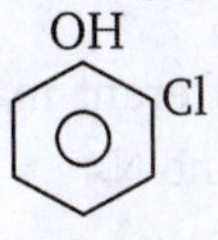
(II)

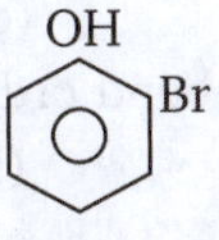
(III)

(a) I > II > III (b) III > II > I
(c) II > I > III (d) III > I > II

144. Which of the following is not true about H_2O molecule?
(a) The molecule has $\mu = 0$
(b) The molecule can act as a base
(c) Shows abnormally high boiling point in comparison to the hydrides of other elements of oxygen group
(d) The molecule has a bent shape

145. The boiling points at atmospheric pressure of HF, H_2S, NH_3 can be arranged in the following order :
(a) $HF > NH_3 > H_2S$ (b) $HF > H_2S > NH_3$
(c) $HF < H_2S < NH_3$ (d) $HF < NH_3 < H_2S$

146. The correct order of strength of H-bond in the following compound :
(a) $H_2O > H_2O_2 > HF$ (b) $HF > H_2O_2 > H_2O$
(c) $HF > H_2O > H_2O_2$ (d) $HF > H_2O > H_2O_2$

147. Which compound does not have electrovalent, covalent, co-ordinate as well as hydrogen bond?
(a) $[Cu(H_2O)_4]SO_4 \cdot H_2O$ (b) $[Zn(H_2O)_6]SO_4 \cdot H_2O$
(c) $[Fe(H_2O)_6]SO_4 \cdot H_2O$ (d) $[Fe(H_2O)_6]Cl_3$

148. Which statement is correct?
(a) m.p. of H_2O, NH_3 are maximum in their respective group due to intermolecular H-bonding
(b) b.p. of CH_4 out of CH_4, SiH_4, GeH_4 and SnH_4 is least due to weak intermolecular force of attraction
(c) formic acid forms dimer by H-bonding
(d) all are correct

149. Which of the following molecules are expected to exhibit intermolecular H-bonding?
(I) Acetic acid (II) *o*-nitrophenol (III) *m*-nitrophenol (IV) *o*-boric acid
Select correct alternate :
(a) I, II, III (b) I, II, IV (c) I, III, IV (d) II, III, IV

150. Which of the following compounds can form H-bonding with each other ?
(a) CH_3COOH and H_2O (b) Phenol and CH_4
(c) CHF_3 and acetone (d) PH_3 and HF

151. Correct order of bond length is:
(a) $O_2 > O_2^+$ (b) $N_2 > N_2^+$
(c) $C_2 > C_2^+$ (d) $H_2 > H_2^+$

152. Select pair of molecules with paramagnetic and diamagnetic nature respectively:
(a) B_2, C_2 (b) C_2, N_2
(c) N_2, O_2 (d) O_2, B_2

153. Which of the following pair has same bond order but different magnetic behaviour?
(a) H_2^+ and H_2^- (b) N_2^{2+} and N_2^{2-}
(c) O_2^+ and O_2^- (d) C_2^+ and C_2^-

154. For which of the following molecule bond length increases by either gain of an electron or removal of an electron?
(a) B_2 (b) C_2 (c) N_2 (d) O_2

155. Select the incorrect order of property mentioned is brackets:
(a) $Li_2 > F_2$ (Bond length) (b) $C_2 > O_2$ (Bond energy)
(c) $H_2 > F_2$ (Bond energy) (d) $O_2 < F_2$ (Bond energy)

156. Which of the following pairs have nearly identical values of bond energy?
(a) O_2 and H_2 (b) F_2 and H_2
(c) N_2 and CO (d) O_2 and Cl_2

157. In which of the following set all the species are paramagnetic in nature?
(a) O_2, O_2^{2+}, N_2^{2-} (b) B_2, C_2, H_2
(c) O_2^-, O_2^+, O_2 (d) N_2, O_2^+, F_2^+

158. Which of the following characteristics are incorrect for order : $F_2 < O_2$?
(a) Bond length (b) Bond energy
(c) HOMO has same symmetry (d) All molecular orbitals are not filled

159. Select correct statement about the following transformation

$$NO^+ \longrightarrow NO$$

(a) Reduction of N — O bond order (b) Increase of magnetic moment
(c) Increase of N — O bond length (d) All of these

160. Which of the following species have the same bond order?
(i) NO^+ (ii) NO (iii) CN^- (iv) OF^-
(a) (i) and (ii) (b) (ii) and (iii)
(c) (i) and (iii) (d) (ii) and (iv)

161. If *s-p* mixing of orbitals is absent in following molecules, then in which of the following molecule only σ-bond is present?
(a) B_2 (b) C_2 (c) N_2 (d) O_2

162. Which of the following species absorb maximum energy in its HOMO-LUMO electronic transition?
(a) O_2 (b) N_2^- (c) C_2 (d) N_2

163. In which of the following transformation, the bond order has increased and the magnetic behaviour has changed?
(a) $C_2^+ \longrightarrow C_2$ (b) $NO^+ \longrightarrow NO$
(c) $O_2 \longrightarrow O_2^+$ (d) $N_2 \longrightarrow N_2^+$

164. N_2 and O_2 are converted into cations N_2^+ and O_2^+ respectively. Which is incorrect statement for these cations?
(a) In O_2^+, paramagnetism decreases w.r.t O_2
(b) N_2^+ becomes diamagnetic
(c) In N_2^+, N — N bond weakens w.r.t N_2
(d) In O_2^+, O — O bond order increases w.r.t O_2

165. Increasing order of bond length in NO, NO^+ and NO^- are:
(a) $NO > NO^- > NO^+$ (b) $NO^+ < NO < NO^-$
(c) $NO < NO^+ < NO^-$ (d) $NO < NO^+ = NO^-$

166. Which of following statement is incorrect?
(a) O_2 is paramagnetic, O_3 is also paramagnetic
(b) O_2 is paramagnetic, O_3 is diamagnetic
(c) B_2 is paramagnetic, C_2 is diamagnetic
(d) C — O bond length decreases when CO^+ is formed from CO

167. N_2 and O_2 are converted to monocations N_2^+ and O_2^+ respectively, which is wrong statement?
(a) In N_2^+, the N — N bond weakens (b) In O_2^+, the O — O bond order increases
(c) In O_2^+, the paramagnetism decreases (d) N_2^+ becomes diamagnetic

168. Which of the following property is different between NO and O_2^+?
(a) *sp* mixing (b) Magnetic behaviour
(c) Bond order (d) σ and π-bond

Level 2

Ionic Bond

1. The ionic bonds X^+Y^- are formed when :

(I) electron affinity of Y is high (II) ionization energy of X is low

(III) lattice energy of XY is high (IV) lattice energy of XY is low

Choose the correct code :

(a) I and II (b) I and III (c) I, II and III (d) All

2. In the Born-Haber cycle for the formation of solid common salt (NaCl), the largest contribution comes from:

(a) the low ionization potential of Na (b) the high electron affinity of Cl

(c) the low ΔH_{vap} of Na(s) (d) the lattice energy

3. Incorrect statement is :

(a) $MgO > AlF_3 > MgF_2$: Lattice energy

(b) $Li > Na > Al > Mg$: Electron affinity

(c) $SF_6 > PF_5 > SiF_4$: Lewis acidic character

(d) $SiCl_4 > SiBr_4 > SiI_4$: Decreasing order of electronegativity of Si

Valence Bond Theory

4. If two different non-axial *d*-orbitals having '*xz*' nodal plane form π-bond by overlapping each other, then internuclear axis will be :

(a) *x* (b) *y*

(c) *z* (d) They don't form π-bond

5. Assuming pure 2*s* and 2*p* orbitals of carbon are used in forming CH_4 molecule, which of the following statement is false?

(a) Three C—H bonds will be at right angle

(b) One C—H bond will be weaker than other three C—H bonds

(c) The shape of molecule will be tetrahedral

(d) The angle of C—H bond formed by *s*-*s* overlapping will be uncertain with respect to other three bonds.

6. The strength of bonds formed by 2*s*-2*s*, 2*p*-2*p* and 2*p* – 2*s* overlap has the order :

(a) $s\text{-}s > p\text{-}p > p\text{-}s$ (b) $s\text{-}s > p\text{-}s > p\text{-}p$

(c) $p\text{-}p > p\text{-}s > s\text{-}s$ (d) $p\text{-}p > s\text{-}s > p\text{-}s$

7. Which of the following statements is incorrect for sigma and π-bonds formed between two carbon atoms?

(a) Sigma-bond is stronger than a π-bond

(b) Bond energies of sigma and π-bonds are of the order of 264 kJ/mol and 347 kJ/mol

(c) Free rotation of surrounding atoms about a sigma-bond is allowed but not in case of a π-bond

(d) Sigma-bond determines the direction between carbon atoms but a π-bond has no primary effect in this regard

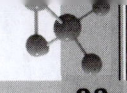

8. Assuming the bond direction to the z-axis, which of the overlapping of atomic orbitals of two atom (A) and (B) will result in bonding?

(I) s-orbital of A and p_x-orbital of B (II) s-orbital of A and p_z orbital of B

(III) p_y-orbital of A and p_z orbital of B (IV) s-orbital of both (A) and (B)

(a) I and IV (b) I and II (c) III and IV (d) II and IV

9. Which of the following orbital can not form π as well as δ-Bond ?

(a) d_{xy} (b) d_{z^2}

(c) $d_{x^2-y^2}$ (d) d_{yz}

VSEPR Theory

10. Which of the following statement is correct about I_3^+ and I_3^- molecular ions ?

(a) Number of lone pairs at central atoms are same in both molecular ions

(b) Hybridization of central atoms in both ions are same

(c) Both are polar species

(d) Both are planar species

11. In which of the following molecular shape d_{z^2}-orbital must not be involved in bonding ?

(a) Pentagonal planar (b) Trigonal planar (c) Linear (d) Square planar

12. The correct statement regarding SO_2 molecule is:

(a) two $p\pi$ - $d\pi$ bonds

(b) molecule has 2 lone pair, 2σ bonds and 2π bonds

(c) two $p\pi$ - $p\pi$ bonds

(d) one $p\pi$ - $p\pi$ and one $p\pi$ - $d\pi$ bond

13. A molecule XY_2 contains two σ, two π-bonds and one lone pair of electron in the valence shell of X. The arrangement of lone pair as well as bond pairs is :

(a) square pyramidal (b) linear (c) trigonal planar (d) unpredictable

14. In which of the following pairs, both the species have the same hybridisation ?

(I) SF_4, XeF_4 (II) I_3^-, XeF_2 (III) $ICl_4^+, SiCl_4$ (IV) ClO_3^-, PO_4^{3-}

(a) I, II (b) II, III (c) II, IV (d) I, II, III

15. Which of the following possess two lone pair of electrons on the central atom and square planar in shape ?

(I) SF_4 (II) XeO_4 (III) XeF_4 (IV) ICl_4^-

(a) I, III (b) II, IV (c) III, IV (d) All

16. Select pair of compounds in which both have different hybridization but have same molecular shape :

(a) BF_3, BrF_3 (b) $ICl_2^{\ominus}, BeCl_2$ (c) BCl_3, PCl_3 (d) PCl_3, NCl_3

17. The species having no $p\pi - p\pi$ bond but has bond order equal to that of O_2 :

(a) ClO_3^- (b) PO_4^{3-} (c) SO_4^{2-} (d) XeO_3

Hybridisation

18. Choose the correct code of characteristics for the given order of hybrid orbitals of same atom,

$$sp < sp^2 < sp^3$$

(i) Electronegativity (ii) Bond angle between same hybrid orbitals
(iii) Size (iv) Energy level
(a) (ii), (iii) and (iv) (b) (iii), (iv)
(c) (ii) and (iv) (d) (i), (ii), (iii) and (iv)

19. Which is correct statement?
As the *s*-character of a hybrid orbital decreases
(I) The bond angle decreases (II) The bond strength increases
(III) The bond length increases (IV) Size of orbitals increases
(a) (I), (III) and (IV) (b) (II), (III) and (IV)
(c) (I) and (II) (d) All are correct

20. Which of the following is incorrectly match ?

	Hybridisation	Geometry	Orbitals use
(a)	sp^3d	Trigonal bipyramidal	$s + p_x + p_y + p_z + d_{z^2}$
(b)	sp^3d^3	Pentagonal bipyramidal	$s + p_x + p_y + p_z + d_{x^2-y^2} + d_{z^2} + d_{xy}$
(c)	sp^3d^2	Capped octahedral	$s + p_x + p_y + p_z + d_{x^2-y^2} + d_{z^2}$
(d)	sp^3	Tetrahedral	$s + p_x + p_y + p_z$

Molecular Geometry/Shape

21. Species having maximum 'Cl—O' bond order is :
(a) ClO_3^- (b) ClO_3 (c) ClO_2 (d) ClO_2^-

22. Which of the following species contains minimum number of atoms in '*XY*' plane?
(a) XeF_5^- (b) SF_6 (c) IF_7 (d) All

23. The molecule ML_x is planar with 7 pairs of electrons around *M* in the valence shell. The value of *x* is :
(a) 6 (b) 5 (c) 4 (d) 3

24. Choose the correct option for the following molecule in view of chemical bonding :

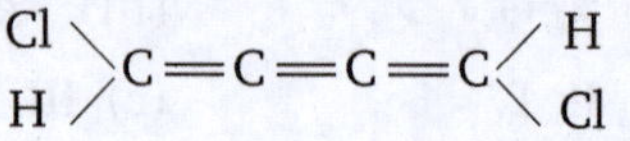

(a) non-planar (b) $\mu \neq 0$ (c) both (a) and (b) (d) $\mu = 0$

Bond Parameters

25. Which of the following fact is directly explained by the statement 'oxygen is a smaller atom than sulphur' ?
(a) H_2O boils at a much higher temperature than H_2S
(b) H_2O undergoes intermolecular hydrogen bonding

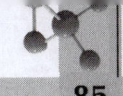

(c) H_2O is liquid and H_2S is gas at room temperature
(d) S—H bond is longer than O—H bond

26. Which of the following compound has maximum "C — C" single bond length ?
(a) CH_2CHCCH
(b) HCCCCH
(c) CH_3CHCH_2
(d) $CH_2CHCHCH_2$

27. Which of the following set contains species having same angle around the central atom?
(a) SF_4, CH_4, NH_3
(b) NF_3, BCl_3, NH_3
(c) $BF_3, NF_3, AlCl_3$
(d) BF_3, BCl_3, BBr_3

28. Which of the following compound has the smallest bond angle ($X — A — X$) in each series respectively?

(A) OSF_2	$OSCl_2$	$OSBr_2$
(B) $SbCl_3$	$SbBr_3$	SbI_3
(C) PI_3	AsI_3	SbI_3

(a) OSF_2, $SbCl_3$ and PI_3
(b) $OSBr_2$, SbI_3 and PI_3
(c) OSF_2, SbI_3 and PI_3
(d) OSF_2, $SbCl_3$ and SbI_3

Molecular Forces

29. The incorrect order of boiling point is :
(a) $H_2O > CH_3OH$
(b) $CH_3NH_2 < NH(CH_3)_2$
(c) $H_3PO_4 > Me_3PO_4$
(d) $CH_3N_3 > HN_3$

30. Iodine molecules are held in the solid lattice by ....
(a) London forces
(b) dipole-dipole interactions
(c) covalent bonds
(d) coulombic force

31. Carbon dioxide is gas, while SiO_2 is solid because :
(a) CO_2 is a linear molecule, while SiO_2 is angular
(b) van der Waals' forces are very strong in SiO_2
(c) CO_2 is covalent, while SiO_2 is ionic
(d) Si cannot form stable bonds with O, hence Si has to form a 3D lattice

32. LUMO [Lowest Unoccupies Molecular Orbital] of which of the following paramagnetic molecular species is not formed by *s-p* mixing:
(a) O_2^+
(b) N_2^{2+}
(c) B_2^-
(d) NO

33. In which of the following molecular species *s*-bond is having fractional bond order equal to 0.5?
(a) N_2^-
(b) O_2^-
(c) NO
(d) N_2^+

34. Select incorrect statement for a diatomic homonuclear +2 cation having molecular orbital configuration $(\sigma 1s^2)(\sigma * 1s)^2(\sigma 2s)^2(\sigma * 2s)^2(\sigma 2p)^2(\pi 2p)^4$
(a) Ion is diamagnetic
(b) It's neutral diatomic molecule is paramagnetic
(c) *s-p* mixing occurs
(d) It has higher bond order than respective neutral molecules

35. The O — O bond length in $O_2, O_2[AsF_4]$ and KO_2 is:
(a) $O_2[AsF_4] < O_2 < KO_2$
(b) $O_2[AsF_4] < KO_2 < O_2$
(c) $O_2 < O_2[AsF_4] < KO_2$
(d) $KO_2 < O_2 < O_2[AsF_4]$

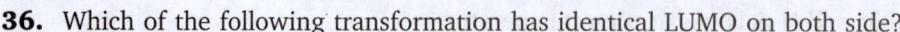

36. Which of the following transformation has identical LUMO on both side?

(a) $N_2 \longrightarrow N_2^{2-}$ (b) $O_2 \longrightarrow O_2^{2+}$

(c) $C_2 \longrightarrow C_2^{2-}$ (d) $B_2 \longrightarrow B_2^{2-}$

37.

List-I	**List-II (Properties)**
(P) $S_2(g)$	(1) Paramagnetic
(Q) $N_2(g)$	(2) Diamagnetic
(R) $O_2(g)$	(3) Paramagnetic
(S) $F_2(g)$	(4) Diamagnetic

Codes:

	P	Q	R	S
(a)	2	3	1	4
(b)	3	1	4	2
(c)	1	4	3	2
(d)	4	2	1	3

38.

List-I	**List-II**
(P) B_2	(1) Paramagnetic
(Q) C_2	(2) Ionization energy is less than parent atom
(R) N_2	(3) Only π-bond is present
(S) O_2	(4) Bond order is equal to 3

Codes:

	P	Q	R	S
(a)	1	3	4	2
(b)	4	1	2	3
(c)	3	2	1	4
(d)	4	2	1	3

Level 3

Passage 1

According to VSEPR model, molecules adopt geometries in which their valence electron pairs position themselves as far from each other as possible. The VSEPR model considers double and triple bonds to have slightly greater repulsive effects than single bonds because of the repulsive effect of π-electrons. However the lone pair creates the maximum repulsive effect.

1. Which of the following statement is false ?
(a) SbF_4^- and SF_4 are isostructural
(b) In IOF_5 the hybridization of central atom is sp^3d^2
(c) Double bond(s) in SOF_4 and XeO_3F_2, is/are occupying equatorial position(s) of their respective geometry
(d) None of these

2. Which of the following does not represent the isostructural pair?
(a) SF_5^- and IF_5 (b) ClO_2F_3 and SOF_4 (c) SeF_3^+ and XeO_3 (d) None

3. Select the incorrect statement with respect to SO_2Cl_2 molecule :
(a) It gives H_2SO_4 and HCl on hydrolysis at room temperature
(b) It has two $d\pi$-$p\pi$ bonds between S and O bonded atoms
(c) It is a polar molecule
(d) None

Passage 2

According to VBT any covalent bond will be formed by overlapping of atomic orbitals of bonded atoms provided atomic orbitals must be half-filled and electrons be in opposite spin. According to type of overlapping covalent bonds can be classified as (a) σ-bond (b) π-bond (c) δ -bond:

1. Which of the following set of orbitals does not produce nodal plane in *xz*-plane ?
(a) $d_{yz} + d_{yz}$ (b) $d_{xy} + d_{xy}$ (c) $p_y + d_{xy}$ (d) None of these

2. The combination of orbital that can not produce non-bonding molecular orbital is (inter-nuclear axis is *z*-axis):
(a) $p_y + d_{x^2-y^2}$ (b) $p_z + d_{yz}$ (c) $s + d_{xz}$ (d) $d_{xy} + d_{xy}$

3. If $F_2C_1 = C_2$ part of $F_2C_1 = C_2 = C_3 = C_4F_2$ lies in *yz*-plane, then incorrect statement is :
(a) Nodal plane of π-bond between C_1 and C_2 lies in *yz*-plane, formed by sideways overlapping of p_x-orbitals
(b) Nodal plane of π-bond between C_2 and C_3 lies in *xz*-plane, formed by sideways overlapping of p_y-orbitals

(c) Nodal plane of π-bond between C_3 and C_4 lies in *yz*-plane, formed by sideways overlapping of p_y-orbitals

(d) Nodal plane of π-bond between C_2 and C_3 lies in *xy*-plane, formed by sideways overlapping of p_z-orbitals

Passage 3

If the central atom is of third row or below this in the periodic table, then lone pair will occupy a stereochemically inactive *s*-orbital and bonding will be through almost pure *p*-orbitals and bond angles are nearly 90°, if the substituent's electronegativity value is $\leq$ 2.5.

1. In which of the following option, covalent bond is having maximum *s*% character?

(a) S — H bond in H_2S (b) P — H bond in PH_3

(c) N — H bond in NH_3 (d) All have equal *s*% character

2. Select incorrect statement regarding P_4 molecule.

(a) Each P atom is joined with three P-atoms

(b) P_4 molecule contains total 12 bond angles

(c) Lone pair of each P atom is present in pure *s*-orbital

(d) Lone pair of each P atom present in hybrid orbital

3. The hybridisation of atomic orbitals of central atom "Xe" in XeO_4, XeO_2F_2 and $XeOF_4$ respectively.

(a) sp^3, sp^3d^2, sp^3d^2 (b) sp^3d, sp^3d, sp^3d^2

(c) sp^3, sp^3d^2, sp^3d (d) sp^3, sp^3d, sp^3d^2

Passage 4

According to V.B.T., atoms of element form bond only to pair up their unpaired electrons present in ground state or excited state. This pairing of unpaired electron will take place by overlapping of orbitals each one having one unpaired electron with opposite spin.

1. Which of the following orbital combination does not form π-bond?

(a) $p_x + p_x$ sideways overlapping (b) $d_{x^2-y^2} + p_y$ sideways overlapping

(c) $d_{xy} + d_{xy}$ sideways overlapping (d) $d_{yz} + p_y$ sideways overlapping

2. Which of the following orbital cannot form δ-bond?

(a) $d_{x^2-y^2}$ orbital (b) d_{xy} orbital

(c) d_{z^2} orbital (d) d_{zx} orbital

3. Which of the following combination of orbitals does not from any type of covalent bond (if *z*-axis is molecular axis)?

(a) $p_z + p_z$ (b) $p_y + p_y$

(c) $s + p_y$ (d) $s + s$

Passage 5

The space model which is obtained by joining the points representing various bonded atoms gives the shape of the molecule. The geometry of the molecule is definite relative arrangement of the bonded atoms in a molecule. The shape and geometry of a molecule is explained by valence shell electron pair repulsion theory given by Gillespie and Nyholm.

1. Select the correct code for the following repulsion orders, according to VSEPR theory :

(I) lone pair–lone pair > lone pair–bond pair

(II) lone pair–bond pair > bond pair–bond pair

(III) lone pair–lone pair > bond pair–bond pair

(IV) lone pair–bond pair > lone pair–lone pair

(a) I, II & III (b) II & IV (c) I, II & IV (d) All

2. Which molecule has both shape and geometry identical?

(I) $SnCl_2$ (II) NH_3 (III) PCl_5 (IV) SF_6

(a) I, III & IV (b) II, III & IV

(c) III & IV (d) All

3. Which is not the electron geometry of covalent molecules?

(a) Pentagonal bipyramidal (b) Octahedral

(c) Hexagonal (d) Tetrahedral

Passage 6

When hybridisation involving *d*-orbitals are considered then all the five *d*-orbitals are not degenerate, rather $d_{x^2-y^2}, d_{z^2}$ and d_{xy}, d_{yz}, d_{zx} form two different sets of orbitals and orbitals of appropriate set is involved in the hybridisation.

1. In sp^3d^2 hybridisation, which sets of *d*-orbitals is involved ?

(a) $d_{x^2-y^2}, d_{z^2}$ (b) d_{z^2}, d_{xy} (c) d_{xy}, d_{yz} (d) $d_{x^2-y^2}, d_{xy}$

2. In sp^3d^3 hybridisation, which orbitals are involved?

(a) $d_{x^2-y^2}, d_{z^2}, d_{xy}$ (b) d_{xy}, d_{yz}, d_{zx}

(c) $d_{x^2-y^2}, d_{xy}, d_{xz}$ (d) d_{z^2}, d_{yz}, d_{zx}

3. Molecule having trigonal bipyramidal geometry and sp^3d hybridisation, *d*-orbitals involved is:

(a) d_{xy} (b) d_{yz} (c) $d_{x^2-y^2}$ (d) d_{z^2}

4. Which of the following orbitals can not undergo hybridisation amongst themselves.

(I) $3d, 4s$ (II) $3d, 4d$

(III) $3d, 4s$ & $4p$ (IV) $3s, 3p$ & $4s$

(a) only II (b) II & III (c) I, II & IV (d) II & IV

Passage 7

Ionic bond is defined as the electrostatic force of attraction holding the oppositely charged ions. Ionic compounds are mostly crystalline solid having high melting and boiling points, electrical conductivity in molten state, solubility in water etc. Covalent bond is defined as the force which binds atoms of same or different elements by mutual sharing of electrons in a covalent bond. Covalent compounds are solids, liquids or gases. They have low melting and boiling points compounds. They are more soluble in non-polar solvents.

1. The valence electrons are involved in formation of covalent bonds is/are called :
(a) non-bonding electrons (b) lone pairs
(c) unshared pairs (d) none of these

2. The amount of energy released when one mole of ionic solid is formed by packing of gaseous ion is called :
(a) Ionisation energy (b) Solvation energy
(c) Lattice energy (d) Hydration energy

3. Which of the following is arranged order of increasing boiling point ?
(a) $H_2O < CCl_4 < CS_2 < CO_2$ (b) $CO_2 < CS_2 < CCl_4 < H_2O$
(c) $CS_2 < H_2O < CO_2 < CCl_4$ (d) $CCl_4 < H_2O < CO_2 < CS_2$

Passage 8

When an ionic compound is dissolved in water (polar solvent), it breaks up into its constituent ions. The given ionic compound will be dissolved in water if its hydration energy is more than lattice energy. If hydration energy is less than lattice energy then ionic compound is usually either sparingly soluble or insoluble in water.

1. Which of the following ionic compound is having maximum lattice energy :
(a) NaF (b) MgF_2 (c) AlF_3 (d) KF

2. Most hydrated cation is :
(a) $Ce^{4+}_{(aq.)}$ (b) $La^{3+}_{(aq.)}$ (c) $Ba^{2+}_{(aq.)}$ (d) $Cs^{+}_{(aq.)}$

Passage 9

A covalent bond will be formed by the overlapping of atomic orbitals having single electron of opposite spin, according to the overlapping of atomic orbitals the covalent bond may be of two types :
(i) Sigma bond (σ) (ii) Pi bond (π)
Sigma bond is stronger bond than the Pi-bond. If atomic orbitals overlap about the nuclear axis then sigma bond is formed but when atomic orbitals overlap sideway then Pi-bond is formed.

1. The correct order of increasing C — O bond length of CO, CO_3^{2-}, CO_2 is :
(a) $CO_3^{2-} < CO_2 < CO$ (b) $CO_2 < CO_3^{2-} < CO$
(c) $CO < CO_3^{2-} < CO_2$ (d) $CO < CO_2 < CO_3^{2-}$

2. Compound having maximum bond angle is :
(a) BBr_3
(b) BCl_3
(c) BF_3
(d) None of these

3. The strength of bonds formed by $2s-2s$, $2p-2p$ and $2p-2s$ overlap has the order :
(a) $s-s>p-p>p-s$
(b) $s-s>p-s>p-p$
(c) $p-p>p-s>s-s$
(d) $p-p>s-s>p-s$

Passage 10

According to VBT the extent of overlapping depends upon types of orbitals involved in overlapping and nature of overlapping. More will be the overlapping and the bond energy will also be high.

1. The incorrect order of bond dissociation energy will be :
(a) H — H > Cl — Cl > Br — Br
(b) Si — Si > P — P > Cl — Cl
(c) C — C > N — N > O — O
(d) H — Cl > H — Br > H — I

2. Which of the following combination of orbitals does not form covalent bond (*x*-axis is inter nuclear axis) :
(a) $s+p_y$
(b) p_y+p_y
(c) $d_{yz}+d_{yz}$
(d) $d_{xy}+d_{xy}$

3. Which of the following compound does not form $p\pi-p\pi$ bond ?
(a) SO_3
(b) NO_3^-
(c) SO_4^{2-}
(d) CO_3^{2-}

Passage 11

Consider the following elements with their period number and valence electrons.

Elements	Period number	Total valence e^-
P	2	4
Q	2	6
R	3	7
S	3	3
T	3	6
U	3	4

According to the given informations, answer the following questions :

1. Choose incorrect statement :
(a) *R* exhibits maximum covalency among all elements given
(b) *Q* does not exhibit variable covalency
(c) *R* exhibits minimum covalency among all elements given
(d) *R* and *S* combine each other and form SR_5 type of compound

2. Choose the correct statement :

(a) Q has maximum value of electron affinity

(b) R has maximum value of electronegativity

(c) S has maximum atomic size

(d) T and U are same group elements

3. Choose the incorrect statement :

(a) SR_3 is a hypovalent compound (b) UR_4 can act as a Lewis acid

(c) PQ_2 can not acts as Lewis acid (d) $UR_4 > SR_3$: Lewis acidic character

Passage 12

Hybridisation involves the mixing of orbitals having comparable energies of same atom. Hybridised orbitals perform efficient overlapping than overlapping by pure s, p or d orbitals.

1. Which of the following is not correctly match between given species and type of overlapping ?

(a) XeO_3: Three $(d\pi - p\pi)$ bonds (b) H_2SO_4: Two $(d\pi - p\pi)$ bonds

(c) SO_3: Three $(d\pi - p\pi)$ bonds (d) $HClO_4$: Three $(d\pi - p\pi)$ bonds

2. Consider the following compounds and select the incorrect statement from the following :

$$NH_3,\ PH_3,\ H_2S,\ SO_2,\ SO_3,\ BF_3,\ PCl_3,\ IF_7,\ P_4,\ H_2$$

(a) Six molecules out of given compounds involves hybridisation

(b) Three molecules are hypervalent compounds

(c) Six molecules out of above compounds are non-planar in structure

(d) Two molecules out of given compounds involves $(d\pi - p\pi)$ bonding as well as also involves $(p\pi - p\pi)$ bonding

Passage 13

Lattice energy is the amount of energy release when one mole of ionic solid is formed from its constitutent gaseous cations and anions.

Hydration energy is the amount of energy release when one mole of gaseous cation or one mole of gaseous anion is completely hydrated.

1. Consider the following conversion and calculate the net energy change for the following conversion :

$$NaCl(s) + H_2O \longrightarrow Na^+(aq) + Cl^-(aq)$$

Given : LE of NaCl $= x$ kJ/mol

HE of Na^+ $= y$ kJ/mol

HE of Cl^- $= z$ kJ/mol

(a) $(x - y + z)$ kJ/mol (b) $(-x + y + z)$ kJ/mol

(c) $(x - y - z)$ kJ/mol (d) $(x + y + z)$ kJ/mol

2. Select the correct order :
(a) $Na_3N > Mg_3N_2 > AlN$ (Lattice energy)
(b) $Na^+(g) < Mg^{2+}(g) < Al^{3+}(g)$ (Ionic radius)
(c) $Li^+(aq) > Na^+(aq) > K^+(aq)$ (Hydrated ion radius)
(d) $F^-(aq) > Cl^-(aq) > I^-(aq)$ (Ionic mobility)

Passage 14

It is cleared from the Kossel and Lewis approach that the formation of an ionic compound would primarily depends upon the ease of formation of the positive and negative ions from the respective neutral atoms.

Conditions for the formation of ionic compounds are :

(i) Electronegativity difference between two combining elements must be larger.

(ii) Ionization enthalpy $[(M(g) \rightarrow M^+(g) + e^-)]$ of electropositive element must be low.

(iii) Negative value of electron gain enthalpy $[(X(g) + e^- \rightarrow X^-(g))]$ of electronegative element should be high.

(iv) Lattice enthalpy $[(M^+(g) + X^-(g) \rightarrow MX(s))]$ of an ionic solid must be high.

1. Select the correct reason for given statement "Flouride of Al is ionic while chloride of Al is covalent".
(a) IE of Al in $AlF_3 > AlCl_3$
(b) EA of Flourine > Chlorine
(c) Lattice energy of $AlF_3 > AlCl_3$
(d) EA of Flourine < Chlorine

2. Which of the following is ionic compound ?
(a) $(NH_4)_2SO_4$
(b) HCN
(c) AlI_3
(d) HBr

Passage 15

ACl_3 is trigonal pyramidal and DCl_3 is trigonal planar compound, when these two compounds ACl_3 and DCl_3 are mixed together then a compound $ADCl_6$ is formed. Structural analysis showed that $ADCl_6$ is an ionic compound, now answer the following with respect to given conditions.

1. If anion has see-saw shape then shape of cation formed is :
(a) linear
(b) bent
(c) pentagonal bipyramidal
(d) trigonal planar

2. If shape of anion is tetrahedral then shape of cation formed is :
(a) tetrahedral
(b) bent
(c) linear
(d) trigonal planar

ONE OR MORE ANSWERS IS/ARE CORRECT

1. In which of the following there is intermolecular hydrogen bonding?
(a) Water (b) Ethanol
(c) Acetic acid (d) H—F

2. Correct order of decreasing boiling points is :
(a) $HF > HI > HBr > HCl$ (b) $H_2O > H_2Te > H_2Se > H_2S$
(c) $Br_2 > Cl_2 > F_2$ (d) $CH_4 > GeH_4 > SiH_4$

3. In which species the hybrid state of central atom is/are sp^3d ?
(a) I_3^- (b) SF_4
(c) PF_5 (d) IF_5

4. Select correct statement(s) is/are :
(a) In AsH_3 molecule lone pair at central atom is present in almost pure *s*-orbital
(b) Number of $p\pi - d\pi$ bond in SO_3 and SO_2 are same
(c) NF_3 is better Lewis base than NCl_3
(d) Stable oxidation state of Lead is +2

5. Which of the following species does/do not exist?
(a) OF_4 (b) NH_2^-
(c) NCl_5 (d) ICl_3^{2-}

6. Which of the following species is/are superoctet molecule?
(a) AlF_3 (b) $SiCl_4$
(c) XeF_2 (d) ICl_3

7. Which of the following statements is incorrect ?
(a) A σ-bond is weaker than a π-bond
(b) There are four co-ordinate bonds in the NH_4^+ ions
(c) The covalent bond is directional in nature
(d) HF is less polar than HCl

8. Which of the following species is/are capable of forming a coordinate bond with BF_3?
(a) PH_3 (b) NH_4^+
(c) OH^- (d) Mg^{2+}

9. Ionic compounds in general do not possess :
(a) high melting points and non-directional bonds
(b) high melting points and low-boiling points
(c) directional bonds and low-boiling points
(d) high solubilities in polar and non-polar solvents

10. Correct stability order of metal cation is/are :
(a) $Pb^{2+} < Sn^{2+}$ (b) $Pb^{4+} < Pb^{2+}$
(c) $Sn^{4+} < Sn^{2+}$ (d) $Pb^{4+} < Sn^{4+}$

11. Consider the following molecule :

$$\underset{(1)}{H_2C} = \underset{(2)}{C} = \underset{(3)}{C} = \underset{(4)}{C} = \underset{(5)}{CF_2}$$

If hybridization of $C_{(1)}$ carbon atom is $sp^2(s + p_y + p_z)$ and hybridization of $C_{(4)}$ carbon atom is $sp(s + p_z)$. Then according to given information the **correct** statement(s) is/are :

(a) Nodal plane of π-bond between $C_{(2)}$ and $C_{(3)}$ lies in *xz*-plane, formed by sideways overlapping of p_y-orbitals

(b) Nodal plane of π-bond between $C_{(3)}$ and $C_{(4)}$ lies in *yz*-plane, formed by side ways overlapping of p_x-orbitals

(c) The orbitals involve in hybridization of $C_{(5)}$ carbon atom are $s + p_x + p_z$

(d) Nodal plane of π-bond between $C_{(1)}$ and $C_{(2)}$ lies in *yz*-plane, formed by side ways overlapping of p_y-orbitals

12. Consider the following two molecules and according to the given information select correct statement(s) about AX_2 and AY_2 :

where *A* : 16th group of 3rd period element

X : more electronegative than (*A*) and same group number of (*A*)

Y : Less atomic size than (*A*) and same period number of (*A*)

(a) The hybridization of central atoms are different in both compounds

(b) The shape of both molecules are same

(c) Both compounds are planar

(d) The $X - \hat{A} - X$ bond angle is less than $Y - \hat{A} - Y$ bond angle

13. Which of the following statements are correct about sulphur hexafluoride ?

(a) all S — F bonds are equivalent

(b) SF_6 is a planar molecule

(c) oxidation number of sulphur is the same as number of electrons of sulphur involved in bonding

(d) sulphur has acquired the electronic structure of the gas argon

14. If AB_4^n, types species are tetrahedral, then which of the following is/are correctly match? (Where *A* is central atom, *B* is surrounding atom and *n* is charge on species.)

	A	**B**	***n***
(a)	Xe	O	0
(b)	Se	F	0
(c)	P	O	−3
(d)	N	H	+1

15. Which of the following statements is correct ?

(a) ClF_3 molecule is bent T-shape

(b) In SF_4 molecule, F—S—F equatorial bond angle is 103° due to *lp* – *lp* repulsion

(c) In $[ICl_4]^-$ molecular ion, Cl—I—Cl bond angle is 90°

(d) In OBr_2, the bond angle is less than OCl_2

16. Which of the following combination of bond pair (b.p.) and lone pair (l.p.) give same shape?

(i) 3 b.p.+1 l.p. (ii) 2 b.p.+2 l.p. (iii) 2 b.p.+1 l.p. (iv) 2 b.p.+0 l.p.

(v) 3 b.p.+2 l.p. (vi) 2 b.p.+3 l.p.

(a) (ii) and (iii) (b) (iv) and (v)
(c) (iv) and (vi) (d) (iii) and (vi)

17. Select the true statement(s) among the following :
(a) Pure overlapping of two d_{xy} orbitals along x-axis results in the formation of π-bond
(b) $NO_2^+ > NO_3^- > NO_2^-$ is the correct order of bond angle as well as N—O bond order
(c) $NF_3 < NCl_3 < NBr_3 < NI_3$ is the correct order of Lewis basic character as well as bond angle
(d) HF > HCl > HBr > HI is the correct order of dipole moment as well as boiling point

18. p_y-orbital can not form π-bond by lateral overlap with :
(a) d_{xz}-orbital (b) $d_{x^2-y^2}$-orbital
(c) d_{xy}-orbital (d) p_z-orbital

19. Which of the following orbital(s) cannot form δ -bond ?
(a) $d_{x^2-y^2}$-orbital (b) d_{xy}-orbital
(c) d_{z^2}-orbital (d) p_x-orbital

20. Select correct statement(s) regarding σ and π-bonds:
(a) σ-bond lies on the line joining the nuclei of bonded atoms
(b) π-electron cloud lies on either side to the line joining the nuclei of bonded atoms
(c) $(2p_\pi - 3d_\pi)$ π-bond is stronger than $(2p_\pi - 3p_\pi)$ π-bond.
(d) σ-bond has primary effect to decide direction of covalent bond, while π -bond has no primary effect in direction of bond

21. Which of the following statements is/are correct?
(a) All carbon to carbon bonds contain a sigma bond and one or more π-bonds
(b) All carbon to carbon bonds are sigma bonds
(c) All oxygen to hydrogen bonds are hydrogen bonds
(d) All carbon to hydrogen bonds are sigma bonds

22. Consider the following three orbitals :

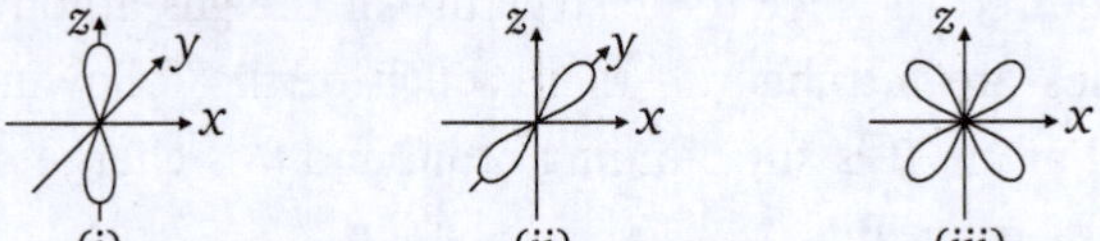

(i) (ii) (iii)

Correct statement(s) regarding given information is/are :
(a) Orbitals (i) and (ii) can never form any type of covalent bond
(b) If internuclear axis is 'x', then combination of (ii) and (iii) orbitals can form π-bond
(c) Orbital (iii) can form δ-bond with other orbital having same orientation of lobes
(d) If internuclear axis is 'x', then combination of (i) and (iii) orbitals can form π-bond

23. Which of the following combination of orbitals do/does not form bond (if x-axis is internuclear axis) ?
(a) $s + p_z$ (b) $s + s$
(c) $p_z + p_x$ (d) $d_{xy} + p_y$

24. Consider the following atomic orbitals :

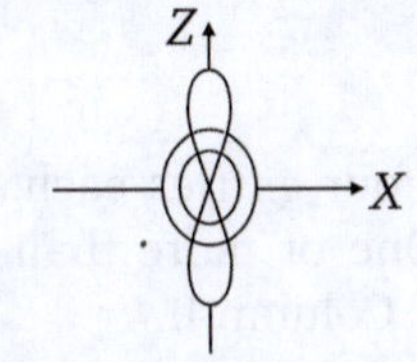

Which of the following statement(s) is/are correct regarding given orbital ?
(a) It is a gerade atomic orbital
(b) It has zero nodal plane
(c) Circular electron density is present in 'XY' plane
(d) Opposite lobes of orbital have same sign of wave function (ψ)

25. Select correct order for $A(g)$ and $B(g)$ where salt $AB(s) = A^+B^-$ is most ionic :
(a) Ionization energy of $A < B$
(b) Electron affinity of $A < B$
(c) Atomic size of $A < B$
(d) Electro negativity of $A < B$

26. Which pair(s) can form 'XY' type compound ?
(a) Al, P
(b) Mg, N
(c) Ca, O
(d) Na, F

27. Correct statement(s) regarding ionic compound is/are :
(a) High melting points and non-directional bonds
(b) Shows structural isomerism
(c) Directional bonds and low-boiling points
(d) High solubilities in polar solvents

28. Pick out among the following species isoelectronic with CO_2 :
(a) N_3^-
(b) $(CNO)^-$
(c) $(NCN)^{2-}$
(d) NO_2^-

29. Which of the following molecular species does/do not exist ?
(a) F_3^-
(b) SCl_6
(c) ICl_6^-
(d) $PCl_6^-(s)$

MATCH THE COLUMN

Column-I and Column-II contains four entries each. Entries of Column-I are to be matched with some entries of Column-II. One or more than one entries of Column-I may have the matching with the same entries of Column-II.

1.

Column-I	Column-II
(A) $B_3N_3H_6$	(P) Planar geometry
(B) I_3^-	(Q) Non-planar geometry
(C) B_2Cl_4 (Solid)	(R) Compound having coordinate bond
(D) SiF_4	(S) Compound having back bond
	(T) Non-polar compound

2.

Column-I (Shape)	Column-II (Hybridisation)
(A) Linear	(P) sp^3
(B) Angular	(Q) sp^3d^2
(C) Square planar	(R) sp^2
(D) Trigonal planar	(S) sp^3d

3.

Column-I	Column-II
(A) SO_3	(P) Largest bond angle
(B) $BeCl_2$	(Q) Lowest bond angle
(C) NH_3	(R) sp^2-hybridisation
(D) NO_2^-	(S) sp^3-hybridisation

4.

Column-I	Column-II
(A) Hypo phosphoric acid	(P) All hydrogen are ionizable in water
(B) Pyro phosphorous acid	(Q) Lewis acid in water
(C) Boric acid	(R) Monobasic
(D) Hypo phosphorous acid	(S) sp^3-hybridised central atom

5.

Column-I	Column-II
(A) NH_2^-	(P) Square pyramidal
(B) $XeOF_2$	(Q) V-shaped
(C) ICl_4^-	(R) T-shaped
(D) $[SbF_5]^{2-}$	(S) Square planar

6.

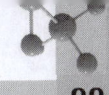

Column-I	Column-II
(A) ICl_2^-	(P) Linear
(B) BrF_2^+	(Q) Pyramidal
(C) ClF_4^-	(R) Tetrahedral
(D) $AlCl_4^-$	(S) Square planar
	(T) Angular

7.

Column-I	Column-II
(A) $Re_2Cl_8^{2-}$	(P) $p\pi - p\pi$ bonding
(B) NO_3^-	(Q) $p\pi - d\pi$ bonding
(C) SO_4^{2-}	(R) $d\pi - d\pi$ bonding
(D) SO_3	(S) δ-bonding

8.

Column-I (Bond order range)	Column-II (Oxyanions)
(A) 1.0 to 1.30	(P) NO_3^-
(B) 1.31 to 1.55	(Q) ClO_4^-
(C) 1.56 to 1.70	(R) PO_4^{3-}
(D) 1.71 to 2.0	(S) ClO_3^-
	(T) SO_4^{2-}

9.

Column-I	Column-II
(A) AsO_4^{3-}	(P) All three *p*-orbitals used in hybridisation
(B) ICl_2^+	(Q) Tetrahedral shape
(C) SOF_4	(R) Axial *d*-orbital with two nodal cones used in hybridisation
(D) $XeOF_4$	(S) All bond lengths are identical
	(T) $p\pi - d\pi$ bond(s) present

10.

Column-I σ-bond pairs + lone pairs around central atom of AB_x type compound	Column-II Characteristics/shape of compound
(A) 2 + 1	(P) Linear
(B) 2 + 3	(Q) Angular
(C) 4 + 2	(R) Polar
(D) 2 + 2	(S) Non-polar
	(T) Planar

11.

Column-I (Type of bond formed)	Column-II [Combining orbitals (Internuclear axis)]
(A) π-bond	(P) $d_{yz} + p_y$, (z)
(B) σ-bond	(Q) $s + p_x$, (y)
(C) δ-bond	(R) $d_{yz} + d_{yz}$, (x)
(D) Non-bonding	(S) $s + s$, (z)
	(T) $s + d_{xy}$, (y)

12.

Column-I	Column-II
(A) XeF_5^-	(P) *d*-orbital with zero nodal plane is used in hybridisation
(B) PBr_4^+	(Q) Non-axial *d*-orbital is used in hybridisation
(C) IOF_3	(R) Planar species
(D) NH_2^-	(S) Non-planar species
	(T) Bond angle 109°28' or less than 109°28'

13.

Column-I	Column-II
(A) $IO_2F_2^-$	(P) Trigonal pyramidal shape
(B) IOF_4^-	(Q) Square pyramidal shape
(C) $SeOF_2$	(R) See-saw shape
(D) $XeOF_2$	(S) Non-planar
	(T) One of the bond angle < 90°

ASSERTION-REASON TYPE QUESTIONS

These questions consist of two statements each, printed as assertion and reason, while answering these questions you are required to choose any one of the following responses.

(A) If assertion is true but the reason is false

(B) If assertion is false but reason is true

(C) If both assertion and reason are true and the reason is the correct explanation of assertion

(D) If both assertion and reason are true but reason is not the correct explanation of assertion

1. **Assertion** : Multiple bond between two bonded atoms can have more than three bonds.
   Reason : Multiple bond between two bonded atoms can not have more than two π-bonds.
2. **Assertion** : 2nd period elements do not involve in excitation of electron.
   Reason : 2nd period elements do not have vacant 2*d*-orbitals.
3. **Assertion** : In SO_3 molecule bond dissociation energy of all S=O bonds are not equivalent.
   Reason : SO_3 molecule is having two types of $(2p\pi - 3p\pi)$ and $(2p\pi - 3d\pi)$ pi-bonds.
4. **Assertion** : PH_4^+ ion is having tetrahedron geometry.
   Reason : P-atom is unhybridised in PH_4^+ ion.
5. **Assertion** : All diatomic molecules with polar bond have dipole moment.
   Reason : Dipole moment is a vector quantity.
6. **Assertion** : Water is a good solvent for ionic compounds but poor for covalent compounds.
   Reason : Hydration energy of ions releases sufficient energy to overcome lattice energy and break hydrogen bonds in water while covalent compounds interact so weakly that even van der Waals' forces between molecules of covalent compounds cannot be broken.
7. **Assertion** : Xe-atom in XeF_2 assumes *sp*-hybrid state.
   Reason : XeF_2 molecule does not follow octet rule.
8. **Assertion** : The atoms in a covalent molecule are said to share electrons, yet some covalent molecules are polar.
   Reason : In polar covalent molecule, the shared electrons spend more time on the average near one of the atoms.
9. **Assertion** : CCl_4 is a non-polar molecule.
   Reason : CCl_4 has polar bonds.
10. **Assertion** : Geometry of ICl_3 is tetrahedral.
    Reason : Its shape is T-shape, due to the presence of two lone pairs.
11. **Assertion** : The covalency of carbon is four in excited state.
    Reason : The four half-filled pure orbitals of carbon form same kind of bonds with an atom as those are with hybridised orbitals.
12. **Assertion** : The shape of XeF_4 is square-planar.
    Reason : In an octahedral geometry, a single lone pair can occupy any position but a second lone pair will occupy the opposite position to the first lone pair.

SUBJECTIVE PROBLEMS

1. Consider following compounds A to E :

(A) XeF_n (B) $XeF^{+}_{(n+1)}$ (C) $XeF^{-}_{(n+1)}$ (D) $XeF_{(n+2)}$

(E) $XeF^{2-}_{(n+4)}$,

If value of n is 4, then calculate value of "$p \div q$" here, 'p' is total number of bond pair and 'q' is total number of lone pair on central atoms of compounds (A) to (E).

2. Consider the following species and find out total number of species which are polar and can act as Lewis acid

CCl_4, CO_2, SO_2, $AlCl_3$, HCHO, SO_3, $SiCl_4$, BCl_3, CF_4

3. Consider the following table regarding interhalogen compounds, XY_n (where Y is more electronegative than X)

Value of *n* for respective interhalogen compound	**Total number of *d*-orbitals used in hybridization of central atom**	**Polarity**	**Planarity**
P_1	1	Polar	Planar
P_2	Q_1	Polar	Non-Planar
P_3	Q_2	Non-Polar	Non-Planar

Then according to given information calculate value of expression $P_2 \times \frac{(P_3 - P_1)}{(Q_1 + Q_2)}$.

4. What is covalency of chlorine atom in second excited state?

5. Sum of σ and π-bonds in NH_4^+ cation is .....

6. Calculate the value of $X - Y$, for $XeOF_4$. (X= Number of σ bond pair and Y= Number of lone pair on central atom)

7. The molecule ML_x is planar with 6 electron pairs around M in the valence shell. The value of x is :

8. Calculate value of $\frac{X+Y+Z}{10}$, here X is O—N—O bond angle in NO_3^- Y is O—N—O bond angle in NO_2^+ and Z is F—Xe—F adjacent bond angle in XeF_4.

9. Calculate $x + y + z$ for H_3PO_3 acid, where x is no. of lone pairs, y is no. of σ bonds and z is no. of π bonds.

10. How many right angle, bond angles are present in TeF_5^- molecular ion?

11. How may possible ∠ FSeF bond angles are present in SeF_4 molecule?

12. In IF_6^- and TeF_5^-, sum of axial d-orbitals which are used in hybridisation in both species.

13. Among the following, total no. of planar species is:

(i) SF_4 (ii) BrF_3 (iii) XeF_2 (iv) IF_5

(v) SbF_4^- (vi) SF_5^- (vii) SeF_3^+ (viii) CH_3^+

(ix) PCl_4^+

14. Calculate the value of "$x + y - z$" here x, y and z are total number of non-bonded electron pair(s), pie(π) bond(s) and sigma(σ) bonds in hydrogen phosphite ion respectively.

15. Consider the following table

Total number of electron pairs (l.p. +σ-bond)	Total number of lone pairs	Shape
5	....p....	linear
....q....	1	see-saw
4	....r....	Bent shape
....s....	2	Square planar
5	....t....	Bent 'T' shape

Then calculate value of "$p + q + r - s - t$".

16. In phosphorus acid, if X is number of non bonding electron pairs. Y is number of σ-bonds and Z is number of π-bonds. Then, calculate value of "$Y \times Z - X$".

17. Calculate the number of $p_\pi - d_\pi$ bond(s) present in SO_4^{2-} :

18. Sum of σ & π-bonds in NH_4^+ cation is ....

19. Consider the following orbitals :

(i) $3p_x$ (ii) $4d_{z^2}$ (iii) $3d_{x^2-y^2}$ (iv) $3d_{yz}$

Then calculate value of '$x + y - z$' here x is total number of gerade orbital and y is total number of ungerade orbitals and z is total number of axial orbital in given above orbitals.

20. Calculate value of $|x - y|$, here, x and y are the total number of bonds in benzene and benzyne respectively which are formed by overlapping of hybridized orbitals.

21. Consider the following compounds :

(i) IF_5 (ii) ClI_4^- (iii) XeO_2F_2 (iv) NH_2^-

(v) BCl_3 (vi) $BeCl_2$ (vii) $AsCl_4^+$ (viii) $B(OH)_3$

(ix) NO_2^- (x) ClO_2^+

Then calculate value of "$x + y - z$", here, x, y and z are total number of compounds in given compounds in which central atom used their all three p-orbitals, only two p-orbitals and only one p-orbital in hybridisation respectively.

22. Total number of species which used all three p-orbitals in hybridisation of central atoms and should be non-polar also.

XeO_2F_2, $SnCl_2$, IF_5, I_3^+, XeO_4, SO_2, XeF_7^+, SeF_4

23. Consider the following species NO_3^-, SO_4^{2-}, ClO_3^-, SO_3, PO_4^{3-}, XeO_3, CO_3^{2-}, SO_3^{2-}

Then calculate value of $|x-y|$, where

x : Total number of species which have bond order 1.5 or greater than 1.5

y : Total number of species which have bond order less than 1.5

24. Consider the following orbitals $3s$, $2p_x$, $4d_{xy}$, $4d_{z^2}$, $3d_{x^2-y^2}$, $3p_y$, $4s$, $4p_z$ and find total number of orbital(s) having even number of nodal plane.

25. For the following molecules :

PCl_5, BrF_3, ICl_2^-, XeF_5^-, NO_3^-, XeO_2F_2, PCl_4^+, CH_3^+

Calculate the value of $\frac{a+b}{c}$

a = Number of species having sp^3d-hybridisation

b = Number of species which are planar

c = Number of species which are non-planar

26. Find out number of transformation among following which involves the change of hybridisation of underlined atom.

(a) $H_2\underline{O} + H^+ \longrightarrow H_3\underline{O}^+$ (b) $\underline{N}H_3 + \underline{B}F_3 \longrightarrow \underline{N}H_3 \cdot \underline{B}F_3$

(c) $\underline{Xe}F_6 \longrightarrow \underline{Xe}F_5^+ + F^-$ (d) $2\underline{P}Cl_5 \longrightarrow PCl_4^+ + PCl_6^-$

(e) $\underline{C}H_3 - CH_3 \longrightarrow \underline{C}H_3^- + CH_3^+$

27. Find total number of orbital which can overlap colaterally, (if inter nuclear axis is z)

$s, p_x, p_y, p_z, d_{xy}, d_{yz}, d_{xz}, d_{z^2}, d_{x^2-y^2}$

Answers

Level-1

1. (c)	2. (b)	3. (d)	4. (a)	5. (c)	6. (b)	7. (d)	8. (c)	9. (b)	10. (b)
11. (d)	12. (b)	13. (a)	14. (c)	15. (d)	16. (a)	17. (d)	18. (c)	19. (c)	20. (b)
21. (d)	22. (d)	23. (c)	24. (c)	25. (d)	26. (c)	27. (d)	28. (c)	29. (b)	30. (d)
31. (c)	32. (d)	33. (d)	34. (d)	35. (a)	36. (a)	37. (b)	38. (d)	39. (a)	40. (a)
41. (c)	42. (d)	43. (d)	44. (b)	45. (b)	46. (b)	47. (d)	48. (d)	49. (a)	50. (b)
51. (c)	52. (b)	53. (d)	54. (b)	55. (d)	56. (b)	57. (d)	58. (d)	59. (a)	60. (c)
61. (d)	62. (a)	63. (c)	64. (c)	65. (c)	66. (a)	67. (b)	68. (b)	69. (a)	70. (b)
71. (a)	72. (a)	73. (c)	74. (a)	75. (a)	76. (d)	77. (b)	78. (c)	79. (d)	80. (a)
81. (b)	82. (b)	83. (c)	84. (b)	85. (a)	86. (a)	87. (c)	88. (c)	89. (c)	90. (c)
91. (d)	92. (b)	93. (b)	94. (c)	95. (b)	96. (c)	97. (a)	98. (d)	99. (b)	100. (b)
101. (b)	102. (a)	103. (a)	104. (b)	105. (c)	106. (c)	107. (c)	108. (d)	109. (b)	110. (b)
111. (c)	112. (a)	113. (c)	114. (b)	115. (c)	116. (d)	117. (a)	118. (c)	119. (c)	120. (c)
121. (b)	122. (b)	123. (d)	124. (d)	125. (c)	126. (d)	127. (b)	128. (c)	129. (a)	130. (d)
131. (b)	132. (c)	133. (d)	134. (a)	135. (c)	136. (b,d)	137. (d)	138. (c)	139. (c)	140. (b)
141. (d)	142. (c)	143. (b)	144. (a)	145. (a)	146. (b)	147. (d)	148. (d)	149. (c)	150. (a)
151. (a)	152. (a)	153. (b)	154. (c)	155. (d)	156. (c)	157. (c)	158. (a)	159. (d)	160. (c)
161. (a)	162. (d)	163. (a)	164. (b)	165. (b)	166. (a)	167. (d)	168. (a)		

Level-2

1. (c)	2. (d)	3. (b,c)	4. (d)	5. (c)	6. (c)	7. (b)	8. (d)	9. (b)	10. (d)
11. (b)	12. (d)	13. (c)	14. (c)	15. (c)	16. (b)	17. (d)	18. (b)	19. (a)	20. (c)
21. (b)	22. (b)	23. (b)	24. (d)	25. (d)	26. (c)	27. (d)	28. (d)	29. (d)	30. (a)
31. (d)	32. (a)	33. (d)	34. (c)	35. (a)	36. (d)	37. (c)	38. (a)		

Level-3

Passage–1	1. (d)	2. (d)	3. (d)	
Passage–2	1. (d)	2. (d)	3. (c)	
Passage–3	1. (c)	2. (d)	3. (d)	
Passage–4	1. (b)	2. (c)	3. (c)	
Passage–5	1. (a)	2. (c)	3. (c)	
Passage–6	1. (a)	2. (a)	3. (d)	4. (d)
Passage–7	1. (d)	2. (c)	3. (b)	
Passage–8	1. (c)	2. (a)		
Passage–9	1. (d)	2. (d)	3. (c)	

Passage–10	1. (b)	2. (a)	3. (c)
Passage–11	1. (d)	2. (c)	3. (c)
Passage–12	1. (c)	2. (c)	
Passage–13	1. (c)	2. (c)	
Passage–14	1. (c)	2. (a)	
Passage–15	1. (a)	2. (b)	

One or More Answers is/are correct

1. (a,b,c,d)	2. (a,b,c)	3. (a,b,c)	4. (a,d)	5. (a,c,d)	6. (c,d)
7. (a,b,d)	8. (a,c)	9. (b,c,d)	10. (b,d)	11. (a,b,c)	12. (a,b,c)
13. (a,c)	14. (a,c,d)	15. (a,c)	16. (a,c)	17. (a,c)	18. (a,b,d)
19. (c,d)	20. (a,b,c,d)	21. (d)	22. (a,c,d)	23. (a,c)	24. (a,b,c,d)
25. (a,b,d)	26. (a,c,d)	27. (a,d)	28. (a,b,c)	29. (a,b,c)	

Match the Column

1.	A→ P, S, T;	B→ P, R, T;	C→ P, S, T;	D→ Q, S, T
2.	A→ P, S;	B→ P, R;	C→ Q;	D→ R
3.	A→ R;	B→ P;	C→ Q, S;	D→ R
4.	A→ P, Q, S;	B→ Q, S;	C→ Q, R;	D→ Q, R, S
5.	A→ Q;	B→ R;	C→ S;	D→ P
6.	A→ P;	B→ T;	C→ S;	D→ R
7.	A→ R, S;	B→ P;	C→ Q;	D→ P, Q
8.	A→ R;	B→ P, T;	C→ S;	D→ Q
9.	A→ P, Q, S, T;	B→ P, S;	C→ P, R, T;	D→ P, R, T
10.	A→ Q, R, T;	B→ P, S, T;	C→ S, T;	D→ Q, R, T
11.	A→ P;	B→ S;	C→ R;	D→ Q, T
12.	A→ P, Q, R, T;	B→ S, T;	C→ P, S, T;	D→ R, T
13.	A→ R, S, T;	B→ Q, S, T;	C→ P, S;	D→ T

Assertion-Reason Type Questions

1. (D)	2. (B)	3. (B)	4. (A)	5. (D)	6. (C)	7. (B)	8. (C)	9. (D)	10. (B)
11. (A)	12. (C)								

Subjective Problems

1. 4	2. 2	3. 4	4. 5	5. 4	6. 4	7. 4
8. 39	9. 13	10. 0	11. 6	12. 4	13. 3	14. 3
15. 2	16. 0	17. 2	18. 4	19. 1	20. 1	21. 8
22. 2	23. 0	24. 5	25. 3	26. 3	27. 6	

Hints and Solutions

Level 1

4. (a) ONCN (Nitrosyl cyanide)

$:\ddot{O}=\ddot{N}-C\equiv N:$

Least formal charge more stable.

5. (c) $NO_3^{\ominus}$ $:\ddot{O}-N=\ddot{O}$ with $:\ddot{O}:(-1)$ bonded to N; formal charges (-1) $(+1)$ (0)

6. (b) CO_2 can be represented as.

(a) $:\ddot{O}-C\equiv O:$

(b) $\ddot{O}=N=\ddot{O}:$

(c) $:O\equiv C-\ddot{O}:$

All are correct.

10. (b) $A^{2+} + BC_4^{3-} \Rightarrow A_3(BC_4)_2$

11. (d) Among given non-metals, O-atom has high electron affinity and strong ionic bond is formed between Al and O-atom.

18. (c) $LE \propto \dfrac{q^+ \cdot q^-}{r^+ + r^-}$

(a) $AlF_3 > MgF_2$ [Charge on cation]

(b) $Li_3N > Li_2O$ [Charge on anion]

(c) NaCl > LiF [Size of cation and anion]

(d) TiC > ScN [Charge on cation and anion]

19. (c) Lattice energy $\propto \dfrac{\text{Charge of cation} \times \text{charge of anion}}{\text{Inter ionic distance}}$

20. (b) Order of lattice energy

NaBr < NaCl < BaO < CaO

$\because$ Lattice energy $\propto \dfrac{|Q^+||Q^{-1}|}{r_+ + r_-}$

21. (d) Lattice energy released in case of MgO is maximum giving highest contribution to ionic nature or ionic bond.

30. (d) In $SiCl_4$ difference between electronegativity of Si (1.8) and chlorine (3.0) is higher than in other given compounds.

31. (c) More effective axial and sideways overlapping between atomic orbitals of carbon and those of oxygen atom is higher due to smaller size of oxygen atom. Oxygen is more electronegative than oxygen atom, due to these factors CO has highest bond energy.

32. (d)

(a) 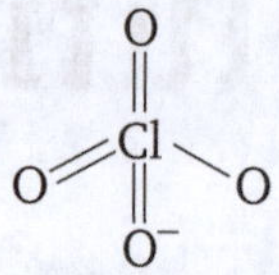 ($14e^-$, hypervalent),

(b) 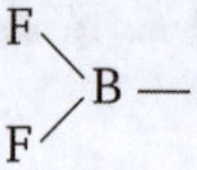 ($6e^-$, hypovalent)

(c) 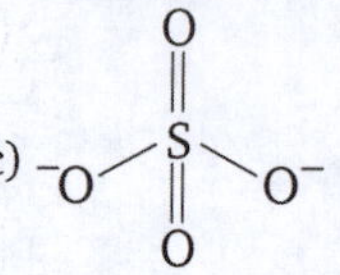 ($12e^-$, hypervalent)

(d) 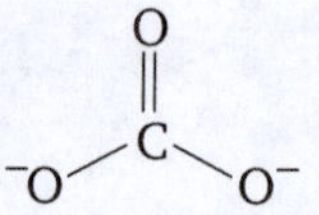 ($8e^-$)

33. (d) In 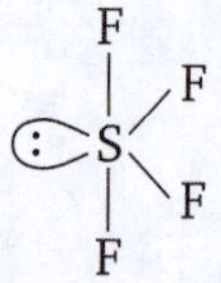 molecule central S-atom is surrounded by 10 valence electrons and it is hypervalent compound.

34. (d) Due to presence of vacant *d*-orbital excitation occurs in Cl-atom and it can have more than eight valence electrons when it is forming hypervalent compound like $HClO_4$.

35. (a) Bond polarity is directly related to difference of electronegativity of bonded atoms.

36. (a) The set of compounds BCl_3, $SiCl_4$, PCl_3 are predominatly covalent compounds. NH_4Br and NaI ionic compounds and Al contains metallic lattice.

37. (b) Maximum covalency of oxygen atom is three, hence OF_4 does not exist.

38. (d) CO_3^{2-} 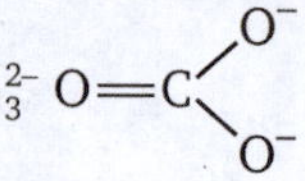

44. (b) Due to inter electronic repulation between lone pairs on both oxygen atoms bond energy of O—O bond is less.

47. (d) Incorrect overlaps (if internulcear axis = Z) :

(B) $2p_x + 2p_x \Rightarrow \pi$-bond; (C) $3d_{xy} + 3d_{xy} \Rightarrow \delta$-bond; (D) $2s + 2p_y \Rightarrow$ No bond formation.

49. (a) 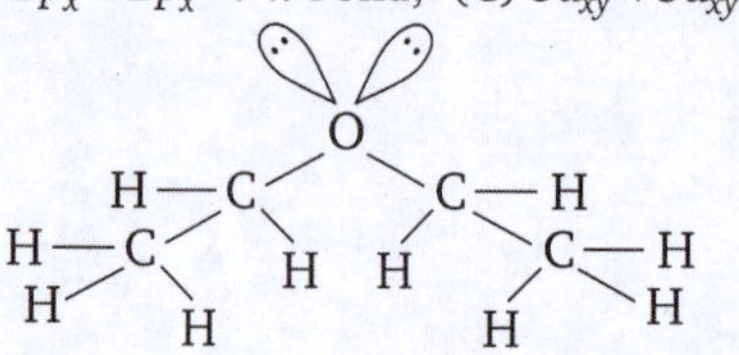 Number of σ-bonds = 14

51. (c) $d_{xz} + p_x \longrightarrow$ 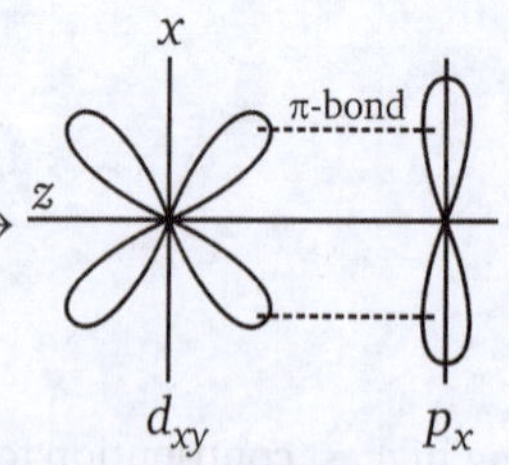

∴ Molecular axis is z-axis.

$d_{xy} + d_{xy} \xrightarrow{z\text{ axis}}$ form δ-bond

52. (b) Correct order $\underbrace{2p\text{-}2p > 2s\text{-}2p > 2s\text{-}2s >}$ $3s\text{-}3s$

In same shell more the directional character more will be strength of σ-bond

53. (d) $d_{x^2-y^2} + d_{x^2-y^2} \xrightarrow{x\text{-axis}} \sigma$-bond

54. (b) $d_{x^2-y^2} + p_y$ (side wise overlap) $\rightarrow$ Non-bonding.

55. (d) $d_{x^2-y^2} + d_{x^2-y^2} \xrightarrow{x\text{-axis}} \sigma$-bond

56. (b) $d_{x^2-y^2} + p_y$

57. (d)

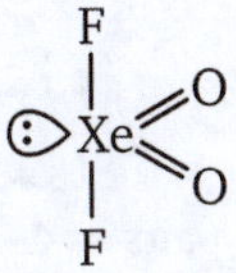
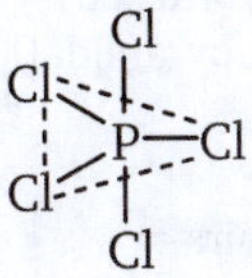
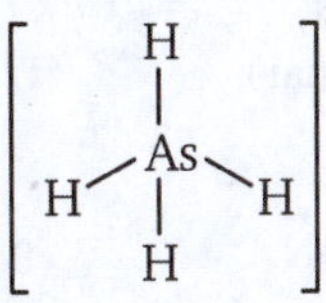
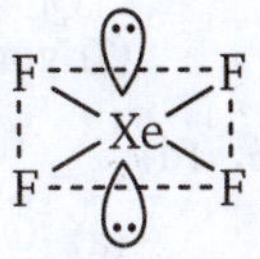

Maximum atoms that $\rightarrow$ can lie in a plane: 3, 4, 3, 5

68. (b) In $\ddot{N}H_3$ central atom is nitrogen which is sp^3 hybridized hence, it will be at the centre of tetrahedron with H-atoms at three vertices.

69. (a) In trigonal by pyramidal geometry lone pair electrons cannot occupy axial positions.

70. (b) (ii) (**F**) In general as the number of lone pair of electrons on central atom increases, value of bond angle from normal bond angle decreases due to $lp - lp > lp - bp$

(iv) (**F**) Structures of xenon fluorides and xenon oxy fluoride are explained on the basis of VSEPR theory.

In $SOBr_2$, S—O bond has maximum bond length in comparison to S—O bond lengths in SOF_2 and $SOCl_2$, because in $SOBr_2$, S—O bond has been formed by hybrid orbital containing less *s*-character.

71. (a)

(a) 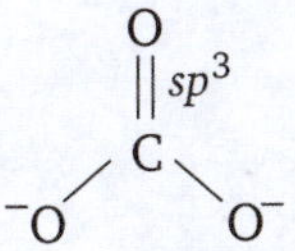 (Trigonal planar)

(b) 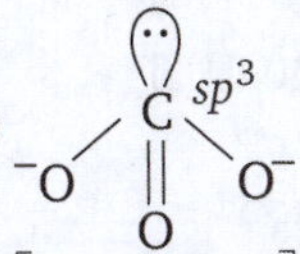 (Trigonal planar)

(c) 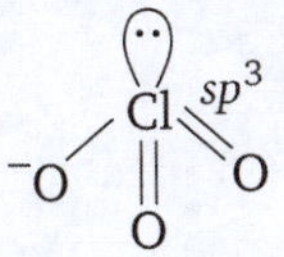 (Trigonal pyramidal)

(d) 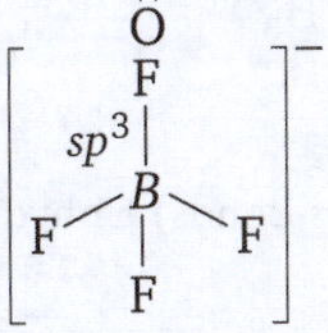 (Tetrahedral)

72. (a) 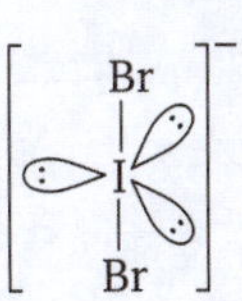 IBr : $X = 2 + \frac{1}{2}[7 - 2 + 1] = (2\sigma\text{-bonds} + 3 \text{ lone pairs})$ sp^3-hybridisation Shape $\rightarrow$ Linear

73. (c) ClF_3 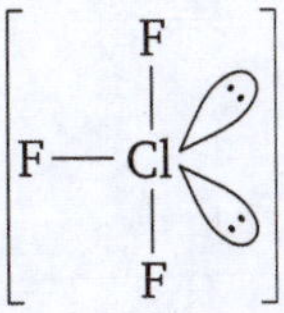 $X = 3 + \frac{1}{2}[7 - 3] = (3\sigma\text{-bonds} + 2 \text{ lone pairs})$ (sp^3d-hybridisation)

Shape $\rightarrow$ Bent - T - shape

74. (a) $NH_3 \longrightarrow$ Trigonal pyramidal

(a) $SO_3^{2-} \longrightarrow$ Trigonal pyramidal

(b) $CO_3^{2-} \longrightarrow$ Trigonal planar

(c) $NO_3^- \longrightarrow$ Trigonal planar

(d) $SO_3 \longrightarrow$ Trigonal planar

75. (a) 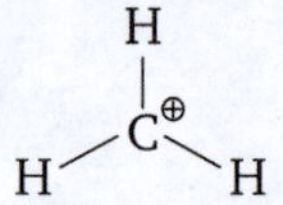

(sp^3-hybrid)
(Trigonal planar)

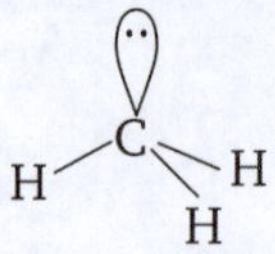

(sp^3-hybridised)
(Trigonal pyramidal)

76. (d)

(a) 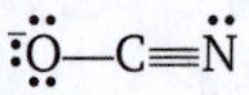 Bond pairs = 4, Lone pairs = 4

(b) 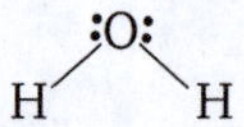 Bond pairs = 2, Lone pairs = 2

(c) 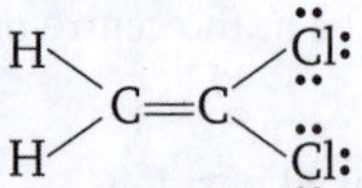 Bond pairs = 6 Lone pairs = 6

(d) 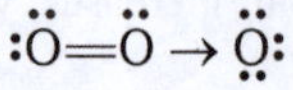 Bond pairs = 3 Lone pairs = 6

82. (b)

$$\underset{sp^3}{\ddot{N}H_3} + H^+ \longrightarrow \underset{sp^3}{NH_4^+}$$

$$\underset{sp^3}{2NH_3} \rightleftharpoons \underset{sp^3}{NH_2^-} + \underset{sp^3}{NH_4^+}$$

$$\underset{sp^2}{H_3BO_3} + OH^- \longrightarrow \underset{sp^3}{[B(OH)_4]^-}$$

$$\underset{sp^3}{H_2O} + H^+ \rightleftharpoons \underset{sp^3}{H_3O^+}$$

89. (c) By sp^2-hybridisation.
Hybridisation orbital = 3 [3σ-bonds] Unhydrised orbital = 1 [1π-bond]

90. (c) 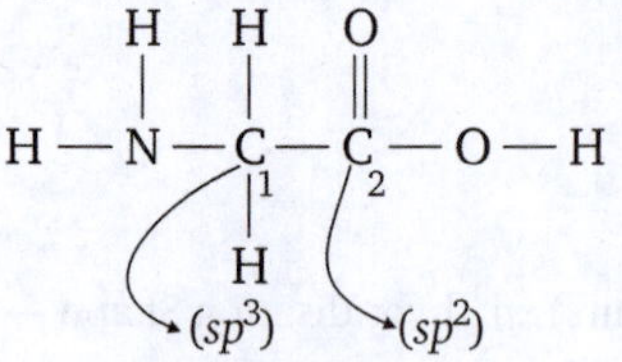

91. (d) 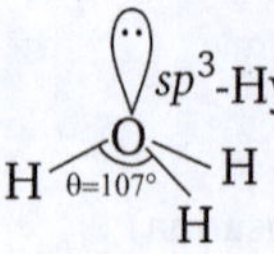

sp^3-Hybridisation

92. (b) 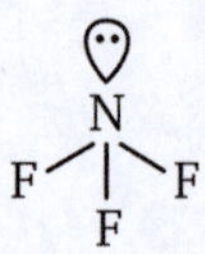

Pyramidal

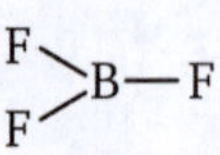

Trigonal planar

(b) 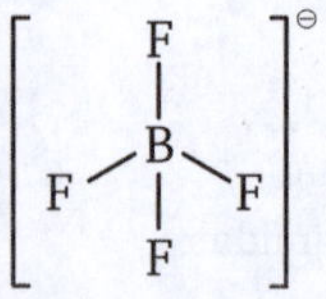

Tetrahedron

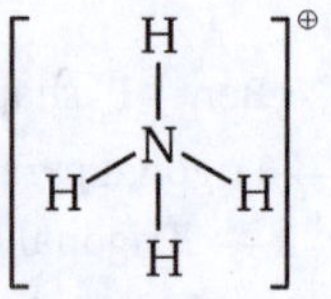

Tetrahedral

(c) 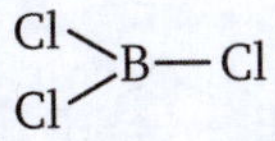

Trigonal planar

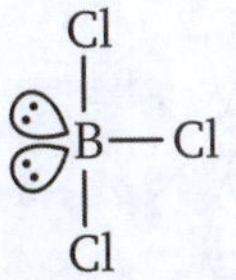

Bent-T-Shape

(d) 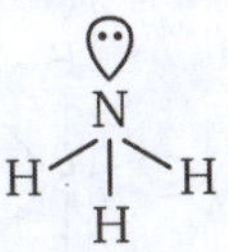

Pyramidal

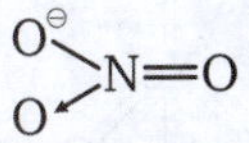

Trigonal planar

95. (b) 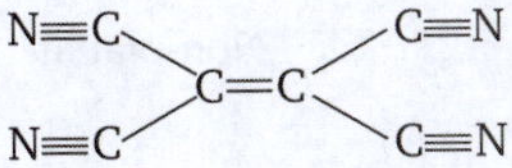

σ-bonds = 9 ; π-bonds = 9

98. (d) 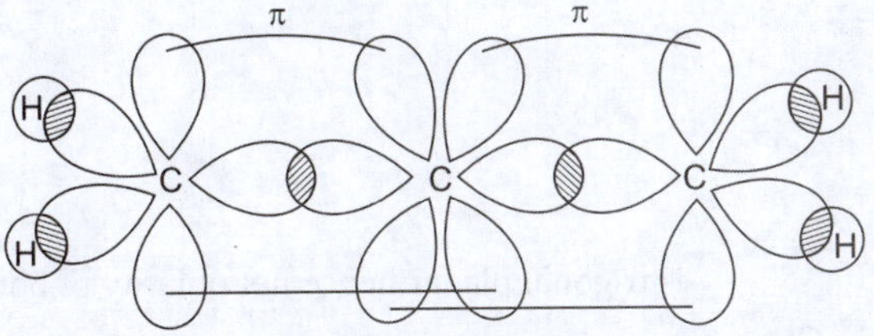

106. (c) XeF_3^+ hybridisation of Xe : sp^3d

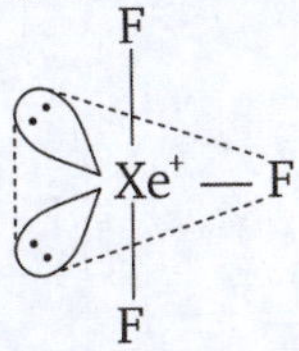

Shape : Bent T

107. (c) In XeF_n, possible value of n is 2, 4, 6, 8, then compound should be XeF_2 (linear), XeF_4 (square planar), XeF_6 (capped octahedral). So in this case trigonal planar molecule does not possible.

108. (d)

(a) 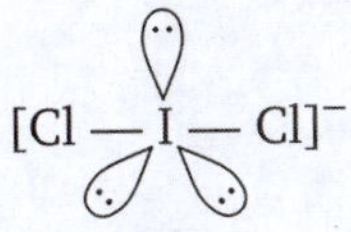

Linear

(b) H — C ≡ C — H

Linear

(c) 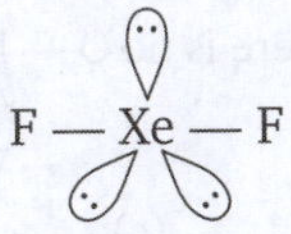

Linear

(d) 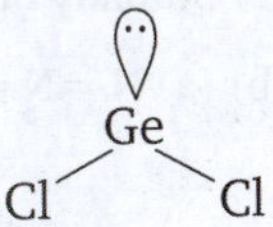

Bent shape

109. (b) CS_2 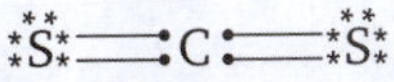

Total lone pairs = 4 Total double bond = 2

All the atoms have complete octet Sulphur is the central atom.

110. (b) $[XeF_3^+]$: 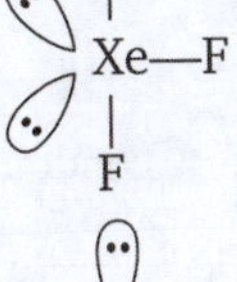 Bent-T-shape (sp^3d-hybridisation)

$[XeF_5^+]$: 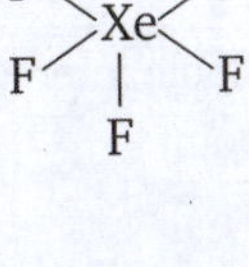 Square pyramidal (sp^3d^2-hybridisation)

115. (c)

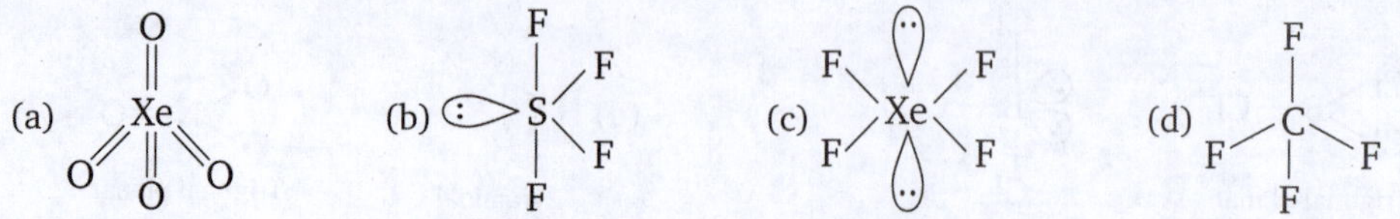

(a)	(b)	(c)	(d)
Non-polar Non-planar	Polar Non-planar	Non-polar Planar	Non-polar Non-planar

116. (d)

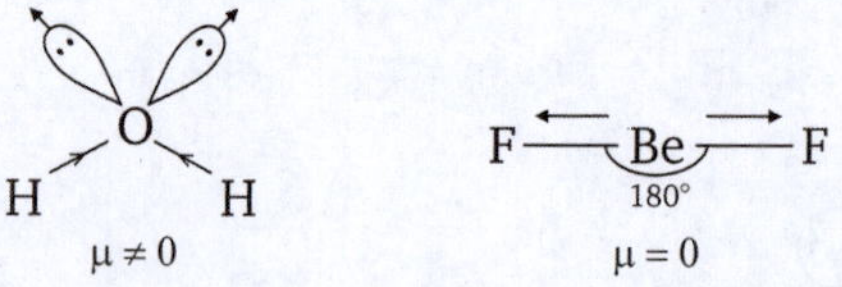

117. (a) O═C═O ($\mu = 0$) is linear and

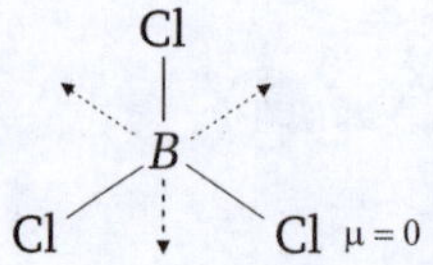

is trigonal planar hence net polarity of both molecules is zero.

118. (c) The net polarity of angular molecules SO_2 and SCl_2 is not equal to zero.

119. (c)

(a) $\overset{\delta+}{H}—\overset{\delta-}{Cl}$ $[EN_{(Cl)} > EN_{(H)}]$ (b) $\overset{\delta+}{Br}—\overset{\delta-}{Cl}$ $[EN_{(Cl)} > EN_{(Br)}]$

(c) 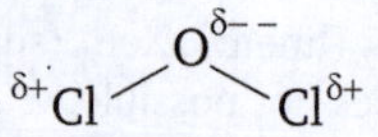 $[EN_{(O)} > EN_{(Cl)}]$ (d) 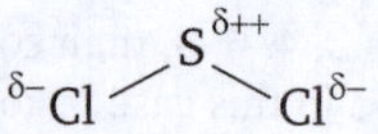 $[EN_{(S)} < EN_{(Cl)}]$

120. (c) Stability order of carbon family hydride Silane > German > Stannane > Plumbane

131. (b) (a) $\overset{-}{N} = \overset{+}{N} = O$ (There is no O — N̂ — O bond angle)

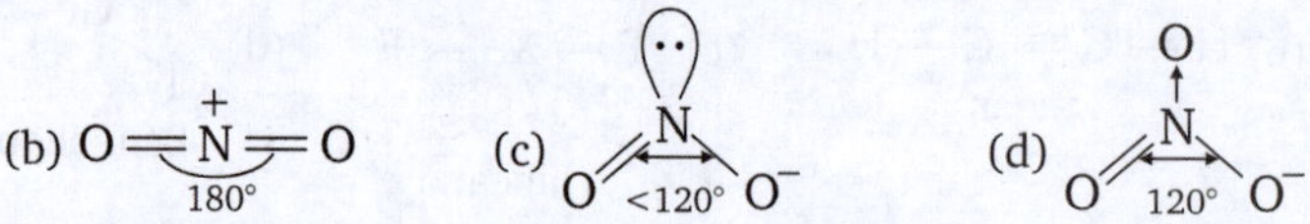

132. (c) Correct order of bond angle:

(a) $NH_3 < PH_3 < AsH_3 < SbH_3$ (As E.N. value of C.A. ↑ bond angle↓)

(b) $OF_2 < OH_2 < OCl_2$

(c) $H_3Te^+ < H_3Se^+ < H_3S^+ < H_3O^+$

(d) $BF_3 = BCl_3 = BBr_3 = BI_3$

133. (d) Strength of molecular forces :

Ion-dipole > dipole-dipole > ion-induced dipole>dipole-induced dipole > London forces.

136. (d) Correct order of molecular force : $\underbrace{H_2O}_{\text{H-bonds}} > \underbrace{O\ \ Br_2 > O(C\ \ H_3)_2}_{\text{Dipole-dipole} \propto \text{molecular mass}}$

137. (d) HCl is highly soluble in water because it ionise in water and form ion-dipole interaction with water.

138. (c) Among given solid, molecular solid is weak, hence, it has low melting point.

139. (c) London dispersion force ∝ molecular mass of covalent molecule.

140. (b) HCl has least boiling point among all halogen acids because it contains V.W. force never contains H-bond $\underbrace{HCl < HBr < HI}_{\text{V.W. force}} < \underbrace{HF}_{\text{H-bond}}$.

141. (d) $\underset{\text{(Molecular lattice)}}{C_2H_6} < \underset{\substack{\text{(Molecular lattice)} \\ \text{(with H-bonding)}}}{CH_3-OH} < \underset{\text{(Ionic lattice)}}{KCl} < \underset{\text{(Covalent lattice)}}{Si}$

142. (c) CO, CO_2 and P_2O_5 are covalent compounds having their molecular lattice. But SiO_2 is a covalent compound having 3-dimensional network structure and it has covalent lattice, so M.P. of SiO_2 is maximum.

146. (b) Strength of H-bonding is higher in H_2O_2 than H_2O, because the amount of formal negative charge on oxygen atom in case of water is more than that of H_2O_2.

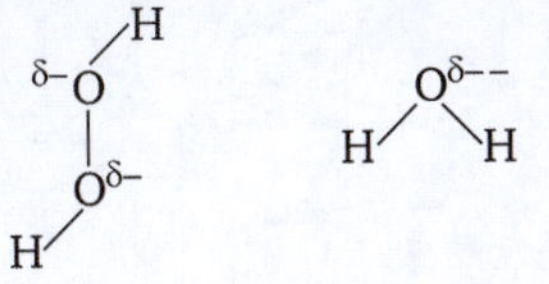

150. (a)

(a) 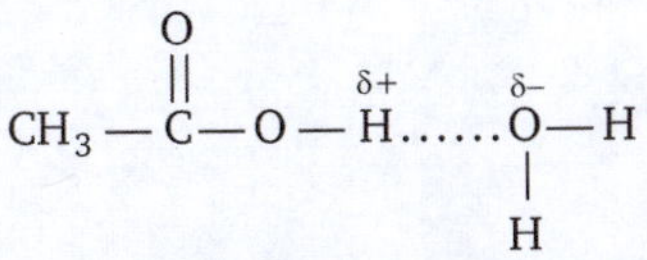

(b), (c), (d) → No scope of hydrogen bonding

Level 2

3. (c) Correct order of Lewis acidic character : $PF_5 > SiF_4 > SF_6$. Although, S has vaccant 3*d*-orbitals but it cannot accept co-ordinate bond from Lewis base due to steric crowding factor as S-atom is already bonded to six F-atoms.

4. (d) Two different non-axial *d*-orbitals will lie in planes perpendicular to each other hence, such *d*-orbital will not form π-bond.

5. (c) C: $2s^2$ $2p^2$

	$2s^2$	$2p^2$
C (In ground state)	↑↓	↑ ↑
C (In excited state)	↑	↑ ↑ ↑
	2*s*	2*p*

In the unhybridized state of carbon, 2*p* orbitals are 90° to one another and each one will overlap with 1*s* orbital of three hydrogen atoms, thus three C—H bonds are formed which are 90° to one another. For the fourth hydrogen atom, its 1*s* orbital may overlap with non-directional 2*s* orbital of the carbon and this σ-bond will be stronger than σC—H bonds formed by 2*p*—1*s* overlap. In such situation CH_4 molecule can never has tetrahedral geometry.

9. (b) d_{z^2} can not form π as well δ-bond but it can form σ-bond.

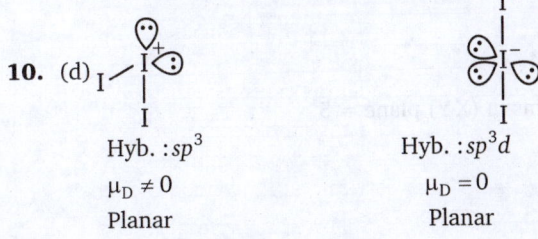

10. (d) 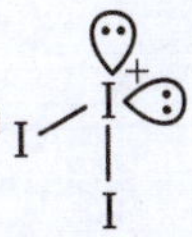

Hyb. : sp^3

$\mu_D \neq 0$

Planar

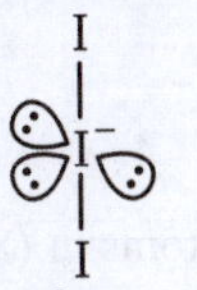

Hyb. : sp^3d

$\mu_D = 0$

Planar

11. (b) (a) Pentagonal planar → $sp^3d^3[s + p_x + p_y + p_z + d_{x^2-y^2} + d_{z^2} + d_{xy}]$

(b) Trigonal planar → $sp^2[s + \text{Any two } p]$

(c) Linear → $sp^2[s + \text{any one } p]$

→ $sp^2[s + \text{any two } p]$

→ $sp^3[s + p_x + p_y + p_z]$

→ $sp^3d[s + p_x + p_y + p_z + d_{z^2}]$

(d) Square planar → $sp^3d^2[s + p_x + p_y + p_z + d_{x^2-y^2} + d_{z^2}]$

16. (b)

BF_3	sp^2	Trigonal planar
BrF_3	sp^3d	Bent 'T' shape
$ICl_2^{\ominus}$	sp^3d	Linear
$BeCl_2$	sp	Linear
BCl_3	sp^2	Trigonal planar
PCl_3	sp^3	Pyramidal
NCl_3	sp^3	Pyramidal

17. (d)

(a) 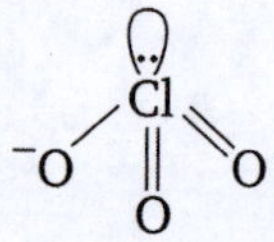 B.O. of Cl—O = 1.67

(b) 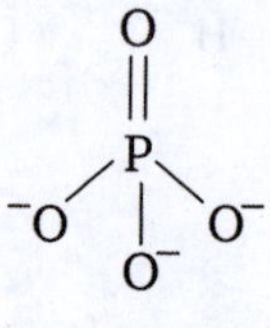 B.O. of P—O = 1.25

(c) 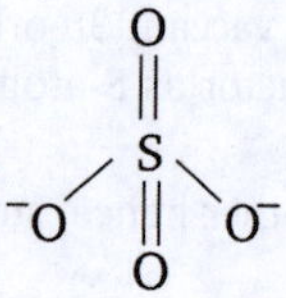 B.O. of S—O = 1.5

(d) 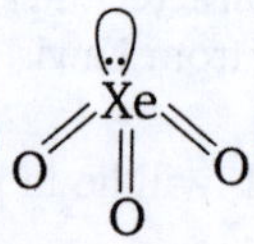 B.O. of Xe—O = 2.0

Bond order of O — O in O_2 = 2.0

21. (b)

(a)	ClO_3^-	B.O. = 1.66
(b)	ClO_3	B.O. = 2 (max.)
(c)	ClO_2	B.O. = 1.75
(d)	ClO_2^-	B.O. = 1.5

22. (b) (a) XeF_5 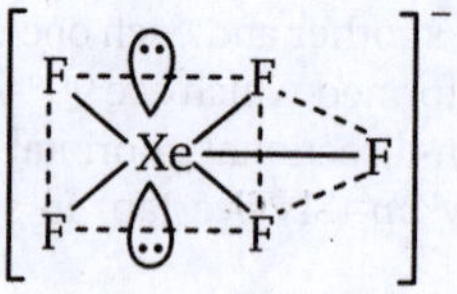 Number of atoms in 'X-Y' plane = 6

(b) SF_6 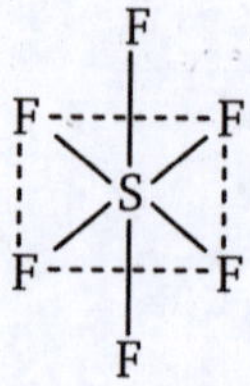 Number of atoms in (X-Y) plane = 5

(c) IF_7 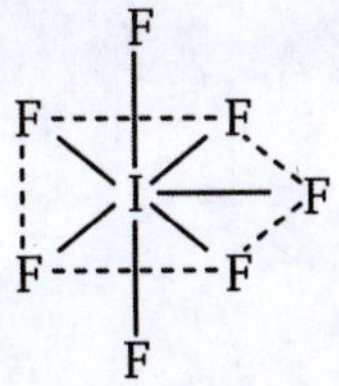 Number of atoms in (X-Y) plane = 5

24. (d)

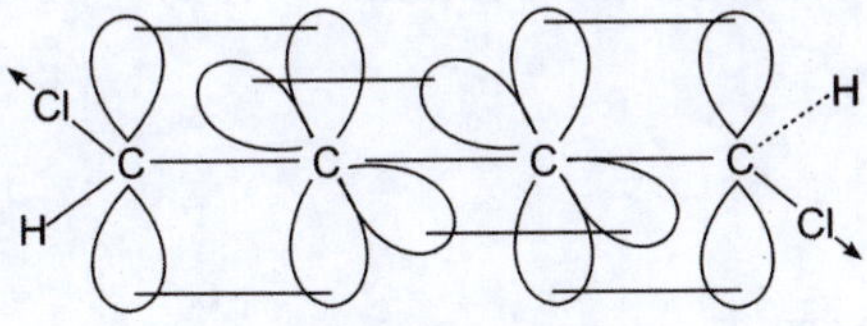

hence, $\mu = 0$

25. (d) As size of sulphur is higher than that of oxygen atom, hence bond length of S—H bond is higher than that of O—H bond.

26. (c)

(a) $CH_2{=}\overset{*}{C}H{-}\overset{*}{C}{\equiv}CH$ (sp^3, sp)

(b) $HC{\equiv}\overset{*}{C}{-}\overset{*}{C}{\equiv}CH$ (sp, sp)

(c) $H_2\overset{*}{C}{-}\overset{*}{C}H{=}CH_2$ (sp^3, sp^2)

(d) $H_2C{=}\overset{*}{C}H{-}\overset{*}{C}H{=}CH_2$ (sp^2, sp^2)

28. (d) Order of decreasing bond angle.

(a) 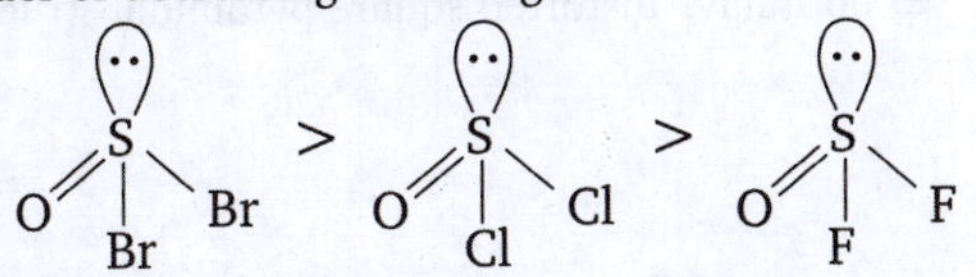 On the basis of electronegativity of halogens

(b) 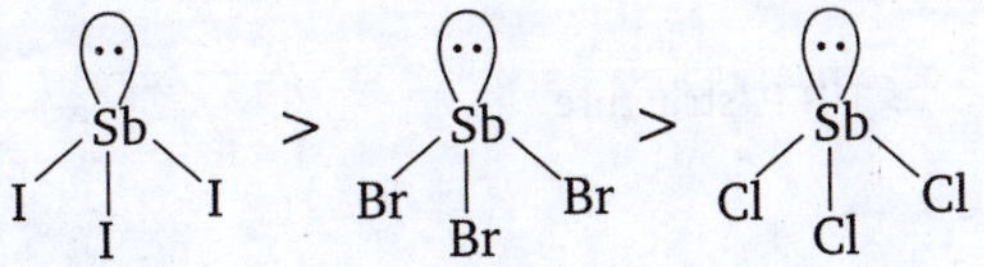 On the basis of electronegativity of halogens

(c) 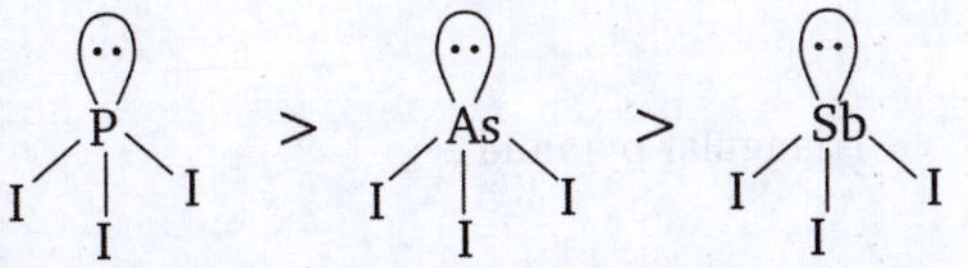

Involvement of *s*-orbital in hybridisation decreases downward in a group

29. (d) Correct order of B.P.

$CH_3N_3 < HN_3$

Among CH_3N_3 there are dipole-dipole interaction while among HN_3 intermolecular H-bonding occurs.

30. (a) (I—I)···(I—I)

London forces between two I_2 molecules in solid lattice.

Level 3

Passage-1

1. (d)

(a) 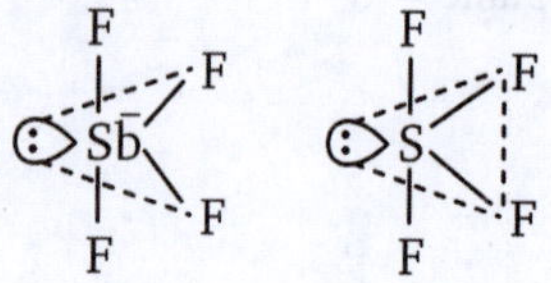

⇒ both have see-saw structure

(b) 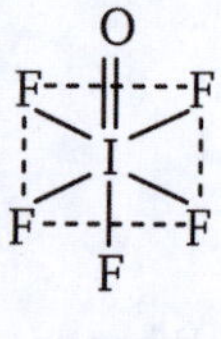

⇒ Hyb : sp^3d^2

(c) 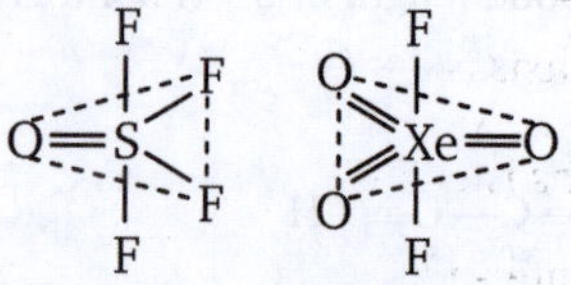

⇒ T.B.P. geometry

2. (d)

(a) 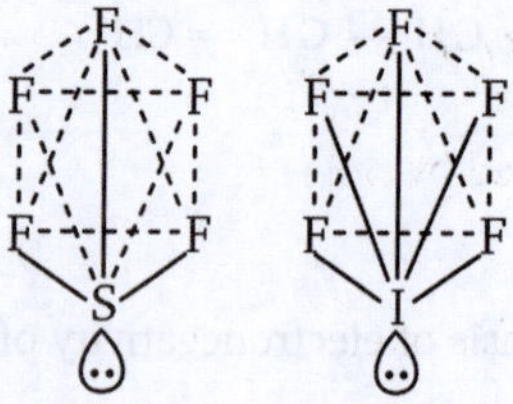

⇒ both have distorted square pyramidal structure

(b) 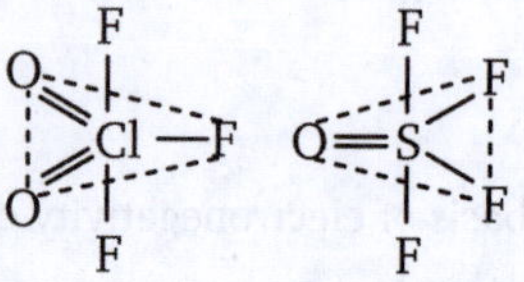

⇒ T.B.P. structure

(c) 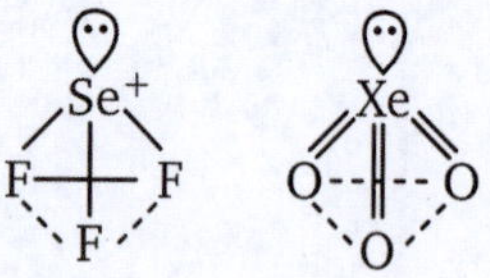

⇒ Triangular pyramid

3. (d)

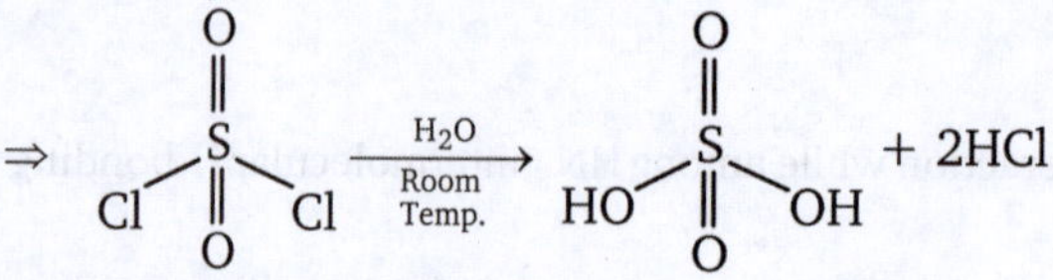

Hyb : sp^3

(No. of $p\pi$-$d\pi$ bonds =2)

Passage-2

1. (d)

Option	Type of orbital combination	For π-bond		For σ-bond	
		Internuclear axis	Nodal plane	axis	Nodal plane
a	$d_{yz} + d_{yz}$	*y*-axis *z*-axis	*xy* *xz*	*x*-axis	*xy* and *xz*
b	$d_{xy} + d_{xy}$	*x*-axis *y*-axis	*xz* *yz*	*z*-axis	*xz* and *yz*
c	$p_y + d_{xy}$	*x*-axis	*xz*	No. δ-bond formation	

2. (d) (a) ⇒ $p_y + d_{x^2-y^2}$: can produce non-bonding if inter-nuclear axis is either *x*, *y* or *z*-axis

(b) ⇒ $p_z + d_{yz}$: can produce non-bonding if inter-nuclear axis is either *x*, *y* or *z*-axis

(c) ⇒ $s + d_{xz}$: will always form non-bonding irrespective of inter-nuclear axis

(d) ⇒ $d_{xy} + d_{xy}$: either form π-bond if inter-nuclear axis is x / y axis or can also form δ-bond if inter-nuclear axis is *z*-axis.

3. (c) Nodal plane of π-bond between C_3 and C_4 lies in *yz*-plane formed by sideways overlapping of p_x-orbitals.

Passage-10

1. (b) Bond dissociation energy : Cl — Cl > P — P > Si — Si

2. (a)

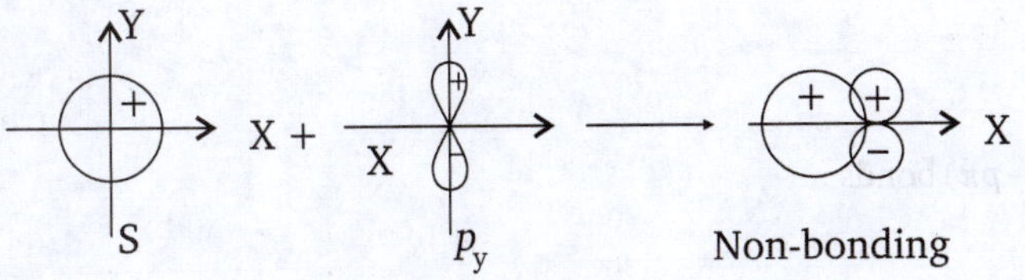

3. (c)

(a) SO_3	No. of $p\pi - p\pi = 1$,	$p\pi - d\pi = 2$
(b) NO_3^-	No. of $p\pi - p\pi = 1$,	$p\pi - d\pi = 0$
(c) SO_4^{2-}	No. of $p\pi - p\pi = 0$,	$p\pi - d\pi = 2$
(d) CO_3^{2-}	No. of $p\pi - p\pi = 1$,	$p\pi - d\pi = 0$

Passage-11

1. (d)

Code element	Actual element	
P	C	
Q	O	exhibits only covalency = 2;
R	Cl	minimum covalency = 1;

S	Al	maximum covalency = 7
T	S	
U	Si	

R and S will combine as SR_3 not as SR_5.

2. (c) Maximum electron affinity is of R. Maximum electronegativity is of Q

T and U belong to different groups.

3. (c) SR_3 : $AlCl_3$ UR_4 : $SiCl_4$ PQ_2 : CO_2 can act as Lewis acid.

Lewis acidic character of $SiCl_4$ > $AlCl_3$

Passage-12

1. (c)

(a) 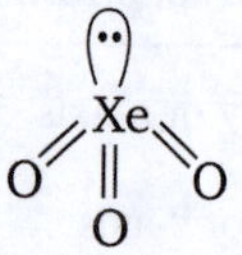

Three ($d\pi - p\pi$) bonds

(b) 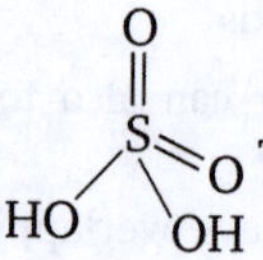

Two ($d\pi - p\pi$) bonds

(c) 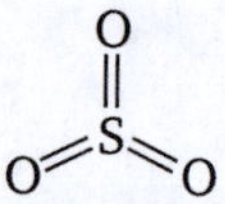

One ($p\pi - p\pi$) and two ($d\pi - p\pi$) bond

(d) 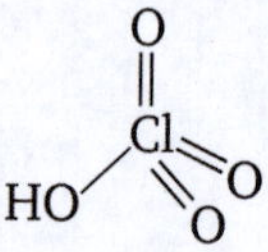

Three ($d\pi - p\pi$) bonds

2. (c)

(a) Involvement of hybridisation (NH_3, SO_2, SO_3, BF_3, PCl_3, IF_7)

(b) Hypervalent compounds (SO_2, SO_3, IF_7)

(c) Non-planar molecules (NH_3, PH_3, PCl_3, IF_7, P_4)

(d) SO_2 [one ($p\pi - p\pi$) bond and one ($d\pi - p\pi$) bond], SO_3 [one ($p\pi - p\pi$) bond and two ($d\pi - p\pi$) bonds]

Passage-13

1. (c) The net energy change during the dissolution or ionisation of ionic compound in water

= Lattice Energy or Ionisation Energy of Compound – Hydration Energy of Cation and Anion.

$= (x - y - z)$ kJ/mol

2. (c) The radius of hydrated ion is directly related to charge of metallic ion and inversely related to size in pure state. Hence the correct order of $Li^+(aq) > Na^+(aq) > K^+(aq)$ (Hydrated ion radius)

Passage-14

1. (c) According to Born Haber cycle, EA and lattice energy should be high for ionic compound formation. In case of AlF_3 and $AlCl_3$.

$(EA)_F < (EA)_{Cl}$

But L.E. of $AlF_3 > AlCl_3$ due to small size of F^- makes overall process exothermic.

2. (a) $2NH_4^+ + SO_4^{2-} \longrightarrow (NH_4)_2SO_4$ (ionic compound)

$H-C \equiv N$; I_2Al-I (Al bonded to three I); $H-Br$ (covalent compound)

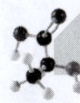

ONE OR MORE ANSWERS IS/ARE CORRECT

4. (a, d)

Correct statement is :

(b) Number of $p\pi - d\pi$ bond(s) in SO_3 is two and in SO_2 is one

(c) Lewis basic order : $NCl_3 > NF_3$

10. (b, d)

Due to phenomenon of inert pair effect Pb^{2+} is more stable than Pb^{4+}.

12. (a, b, ,c)

AX_2: SO_2 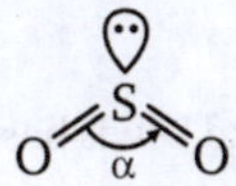 → Hyb. of S : sp^2; shape : Bent

AY_2: SCl_2 → Hyb. of S : sp^3; shape : Bent

→ $\alpha > \beta$

→ Both are planar

16. (a, c)

No.	Total no. of b.p. + l.p.	Hybridisation	Geometry	Shape
(i)	3 + 1	sp^3	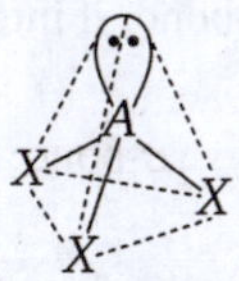	Pyramidal
(ii)	2 + 2	sp^3	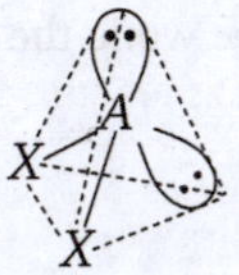	V-shape/bent
(iii)	2 + 1	sp^2	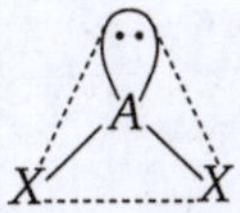	V-shape/bent
(iv)	2 + 0	sp	$X - A - X$ (180°)	Linear

(v) 3 + 2 sp^3d 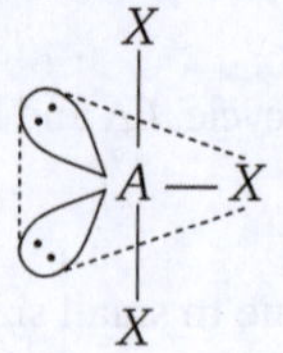 Bent T-shape

(vi) 2 + 3 sp^3d 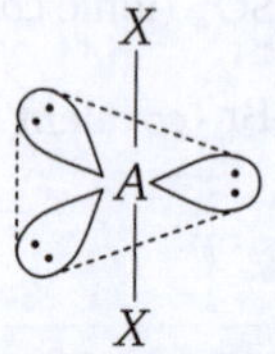 Linear

17. (a, c)

(a) 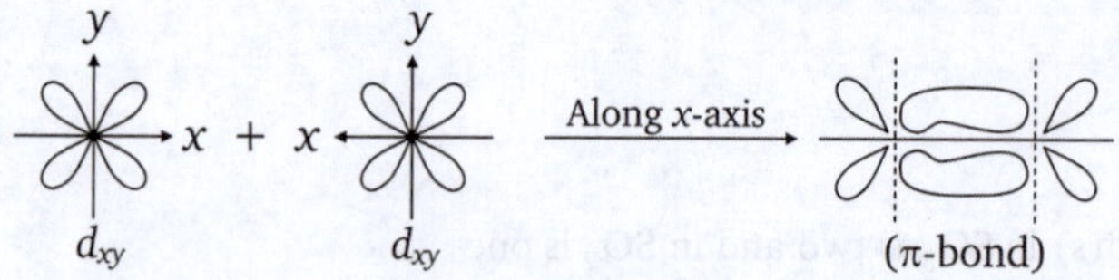

(b) 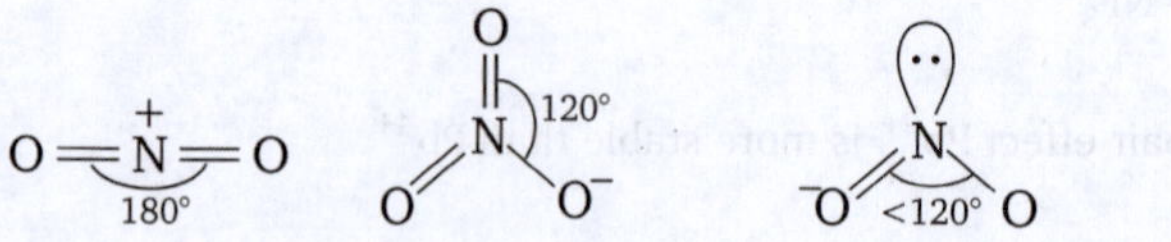

B.O. = 2   B.O. = $4/3 = 1.33$ B.O. = $3/2 = 1.5$

(c) $NF_3 < NCl_3 < NBr_3 < NI_3$ (As E.N. value of C.A. ↓ bond angle and Lewis basic character ↑)

(d) $HF > HCl > HBr > HI$ (Dipole moment order)

$HF > HI > HBr > HCl$ (Boiling point order)

22. (a, c, d)

(a) $p_z + p_y$ ⇒ Non-bonding if internuclear axis is *x*-axis

(b) $p_y + d_{xz}$ ⇒ Form non-bonding if internuclear axis is *x*-axis

(c) $d_{xz} + d_{xz}$ ⇒ Can form δ-bond if internuclear axis is *y*-axis

(d) $p_z + d_{xz}$ ⇒ Can form π-bond, if internuclear axis is *x*-axis.

23. (a, c)

$s + p_z$: Non-bonding; $s + s$: σ-bond; $p_z + p_x$: Non-bonding; $d_{xy} + p_y$: π-bond

24. (a, b, ,c ,d)

It has two angular nodes modified in shape of nodal cones.

One lobe is dumb-bell shape while the other is in the shape of circular ring (in *XY* plane)

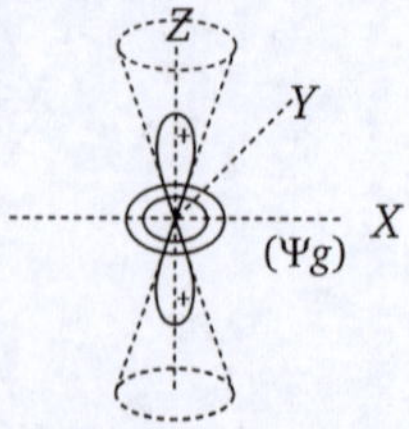

25. (a, b, d)

A^+B^- is ionic when ionisation energy of cation (A^+) is low and electron affinity of anion (B^-) is high.

26. (a, c, d)

Mg^{2+}, N^{3-} from Mg_3N_2, X_3Y_2 type compound.

27. (a, d)

Ionic compound have high melting point and high boiling points. These have high solubilities in polar solvents and have non-directional nature of bonds.

MATCH THE COLUMN

1. (A) 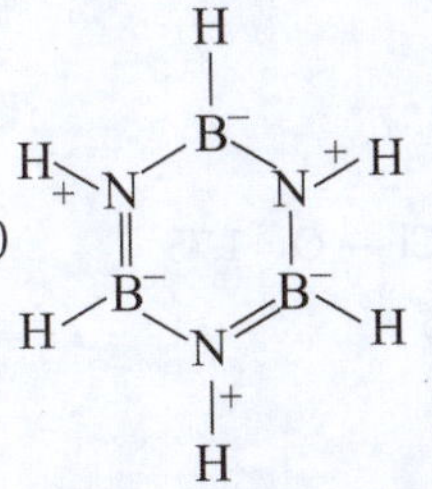

→ Planar as both B and N are sp^2 -hybridized

→ $\mu_D = 0$ (non-polar)

→ has $2p_\pi - 2p_\pi$ back bonding between B—N bond.

→ has no co-ordinate bond

(B) 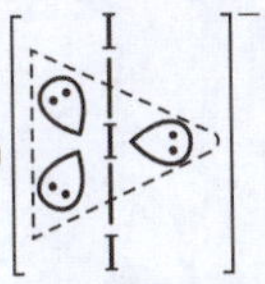

→ Planar structure

→ $\mu_0 = 0$

→ has no back bond

$:\ddot{I}-\ddot{I}: + :\ddot{I}: \rightleftharpoons :\ddot{I} - \ddot{I} \leftarrow \ddot{I}:$

(C) 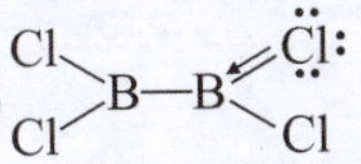

→ Planar structure as both B-atoms are sp^2-hybridised

→ $\mu_D = 0$

→ has $2p_\pi$-$3p_\pi$ back bonding in B—Cl bond

→ has no co-ordinate bond

(D) $2p_\pi$-$3d_\pi$ back bonding

→ Non-planar

→ $\mu_D = 0$

→ has no co-ordinate bond

4. (A) Hypophosphoric Acid ($H_4P_2O_6$) 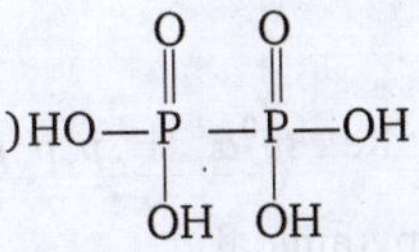 ; Basicity = 4

(B) Pyrophosphoric Acid ($H_4P_2O_5$) 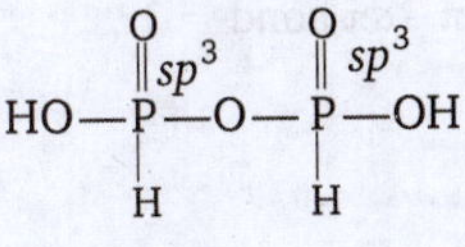 ; Basicity = 2

(C) Boric Acid (H_3BO_3)

$$\underset{(L.A.)}{H_3BO_3} + \underset{(L.B.)}{OH^-} \rightleftharpoons \underset{\text{borate ion}}{[B(OH)_4]^-}$$

(D) Hypophosphorus acid (H_3PO_2) 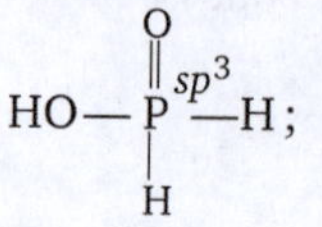 ; Basicity = 1

8. ⇒ 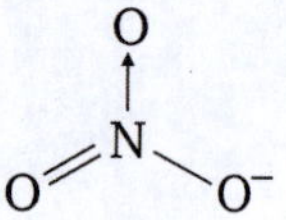 B.O. of N — O = 1.33 ⇒ 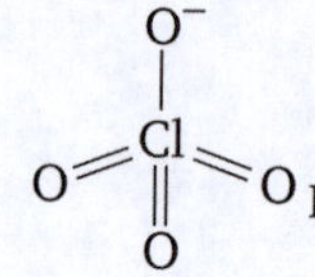 B.O. of Cl — O = 1.75

⇒ 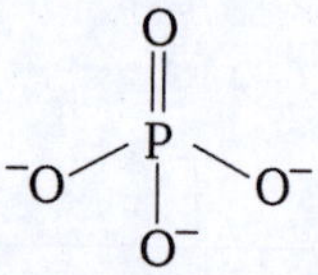 B.O.of P — O = 1.25 ⇒ 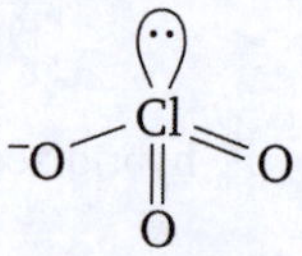 B.O. of Cl — O = 1.67

⇒ 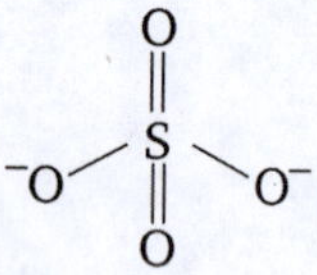 B.O.of S — O = 1.50

9. (a) 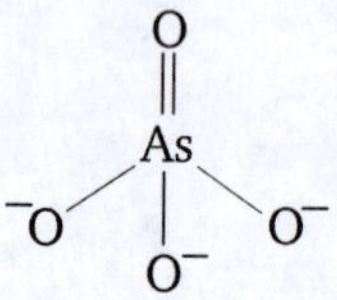

Hybridisation of As : sp^3

Shape : Tetrahedron

All As—O bonds are of equal length due to resonance

Number of $p\pi - d\pi$ bond = 1

(b) 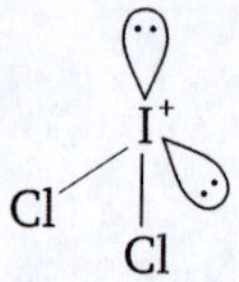

Hydridisation : sp^3

Shape : V-shape

All I—Cl bonds are of equal length.

(c) 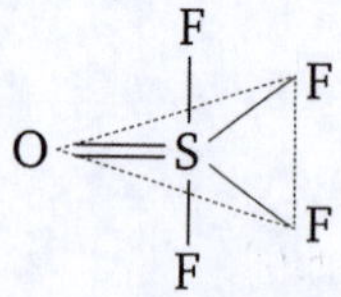

Hybridisation of S : sp^3d $(sp_xp_y + p_zd_{z^2})$

Shape : T.B.P.

Number of $p\pi - d\pi$ bond = 1

(d) 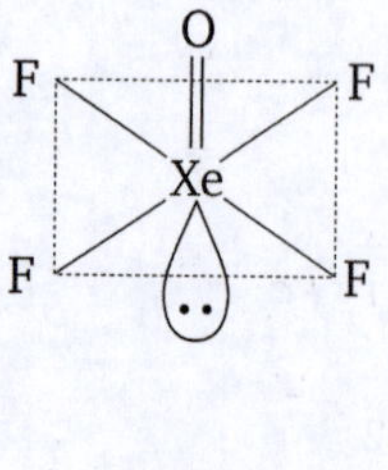

Hybridisation of Xe : sp^3d^2 $(\equiv sp_xp_yp_zd_{x^2-y^2}d_{z^2})$

Shape : Square pyramidal

Number of $p\pi - d\pi$ bond = 1

10. (a) 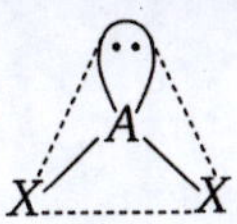

Hybridisation : sp^2; Shape : Angular; Polar; Planar

(b) 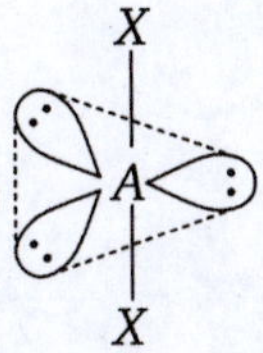

Hybridisation : sp^3d; Shape : Linear; Non-polar; Planar

(c) 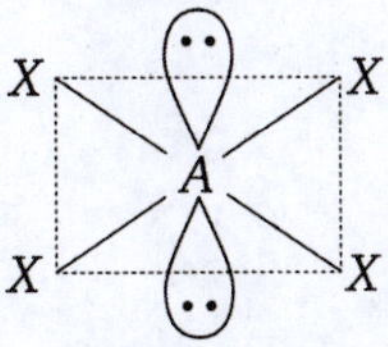

Hybridisation : sp^3d^2; Shape : Square planar; Non-polar; Planar

(d) 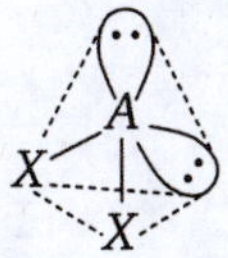

Hybridisation : sp^3;Shape : Angular; Polar; Planar

11.

	Combining orbitals (internuclear axis)	Type of bond formed
P	$d_{yz} + p_y$, (z)	π-bond
Q	$s + p_x$, (y)	Non-bonding
R	$d_{yz} + d_{yz}$, (x)	δ-bond
S	$s + s$, (z)	σ-bond
T	$s + d_{xy}$, (y)	Non-bonding

12. (a) 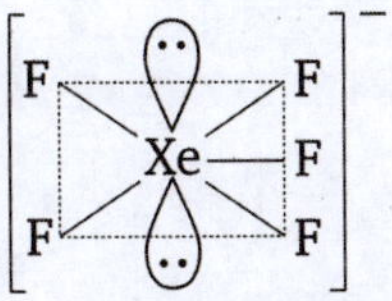

sp^3d^3-hybridisation $(s + p_x + p_y + p_z + d_{x^2-y^2} + d_{z^2} + d_{xy})$, d-orbital with zero nodal Plane (d_{z^2}) and non-axial d-orbital (d_{xy}) used in hybridisation.

Planar.

Bond angle, 72°

(b) 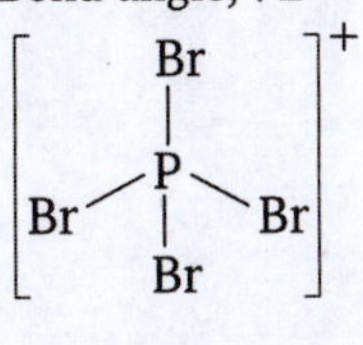

Hybridisation sp^3d $(s + p_x + p_y + p_z + d_z)$

Non-planar species

Bond angle 109°28'

(c) 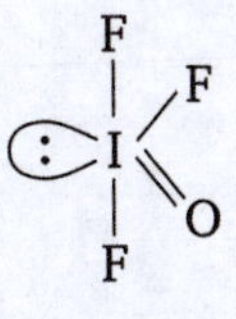

Hybridisation sp^3d $(s + p_x + p_y + p_z + d_{z^2})$

d-orbital with zero nodal plane (d_{z^2}) used

Non-planar

Bond angle < 90°

(d) 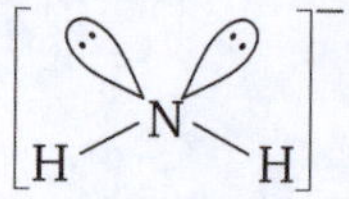

Hybridisation sp^3

Planar

Bond angle < 109°28′

13. (a) $IO_2F_2^-$: 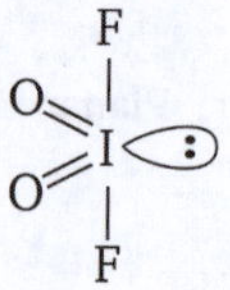

See-saw, Non-planar

(b) IOF_4^- : 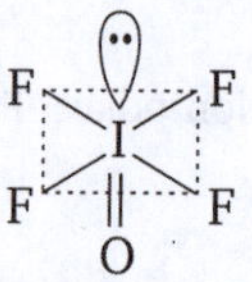

Square pyramidal, non-planar

(c) $SeOF_2$: 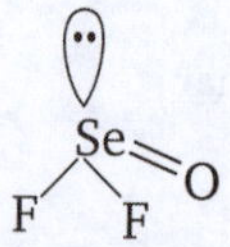

Trigonal pyramidal, non-planar

(d) $XeOF_2$: 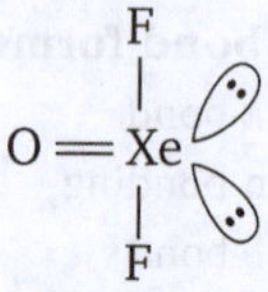

Bent-T-shape, Planar

ASSERTION-REASON TYPE QUESTIONS

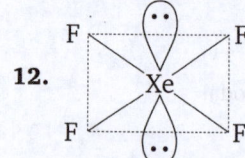

12. 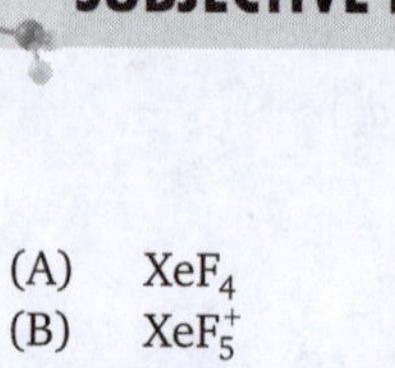

Hybridisation of Xe : sp^3d^2, shape: square planar

SUBJECTIVE PROBLEMS

1.

		b.p.	l.p.
(A)	XeF_4	4	2
(B)	XeF_5^+	5	1
(C)	XeF_5^-	5	2
(D)	XeF_6	6	1
(E)	XeF_8^{2-}	8	1
		28	**7**

$$\Rightarrow \frac{p}{q} = \frac{28}{7} = 04$$

2. SO_2, HCHO

3. $P_1 = 3$, $P_2 = 5$, $Q_1 = 2$, $P_3 = 7$, $Q_2 = 3$

$$= \frac{5(7-3)}{3+2} = 4$$

6. $X = 5$ and $Y = 1$

so, $X - Y = 5 - 1 = 4$

8. $X = 120$ (sp^2-hybridization)

$Y = 180$ (sp-hybridization)

$Z = 90$ (sp^3d^2-hybridization)

$$\frac{120+180+90}{10} = \frac{390}{10} = 39$$

14. 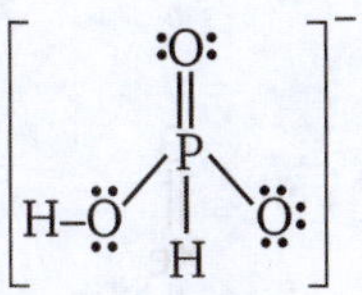

$x = 7, y = 1, z = 5$

$7 + 1 - 5 \Rightarrow 3$

15. $p = 3$, $q = 5$, $r = 2$

$s = 6$, $t = 2$

$3 + 5 + 2 - 6 - 2 \Rightarrow 2$

16. 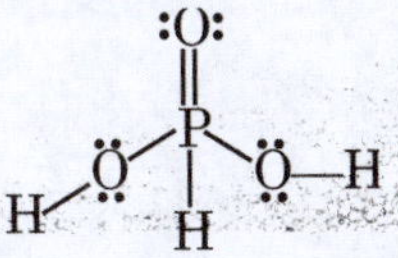

$x = 6$ $y = 6$ $z = 1$

$\therefore\ y \times z - x = 6 \times 1 - 6 = 0$

17. 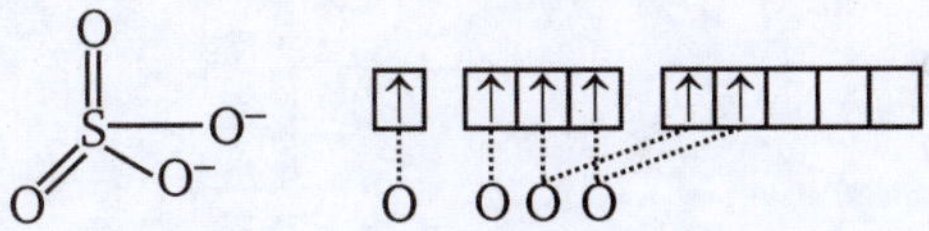

19. $x = 3$, $y = 1$, $z = 3$; $x + y - z = 3 + 1 - 3 = 1$

20. 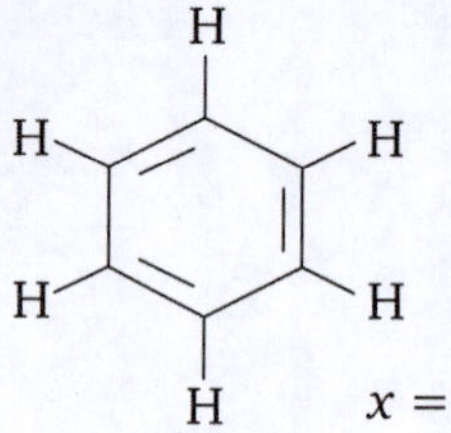

$x = 12$

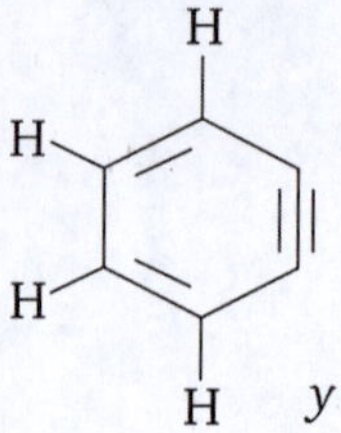

$y = 11$

$|x-y|=1$

21. (i) $IF_5(sp^3d)$ (ii) $ClI_4^-(sp^3d^2)$ (iii) $XeO_2F_2(sp^3d)$ (iv) $NH_2^-(sp^3)$

(v) $BCl_3(sp^2)$ (vi) $BeCl_2(sp)$ (vii) $AsCl_4^+(sp^3)$ (viii) $B(OH)_3(sp^2)$

(ix) $NO_2^-(sp^2)$ (x) $ClO_2^+(sp^2)$

$x = (sp^3)2 + sp^3d(1) + sp^3d^2(2) = 5$

$y = 4, \quad z = 1; \quad 5 + 4 - 1 = 8$

22. XeO_4, XeF_7^+

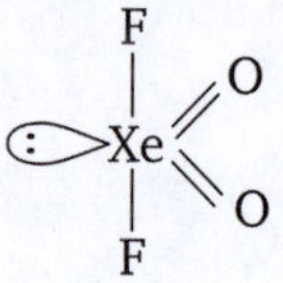

→ sp^3d
→ polar

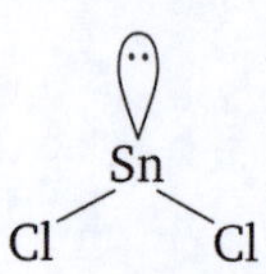

→ sp^2
→ polar

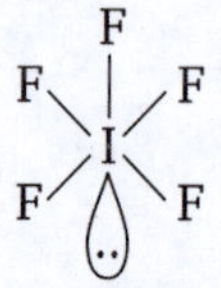

→ sp^3d^2
→ polar

→ sp^3
→ polar

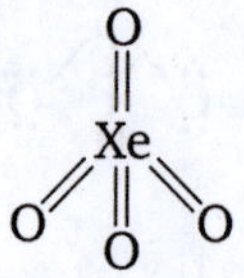

→ sp^3
→ polar

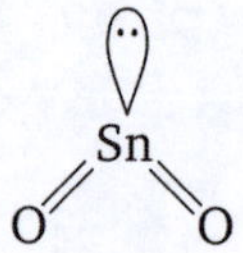

→ sp^2
→ polar

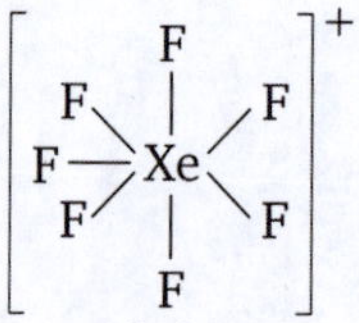

→ sp^3d^3
→ non-polar

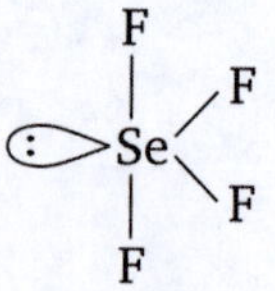

→ sp^3d
→ polar

23.

Species	Bond order
NO_3^-	1.33
SO_4^{2-}	1.50
ClO_3^-	1.66
SO_3	2.00
PO_4^{3-}	1.25
XeO_3	2.00
CO_3^{2-}	1.33
SO_3^{2-}	1.33

$x = 4 \quad y = 4 \quad$ so, $4 - 4 = 0$

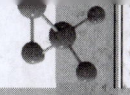

24. $3s$: 0 Nodal plane　　$4d_{z^2}$: 0 Nodal plane　　$4s$: 0 Nodal plane

$2p_x$: 1 Nodal plane　　$3d_{x^2-y^2}$: 2 Nodal plane　　$4p_z$: 1 Nodal plane

$4d_{xy}$: 2 Nodal plane　　$3p_y$: 1 Nodal plane

$3s$, $4d_{xy}$, $4d_{z^2}$, $3d_{x^2-y^2}$, $4s$ (Five)

25. $PCl_5 \longrightarrow sp^3d$, non-planar　　$BrF_3 \longrightarrow sp^3d$, bent, T-shape, planar

$ICl_2^- \longrightarrow sp^3d$, linear, planar　　$XeF_5^- \longrightarrow sp^3d^3$, pentagonal planar

$NO_3^- \longrightarrow sp^2$, planar　　$XeO_2F_2 \longrightarrow sp^3d$, see-saw, non-planar

$PCl_4^+ \longrightarrow sp^3$, tetrahedral, non-planar　　$CH_3^+ \longrightarrow sp^2$, Trigonal planar

$a = 4, \quad b = 5, \quad c = 3$　　so, $\dfrac{a+b}{c} = 3$

26. Transformations (b), (c) and (d) involve change in hybridisation.

27. $(p_x, p_y, d_{xy}, d_{yz}, d_{xz}, d_{x^2-y^2})$

3

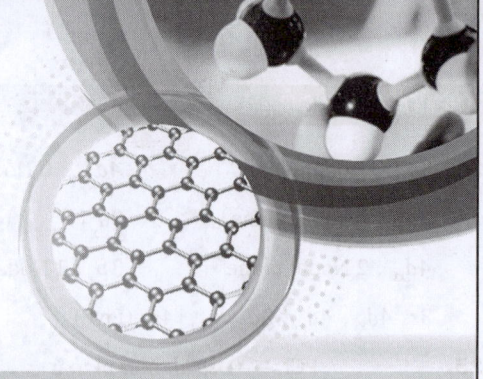

CHEMICAL BONDING (ADVANCED)

Level 1

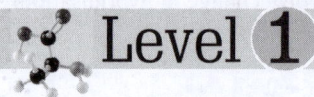

Introductory Question

1. On decreasing internuclear distance below, the optimum distance (where potential energy is minimum), there is steep increase in potential energy due to :
(a) Increase in force of attraction between electrons and nucleus
(b) Increase in stability of bonded atoms
(c) Equal probability of finding bonding electrons near to either of nuclei
(d) Increase in interelectronic and internuclear repulsions

Lewis Acid-Base

2. Which of the following halides is inert towards hydrolysis at room temperature?
(a) $SiCl_4$ (b) PCl_3
(c) NCl_3 (d) NF_3

3. Amongst the following trihalide, which one is least basic?
(a) NF_3 (b) NCl_3 (c) NBr_3 (d) NI_3

4. Which of the following statement is correct ?
(a) PH_3 is more basic than NH_3 (b) PH_3 is less basic than NH_3
(c) PH_3 is equally basic as NH_3 (d) PH_3 is amphoteric while NH_3 is basic

5. Which of the following molecule can act as lewis acid as well as lewis base ?
(a) CO_2 (b) SO_2 (c) SO_3 (d) NH_3

6. Lewis acid-base interaction does not occur at room temperature in :
(a) $Al(OH)_3 + KOH$ (b) $CO_2 + H_2O$ (c) $I_2 + I^-$ (d) $NH_3 + CCl_4$

7. Which of the following is Lewis acid-Lewis base interaction ?
(i) $B(CH_3)_3$ and $N(CH_3)_3$ form addition compound
(ii) H_3BO_3 and C_2H_5OH form addition compound
(iii) Ammonium ion is formed by protonation of ammonia molecule

(iv) BF_3 and NH_3 form addition compound

(a) Only (ii), (iii) are correct (b) Only (iv) is correct

(c) (ii), (iii) and (iv) are correct (d) All are correct

8. Incorrect order of lewis acidic character :

(a) $AlCl_3 > AlBr_3 > AlI_3$ (b) $PCl_5 > SiCl_4 > AlCl_3$

(c) $SF_6 > SF_4 > CCl_4$ (d) $SiF_4 > SiCl_4 > SiBr_4$

9. Which of the following molecule when combines with water, then H_2O molecule does not attack at central atom ?

(a) PCl_3 (b) NCl_3 (c) ClF_5 (d) CO_2

10. In protonation of H_2O change occur in :

(a) Hybridisation state of oxygen atom (b) Shape of molecule

(c) Hybridisation and shape both (d) None of these

11. Which one is least basic among the following trihalide ?

(a) NF_3 (b) NCl_3 (c) NBr_3 (d) NI_3

12. Acidic character of liquid HF increases on addition of which of the following compound ?

(a) SiF_4 (b) SF_6 (c) BF_3 (d) (a) and (c) both

Resonance

13. The correct order of 'S—O' bond length is :

(a) $SO_3^{2-} > SO_4^{2-} > SO_3 > SO_2$ (b) $SO_3^{2-} > SO_4^{2-} > SO_2 > SO_3$

(c) $SO_4^{2-} > SO_3^{2-} > SO_2 > SO_3$ (d) $SO_4^{2-} > SO_3^{2-} > SO_3 > SO_2$

14. What is not true about resonance?

(a) The resonating structures are hypothetical

(b) The unpaired electrons in various resonating structures are same

(c) Hybrid structure is most energetic

(d) Hybrid structure is least energetic

15. Which of the following conditions is not correct for resonating structures?

(a) The contributing structures must have the same number of unpaired electrons

(b) The contributing structures should have almost similar energies

(c) The contributing structures should be so written that unlike charges reside on atoms that are far apart

(d) The positive charge should be present on the electropositive element and the negative charge on the electronegative element

16. A molecule may be represented by three structures having energies E_1, E_2 and E_3, respectively. The energies of these structures follow the order $E_3 < E_2 < E_1$, respectively. If the experimental bond energy of the molecule is E_0, the resonance energy is :

(a) $(E_1 + E_2 + E_3) - E_0$ (b) $E_0 - E_3$

(c) $E_0 - E_1$ (d) $E_0 - E_2$

17. The correct order of increasing C—O bond strength of CO, CO_3^{2-}, CO_2 is :

(a) $CO_3^{2-} < CO_2 < CO$ (b) $CO_2 < CO_3^{2-} < CO$ (c) $CO < CO_3^{2-} < CO_2$ (d) $CO < CO_2 < CO_3^{2-}$

18. Resonance structures can be written for :

(a) O_3 (b) NH_3 (c) CH_4 (d) H_2O

19. The correct order of Cl — O bond order is :

(a) $ClO_3^- < ClO_4^- < ClO_2^- < ClO^-$ (b) $ClO^- < ClO_4^- < ClO_3^- < ClO_2^-$

(c) $ClO^- < ClO_2^- < ClO_3^- < ClO_4^-$ (d) $ClO_4^- < ClO_3^- < ClO_2^- < ClO^-$

20 How many resonance forms can be written for the nitrate ion, (NO_3^-)?

(a) 1 (b) 2 (c) 3 (d) 4

Hybridisation

21. Two hybrid orbitals have a bond angle of 120°. The percentage of *s*-character in the hybrid orbital is nearly:

(a) 25% (b) 33% (c) 50% (d) 66%

22. The state of hybridisation of central atom in dimer of BH_3 and BeH_2 is :

(a) sp^2, sp^2 (b) sp^3, sp^2 (c) sp^3, sp^3 (d) sp^2, sp^3

23. In NO_2 molecule N atom undergoes in :

(a) sp^3 hybridization (b) sp^2 hybridization

(c) sp hybridization (d) sp^2d hybridization

Molecular Geometry/Shape

24. Identify the correct sequence of increasing number of π-bonds in the structure of the following molecules :

(I) $H_2S_2O_6$ (II) $H_2S_2O_3$ (III) $H_2S_2O_5$

(a) I, II and III (b) II, I and III

(c) II, III and I (d) I, III and II

25. C_2H_2 is isostructural with :

(a) H_2O_2 (b) NO_2 (c) $SnCl_2$ (d) CO_2

26. The shapes of nitrite and nitrile respectively are :

(a) Linear and angular (b) Angular and linear

(c) Both angular (d) Both linear

27. Linear structure is assumed by :

(I) NCO^- (II) CS_2 (III) $\overset{+}{N}O_2$ (IV) Solid BeH_2

(a) all four (b) (II), (III) and (IV)

(c) (I), (II) and (III) (d) (II) and (III)

28. Among the oxides of nitrogen, N_2O, NO and NO_2, molecules with unpaired electrons are :

(a) N_2O and NO (b) NO and NO_2

(c) N_2O and NO_2 (d) NO_2 and its dimer

29. Which of the following pair consists of only network solid ?

(a) SiO_2, P_4O_{10} (b) P_4O_{10}, SO_3

(c) P_4O_{10}, P_4O_6 (d) Diamond, SiO_2

30. Which of the following ions does not have S—S linkage?

(a) $S_2O_8^{2-}$ (b) $S_2O_6^{2-}$ (c) $S_2O_5^{2-}$ (d) $S_2O_3^{2-}$

31. Among KO_2, $KAlO_2$, CaO_2 and NO_2^+, unpaired electron is present in :

(a) NO_2^+ and CaO_2 (b) KO_2 and $KAlO_2$ (c) KO_2 only (d) CaO_2 only

32. Structure of S_2Cl_2 is analogous to :

(a) $SOCl_2$ (b) CO_2 (c) H_2S (d) H_2O_2

33. Number of P—H, P—O — P, P—O—H and P—O bonds in sodium dihydrogen pyrophosphate respectively are :

(a) 1, 1, 1, 2 (b) 0, 1, 2, 2 (c) 0, 1, 2, 4 (d) 2, 0, 0, 2

Dipole Moment

34. Which of the following pair of molecules will have permanent dipole moment?

(a) NO_2 and CO_2 (b) NO_2 and O_3
(c) SiF_4 and CO_2 (d) SiF_4 and NO_2

35. The dipole moment of HCl is 1.03 D, if H—Cl bond distance is 1.26 Å, what is the percentage of ionic character in the H—Cl bond?

(a) 60% (b) 39% (c) 29% (d) 17%

36. The dipole moment of *o*, *p* and *m*-dichlorobenzene will be in the order :

(a) $o > p > m$ (b) $p > o > m$
(c) $m > o > p$ (d) $o > m > p$

37. Which of the following molecules has highest dipole moment?

(a) BF_3 (b) NH_3 (c) NF_3 (d) B_2H_6

38. In terms of polar character, which of the following order is correct?

(a) $NH_3 < H_2O < HF < H_2S$ (b) $H_2S < NH_3 < H_2O < HF$
(c) $H_2O < NH_3 < H_2S < HF$ (d) $HF < H_2O < NH_3 < H_2S$

39. The correct order of dipole moment is :

(a) $CH_4 < NF_3 < NH_3 < H_2O$ (b) $NF_3 < CH_4 < NH_3 < H_2O$
(c) $NH_3 < NF_3 < CH_4 < H_2O$ (d) $H_2O < NH_3 < NF_3 < CH_4$

Bond Parameters

40. The strongest P—O bond is found in the molecule :

(a) F_3PO (b) Cl_3PO (c) Br_3PO (d) $(CH_3)_3PO$

41. O_2F_2 is an unstable yellow orange solid and H_2O_2 is a colourless liquid, both have O—O bond and O—O bond length in H_2O_2 and O_2F_2 respectively is :

(a) 1.22 Å, 1.48 Å (b) 1.48 Å, 1.22 Å
(c) 1.22 Å, 1.22 Å (d) 1.48 Å, 1.48 Å

42. The bond length of the S—O bond is maximum in which of the following compounds?

(a) $SOCl_2$ (b) $SOBr_2$
(c) SOF_2 (d) All have same length

43. ∠ FAsF bond angle in AsF_3Cl_2 molecule is :

(a) 90° and 180° (b) 120° (c) 90° (d) 180°

44. Which of the following has largest bond angle ?

(a) H_2O (b) F_2O (c) Cl_2O (d) H_2S

45. The incorrect order of bond angle is :

(a) $ClO_2 > OCl_2$ (b) $NO_2^- < NO_2$ (c) $\dot{C}H_3 > \dot{C}F_3$ (d) $O(SiH_3)_2 < ClO_2$

Fajan's Rule (Ionic Bond)

46. In an ionic compound A^+X^- the degree of covalent bonding is greatest when :
(a) A^+ and X^- ion are small
(b) A^+ is small and X^- is large
(c) A^+ and X^- ions are approximately of the same size
(d) X^- is small and A^+ is large

47. In which of the following species the bonds are non-directional?
(a) NCl_3 (b) RbCl (c) $BeCl_2$ (d) BCl_3

48. Which of the following when dissolved in water forms a solution which is non-conducting?
(a) Green vitriol (b) Chile or Indian salt petre
(c) Alcohol (d) Potash alum

49. Which of the following statements about LiCl and NaCl is wrong?
(a) LiCl has lower melting point than NaCl
(b) LiCl dissolves more in organic solvents whereas NaCl does not
(c) LiCl would ionise in water less than NaCl
(d) Fused LiCl would be less conducting than fused NaCl

50. Which of the following substances has the highest melting point?
(a) NaCl (b) KCl (c) MgO (d) BaO

51. The stability of ionic crystal principally depends on :
(a) high electron affinity of anion forming species
(b) the lattice energy of crystal
(c) low I.E. of cation forming species
(d) low heat of sublimation of cation forming solid

52. In which of the following solvents, KI has highest solubility?
(a) $C_6H_6(\epsilon = 0)$ (b) $(CH_3)_2CO(\epsilon = 2)$
(c) $CH_3OH(\epsilon = 32)$ (d) $CCl_4(\epsilon = 0)$

53. Amongst LiCl, $BeCl_2$, $MgCl_2$ and RbCl the compounds with greatest and least ionic character, respectively are :
(a) LiCl and RbCl (b) RbCl and $BeCl_2$
(c) RbCl and $MgCl_2$ (d) $MgCl_2$ and $BeCl_2$

54. The compound with the highest degree of covalency is :
(a) NaCl (b) $MgCl_2$ (c) AgCl (d) CsCl

55. The salt having the least solubility in water is :
(a) $BaCl_2$ (b) $Ba(NO_3)_2$ (c) $MgSO_4$ (d) $BaSO_4$

56. The solubility of Na_2SO_4, $BeSO_4$, $MgSO_4$ and $BaSO_4$ in water follow the order :
(a) $BaSO_4 > BeSO_4 > MgSO_4 > Na_2SO_4$ (b) $Na_2SO_4 > BeSO_4 > MgSO_4 > BaSO_4$
(c) $BeSO_4 > MgSO_4 > BaSO_4 > Na_2SO_4$ (d) $MgSO_4 > BeSO_4 > Na_2SO_4 > BaSO_4$

57. Solubility of alkali metal fluorides increases down the group." Select correct explanation for given statement :
(a) Hydration energy increases and lattice energy decreases down the group
(b) Both energy decrease down the group but decrease in hydration energy is rapid
(c) Both energy decrease down the group but decrease in lattice energy is rapid
(d) Both energy increase down the group but increase in hydration energy is rapid

58. Covalency favoured in the following case :
(a) smaller cation (b) larger anion
(c) large charge on cation and anions (d) all of these

59. The melting point of RbBr is 682°C while that of NaF is 988°C. The principal reason for this fact is :
(a) the molar mass of NaF is smaller than that of RbBr
(b) the bond in RbBr has more covalent character than the bond in NaF
(c) the difference in electronegativity between Rb and Br is smaller than the difference between Na and F
(d) the internuclear distance, $r_c + r_a$ is greater for RbBr than for NaF

Molecular Forces

60. The boiling points of noble gases are illustrative of the operation of forces of the type :
(a) ion-dipole (b) dipole-induced dipole
(c) ion-induced dipole (d) London dispersion forces

61. Among the following, which has the lowest enthalpy of fusion ?
(a) Fluorine (b) Hydrogen (c) Chlorine (d) Helium

62. Out of the two compounds shown below, the vapour pressure of *B* at a particular temperature is expected to be :

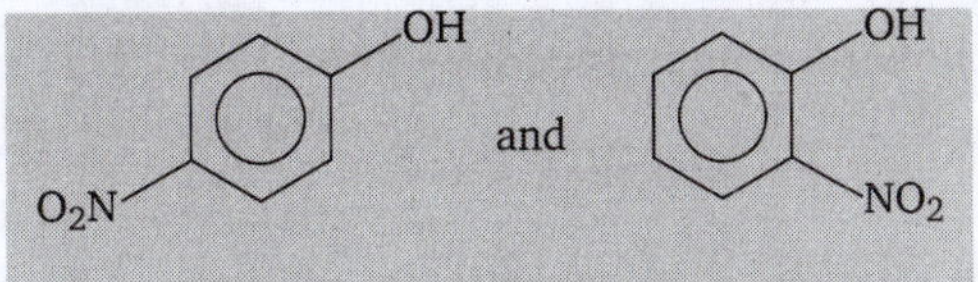

(*A*) (*B*)

(a) higher than that of *A*
(b) lower than that of *A*
(c) same as that of *A*
(d) can be higher or lower depending upon the size of the vessel

63. The crystal lattice of ice is mostly formed by :
(a) ionic forces (b) covalent bonds
(c) intermolecular H-bonds (d) intramolecular H-bonds

64. The boiling points of methanol, water and dimethyl ether are respectively 65° C, 100° C and 34.5° C. Which of the following best explains these wide variations in b.p.?
(a) The molecular mass increases from water (18) to methanol (32) to diethyl ether (74)
(b) The extent of H-bonding decreases from water to methanol while it is absent in ether
(c) The extent of intramolecular H-bonding decreases from ether to methanol to water
(d) The density of water is 1.00 $g\,mL^{-1}$, methanol 0.7914 $g\,mL^{-1}$ and that of diethyl ether is 0.7137 $g\,mL^{-1}$

65. In ice, the length of H-bonds :
(a) is less than that of covalent bonds
(b) is greater than that of covalent bonds
(c) is same as that of covalent bonds
(d) can be less greater or same as that of covalent bonds

66. The correct order of the strength of H-bonds in same species :

(a) H...F > H...O > H...N
(b) H...N > H...O > H...F
(c) H...O > H...N > H...F
(d) H...F > H...N > H...O

67. *o*-nitrophenol can be easily steam distilled whereas *p*-nitrophenol cannot be. This is because of :

(a) strong intermolecular hydrogen bonding in *o*-nitrophenol
(b) strong intramolecular hydrogen bonding in *o*-nitrophenol
(c) strong intramolecular hydrogen bonding in *p*-nitrophenol
(d) dipole moment of *p*-nitrophenol is larger than that of *o*-nitrophenol

68. What is not true about ice?

(a) It has open cage like structure
(b) It has less density than water
(c) Each O atom is surrounded by 4 H atoms
(d) Each O atom has four H-bonds around it

69. When ice melts to form liquid water at 0° C, there is a contraction in volume. This is due to :

(a) the molecules contracting in size
(b) a partial disruption of the hydrogen bonded network of ice on melting
(c) the absorption of heat during the melting process
(d) the dissolving of air into the water during the melting process

Back Bond

70. In which of the following compounds B—F bond length is shortest?

(a) BF_4^-
(b) $BF_3 \leftarrow NH_3$
(c) BF_3
(d) $BF_3 \leftarrow N(CH_3)_3$

71. The geometry with respect to the central atom of the following molecules are:

$N(SiH_3)_3$; Me_3N ; $(SiH_3)_3P$

(a) planar, pyramidal, planar
(b) planar, pyramidal, pyramidal
(c) pyramidal, pyramidal, pyramidal
(d) pyramidal, planar, pyramidal

72. Which of the following is correct skeleton for Ge — N — C — O in H_3GeNCO molecule?

(a) 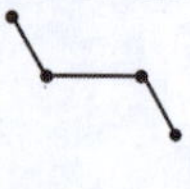
(b) 
(c) 
(d) 

73. Among following molecules, in which molecule N — Si bond length is shortest:

(a) $N(SiH_3)_3$
(b) $NH(SiH_3)_2$
(c) $NH_2(SiH_3)$
(d) All have equal N — Si bond length

74. B — F bond length is minimum in:

(a) BF_3
(b) BF_2OH
(c) BF_2NH_2
(d) BF_3NMe_3

75. Which of the *d*-orbital(s) of silicon atoms can form back bond in $N(SiH_3)_3$? If $N(SiH_3)_3$ is present in *xy* plane:

(I) d_{xy}
(II) d_{xz}
(III) d_{yz}
(IV) $d_{x^2-y^2}$

(a) All I, II, III, IV
(b) Only I, II, III
(c) Only II, III, IV
(d) Only II, III

76. Both BF_3 and BHF_2 compounds have trigonal planer geometry. Incorrect statement about both compounds is:
(a) $F\hat{B}F$ bond angle in $BHF_2 > F\hat{B}F$ bond angle in BF_3
(b) B — F bond length in $BHF_2 >$ B — F bond length in BF_3
(c) B — F bond order in $BHF_2 >$ B — F bond order in BF_3
(d) Back bond strength in $BHF_2 >$ Back bonding strength in BF_3

77. Species in which hybridization of underlined atom remains same by replacing all SiH_3 group(s) by CH_3 group(s):
(a) $\underline{O}(SiH_3)_2$ (b) $\underline{N}(SiH_3)_3$
(c) $H_3Si\underline{N}CS$ (d) $\underline{P}(SiH_3)_3$

78. In which of the following compound B — O bond length is shortest?
(a) H_3BO_3 (b) $B(OH)_4^-$ (c) $B(OH)(CH_3)_2$ (d) $BF_2(OH)$

Bridge Bond

79. The number of three centre two electron bonds in a molecule of diborane is :
(a) 0 (b) 2 (c) 4 (d) 6

80. In which of the following compounds octet is complete and incomplete for all atoms :

	Al_2Cl_6	$Al_2(CH_3)_6$	AlF_3	Dimer of $BeCl_2$	Dimer of BeH_2
(a)	IC	IC	IC	C	C
(b)	C	IC	IC	C	IC
(c)	C	IC	C	IC	IC
(d)	IC	C	IC	IC	IC

(Note : C for complete octet and IC for incomplete octet.)

81. In which of the following molecular species both σ-dative and π-dative bonds are present ?
(a) BF_4^- (b) Be_2Cl_4 (c) NH_4^+ (d) $[BeF_4]^{2-}$

Odd Electron Species

82. Incorrect order of bond angle is :
(a) $\overset{+}{NO_2} > NO_2 > NO_2^-$ (b) $BF_3 > NF_3 > PF_3$
(c) $ClO_2 > Cl_2O > ClO_2^-$ (d) $PF_3 > PCl_3 > PBr_3$

83. Hybridization of central atom changes for which of the following molecule when undergoes dimerization :
(a) CF_3 (b) ClO_3 (c) NO_2 (d) CH_3

84. Which of the following statement is not correct for

$$NO_2, NO_2^+, NO_2^-$$

(a) NO_2 is paramagnetic
(b) NO_2^+ is linear, NO_2 is bent and bond angle is slightly less than 120°
(c) NO_2^+ ion has the shortest and strongest bonds among these
(d) NO_2^- ion has longest and weakest bond among these

85. Correct order of bond angle is :

(a) $\dot{C}H_3 > \dot{C}F_3$ (b) $CH_3^- > CH_3^+$ (c) $CH_4 > CF_4$ (d) $CH_4 > \dot{C}H_3$

86. In which of the following conversion both hybridisation as well as shape changes with respect to central atom?

(a) $CH_3 \rightarrow C_2H_6$ (b) $NH_3 \rightarrow \overset{+}{N}H_4$ (c) $H_2O \rightarrow H_3O^+$ (d) All of these

87. The shape of methyl radical ($\dot{C}H_3$) is :

(a) linear (b) pyramidal (c) planar (d) spherical

Level 2

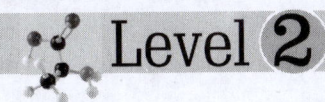

Introductory Question

1. Consider the given figure showing the formation of H_2^+ ion depending on internuclear distance *versus* potential energy of the system.

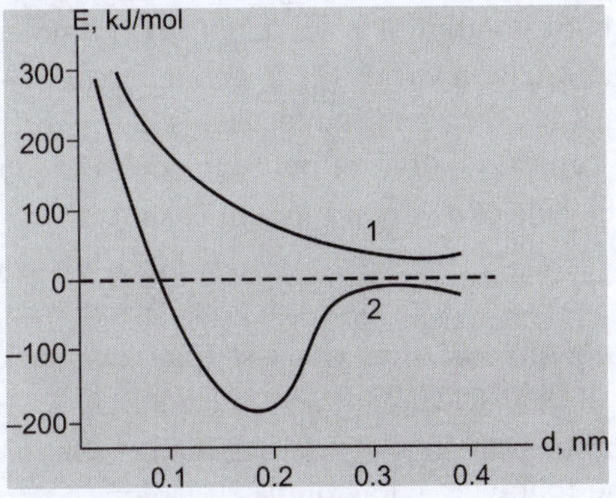

which is correct statement :

(a) Curve-1 represents the most stable state of the system for H_2^+ ion

(b) Curve-2 represents the most stable state of the system for H_2^+ ion

(c) Curve-1 indicates that the molecular hydrogen ion is formed

(d) Curve-2 represents the energy level of the antibonding region

Lewis Acid-Base

2. The correct increasing order of extent of hydrolysis is :

(a) $CCl_4 < MgCl_2 < AlCl_3 < SiCl_4 < PCl_5$ (b) $CCl_4 < AlCl_3 < MgCl_2 < PCl_5 < SiCl_4$

(c) $CCl_4 < SiCl_4 < PCl_5 < AlCl_3 < MgCl_2$ (d) $CCl_4 < PCl_5 < SiCl_4 < AlCl_3 < MgCl_2$

3. Inorganic benzene reacts with HCl to form a compound $B_3N_3H_9Cl_3$. The protonation occurs at :

(a) B-atom

(b) N-atom

(c) First at B-atom then rearranges into N-atom

(d) First at N-atom then rearranges into B-atom

4. Select correct statement about hydrolysis of BCl_3 and NCl_3 :

(a) NCl_3 is hydrolysed and gives HOCl but BCl_3 is not hydrolysed

(b) Both NCl_3 and BCl_3 on hydrolysis gives HCl

(c) NCl_3 on hydrolysis gives HOCl but BCl_3 gives HCl

(d) Both NCl_3 and BCl_3 on hydrolysis gives HOCl

Back Bond

5. Both $N(SiH_3)_3$ and $NH(SiH_3)_2$ compounds have trigonal planar skeleton. Incorrect statement about both compounds is :
(a) $Si\hat{N}Si$ bond angle in $NH(SiH_3)_2$ > $Si\hat{N}Si$ bond angle in $N(SiH_3)_3$
(b) N—Si bond length in $NH(SiH_3)_2$ > N — Si bond length in $N(SiH_3)_3$
(c) N—Si bond length in $NH(SiH_3)_2$ < N — Si bond length in $N(SiH_3)_3$
(d) Back bonding strength in $NH(SiH_3)_2$ > Back bonding strength in $N(SiH_3)_3$

6. The incorrect statement regarding $O(SiH_3)_2$ and OCl_2 molecule is/are :
(a) The strength of back bonding is more in $O(SiH_3)_2$ molecule than OCl_2 molecule
(b) Si — Ô — Si bond angle in $O(SiH_3)_2$ is greater than Cl — Ô — Cl bond angle in OCl_2
(c) The nature of back bond in both molecules is $(2p_\pi - 3d_\pi)$
(d) Hybridisation of central O-atom in both molecules is same

7. Among following molecule N—Si bond length is shortest :
(a) $N(SiH_3)_3$ (b) $NH(SiH_3)_2$
(c) $NH_2(SiH_3)$ (d) All have equal N—Si bond length

8. Which of the following molecule has weakest $(p\pi - d\pi)$ back bonding ?
(a) OCl_2 (b) $N(SiH_3)_3$ (c) SiF_4 (d) $O(SiH_3)_2$

9. "Hybridisation of central atom does not always change due to back bonding". This statement is valid for which of the following compounds ?
(i) CCl_3^- (ii) CCl_2 (iii) $(SiH_3)_2O$ (iv) $N(SiH_3)_3$
(a) (i), (ii) (b) (i), (iii) (c) (ii), (iii) (d) All

10. The geometry with respect to the central atom of the following molecules are :
$N(SiH_3)_3$; Me_3N; $(SiH_3)_3P$
(a) planar, pyramidal, planar
(b) planar, pyramidal, pyramidal
(c) pyramidal, pyramidal, pyramidal
(d) pyramidal, planar, pyramidal

11. Incorrect statement regarding BF_2NH_2 molecule is :
(a) FBF bond angle < 120° (b) HNH bond angle > 109°28'
(c) Exhibits intermolecular H-bond (d) Hybridization of N-atom is sp^3

Molecular Forces

12. Which of the following solid has maximum melting point ?
(a) NaCl (b) Ice (c) Dry ice (d) SiO_2

13. The melting point of AlF_3 is 104°C and that of SiF_4 is – 77°C (it sublimes) because :
(a) there is a very large difference in the ionic character of the Al – F and Si – F bonds
(b) in AlF_3, Al^{3+} interacts very strongly with the neighbouring F^- ions to given a three dimensional structure but in SiF_4 no such interaction is possible
(c) the silicon ion in the tetrahedral SiF_4 molecule is not shielded effectively from the fluoride ions whereas in AlF_3, the Al^{3+} ion is shielded on all sides
(d) the attractive forces between the SiF_4 molecules are strong whereas those between the AlF_3 molecule are weak

14. The correct order of boiling point is :

(a) $T_2 < D_2 < H_2$
(b) n –pentane < neo-pentane
(c) Xe < Ar < He
(d) m –nitrophenol > o –nitrophenol

Valence Bond Theory

15. Correctly match is :

(a) $d_{x^2-y^2}$ atomic orbital — One nodal plane
(b) p_y atomic orbital — Two nodal planes
(c) σ_{p_x} — ψ (gerade)
(d) $\pi^*_{p_y}$ — ψ (ungerade)

16. Select correct statement(s) :

(a) Acidic strength of HBr > HCl but reverse is true for their reducing property
(b) Basic strength of $PH_3 > AsH_3$ but reverse is true for their bond angle
(c) Dipole moment of $CH_3Cl > CH_3F$ but reverse is true for their $H\hat{C}H$ bond angle
(d) K_{a_1} of fumaric acid is higher than maleic acid but reverse is true for their K_{a_2}

17. The structure of $B_3N_3H_6$ is as follows :

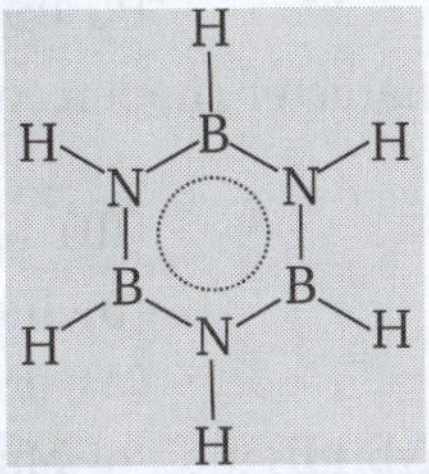

How may derivative structures of $B_3N_3H_4X_2$ can be derived from the basic structure, by the replacement of two hydrogen atoms?

(a) 2
(b) 3
(c) 4
(d) 5

Hybridisation

18. Consider the following reaction :

$MX_4 + X'_2 \longrightarrow MX_4X'_2$

If atomic number of M is 52 and X and X' are halogens and X' is more electronegative than X. Then choose correct statement regarding given information:

(a) Both X' atoms occupy axial positions which are formed by overlapping of p and d-orbitals only
(b) All M — X bond lengths are identical in both MX_4 and $MX_4X'_2$ compounds
(c) Central atom 'M' does not use anyone valence non-axial set of d-orbital in hybridization of final product
(d) Hybridization of central atom 'M' remains same in both reactant and final product.

19. Select the incorrect match :

	Statement	Shape	Example
(a)	Bond pair has > 75% *p*-character		HF
(b)	Reduction in axial bond angle is more than that of in equatorial bond angle		SF_4
(c)	Two axial *d*-orbitals and one non-axial *d*-orbital are used in hybridization		XeF_5^-
(d)	Two *p*-orbitals are used in hybridization		$SnCl_2$

20. In which of the following species, *d*-orbitals having *xz* and *yz* two nodal planes involved in hybridization of central atom?

(a) $IO_2F_2^-$ (b) ClF_4^- (c) IF_7 (d) None of these

21. The correct order of increasing *s*-character (in percentage) in the hybrid orbitals of following molecules/ions is :

(I) CO_3^{2-} (II) XeF_4 (III) I_3^- (IV) NCl_3 (V) $BeCl_2$

(a) II < III < IV < I < V (b) II < IV < III < V < I
(c) III < II < I < V < IV (d) II < IV < III < I < V

22. The shape of MnO_4^- ion and the hybridisation of Mn in MnO_4^- is :

(a) tetrahedral, sp^3 (b) tetrahedral, d^3s
(c) square planar, dsp^2 (d) square planar, sp^3

Molecular Geometry/Shape

23. Molecule having non-polar as well as polar bonds but the molecule as a whole is polar :

(a) S_2F_2 (b) N_2O_4 (c) Si_2H_6 (d) I_2Cl_6

24. Choose the correct statement regarding $SeOCl_2$ molecule :

(a) It does not contain plane of symmetry
(b) '$Cl-\hat{Se}-Cl$' bond angle is greater than '$Cl-\hat{Se}-O$' bond angle
(c) Lone pair has greater than 33.3% *s*-character
(d) Central atom used one *d*-orbital in bonding

25. In which species, X—O bond order is 1.5 and contains $p\pi - d\pi$ bond(s).

(a) $IO_2F_2^-$ (b) $HCOO^-$ (c) SO_3^{2-} (d) XeO_2F_2

26. Which of the following species has polar and non-polar bonds but molecule as a whole is non-polar ?

(a) $S_2O_3^{2-}$ (b) $(SCN)_2$ (c) Be_2Cl_4 (d) Si_2H_6

27. The incorrect statement(s) regarding $\dot{C}X_3$ species is :

(a) If electronegativity of surrounding element '*X*' is less than 2.5, then central carbon atom used almost 33% *s*-character in their hybrid bonding orbitals

(b) If electronegativity of surrounding element '*X*' is greater than 2.5, then central carbon atom used almost 25% *s*-character in their hybrid bonding orbitals

(c) If '*X*' is 'F', then species should be polar and pyramidal

(d) If '*X*' is H, then speçies should be polar and planar

28. Consider following compounds :

(I) H_3X-NCS (II) H_3Y-NCS (III) $(H_3X)_2O$ (IV) $(H_3Y)_2O$

The incorrect statement regarding given compound is :

(a) IF *Y* is carbon in compounds (II) and (IV), then both are bent

(b) If *X* is silicon in compounds (I) and (III), then both are linear

(c) If *X* is carbon and *Y* is silicon then compound (I) is more basic than compound (II)

(d) If *X* is silicon and Y is carbon then $X-\hat{O}-X$ bond angle compounds (III) is greater than $Y-\hat{O}-Y$ bond angle in compounds (IV)

29. The incorrect statement about carbene (CH_2) is :

(a) In singlet carbene, carbon is sp^2-hybridized whereas in triplet carbene, carbon is *sp*-hybridized

(b) Triplet carbene is less stable than singlet carbene

(c) Stability order of singlet halocarbenes is : CHF > CHCl > CHBr

(d) None of the above

30. The lowest O—O bond length in the following molecule is :

(a) O_2F_2 (b) O_2 (c) H_2O_2 (d) O_3

31. Out of $CHCl_3$, CH_4 and SF_4 the molecules do not having regular geometry are :

(a) $CHCl_3$ only (b) $CHCl_3$ and SF_4 (c) CH_4 only (d) CH_4 and SF_4

32. When iodine is dissolved in aqueous potassium iodide, the shape of the species formed is :

(a) linear (b) angular (c) triangular (d) see-saw

33. Which of the following set of species have planar structures?

(a) $I_3^-, \dot{C}H_3, ClO_3^-, SiF_6^{2-}$ (b) $I_3^+, ICl_4^-, Al_2Cl_6, TeCl_4$

(c) $SCl_2, N_2O_5, SF_4, XeOF_4$ (d) $I_2Cl_6, XeF_2, BrF_4^-, XeF_5^-$

34. Which of the following compounds have the same no. of lone pairs with their central atom?

(I) XeF_5^- (II) BrF_3 (III) XeF_2 (IV) H_3S^+ (V) Triple Methylene

(a) IV and V (b) I and III (c) I and II (d) II, IV and V

35. Given the correct order of initials **T** or **F** for following statements. Use **T** if statements is true and **F** if it is false :

(I) $(CH_3)_2P(CF_3)_3$ is non-polar and $(CH_3)_3P(CF_3)_2$ is polar molecule

(II) $CH_3\hat{P}CH_3$ bond angles are equal in $(CH_3)_3P(CF_3)_2$ molecule

(III)PF_3 will be more soluble in polar solvent than SiF_4

(a) TTF (b) FFT (c) FFF (d) FTT

36. The correct sequence of polarity of the following molecule

(1) Benzene (2) Inorganic Benzene

(3) PCl_3F_2 (4) PCl_2F_3

	1	2	3	4		1	2	3	4
(a)	P	NP	NP	P	(b)	NP	NP	NP	P
(c)	NP	P	NP	P	(d)	NP	P	P	NP

(Where, P = polar, NP = non-polar)

37. Which among the following molecules is not perfect flat?

(a) $B_3N_3H_6$ (b) $C_3N_3(NH_2)_3$

(c) SO_3 (d) $C_3N_3(N_3)_3$

38. Which of the following structure(s) is/are non-planar?

(a) $Na_3B_3O_6$ (b) I_2Cl_6

(c) Sheet silicate (d) Inorganic graphite layer

39. Nodal planes of π-bond(s) in $CH_2{=}C{=}C{=}CH_2$ are located in :

(a) all are in molecular plane

(b) two in molecular plane and one in a plane perpendicular to molecular plane which contains C—C σ-bond

(c) one in molecular plane and two in plane perpendicular to molecular plane which contains C—C σ-bonds

(d) two in molecular plane and one in a plane perpendicular to molecular plane which bisects C—C σ-bonds at right angle

40. Which of the following have X—O—X linkage?

(where X is central atom) :

(i) $Cr_2O_7^{2-}$ (ii) $S_2O_3^{2-}$ (iii) Pyrosilicate (iv) Hyponitrous acid

(a) (i) (iii) (b) (iiii) (iv)

(c) (i) (iii) (iv) (d) (i) (ii)

41. Select the correct statement :

(a) HSO_5^- ion has one S—O—H linkage

(b) Number of B—O—B linkages in Borax is equal to number of P—O—P linkages in P_4O_{10}

(c) Hybridization of both sulphur in $H_2S_2O_5$ (pyrosulphurous acid) is same but oxidation state of both sulphur are different

(d) Tetra-polyphosphoric acid has four P—O—P and no P—P linkage

42. Oxidation state of '*S*' in peroxodisulphuric acid and sodium tetrathionate :

(a) +6, +5, 0 (b) +6, +6, +6

(c) +6, +4, +2 (d) +6, +2, 0

43. Structure of $Na_2[B_4O_5(OH)_4]\cdot 8H_2O$ contains :

(a) two triangular and two tetrahedral units

(b) three triangular and one tetrahedral units

(c) all tetrahedral units

(d) all triangular units

44. Which of the following molecular species is not linear ?

(a) $(CN)_2$ (b) OCN^- (c) XeF_2 (d) S_3^{2-}

45. Incorrect match is :

	Electron geometry		**Possible molecular shape from respective electron geometry**
(a)	Tetrahedron	—	Bent
(b)	Trigonal bipyramidal	—	Triangular planar
(c)	Octahedron	—	Square pyramidal
(d)	Pentagonal bipyramidal	—	Pentagonal planar

Dipole Moment

46. In which of the following molecule μ (observed) is found to be greater than μ(theoretical) :

(a) 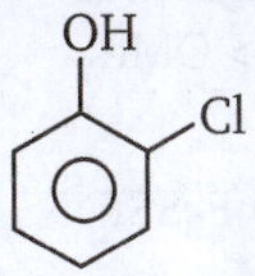

(b) 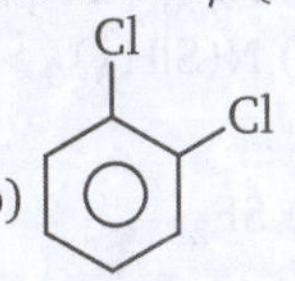

(c) 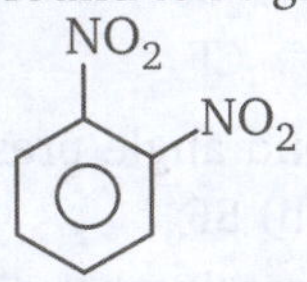

(d) None of these

47. Among the following, the molecule with highest dipole moment is :

(a) CH_3Cl (b) CH_2Cl_2
(c) $CHCl_3$ (d) CCl_4

48. Which of the following compounds has dipole moment approximately equal to that of chlorobenzene?

(a) *o*-dichlorobenzene (b) *m*-dichlorobenzene
(c) *p*-dichlorobenzene (d) *p*-chloronitrobenzene

Bond Parameters

49. Which one of the following molecule will have all equal X—F bond length? (where X = central atom)

(a) $SOCl_2F_2$ (b) SeF_4 (c) PBr_2F_3 (d) IF_7

50. Consider the following information (X = F or Cl)

Molecule	P—X(axial) bond length	P—X(Equitorial) bond length
PF_5	a	b
PF_4CH_3	c	d
$PF_3(CH_3)_2$	e	f
PCl_5	g	h

According to given information choose the incorrect order of bond length :

(a) $g > a > d > b$ (b) $g > e > f > b$ (c) $f > d > a > b$ (d) $c > f > d > b$

51. In which of the following cases C—C bond length will be highest?

(a) CH_3—CF_3 (b) FCH_2—CH_2F (c) F_2CH—CHF_2 (d) CF_3—CF_3

52. Select the incorrect statement about N_2F_4 and N_2H_4 :

(I) In N_2F_4, *d*-orbitals are contracted by electronegative fluorine atoms, but *d*-orbital contraction is not possible by H-atom in N_2H_4

(II) The N—N bond energy in N_2F_4 is more than N—N bond energy in N_2H_4

(III)The N—N bond length in N_2F_4 is more than that of in N_2H_4
(IV)The N—N bond length in N_2F_4 is less than that of in N_2H_4
Choose the correct code :
(a) I, II and III (b) I and III (c) II and IV (d) II and III

53. The correct order of equatorial FSF bond angle in the following compound.
(I) SF_4 (II) OSF_4 (III) H_2CSF_4
(a) (III) > (II) > (I) (b) (I) > (III) > (II)
(c) (I) > (II) > (III) (d) (II) > (III) > (I)

54. Incorrect order of bond angle is :
(a) $OCl_2 > SF_2 > AsH_3 > H_2Se$ (b) $NH_3 > PF_3 > PH_3 > H_2S$
(c) $XeO_4 > ClO_4^- > SO_4^{2-} > CF_4$ (d) $N(SiH_3)_3 > O(SiH_3)_2 > OMe_2$

55. Minimum F — $\hat{S}$ — F bond angle present in :
(a) SSF_2 (b) SF_6 (c) SF_2 (d) F_3SSF

56. The correct order of increasing bond angles is :
(a) $OF_2 < ClO_2 < H_2O < Cl_2O$ (b) $OF_2 < H_2O < Cl_2O < ClO_2$
(c) $OF_2 < H_2O < ClO_2 < Cl_2O$ (d) $ClO_2 < OF_2 < H_2O < Cl_2O$

57. The correct order of bond angles is :
(a) $NO_2^- > NO_2^+ > NO_2$ (b) $NO_2^+ > NO_2^- > NO_2$
(c) $NO_2 > NO_2^+ > NO_2^-$ (d) $NO_2^+ > NO_2 > NO_2^-$

58. Which one is correct for bond angle?
(a) $PF_3 > PCl_3$ (b) $OCl_2 = ClO_2$
(c) $NF_3 > NH_3$ (d) $PCl_3 > PF_3$

59. In molecules of the type AX_2L_n (where L represents lone pairs and n is its number) there exists a bond between element A and X. The $\angle XAX$ bond angle.
(a) Always decreases if n increases (b) Always increases if n increases
(c) Will be maximum for n=3 (d) generally decreases if n decreases

Molecular Orbital Theory

60. The incorrect statement regarding molecular orbital(s) is :
(a) If there is a nodal plane perpendicular to the internuclear axis and lying between the nuclei of bonded atoms then corresponding orbitals is antibonding M.O.
(b) If a nodal plane lies in the inter-nuclear axis, then corresponding orbitals is pi(π) bonding M.O.
(c) The σ-bonding molecular orbital does not contain nodal planes containing the internuclear axis
(d) The δ-bonding molecular orbital possesses three nodal planes containing the internuclear axis.

61. Which of the following species absorb maximum energy in its HOMO-LUMO electronic transition?
(a) O_2 (b) N_2^- (c) C_2 (d) N_2

62. If *P* to *T* are second period *p*-block elements then which of the following graph show correct relation between valence electrons in P_2 to T_2 (corresponding molecules) and their bond order is :

(a) 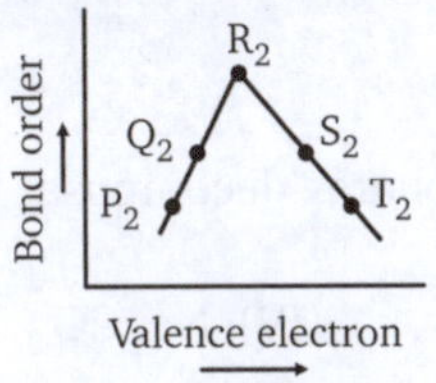

(b) 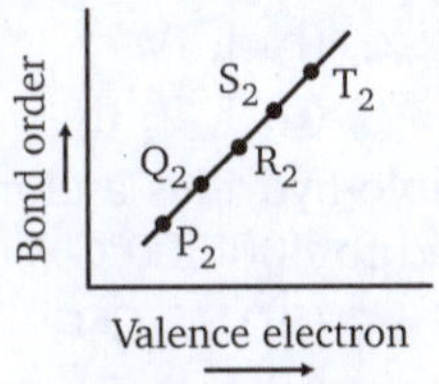

(c) 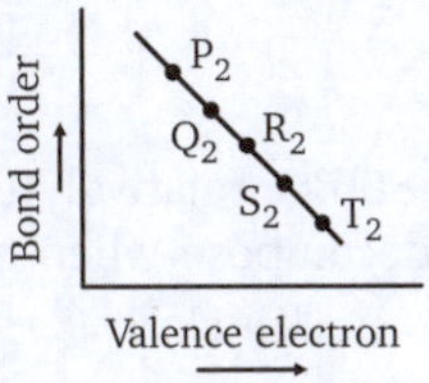

(d) 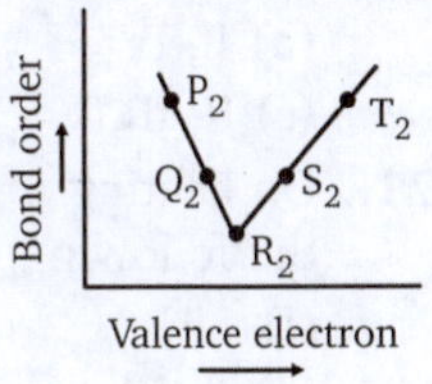

63. Which of the following facts given is not correct ?

(I) Bond length order : $H_2^- = H_2^+ > H_2$

(II) O_2^+, NO, N_2^- have same bond order of $2\frac{1}{2}$

(III) Bond order can assume any value including zero upto four

(IV) NO_3^- and BO_3^- have same bond order for X — O bond (where X is central atom)

(a) I, II & III (b) I & IV (c) II & IV (d) I & II

64. N_2 and O_2 are converted to monocations N_2^+ and O_2^+ respectively, which is wrong statement :

(a) In N_2^+, the N—N bond weakens (b) In O_2^+, the O—O bond order increases

(c) In O_2^+, the paramagnetism decreases (d) N_2^+ becomes diamagnetic

65. In which of the following transformations, the bond order has increased and the magnetic behaviour has changed?

(a) $C_2^+ \rightarrow C_2$ (b) $NO^+ \rightarrow NO$ (c) $O_2 \rightarrow O_2^+$ (d) $N_2 \rightarrow N_2^+$

66. H.O.M.O. (Highest Occupied Molecular Orbital) of CO molecular is :

(a) Non-bonding M.O. with slight antibonding character

(b) Non-bonding M.O. with slight bonding character

(c) Pure non-bonding M.O.

(d) None of the above

Fajan's Rule (Ionic Bond)

67. The incorrect order is :

(a) Covalent character : $PbCl_2 > CaCl_2 > SrCl_2 > BaCl_2$

(b) Thermal stability : $PbF_4 > PbCl_4 > PbBr_4 > PbI_4$

(c) Melting point : KF > KCl > KBr > KI

(d) Boiling point : $CHCl_3 > CH_3Cl > CCl_4$

68. If CdI_2 is pink in colour, the $CdCl_2$ will be '———' coloured.

(a) yellow (b) red (c) blue (d) cannot be predicted

69. Which order are correct?

(I) Thermal stability : $BeSO_4 < MgSO_4 < CaSO_4 < SrSO_4 < BaSO_4$

(II) Basic nature : $ZnO > BeO > MgO > CaO$

(III) Solubility in water : $LiOH > NaOH > KOH > RbOH > CsOH$

(IV) Melting point : $NaCl > KCl > RbCl > CsCl > LiCl$

(a) (I), (IV) (b) (I), (II) and (IV) (c) (II), (III) (d) All correct

70. The correct solubility in water order is/are :

(I) $CaCO_3 > SrCO_3 > BaCO_3$ (II) $Li_2CO_3 < Na_2CO_3 < K_2CO_3$

(III) $K_2CO_3 < Rb_2CO_3 < Cs_2CO_3$ (IV) $Na_2CO_3 > K_2CO_3 > Rb_2CO_3$

(a) II, IV (b) I, IV
(c) II, III,IV (d) I, II, III

71. On heating to 400-500°C, relatively unstable hydrides and carbonates decompose. Which of the following will decompose when heated to 400-500°C ?
(I) LiH (II) NaH (III) Li_2CO_3 (IV) Na_2CO_3
(a) II, III (b) I, II, III
(c) I, III (d) III, IV

Hydrogen Bonding

72. *Cis*-butene dioic acid $\underset{}{\overset{K_{a_1}(-H^+)}{\rightleftharpoons}} X_1^- \overset{K_{a_2}(-H^+)}{\rightleftharpoons} X_2^{2-}$

Trans-butene dioic acid $\overset{K'_{a_1}(-H^+)}{\rightleftharpoons} Y_1^- \overset{K'_{a_2}(-H^+)}{\rightleftharpoons} Y_2^{2-}$

The incorrect statement regarding above information is :
(a) X_2^{2-} species is more basic than Y_2^{2-} species
(b) X_1^- species is more basic than Y_1^- species
(c) K_{a_1} is greater than K'_{a_1}
(d) K'_{a_2} is greater than K_{a_2}

73. Which of the following is not a best representation of the H-bond?

(a) 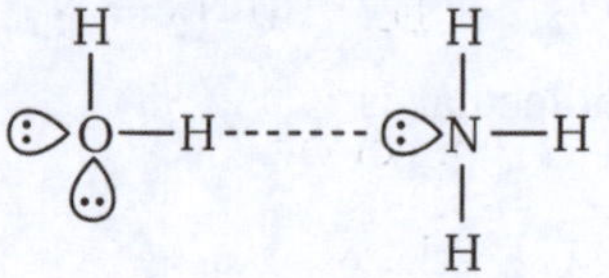

(b) 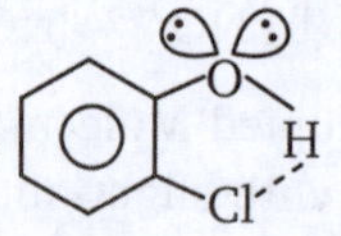

(c) 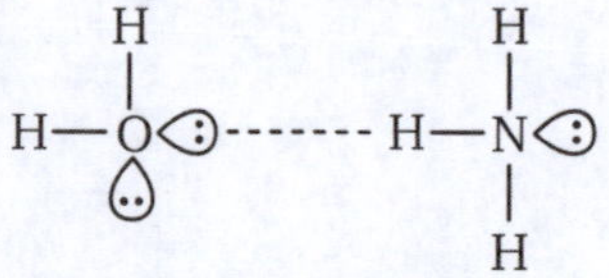

(d) None

74. The H-bonds in solid HF can be best represented as :
(a) H—F----H—F----H—F
(b) 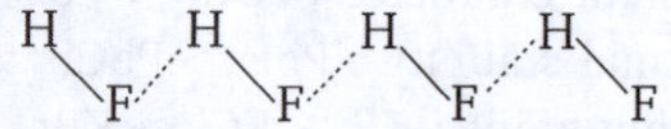

(c) 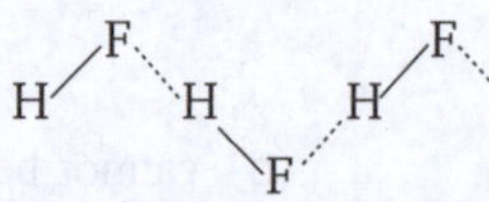

(d) 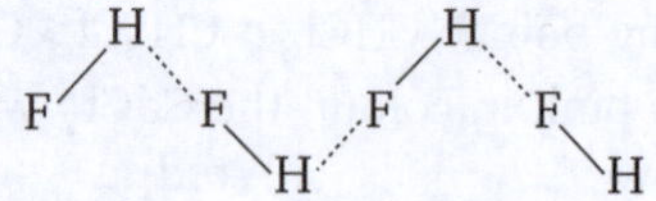

75. The type of molecular forces of attraction present in the following compound is :

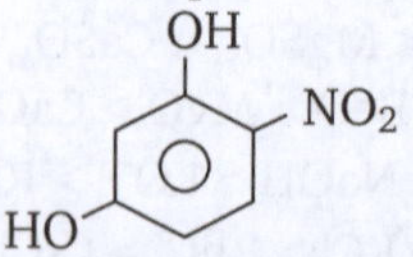

(a) Intermolecular H-bonding (b) Intramolecular H-bonding
(c) van der Waals' force (d) All of these

76. Which of the following interaction lies in the range of 8 – 42 kJ/mol ?
(a) $H_2...H_2O$ (b) HCl...HCl (c) F^-...HF (d) $HCN...NH_3$

Level 3

Passage 1

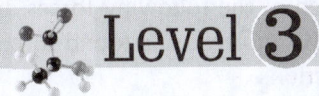

Colour of compounds occurs due to phenomenon of polarisation, charge transfer, *d-d* transition and H.O.M.O.-L.U.M.O. transition. Most of the transition metal complex compound are coloured either due to *d-d* electron transition or charge transfer and ionic compounds are coloured due to polarisation of anion.

1. Which of the following is correct about $\underset{(I)}{KFe^{II}[Fe(CN)_6]}$ and $\underset{(II)}{KFe^{III}[Fe(CN)_6]}$ complex compounds ?

(a) Both are blue coloured compound because colour arises due to *d-d* electron transition in Fe cation present outside the complex ion.

(b) Both are blue coloured compound because colour arises due to transfer of electron between Fe^{II} and Fe^{III} cation

(c) Both are blue coloured compound because in complexes Fe^{II} cation shows same *d-d* transition band

(d) Complex (I) has blue colour while complex (II) has brown colour.

2. If MCl_2 salt is white, then comment on colour of its iodide salt.

(a) Coloured (b) White

(c) May be white or coloured (d) Black

3. Choose incorrect statement.

(a) Halogens are coloured due to HOMO-LUMO transition

(b) During charge transfer, oxidation state of atoms changes

(c) Higher the polarisation, more is colour intensity

(d) Complex compound having no unpaired electron can not undergo *d-d* transition and therefore it is colourless

Passage 2

Hydrogen bond is the term given to the relatively weak secondary interaction between a hydrogen atom bound to an electronegative atom and another atom which is also generally electronegative and which has one or more lone pairs and can thus acts as a base. We can give the following generalized representation of a hydrogen bond.

$$\overset{\delta-}{X}-\overset{\delta+}{H}\ldots Y$$

Bond dissociation energy of H-bond ranges from 8 to 42 kJ/mol, and the most commonly encountered hydrogen bonds are O—H...O, N—H...O and F—H...F.

1. Among molecules of HCl, which of the following forces are present.
(a) Interaction between two HCl molecules is found to be greater than 8 kJ/mol
(b) Weak dipole-dipole interactions
(c) Weak ion-dipole interactions
(d) All of the above

2. Which of the following interaction has energy between 8-42 kJ/ mol ?
(a) $Na^+ : CCl_4$ (b) $CHCl_3 : Br^-$ (c) $C_6H_6 : CCl_4$ (d) $H_2O : HCN$

Passage 3

The intermolecular forces of attraction (*i.e.*, H-bonding and van der Waals' forces) exist among polar and non-polar species which affect melting point, boiling point, solubility and viscosity of covalent compounds :

1. Melting and boiling point of halogens increase down the group due to :
(a) Increase in London dispersion forces (b) Increase in extent of polarity
(c) Increase in molecular mass (d) Both (a) and (c)

2. The type of molecular force of attraction present in the following compound is :

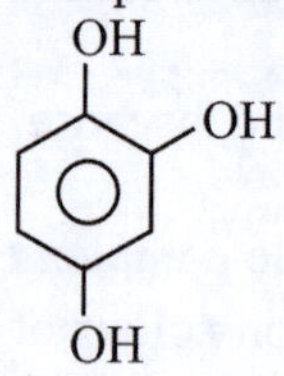

(a) Intermolecular H-bonding (b) Intramolecular H-bonding
(c) van der Waals' force (d) All of these

3. Select the incorrect order of boiling point between the following compounds :
(a) $N_3H < CH_3N_3$ (b) $Me_2SO_4 < H_2SO_4$
(c) $Me_3BO_3 < B(OH)_3$ (d) $BF_3 < BI_3$

Passage 4

There are five species *P*, *Q*, *R*, *S* and *T*. Spectroscopical analysis shows that *P*, *Q* and *R* are homonuclear diatomic species and have their bond order 2.5, 1.5 and 2.5 respectively and rest two species *S* and *T* are heteronuclear diatomic species and have bond order 3 and 2 respectively. All homonuclear diatomic species are paramagnetic and all heteronuclear diatomic species are diamagnetic in nature. *P*, *R*, *S* and *T* are monovalent positive ion and *Q* is monovalent negative ion :

1. According to given information the incorrect match is :
(a) $P = N_2^+$ (b) $R = O_2^+$ (c) $S = CO^+$ (d) $T = CN^+$

2. The correct statement is :
(a) If P is having 13 electrons then removal of one electron retains its magnetic behaviour
(b) If Q is having 17 electrons then addition of one electron retains its magnetic behaviour
(c) If R is having 15 electrons then addition of one e^- retains its magnetic behaviour
(d) If T is having 12 electrons then addition of one e^- retains its magnetic behaviour

3. The incorrect statement is :
(a) If R has 15 electrons then bond order of R is greater than its parent molecule
(b) If Q has 17 electrons then bond order of Q is less than its parent molecule
(c) If P has 13 electrons then bond order of P is greater than its parent molecule
(d) On addition of two electrons in P(having 13 electrons) the bond order remains same

Passage 5

Compound, MX_n type ($n = 2$ or 3 or 4)	Value of $\cos\theta$ (θ = bond angle between equivalent hybrid orbitals)
P	−0.241
Q	−0.292
R	−0.5
S	−0.325
T	−0.469

In all expected compounds each central atom only uses its s and p-orbitals in hybridization. The relationship between bond angle 'θ' and decimal fraction of s and p character present in the equivalent hybrid orbitals is given by :

$\cos\theta = \dfrac{S}{S-1} = \dfrac{P-1}{P}$, S = decimal fraction of s-character in the equivalent hybrid orbital

P = decimal fraction of p-character in the equivalent hybrid orbital.

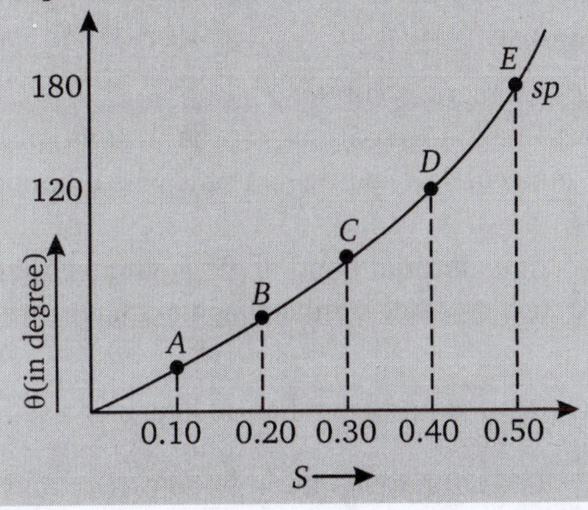

1. The correct order of % *p*-character in bond pairs of central atoms in the following compounds is :

(a) $P > T > S > Q > R$ (b) $S > R > T > P > Q$

(c) $P > Q > S > R > T$ (d) $P > Q > S > T > R$

2. If the value of *n* is 2 for compound *T*, then number of lone pair present at central atom of compound *T* will be :

(a) 0 (b) 1 (c) 2 (d) 3

3. The incorrect statement is :

(a) The ratio of % p-character *to* % *s*-character is less than four, for the bond pair of central atom of compound *S*

(b) Central atom uses three hybrid orbitals to form compound *R*

(c) Central atom uses four hybrid orbitals to form compound *S*

(d) There are three compounds present between point *C* to *E*, according to % *s*-character in bond pair of central atom

Passage 6

The concept of redistribution of energy in different orbitals of an atom associated with different energies to give new orbitals of equal (or sometimes it may be non-equal) energy oriented in space in definite directions is called hybridisation and formed new orbitals are called hybrid orbitals. The bonds formed by such orbitals are called hybrid bonds. The process of mixing of orbitals itself requires some energy. Thus, some additional energy, is needed for the hybridisation (mixing) of atomic orbitals.

1. Select from each set the molecule or ion having the smallest bond angle :

(i) H_2Se, H_2Te and PH_3

(ii) NO_2^- and NH_2^-

(iii) POF_3 and $POCl_3$ ($X — \hat{P} — X$ angle)

(iv) OSF_2Cl_2 and $SF_2(CH_3)_2$($F — \hat{S} — F$ angle)

(a) H_2Se, NH_2^-, POF_3 and OSF_2Cl_2 (b) H_2Te, NO_2^-, POF_3 and $SF_2(CH_3)_2$

(c) PH_3, NH_2^-, $POCl_3$ and $SF_2(CH_3)_2$ (d) H_2Te, NH_2^-, POF_3 and $SF_2(CH_3)_2$

2. Which of the following statement is correct ?

(a) In BrF_3, maximum three halogen atoms can lie in same plane

(b) In $CH_2SF_2(CH_3)_2$ molecule all hydrogen atoms which bonded to $s - sp^2$ overlapping, lie in equatorial plane

(c) In $OSCl_4$, $Cl — \hat{S} — Cl$ equatorial bond angle is greater than 120°

(d) Molecules IOF_5 and XeO_2F_4 have similar shape but have different number of lone pairs in whole molecule

3. In neutral molecule $XeO_{n_1}F_{n_2}$, central atom has no lone pair and ratio of $\frac{n_2}{n_1}$ is two, then which of the following orbital does not participate in bonding (n_1 and n_2 are natural numbers) :

(a) d_{z^2} (b) p_z (c) $d_{x^2-y^2}$ (d) None of these

Passage 7

Drago suggested an emprical rule which is compatible with the energetics of hybridization. It states that if the central atom is in the third row or below in the periodic table, the lone pair will occupy a stereochemically inactive *s*-orbital, and the bonding will be through *p*-orbitals and bond angles will be nearly 90° if the electronegativity of the surrounding atom is ≤ 2.5.

1. In which of the following molecule central atom has higher % *s*-character in its bond pair :

(a) AsH_3 (b) GeH_4 (c) P_4 (d) H_2Se

2. Correct order of bond angle is :

(a) $PH_4^+ > OF_2 > SF_2 > SbH_3 > H_2Te$
(b) $OF_2 > SF_2 > PH_4^+ > SbH_3 > H_2Te$
(c) $PH_4^+ > SF_2 > OF_2 > SbH_3 > H_2Te$
(d) $SF_2 > OF_2 > PH_4^+ > SbH_3 > H_2Te$

Passage 8

According to hybridisation theory, the % *s*-character in *sp*, sp^2 and sp^3-hybrid orbitals is 50, 33.3 and 25 respectively, but this is not true for all the species. When θ is the bond angle between equivalent hybrid orbitals then % *s* and *p*-character in hybrid orbital (when only *s*- and *p*-orbitals are involved in hybridisation) can be calculated by the following formula :

$$\cos\theta = \frac{S}{S-1} = \frac{P-1}{P}$$

1. Two elements *X* and *Y* combined together to form a covalent compound. If % *p*-character is found to be 80% in a hybrid orbital then the hybridised state of central atom *X* for the orbital is:

(a) sp^2 (b) sp^3 (c) sp^4 (d) sp^5

2. Smallest $O\hat{S}O$ bond angle is found in :

(a) SO_2F_2 (b) SO_2Cl_2 (c) $SO_2(CF_3)_2$ (d) $SO_2(CH_3)_2$

3. Correct order of P—P bond length in the following compound is :

(a) $P_2F_4 < P_2(CH_3)_4 < P_2(CF_3)_4 < P_2H_4$
(b) $P_2F_4 < P_2(CF_3)_4 < P_2(CH_3)_4 < P_2H_4$
(c) $P_2F_4 < P_2H_4 < P_2(CH_3)_4 < P_2(CF_3)_4$
(d) $P_2F_4 < P_2(CH_3)_4 < P_2H_4 < P_2(CF_3)_4$

Passage 9

PCl_5 is an example of a molecule having sp^3d-hybridisation. Three out of the five orbitals involved in sp_xp_y-hybridization while remaining two have $p_zd_{z^2}$-hybridization. If P-atom is attached to substituents differ in electronegativity, as in PCl_xF_{5-x}, then it has been experimentally observed that the more electronegative substituent occupies the axial position of t.b.p geometry.

1. The correct statement is :
(a) in CH_2F_2 the F—C—F bond angle is larger 109° 28'
(b) in CH_2F_2 the C—F bond has more than 25% *s*-character
(c) in CH_2F_2 the H—C—H bond angle is larger than 109° 28'
(d) in CH_2F_2 the C—H bond has less than 25% *s*-character

2. The incorrect statement regarding PCl_2F_3 molecule will be :
(a) given compound is polar
(b) both axial position occupied by F-atoms
(c) both Cl atoms present in equatorial position
(d) one Cl atom present at axial and other Cl atom is present at equatorial position of geometry

3. The highest H — C — H bond angle present in :
(a) CH_2F_2 (b) CH_4 (c) CH_3Cl (d) CH_3F

Passage 10

The first compound of the noble gases was made in 1962. Bartlett and Lohman had previously used the highly oxidizing compound platinum hexafluoride to oxidize dioxygen.

$$O_2 + PtF_6 \longrightarrow O_2^+[PtF_6]^-$$

The first ionization energy for $O_2 \rightarrow O_2$ is 1165 kJ mol^{-1}, which is almost the same as the value of 1170 kJ mol^{-1} for $Xe \rightarrow Xe^+$. It was predicated that xenon should react with PtF_6. Experiments showed that when deep red PtF_6 vapour was mixed with an equal volume of Xe, the gases combined immediately at room temperature to produce a solid.

$$Xe + PtF_6 \longrightarrow Xe[PtF_6]$$

1. IUPAC name of first xenon-compound synthesized by scientist Bartlett is :
(a) xenonhexafluoroplatinate (IV) (b) xenonhexafluoroplatinate (V)
(c) hexafluoroplatinum (V) xenon (d) xenoniumhexafluoroplatinum (V)

2. Noble gases are water insoluble, however their insolubility in water decreases down the group due to increases in :
(a) dipole-dipole attraction
(b) dipole-induced dipole attraction
(c) instantaneous dipole-induced dipole attraction
(d) none of these

3. Which of the following species is not having perfect octahedron structure?
(a) XeF_6 (b) SiF_6^{2-}
(c) PCl_6^- (d) XeO_6^{4-}

Passage 11

According to MOT, two atomic orbitals overlap resulting in the formation of molecular orbitals. Number of atomic orbitals overlapping together is equal to the molecular orbital formed. The two atomic orbital thus formed by LCAO (linear combination of atomic orbital) in the same phase or in the different phase are known as bonding and antibonding molecular orbitals respectively. The energy of bonding molecular orbital is lower than that of the pure atomic orbital by an amount Δ. This known as the stabilization energy. The energy of antibonding molecular orbital is increased by Δ′ (destabilisation energy).

1. The bond order of N_2^- is equal to that of :

(a) O_2 (b) O_2^{2-}

(c) O_2^+ (d) None

2. Which among the following pairs contain both paramagnetic species.

(a) O_2^{2-} and N_2^- (b) O_2^- and N_2 (c) O_2 and N_2 (d) O_2 and N_2^-

3. Which of the following statement(s) is true :

(a) Higher the bond order lesser the bond length

(b) Higher the bond order greater the bond length

(c) Higher the bond order lesser the bond energy

(d) Higher the bond order lesser the number of bonds

4. Which of the following pairs of molecule can exist ?

(a) He_2 and Be_2 (b) O_2^{2-} and Na_2 (c) O_2^{2-} and H_2^{2-} (d) Be_2 and Mg_2

5. How many nodal plane is present in $\sigma_{(s \text{ and } p)}$ bonding molecular orbital?

(a) zero (b) 1 (c) 2 (d) 3

6. Which of the following combination of orbitals is correct?

(a) 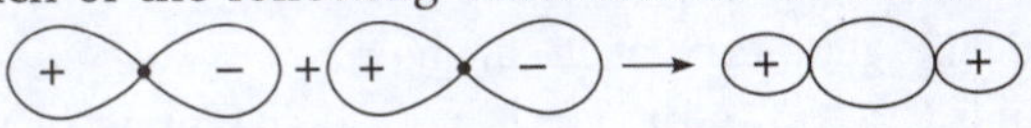

(b) 

(c) 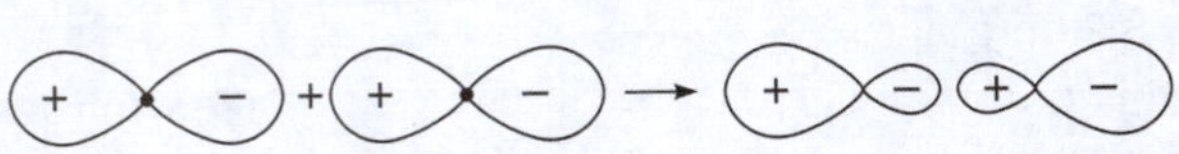

(d) 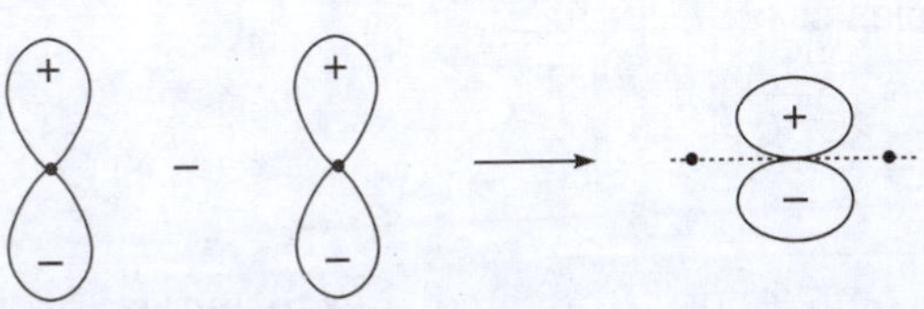

7. Which of the following statements is not correct regarding bonding molecular orbitals?

(a) Bonding molecular orbitals possess less energy than the atomic orbitals from which they are formed

(b) Bonding molecular orbitals have low electron density between the two nuclei

(c) Electron in bonding molecular contributes to the attraction between atoms
(d) They are formed when the lobes of the combining atomic orbitals have the same sign

8. If x-axis is the molecular axis, then π-molecular orbitals are formed by the overlap of :
(a) $s + p_z$ (b) $p_x + p_y$ (c) $p_z + p_z$ (d) $p_x + p_x$

Passage 12

Polar covalent molecules exhibit dipole moment. Dipole moment is equal to the product of charge separation, q and the bond length d for the bond. Unit of dipole moment is debye. One debye is equal to 10^{-18} esu cm.

Dipole moments is a vector quantity. It has both magnitude and direction. Hence, dipole moment of a molecule depends upon the relative orientation of the bond dipoles, but not on the polarity of bonds alone. A symmetrical structure shows zero dipole moment. Thus, dipole moment helps to predict the geometry of a molecules. Dipole moment values can be used to distinguish between *cis*-and *trans*-isomers; *ortho*-, *meta*- and *para*-forms of a substance, etc.

1. Which is a polar molecule?
(a) XeF_4 (b) BF_3
(c) I_2Cl_6 (d) PCl_2F_3

2. A diatomic molecule has a dipole moment of 1.2 D. If the bond length is 1.0×10^{-8} cm, what fraction of charge does exist each atom?
(a) 0.1 (b) 0.2 (c) 0.25 (d) 0.3

3. Arrange the following compounds in increasing order of dipole moments, toluene (I) *o*-dichlorobenzene (II), *m*-dichlorobenzene (III) and *p*-dichlorobenzene (IV) :
(a) IV < I < II < III (b) I < IV < II < III
(c) IV < I < III < II (d) IV < II < I < III

4. μ of the AX_4 type of molecule is zero. The geometry of it can be :
(a) tetrahedral (b) square planar (c) *A* or *B* (d) none of these

5. Which of the following statement is correct regarding $C_2H_2F_2$ molecule?
(a) One isomer is polar, one is non-polar
(b) Two isomers are polar, one is non-polar
(c) Two isomers are planar, one is non-planar
(d) Two isomers are only possible and planar

Passage 13

In general boiling point of covalent compounds is affected due to increasing molecular weight and hydrogen bonding. Thus it is observed that the boiling point of octanol is greater that water while that of methanol is lesser than water. The other properties which are considerably affected due to hydrogen bond formation are acidic nature, melting point, anamalous behaviour of water below 4°C., It is therefore concluded that hydrogen bonding plays a vital role in explaning many observable facts.

1. Which among the following has maximum boiling point ?

(a) $CH_3-CH_2-(CH_2)_2-CH_2OH$ (b) $CH_3-CH_2-CH_2-CH(OH)-CH_3$

(c) $CH_3-CH_2-CH(OH)-CH_2-CH_3$ (d) $CH_3-C(CH_3)(OH)-CH_2-CH_3$

2. Which of the following statements is true ?

(a) the lattice structure of ice involves true covalent bond

(b) the lattice structure of ice is the result of dipole-dipole interaction

(c) the lattice structure of ice is the result of intra and inter-molecular hydrogen bond formation

(d) the lattice structure of ice is only due to inter-molecular hydrogen bonding

3. K_{a_2} of Maleic acid is lesser than K_{a_2} of fumaric acid due to :

(a) intramolecular hydrogen bonding in the formed after one proton removal in fumaric acid

(b) intermolecular hydrogen bonding in the ion formed after one proton removal in maleic acid

(c) intramolecular hydrogen bonding in the ion formed after one proton removal in maleic acid

(d) intermolecular hydrogen bonding in the ion formed after one proton removal in fumaric acid

Passage 14

The molecule in which an atom is associated with more than 8 electrons is known as hypervalent molecule and less than 8 electrons is known as hypovalent molecule. All hypervalent molecules must have $p\pi$-$d\pi$ bonding but the molecules having back bonding need not to have always $p\pi$-$d\pi$ bonding.

1. Which of the molecule is not hypovalent but complete its octet :

(a) $AlCl_3$ (b) $AlBr_3$

(c) AlF_3 (d) BF_3

2. Which of the following molecule is having complete octet :

(a) $BeCl_2$ (dimer) (b) BeH_2 (dimer)

(c) BeH_2(s) (d) $BeCl_2$(s)

3. Which of the following molecule is not having $p\pi$-$d\pi$ bonding :

(a) SO_2 (b) P_4O_{10} (c) PF_3 (d) $B_3N_3H_6$

Passage 15

According to Pauling and Slater the atomic orbitals combine to form new set of equivalent orbitals known as **hybrid orbitals.** Unlike pure orbitals, the hybrid orbitals are used in bond formation. The phenomenon is known as **hybridisation** which can be defined as the process of intermixing of the orbitals of slightly different energies in the formation of new set of orbitals of equivalent energies.

1. Which pair of species uses '*d*' orbital in hybridization ?
(a) BrF_2^+, BrF_2^- (b) BrF_4^+, BrF_4^- (c) NO_2^+, NO_3^- (d) SO_3^{2-}, SO_4^{2-}

2. Which molecule is non-planar as well as non-polar ?
(a) IF (b) IF_3 (c) IF_5 (d) IF_7

3. Which molecule is having same electronic geometry as well as molecular geometry ?
(a) NCl_3 (b) PCl_5 (c) SF_4 (d) XeF_4

Passage 16

In 1923 G.N. Lewis proposed a definition of acid-base behaviour in terms of electron-pair donation and acceptance. The Lewis definition is perhaps the most widely used of all because of its simplicity and wide applicability, especially in the field of organic reactions. Lewis defined a base as an electron-pair donor and an acid as an electron-pair acceptor.

1. In which of the following interaction hybridization of underlined atom does not change ?
(a) $\underline{Xe}F_4 + F^-$ (b) $H_3\underline{B}O_3 + OH^-$ (c) $\underline{N}H_3 + H^+$ (d) $\underline{S}O_3 + OH^-$

2. Select the incorrect statement :
(a) CH_4 is neither lewis acid nor lewis base
(b) SO_2 can act as lewis acid as well as lewis base
(c) SF_6 act as lewis acid but not as lewis base
(d) OH^- act as lewis base but not as lewis acid

ONE OR MORE ANSWERS IS/ARE CORRECT

1. Which is correct statement ?
(a) LiCl is more soluble in polar solvent (water) than NaCl
(b) K_{a_2} fumaric acid is more than K_{a_2} of maleic acid
(c) The O—O bond length in $O_2[AsF_4]$ is shorter than KO_2
(d) In $CF_2{=}C{=}CF_2$ molecule all the four fluorine atoms are in the same plane

2. Select correct statement(s) :
(a) Thermodynamic stability of graphite > diamond, but reverse order is true for their kinetic stability
(b) Melting point of NaCl > LiCl, but reverse order is true for their thermal stability
(c) Ionisation energy of $N_2 > O_2$, but reverse order of ionisation energy is true for their corresponding atoms
(d) Lewis acidic strength of $BeI_2 > BeF_2$, but reverse order is true for their melting point

3. Select correct statements regarding σ and π-bonds :
(a) σ-bond lies on the line joining the nuclei of bonded atoms
(b) π-electron cloud lies on either side to the line joining the nuclei of bonded atoms
(c) ($2p\pi$ — $3d\pi$) Pi-bond is stronger than ($2p\pi - 3p\pi$) Pi-bond
(d) σ-bond has primary effect to decide direction of covalent bond, whereas π-bond has no primary effect in direction of bond.

4. Which of the following molecular species is/are having π_{2p} as H.O.M.O. (highest occupied molecular orbital):

(a) N_2^- (b) O_2^{2+} (c) NO^+ (d) B_2^+

5. Select correct order between given compounds.

(a) $COCl_2 > COF_2$: $X\hat{C}X$ bond angle

(b) $NO_2F > NO_2Cl$: $O\hat{N}O$ bond angle

(c) $SO_2F_2 < SOF_2$: $F\hat{S}F$ bond angle

(d) $N_2F_2 < N_2(CH_3)_2$: N—N bond length

6. Select the correct statement(s) regarding BF_2NH_2 molecule :

(a) FBF bond angle < 120° (b) HNH bond angle > 109°28'

(c) HNH bond angle < 109°28' (d) FBF bond angle > 120°

7. Which of the folowing exists as polymeric (covalent) solid at room temperature with coordination number '6' for the central atom?

(a) AlF_3 (b) $AlCl_3$ (c) $AlBr_3$ (d) AlI_3

8. In which of the following compound, observed bond angle is found to be greater than expected, but not due to back bonding.

(a) $N(SiH_3)_3$ (b) $N(CH_3)_3$ (c) $O(CH_3)_2$ (d) $O(SiH_3)_2$

9. Two compounds PX_2Y_3 and PX_3Y_2. (Where P = Phosphorous atom and X, Y = monovalent atoms). If all 'X' atoms are replaced by 'Z' atoms and electronegativity order is $X > Y > Z$. Then incorrect statement(s) is/are :

(a) The dipole moment of product obtained from PX_2Y_3 is non-zero

(b) The dipole moment of product obtained from PX_2Y_3 is zero

(c) The dipole moment of product obtained from PX_3Y_2 is zero

(d) The dipole moment of product obtained from PX_3Y_2 is non-zero

10. Correct order of bond angles in the given compounds is/are :

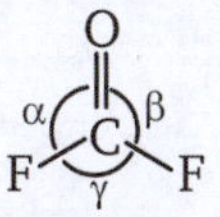

and

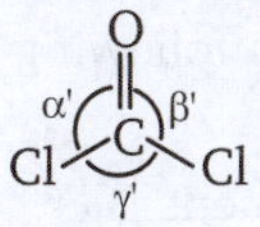

(a) $\gamma < \gamma'$ (b) $\gamma < \beta = \alpha$ (c) $\alpha > \alpha'$ (d) $\beta > \beta'$

11. The correct statement(s) is/are :

(a) Boiling point of *m*-hydroxybenzaldehyde is greater than *o*-hydroxybenzaldehyde

(b) Boiling point of $CHCl_3$ is higher than CCl_4

(c) Melting point of $BeCl_2$ is higher than BeF_2

(d) Boiling point of HF is greater than CH_3F

12. Consider the following reactions

$$CHF_3 \xrightarrow{K_a} CF_3^- + H^+$$

$$CHCl_3 \xrightarrow{K'_a} CCl_3^- + H^+$$

Then regarding given reactions which of the following statement(s) is/are correct :

(a) $K_a > K'_a$
(b) CHF_3 act as a stronger bronsted acid than $CHCl_3$
(c) CCl_3^- is more stable than CF_3^-
(d) CCl_3^- is weaker lewis base than CF_3^-

13. In which of the following molecule $\mu_{exp.}$ (observed dipole moment) is found to be greater than $\mu_{th.}$ (expected dipole moment) ?

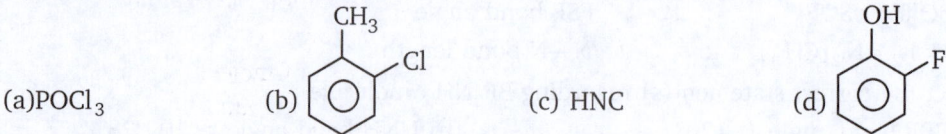

(a) $POCl_3$ (b) 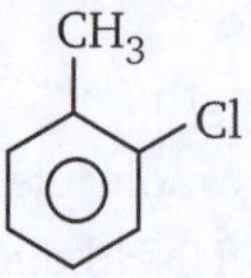 (c) HNC (d) 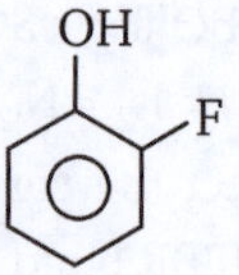

14. Correct statement(s) regarding $As(CH_3)F_2Cl_2$ molecule is/are :
(a) Maximum three halogen atoms can lie in same plane
(b) Both axial and equatorial plane may have equal number of atoms
(c) As—Cl bond length is longer than As—F bond length
(d) Maximum five atoms can lie in equatorial plane

15. Which of the following species is/are having 'N—N' bond order = 2?
(a) N_3^- (b) N_2F_2 (c) N_2O_4 (d) N_2O

16. Which of the following statements is correct ?
(a) ClF_3 molecule is bent 'T' shape
(b) In SF_4 molecule, F—S—F equatorial bond angle is 103° due to *lp-lp* repulsion
(c) In $[ICl_4]^-$ molecular ion, Cl—I—Cl bond angle is 90°
(d) In OBr_2, the bond angle is less than OCl_2

17. Which of the following species does/do not exist ?
(a) FeI_3 (b) SH_6 (c) PbI_4 (d) PI_5

18. Select correct order between following compounds:
(a) $NH_3 > NF_3$: Bond angle
(b) $NH_3 > NF_3$: Dipole moment
(c) $NH_3 > NF_3$: % *s*-Character of lone pair
(d) $NH_3 > NF_3$: Reactivity towards Lewis acid

19. Which of the following is (are) V-shaped ?
(a) S_3^{2-} (b) I_3^- (c) N_3^- (d) I_3^+

20. Select correct order between given compounds:

(a) $COCl_2 > COF_2$: $X\hat{C}X$ bond angle
(b) $NO_2F > NO_2Cl$: $O\hat{N}O$ bond angle
(c) $SO_2F_2 < SOF_2$: $F\hat{S}F$ bond angle
(d) $N_2F_2 < N_2(CH_3)_2$: N — N bond length

21. Which of the following equilibria would have highest and lowest value of K_p at a common temperature ?
(a) $BeCO_3 \rightleftharpoons BeO + CO_2$ (b) $CaCO_3 \rightleftharpoons CaO + CO_2$
(c) $SrCO_3 \rightleftharpoons SrO + CO_2$ (d) $BaCO_3 \rightleftharpoons BaO + CO_2$

22. Which of the following process is/are associated with change of hybridization of the underlined compound?
(a) $Al(OH)_3$ ppt. dissolved in NaOH (b) B_2H_6 is dissolved in THF
(c) SiF_4 vapour is passed through liq. HF (d) Solidification PCl_5 vapour

23. Which of the following are true ?
(a) van der Waals forces are responsible for the formation of molecular crystals
(b) Branching lower the boiling points of isomeric organic compounds due to decrease in van der Waals forces
(c) In graphite, van der Waals forces act between the carbon layers
(d) In diamond, van der Waals forces act between the carbon layers

24. Which of the following statement is incorrect :
(a) O_2 is paramagnetic, O_3 is also paramagnetic
(b) O_2 is paramagnetic, O_3 is diamagnetic
(c) B_2 is paramagnetic, C_2 is also paramagnetic
(d) Different observation is found in their bond length when $NO \rightarrow NO^+$ and $CO \rightarrow CO^+$

25. Which of the following statements are not correct?
(a) All C—O bonds in CO_3^{2-} are equal but not in H_2CO_3
(b) All C—O bonds in HCO_2^- are equal but not in HCO_2H
(c) C—O bond length in HCO_2^- is longer than C—O bond length in CO_3^{2-}
(d) C—O bond length in HCO_2^- and C—O bond length in CO_3^{2-} are equal

26. In the structure of H_2CSF_4, which of the following statement is/are correct?
(a) Two C—H bonds are in the same plane of axial S—F bonds
(b) Two C—H bonds are in the same plane of equitorial S—F bonds
(c) Total six atoms are in the same plane
(d) Equitorial S—F plane is perpendicular to the nodal plane of π-bond

27. In which compound vacant hybride orbital take part in bonding :
(a) B_2H_6 (b) Al_2Cl_6 (c) C_2H_5Cl (d) H_3BO_3

28. Which of the following is true for N_2O ?
(a) Its molecule is linear
(b) Symmetric N — O — N is a favoured structure as compared to N — N — O skeleton
(c) Bond orders are fractional for N — N and N — O bonds
(d) It is a neutral oxide

29. Silane is more reactive than CH_4 towards Nu^- substitution due to :
(a) larger size of Si compared to C which facilitate the attack by nucleophile
(b) Polarity of Si—H bond is opposite to that of C—H bond
(c) Availability of vacant 3*d* orbitals in case of Si to form the reaction intermediate easily for nucleophilic attack
(d) Si—H bond energy is lower than that of C—H bond

30. Which of the following statements is/are not correct for following compounds?
(I) $SCl_2(OCH_3)_2$ and (II) $SF_2(OCH_3)_2$
(a) $—OCH_3$ groups in both cases occupy the same position
(b) Cl-atoms occupy equitorial position in case of (I) and F-atoms occupy equitorial position in case of (II)
(c) Cl-atoms occupy axial position in case of (I) & F-atoms occupy equitorial position in case of (II)
(d) Cl and F-atoms occupy either axial or equitorial position in case of (I) and (II) respectively

31. If N_B is the number of bonding electrons and N_A is the number of antibonding electrons of a molecule. Then choose the incorrect statement(s) for the relationship, $N_B > N_A$:
(a) Molecule may be stable or unstable
(b) Molecule may have any integral, fractional or zero value of bond order
(c) Molecule is only paramagnetic species
(d) Molecule does not exist

32. Stepwise hydrolysis of P_4O_{10} takes place via formation of :
(a) tetrametaphosphoric acid (b) tetrapolyphosphoric acid
(c) pyrophosphoric acid (d) orthophosphoric acid

33. Select the correct statement(s) about the compound $NO[BF_4]$:
(a) If has 5σ and 2π bond
(b) Nitrogen-oxygen bond length is higher than nitric oxide (NO)
(c) It is a diamagnetic species
(d) B—F bond length in this compound is lower than in BF_3

34. Which of the following molecules has as O—O bond?
(a) $H_2S_2O_8$ (b) $H_2S_2O_7$ (c) H_2SO_5 (d) $H_2S_2O_6$

35. Which of the following species is paramagnetic :
(a) CN^- (b) NO (c) O_2^{2-} (d) O_2

36. CO_2 molecule is not isostructural with :
(a) $HgCl_2$ (b) $SnCl_2$ (c) C_2H_2 (d) NO_2

37. Which of the following have a linear structure?
(a) $HgCl_2$ (b) $SnCl_2$ (c) ICl_2^- (d) CS_2

38. Which of the following compounds is/are non-polar?
(a) NO_2 (b) B_2H_6 (c) PF_3Cl_2 (d) $B_3N_3H_6$

39. Non-polar molecules are :
(a) CH_4 (b) C_2F_2 (c) C_2F_4 (d) OF_2

40. Which of the following molecular species is/are having π_{2p} as HOMO (highest occupied molecular orbital) ?
(a) N_2^- (b) O_2^{2+} (c) NO^+ (d) B_2^+

41. Correct order of B.pt. is/ are:
(a) $H_2 < He$ (b) $H_2 < D_2$ (c) $H_2O < D_2O$ (d) $NH_3 < SbH_3$

42. Incorrect order between following compounds is/are:
(a) $O(CH_3)_2 < O(SiH_3)_2$: number of sp^3-hybrid atoms
(b) $O(CH_3)_2 < O(SiH_3)_2$: Bond angle w.r.t. common atom
(c) $O(CH_3)_2 < O(SiH_3)_2$: % s-character of hybrid orbital on central atom
(d) $O(CH_3)_2 < O(SiH_3)_2$: reactivity towards Lewis acid

43. Correct order(s) of Lewis basic character :
(a) $NH_3 > H_2O > HF$
(b) $NH_3 > PH_3 > PF_3$
(c) $H_2O > SCl_2 > SeF_2$
(d) $NMe_3 > NH_3 > NF_3$

44. Which of the following statement(s) is/are correct for combination between H_3BO_3 and ethyl alcohol?
(a) H_3BO_3 acts as electrolyte in presence of C_2H_5OH
(b) Acidic character of C_2H_5OH increases in presence of H_3BO_3
(c) H_3BO_3 and C_2H_5OH combine in Lewis acid-base interaction
(d) H_3BO_3 furnishes hydrogen ion in the presence of C_2H_5OH

45. Acidic character of HF increases when it combines with :
(a) BF_3
(b) SiF_4
(c) SF_6
(d) PF_5

46. Select the species in which dative coordinate bond is present
(a) O_3
(b) BrF_2^+
(c) BH_4^-
(d) NH_4^+

47. Which of the following combination(s) of atomic orbitals can form π-bond having nodal plane in yz plane ?
(a) $p_x + p_x$
(b) $d_{xz} + p_x$
(c) $d_{yz} + d_{yz}$
(d) $d_{xy} + d_{xy}$

MATCH THE COLUMN

Column-I and Column-II contains four entries each. Entries of Column-I are to be matched with some entries of Column-II. One or more than one entries of Column-I may have the matching with the same entries of Column-II.

1.

Column-I	Column-II
(A) $O(SiH_3)_2$	(P) Hybridization of central atom does not change due to back bonding
(B) Singlet CCl_2	(Q) Bond angle of central atom increases due to combined effect of back bonding and steric factor
(C) H_4SiO_4	(R) Anyone of t_{2g} d-orbital is involved in back bonding
(D) $B(NMe_2)_3$	(S) Electron density on central atom decreases due to back bonding
	(T) Electron density on central atom increases due to back bonding

2.

Column-I	Column-II
(A) CO, CN^-, NO^+, O_2^{2+}	(P) All are paramagnetic
(B) N_2^+, O_2^+, O_2^-, NO	(Q) All are diamagnetic
(C) NO^-, N_2^{2+}, C_2, B_2^{2-}	(R) All have intermixing of s and p-orbitals
(D) CN, C_2^+, B_2^+, N_2^-	(S) All have same bond order
	(T) All have fractional bond order

3.

Column-I (Reactions)	Column-II (Characteristics of final products)
(A) Formation of cation and anion by self ionization of iodine	(P) Lone pair(s) is/are present at central atom
(B) Attack of hydroxide ion on boric acid	(Q) *d*-orbital(s) involved in hybridization of central atom of either of product
(C) $Ba^{2+}(aq) + SO_4^{2-}(aq) \longrightarrow BaSO_4 \downarrow$ (white ppt.)	(R) *d*-orbital(s) not involved in hybridization of central atom of either of product
(D) $MgSO_4 \xrightarrow{T>800^\circ C} MgO + SO_2 + \frac{1}{2}O_2$	(S) $d\pi - p\pi$ bond(s)
	(T) Planar covalent species is formed

4.

Column-I (Compounds)	Column-II (Characteristics)
(A) H_4SiO_4	(P) Back bond
(B) H_2SeO_4	(Q) Intermolecular hydrogen bond
(C) H_3BO_3	(R) Hypovalent compound
(D) H_2NBF_2	(S) Proton donor acid
	(T) Hypervalent compound

5.

Column-I (Characteristics)	Column-II (Species)
(A) The distribution of *s*-character in hybrid orbitals of central atom is not equal and all bond lengths (CA—X) are equivalent	(P) $(CH_3)_2O$
(B) The distribution of *s*-character in hybrid orbitals of central atom is equal and all bond lengths (CA—*X*) are equivalent	(Q) NH_3
(C) The distribution of *s*-character in hybrid orbitals of central atom is not equal and bond angle (*X*—CA—*X*) is greater than 109°28'	(R) PBr_4^+
(D) The distribution of s-character in hybrid orbitals of central atom is equal and bond angle (*X*—CA—*X*) is either equal or less than 109°28'	(S) H_2O
	(T) XeO_6^{4-}

6.

Column-I	Column-II
(A) NH_2BF_2	(P) Six-atoms are in same plane
(B) Be_2Cl_4	(Q) Polar ($\mu \neq 0$)
(C) CH_2SF_4	(R) Non-planar
(D) IF_7	(S) All 'CA—*X*' (*X*= halogen) bond lengths are identical
	(T) All surrounding atoms contain non-bonding electron pair (lone pair)

7.

Column-I	Column-II
(A) $Re_2Cl_8^{2-}$	(P) $p\pi$ - $p\pi$ bonding
(B) NO_3^-	(Q) $p\pi$ - $d\pi$ bonding
(C) SO_4^{2-}	(R) $d\pi$ - $d\pi$ bonding
(D) SO_3	(S) δ-bonding

8.

Column-I	Column-II
(A) 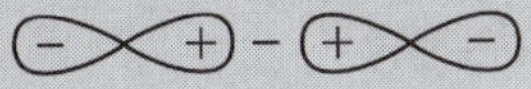	(P) Resulting H. O. M. O. of O_2 molecule
(B) 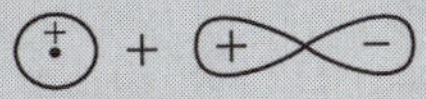	(Q) Resulting H. O. M. O. of C_2 molecule
(C) 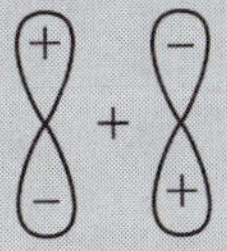	(R) Resulting molecular orbital having one nodal plane
	(S) Resulting M. O. having lower energy than participating atomic orbitals

9.

Column-I (Species)	Column-II (Characteristics)
(A) XeF_5^-	(P) Non-polar and planar
(B) MnO_4^-	(Q) Species having equal bond angle and bond length
(C) $\dot{C}H_3$	(R) Both axial *d*-orbitals are involved in hybridisation
(D) I_2Cl_6	(S) All non-axial *d*-orbitals are involved in hybridisation

10.

Column-I (Axial/sideways combination of appropriate/ inappropriate pure orbitals)	Column-II (Types of molecular orbital)
(A) $p + p$ pure orbitals	(P) σ - bonding molecular orbital
(B) $s + p$ pure orbitals	(Q) π - anti-bonding molecular orbital
(C) (non-axial) $d + p$ pure orbitals	(R) σ - anti-bonding molecular orbital
(D) (axial) $d + p$ pure orbitals	(S) π - bonding molecular orbital
	(T) Non- bonding molecular orbital

11.

Column-I (Oxyacids)	Column-II (Oxidation state of S-atom)
(A) $H_2S_4O_6$	(P) +6
(B) $H_2S_2O_3$	(Q) +5
(C) H_2SO_5	(R) 0
(D) $H_2S_2O_5$	(S) –2
	(T) +3

12.

Column-I	Column-II
(A) NH_4Cl	(P) Hydrogen bond
(B) $CuSO_4 \cdot 5H_2O$	(Q) Co-ordinate bond
(C) HNC	(R) Ionic bond
(D) Liquid H_2O_2	(S) Covalent bond

13.

Column-I	Column-II
(A) $B_3N_3H_6$	(P) Planar geometry
(B) S_2Cl_2	(Q) Non-planar geometry
(C) B_2H_6	(R) No lone pair
(D) I_2Cl_6	(S) Non-polar molecule

14.

Column-I (Pair of species)	Column-II (Identical Property in pairs of species)
(A) PCl_3F_2, PCl_2F_3	(P) Hybridisation of central atom
(B) BF_3 and BCl_3	(Q) Shape of molecule/ion
(C) CO_2 and CN_2^{-2}	(R) μ (dipole moment)
(D) C_6H_6 and $B_3N_3H_6$	(S) Total number of electrons

15.

Column-I (Species)	Column-II (Bond angle)
(A) NO_2^+	(P) 180°
(B) NO_2^-	(Q) 120°
(C) NO_2	(R) 134°
(D) NO_3^-	(S) 115°
	(T) 109°

ASSERTION-REASON TYPE QUESTIONS

These questions consist of two statements each, printed as assertion and reason, while answering these questions you are required to choose any one of the following responses.

(A) If assertion is true but the reason is false

(B) If assertion is false but reason is true

(C) If both assertion and reason are true and the reason is the correct explanation of assertion

(D) If both assertion and reason are true but reason is not the correct explanation of assertion

1. Assertion : C_3O_2 is non-planar molecule.

Reason : Terminal π-bonds of the molecule are lying in different planes.

2. Assertion : If $d_{x^2-y^2}$ and p_y-orbital come close together along z-axis, then they can form π-bond by sideways overlapping.

Reason : Both orbitals do not have electron density along z-axis.

3. Assertion : BF_3 undergoes in partial hydrolysis.

Reason : Due to strong back bonding in BF_3 only two fluoride groups have come out on nucleophilic attack by H_2O.

4. Assertion : The central carbon atom in $F_2C=C=CF_2$ and both carbon atoms in $F_2B-C\equiv C-BF_2$ are *sp*-hybridized.

Reason : Both molecules are planar.

5. Assertion : Formation of PH_4^+ ion is relatively difficult in comparison to NH_4^+ ion.

Reason : Lone pair of phosphorus atom in PH_3 resides in stereochemically inactive pure *s*-orbital.

6. Assertion : Bond dissociation energy of $B-F$ bond in BF_3 molecule is lower than $C-F$ bond in CF_4 molecule.

Reason : Atomic size of B-atom is larger than that of C-atom.

7. Assertion : PF_3 is stronger Lewis base than PH_3.

Reason : l.p. of P-atom in PF_3 molecule is present in sp^3-hybrid orbital, whereas l.p. of P-atom in PH_3 is present in almost pure *s*-orbital.

8. Assertion : NiO is less basic than CaO.
Reason : Ni^{2+} is pseudo noble gas configuration cation whereas Ca^{2+} is noble gas configuration cation.

9. Assertion : When two gaseous OF molecules are allowed to cool, then they undergo dimerisation through O-atom.
Reason : Dimer-form of OF molecule (*i.e.*, O_2F_2) is having one peroxy linkage in its structure.

10. Assertion : Bond dissociation energy of N—F bond in NF_3 molecule is lower than that of in NCl_3 molecule.
Reason : Interelectronic repulsion exists between small size N and F atoms in N—F bond of NF_3 molecule.

11. Assertion : If $d_{x^2-y^2}$ and p_y orbitals come close together along z-axis, they can form π-bond by sideways overlapping.
Reason : Both orbitals do not have electron density along z-axis.

12. Assertion : $H\hat{O}F$ bond angle is higher than $H\hat{O}Cl$.
Reason : Oxygen is more electronegative than chlorine.

13. Assertion : NaCl is more ionic than NaI.
Reason : Chlorine is more electronegative than iodine.

14. Assertion : PbI_4 doesn't exist and converts into PbI_2 and I_2 spontaneously at room temperature but $PbCl_4$ needs heating to convert into $PbCl_2$ and Cl_2.
Reason : Pb^{2+} is more stable than Pb^{4+} due to inert pair effect.

15. Assertion : Dipole moment of NF_3 is less than that of NH_3.
Reason : Polarity of N—F bond is less than that of N—H bond.

16. Assertion : Solubility of *n*-alcohol in water decreases with increase in molecular weight.
Reason : The hydrophobic nature of alkyl chain increase.

17. Assertion : The unpaired electron of $\dot{C}H_3$ free radical occupies *p*-orbital.
Reason : $\dot{C}H_3$ possesses sp^2 hybridization.

18. Assertion : Nitrogen is inactive at room temperature but becomes reactive at elevated temperature (on heating or in the presence of catalyst).
Reason : In nitrogen molecule, there is delocalization of electrons.

19. Assertion : The *p*-isomer of dichlorobenzene has higher melting point than *o*- and *m*-isomer.
Reason : *p*- isomer is symmetrical and thus shows more closely packed structure.

20. Assertion : Na_2SO_4 is soluble in water while $BaSO_4$ is water insoluble.
Reason : Lattice energy of $BaSO_4$ exceeds its hydration energy.

21. Assertion : N_2 and NO^+ both are diamagnetic substances.
Reason : NO^+ is isoelectronic with N_2.

22. Assertion : Bond order can assume any value including zero.
Reason : Higher the bond order, shorter is the bond length and greater is the bond energy.

23. Assertion : C_3O_2 has linear structures.
Reason : Each C atom in C_3O_2 is *sp*-hybridised.

24. Assertion : H bonding occurs in H_2O due to larger size of O-atom.

Reason : The size of O- atom is larger than H atom.

25. Assertion : $(CH_3)_3N$ geometry is pyramidal but in case $(SiH_3)_3N$ it is planar.

Reason : The maximum covalency of Si is six but that of C is four.

26. Assertion : Superoxides of alkali metals are paramagnetic.

Reason : Superoxides contain the ion O_2^- which has one unpaired electron in its anti-bonding molecular orbital.

27. Assertion : The HF_2^- ion exists in the solid state & also in liquid state but not in aqueous state.

Reason : The magnitude of hydrogen bonds among HF molecules is weaker than that in between HF and H_2O.

28. Assertion : If $d_{x^2-y^2}$ and p_y-orbitals come close together along z-axis, then they can form π –bond by sideways overlapping.

Reason : Both orbitals do not have electron density along z-axis.

29. Assertion : The H-bond present in NH_3 dissolved in water is best represented by :

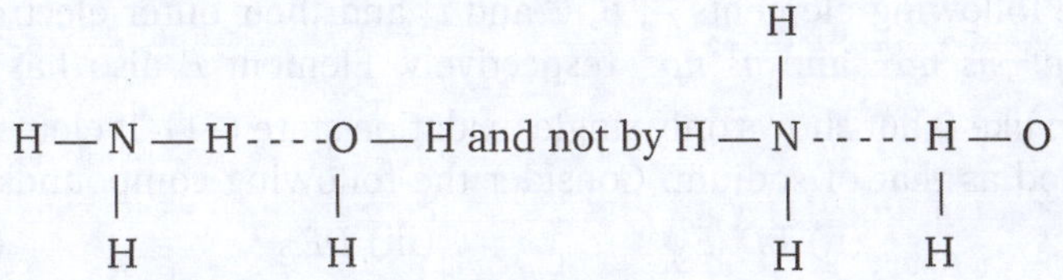

Reason : The O—H bond polarity is more compared to that of N—H bond.

SUBJECTIVE PROBLEMS

1. There are two groups of compounds A and B. Group A contains three compounds Px_4, Qy_3, Rz_2. Group B also contains three compounds Sx_4, Ty_3, Uz_2. Hybridization of each central atom of group A compounds is same as that of iodine in $IBrCl^-$ while in group B compounds it is same as that of iodine in $IBrCl^+$. Substituents X, Y and Z exhibit covalency of one in ground state. Then find the value of x/y.
Where, x and y are total number of lone pairs present at central atoms of compounds of group A and B respectively.

2. Consider the following three compounds (i) AX_{2n}^{n-}, (ii) AX_{3n} and (iii) AX_{4n}^{n+}, where central atom A is 15th group element and their maximum covalency is $3n$. If total number of proton in surrounding atom X is n and value of n is one, then calculate value of "$x^3 + y^2 + z$". (Where x, y and z are total number of lone pair at central atom in compound (i), (ii) and (iii) respectively.

3. Consider the following combination of atomic orbitals :

Combinding orbitals (internuclear axis)	Combinding orbitals (Internuclear axis)
(i) $s + p_x(x)$	(ii) $d_{xy} + d_{xy}(x)$
(iii) $d_{yz} + p_z(z)$	(vi) $s + s(z)$
(v) $d_{yz} + d_{yz}(x)$	(iv) $p_y + p_y(y)$

(vii) $d_{z^2} + d_{z^2}(z)$ (viii) $d_{xy} + d_{xy}(z)$
(ix) $p_x + p_x(y)$ (x) $s + p_z(x)$

Then calculate value of "$a^2 + b^2 + 2cd$". (where $a = \sigma$ M.O.; $b = \pi$ M.O.; $c = \delta$ M.O.; d = non-bonding M.O.)

4. Consider the following six changes

(i) $NO \longrightarrow NO^+$ (ii) $O_2^- \longrightarrow O_2^{2-}$ (iii) $O_2 \longrightarrow O_2^+$ (iv) $NO^+ \longrightarrow NO^-$
(v) $NO^+ \longrightarrow NO^{2+}$ (vi) $CO \longrightarrow CO^+$

Then calculate value of "$c^3 - b^2 - a$", where a, b and c are total number of transformations in which magnetic property will be changed, bond order increases and bond order decreases respectively.

5. When B_2H_6 is allowed to react with following Lewis bases, then how many given Lewis bases form adduct through symmetrical cleavage of B_2H_6?

NH_3, $MeNH_2$, Pyridine, CO, T.H.F., PH_3, PF_3, Me_3N, Me_2NH

6. Consider the following elements A, B, C and D and their outer electronic configurations are $ns^2np^1, ns^2np^3, ns^2np^4$ and ns^2np^5 respectively. Element E also has same outer electronic configuration like D but shows only single oxidation state (–1). If element A, B, C and D belong to same period as that of sodium. Consider the following compounds.

(i) CE_4 (ii) BD_2E_3 (iii) DE_3 (iv) CE_2
(v) BD_3E_2 (vi) C_2E_2 (vii) DE (viii) A_2D_6

Then calculate the value of "$x \div y$", (where x and y are total number of polar and non-polar compounds).

7. Consider following four compounds :

(a) C_xO_y (b) C_xO_{y+1}
(c) $C_{x+2}O_{y+1}$ and (d) $C_{x+11}O_{y+8}$

If "$x = y = 1$", then calculate the value of $|p - q|$, where p and q are total number of sp^2 and sp-hybridized carbon atoms respectively in given four compounds :

8. Total number of species among following which can use any one t_{2g} d-orbital in back bonding.

$H_4SiO_4, H_2NBF_2, O(SiH_3)_2, \overset{\uparrow\downarrow}{C}Cl_2, N(SiH_3)_3, (BN)_x, R_3PO, P_4O_{10}, CCl_3^-$

9. Calculate expression $(x + y + z)$ for diatomic molecules.

Where x = Total number of singly occupied molecular orbital (SOMO) in O_2
y = Total number of singly occupied molecular orbital (SOMO) in B_2
z = Total number of singly occupied molecular orbital (SOMO) in NO

10. If Hund rule violats, then find the total number of species among following which will be diamagnetic :

$B_2, O_2, N_2, C_2, NO, OF, N_2^{2-}, BN$

11. Consider the following table

Compounds (X are monovalent surrounding atoms)		Central atoms(A to D) belong to group	Characteristics of compounds	Number of lone pair(s) at central atom
(i)	AX_{n_1}	16	Planar and polar	m_1
(ii)	BX_{n_2}	15	Trigonal pyramidal	m_2
(iii)	CX_{n_3}	14	Zero dipole moment	m_3
(iv)	DX_{n_4}	13	All $X - \hat{D} - X$ bond angle are 120°	m_4

Than calculate value of expression $\left|\dfrac{n_1+n_2+n_3+n_4}{m_1+m_2+m_3+m_4}\right|^2$

12. Total number of species among following, in which bond angle (w.r.t. central atom) is equal to or less than 109°28' and also they act as lewis base :

NH_3, NMe_3, $O(SiH_3)_2$, ICl_4^-, XeO_3, BF_2Cl, SiF_4, AsH_3, SO_2F_2

13. Total number of unpaired electron(s) present in both cationic and anionic part of compound $O_2[PtF_6]$.

14. Total number of species which has/have symmetrical electronic distribution in their HOMO and also paramagnetic.

N_2^+, O_2^{2-}, C_2, O_2, B_2, C_2^{2-}, N_2^{2-}

15. Total number of molecules, in which each covalent bond is comprised of back bond.

BF_3, $N(SiH_3)_3$, PF_3, POF_3, $B(OH)_3$, $O(SiH_3)_2$, $NH(SiH_3)_2$, BFH_2, $BF_2(NH_2)$

16. Total number of angle in $SeCl_4$ which are less than 90°.

17. Consider the following species

$O(Me)_2$, $N(SiH_3)_3$, CO, $O(SiH_3)_2$, CCl_2(Singlet), CCl_3^-, H_4SiO_4, OCl_2, MeNCS

Then calculate total number of species which have $(p_\pi - p_\pi)$ back bond or $(p_\pi - d_\pi)$ back bond.

18. Total number of molecules which can form H-bond among themselves.

SiH_3OH, HCN, $B(OMe)_3$, $NHMe_2$, CH_3CONH_2, HCHO, HCOOH, NH_2OH, H_4SiO_4

19. Consider two covalent compounds AL_{n_1} and BL_{n_2}, if central atom (A) of first compounds has total six electron pairs and central atom (B) of second compound contains total five electron pairs in its valence shell and both compounds are planar and non-polar then calculate value of expression $(n_1 - n_2)^2$.

[where n_1 and n_2 are number of monovalent surrounding atom (L)]

20. Calculate the I — I distance in (Å) for given compound H_2CCl_2 if C — I bond length is 2.35 Å. (sin 60° = 0.866)

21. There are some arrangements of atomic orbitals which are given below :

(i) 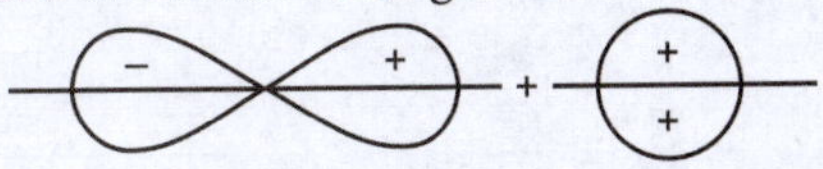

(ii) 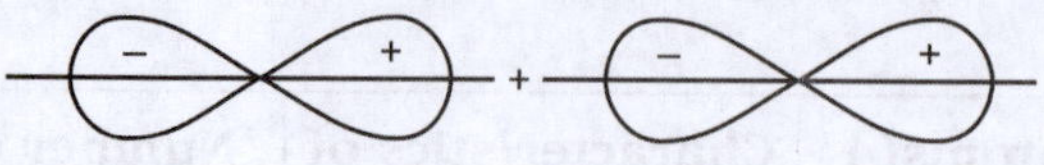

(iii) 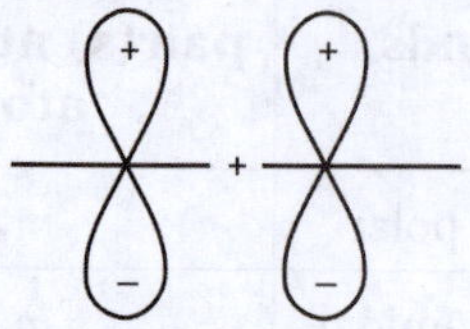

(iv) 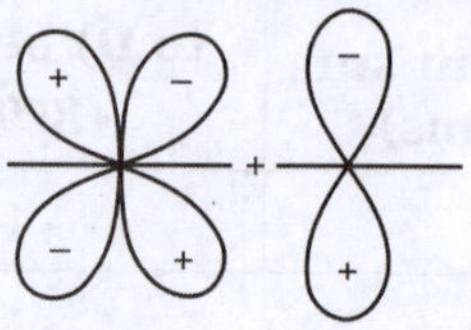

(v) 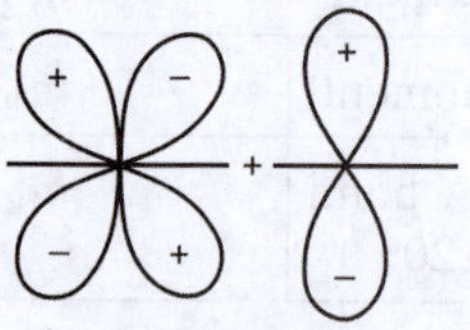

(vi) 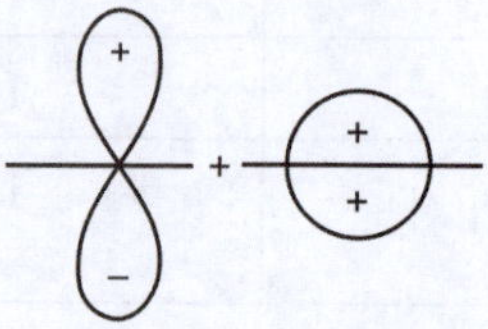

(vii) 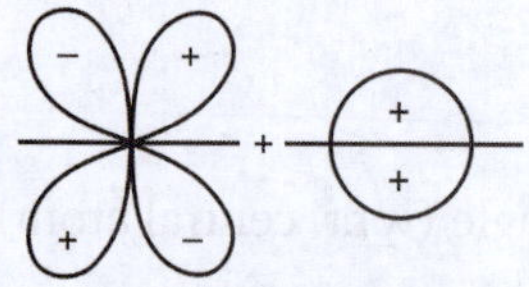

(viii) 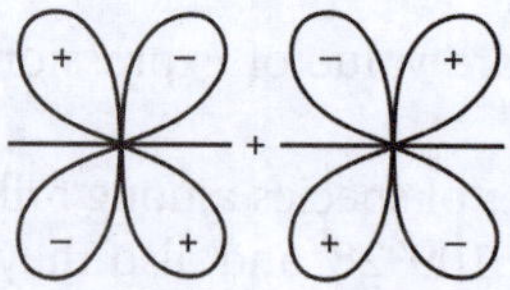

(ix) 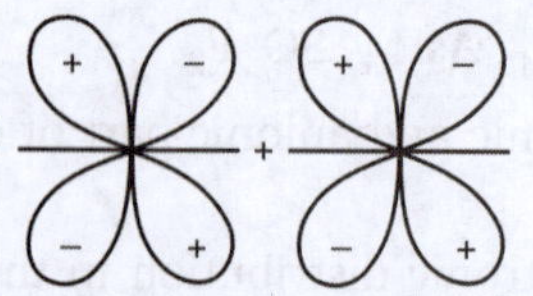

Then calculate the value of "$Q \times R - P$" where, P, Q and R are no. of arrangements which give bonding molecular orbitals (positive overlap), antibonding molecular orbitals (negative overlap) and non-bonding molecular orbitals (zero overlap) respectively.

22. Number of hybrid orbital C atoms which have 33% *s* character in $C(CN)_4$.

23. Max. no. of equal P — O bonds in $P_2O_7^{4-}$ ion is :

24. Consider the following species :

(i) CH_3^+ (ii) $(CH_3)_3Al$ (iii) HCHO (iv) CH_4

(v) $(C_2H_5)_3N$ (vi) $TiCl_4$ (vii) CO_2 (viii) $SiCl_4$

(ix) BF_3

Then find out total number of species which can act as Lewis acid.

25. Calculate value of $|x - y|$, here x and y are the total number of bonds in benzene and benzyne respectively which are formed by overlapping of hybridized orbitals.

26. Consider the following compounds:

(i) IF_5 (ii) ICl_4^- (iii) XeO_2F_2 (iv) NH_2^-

(v) BCl_3 (vi) $BeCl_2$ (vii) $AsCl_4^+$ (viii) $B(OH)_3$

(ix) NO_2^- (x) ClO_2^+

Then, calculate value of "$x + y - z$", here x, y and z are total number of compounds in given compounds in which central atom used their all three *p*-orbitals, only two *p*-orbitals and only one *p*-orbital in hybridisation respectively :

27. Consider the following molecule

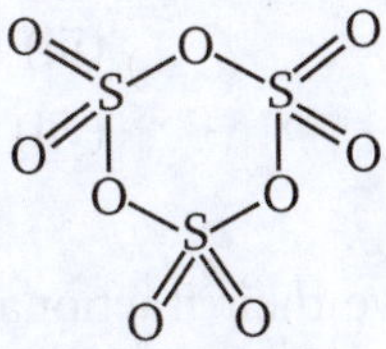

Calculate value of $p \div q$, here p and q are total number of $d\pi$-$p\pi$ bonds and total number of sp^3 hybridised atoms respectively in given molecule.

28. Consider the following orbitals (i) $3p_x$ (ii) $4d_{z^2}$ (iii) $3d_{x^2-y^2}$ (iv) $3d_{yz}$

Then, calculate value of "$x + y - z$" here x is total number of gerade orbital and y is total number of ungerade orbitals and z is total number of axial orbitals in given above orbitals.

29. Consider the following oxyanions :

PO_4^{3-}, $P_2O_6^{4-}$, SO_4^{2-}, MnO_4^-, CrO_4^{2-}, $S_2O_5^{2-}$, $S_2O_7^{2-}$

and find the value of $R + Q - P$

Where

P = Number of oxy anions having three equivalent X — O bonds per central atom

Q = Number of oxy anions having two equivalent X — O bonds per central atom

R = Number of oxy anions having four equivalent X — O bonds per central atom

30. Consider the following three compounds (i) AX_{2n}^{n-}, (ii) AX_{3n} and (iii) AX_{4n}^{n+}, where central atom A is 15th group element and their maximum covalency is $3n$. If total number of proton in surrounding atom X is n and value of n is one, then calculate value of "$x^3 + y^2 + z$". (Where x, y and z are total number of lone pair at central atom in compound (i), (ii) and (iii) respectively).

31. Consider the following compounds and Calculate value of $\left(\dfrac{P^2 - Q^2}{R + S}\right)$.

(i) BrF	(ii) ICl	(iii) BrF_3	(iv) BrF_5
(v) ICl_3	(vi) IF_3	(vii) IF_5	(viii) IF_7,

Where P : Total number of polar compounds,

Q : Total number of planar compounds

R : Total number of non-polar compounds

S : Total number of non-planar compounds

32. Consider the following compounds

(1) H_3CF	(2) H_2CF_2	(3) CH_4
(4) H_3CCF_3	(5) $CH_3\overset{+}{C}H_2$	(6) C_2H_4

and calculate value of $Y \div X$, (Where X is the total number of compounds which have H — C — H bond angles equal to 109°28′ and Y is the total number of compounds which have H — C — H bond angles greater than 109°28′ and less than 120°)

33. There are some species given below.

(i) O_2^+ (ii) CO (iii) B_2 (iv) O_2^-

(v) NO^+ (vi) He_2^+ (vii) C_2^{2+} (viii) CN^-

(ix) N_2^-

Total number of species which have their fractional bond order.

34. Following compounds *A* and *B* have similar structure with delocalization of π-electron system.

(A) $(PNCl_2)_{x/2}$ (B) $(CH)_x$

If value of *x* is 6, then calculate value of "$P \div Q$", where '*P*' is total no. of σ -bonds in compound *A* and *B* and '*Q*' is total no. of π bond in compound *A* and *B*.

35. The hybridization of central atoms of compounds *A*, *B*, *C* and *D* are sp^3d, sp^3, sp^2 and sp respectively. If compounds *A* and *D* have same shape like I_3^- and compounds *B* and *C* have same shape like water molecule. Then calculate value of "$P + Q + R + S$", where *P*, *Q*, *R* and *S* are number of lone pairs on central atoms of compounds *A*, *B*, *C* and *D* respectively.

36. In compound PCl_xF_{5-x}, possible values of *x* are 0 to 5, then calculate value of $x_1 + x_2 + x_3$ (where x_1, x_2 and x_3 ...... are possible values of *x*, with zero dipole moment for given compound).

37. Consider the following five groups (According to modern periodic table) of elements with their increasing order of atomic numbers :

Group 1 → A, B, C, D, E Group 2 → F, G, H, I, J

Group 13 → K, L, M, N, O Group 15 → P, Q, R, S, T Group 17 → U, V, W, X, Y

If first and last element of each group belongs to 2nd and 6th period respectively and Z represents to carbonate ion (CO_3^{2-}) then consider the following orders.

(i) $O^+ > H^{2+}$; Polarising power

(ii) $T^{3+} > S^{3+} > R^{3+}$; Stability of cation

(iii) $U^-(aq) > V^-(aq) > W^-(aq) > X^-(aq)$; Size

(iv) $JV_2 < IV_2 < GV_2 < LV_3$; Covalent character

(v) GZ > IZ > JZ; Thermal stability

(vi) AV > BV > CV > DV > EV; Thermal stability

(vii) $C_3P > B_3P > A_3P$; Lattice energy

(viii) $KU_3 < KV_3 < KW_3 < KX_3$; Melting point

Then calculate value of $|p - q|^2$, here *p* and *q* are correct and incorrect orders in the given eight orders respectively.

Answers

Level-1

1. (d)	2. (d)	3. (a)	4. (b)	5. (b)	6. (d)	7. (d)	8. (c)	9. (b)	10. (b)
11. (a)	12. (d)	13. (b)	14. (c)	15. (c)	16. (b)	17. (a)	18. (a)	19. (c)	20. (c)
21. (b)	22. (b)	23. (b)	24. (c)	25. (d)	26. (b)	27. (c)	28. (b)	29. (d)	30. (a)
31. (c)	32. (d)	33. (c)	34. (b)	35. (d)	36. (d)	37. (b)	38. (b)	39. (a)	40. (a)
41. (b)	42. (b)	43. (a)	44. (c)	45. (d)	46. (b)	47. (b)	48. (c)	49. (c)	50. (c)
51. (b)	52. (c)	53. (b)	54. (c)	55. (d)	56. (b)	57. (c)	58. (d)	59. (d)	60. (d)
61. (d)	62. (a)	63. (c)	64. (b)	65. (b)	66. (a)	67. (b)	68. (d)	69. (b)	70. (c)
71. (b)	72. (d)	73. (c)	74. (a)	75. (d)	76. (b)	77. (d)	78. (c)	79. (b)	80. (c)
81. (b)	82. (d)	83. (d)	84. (b)	85. (a)	86. (a)	87. (c)			

Level-2

1. (b)	2. (a)	3. (b)	4. (c)	5. (b)	6. (d)	7. (c)	8. (a)	9. (a)	10. (b)
11. (d)	12. (d)	13. (b)	14. (d)	15. (c)	16. (c)	17. (c)	18. (c)	19. (b)	20. (c)
21. (a)	22. (b)	23. (a)	24. (d)	25. (a)	26. (d)	27. (d)	28. (b)	29. (b)	30. (b)
31. (b)	32. (a)	33. (d)	34. (c)	35. (d)	36. (b)	37. (b)	38. (c)	39. (b)	40. (a)
41. (c)	42. (a)	43. (a)	44. (d)	45. (b)	46. (d)	47. (a)	48. (b)	49. (a)	50. (c)
51. (b)	52. (b)	53. (d)	54. (c,d)	55. (d)	56. (b)	57. (d)	58. (d)	59. (c)	60. (d)
61. (d)	62. (a)	63. (b)	64. (d)	65. (a)	66. (a)	67. (d)	68. (d)	69. (a)	70. (d)
71. (a)	72. (b)	73. (c)	74. (c)	75. (d)	76. (d)				

Level-3

Passage–1	1. (b)	2. (c)	3. (d)
Passage–2	1. (b)	2. (d)	
Passage–3	1. (d)	2. (d)	3. (a)
Passage–4	1. (c)	2. (c)	3. (c)
Passage–5	1. (d)	2. (b)	3. (d)
Passage–6	1. (d)	2. (d)	3. (d)
Passage–7	1. (b)	2. (a)	
Passage–8	1. (c)	2. (d)	3. (b)
Passage–9	1. (c)	2. (d)	3. (a)
Passage–10	1. (b)	2. (b)	3. (a)

Passage–11	**1.** (c)	**2.** (d)	**3.** (a)	**4.** (b)	**5.** (a)	**6.** (c)	**7.** (b)	**8.** (c)
Passage–12	**1.** (d)	**2.** (c)	**3.** (c)	**4.** (c)	**5.** (b)			
Passage–13	**1.** (a)	**2.** (d)	**3.** (c)					
Passage–14	**1.** (c)	**2.** (d)	**3.** (d)					
Passage–15	**1.** (b)	**2.** (d)	**3.** (b)					
Passage–16	**1.** (c)	**2.** (c)						

One or More Answers is/are correct

1.	(a,b,c)	**2.**	(a,b,d)	**3.**	(a,b,c,d)	**4.**	(b,c,d)	**5.**	(a,b,d)	**6.**	(a,b)
7.	(b)	**8.**	(b,c)	**9.**	(b,d)	**10.**	(a,b,c,d)	**11.**	(a,d)	**12.**	(c,d)
13.	(a,b,c)	**14.**	(a,b,c,d)	**15.**	(a,b)	**16.**	(a,c)	**17.**	(a,b,c)	**18.**	(a,b,d)
19.	(a,d)	**20.**	(a,b,d)	**21.**	(a,d)	**22.**	(a,c,d)	**23.**	(a,b,c)	**24.**	(a,c,d)
25.	(c,d)	**26.**	(a,c,d)	**27.**	(a,b)	**28.**	(a,c,d)	**29.**	(a,b,c,d)	**30.**	(a,b,c,d)
31.	(b,c,d)	**32.**	(a,b,c,d)	**33.**	(a,c)	**34.**	(a,c)	**35.**	(b,d)	**36.**	(b,d)
37.	(a,c,d)	**38.**	(b,d)	**39.**	(a,b,c)	**40.**	(b,c,d)	**41.**	(b,c,d)	**42.**	(a,d)
43.	(a,b,c,d)	**44.**	(a,b,c)	**45.**	(a,b,d)	**46.**	(a,c,d)	**47.**	(a,b,d)		

Match the Column

1. A→ Q, R, S;	B→ P, Q, T;	C→ P, R, T;	D→ P, T	
2. A→ Q, S;	B→ P, T;	C→ R, S;	D→ P, R, T	
3. A→ P, Q, R, T;	B→ R;	C→ R, S;	D→ P, R, S, T	
4. A→ P, Q, S;	B→ Q, S, T;	C→ P, Q, R;	D→ P, Q, R	
5. A→ P, Q, S;	B→ R, T;	C→ P;	D→ R, T	
6. A→ Q, R, S;	B→ P, T;	C→ P, Q, R;	D→ P, R, T	
7. A→ R, S;	B→ P;	C→ Q;	D→ P, Q	
8. A→ R;	B→ S;	C→ P		
9. A→ P, Q, R;	B→ Q, S;	C→ P, Q;	D→ P, R	
10. A→ P, Q, R, S, T;		B→ P, R, T;	C→ Q, S, T;	D→ P, R,T
11. A→ Q, R;	B→ P, S;	C→ P;	D→ Q, T	
12. A→ Q, R, S;	B→ P, Q, R, S;	C→P, S;	D→ P, S	
13. A→ P, R, S;	B→ Q;	C→ Q, R, S;	D→ P, S	
14. A→ P,Q;	B→ P, Q, R;	C→ P, Q, R, S;	D→ P, Q, R, S	
15. A→ P;	B→ S;	C→ R;	D→ Q	

Assertion-Reason Type Questions

1. (B)	**2.** (B)	**3.** (A)	**4.** (A)	**5.** (C)	**6.** (B)	**7.** (B)	**8.** (A)	**9.** (A)	**10.** (B)
11. (B)	**12.** (B)	**13.** (D)	**14.** (D)	**15.** (A)	**16.** (C)	**17.** (C)	**18.** (A)	**19.** (C)	**20.** (C)
21. (D)	**22.** (D)	**23.** (C)	**24.** (B)	**25.** (A)	**26.** (C)	**27.** (C)	**28.** (B)	**29.** (B)	

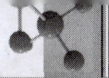

Subjective Problems

1. 2	**2.** 9	**3.** 28	**4.** 13	**5.** 6	**6.** 3	**7.** 7
8. 6	**9.** 5	**10.** 5	**11.** 16	**12.** 4	**13.** 2	**14.** 4
15. 3	**16.** 4	**17.** 7	**18.** 7	**19.** 4	**20.** 4	**21.** 2
22. 0	**23.** 6	**24.** 7	**25.** 1	**26.** 8	**27.** 1	**28.** 1
29. 2	**30.** 9	**31.** 6	**32.** 5	**33.** 4	**34.** 4	**35.** 6
36. 8	**37.** 4 or 16					

Hints and Solutions

Level 1

10. (b) During protonation hybridisation same but shape changes.

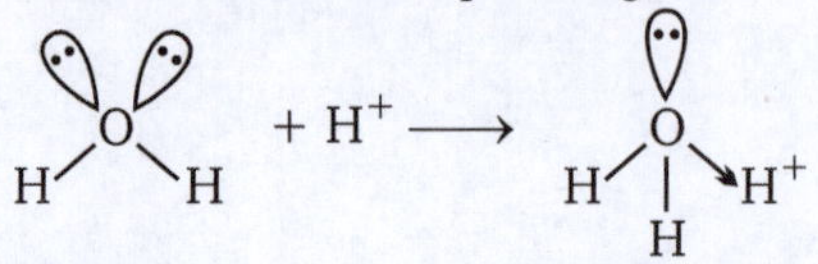

(V shape) sp^3 (Pyramidal) sp^3

11. (a) $\ddot{N}F_3 < \ddot{N}Cl_3 < \ddot{N}Br_3 < \ddot{N}I_3$

Correct order of lewis base character in nitrogen halides.

12. (d) $SiF_6 + 2F^- \longrightarrow SiF_6^{2-}$

$SF_6 + F^- \longrightarrow$ No reaction

$BF_3 + F^- \longrightarrow BF_4^-$

Due to complex formation F^- concentration decreases, ionization of $HF \rightleftharpoons H^+ + F^-$ increases.

13. (b)

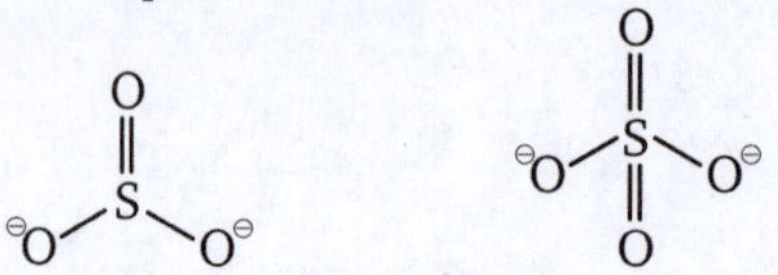

$B.O. = \frac{4}{3} = 1.33$ $\quad B.O. = \frac{6}{4} = 1.5$

$\left[B.L. \propto \frac{1}{B.O.}\right]$

$\therefore \quad SO_3^{2-} > SO_4^{2-} > \underbrace{SO_2 > SO_3}_{\text{Bent's Rule}}$

20. (c)

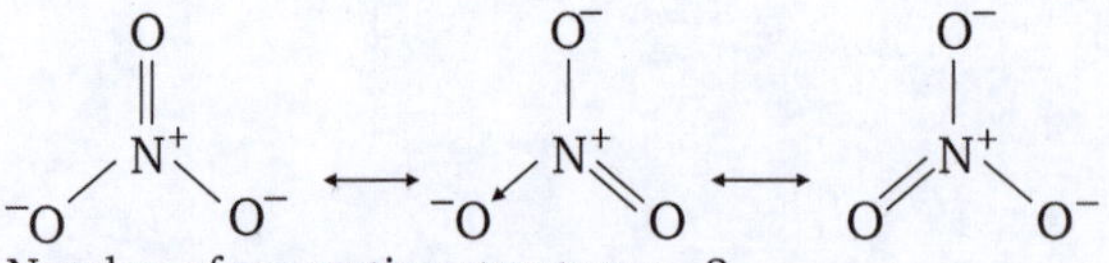

Number of resonating structures = 3

22. (b) $2BH_3 \rightarrow B_2H_6$

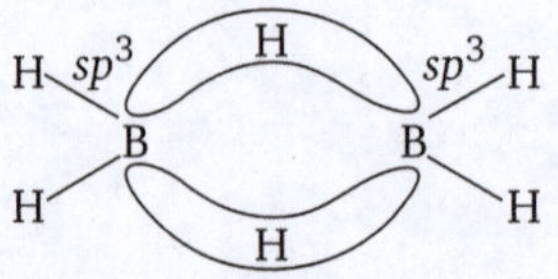

$2BeH_2 \rightarrow Be_2H_4$

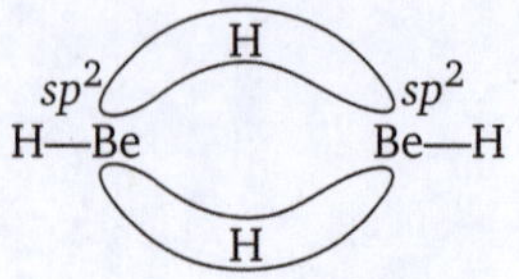

24. (c) 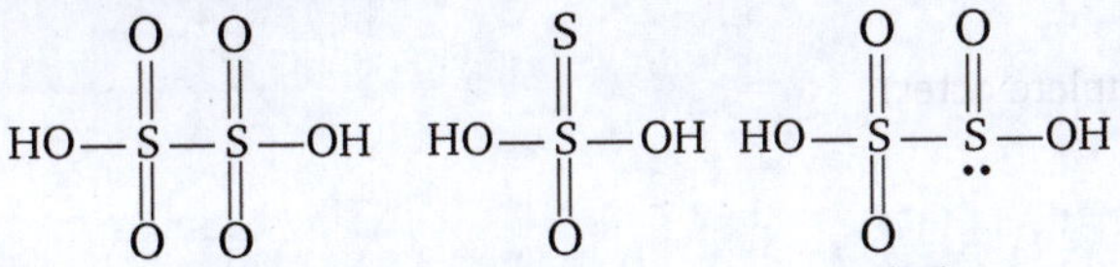

(I) (II) (III)

38. (b) As electronegativity difference of bond increases, polar character also increases.

41. (b) 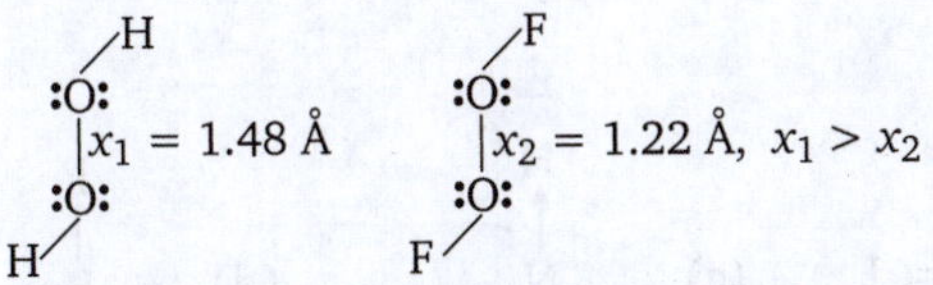

According to Bent's Rule in O_2F_2, there is more *p*-character in O—F bond in comparison to O—H bond in H_2O_2; hence *s*-character in O—O bond is greater in O_2F_2.

42. (b) 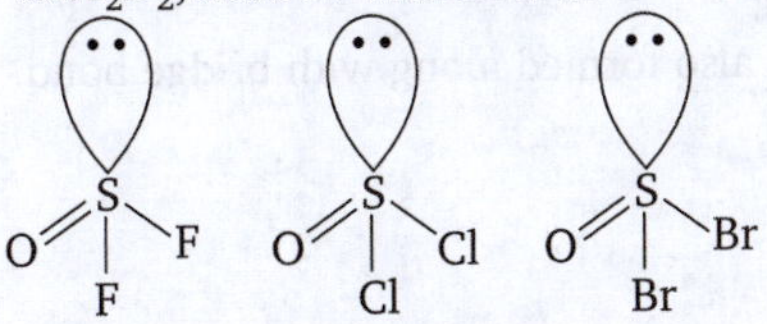

According to Bent's Rule

57. (c) Although both hydration and lattice energies of alkali metal fluorides decrease down the group and hydration energy dominates over lattice energy, therefore, solubility increases down the group.

62. (a) Compound (B) exhibits intramolecular H-bonding has more vapour pressure than compound (A) involved in intermolecular H-bonding.

68. (d) 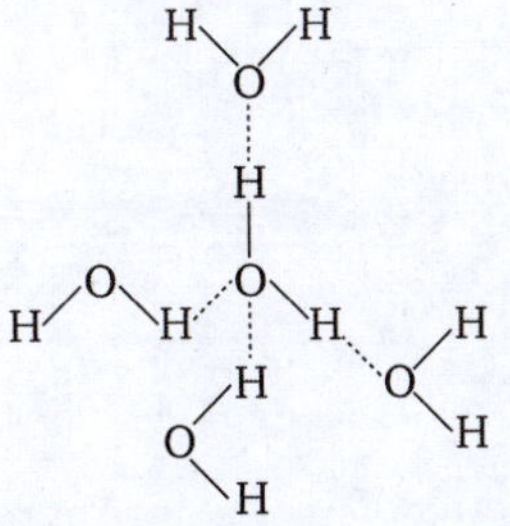

70. (c) Only in BF_3 $p\pi$-$p\pi$ back bonding is possible due to which B—F bond length is shortest. In other compounds, *p*-orbital at boron is not vacant hence, $p\pi$-$p\pi$ back bonding is not possible.

Water molecules are hexagonally closed packed in ice with the help of H-bonds, hence due to existance of voids/interstitial spaces it has cage like structure with less density than water.

80. (c) (i) 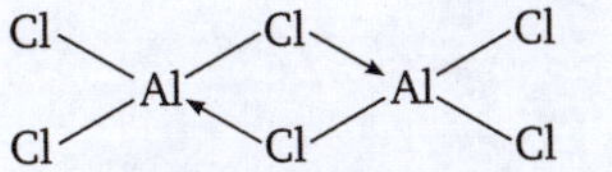

(complete octet)

(ii) 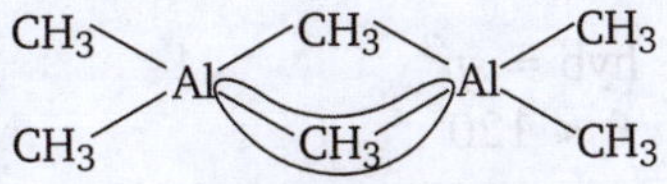

(3c-2e) bond
(incomplete octet)

(iii) AlF_3 (ionic compound) $\longrightarrow$ Al^{3+} $2s^22p^6$ (octet complete) + $3F^-$ $2s^22p^6$ (octet complete)

(iv) 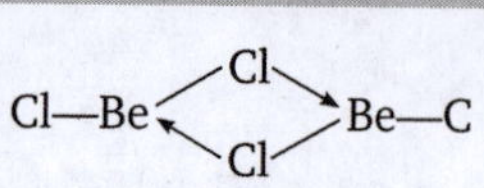 (Incomplete octet)

(Incomplete octet)

(v) 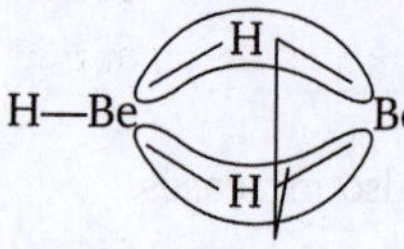 (Incomplete octet)

$(3c - 2e^-)$ bond

81. (b)

(a) 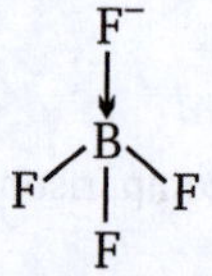 (b) 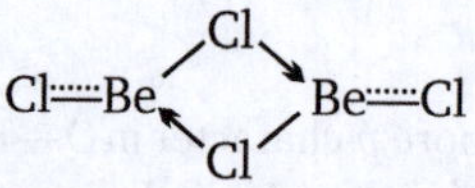 (c) 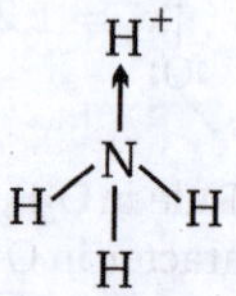 (d) 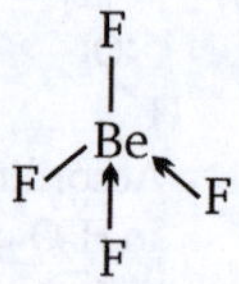

In Be_2Cl_4 octet of Be was not complete, so back bond also formed along with bridge bond.

82. (d) %P ↑↑ 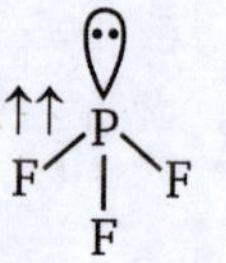 < 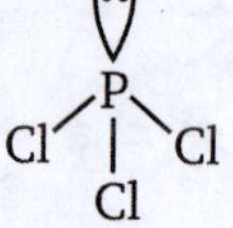 < 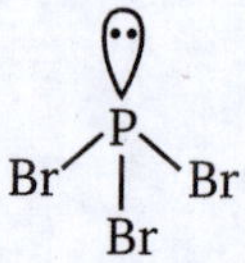

%P character increases in PF_3, as EN of F is maximum so bond angle is minimum in PF_3.

83. (d) $2\dot{C}F_3 \longrightarrow C_2F_6$
(sp^3) (sp^3)

$2\dot{C}lO_3 \longrightarrow Cl_2O_6$
(sp^3) (sp^3)

$2\dot{N}O_2 \longrightarrow N_2O_4$
(sp^2) (sp^2)

$2\dot{C}H_3 \longrightarrow C_2H_6$
(sp^2) (sp^2)

84. (b) NO_2 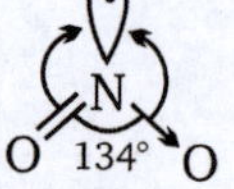

85. (a) 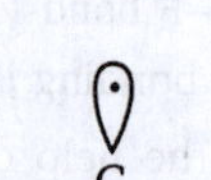

hyb = sp^2 hyb = sp^3
$\theta = 120°$ $\theta < 120°$

Level 2

2. (a) Aqueous hydrolysis of CCl_4 is not possible due to absence of vacant orbital on carbon, while hydrolysis of $MgCl_2$, $AlCl_3$, $SiCl_4$ and PCl_5 is possible. Extent of hydrolysis is proportional to the amount of positive formation charge present on the atomic site prone to attack of H_2O molecules.

$$CCl_4 < MgCl_2 < AlCl_3 < SiCl_4 < PCl_5$$

3. (b)

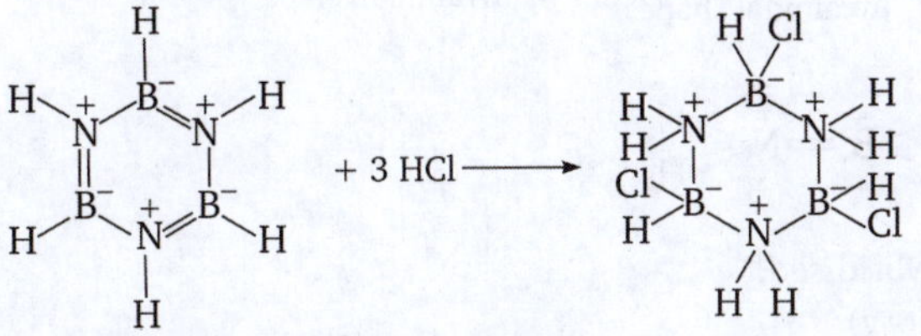

4. (c) $BCl_3 + 3H_2O \longrightarrow H_3BO_3 + 3HCl$

$NCl_3 + 3H_2O \longrightarrow NH_3 + 3HOCl$

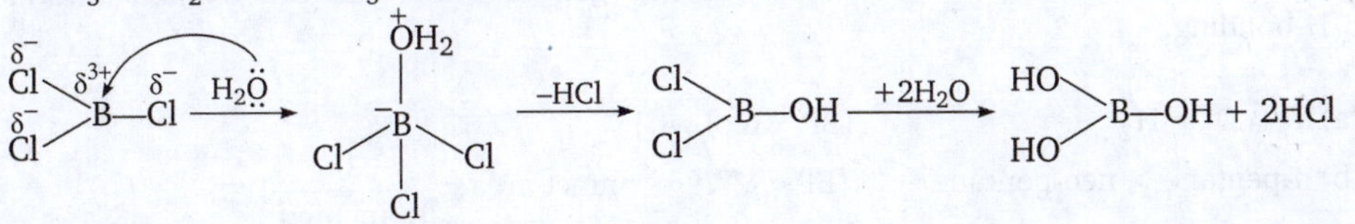

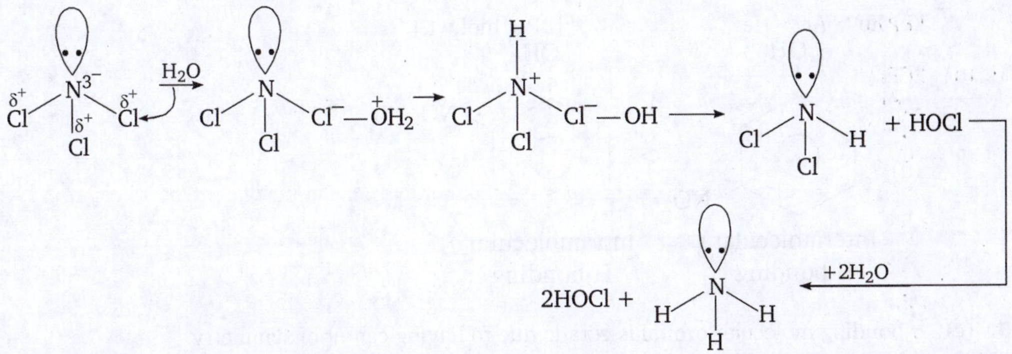

5. (b) → In $NH(SiH_3)_2$ electron density or lone pair at N-atom is involved in back bonding only with two empty 3*d*-orbitals of two silicon atoms while in $N(SiH_3)_3$ it is involved with three empty 3*d*-orbitals of three silicon atoms.

→ Strength of back bonding in $NH(SiH_3)_2$ is higher than in $N(SiH_3)_3$ hence N—Si bond length in $NH(SiH_3)_2$ is less than that of in $N(SiH_3)_3$.

6. (d)

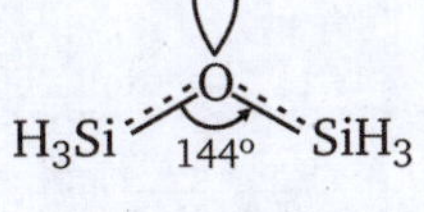

Hybridisation of O-atom : sp^2 due to more extent of $(2p_\pi\text{-}3d_\pi)$ back bonding

Hybridisation of O-atom remains sp^3, because of less effective $(2p_\pi\text{-}3d_\pi)$ back bonding due to *d*-orbital resonance

7. (c) More stronger the back bond, smaller will be the bond length.

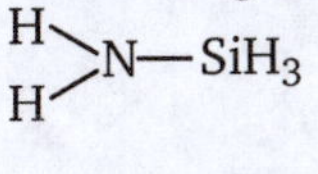

[Strongest back bond ∴ Smallest bond length]

10. (b)

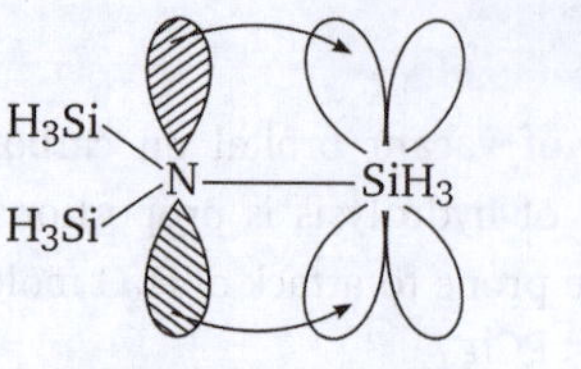

due pπ-pπ back bonding
Hybridisation of Nitrogen : sp^2
planar shape

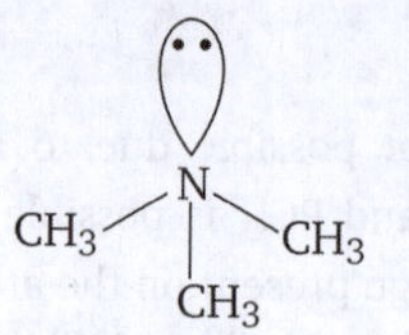

Hybridisation : sp^2
pyramidal shape

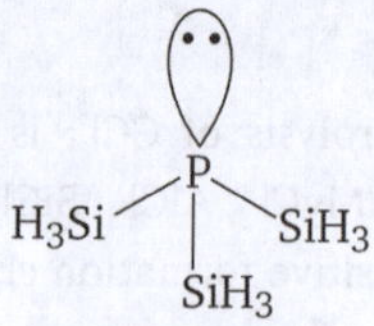

No back bonding
pyramidal shape

11. (d) BF_2NH_2

* Both boron and nitrogen are sp^2-hybridised.
* FBF bond angle $< 120°$ (VSPER theory)
* HNH bond angle is less than $120°$ but greater than $109°28'$ due to back bonding.
* Due to presence of H-atom attached to nitrogen this molecule can exhibits intermolecular H-bonding.

14. (d)

(a) $T_2 > D_2 > H_2$ [BP $\propto$ mol.wt.]

(b) *n*-pentane > neo-pentane [BP $\propto$ VWf $\propto$ contact area $\propto \frac{1}{\text{Branching}}$]

(c) Xe > Ar > He [BP $\propto$ mol.wt.]

(d)

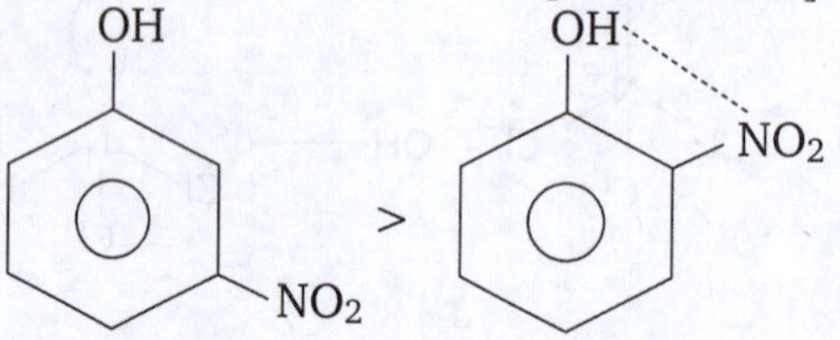

Intermolecular H-bonding   Intramolecular H-bonding

15. (c) σ-bonding molecular orbital is gerade due to having center of symmetry.

16. (c) (a)Acidic strength of HBr > HCl and their reducing properties are also in same order

(b)Basic strength of $PH_3 > AsH_3$, their bond angles are also in same order

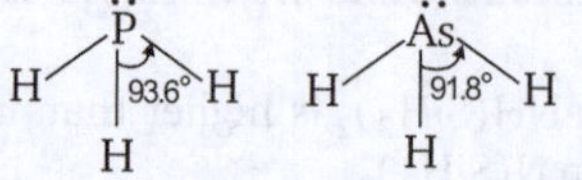

(c) $\theta_2 > \theta_1$ because C—H bond has more *s*-character in CH_3F than in CH_3Cl.

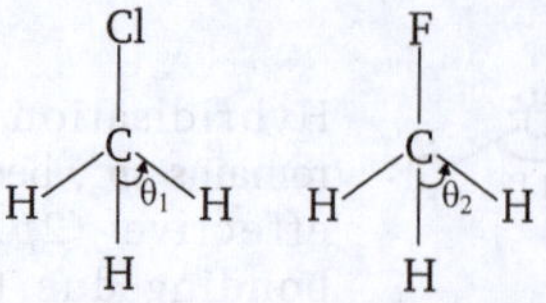

(d) K_{a_1} of maleic acid is higher than K_{a_1} of fumaric acid but reverse is true for their K_{a_2}

17. (c)

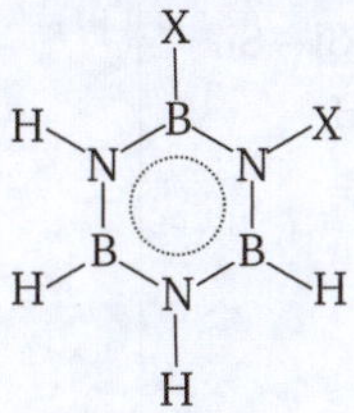

ortho-form

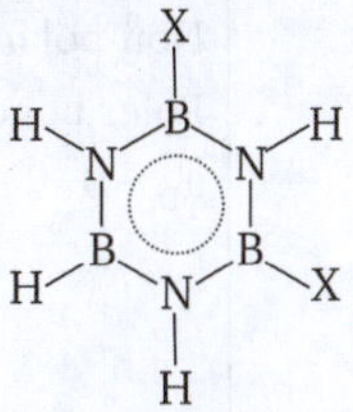

meta-form

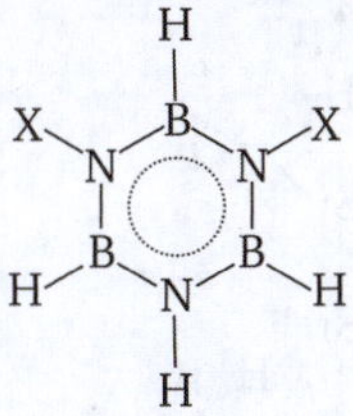

meta-form

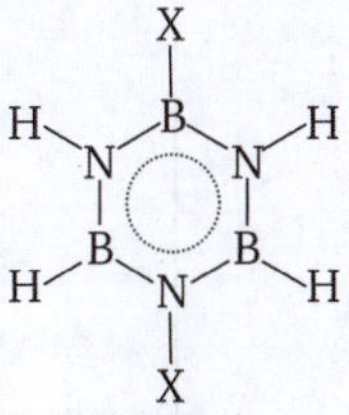

para-form

18. (c) $MX_2 + X'_2 \longrightarrow MX_4X'_2 \quad (M = \text{Te})$

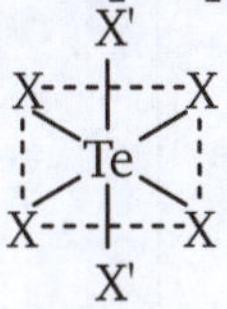

→ Hybridization of Te : $sp^3d^2(sp_xp_yp_zd_{x^2-y^2}d_{z^2})$

→ Axial positions are formed by hybrid orbitals.

→ All *M*—*X* bond lengths are identical.

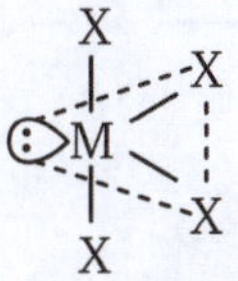

→ Hybridization of Te : $sp^3d(\equiv sp_xp_y + p_zd_{z^2})$

→ All *M* — *X* bond lengths are not identical

19. (b) In see-saw structure, as lone pair lies in equatorial position, hence there is more reduction in equatorial bonds than in axial bonds.

20. (c) $IO_2F_2^-$: Hyb. sp^3d, $[\equiv sp_xp_yp_zd_{z^2}]$

ClF_4^-: Hyb. sp^3d^2 $[\equiv sp_xp_yp_zd_{x^2-y^2}d_{z^2}]$

IF_7: Hyb. sp^3d^3. $[sp_xp_yp_zd_{x^2-y^2}d_{xy}d_{z^2}]$

d_{xy}: orbital has two nodal planes *xz* and *yz*

21. (a)

CO_3^-	XeF_4	I_3^-	NCl_3	$BeCl_2$
sp^2	sp^3d^2	sp^3d	sp^3	sp

23. (a)

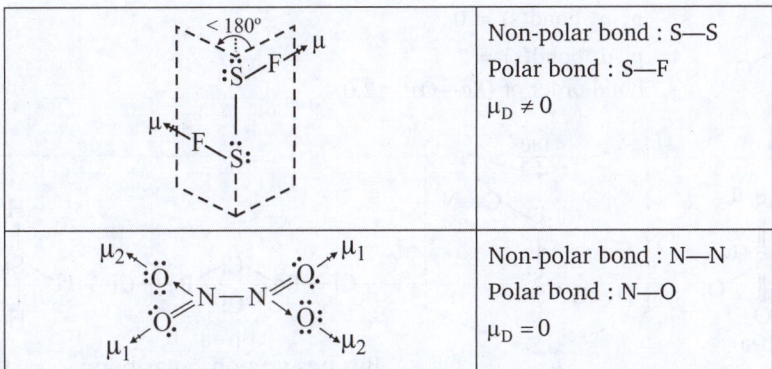

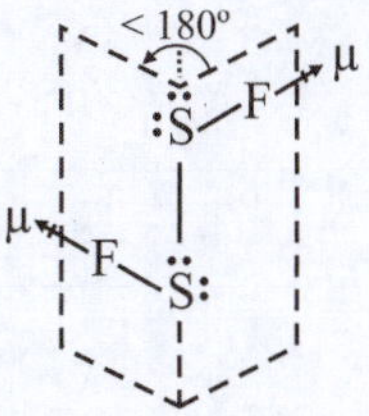	Non-polar bond : S—S Polar bond : S—F $\mu_D \neq 0$
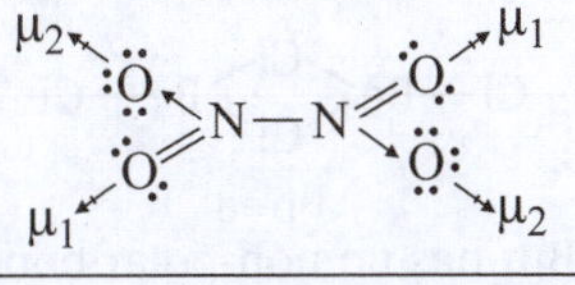	Non-polar bond : N—N Polar bond : N—O $\mu_D = 0$

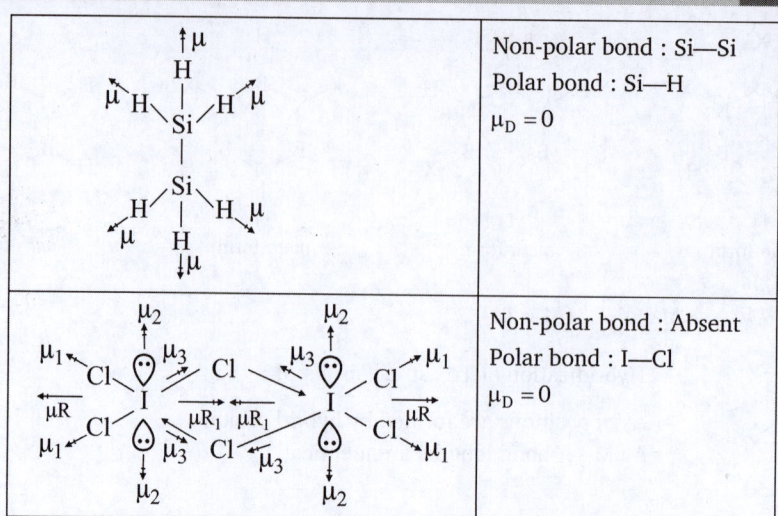

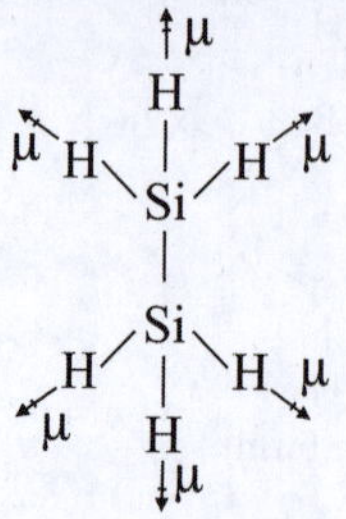	Non-polar bond : Si—Si Polar bond : Si—H $\mu_D = 0$
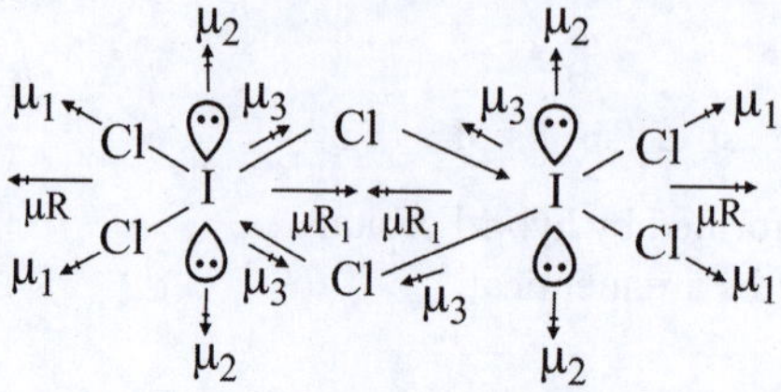	Non-polar bond : Absent Polar bond : I—Cl $\mu_D = 0$

25. (a)

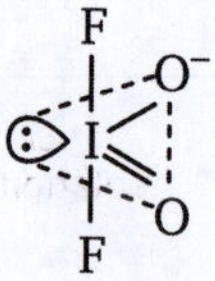

p_π-p_π bond(s) = 0
p_π-d_π bond(s) = 1
Bond order of (I—O) = 1.5

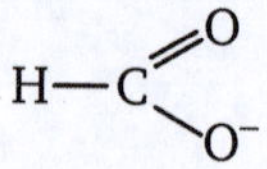

p_π-p_π bond(s) = 1
p_π-d_π bond(s) = 0
Bond order of (C—O) = 1.5

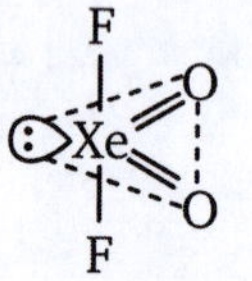

p_π-p_π bond(s) = 0
p_π-d_π bond(s) = 1
Bond order of (S—O) = 1.33

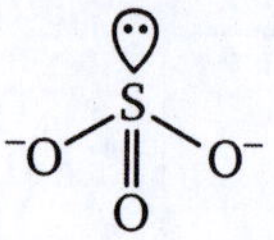

p_π-p_π bond(s) = 0
p_π-d_π bond(s) = 2
Bond order of (Xe—O) = 2.0

26. (d)

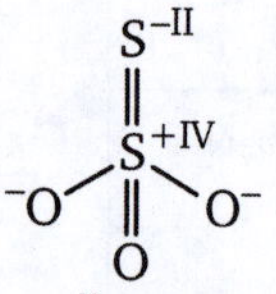

$\mu_{D\neq0}$

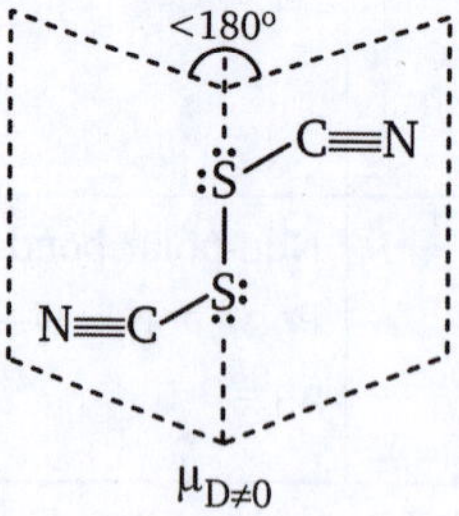

$\mu_{D\neq0}$

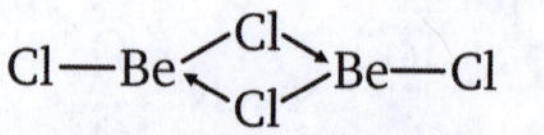

$\mu_{D=0}$

But has no non-polar bond

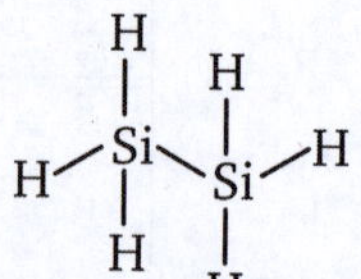

$\mu_{D=0}$

27. (d) ⇒

Hyb. of carbon : sp^3, hence % *s*-character in C—F bond ≈ 25%
→ Non-planar
→ Polar

⇒ 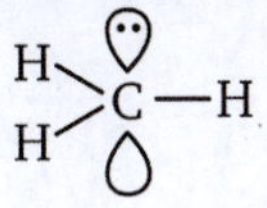

Hyb. of carbon : sp^2, hence % *s*-character in C—H bond ≈ 33%

→ Planar

→ Non-polar

28. (b)

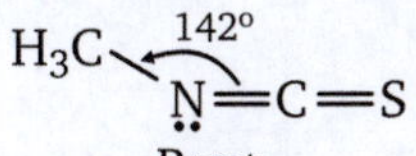

Bent

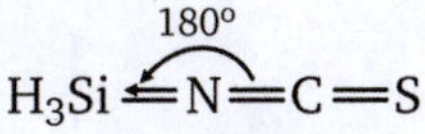

Linear

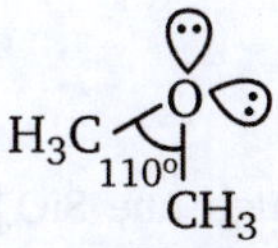

Bent

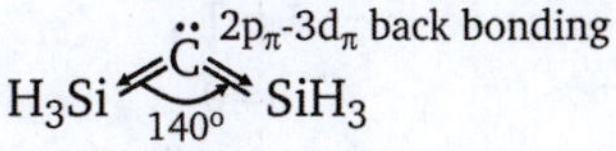

Bent

29. (b) Triplet carbene is more stable than singlet carbene.

33. (d)

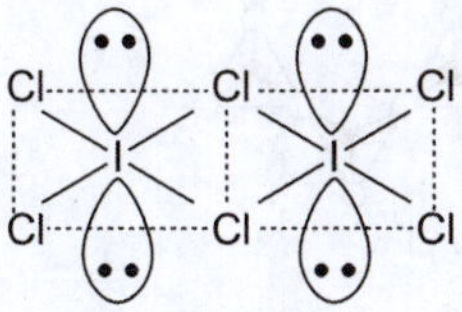

sp^3d^2
Planar

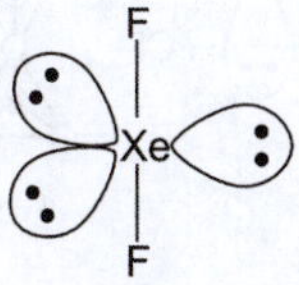

sp^3d
Linear: It is planar as three points are in same plane

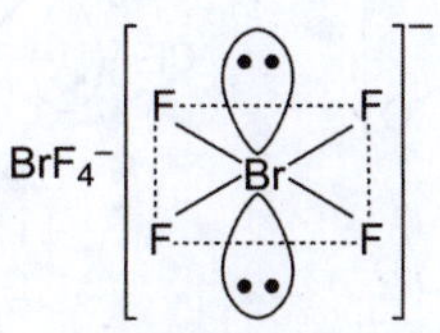

sp^3d^2
square planar

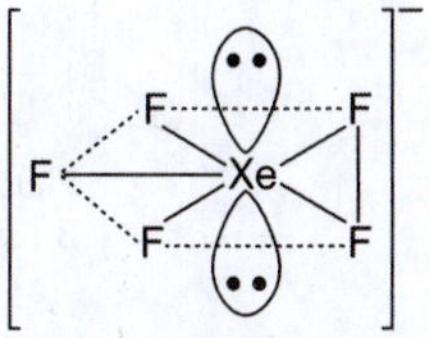

sp^3d^3
pentagonal planar

34. (c)

XeF_5^-	:	2 lone pairs	;	pentagonal planar
BrF_3	:	2 lone pairs	;	Bent-T-shape
XeF_2	:	3 lone pairs	;	Linear
H_3S^+	:	1 lone pairs	;	Pyramidal
$\overset{\uparrow\uparrow}{C}H_2$	:	2 unpaired $\bar{e}s$ (No lone pair)	;	Linear

35. (d) (I)

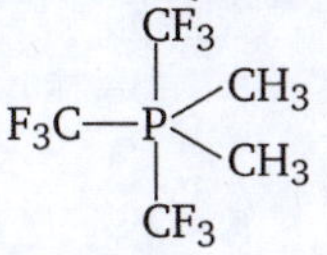

$\mu \neq 0$

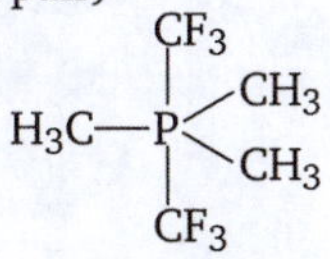

$\mu = 0$

(II) 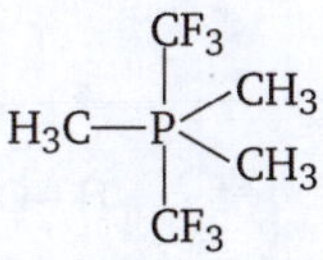

$CH_3\hat{P}CH_3$ bond angles are equal

(III) 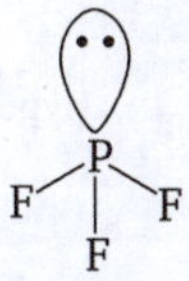

$\mu \neq 0$
(Polar)

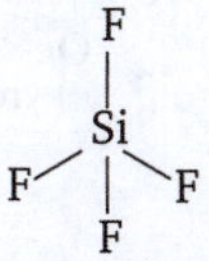

$\mu = 0$
(No Polar)

36. (b) 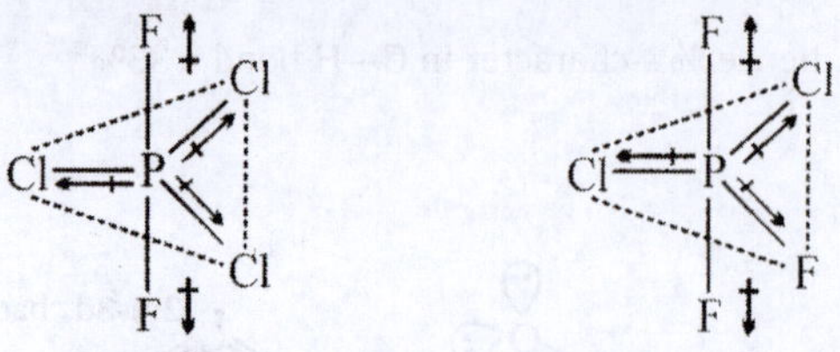

$\mu = 0$ $\mu \neq 0$

In sheet silicates although one SiO_4^{4-} tetrahedron is linked to other three tetrahedrons but the layer/sheet obtained is not planar, as fourth oxygen atom is projecting away from sheet.

38. (c) 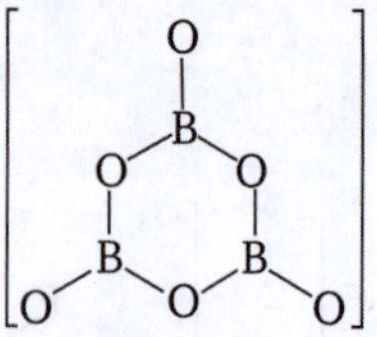

Planar
B : sp^2
(a)

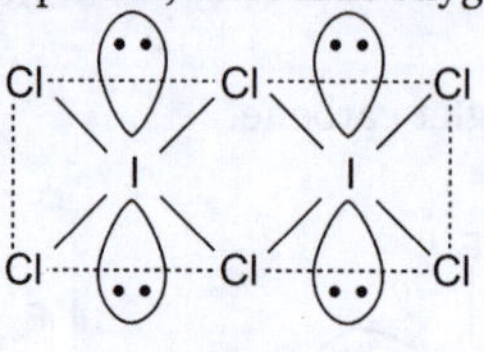

Planar
I : sp^3d^2
(b)

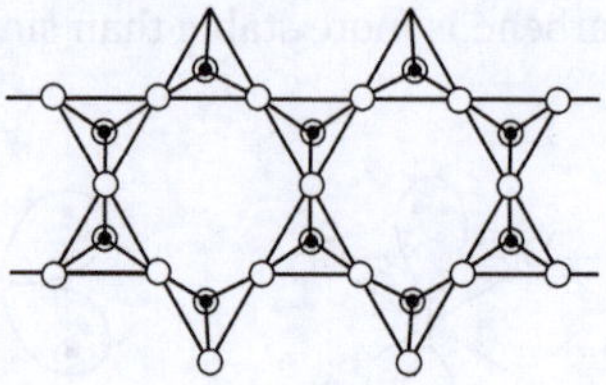

(c)

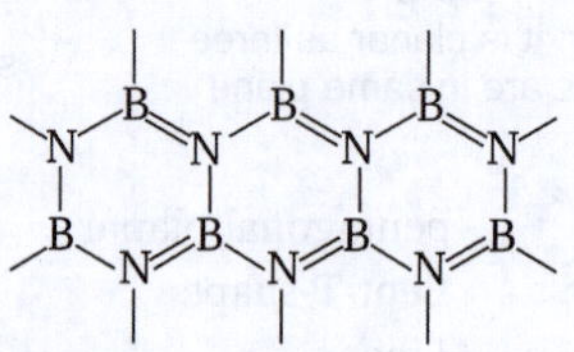

each layer is planar as both B and N are sp^2 hybridized
(d)

39. (b) 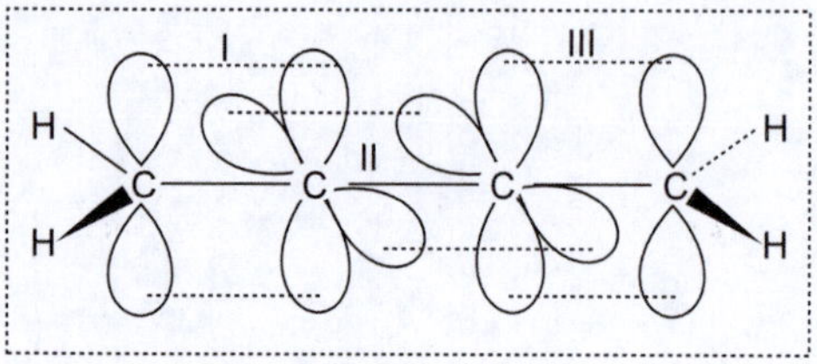

40. (a) 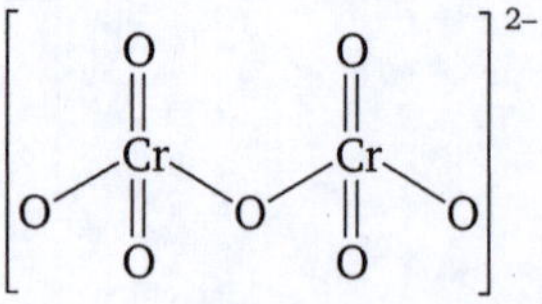

$Cr_2O_7^{2-}$

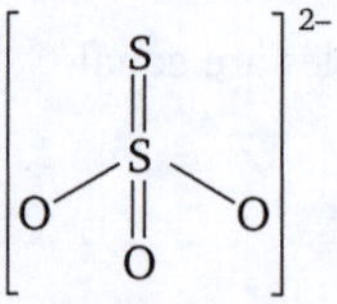

$S_2O_3^{2-}$

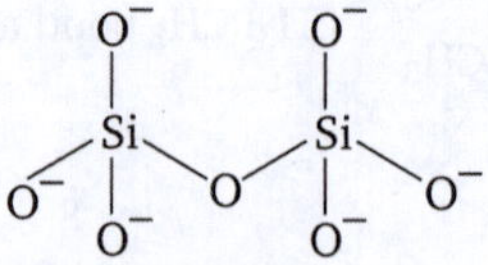

Pyrosilicate

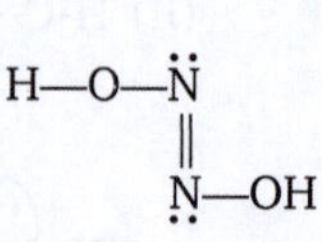

Hyponitrous acid

41. (c) 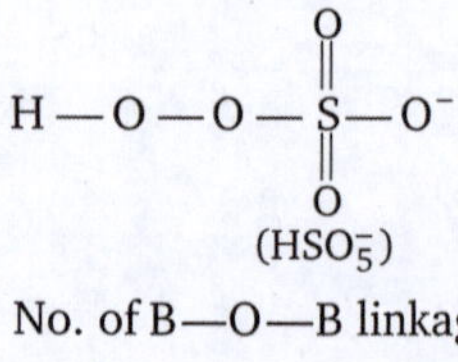

(HSO_5^-)

No. of B—O—B linkages = 5; No. of P—O—P linkages = 6

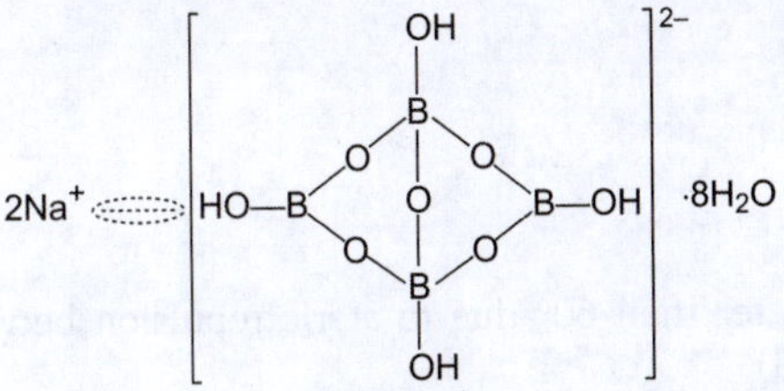

(Borax)

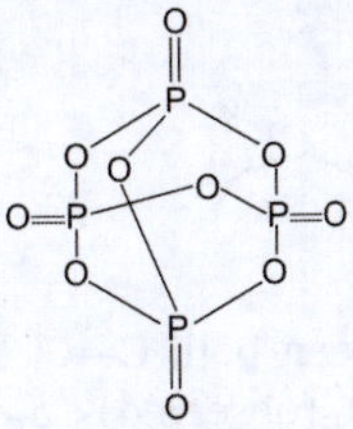

(P_4O_{10})

Pyrosulphurous Acid : 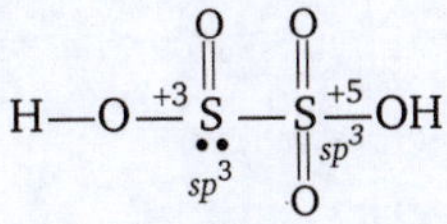

Tetra Polyphosphoric Acid : $(H_6P_4O_{13})$

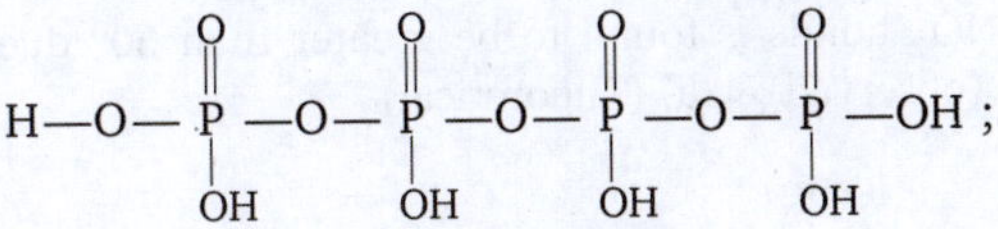

No. of P—O—P linkages = 3

44. (d)

(a) $N \equiv C - C \equiv N$ (Linear)

(b) $^{-}O - C \equiv N$ (Linear)

(c) 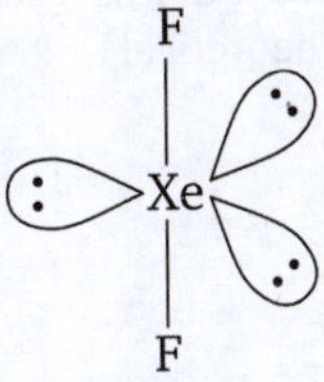

(Linear)

(d) 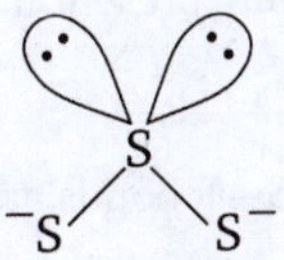

(Bent shape)

45. (b) In trigonal bipyramidal geometry lone pairs (if present) never placed at axial positions.

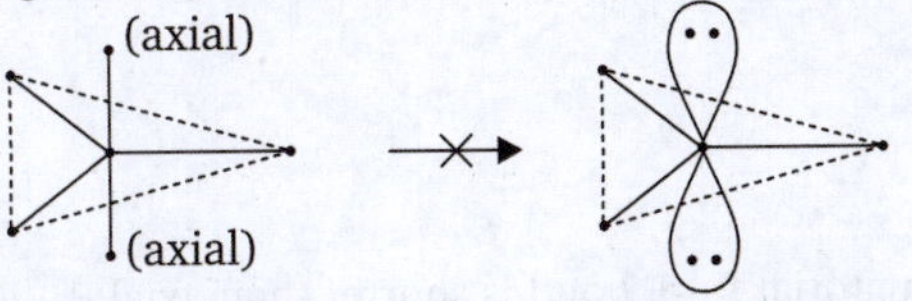

(Trigonal bipyramidal geometry) (Trigonal planer shape is not possible)

46. (d) → 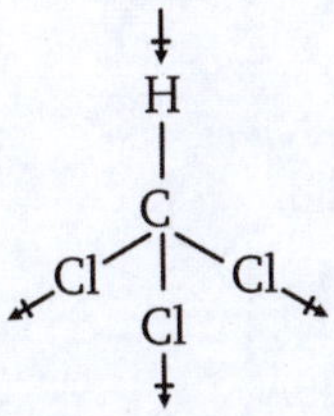

Due to steric repulsion among Cl-atoms observed ∠Cl C Cl is found to be greater than expected.

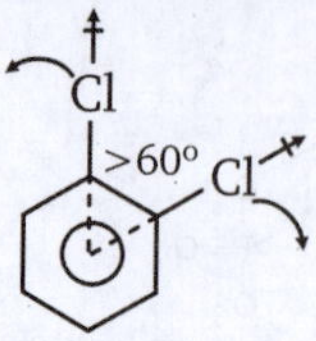

Bond angle between both C—Cl bonds is greater than 60° due to steric repulsion between both Cl-atoms, hence μ_D(observed) < μ_D (Theoretical)

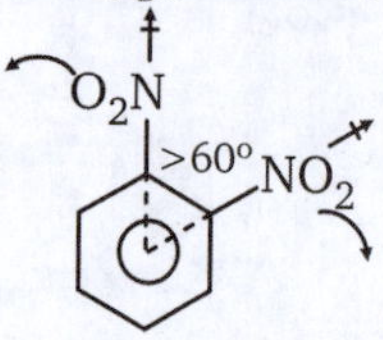

Observed bond angle between both C—NO_2 bonds is found to be greater than 60° due to steric repulsion, between NO_2 groups, hence μ_D (observed) < μ_D (Theoretical)

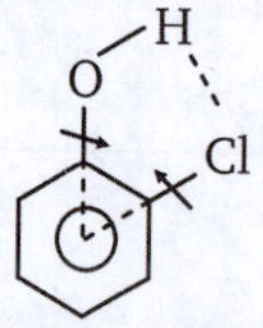

Observed bond angle between C—O and C—Cl bond is found to be less than 60° due to intramolecular H-bonding present in it, hence, μ_D (observed) < μ_D (Theoretical)

49. (a) ⇒ 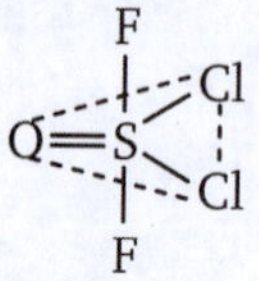 : both S—F bonds are of equal length.

⇒ 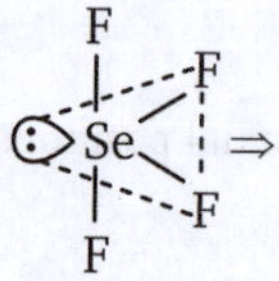 ⇒ Equatorial Se—F bond is shorter than axial Se—F bond

⇒ 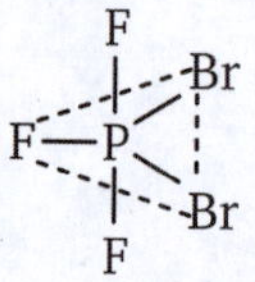 ⇒ Equatorial P—F bond is shorter than axial P—F bond

⇒ 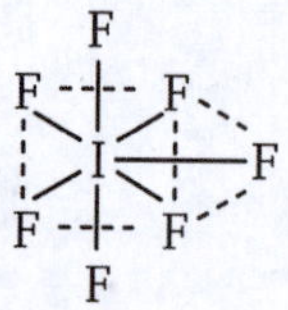 ⇒ Equatorial I—F bond is longer than axial I—F bond.

50. (c) $a = 1.577$Å $b = 1.534$Å $c = 1.612$Å $d = 1.543$Å $e = 1.643$Å
$f = 1.553$Å $g = 2.19$Å $h = 2.04$Å

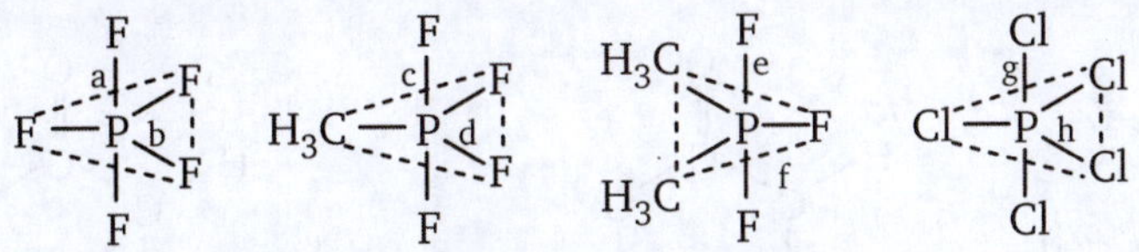

→ According to Bent's Rule : $f > d > b$ and

$h > f$ as $r_{Cl} > r_F$

$g > e$ as $r_{Cl} > r_F$

51. (b) According to Bent's Rule more electronegative substituents attached to hybrid orbital that contains more *p*-character. Hence, more *p*-character, longer will be bond length.

52. (b)

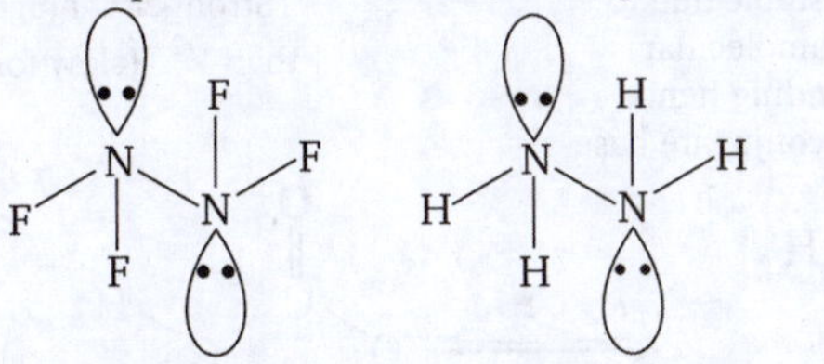

It can be explained on the basis of Bent's rule. In N_2F_4, N—N bond has more *s*-character hence bond length decreases.
While in N_2H_4, N—N bond has less *s*-character (*i.e.*, more *p*-character), hence bond lengths

54. (c, d)

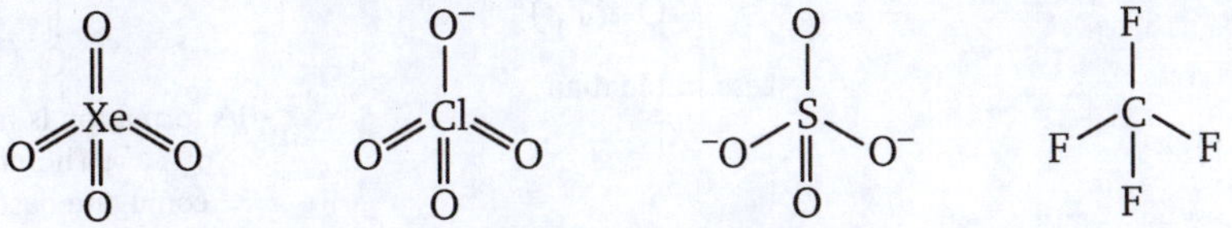

$\angle OXeO = 109°28'$ $\angle OClO = 109°28'$ $\angle OSO = 109°28'$ $\angle FCF = 109°28'$

⇒ Order of bond angle $O(SiH_3)_2 > N(SiH_3)_2 > OMe_2$

55. (d)

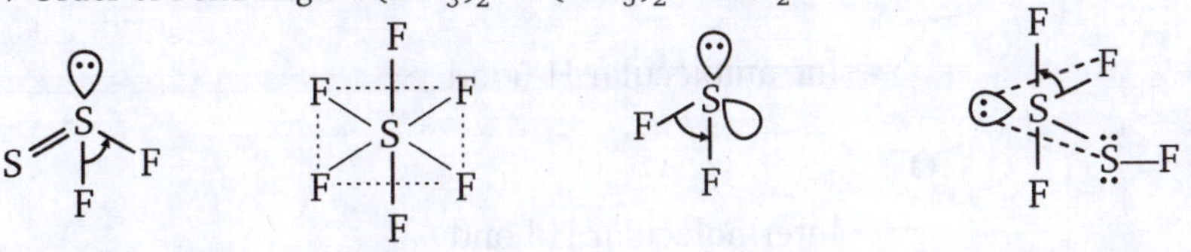

$\angle FSF < 109°28'$ $\angle FSF < 90°$ $\angle FSF < 109°28'$ $\angle FSF < 90°$

62. (c)

Species :	P_2: (B_2)	Q_2:(C_2)	R_2: (N_2)	S_2(O_2)	T_2: (F_2)
Bond order	1.0	2.0	3.0	2.0	1.0
Total No. of valence e^-s	6	8	10	12	14

65. (a)

(a) C_2^+ (BO = 1.5, Paramagnetic) → C_2 (BO = 2, Diamagnetic)

(b) NO^+ (BO = 3, Diamagnetic) → NO (BO = 2.5, Paramagnetic)

(c) O_2 (BO = 2, Paramagnetic) → O_2^+ (BO = 2.5, Paramagnetic)

(d) N_2 (BO = 3, Diamagnetic) → N_2^+ (BO = 2.5, Paramagnetic)

66 (a) According to coulsion model, H.O.M.O. (Highest Occupied Molecular Orbital) of CO molecule is non-bonding M.O. with slight antibonding character.

68. (d) In CdI_2, Pink colour is due to polarization of I^- by Cd^{2+} has pseudonoble gas configuration. In $CdCl_2$, extent of polarization of Cl^- by Cd^{2+} is relatively less, hence specific colour cannot be predicted.

72. (b)

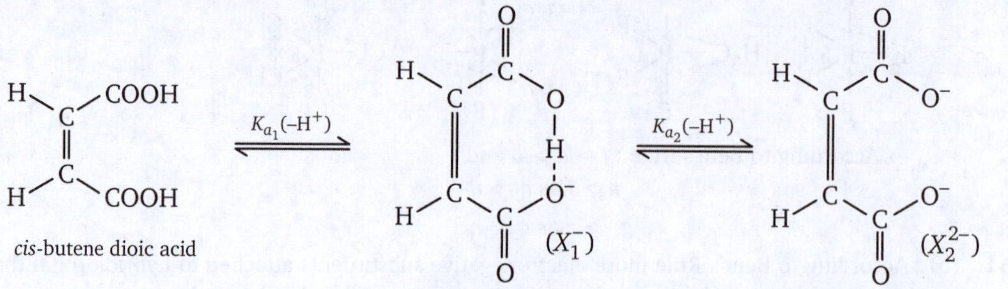

cis-butene dioic acid

More stable due to intramolecular H-bonding hence weaker conjugate base

Stronger conjugate base than Y_2^{2-} (slow formation)

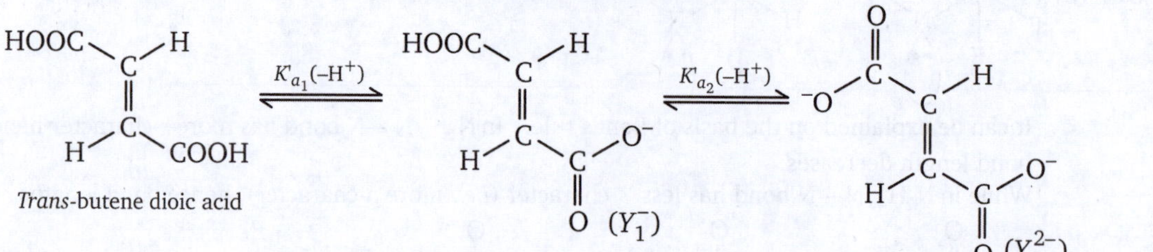

Trans-butene dioic acid

Less stable than X_1^-

Its formation is faster than that of X_2^{2-}; Therefore weaker conjugate base than X_2^{2-}

73. (c) NH_3 is stronger lewis base than H_2O and H_2O has more acidic H-atom than NH_3.

75. (d)

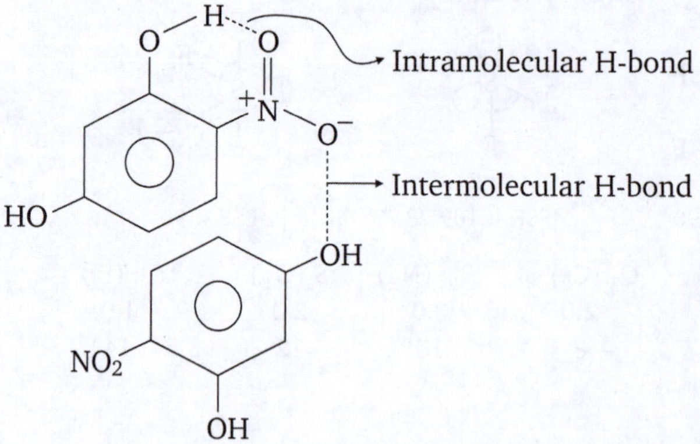

76. (d)

(a) H_2.....H_2O	Dipole-induced dipole interaction (van der Waals' force) energy < 8 kJ/mol
(b) H—Cl.....H—Cl	Dipole-dipole interaction (van der Waals' force) < 8 kJ/mol
(c) F^-.....HF	Ion-dipole H-bond (very strong H-bond energy) > 42 kJ/mol
(d) HCN.....NH_3	H-bond energy ranges from 8-42 kJ/mol

Level 3

Passage-2

1. (b) $\overset{\delta+}{H}—\overset{\delta-}{Cl} \overset{E}{\cdots} \overset{\delta+}{H}—\overset{\delta-}{Cl}$. The bond energy ($E$) between two H—Cl molecules, caused by dipole-dipole interaction is not found to be in the range of unsymmetrical H-bond energy, rather it is less than 8 kJ/mol, hence this interaction is called weak dipole-dipole interaction.

2. (d) $Na^+:CCl_4$: ion-induced dipole < 8 kJ/mol
$CHCl_3$: Br : Weaker ion-dipole < 8 kJ/mol
$C_6H_6:CCl_4$: London dispersion forces < 8 kJ/mol
H_2O : HCN : Unsymmetrical H-bond : 8-42 kJ/mol

Passage-3

1. (d) → Halogens are non-polar species, hence London dispersion forces act among them and these forces are directly proportional to molecular weight.
→ London dispersion forces ∝ B.P. and M.P. in such non-polar species.

2. (d) 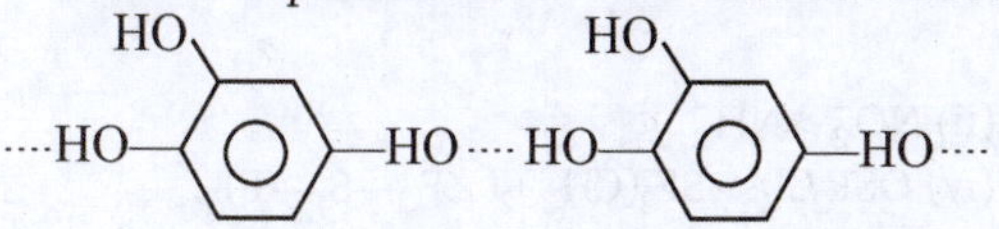 → Intermolecular H-bonding

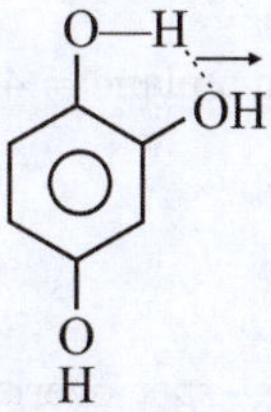 intramolecular H-bonding

3. (a) → Boiling point of $HN_3 > CH_3N_3$ as in hydrazoic acid (HN_3) intermolecular H-bonding occurs and its bond energy is higher than weak dipole-dipole interactions present in CH_3N_3.
→ Boiling point of BI_3 is greater than that of BF_3 as molecular weight of BI_3 is higher than that of BF_3.
→ Due to intermolecular H-bonding in H_2SO_4 its boiling point is higher than Me_2SO_4.
→ Similarly due to intermolecular H-bonding in $B(OH)_3$ its boiling point is higher than that of Me_3BO_3.

Passage-4

1. (c) **P** : $\sigma 1s^2 < \overset{*}{\sigma} 1s^2 < \sigma 2s^2 < \overset{*}{\sigma} 2s^2 < \pi 2p_{x^2} < \pi 2p_{y^2} < \sigma 2p_{z^1}$

→ by removing one $\bar{e}$, P becomes diamagnetic from paramagnetic.
→ Bond order of P(*i.e.*, N_2^+) < Bond order of N_2

Q : $\sigma 1s^2 < \overset{*}{\sigma} 1s^2 < \sigma 2s^2 < \overset{*}{\sigma} 2s^2 < \sigma 2p_{z^2} < \pi 2p_{x^2} = \pi 2p_{y^2} < \overset{*}{\pi} 2p_{y^2} = \overset{*}{\pi} 2p_{y^1}$

→ by adding one $\bar{e}$, Q become diamagnetic from paramagnetic
Bond order of Q(*i.e.*, O_2^-) < bond order of O_2

R : $\sigma 1s^2 < \overset{*}{\sigma} 1s^2 < \sigma 2s^2 < \overset{*}{\sigma} 2s^2 < \sigma 2p_{z^2} < \pi 2p_{x^2} = \pi 2p_{x^2} < \overset{*}{\pi} 2p_{y^1} = \overset{*}{\pi} 2p_{y^0}$

→ by adding one $\bar{e}$, R retains its paramagnetic behaviour

T : $\sigma 1s^2 < \overset{*}{\sigma} 1s^2 < \sigma 2s^2 < \overset{*}{\sigma} 2s^2 < \pi 2p_{x^2} = \pi 2p_{y^2}$

→ by adding one $\bar{e}$, T becomes paramagnetic from diamagnetic

Passage-5

3. (d)

Compound, MX_n type (n = 2 or 3 or 4)	**Value of cos θ (θ = bond angle between equivalent hybrid orbitals)**
P	–0.241 ⟶ close to sp^3
Q	–0.292 ⟶ close to sp^3
R	–0.5 ⟶ sp^2
S	–0.325 ⟶ sp^3
T	–0.469 ⟶ close to sp^2

Passage-6

1. (d) Order of bond angle :

(i) $PH_3 > H_2Se > H_2Te$ (ii) $NO_2^- > NH_2^-$

(iii) $POCl_3 > POF_3 (X — P — X$ angle) (iv) $OSF_2Cl_2 > SF_2(CH_3)_2 (\angle F — S — F)$

2. (d)

(a) 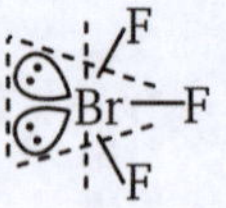 ⇒ Maximum number of atoms that can lie in a plane = 4

(b) 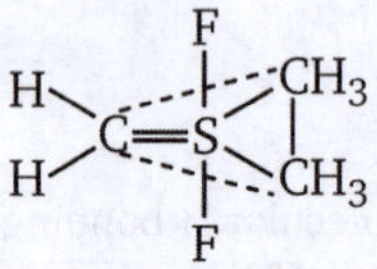 ⇒ Hydrogen atoms bonded by $1s - sp^2$ overlapping lie in axial plane.

(c) 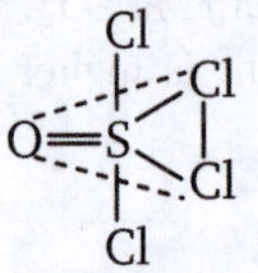 ⇒ $\angle Cl — S — Cl$ is less than 120°, due to shifting of s-character in S = O bond.

(d) 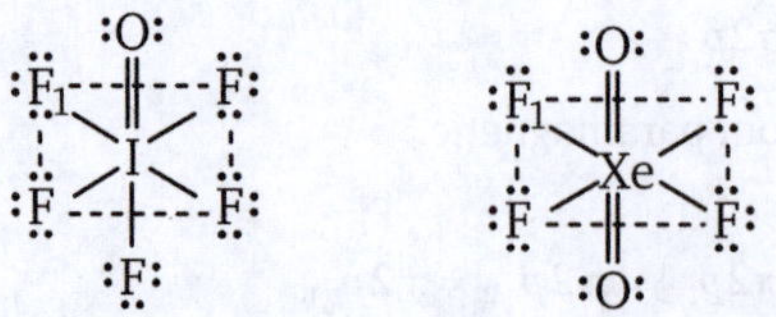

No. of lone pairs = 17 No. of lone pairs = 16

3. (d) For XeO_2F_4, $= \frac{n_2}{n_1} = 1$

Hyb. of Xe : $sp^3d^2 [sp_xp_yp_zd_{x^2-y^2}d_{z^2}]$

Passage-7

1. (b) In AsH_3, P_4 and H_2Se → No Hybridisation [Acc. to Drago's rule]

$GeH_4 \rightarrow sp^3$-hybridisation [% s = 25%] maximum.

2. (a) $PH_4^{\oplus} \rightarrow sp^3[109°28']$
$OF_2 \rightarrow sp^3$ [B.A. < 109°28′]
$SF_2 \rightarrow sp^3$[B. A.<< 109°28′]
$SbH_3 \rightarrow$ No hybridisation [B.A. ≈ 90°]
Order of B.A. : $PH_4^{\oplus} > OF_2 > SF_2 > SbH_3 > H_2Te$

Passage-11

3. (a) Bond order ∝ Bond energy $\propto \dfrac{1}{\text{Bond length}}$

5. (a) 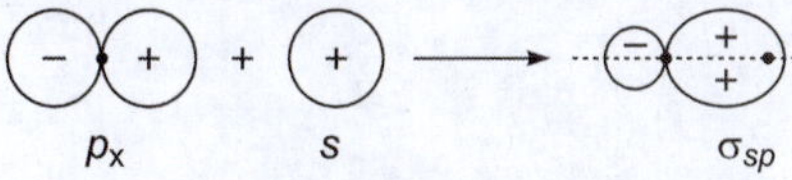

(No nodal plane between both nuclei)

6. (c) (a) 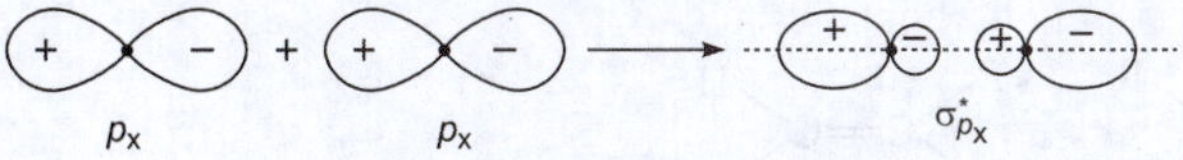

(b) 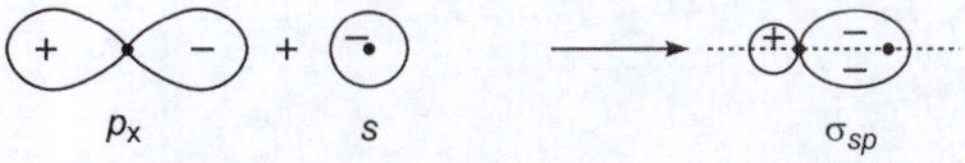

(d) 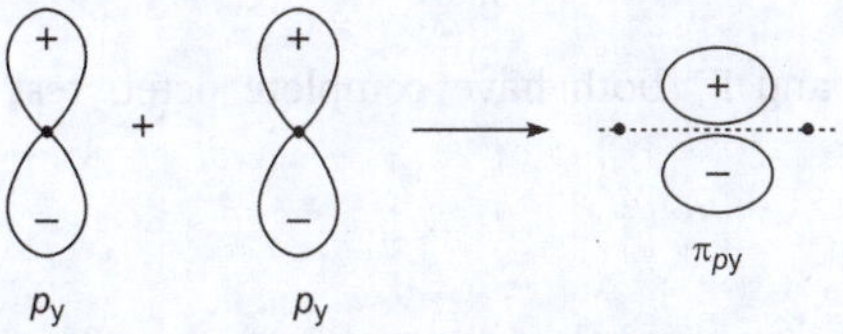

7. (b) bonding M.O. has maximum electron density between two nuclei

8. (c) 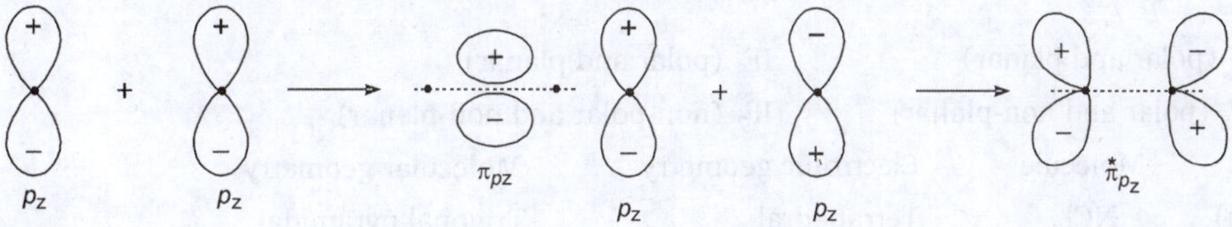

Passage-12

1. (d) 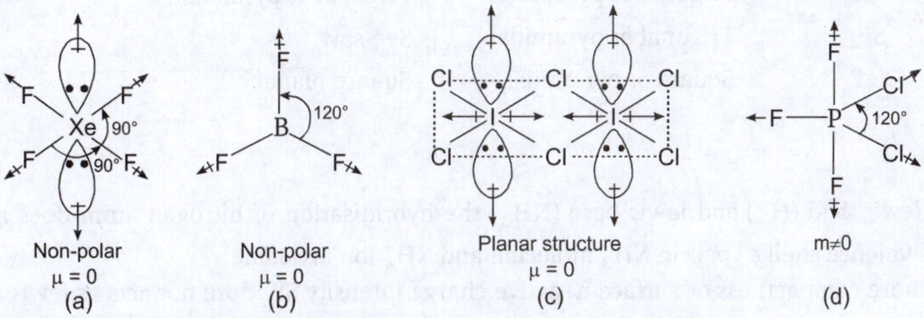

2. (c) Fraction of charge $= \dfrac{1.2 \times 10^{-18}}{4.8 \times 10^{-10} \times 10^{-8}} = 0.25$

3. (c)

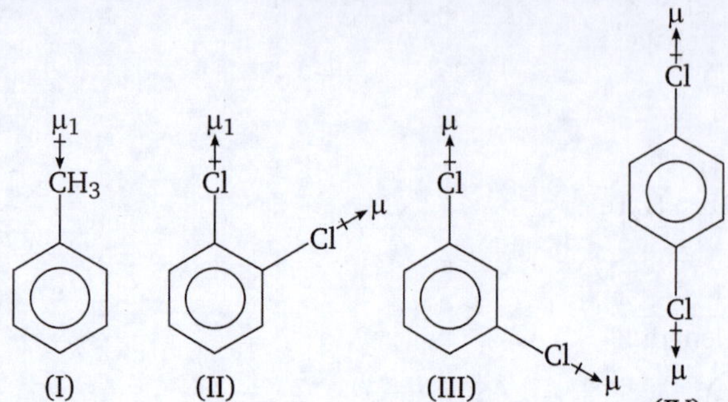

(I) (II) (III) (IV)

μ_1 2μ μ $\mu=0$

$\mu>\mu_1$

5. (b)

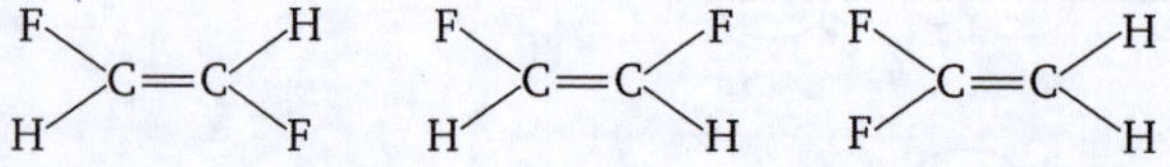

$\mu=0$ $\mu\neq0$ $\mu\neq0$

Passage-14

1. (c) AlF_3 is ionic compound, hence Al^{3+} and F^- both have complete octet, rest compounds do not complete, their octet.

Passage-15

1. (b) $BrF_2^+(sp^3)$, $BrF_2^-(sp^3d)$, $BrF_4^+(sp^3d)$, $BrF_4^-(sp^3d^2)$, $NO_2^+(sp)$, $NO_3^-(sp^2)$, $SO_3^{2-}(sp^3)$, $SO_4^{2-}(sp^3)$

2. (d) IF (polar and planar) IF_3 (polar and planar)

IF_5 (polar and non-planar) IF_7 (non-polar and non-planar)

3. (b)

	Molecule	Electronic geometry	Molecular geometry
(a)	NCl_3	Tetrahedral	Trigonal pyramidal
(b)	PCl_5	Trigonal *bi*-pyramidal	Trigonal *bi*-pyramidal
(c)	SF_4	Trigonal *bi*-pyramidal	See-saw
(d)	XeF_4	Square *bi*-pyramidal	Square planar

Passage-16

1. (c) During lewis acid (H^+) and lewis base ($\ddot{N}H_3$) the hybridisation of nitrogen atom does not change because valence shell e^- pair in NH_3 molecule and NH_4^+ ion are same.

2. (c) Due to more compactness or surface negative charge intensity SF_6 dose not acts as lewis acid.

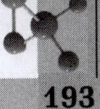

ONE OR MORE ANSWERS IS/ARE CORRECT

6. (a, b)

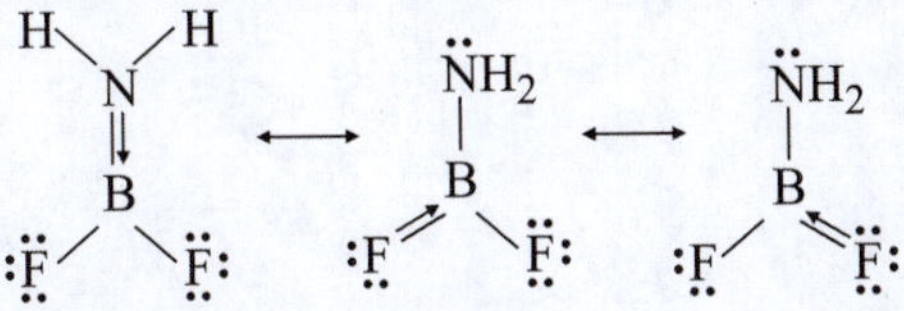

$2p_\pi$-$2p_\pi$ back bonding

According to Bent's rule there is more *p*-character in B—F bond than in B—N bond; hence FBF is less than 120º

As size of —NH_2 group is larger than F-atom hence repulsion between —NH_2 group and F-atoms is higher than between two F-atoms.

As lone pair of N-atom in NH_2 group participate in back bonding hence H—N—H is greater than 109º28', as hybridization of N is changing from sp^3 towards close to sp^2

8. (b, c)

Due to $2p_\pi \cdot 3d_\pi$ back bonding observed bond angle in $N(SiH_3)_3$ and $O(SiH_3)_2$ is higher than expected

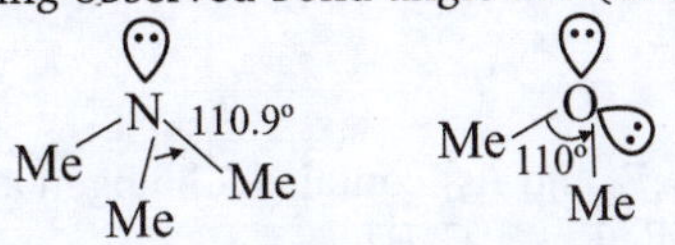

both have no back bonding but higher bond angle is due to steric repulsions between methyl groups.

9. (b, d)

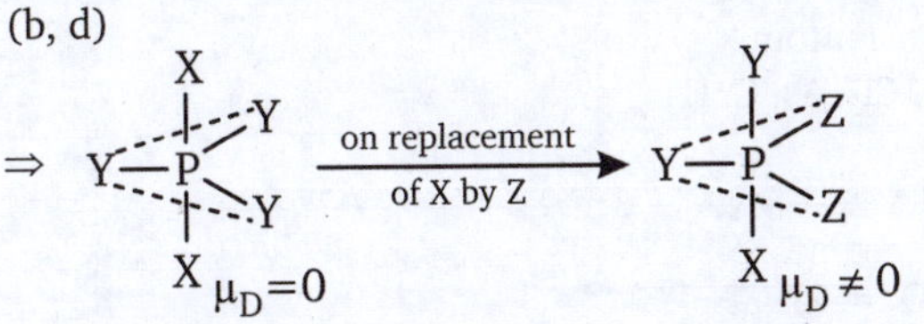

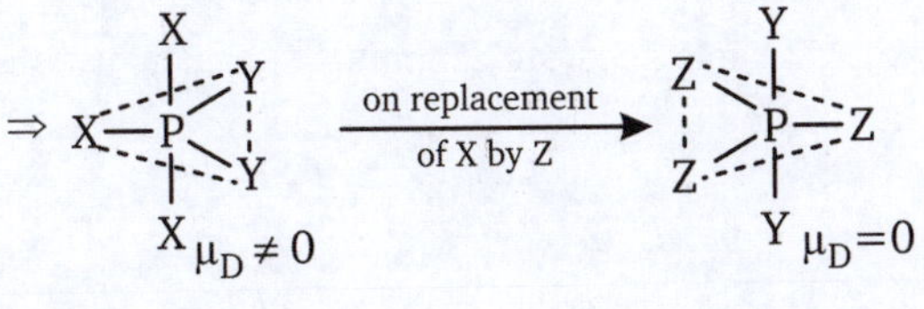

10. (a, b, c, d)

According to Bent's rule, there is less *s*-character in C—F bonds in COF_2 than in C—Cl bonds in case of $COCl_2$ hence $\gamma' > \gamma$ and $\angle FCF$ is less than 120º.

$\Rightarrow \alpha = \beta$ as both C—F bonds are equivalent similarly $\alpha' = \beta'$ as both C—Cl bonds are equivalent $\alpha = \beta > \gamma$

$\alpha > \alpha'$

$\beta > \beta'$

11. (a, d)

[Melting point of a covalent compound having bond between metal and non-metal]

$$\propto \frac{1}{\text{Polarization}}$$

Hence, melting point of $BeF_2 > BeCl_2$

12. (c, d)

$K_a' > K_a$

$CHF_3 \overset{K_a}{\rightleftharpoons} CF_3^- + H^+$

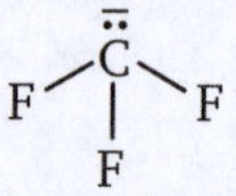

Stabilized by inductive effect of F-atoms

$CHCl_3 \overset{K_a'}{\rightleftharpoons} CCl_3^- + H^+$

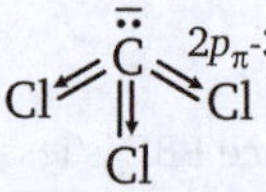

Due to combined effect of inductive effect of Cl-atoms and $2p_\pi$-$3d_\pi$ back bonding, lone pair at C-atom (negative charge) in CCl_3^- is more delocalized than in CF_3^-. Hence CCl_3^- is more stable than CF_3^- and CCl_3^- is weaker lewis base than CF_3^-.

14. (a, b, c, d)

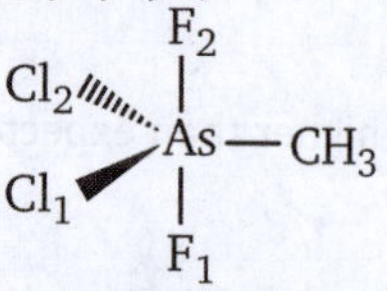

(a) The plane which passes from (Cl_1, F_1, F_2 and As) contains 3-halogen atoms.
(b) Axial plane → maximum atom = 5[F_1, F_2, As, C, H]
equatorial plane → maximum atom = 5[Cl_1, Cl_2, As, C, H]
(c) $(B.L.)_{As-Cl} > (B.L.)_{As-F}$ As size of Cl-atom >> F-atom.
(d) Equatorial plane → maximum atoms = 5[Cl_1, Cl_2, As, C, H]

15. (a, b)

(a) $N_3^{\ominus}$,

$\overset{\ominus}{N}=\overset{\oplus}{N}=\overset{\ominus}{N} \leftrightarrow \overset{\ominus}{N}^{2}-\overset{\oplus}{N}\equiv N \leftrightarrow N\equiv\overset{\oplus}{N}-\overset{2-}{N}$ (B. O. = 2)

(b) N_2F_2, 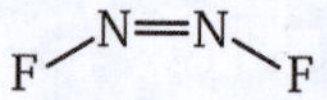 $(B.O.)_{N-N} = 2$

(c) N_2O_4, 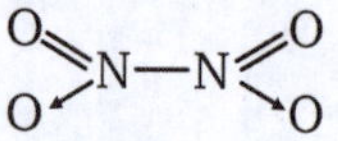 $(B.O.)_{N-N} = 1$

(d) N_2O, $N\equiv N \rightarrow O$ $(B.O.)_{N-N} \approx 3$

22. (a, c, d)

(a) $\underline{Al}(OH)_3 + NaOH \longrightarrow Na[\underline{Al}(OH)_4]$
(sp^2) (sp^3)

(b) $\underline{B_2}H_6 + 2$ 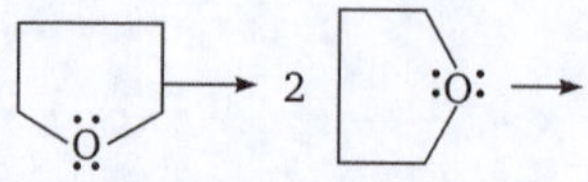 BH_3
(sp^3) THF (sp^3)

(c) $\underline{Si}F_4 + 2HF \longrightarrow H_2\underline{Si}F_6$
sp^3d (sp^3d^2)

(d) $2\underline{P}Cl_5 \xrightarrow{\text{solidification}} \underline{P}Cl_4^{\oplus} + \underline{P}Cl_6^{\ominus}$
(sp^3d) (sp^3) (sp^3d^2)

24. (a, c, d)

O_2 = Paramagnetic molecule with 2 unpaired electrons in antibonding *p*-orbital

O_3 = diamagnetic molecule

B_2 = Paramagnetic with 2 unpaired electron in bonding π-orbitals

C_2 = Diamagnetic molecule

$NO \longrightarrow \overset{\oplus}{N}O$ (Electron removes from antibonding orbital

$\because$ bond length decreases)

$CO \longrightarrow C\overset{\oplus}{O}$ (Electron removes from antibonding orbital

$\because$ bond length decreases)

25. (c,d) 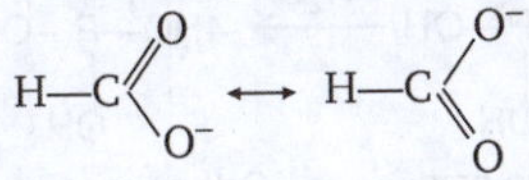 B.O. $= \frac{2+1}{2} = 1.5$

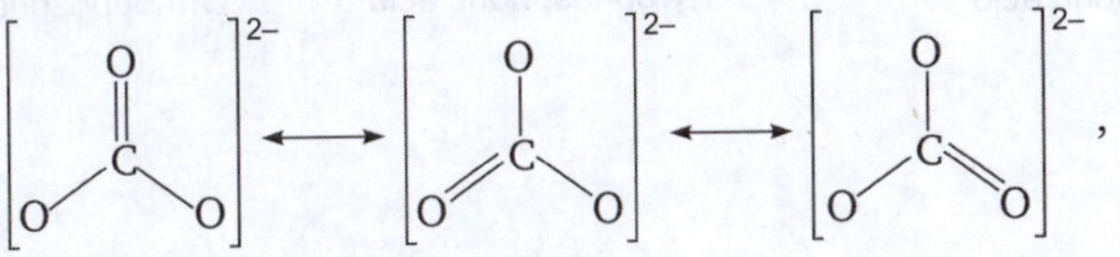

$$B.O. = \frac{2+1+1}{3} = \frac{4}{3} = 1.33$$

C—O bond length in $HCOO^-$ is less than C—O bond length in CO_3^{2-}

26. (a,c,d) 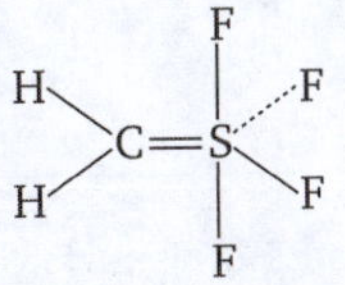

Hydrogen atoms are in a vertical plane with axial fluorine atoms π-bond involving a *p*-orbital of carbon atom must lie in equatorial plane of the molecule.
Six atoms, *i.e.*, 2 H-atoms, C, S and both axial F-atoms lie in one plane.

29. (a,b,c,d) $\overset{\delta+}{Si}—\overset{\delta-}{H}$ $\overset{\delta-}{C}—\overset{\delta+}{H}$

30. (a,b,c,d) 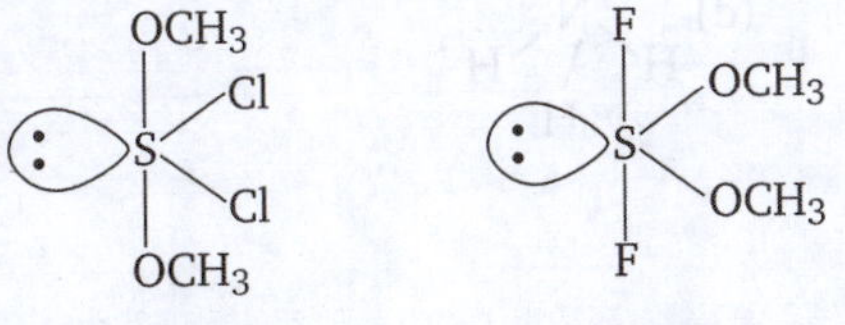

$SCl_2(OCH_3)_2$ (I) $SF_2(OCH_3)_2$ (II)

31. (b,c,d)

Molecule may have only integral/fractional value of bond order
Molecule may or not be paramagnetic
Molecule will exist

32. (a, b, c, d)

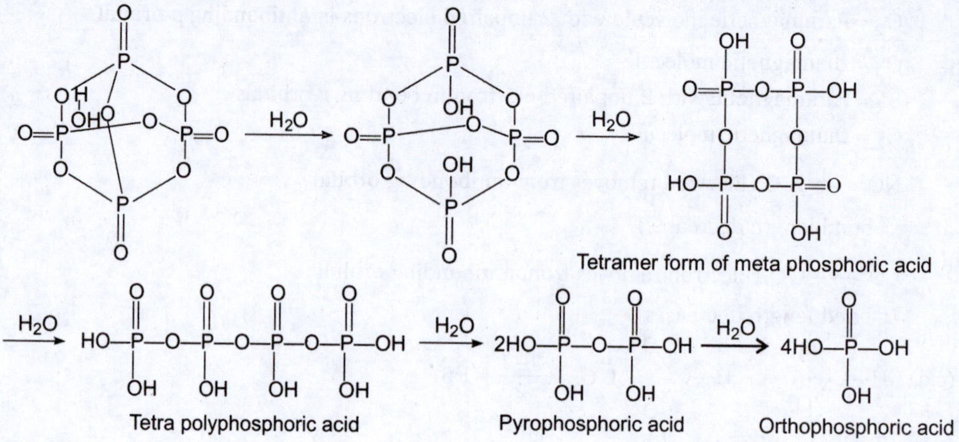

33. (a,c) $NO^+[BF_4]^-$

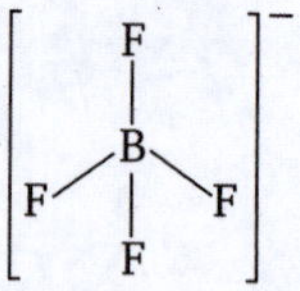

No. of σ bonds in $[BF_4]^- = 4$

⇒ B.O. of $NO^+ = 3.0$, *i.e.*, one sigma bond and two π bonds

∴ No. of π bonds = 2

No. of σ bonds = 5

⇒ B.O. of $NO^+ = 3.0$

and B.O. of NO = 2.5

⇒ NO^+ is diamagnetic and BF_4^- is also diamagnetic

⇒ B—F bonds are longer in BF_4^- than in BF_3 due to absence of *pπ-pπ* back bonding in $[BF_4]$

46. (a, c, d)

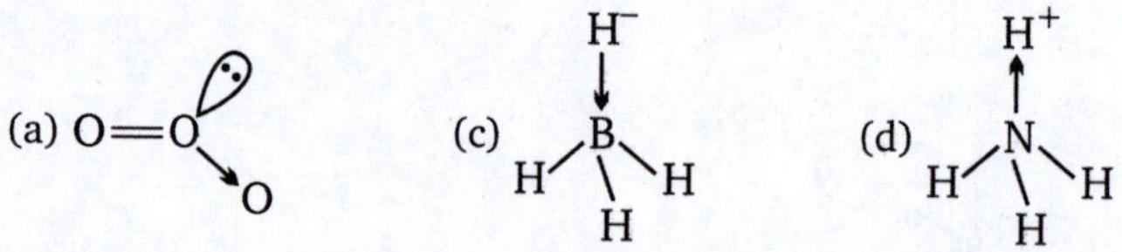

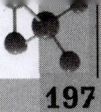

MATCH THE COLUMN

1. (a)

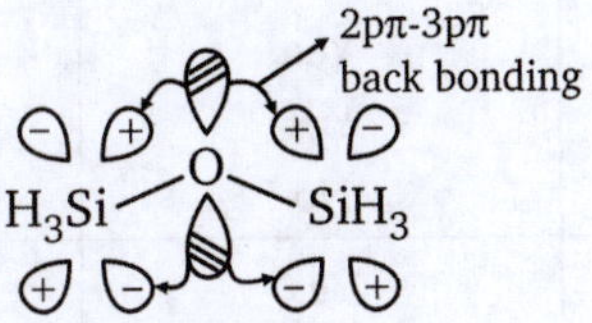

→ Si—O—Si ≈ 144°
→ Hybridization of O-atom changed to sp^2
→ In $2p_\pi$ - $3d_\pi$ back bonding non-axial *d*-orbital of t_{2g} is used
→ Electron density at O-atom decreases

(b)

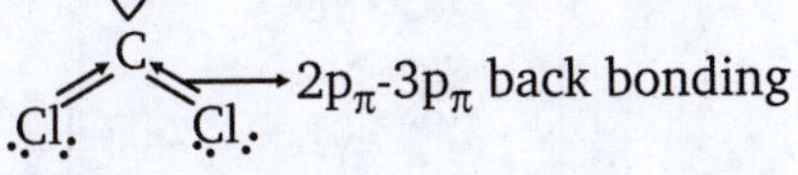

→ ∠Cl — O — Cl increases due to back bonding and steric repulsion between both Cl-atoms
→ Hybridization of C remains sp^2
→ Electron density increases at central C-atom.

(c)

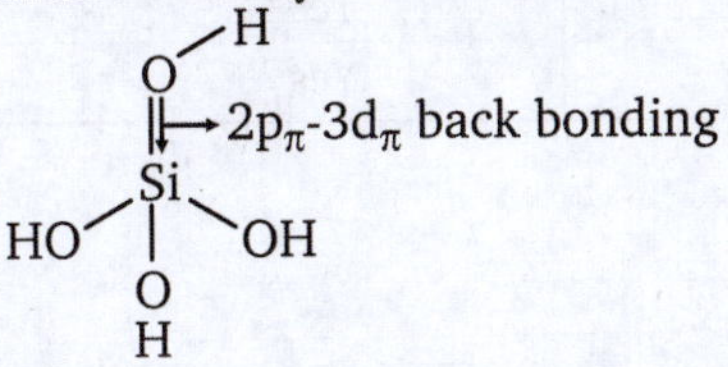

→ Electron density at Si-atom increases due to $2p_\pi - 3d_\pi$ back bonding
→ Non-axial *d*-orbital of t_{2g} set of orbitals is involved in back bonding
→ All O—Si—O remains at 109°28' because all four substituents are same

(d)

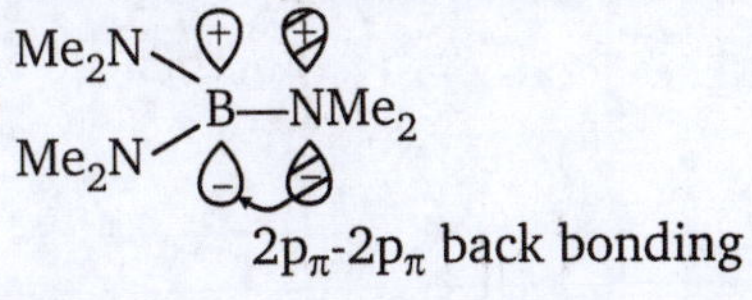

→ Hybridization of central does not change
→ Electron density at B-atom increases
→ All N—B—N remain same as all three substituents are same.

2. M.O. configuration for molecules having total number electron less or equal to 14.

$$\sigma 1s < \overset{*}{\sigma} 1s < \sigma 2s < \overset{*}{\sigma} 2s < \begin{matrix}\pi 2p_x \\ \pi 2p_y\end{matrix} < \sigma 2p_z < \begin{matrix}\overset{*}{\pi} 2p_x \\ \overset{*}{\pi} 2p_x\end{matrix} < \overset{*}{\sigma} 2p_z$$

For molecules having total number of e^-s greater than 14

$$\sigma 1s < \overset{*}{\sigma} 1s < \sigma 2s < \overset{*}{\sigma} 2s < \sigma 2p_z < \begin{matrix}\pi 2p_x \\ \pi 2p_y\end{matrix} < \begin{matrix}\overset{*}{\pi} 2p_x \\ \overset{*}{\pi} 2p_y\end{matrix} < \overset{*}{\sigma} 2p_z$$

S. No.	species	Total No. of e^-s	No. of unpaired e^-s and lieff unpaired e^-s and lieff	Mixing of *s* and *p*-orbitals	Bond order
a	CO	14	diamagnetic	Yes	3.0
	CN^-	14	diamagnetic	Yes	3.0
	NO^+	14	diamagnetic	Yes	3.0
	O_2^{2+}	14	diamagnetic	No	3.0
b	N_2^+	13	paramagnetic	Yes	2.5
	O_2^+	15	paramagnetic	No	2.5
	O_2^-	17	paramagnetic	No	1.5
	NO	15	paramagnetic	Yes	2.5
c	NO^-	16	paramagnetic	Yes	2.0
	N_2^{2+}	13	diamagnetic	Yes	2.0
	C_2	12	diamagnetic	Yes	2.0
	B_2^{2-}	12		Yes	2.0
d	CN	13	paramagnetic	Yes	2.5
	C_2^+	11	paramagnetic	Yes	1.5
	B_2^+	9	diamagnetic	Yes	0.5
	N_2^-	15	diamagnetic	Yes	2.5

3. (a) $3I_2 \rightarrow I_3^+ + I_3^-$

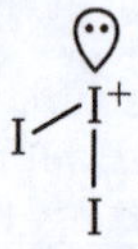

(I_3^+)

Hybridization : sp^3
planar

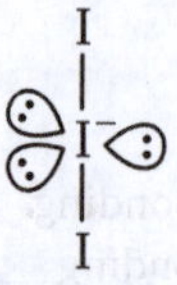

(I_3^-)

Hybridization : sp^3d
planar

(b) $B(OH)_3 + OH^- \rightarrow B(OH)_4^-$

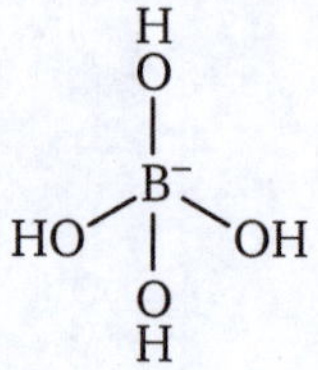

→ Hybridization of B : sp^3

→ Non-planar

(c) $Ba^{2+}SO_4^{2-}$:

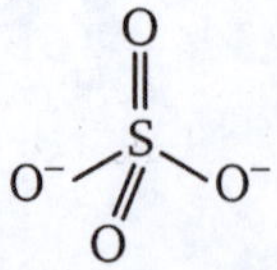

; Hybridization of S : sp^3

Non-planar

$p\pi$-$d\pi$ bonds = 2

(d) MgO ⇒ Ionic; SO_2: covalent

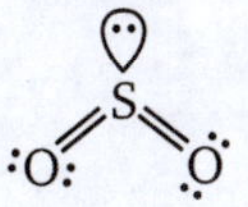

Hybridization of S : sp^2,

Planar

$p\pi$-$d\pi$ bonds = 1

4. ⇒ 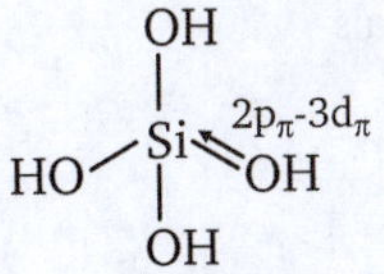

→ $2p_\pi$-$3d_\pi$ back bond

→ Can exhibit intermolecular H-bonding as H-atom is bonded to O-atom.

→ Proton donor acid; basicity = 4

⇒ 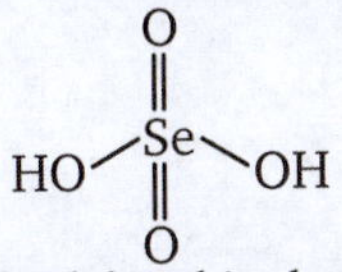

→ back bond is absent

→ can form intermolecular H-bond as H-atom is directly bonded to O-atom

→ Proton donor acid, basicity = 2

→ Hypervalent, Number of e^-s at Se = 12

⇒ 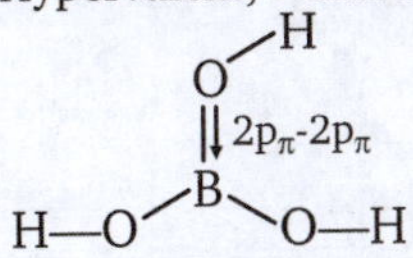

→ $2p_\pi$-$2p_\pi$ back bond is present

→ Hypovalent, as number of e^-s at B-atom = 6

→ Does not furnish H^+

⇒ 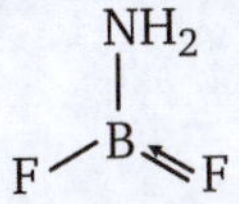

→ $2p_\pi$-$2p_\pi$ back bond is present

→ Can form intermolecular H-bonding as H-atom is directly bonded to N-atom

Hypovalent number of e^-s at B-atom = 6

→ Does not furnish H^+

5. (a) 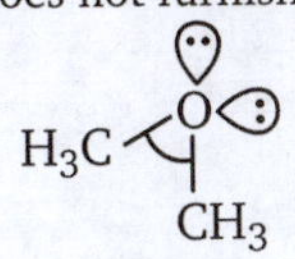

→ Unequal distribution of s-character in hybrid orbitals

→ ∠C—O—C > 109°28'

→ Both O—C bonds are equivalent

(b) 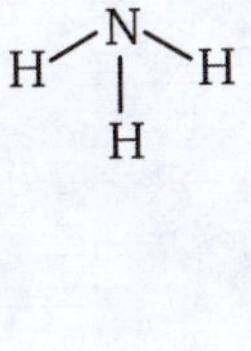

→ Unequal distribution of s-character in hybrid orbitals

→ ∠HNH < 109°28'

→ All three N—H bonds are equivalent

(c) 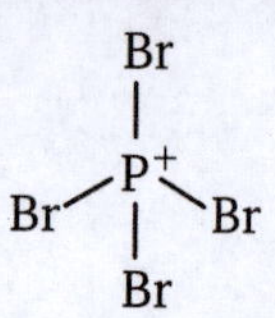

→ Equal distribution of s-character in hybrid orbitals
→ $\angle$Br — P — Br = 109°28′
→ All P—Br bonds are equivalent

(d) 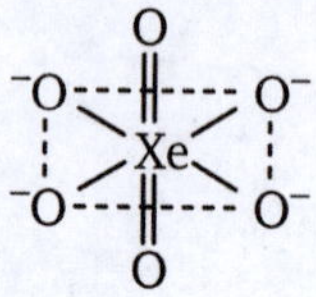

→ Equal distribution of s-character in all hybrid orbitals
→ $\angle$O—Xe—O = 90°
→ All Xe—O bonds are equivalent

11. $H_2S_4O_6$: 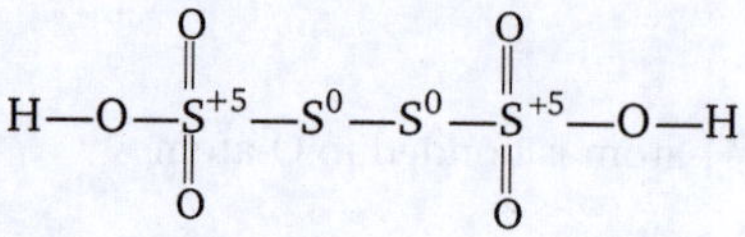

$H_2S_2O_3$: 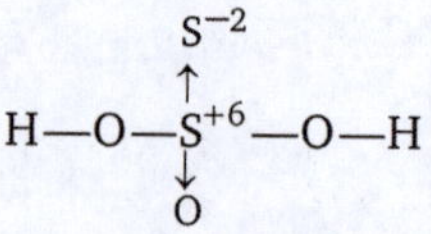

H_2SO_5 : 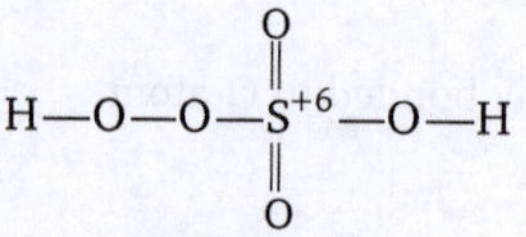

$H_2S_2O_5$: 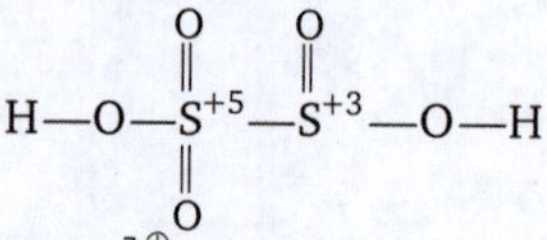

12. (A) NH_4Cl 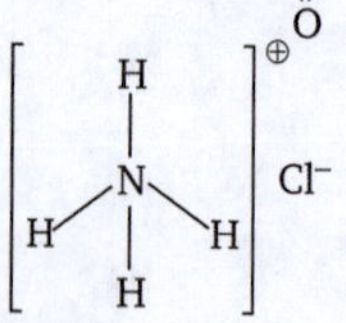

(B) $CuSO_4.5H_2O$ 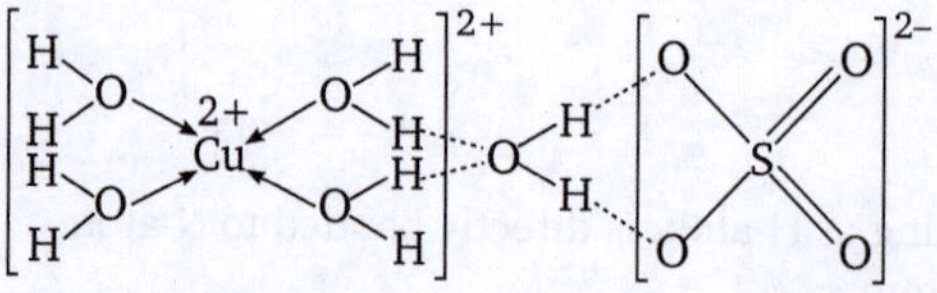

(C) HNC 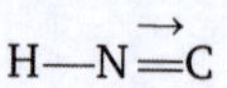

(D) Liquid H_2O_2 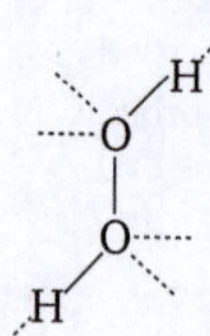

13. (A) $B_3H_3H_6$ 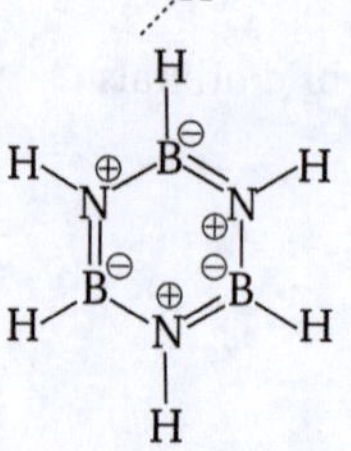

(B) S_2Cl_2 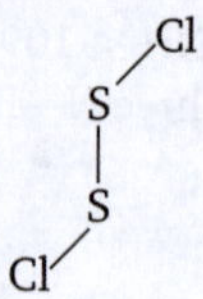

(C) B_2H_6

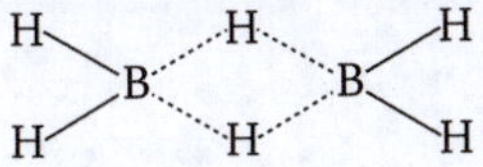

(D) I_2Cl_6

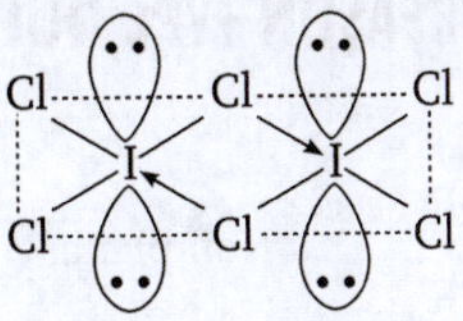

14. (A)

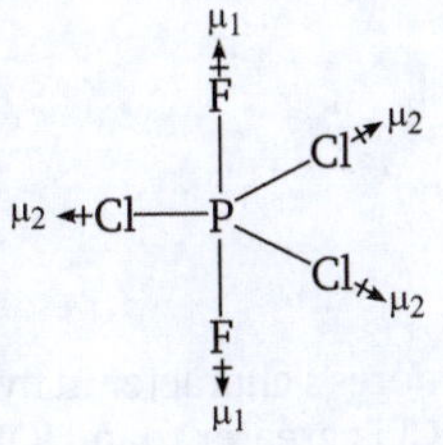

$\mu = 0$

sp^3*d* hybridisation
Trigonal bipyramidal

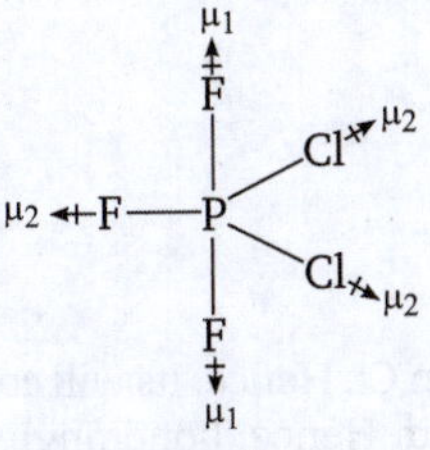

$\mu \neq 0$

sp^3*d* hybridisation
Trigonal bipyramidal

(B)

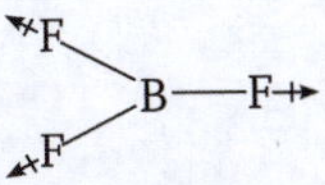

$\mu = 0$

sp^2 hybridisation
Trigonal planar

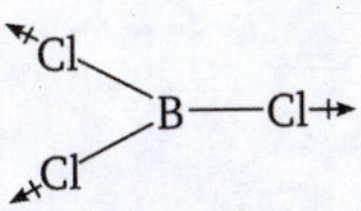

$\mu = 0$

sp^2 hybridisation
Trigonal planar

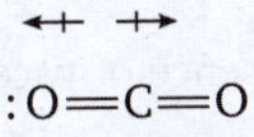

sp hybridisation
linear
$\mu = 0$
No. of $e^-s = 22$

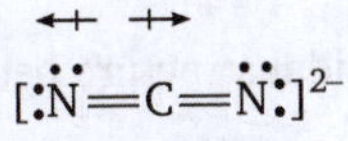

sp hybridisation
linear
$\mu = 0$
No. of $e^-s = 22$

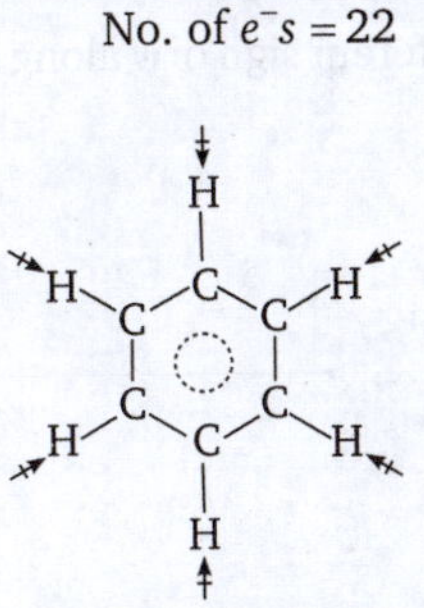

sp^2
planar
$\mu = 0$
No. of $e^-s = 42$

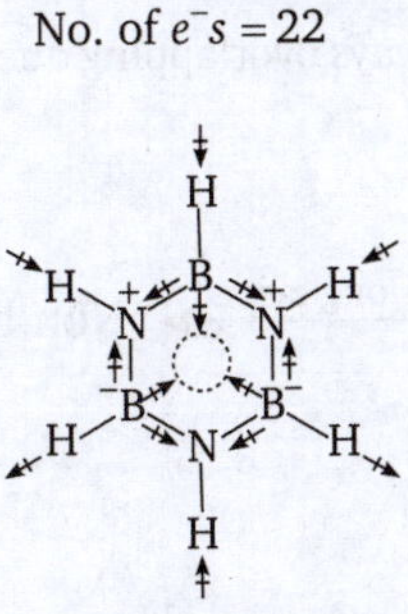

B: *sp*^{2} N: *sp*^{2}
planar
$\mu = 0$
No. of $e^-s = 42$

ASSERTION-REASON TYPE QUESTIONS

4. 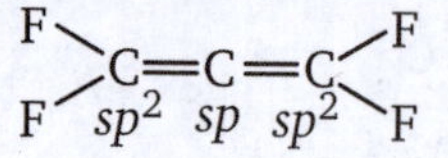 : Non-planar

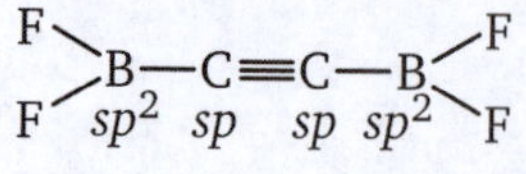 : Planar

12. (B) In $H{-}O{-}Cl$, O is more electronegative than Cl. Hence, its will contain mores *s* character in hybrid orbital hence bond angle will be more than expected. Hence, bond angle is HOCl is greater than HOF.

14. (D) $\underset{\text{Oxidizing agent}}{Pb^{4+}} + \underset{\text{strong reducing agent}}{4I^-} \longrightarrow PbI_2 + I_2$

hence, PbI_4 does not exist

$\underset{\text{oxidizing agent}}{Pb^{4+}} + \underset{\text{not good red, agent like } I^-}{4Cl^-} \longrightarrow \underset{\text{unstable}}{PbCl_4} \xrightarrow[50°C]{\text{above}} PbCl_2 + Cl_2$

Since Cl_2 is a strong oxidizing agent, hence Cl^- is poor reducing agent, therefore $PbCl_4$ does from but decomposes on heating.

25. (A) In $(CH_3)_3\ddot{N}$, N is sp^3 hybridized, having pyramidal structure because of absence of vacant orbital on carbon atom therefore no back bonding is possible.
In $(SiH_3)_3N$, N is sp^2 hybridized, on the basis of $p\pi$-$d\pi$ back bonding $(SiH_3)_3N$ resulting into triangular planar structure
Covalency of both C and Si is four.

28. (B) This combination can not form π-bond by sideways overlapping due to different sign of ψ along *z*-axis.

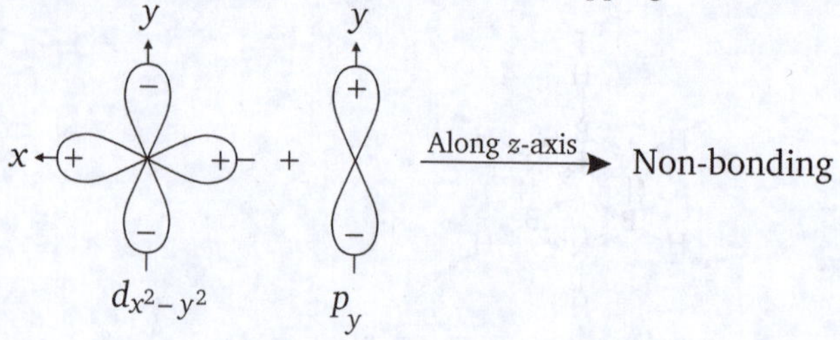

29. (B) The correct representation of hydrogen bonding is 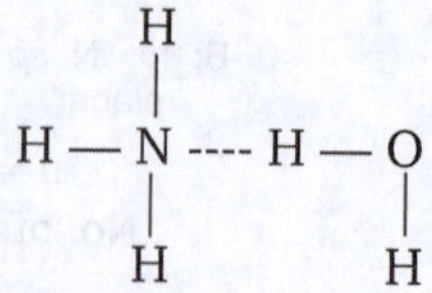

$$NH_3 + H_2O \longrightarrow NH_4^+ + OH^-$$

and ammonia never acts as acid in aqueous medium.

$$NH_3 + H_2O \longrightarrow NH_2^- + H_3O^+$$

SUBJECTIVE PROBLEMS

1. $I_3^- \Rightarrow sp^3d$

Group A

	l.P.
Px_4	1
Qy_3	2
Rz_2	3

$\boldsymbol{x}$ **= Total** *l.P.* **= 6**

$AsF_4^+ \Rightarrow sp^3$

Group B

	l.P.
Sx_4	0
Ty_3	1
Uz_2	2

$\boldsymbol{y}$ **= Total** *l.P.* **= 3**

$x/y = 6/3 \Rightarrow 2$

2. $n = 1$, then X = H; A = N

(i) NH_2^- (ii) NH_3 (iii) NH_4^+

lone pair $x = 2, y = 1, z = 0$

$x^3 + y^2 + z = (2)^3 + (1)^2 + (0) = 9$

4. (i) NO ⟶ NO^+

2.5 ⟶ 3.0

Paramagnetic

(ii) O_2^- ⟶ O_2^{2-}

(1.5) ⟶ (1)

(iii) O_2 ⟶ O_2^+

(2) ⟶ (2.5)

Paramagnetic ⟶ Paramagnetic

(iv) NO^+ ⟶ NO^-

(3) ⟶ (2)

Diamagnetic ⟶ Paramagnetic

(v) NO^+ ⟶ NO^{2+}

(3) ⟶ (2.5)

Diamagnetic ⟶ Diamagnetic

(vi) CO ⟶ CO^+

(3) ⟶ (3.5)

Diamagnetic ⟶ Paramagnetic

$c^3 - b^2 - a = 3^3 - 3^2 - 5 = 27 - 9 - 5 = 13$

5. → Unsymmetrical cleavage of B_2H_6: with small sized strong Lewis base like : NH_3, MNH_2, Me_2NH

→ Symmetrical cleavage of B_2H_6: with large sized strong Lewis base or weaker Lewis base like: PH_3, PF_3, H^-, CO, T.H.F. Me_3N, pyridine.

$+ 2L \longrightarrow 2BH_3L$

6. $\frac{6}{2} = 3$, Elements A = Al, B = P, C = S, D = Cl, E = F

	Compounds	Polarity
(i)	$CE_4(SF_4)$	P
(ii)	$BD_2E_3(PCl_2F_3)$	P
(iii)	$DE_3(ClF_3)$	P
(iv)	$CE_2(SF_2)$	P
(v)	$BD_3E_2(PCl_3F_2)$	NP
(vi)	$C_2E_2(S_2F_2)$	P
(vii)	$DE(ClF)$	P
(viii)	$A_2D_6(Al_2Cl_6)$	NP

7.

Compounds		Geometry	sp^2 (C)	sp (C)
(i)	CO	$C \equiv O$	0	1
(ii)	CO_2	$O = C = O$	0	1
(iii)	C_3O_2	$O = C = C = C = O$	0	3
(iv)	$C_{12}O_9$	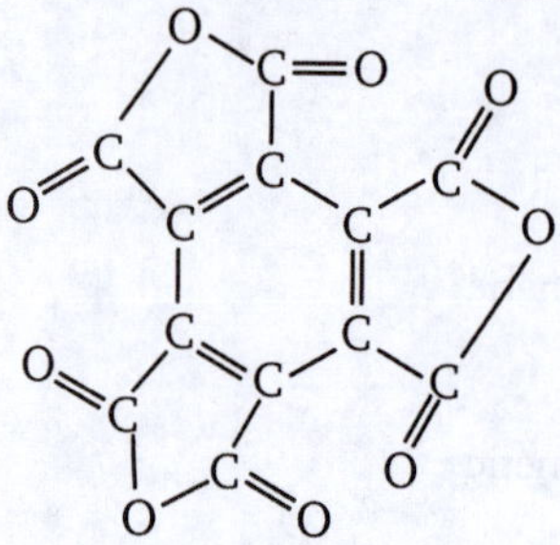	12	0

$\Rightarrow \quad |p - q| = |12 - 5| = 7$

11. Compound

SX_2	$n_1 = 2$	$m_1 = 2$
PX_3	$n_2 = 3$	$m_2 = 1$
SiX_4	$n_3 = 4$	$m_3 = 0$
AlX_3	$n_4 = 3$	$m_4 = 0$

$$\left|\frac{2+3+4+3}{2+1}\right|^2 = \left|\frac{12}{3}\right|^2 = |4|^2 = 16$$

12. Species having bond angle less or equal to 109°28' and also can act as lewis base are :

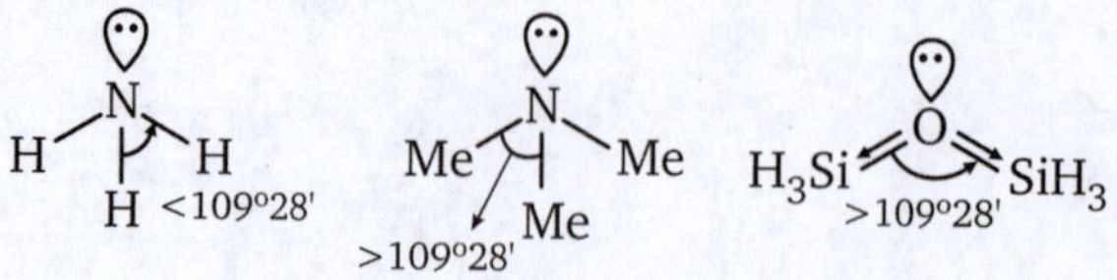

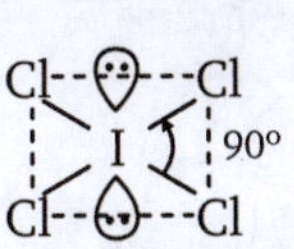

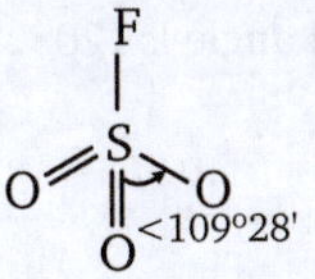

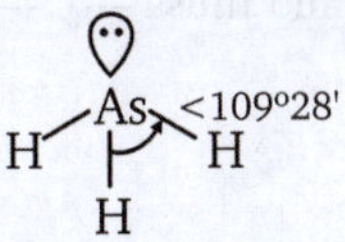

13. $O_2^+[PtF_6]^-$

O_2^+ has one unpaired e^-

$[PtF_6]^-$ has one unpaired e^-, because Pt is in +5 oxidation state so total unpaired electron is 2.

14. $N_2^+, O_2, B_2, N_2^{2-}$ have symmetrical electronic distribution in their HOMO and are also paramagnetic.

N_2^+ paramagnetic and symmetrical electronic distribution in their HOMO.

O_2 paramagnetic and symmetrical electronic distribution in their HOMO.

B_2 paramagnetic and symmetrical electronic distribution in their HOMO.

N_2^{2-} paramagnetic and symmetrical electronic distribution in their HOMO.

O_2^{2-} diamagnetic and symmetrical electronic distribution in their HOMO.

C_2 diamagnetic and symmetrical electronic distribution in their HOMO.

C_2^{2-} diamagnetic and symmetrical electronic distribution in their HOMO.

15. Back bond found in each covalent bond in → BF_3, PF_3, POF_3

16. 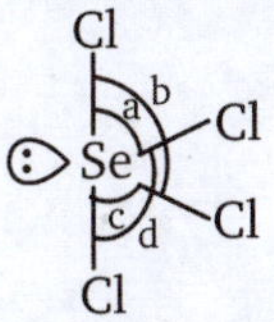

(a = b = c = d) < 90° due to lone pair-bond pair repulsion.

17. In $O(Me)_2$ and MeNCS back bonding is absent.

18. $B(OMe)_2$ and HCHO can not form H-bond.

19. ⇒ AL_{n_1}:

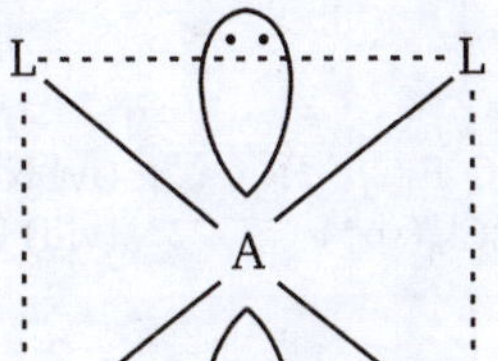

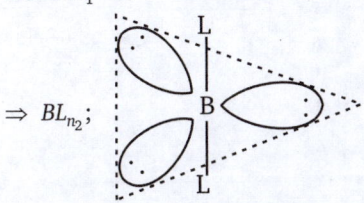

⇒ Number of electron pair on $A = 6$

⇒ Non-polar

⇒ Planar

Hence $n_1 = 4$

⇒ BL_{n_2};

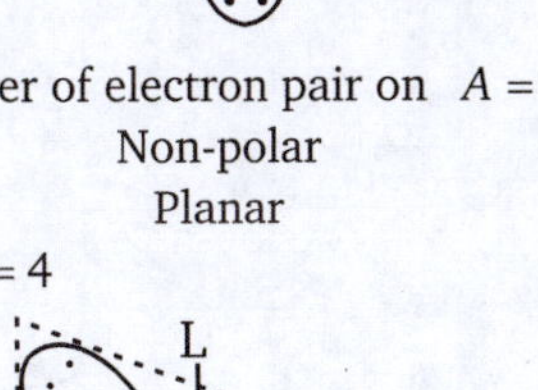

⇒ Number of electron pair on $B = 5$

⇒ Non-polar

⇒ Planar

Hence $n_2 = 2$

$(n_1 - n_2)^2 = (4-2)^2 = 4$

20. $H_2C = CI_2$, has sp^2 hybridised carbon and thus I—C—I bond angle is 120°.

$\therefore \quad \frac{IO}{CI} = \sin 60°$

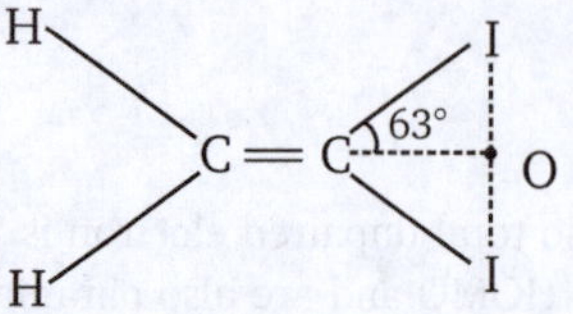

[In $\Delta ICO \angle ICO = 60°$ and $\angle IOC = 90°$]

$IO = CI \sin 60° = 2.35 \times 0.866$

$= 2.0351$ Å

I—I distance $= 2.0351 \times 2 = 4.07$ Å ≈ 4

21. $(P) = (i), (iii), (iv), (vii) (4)$

$(Q) = (ii), (v) (ix) (3)$

$(R) = (vi), (vii) (2)$

then $Q \times R - P = 3 \times 2 - 4 \Rightarrow 2$

24. $CH_3^+, (C_3H_5)_3Al, HCHO, TiCl_4, CO_2, SiCl_4, BF_3$

25.

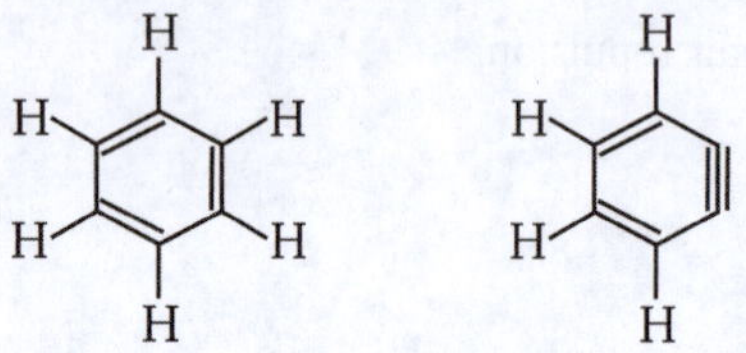

$x = 12$ $\quad\quad$ $y = 11$

$|x - y| = 1$

26. (i) $IF_5 (sp^3d)$ (ii) $ClI_4^- (sp^3d^2)$ (iii) $XeO_2F_2 (sp^3d)$ (iv) $NH_2^- (sp^3)$

(v) $BCl_3 (sp^2)$ (vi) $BeCl_2 (sp)$ (vii) $AsCl_4^+ (sp^3)$ (viii) $B(OH)_3 (sp^2)$

(ix) $NO_2^- (sp^2)$ (x) $ClO_2^+ (sp^2)$

$x = (sp^3)2 + sp^3d(1) + sp^3d^2(2) = 5$

$y = 4, \quad z = 1; \quad 5 + 4 - 1 \Rightarrow 8$

27.

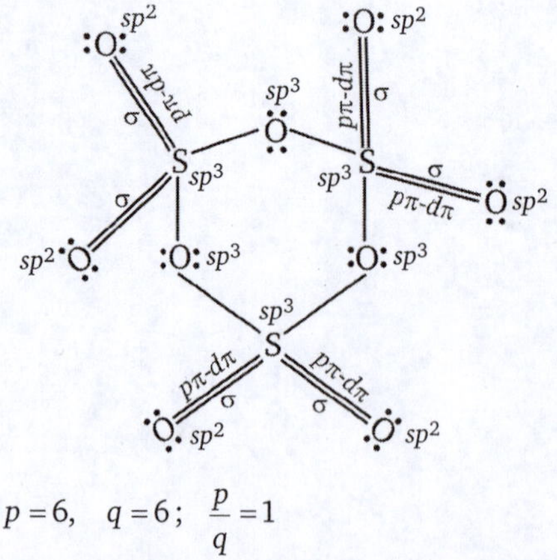

$p = 6, \quad q = 6; \quad \frac{p}{q} = 1$

28. $x = 3, \quad y = 1, \quad z = 3$

29.

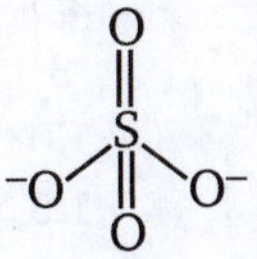

(*R*)

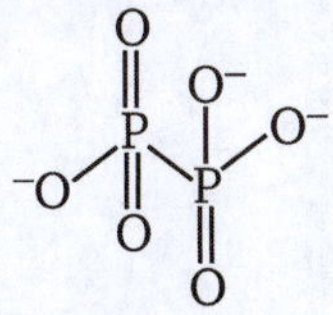

(*P*)

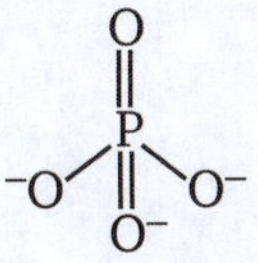

(*R*)

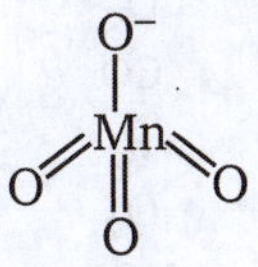

(*R*)

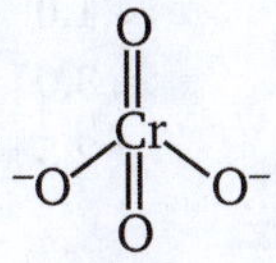

(*R*)

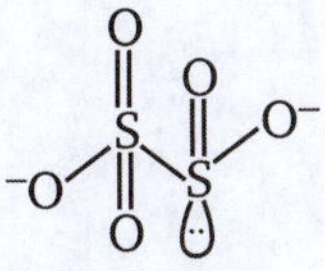

(*P* and *Q*)

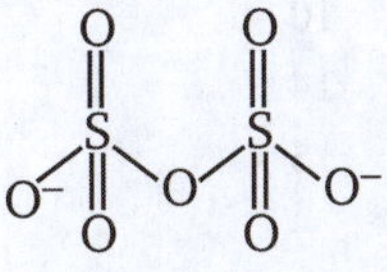

(*P* and *Q*)

$P = 3, R = 4, Q = 2$

30. $n = 1$, then $X = H; A = N$

(i) NH_2^- (ii) NH_3 (iii) NH_4^+

lone pair $x = 2, \quad y = 1, \quad z = 0$

$x^3 + y^2 + z = (2)^3 + (1)^2 + (0) = 9$

32.

(1)

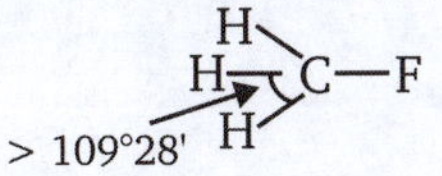

(2)

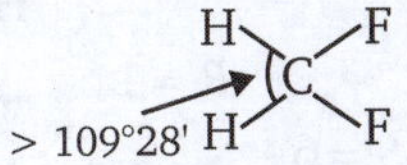

(3)

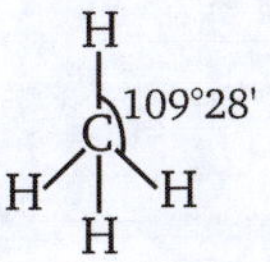

(4)

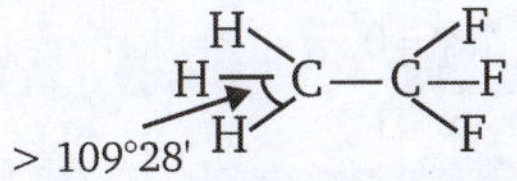

(5)

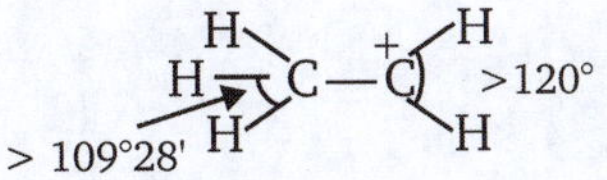

(6)

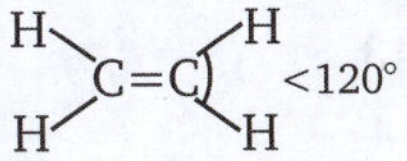

33. → Molecular orbital configuration for upto 14 electrons

$\sigma_{1s} < \overset{*}{\sigma}_{1s} < \sigma_{2s} < \overset{*}{\sigma}_{2s} < \pi_{2px}\pi_{2py} < \sigma_{2pz} < \overset{*}{\pi}_{2px}$

$= \overset{*}{\pi}_{2py} < \overset{*}{\sigma}_{2pz}$

For more than 14 electrons

$\sigma_{1s} < \overset{*}{\sigma}_{1s} < \sigma_{2s} < \overset{*}{\sigma}_{2s} < \sigma_{2pz} < \pi_{2px} = \pi_{2py} < \overset{*}{\pi}_{2px}$

$= \overset{*}{\pi}_{2py} < \overset{*}{\pi}_{2pz}$

Bond order $= \frac{1}{2}$ number of electrons in [Bonding M.O. – Antibonding M.O.]

No.	Species	Total no.	No. of electrons in	No. of electrons	Bond order
(i)	O_2^+	15	10	5	2.5
(ii)	CO	14	10	4	3
(iii)	B_2	10	6	4	1.0
(iv)	O_2^-	17	10	7	1.5
(v)	NO^+	14	10	4	3
(vi)	He_2^+	3	2	1	0.5
(vii)	C_2^{++}	10	6	4	1.0
(viii)	CN^-	14	10	4	3.0
(ix)	N_2	15	10	5	2.5

34.

	A		B
σ-bond	12	+	12
π-bond	3	+	3

$\Rightarrow \frac{24}{6} = 4$

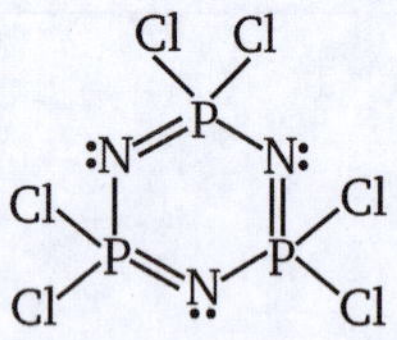

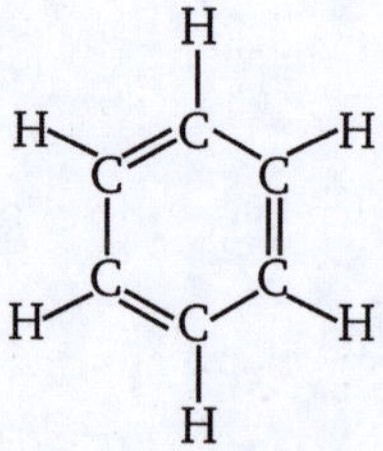

35. $P = 3$ $Q = 2$ $R = 1$ $S = 0$

Hence $P + Q + R + S = 6$

36.

Value of x	Dipole moment
$x_1 = 0$	$\mu = 0$
$x = 1$	$\mu \neq 0$
$x = 2$	$\mu \neq 0$
$x_2 = 3$	$\mu = 0$
$x = 4$	$\mu \neq 0$
$x_3 = 5$	$\mu = 0$

Then, $0 + 3 + 5 = 8$

37. G-1 A(Li), B(Na), C(K), D(Rb), E(Cs)

G-2 F(Be), G(Mg), H(Ca), I(Sr), J(Ba)

G-13 K(B), L(Al), M(Ga), N(In), O(Tl)

G-15 P(N), Q(P), R(As), S(Sb), T(Bi)

G-17 U(F), V(Cl), W(Br), X(I), Y(At)

(i) $Tl^+ > Ca^{2+}$; Polarising power (T)

(ii) $Bi^{3+} > Sb^{3+} > As^{3+}$; Stability of cation (T)

(iii) $F^-(aq) > Cl^-(aq) > Br^-(aq) > I^-(aq)$; Size (T)

(iv) $BaCl_2 > SrCl_2 < MgCl_2 < AlCl_3$; Covalent nature (T)

(v) $MgCO_3 > CaCO_3 > SrCO_3 > BaCO_3$; Thermal stability (F)

(vi) LiCl > NaCl > KCl > RbCl > CsCl ; Thermal stability (T)

(vii) $K_3N > Na_3N > Li_3N$; Lattice energy (F)

(viii) $BF_3 < BCl_3 < BBr_3 < BI_3$; Melting point (T)

$\Rightarrow |p - q|^2$ $|6 - 2|^2 = 16$

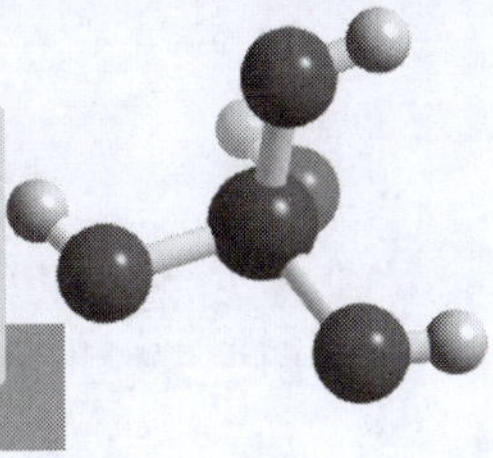

4

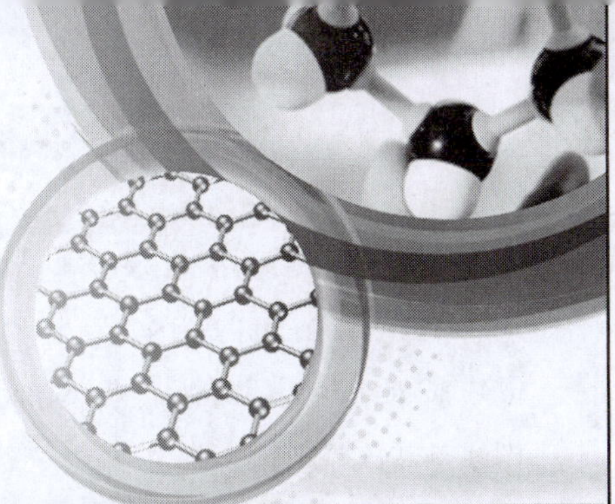

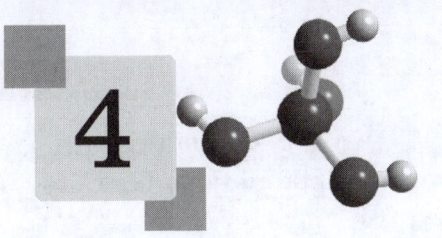

CO-ORDINATION COMPOUNDS

Level 1

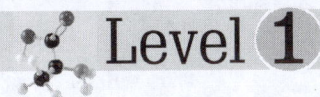

Classification of Ligands

1. The common features among the species CN^-, CO and NO^+ are :
(a) Bond order three and diamagnetic
(b) Bond order three and weak field ligands
(c) Paramagnetic and strong field ligands
(d) Paramagnetic and π - acceptor ligands

2. Ni^{2+} ion can be estimated by using dimethyl glyoxime and forms a cherry-red precipitate. The complex is stabilized by :
(a) ionic bonds
(b) coordinate covalent bonds
(c) dative π-bonds
(d) hydrogen bonds

3. Ammonia forms the complex $[Cu(NH_3)_4]^{2+}$ with copper ions in alkaline solution but not in acidic solution. The reason for this is :
(a) In alkaline solution $Cu(OH)_2$ is precipitated which is soluble in excess of alkali
(b) Copper hydroxide is amphoteric substance
(c) In acidic solution hydration protects Cu^{2+} ions
(d) In acidic solution protons are coordinated with ammonia molecules forming NH_4^+ ions

4. Select the wrong statement about alum :
(a) Its aqueous solution gives test of three types of ions
(b) Its aqueous solution is acidic in nature
(c) Its constituent ions retain their identity in aqueous solution
(d) Its constituent ions loose their identity in aqueous solution

5. Match the compounds given in column-I with the oxidation state of cobalt present in it (given in column-II) and assign the correct code.

Column-I (Complexes)	Column-II (Oxidation state of Co)
(P) $[Co(NCS)(NH_3)_5]SO_3$	(1) +4
(Q) $[Co(NH_3)_4Cl_2]SO_4$	(2) 0
(R) $Na_4[Co(S_2O_3)_3]$	(3) +1
(S) $[Co_2(CO)_8]$	(4) +2
	(5) +3

Codes :

	P	Q	R	S
(a)	5	2	4	5
(b)	4	3	2	1
(c)	5	1	4	2
(d)	4	1	2	3

Synergic Bonding

6. In the isoelectronic series of metal carbonyl, the CO bond strength is expected to increase in the order :

(a) $[Mn(CO)_6]^+ < [Cr(CO)_6] < [V(CO)_6]^-$
(b) $[V(CO)_6]^- < [Cr(CO)_6] < [Mn(CO)_6]^+$
(c) $[V(CO)_6]^- < [Mn(CO)_6]^+ < [Cr(CO)_6]$
(d) $[Cr(CO)_6] < [Mn(CO)_6]^+ < [V(CO)_6]^-$

7. Which is not true about metal carbonyls?

(a) Here CO acts as a Lewis base as well as Lewis acid
(b) Here metal acts as Lewis base as well as Lewis acid
(c) Here $d\pi$-$p\pi$ back bonding takes place
(d) Here $p\pi$-$p\pi$ back bonding takes place

8. Select **correct** order of C—O bond length :

(a) $(C-O)_{Cr(CO)_6} > (C-O)_{CO} > (C-O)_{CO^+}$
(b) $(C-O)_{Cr(CO)_6} > (C-O)_{CO^+} > (C-O)_{CO}$
(c) $(C-O)_{CO} > (C-O)_{Cr(CO)_6} > (C-O)_{CO^+}$
(d) $(C-O)_{CO} > (C-O)_{CO^+} > (C-O)_{Cr(CO)_6}$

9. The C—O bond length is found to maximum in :

(a) $H_3B \leftarrow CO$
(b) $[V(CO)_6]^-$
(c) $[Cr(CO)_6]^0$
(d) $[Mn(CO)_6]^+$

Oxidation State and Coordination Number

10. What is the oxidation number of Fe in $[Fe(H_2O)_5(NO)]^{2+}$ ion?

(a) +2
(b) +3
(c) +1
(d) 0

11. The oxidation state of iron in $Na_4[Fe(CN)_5(NOS)]$ is :

(a) +1
(b) +2
(c) +3
(d) zero

12. The coordination number of a central metal atom in a complex is determined by :
(a) the number of only anionic ligands bonded to the metal ion
(b) the number of monodentate ligands around a metal ion bonded by pi-bonds
(c) the number of monodentate ligands around a metal ion bonded by σ and pi-bonds both
(d) the number of monodentate ligands around a metal ion bonded by σ-bonds

13. Which statement about coordination number of a cation is true?
(a) Metal ions exhibit only a single characteristic coordination number
(b) The coordination number is equal to the number of ligands bonded to the metal atom
(c) The coordination number is determined solely by the tendency to surround the metal atom with the same number of electrons as one of the rare gases
(d) For most cations, the coordination number depends on the size, and charge of the cation

Sidwick's Rule of EAN

14. If EAN of central metal cation M^{2+} in a non-chelating complex is 36 and atomic no. of metal M is 26, then the number of monodentate ligand in this complex are :
(a) 5 (b) 4
(c) 6 (d) none of these

15. Which of the following is an oxidizing agent?
(a) $Mn(CO)_5$ (b) $Fe(CO)_5$
(c) $Mn_2(CO)_{10}$ (d) $Fe_2(CO)_9$

16. An effective atomic number of $Co(CO)_4$ is 35 and hence is less stable. It attains stability by :
(a) Oxidation of Co (b) Reduction of Co
(c) Dimerisation (d) Both (b) and (c)

17. Which of the following pair the EAN of central metal atom is not same?
(a) $[Fe(CN)_6]^{3-}$ and $[Fe(NH_3)_6]^{3+}$ (b) $[Cr(NH_3)_6]^{3+}$ and $[Cr(CN)_6]^{3-}$
(c) $[FeF_6]^{3-}$ and $[Fe(CN_6)]^{3-}$ (d) $[Ni(CO)_4]$ and $[Ni(CN)_4]^{2-}$

18. If complex compound, $[Fe(\pi - C_5H_5)_x(\pi - C_3H_5)_y(CO)_z]$ is following the Sidwick's rule of EAN then value of expression "$x + y + z$" is :
(Where x, y and z are natural numbers)
(a) 6 (b) 5
(c) 4 (d) 3

19. Select correct set of value of x, y respectively if complex $[Mn(CO)_x(\eta^y - C_5H_5)]$ follows EAN rule.
(a) 2, 5 (b) 4, 1
(c) 3, 5 (d) 3, 3

20. For complex compound, $[Cr(CO)_x(\pi - B_3N_3H_6)_y]$, the sum of $(x + y)$ is :
(a) 3 (b) 4
(c) 5 (d) 6

21. Which of the following pair the EAN of central metal atom is not same ?
(a) $[Fe(CN)_6]^{3-}$ and $[Fe(NH_3)_6]^{3+}$ (b) $[Cr(NH_3)_6]^{3+}$ and $[Cr(CN)_6]^{3-}$
(c) $[FeF_6]^{3-}$ and $[Fe(CN)_6]^{3-}$ (d) $[Ni(CO)_4]$ and $[Ni(CN)_4]^{2-}$

22. Which of them follow EAN rule

(a) 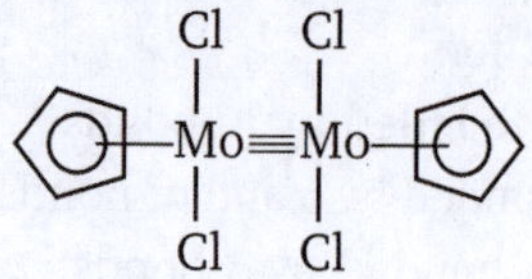

(b) 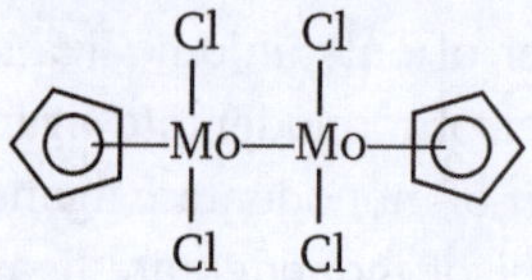

(c) 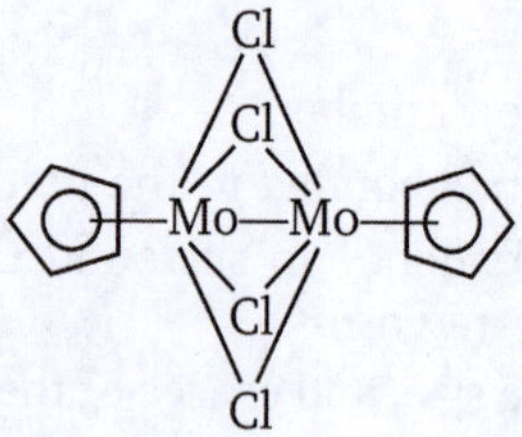

(d) 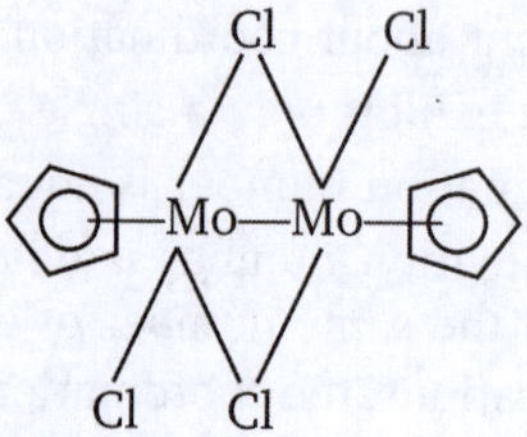

23. Which of the given complex species is following E.A.N. Rule ?

(a) $[Ca(EDTA)]^{2-}$ (b) $[Cr(en)_3]^{3+}$ (c) $[CoBrCl(trien)]^{+}$ (d) $[Ni(dmg)_2]$

24. EAN of the central metal atom/ion are equal in :

(a) $[\overset{*}{Ni}(CO)]_4, [\overset{*}{Fe}(CN)_6]^{4-}$ (b) $[\overset{*}{Ni}(en)_2]^{2+}, [\overset{*}{Fe}(H_2O)_6]^{2+}$

(c) $[\overset{*}{Co}(CN)_6]^{3-}, [\overset{*}{Fe}(CN)_6]^{3-}$ (d) $[\overset{*}{Ni}(en)_2]^{2+}, [\overset{*}{Fe}(H_2O)_6]^{3+}$

IUPAC Name

25. The correct name for the complex ion $[CoCl(ONO)(en)_2]^{+}$ is :

(a) chlorobis(ethylenediamine)nitrito-O-cobaltate (III) ion
(b) chlorodiethyldiaminenitrito-O-cobalt (III) ion
(c) chloronitrito-O-diethyldiamine cobaltate (III) ion
(d) chlorobis(ethylenediamine)nitrito-O-cobalt (III) ion

26. IUPAC name of $[Fe(O_2)(CN)_4Cl]^{4-}$ is :

(a) Chlorotetracyano dioxoferrate (II)ion (b) Chlorotetracyano peroxoferrate (II)ion
(c) Chlorotetracyano superoxoferrate (II)ion (d) Tetracyanochloro superoxoferrate (II)ion

27. The IUPAC name of the Wilkinson's catalyst $[RhCl(PPh_3)_3]$ is :

(a) Chlorotris (triphenylphosphine) rhodium (I)
(b) Chlorotris (triphenylphosphine) rhodium (IV)
(c) Chlorotris (triphenylphosphine) rhodium (0)
(d) Chlorotris (triphenylphosphine) rhodium (VI)

28. The correct formula of diammine dichlorodicyano chromate (III) ion is :

(a) $[CrCl_2(CN)_2(NH_3)_2]^{3+}$ (b) $[CrCl_2(CN)_2(NH_3)_2]^{3-}$
(c) $[CrCl_2(CN)_2(NH_3)_2]$ (d) $[CrCl_2(CN)_2(NH_3)_2]^{-}$

29. The IUPAC name for $K_2[Cr(CN)_2(O)_2(O_2)NH_3]$ is :

(a) Potassium amminedicyanotetraoxo chromium (III)
(b) Potassium amminedicyanodioxygendioxo chromate (IV)
(c) Potassium amminedicyanosuperoxoperoxo chromate (III)
(d) Potassium amminedicyanodioxoperoxo chromate (VI)

30. IUPAC name of $H_2[PtCl_6]$ is :

(a) hydrogen hexachloroplatinate (IV) (b) dihydrogen hexachloroplatinate (IV)
(c) hydrogen hexachloroplatinic (IV) acid (d) hexachloroplatinic (IV) acid.

31. The IUPAC name for $[PtCl(NH_2CH_3)(NH_3)_2]Cl$ is :

(a) diamminechloro(methylamine)platinum(II)chloride
(b) (dimethylamine)chlorodiamminoplatinum(II)chloride
(c) bis(ammine)chloro(methylamine)platinate(II)chloride
(d) diaminechloro(mehylamine)platinum(II)chloride

32. The IUPAC nomenclature for the complex $Na[PtBrCl(NO_2)(NH_3)]$ is :

(a) Sodium amminechlorobromonitro-N-platinum(II)
(b) Sodium nitrochlorobromoammine-N-platinate(II)
(c) Sodium amminebromochloronitro-N-platinate(II)
(d) Sodium amminebromochloronitro-N-platinum(II)

33. The IUPAC name of $Xe[PtF_6]$ is :

(a) Hexafluoroplatinate(VI)xenon (b) Xenonhexafluoroplatinate(V)
(c) Xenonhexafluoroplatinate(VI) (d) Xenoniumhexafluoroplatinum(V)

34. What is the correct IUPAC name of $[Ni(en)_2(NH_3)_2]Cl_2$?

(a) Diaminebis(ethylenediamine)nickel(II)chloride
(b) Diamminebis(ethylenediamine)nickel(II)chloride
(c) Diamminebis(ethylenediammine)nickel(II)chloride
(d) Diaminebis(ethylenediammine)nickel(II)chloride

35. Correct IUPAC name of complex compound $[Co(NCS)(NH_3)_5][Zn(CN)_4]$:

(a) Pentaamminethiocyanato-N-cobalt (III) tetracyanidozinc(II)
(b) Pentaamminethiocyanato-S-cobalt (III) tetracyanidozincate(II)
(c) Pentaamminethiocyanato-N-cobalt(II) tetracyanidozincate(II)
(d) Pentaamminethiocyanato-N-cobalt(III) tetracyanidozincate(II)

36. Select the correct IUPAC name of prussian blue :

(a) Iron(II) hexacyanoferrate(II) (b) Iron(II) hexacyanoferrate(III)
(c) Iron(III) hexacyanoferrate(II) (d) Iron(III) hexacyanoferrate(III)

37. Correct IUPAC name of complex compound $[Co(NCS)(NH_3)_5][Zn(CN)_4]$.

(a) Pentaamminethiocyanato-N-cobalt (III) tetracyanidozinc(II)
(b) Pentaamminethiocyanato-S-cobalt (III) tetracyanidozincate(II)
(c) Pentaamminethiocyanato-N-cobalt(II) tetracyanidozincate(II)
(d) Pentaamminethiocyanato-N-cobalt(III) tetracyanidozincate(II)

38. Which of the following complex compound is "Pentaaquacyanidoiron (III) trichloridotricyanido cobaltate (III)" ?

(a) $[Fe(CN)(H_2O)_5][CoCl_3(CN)_3]$ (b) $[Fe(CN)(H_2O)_5]_2[CoCl_3(CN)_3]_3$
(c) $[Fe(CN)_2(H_2O)_4]_3[FeCl_3(CN)_3]_2$ (d) $[Fe(CN)(H_2O)_5]_3[CoCl_3(CN)_3]_2$

39. Select correct IUPAC name of $K[Co(CH_3NH_2)_2Cl_4]$ complex compound.

(a) Potassium tetrachloridodi(methylammine)cobaltate(III)
(b) Potassium tetrachloridodi(methylamine)cobaltate(III)
(c) Potassium tetrachloridodimethylaminecobaltate(III)
(d) Potassium tetrachloridodimethylamminecobaltate(III)

40. Which of the following pair of IUPAC name is not matched with its formula ?
(a) $[Fe(H_2O)_5(NO^+)]SO_4$: Pentaaquanitrosoniumiron(I)sulphate
(b) $Li[AlH_4]$: Lithiumtetrahydridoaluminate(III)
(c) $Na[Ag(CN)_2]$: Sodiumdicyanidoargentate(I)
(d) $Na_2[Fe(CN)_5(NO^+)]$: Sodiumpentacyanidonitrosylferrate(II)

41. The IUPAC name of Wilkinson's catalyst is :
(a) chloridotris (triphenyl phosphine) rhodium (I)
(b) chloridotris (triphenyl phosphine) rhodium (IV)
(c) chloridotris (triphenyl phosphine) rhodium (0)
(d) chloridotris (triphenyl phosphine) rhodium (VI)

42. The IUPAC name of the complex compound $[CoCl_2(en)_2]Cl$ is :
(a) Dichloridobis(ethane-1, 2-diamine)cobalt(III) chloride
(b) Dichloridobis(ethane-1, 2-diammine)cobalt(III) chloride
(c) Dichloridobis(ethylenediammine)cobalt(III) chloride
(d) Bis(ethylenediamine)dichlorido cobalt(III) chloride

Werner's Coordination Theory

43. A six coordinate complex of formula $CrCl_3.6H_2O$ has green colour. A 0.1 *M* solution of the complex when treated with excess of $AgNO_3$ gave 28.7g of white precipitate. The formula of the complex would be :
(a) $[Cr(H_2O)_6)]Cl_3$
(b) $[CrCl(H_2O)_5]Cl_2 \cdot H_2O$
(c) $[CrCl_2(H_2O)_4]Cl \cdot 2H_2O$
(d) $[Cr(H_2O)_3Cl_3]$

44. A complex has a composition corresponding to the formula $CoBr_2Cl.4NH_3$. What is the structural formula if conductance measurements show two ions per formula unit? Silver nitrate solution given an immediate precipitate of AgCl but no AgBr.
(a) $[CoBrCl(NH_3)_4]Br$
(b) $[CoCl(NH_3)_4]Br_2$
(c) $[CoBr_2Cl(NH_3)_4]$
(d) $[CoBr_2(NH_3)_4]Cl$

45. Mixture *X* of 0.02 mole of $[Co(NH_3)_5SO_4]Br$ and 0.02 mole of $[Co(NH_3)_5Br]SO_4$ was prepared in 2 litre of solution :
1 litre of mixture X + excess of $AgNO_3 \rightarrow Y$
1 litre of mixture X + excess of $BaCl_2 \rightarrow Z$
Number of moles of *Y* and *Z* respectively are :
(a) 0.01, 0.02
(b) 0.02, 0.01
(c) 0.01, 0.01
(d) 0.02, 0.02

46. A Pt complex of ammonia and chlorine produces four ions per molecule in the solution is :
(a) $[Pt(NH_3)_5Cl]Cl_3$
(b) $[Pt(NH_3)_6]Cl_4$
(c) $[Pt(NH_3)_2Cl_4]$
(d) $[Pt(NH_3)_4Cl_2]Cl_2$

47. Select the compound having maximum conductivity in aqueous medium.
(a) $[Cr(NH_3)_6]Cl_3$ (b) $[Cr(NH_3)_5Cl]Cl_2$ (c) $[Cr(NH_3)_4Cl_2]Cl$ (d) $[Cr(NH_3)_3Cl_3]$

48. 100 mL 0.01*M* solution of complex compound $Ir\ Br_3 5NH_3$ was treated with excess $AgNO_3$ solution and precipitate of AgBr was obtained, then number of moles of AgBr obtained is :
(a) 0.01 (b) 0.001 (c) 0.02 (d) 0.002

49. Which of the following compound gives one mole AgCl precipitate with 100 mL of a 10 M solution of $AgNO_3$?
(a) $CoCl_3 \cdot 6NH_3$ (b) $CoCl_3 \cdot 5NH_3$ (c) $CoCl_3 \cdot 4NH_3$ (d) All of these

50. On adding excess of $AgNO_3$ solution into 0.01 mole complex compound $PtBr_4 \cdot xNH_3$, 0.03 moles yellow precipitate was obtained, then value of 'x' is :
(a) 2 (b) 3 (c) 4 (d) 5

51. Select correct statement for $Cr \cdot 6NH_3 \cdot Cl_3$ and $Cr \cdot 5NH_3 \cdot Cl_3$
(a) In both complex compounds secondary valency is satisfied by only NH_3
(b) In both complex compounds Cl^- are satisfying only primary valency
(c) In both complex compounds primary valency is satisfied by only Cl^-
(d) In both complex compounds all Cl^- are ionizable

52. Which of the following complexes have lowest molar conductance?
(a) $CoCl_3 \cdot 3NH_3$ (b) $CoCl_3 \cdot 4NH_3$
(c) $CoCl_3 \cdot 5NH_3$ (d) $CoCl_3 \cdot 6NH_3$

Valence Bond Theory

53. There are four complexes of Ni. Select the complex(es) which will be attracted by magnetic field :
(I) $[Ni(CN)_4]^{2-}$ (II) $[NiCl_4]^{2-}$ (III) $Ni(CO_4)$ (IV) $[Ni(H_2O)_6]^{2+}$
(a) I only (b) IV only (c) II, III and IV (d) II and IV

54. Which of the following complex is an outer orbital complex?
(a) $[Ni(NH_3)_6]^{2+}$ (b) $[Mn(CN)_6]^{4-}$
(c) $[Co(NH_3)_6]^{3+}$ (d) $[Fe(CN)_6]^{4-}$

55. Which of the following complex is an outer orbital complex ?
(a) $[Ni(NH_3)_6]^{2+}$ (b) $[Mn(CN)_6]^{4-}$
(c) $[Co(NH_3)_6]^{3+}$ (d) $[Fe(CN)_6]^{4-}$

56. The magnetic moment of $[MnX_4]^{2-}$ is 5.9 BM. The geometry of the complex ion is :
(X = monodentate halide ion)
(a) tetrahedral (b) square planar (c) both are possible (d) none of these

57. The geometry of $[Ni(CO)_4]$ and $[NiCl_2(PPh_3)_2]$ are :
(a) both square planar
(b) tetrahedral and square planar respectively
(c) both are tetrahedral
(d) square planar and tetrahedral respectively

58. $[Fe(H_2O)_6]^{2+}$ and $[Fe(CN)_6]^{4-}$ differ in :
(a) geometry, magnetic moment (b) geometry, hybridization
(c) magnetic moment, colour (d) hybridization, number of d-electrons

59. Which of the following order is correct in spectrochemical series of ligands?
(a) $Cl^- < F^- < C_2O_4^{2-} < NO_2^- < CN^-$ (b) $NO_2^- < C_2O_4^{2-} < Cl^- < F^- < CN^-$
(c) $C_2O_4^{2-} < F^- < Cl^- < NO_2^- < CN^-$ (d) $F^- < Cl^- < NO_2^- < CN^- < C_2O_4^{2-}$

60. The species with spin only magnetic moment of $\sqrt{24}$ BM is :
(a) $[CoF_3(H_2O)_3]$ (b) $[CoCl_4]^{2-}$ (c) $[NiCl_4]^{2-}$ (d) $[Ni(H_2O)_6]^{2+}$

61. For the complexes showing the square pyramidal structure, the *d*-orbital involved in the hybridisation is :
(a) $d_{x^2-y^2}$ (b) d_{z^2} (c) d_{xy} (d) d_{xz}

62. Which of the following aquated metal ions has the highest paramagnetism?
(a) $[Cr(H_2O)_6]^{3+}$ (b) $[Fe(H_2O)_6]^{2+}$
(c) $[Cu(H_2O)_6]^{3+}$ (d) $[Zn(H_2O)_2]^{2+}$

63. The hybridization states of the central atom in the complexes $[Fe(CN)_6]^{3-}$, $[Fe(CN)_6]^{4-}$ and $[Co(NO_2)_6]^{3-}$ are :
(a) d^2sp^3, sp^3d^2 and dsp^2 respectively (b) d^2sp^3, sp^3d^2 and sp^3d^2 respectively
(c) d^2sp^3, sp^3d^2 and d^2sp^3 respectively (d) all d^2sp^3

64. Which of the following is incorrectly matched?

Complex	Number of unpaired electrons
(a) $[FeF_6]^{3-}$	5
(b) $[Cr(en)_3]^{2+}$	2
(c) $[Co(NH_3)_6]^{3+}$	4
(d) $[Mn(H_2O)_6]^{2+}$	5

65. Which of the following complexes have a maximum number of unpaired electrons?
(a) $[Ni(CO)_4]$ (b) $[Co(NH_3)_4(NO_2)_2]^+$
(c) $[Ag(CN)_2]^-$ (d) $[CuBr_4]^{2-}$

66. The degeneracy of *d*-orbitals is lost under :
(I) Strong field ligand (I) Weak field ligand
(III) Mixed field ligand (IV) Chelated ligand field
Choose the correct code :
(a) I, II and IV (b) I and II
(c) I, II, III and IV (d) I, II and III

67. The complex ion $[Fe(CN)_6]^{4-}$ contains :
(a) total of 36 electrons on Fe^{2+} cation
(b) sp^3d^2 hybrid orbitals with octahedral structure
(c) total of 104 electrons
(d) six sigma bonds

68. In $[Pt(NH_3)_2Cl_2]$, pt—Cl bond length is 2 Å and Cl—Cl distance is 2.88 Å then the compound is :
(a) tetrahedral (b) square pyramidal
(c) *cis*-square planar (d) *trans*-square planar

69. The magnetic moment of $[NiX_4]^{2-}$ ion is found to be zero. Then the ion is :
(X = monodentate anionic ligand)

(a) sp^3 hybridised (b) spd^2 hybridised
(c) dsp^2 hybridised (d) d^2sp hybridised

70. The hybridised orbitals used by silver in the complex $[Ag(NH_3)_2]^+$ are of the type :
(a) sp^2 (b) sp (c) sp^3 (d) dsp^2

71. Select the correct match
(a) $[Mn(NH_3)_6]^{2+}$-inner orbital complex (b) $[Co(H_2O)_6]^{3+}$-outer orbital complex
(c) $[PtCl_4]^{2-}$-diamagnetic complex (d) $K_3[Cu(CN)_4]$-paramagnetic complex

72. Which of the following complex compound is paramagnetic
(a) $[Ni(dmg)_2]$ (b) $[Fe(H_2O)_5(NO)]SO_4$
(c) $Na_2[Fe(CN)_5(NO)]$ (d) $[Co(NH_3)_6]^{3+}$

73. In which complex, d_{z^2} orbital of inner shell is not used in the hybridization of central metal cation
(a) $Fe(CO)_5$ (b) $[Cu(NH_3)_5]^{2+}$ (c) $[Co(NH_3)_6]^{2+}$ (d) $[IrF_6]^{3-}$

74. Arrange the following cyano complexes in decreasing order of their magnetic moment.
(a) $[Cr(CN)_6]^{3-} > [Mn(CN)_6]^{3-} > [Fe(CN)_6]^{3-} > [Co(CN)_6]^{3-}$
(b) $[Mn(CN)_6]^{3-} > [Cr(CN)_6]^{3-} > [Fe(CN)_6]^{3-} > [Co(CN)_6]^{3-}$
(c) $[Fe(CN)_6]^{3-} > [Cr(CN)_6]^{3-} > [Mn(CN)_6]^{3-} > [Co(CN)_6]^{3-}$
(d) $[Co(CN)_6]^{3-} > [Cr(CN)_6]^{3-} > [Mn(CN)_6]^{3-} > [Fe(CN)_6]^{3-}$

75. The magnetic moments of complexes given below are in the order :
(I) $[Ni(CO)_4]$ (II) $[Mn(CN)_6]^{4-}$ (III) $[Cr(NH_3)_6]^{3+}$ (IV) $[CoF_6]^{3-}$
(a) I > II > III > IV (b) I < II < III < IV (c) IV > II > I > III (d) IV < II < I < III

76. The magnetic moment of a complex ion is 2.83 B.M. The complex ion is :
(a) $[V(H_2O)_6]^{3+}$ (b) $[Cr(H_2O)_6]^{3+}$ (c) $[Cu(CN)_4]^{2-}$ (d) $[MnCl_4]^{2-}$

77. The diamagnetic species is :
(I) $[Cu(CN)_4]^{3-}$ (II) $[Co(NH_3)_6]^{3+}$ (III) $[Ni(NH_3)_6]^{2+}$ (IV) $[Fe(CN)_6]^{3-}$
(a) I, III (b) I, II (c) III, IV (d) only IV

78. Which of the following complex is an outer orbital complex ?
(a) $[Ni(NH_3)_6]^{2+}$ (b) $[Mn(CN)_6]^{4-}$ (c) $[Co(NH_3)_6]^{3+}$ (d) $[Fe(CN)_6]^{4-}$

79. The species which has four unpaired electron is :
(a) $[Co(CN)_6]^{4-}$ (b) $[Cr(H_2O)_6]^{3+}$ (c) $[FeCl_4]^{2-}$ (d) $[Fe(H_2O)_6]^{3+}$

80. Which of the characteristic is not common between $[Cu(en)_2]^{2+}$ and $[Ni(dmg)_2]$?
(a) Geometry of complexes (b) Hybridization of central metal cation
(c) Magnetic behaviour (d) Number of stereoisomers

81. Which of the following species is "Diamagnetic" ?
(a) $[NiCl_4]^{2-}$ (b) $K_3[Fe(CN)_6]$ (c) $[Ni(CO)_4]$ (d) $[Co(CN)_6]^{4-}$

82. Which of the following outer orbital complex has highest magnetic moment ?
(a) $[Mn(NH_3)_6]Cl_2$ (b) $[Cr(NH_3)_6]Cl_3$ (c) $[Ni(NH_3)_6]Cl_2$ (d) $[Co(NH_3)_6]Cl_3$

83. Which complex is diamagnetic ?
(a) $Na_3[Co(OX)_3]$ (b) $[Ni(NH_3)_6]^{2+}$ (c) $[Fe(CN)_6]^{3-}$ (d) $[Mn(CN)_6]^{3-}$

84. Which complex compound has highest value of C.F.S.E. ?
(a) $K_2[PtCl_4]$ (b) $K[Pt(NH_3)Cl_3]$ (c) $[Pt(NH_3)_2Cl_2]$ (d) $[Pt(NH_3)_4]Cl_2$

85. In which of the following complex hybridization of central metal is not same as that of donor atom of ligand
(a) $[Ni(PF_3)_4]$ (b) $[Fe(dmg)_2]$ (c) $[Zn(en)_2]^{2+}$ (d) $[Ni(PMe_3)_4]^{2+}$

86. The oxidation number, coordination number and magnetic moment in the following complex is $[Cr(C_2O_4)_2(NH_3)_2]^-$
(a) O.N. = +3, C.N. = 6, M.M. = $\sqrt{15}$ B.M. (b) O.N. = +1, C.N. = 6, M.M. = $\sqrt{15}$ B.M.
(c) O.N. = +3, C.N. = 6, M.M. = $\sqrt{3}$ B.M. (d) O.N. = +3, C.N. = 6, M.M. = $\sqrt{24}$ B.M.

87. Which of the following complex is an outer orbital complex ?
(a) $[Ni(NH_3)_6]^{2+}$ (b) $[Mn(CN)_6]^{4-}$ (c) $[Co(NH_3)_6]^{3+}$ (d) $[Fe(CN)_6]^{4-}$

88. Pair of complexes, which do not have equal number of unpaired electron(s) ?
(a) $[Co(CO)_4]^-$, $[Ni(CN)_4]^{4-}$ (b) $[Co(H_2O)_6]^{3+}$, $[NiF_6]^{2-}$
(c) $[Ni(en)_3]^{2+}$ $[Cr(CN)_6]^{4-}$ (d) $[Co(CN)_6]^{4-}$, $[Cr(NH_3)_6]^{3+}$

89. In which of the following pairs both the complexes have same geometry ?
(a) $[NiCl_4]^{2-}$, $[Ni(CN)_4]^{2-}$ (b) $[CoF_6]^{3-}$, $[Co(NH_3)_6]^{3+}$
(c) $[Cu(NH_3)_4]^+$, $[Ni(NH_3)_4]^{2+}$ (d) $[Ni(CO)_4]$, $[Ni(CN)_4]^{2-}$

90. Pair of complexes, which do not have equal number of unpaired electron(s) ?
(a) $[Co(CO)_4]^-$, $[Ni(CN)_4]^{4-}$ (b) $[Co(H_2O)_6]^{3+}$, $[NiF_6]^{2-}$
(c) $[Ni(en)_3]^{2+}$, $[Cr(CN)_6]^{4-}$ (d) $[Co(CN)_6]^{4-}$, $[Cr(NH_3)_6]^{3+}$

91. Spin only magnetic moment of which of the following complex ion is 4.9 B.M. ?
(a) $[Cr(NH_3)_6]^{2+}$ (b) $[Fe(NH_3)_6]^{2+}$ (c) $[Co(H_2O)_6]^{3+}$ (d) $[NiF_6]^{2-}$

92. Which of the following complex compound is low spin, inner orbital, diamagnetic complex ?
(a) $[Ni(NH_3)_6]Cl_2$ (b) $K_3[Fe(CN)_6]$ (c) $K_2[PtCl_6]$ (d) $[Cr(H_2O)_6]Cl_3$

93. Same characteristics between $[NiF_6]^{4-}$ and $[IrF_6]^{3-}$ complexes is :
(a) Magnetic behaviour (b) Type of hybridisation
(c) High spin complex (d) Geometry of complexes

94. Arrange the following cyano complexes in increasing order of magnetic moment.
(a) $[Fe(CN)_6]^{4-} < [Fe(CN)_6]^{3-} < [Mn(CN)_6]^{3-} < [Cr(CN)_6]^{3-}$
(b) $[Fe(CN)_6]^{3-} < [Cr(CN)_6]^{3-} < [Mn(CN)_6]^{3-} < [Fe(CN)_6]^{4-}$
(c) $[Mn(CN)_6]^{3-} < [Fe(CN)_6]^{3-} < [Fe(CN)_6]^{4-} < [Cr(CN)_6]^{3-}$
(d) $[Fe(CN)_6]^{3-} < [Cr(CN)_6]^{3-} < [Fe(CN)_6]^{4-} < [Mn(CN)_6]^{3-}$

95. Which of the following is correctly matched ?

Column-I	Column-II	Column-III
(a) $[Cr(CO)_6]$	Paramagnetic	Octahedral, sp^3d^2
(b) $[Fe(CO)_5]$	Paramagnetic	Trigonal bipyramidal, sp^3d
(c) $[Co(CO)_4]$	Paramagnetic	Square planar, dsp^2
(d) $[Ni(CO)_4]$	Diamagnetic	Square planar, dsp^2

Crystal Field Theory

96. $[PdCl_2(PMe_3)_2]$ is a diamagnetic complex of Pd (II). How many unpaired electrons are present in analogous complex of Ni (II) ?

(a) Zero (b) 1 (c) 2 (d) 3

97. Magnetic moment (spin only) of octahedron complex having CFSE$= -0.8\Delta_0$ and surrounded by weak field ligands can be:

(a) $\sqrt{15}$ BM (b) $\sqrt{8}$ BM (c) (a) & (b) both (d) None of these

98. Consider the following complex : $[Co(NH_3)_5CO_3]ClO_4$

The coordination number, oxidation number, no. of *d*-electrons and number of unpaired *d*-electrons on the metal are respectively :

(a) 6, 2, 7, 3 (b) 7, 2, 7, 1

(c) 5, 3, 6, 4 (d) 6,3, 6, 0

99. Consider the following complex : $[Co(CO_3)(NH_3)_5]ClO_4$

Mark the correct option :

	Coordination no.	Oxidation no.	No. of *d*-electrons	Unpaired *d*-electrons
(a)	6	3	6	0
(b)	7	2	7	1
(c)	7	1	6	4
(d)	6	2	7	3

100. The magnetic moments of complexes given below are in the order :

(I) $[Ni(CO)_4]$ (II) $[Mn(CN)_6]^{4-}$ (III) $[Cr(NH_3)_6]^{3+}$ (IV) $[CoF_6]^{3-}$

(a) I > II > III > IV (b) I < II < III < IV (c) IV > II > I > III (d) IV < II < I < III

101. Which is low spin complex?

(a) $[Fe(CN_6)]^{3-}$ (b) $[Co(NO_2)_6]^{3-}$ (c) $[Mn(CN)_6]^{3-}$ (d) All of these

102. Which of the following are diamagnetic?

(I) $K_4[Fe(CN)_6]$ (II) $K_3[Cr(CN)_6]$ (III) $K_3[Co(CN)_6]$ (IV) $K_2[Ni(CN)_4]$

Select the correct answer using the codes given below :

(a) I, II and IV (b) I, III and IV (c) II and III (d) I and IV

103. The spin magnetic moment of cobalt in $Hg[Co(SCN)_4]$ is :

(a) $\sqrt{3}$ (b) $\sqrt{8}$ (c) $\sqrt{15}$ (d) $\sqrt{24}$

104. The species having tetrahedral shape is :

(a) $[PdCl_4]^{2-}$ (b) $[Ni(CN)_4]^{2}$ (c) $[Pd(CN)_4]^{2-}$ (d) $[NiCl_4]^{2-}$

105. Which one of the following has lowest value of magnetic behaviour?

(a) $[Cr(CN)_6]^{3-}$ (b) $[Mn(CN)_6]^{3-}$

(c) $[Fe(CN)_6]^{3-}$ (d) $[Co(CN)_6]^{3-}$

106. Which of the following statements is correct?

(a) $[CoF_6]^{3-}$ and $[Co(NH_3)_6]^{3+}$ both are paramagnetic complexes

(b) $[CoF_6]^{3-}$ and $[Co(NH_3)_6]^{3+}$ both are high spin complexes

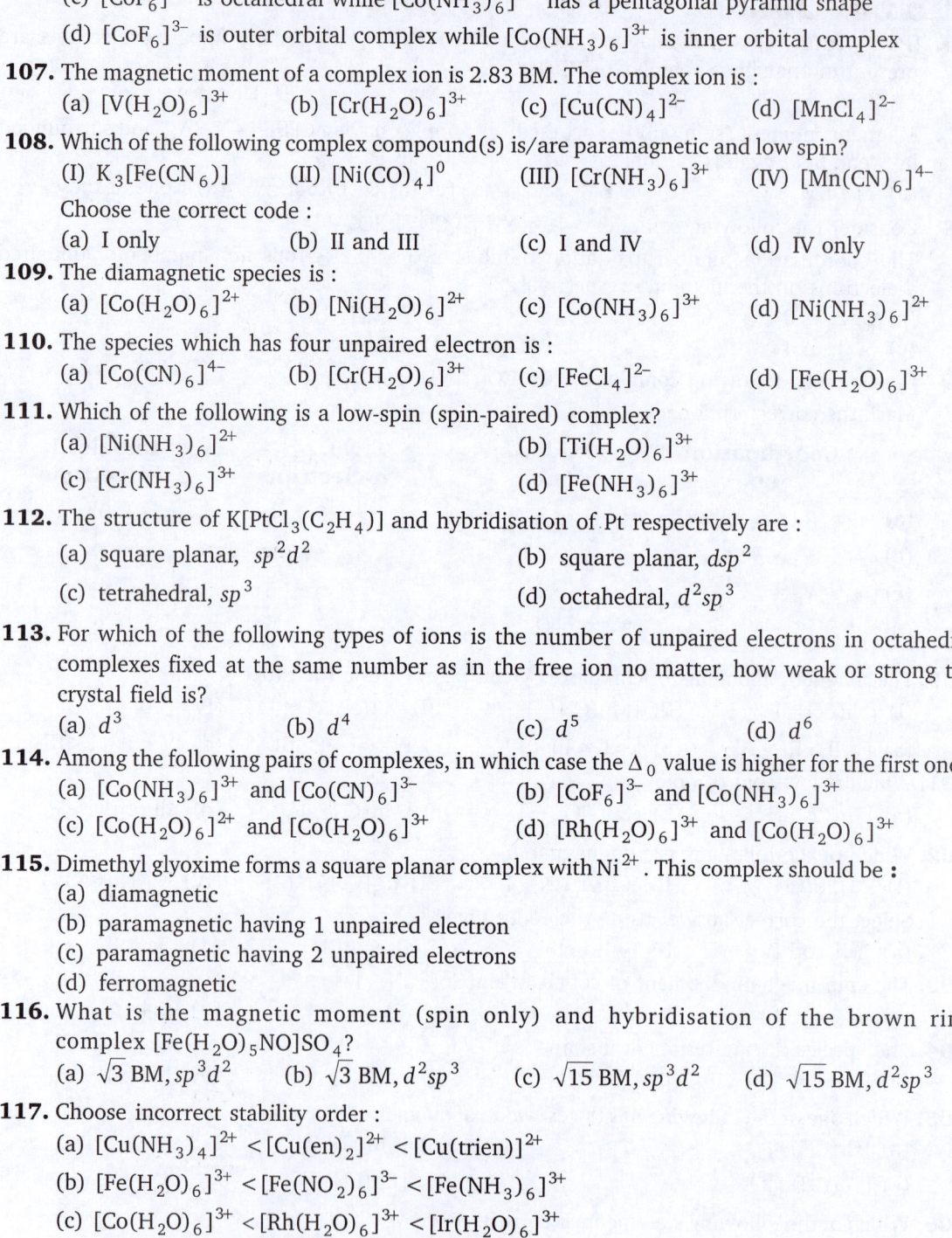

(c) $[CoF_6]^{3-}$ is octahedral while $[Co(NH_3)_6]^{3+}$ has a pentagonal pyramid shape
(d) $[CoF_6]^{3-}$ is outer orbital complex while $[Co(NH_3)_6]^{3+}$ is inner orbital complex

107. The magnetic moment of a complex ion is 2.83 BM. The complex ion is :
(a) $[V(H_2O)_6]^{3+}$ (b) $[Cr(H_2O)_6]^{3+}$ (c) $[Cu(CN)_4]^{2-}$ (d) $[MnCl_4]^{2-}$

108. Which of the following complex compound(s) is/are paramagnetic and low spin?
(I) $K_3[Fe(CN_6)]$ (II) $[Ni(CO)_4]^0$ (III) $[Cr(NH_3)_6]^{3+}$ (IV) $[Mn(CN)_6]^{4-}$
Choose the correct code :
(a) I only (b) II and III (c) I and IV (d) IV only

109. The diamagnetic species is :
(a) $[Co(H_2O)_6]^{2+}$ (b) $[Ni(H_2O)_6]^{2+}$ (c) $[Co(NH_3)_6]^{3+}$ (d) $[Ni(NH_3)_6]^{2+}$

110. The species which has four unpaired electron is :
(a) $[Co(CN)_6]^{4-}$ (b) $[Cr(H_2O)_6]^{3+}$ (c) $[FeCl_4]^{2-}$ (d) $[Fe(H_2O)_6]^{3+}$

111. Which of the following is a low-spin (spin-paired) complex?
(a) $[Ni(NH_3)_6]^{2+}$ (b) $[Ti(H_2O)_6]^{3+}$
(c) $[Cr(NH_3)_6]^{3+}$ (d) $[Fe(NH_3)_6]^{3+}$

112. The structure of $K[PtCl_3(C_2H_4)]$ and hybridisation of Pt respectively are :
(a) square planar, sp^2d^2 (b) square planar, dsp^2
(c) tetrahedral, sp^3 (d) octahedral, d^2sp^3

113. For which of the following types of ions is the number of unpaired electrons in octahedral complexes fixed at the same number as in the free ion no matter, how weak or strong the crystal field is?
(a) d^3 (b) d^4 (c) d^5 (d) d^6

114. Among the following pairs of complexes, in which case the Δ_0 value is higher for the first one?
(a) $[Co(NH_3)_6]^{3+}$ and $[Co(CN)_6]^{3-}$ (b) $[CoF_6]^{3-}$ and $[Co(NH_3)_6]^{3+}$
(c) $[Co(H_2O)_6]^{2+}$ and $[Co(H_2O)_6]^{3+}$ (d) $[Rh(H_2O)_6]^{3+}$ and $[Co(H_2O)_6]^{3+}$

115. Dimethyl glyoxime forms a square planar complex with Ni^{2+}. This complex should be :
(a) diamagnetic
(b) paramagnetic having 1 unpaired electron
(c) paramagnetic having 2 unpaired electrons
(d) ferromagnetic

116. What is the magnetic moment (spin only) and hybridisation of the brown ring complex $[Fe(H_2O)_5NO]SO_4$?
(a) $\sqrt{3}$ BM, sp^3d^2 (b) $\sqrt{3}$ BM, d^2sp^3 (c) $\sqrt{15}$ BM, sp^3d^2 (d) $\sqrt{15}$ BM, d^2sp^3

117. Choose incorrect stability order :
(a) $[Cu(NH_3)_4]^{2+} < [Cu(en)_2]^{2+} < [Cu(trien)]^{2+}$
(b) $[Fe(H_2O)_6]^{3+} < [Fe(NO_2)_6]^{3-} < [Fe(NH_3)_6]^{3+}$
(c) $[Co(H_2O)_6]^{3+} < [Rh(H_2O)_6]^{3+} < [Ir(H_2O)_6]^{3+}$
(d) $[Cr(NH_3)_6]^{1+} < [Cr(NH_3)_6]^{2+} < [Cr(NH_3)_6]^{3+}$

118. Aqueous solution of Ni^{2+} contains $[Ni(H_2O)_6]^{2+}$ and its magnetic moment is 2.83 BM. When ammonia is added in it, comment on the magnetic moment of solution :

(a) It will remain same
(b) It increases from 2.83 BM.
(c) It decreases from 2.83 BM.
(d) It cannot be predicted theoretically

119. The correct order of energies of *d*-orbitals of metal ion in a square planar complex is :

(a) $d_{xy} = d_{yz} = d_{zx} > d_{x^2-y^2} = d_{x^2}$
(b) $d_{x^2-y^2} = d_{z^2} > d_{xy} = d_{yz} = d_{zx}$
(c) $d_{x^2-y^2} > d_{z^2} > d_{xy} = d_{yz} = d_{zx}$
(d) $d_{x^2-y^2} > d_{xy} > d_{z^2} > d_{zx} = d_{yz}$

120. Which of the following is true about the complex $[PtCl_2(H_2O)(NH_3)]$?

(a) It exhibits geometrical isomerism
(b) It is paramagnetic complex
(c) Its geometry is tetrahedron
(d) Platinum is sp^3 hybridised

121. The crystal fieldstabilisation energy of $[Co(NH_3)_6]Cl_3$ is :

(a) $-7.2\,\Delta_0$
(b) $-0.4\,\Delta_0$
(c) $-2.4\,\Delta_0$
(d) $-3.6\,\Delta_0$

122. The magnitude of crystal field stabilisation energy in octahedral field depends on :

(I) the nature of the ligand
(II) the charge on the metal ion
(III) whether the metal is in the first, second or third row of the transition elements

(a) I, II, III correct
(b) I, II correct
(c) II, III correct
(d) III correct

123. Complex compound $[Cr(NCS)(NH_3)_5][ZnCl_4]$ will be :

(a) colourless and diamagnetic
(b) green coloured and diamagnetic
(c) green coloured and shows coordination isomerism
(d) diamagnetic and shows linkage isomerism

124. The most stable ion is :

(a) $[Fe(C_2O_4)_3]^{3-}$
(b) $[Fe(CN)_6]^{3-}$
(c) $[Fe(CN)_6]^{4-}$
(d) $[Fe(H_2O)_6]^{3+}$

125. In the complex $K_2Fe[Fe(CN)_6]$:

(a) both Fe atoms are in the same oxidation state
(b) both Fe atoms are in different oxidation state
(c) the coordination number of ion is 4
(d) the complex is a high spin complex

126. In $Na_2[Fe(CN)_5NO]$, sodium nitroprusside :

(a) oxidation state of Fe is +2
(b) this has NO^+ as ligand
(c) both are correct
(d) none is correct

127. An aqueous solution of titanium chloride, when subjected to magnetic measurement, measured zero magnetic moment. Assuming the octahedral complex in aqueous solution, the formulae of the complex is :

(a) $[Ti(H_2O)_6]Cl_2$
(b) $[Ti(H_2O)_6]Cl_4$
(c) $[TiCl_3(H_2O)_3]$
(d) $[TiCl_2(H_2O)_4]$

128. Amongst the following, the most stable complex is :
(a) $[Co(H_2O)_6]^{3+}$ (b) $[Co(ox)_3]^{3-}$ (c) $[Co(ONO)_6]^{3-}$ (d) $[CoF_6]^{3-}$

129. For an octahedral complex, whcih of the following *d*-electron configuration will give maximum CFSE ?
(a) High spin with d^6 configuration (b) Low spin with d^4 configuration
(c) Low spin with d^5 configuration (d) High spin with d^7 configuration

130. For octahedral complex, which of the following d^n configurations of metal cation cannot exist in high spin and low spin forms ?
(a) d^3 and d^8 (b) d^3 and d^5 (c) d^3 and d^6 (d) d^4 and d^8

131. Which of the following order of stability of complex ion is **Incorrect** ?
(a) $[Fe(C_2O_4)_3]^{3-} > [Fe(H_2O)_6]^{3+}$ (b) $[Fe(edta)]^{-} > [Fe(en)_3]^{3+}$
(c) $[Ni(en)_2]^{2+} > [Ni(DMG)_2]$ (d) $[Fe(CN)_6]^{3-} > [Fe(CN)_6]^{4-}$

132. Which of the following is tetrahedral paramagnetic complex ?
(a) $K_2[PtCl_4]$ (b) $K_2[MnCl_4]$ (c) $K_2[ZnCl_4]$ (d) $K_2[HgI_4]$

133. In an octahedral crystal field, the t_{2g} orbitals are :
(a) Raised in energy by 0.4 Δ_o (b) Lowered in energy by 0.4 Δ_o
(c) Raised in energy by 0.6 Δ_o (d) Lowered in energy by 0.6 Δ_o

134. Identify the complex which are excepted to be coloured
(a) $[Ti(NO_3)_4]$ (b) $Na_2[CdCl_4]$ (c) $K_3[VF_6]$ (d) $[Sc(H_2O)_6]^{3+}$

135. Select the complex having highest value of stability contant (K_s)
(a) $[Pt(NH_3)_4]^{2+}$ (b) $[Pt(NH_3)_3Cl]^{+}$ (c) $[Pt(NH_3)Cl_3]^{-}$ (d) $[PtCl_4]^{2-}$

136. Select the **Incorrect** match
(a) $Fe^{3+} + [Fe(CN)_6]^{4-} \rightarrow$ Blue colour ppt.
(b) $Fe^{3+} + [Fe(CN)_6]^{3-} \rightarrow$ Red brown colouration
(c) $Fe^{2+} + [Fe(CN)_6]^{3-} \rightarrow$ Blue colour ppt.
(d) $Fe^{2+} + [Fe(CN)_6]^{4-} \rightarrow$ Red brown colouration

137. The complex ion having minimum wavelength of absorption in the visible region is :
(a) $[Co(NH_3)_6]^{3+}$ (b) $[CoCl(NH_3)_5]^{2+}$
(c) *Cis* - $[CoCl_2(NH_3)_4]^{+}$ (d) *Trans* - $[CoCl_2(NH_3)_4]^{+}$

138. Incorrect order of stability is :
(a) $[Co(ox)_3]^{3-} > [Co(H_2O)_6]^{3+}$ (b) $[PtF_6]^{2-} > [NiF_6]^{2-}$
(c) $[Ni(trien)]^{2+} > [Ni(en)_2]^{2+}$ (d) $[Ni(NH_3)_6]^{2+} > [Ni(dmg)_2]$

139. Select two isomers having colour violet and green respectively
(a) $[Cr(H_2O)_6]Cl_2$; $[Cr(H_2O)_6]Cl_3$
(b) $[Co(H_2O)_6]Cl_3$; $[Co(H_2O)_4Cl_2]Cl \cdot 2H_2O$
(c) $[Co(ONO)(H_2O)_5]Cl_2$; $[Co(NO_2)(H_2O)_5]Cl_2$
(d) $[Pt(Br)(NH_3)_3]NO_2$; $[Pt(NO_2)(NH_3)_3]Br$

140. In which of the following splitting of *d*-orbitals of metal atom/ion electrons are incorrectly distributed ?

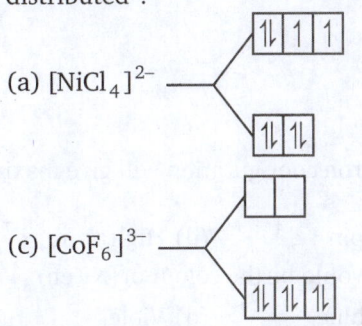

(a) $[NiCl_4]^{2-}$ 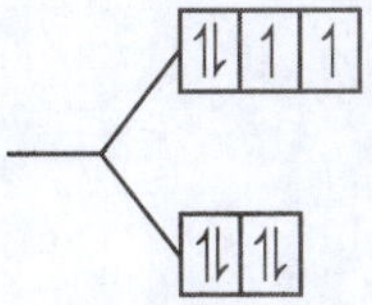

(b) $[Ni(NH_3)_6]^{2+}$ 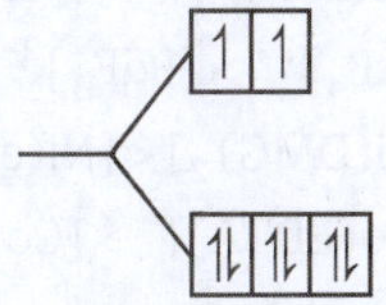

(c) $[CoF_6]^{3-}$ 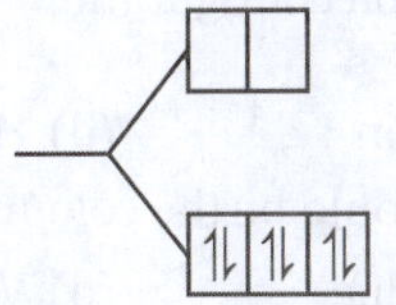

(d) $[Co(SCN)_4]^{2-}$ 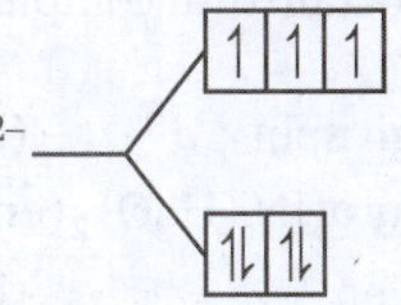

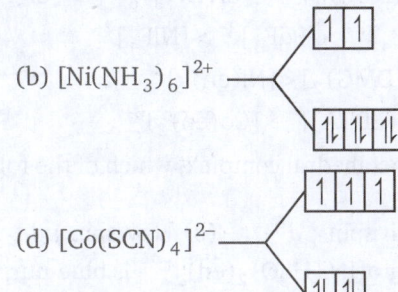

141. The value of CFSE (Δ_o) for complexes given below follow the order.

(I) $[Co(NH_3)_6]^{3+}$ (II) $[Rh(NH_3)_6]^{3+}$ (III) $[Ir(NH_3)_6]^{3+}$

(a) I < II < III (b) I > II > III (c) I < II > III (d) I = II = III

142. Find out **wrong** statement for an octahedral complex-

(a) Central metal cation with d^6 configuration is diamagnetic in strong ligand field

(b) Central metal cation with d^5 configuration has one unpaired electron in both weak and strong ligand field

(c) Central metal cation with d^8 configuration has two unpaired electrons in weak, strong and also in mixed ligand field

(d) Central metal cation with d^4, d^5, d^6 and d^7 configuration have different number of unpaired electrons in weak and strong ligand field.

143. Select correct pair of co-ordination compounds in which first complex compound/ion is more stable than second compound/ion.

(a) $[Ni(CN)_4]^{2-}, [Ni(NH_3)_6]^{2+}$ (b) $[PdBr_2(NH_3)_2], [PdBr(ONO)(NH_3)_2]$

(c) $[Co(SCN)_4]^{2-}, [CoF_6]^{3-}$ (d) $[Cr(NH_3)_2(en)_2]^{3+}, [Cr(en)_3]^{3+}$

144. Coloured compound among the following is :

(a) $Na_2[CdCl_4]$ (b) $K_3[Cu(CN)_4]$

(c) $Na_2[CuCl_4]$ (d) $[Cu(CH_3CN)_4]BF_4$

145. Select **incorrect** match between compound and reason for its observed colour

(a) $KMnO_4$: Charge transfer spectrum (b) $[Fe(H_2O)_5(NO)]SO_4$: $d-d$-transition

(c) Ag_2PO_4 : Polarization (d) HgI_2 : Polarization

146. Among the following pair of complexes, in which case the value of Δ_o is higher for the first one?

(a) $[Co(NH_3)_6]^{3+}$ and $[Co(CN)_6]^{3-}$ (b) $[CoF_6]^{3-}$ and $[Co(NH_3)_6]^{3+}$

(c) $[Co(H_2O)_6]^{2+}$ and $[Co(H_2O)_6]^{3+}$ (d) $[Rh(H_2O)_6]^{3+}$ and $[Co(H_2O)_6]^{3+}$

147. Amongst TiF_6^{2-}, CoF_6^{3-}, CuCl and $NiCl_4^{2-}$ the colourless species are :

(a) CoF_6^{3-} and $NiCl_4^{2-}$ (b) TiF_6^{2-} and CoF_6^{3-} (c) Cu_2Cl_2 and $NiCl_4^{2-}$ (d) TiF_6^{2-} and CuCl

148. Correct relationship between pairing energy (*P*) and C.F.S.E. (Δ_o) in complex ion; $[Ir(H_2O)_6]^{3+}$ is :

(a) $\Delta_o < P$ (b) $\Delta_o > P$ (c) $\Delta_o = P$ (d) Cannot comment

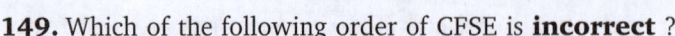

149. Which of the following order of CFSE is **incorrect** ?
(a) $[Cr(NO_2)_6]^{3-} > [Cr(NH_3)_6]^{3+} > [Cr(H_2O)_6]^{3+}$
(b) $[PtF_4]^{2-} > [PdF_4]^{2-} > [NiF_4]^{2-}$
(c) $[Ni(DMG)_2] < [Ni(en)_2]^{2+}$
(d) $[Co(EDTA)]^- > [Co(en)_3]^{3+}$

150. For an octahedral complex, which of the following *d*-electron configuration will give maximum CFSE ?
(a) High spin ; d^6 (b) Low spin ; d^5 (c) Low spin ; d^4 (d) High spin ; d^7

151. If colour of $[Ni(H_2O)_2(en)_2]^{2+}$ is blue-purple then what would be the colour of $[Ni(en)_3]^{2+}$?
(a) Green (b) Pale blue (c) Deep blue (d) Violet

152. Which of the following hydrate isomer of $CrCl_3 \cdot 6H_2O$ absorb shorter wavelength in visible spectrum ?
(a) $[Cr(H_2O)_6]Cl_3$ (b) $[CrCl(H_2O)_5]Cl_2 \cdot H_2O$
(c) $[CrCl_2(H_2O)_4]Cl \cdot 2H_2O$ (d) $[CrCl_3(H_2O)_3] \cdot 3H_2O$

153. CFSE value of $[Fe(H_2O)_5(NO)]SO_4$ (Brown ring complex) is :
(a) $-0.8\,\Delta_o + P$ (b) $-0.4\,\Delta_o + P$ (c) $-1.8\,\Delta_o + 2P$ (d) $-2.4\,\Delta_o$

154. Which of the following complex ion absorb visible light ?
(a) $[Sc(H_2O)_3(NH_3)_3]^{3+}$ (b) $[Ti(en)_2(NH_3)_2]^{4+}$
(c) $[Cr(NH_3)_6]^{3+}$ (d) $[Zn(NH_3)_4]^{2+}$

155. Which of the following statement is not true for the reaction given below ?
$$[Cu(H_2O)_4]^{2+} + 4NH_3 \rightleftharpoons [Cu(NH_3)_4]^{2+} + 4H_2O$$
(a) It is a ligand substitution reaction
(b) NH_3 is relatively strong field ligand while H_2O is a weak field ligand
(c) During the reaction, there is a change in colour form light blue to dark blue
(d) $[Cu(NH_3)_4]^{2+}$ has tetrahedral structure and is paramagnetic

156. From the stability constant (hypothetical values) given below predict which is the strongest ligand ?
(a) $Cu^{2+} + 4NH_3 \rightleftharpoons [Cu(NH_3)_4]^{2+}$ $K = 4.5 \times 10^{11}$
(b) $Cu^{2} + 4CN^- \rightleftharpoons [Cu(CN)_4]^{2-}$ $K = 2.0 \times 10^{27}$
(c) $Cu^{2+} + 2en \rightleftharpoons [Cu(en)_2]^{2+}$ $K = 3 \times 10^{15}$
(d) $Cu^{2+} + 4H_2O \rightleftharpoons [Cu(H_2O)_4]^{2+}$ $K = 9.5 \times 10^{8}$

Isomerism

157. Which of the following pairs of complexes are isomeric with each other but their aqueous solutions exhibit different molar conductivities?
(a) $[PtCl_2(NH_3)_4]Br_2$ and $[PtBr_2(NH_3)_4]Cl_2$
(b) $[CoCl_2(NH_3)_4]NO_2$ and $[CoCl(NO_2)(NH_3)_4]Cl$
(c) $[Co(NO_2)(NH_3)_5]Cl_2$ and $[Co(ONO)(NH_3)_5]Cl_2$
(d) $[CoBr(NH_3)_5]SO_4$ and $[Co(SO_4)(NH_3)_5]Br$

158. The compounds $[Cr(H_2O)_6]Cl_3$, $[Cr(H_2O)_5Cl]Cl_2 \cdot H_2O$ and $[Cr(H_2O)_4Cl_2]Cl \cdot 2H_2O$ exhibits :
(a) linkage isomerism (b) geometrical isomerism
(c) ionization isomerism (d) hydrate isomerism

159. Which one of the following pairs of isomers and types of isomerism are correctly matched?
(i) $[Co(NH_3)_5(NO_2)]Cl_2$ and $[Co(NH_3)_5(ONO)]Cl_2$...(Linkage)
(ii) $[Cu(NH_3)_4][PtCl_4]$ and $[Pt(NH_3)_4][CuCl_4]$...(Coordination)
(iii) $[PtCl_2(NH_3)_4]Br_2$ and $[PtBr_2(NH_3)_4]Cl_2$...(Ionization)
Select the correct answer using the codes given below :
(a) (ii) and (iii) (b) (i), (ii) and (iii) (c) (i) and (iii) (d) (i) and (ii)

160. The two compounds pentaamminesulphatocobalt (III) bromide and pentaamminesulphatocobalt (III) chloride represent :
(a) Linkage isomerism (b) Ionization isomerism
(c) Coordination isomerism (d) No isomerism

161. Select the correct code about complex $[Cr(NO_2)(NH_3)_5][ZnCl_4]$:
(I) IUPAC name of compound is pentaamminenitrito-N-chromium (III) tetrachlorozincate(II)
(II) It shows geometrical isomerism
(III) It shows linkage isomerism
(IV) It shows coordination isomerism
(a) III, IV (b) I, III and IV (c) II, III and IV (d) I, II, III and IV

162. Which of the following order is representing increasing order of geometrical isomers of given complexes ?
(a) $[M(AA)b_2c_2]^{n\pm}$; $[Ma_2b_2c_2]^{n\pm}$; $[Ma_3bcd]^{n\pm}$; $[Ma_2bcde]^{n\pm}$
(b) $[M(AA)b_2c_2]^{n\pm}$; $[Ma_3bcd]^{n\pm}$; $[Ma_2b_2c_2]^{n\pm}$; $[Ma_2bcde]^{n\pm}$
(c) $[Ma_3bcd]^{n\pm}$; $[Ma_2b_2c_2]^{n\pm}$; $[M(AA)b_2c_2]^{n\pm}$; $[Ma_2bcde]^{n\pm}$
(d) $[Ma_2b_2c_2]^{n\pm}$; $[M(AA)b_2c_2]^{n\pm}$; $[Ma_3bcd]^{n\pm}$; $[Ma_2bcde]^{n\pm}$

163. Consider the following balanced reactions :
(i) $K_2[PtCl_4] + 2NH_3 \rightarrow$ 'X' $+ 2KCl$
(ii) $[Pt(NH_3)_4](NO_3)_2 + 2KCl \rightarrow$ 'Y' $+ 2NH_3 + 2KNO_3$
Both X and Y have same molecular formula $Pt \cdot 2NH_3 \cdot Cl_2$ and X is more soluble in polar solvent such as ehtanol while Y is soluble in non-polar solvent like petroleum, ether and CCl_4. Complex X and Y are :
(a) Ionization isomers (b) Geometrical isomers
(c) Solvate isomers (d) Co-ordination isomers

164. Complex ion/compound having only two stereoisomers :
(a) $[CrBr_2(H_2O)(NH_3)_3]$ (b) $[Zn(gly)_2]$
(c) $[PtBrCl(CN)(H_2O)]^-$ (d) $[Co(en)(NH_3)_4]^{3+}$

165. Which type of isomerism is not exhibited by complex $[CrCl_2(H_2O)_2(NH_3)_2]Br$?
(a) Ionization isomerism (b) Hydrate isomerism
(c) Geometrical isomerism (d) Optical isomerism

166. Select correct match :
(a) $[Co(ox)(H_2O)_3(NH_3)]Br$: Optical isomerism
(b) $[Cr(SCN)(H_2O)_3(en)](C_2O_4)$: Ionization isomerism
(c) $[ZnBr(CN)(SCN)(NH_3)]^-$: Geometrical isomerism
(d) $[CoBrCl(H_2O)_4][Ag(CN)_2]$: Co-ordination isomerism

167. Which of the following complex compound does not show stereoisomerism ?
(a) $[PdBrCl(NO_2)(NH_3)]^-$ (b) $[Zn(SCN)(H_2O)(gly)]$
(c) $[Co(acac)_3]$ (d) $[PtBr(H_2O)(en)]$

168. $[Pt(NH_3)_4Cl_2]Br_2$ complex can show :
(a) Hydrated as well as ionization isomerism
(b) Ionization as well as geometrical isomerism
(c) Linkage as well as geometrical isomerism
(d) Ionization as well as optical isomerism

169. Which of the following type of isomerism is not exhibited by $[Co(H_2O)_3(NH_3)_2(NO_3)]Br_2$?
(a) Linkage isomerism (b) Ionization isomerism
(c) Hydrate isomerism (d) Geometrical isomerism

170. Select incorrect match.
(a) $[Co(acac)\,Br_2(H_2O)_2]$: One pair of enantiomers
(b) $[IrBr_4(en)]^-$: Does not exhibit *cis-trans* isomerism
(c) $[ZnBrCl(CN)(NO_2)]^{2-}$: Number of stereoisomers = 2
(d) $[Cr(en)_3]^{3+}$: Numebr of stereoisomers is equal to number of geometrical isomers.

171. Which kind of isomerism is exhibited by octahedral $[Co(NH_3)_4Br_2]Cl$?
(a) Geometrical and ionization (b) Geometrical and optical
(c) Optical and ionization (d) Geometrical only

172. Select incorrect statement about complex $[Cr(NH_3)_5(NO_2)][Zn(SCN)_4]$.
(a) It show coordination isomerism
(b) It show optical isomerism
(c) It show linkage isomerism
(d) IUPAC name is pentaammine nitrito-N-chromium(III)tetrathiocyanato-S-zincate(II)

173. Which of the following statement is **false** ?
(a) Optical isomerism is observed in $[Mabcd]^{n\pm}$ tetrahedral complexes.
(b) Geometrical isomerism does not exist while optical isomerism exists in complex $[Fe(C_2O_4)_3]^{3-}$.
(c) Both *cis*-form and *trans* form is optically inactive in $[PtCl_2(NH_3)_4]^{2+}$ complex ion.
(d) $[Pt(en)_2]^{2+}$ show geometrical isomerism as well as optical isomerism.

174. Select correct pair of complexes that exhibit same type of isomerism.
(a) $[CoBr(NH_3)_5]Cl_2, [IrBr_3(H_2O)_3]$
(b) $[Cr(NO_2)_2(en)_2]^+, [Rh(SCN)(H_2O)(ox)_2]^{2-}$
(c) $[Pt(gly)(NH_3)(H_2O)]^+, [Zn(gly)(NH_3)_2]^+$
(d) $[CoCl_2(NH_3)_4]^+, [CrBr(H_2O)_5]Br_2$

175. Which of the following has largest number of isomers ?
(a) $[Co(en)_2Cl_2]^+$ (b) $[Co(NH_3)_5Cl]^{2+}$
(c) $[Ir(PR_3)_2H(CO)]^{2+}$ (d) $[Ru(NH_3)_4Cl_2]^+$

176. Which of the following will have three stereoisomeric forms ?
(i) $[Cr(NO_3)_3(NH_3)_3]$ (ii) $K_3[Co(C_2O_4)_3]$
(iii) $K_3[CoCl_2(C_2O_4)_2]$ (iv) $[CoBrCl(en)_2]$
(a) (iii) and (iv) (b) (i), (iii) and (iv)
(c) (iv) only (d) all four

177. The complexes $[Co(NH_3)_6][Cr(CN)_6]$ and $[Cr(NH_3)_6][Co(CN)_6]$ are the examples of type of isomerism?
(a) Geometrical isomerism (b) Linkage isomerism
(c) Ionisation isomerism (d) Coordination isomerism

178. Possible isomerism in complexes $[Co(NH_3)_3(NO_2)_3]$ and $[Co(NH_3)_5(NO_2)]Cl_2$, respectively are :
(a) Linkage and optical (b) Geometrical and linkage
(c) Optical and ionization (d) Linkage and geometrical

179. Which of the following co-ordination ion/compound does not exhibit structural isomerism?
(a) $[PtBrCl(H_2O)_4]SO_4$ (b) $[CoBr(NH_3)_5][Cd(CN)_4]$
(c) $[Co(ox)(H_2O)_4]Br$ (d) $[Ir(ONO)_3(H_2O)_3]$

180. Which of the following co-ordination compound has three stereoisomers ?
(a) $[Cd(gly)(H_2O)(NH_3)]^+$ (b) $[PtBr_2(H_2O)_2]$
(c) $[Cr(en)_3]^{3+}$ (d) $[CoBr(NO_2)(en)_2]^+$

181. Complex showing *cis-trans* isomerism is :
(a) $[Pt(NH_3)_3Cl]Cl$ (b) $[Zn(NH_3)_2Cl_2]$ (c) $K_3[Fe(C_2O_4)_3]$ (d) $[Co(gly)_3]$

182. $[Ni(NH_3)_6]^{2+} + en \longrightarrow X + 2NH_3$
$[Ni(NH_3)_6] + 2en \longrightarrow Y + 4NH_3$
$[Ni(NH_3)_6] + 3en \longrightarrow Z + 6NH_3$
Which of them show optical as well as geometrical isomerism ?
(a) *X* (b) *Y* (c) *Z* (d) All of these

183. Select the complex compound which does not show stereoisomerism.
(I) $[M(en)_2]$ (II) $[M(en)(gly)]$ (III) $[M(gly)(NH_3)_2]$ (IV) $[M(gly)_2]$
(a) All I,II,III,IV (b) Only I,II,III
(c) Only II,III,IV (d) Only II, III

184. Which of the following paramagnetic complex ion exhibits optical activity ?
(a) $[Co(ox)_3]^{3-}$ (b) $[Zn(gly)_2]$
(c) $[Ni(NH_3)_2(en)_2]^{2+}$ (d) $[FeF_3(H_2O)_2(NH_3)]$

185. Which of the following complexes cannot exhibit both geometrical and optical isomerism ?
(A) $[Ru(en)_3]^{3+}$ (B) $[Co(H_2O)Cl_3]$
(C) $[Pt\ Br\ Cl(H_2O)NH_3]$ (D) $[CoBr_2(en)_2]^+$
correct code is :
(a) A, B, C (b) B, C (c) C, D (d) only B

186. Which of the following co-ordination compound has three stereoisomers ?
(a) $[Cd(gly)(H_2O)(NH_3)]^+$ (b) $[Pt\ Br_2(H_2O)_2]$
(c) $[Cr(en)_3]^{3+}$ (d) $[Co\ Br(NO_2)(en)_2]^+$

187. Which one of the following can show optical isomerism ?
(a) $FeSO_4 \cdot 7H_2O$ (b) $K_3[Cr(C_2O_4)_3]$
(c) $K_3[Fe(CN)_6]$ (d) $[Cr(NH_3)_4(H_2O)_2]Cl_3$

188. Consider the following two reactions :
$$Cd^{2+}(aq.) + 2H_2NCH_2CH_2NH_2 \xrightarrow{K_1} A$$
$$Cd^{2+}(aq.) + 2CH_3CH(NH_2)CH(NH_2)CH_3 \xrightarrow{K_2} B$$
According to given information the correct statement is are :
(a) A is optically active while B is optically inactive.
(b) A is optically inactive while B is optically active.
(c) Both are optically inactive.
(d) Both are optically active.

189. Select the complex compound which show geometrical as well as optical isomerism.
(a) $[Cr(H_2O)_4(NH_3)_2]^{3+}$ (b) $[Ni(en)_3]^{2+}$
(c) $[CoBrCl(en)_2]^+$ (d) $[Zn(gly)_2]$

190. Which of the following complex ion has a pair of enantiomers ?
(a) $[Zn(bcac)(en)]^+$ (b) $[PtBrCl(CN)(SCN)]^{2-}$
(c) $[Ir(acac)_2(H_2O)(NH_3)]^+$ (d) $[CrCl_3(SCN)(H_2O)_2]^-$

191. Complex compound with coordination number two and +1 oxidation state of central metal cation can not exhibit :
(a) Ionization isomerism (b) Hydrate isomerism
(c) Geometrical isomerism (d) Linkage isomerism

192. Which of the following complex is non-ionisable and has two geometrical isomers ?
(a) $PtCl_4 \cdot 3NH_3$ (b) $PtCl_4 \cdot 6NH_3$ (c) $PtCl_4 \cdot 2NH_3$ (d) $PtCl_4 \cdot 4NH_3$

193. Which of the following complex is optically inactive ?
(a) $[Co(en)_3]Cl_3$ (b) *cis* - $[Co(NH_3)_3Cl_3]$
(c) *cis* - $[Co(en)_2Cl_2]Cl$ (d) *cis* - $[Co(en)(NH_3)_2Cl_2]Cl$

194. Complex compound/ion which exhibits optical activity :
(a) $[CoBr_3(H_2O)_2(NH_3)]$ (b) $[IrBr_4(en)]^-$
(c) $[PtBr_2(NO_2)_2(en)]$ (d) $[Cr(CN)_3(NO_2)(en)]^-$

195. For complex ion/compound formation reactions
(I) $Co^{3+}(aq) + EDTA^{4-} \longrightarrow P$
(II) $Ni^{2+}(aq) + \text{dmg (excess)} \xrightarrow{NH_4OH} Q$
(III) $Zn^{2+}(aq) + \text{gly (excess)} \longrightarrow R$
(IV) $Pt^{4+}(aq) + \text{en (excess)} \longrightarrow S$
which of the following complex ion/compound does not exhibit optical activity ?
(a) P (b) Q (c) R (d) S

196. Which one of the following has largest number of isomers ?
(a) $[Co(en)_2(SCN)_2]^+$ (b) $[Pt(NH_3)Cl(NO_2)py]$
(c) $[Ir(ox)_3]^{3-}$ (d) $[Ru(NH_3)_4Cl_2]^+$

197. Which of the following isomerism, exhibited by $[CrCl_2(OH)_2(NH_3)_2]^-$?

(a) Ionization (b) Geometrical

(c) Hydrate (d) Linkage

198. Which kind of isomerism is exhibited by octahedral $[Co(NH_3)_4Br_2]Cl$?

(a) Geometrical and ionization (b) Geometrical and optical

(c) Optical and ionization (d) Geometrical only

199. A metal complex of coordination number six having three different types of ligands a, b and c of composition $Ma_2b_2c_2$ can exist in several geometrical isomeric forms; the total number of such isomers is :

(a) 3 (b) 5 (c) 7 (d) 9

200. How many geometrical isomers and stereoisomers are possible for $[Pt(NO_2)(NH_3)(NH_2OH)(Py)]^+$ and $[Pt(Br)(Cl)(I)(NO_2)(NH_3)(Py)]$ respectively?

(a) 3 and 15 (b) 3 and 30 (c) 4 and 15 (d) 4 and 30

201. Complexes given below show :

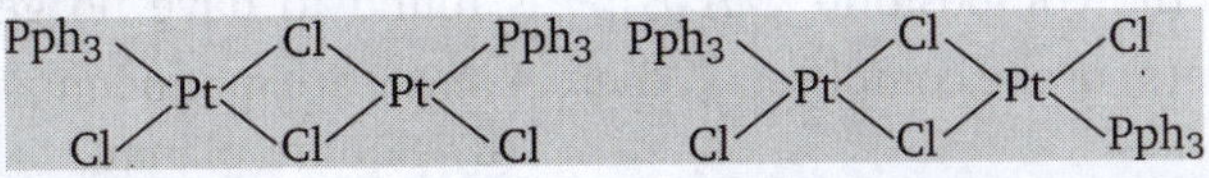

(a) Optical isomerism (b) Coordinate isomerism

(c) Geometrical isomerism (d) Bridge isomerism

202. Fac and Mer isomerism is associated with which of the following general formula?

(a) $[M(AA)_2]$ (b) $[M(AA)_3]$ (c) $[MABCD]$ (d) $[MA_3B_3]$

203. Which of the following will have two stereoisomeric forms?

(I) $[Cr(NO_3)_3(NH_3)_3]$ (II) $K_3[Fe(C_2O_4)_3]$ (III) $[CoCl_2(en)_2]^+$ (IV) $[CoBrCl(ox)_2]^{3-}$

(a) I only (b) I and II

(c) III and IV (d) All of these

204. Three arrangements are shown for the complex $[CoBr_2(NH_3)_2(en)]^{\oplus}$. Which one is wrong statement?

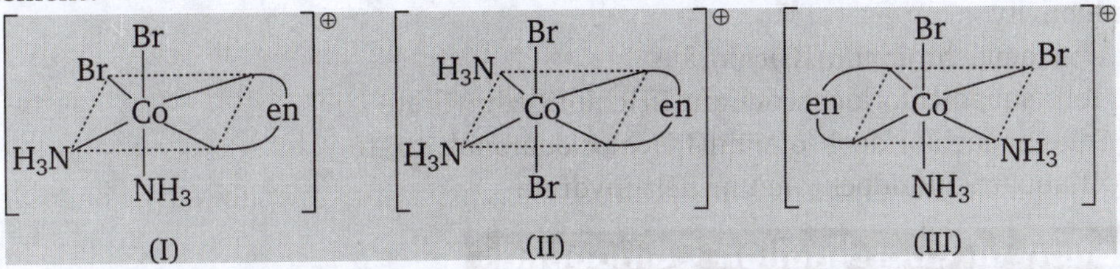

(a) I and II are geometrical isomers (b) II and III are optically active isomers

(c) I and III are optically active isomers (d) II and III are geometrical isomers

205. Which of the following is not optically active?

(a) $[Co(en)_3]^{3+}$ (b) $[Cr(Ox)_3]^{3-}$

(c) *cis*-$[CoCl_2(en)_2]^+$ (d) *trans*-$[CoCl_2(en)_2]^+$

206. Where among the following metal complexes the one which exhibits optical activity is : (AA=bidentate ligand; A, X= monodentate ligand)

(a) *cis*-$[MA_4X_2]$ (b) *trans*-$[MA_4X_2]$

(c) *cis*-$[M(AA)_2X_2]$ (d) *trans*-$[M(AA)_2X_2]$

207. The optically active species among the following is :
(a) $[Cr(NH_3)_6]^{3+}$ (b) $[Co(CN)_6]^{3-}$ (c) $[Co(gly)_3]$ (d) $[Ru(NH_3)_6]^{3+}$

208. *Cis-trans* isomerism is exhibited by :
(a) $[PtCl(NH_3)_3]^+$ (b) $[Pt(NH_3)_4]^{2+}$ (c) $[PtCl_4]^{2-}$ (d) $[PtCl_2(NH_3)_2]$

209. Which of the following will show optical isomers?
(I) *cis*-$[Co(NH_3)_2(en)_2]^{3+}$ (II) *trans*-$[IrCl_2(C_2O_4)_2]^{3-}$
(III) $[Rh(en)_3]^{3+}$ (IV) *cis*-$[Ir(H_2O)_3Cl_3]$
(a) I, III only correct (b) II, IV only correct
(c) I, III, IV only correct (d) III only correct

210. The complex with a maximum number of stereoisomers is :
(a) $[PtCl_3(C_2H_4)]^-$ (b) $[CuBr_2Cl_2]^{2-}$
(c) $[Co(C_2O_4)_3]^{3-}$ (d) $[Cr(NH_3)_2(en)_2]^{3+}$

211. A complex with the composition $[MA_3B]^{n\pm}$ is found to have no geometrical isomers. The possible structure(s) of the complex is (Where *A* and *B* are monodentate ligands)
(a) Tetrahedral (b) Square planar
(c) Both (a) and (b) (d) Cannot be predicted

212. Which of the following isomerism is not possible for complexes having molecular formulae ?
(I) $Pt(SCN)_2 \cdot 3PEt_3$, (II) $CoBr \cdot SO_4 \cdot 5NH_3$ (III) $FeCl_2 \cdot 6H_2O$
(a) Optical (b) Linkage (c) Ionisation (d) Hydrate

213. Incorrect match for given complex compound/ion and its characteristics :
(a) $[CrBrCl(en)_2]Br$ Ionization and optical isomerism
(b) $[CoBr_3(H_2O)_3]$ Fac-mer and hydrate isomerism
(c) $[PtCl_2(NH_3)_4][Co(SCN)_4]$ Linkage isomerism and paramagnetic character
(d) $[Co(ox)_3]^{3-}$ Inner orbital complex and optical isomerism

214. Find IUPAC name of the **hydrate isomer** of $CrCl_3 \cdot 6H_2O$, which is having lowest electrical conductivity.
(a) Hexaaquachromium(III)chloride
(b) Tetraaquadichloridochromium(III)chloridedihydrate
(c) Pentaaquachloridochromium(III)chloridemonohydrate
(d) Triaquatrichloridochromium(III)trihydrate

Application of Coordination Compounds

215. Coordination compounds have great importance in biological systems. In this context which of the following statements is incorrect?
(a) Carboxypeptidase–A is an enzyme and contains zinc
(b) Haemoglobin is the red pigment of blood and contains iron
(c) Cyanocobalamin is B^{12} and contains cobalt
(d) Chlorophylls are green pigments in plants and contain calcium

216. Which one of the following platinum complexes is used in cancer chemotherapy?
(a) *cis*-$[PtCl_2(NH_3)_2]$ (b) *trans*-$[PtCl_2(NH_3)]$
(c) $[Pt(NH_3)_4]^{2+}$ (d) $[Pt(Cl_4)]^{2-}$

217. The cyanide complex of silver formed in the silver extraction in Mac-Arthur's Forrest cyanide process is :
(a) $[Ag(CN)_2]^-$ (b) $K_2[Ag(CN)_3]$ (c) $[Ag(CN)_4]^{2-}$ (d) $Na_3[Ag(CN)_4]$

218. Complexes formed in the following methods are :
(I) Mond's process for purification of nickel
(II) Removal of unreacted AgBr from photographic plate
(III) Removal of lead poisoning from the body

	I	II	III
(a)	$Ni(CO)_4$	$[Ag(CN)_2]^-$	$[Pb(EDTA)]^{2-}$
(b)	$Ni(CO)_4$	$[Ag(S_2O_3)_2]^{3-}$	$[Pb(EDTA)]^{2-}$
(c)	$Ni(CO)_6$	$[Ag(S_2O_3)_2]^{3-}$	$[Pb(EDTA)]^{4-}$
(d)	$Ni(CO)_6$	$[Ag(S_2O_3)]^-$	$[Pb(EDTA)]^{2-}$

219. Metal cation present in Sodium nitroprusside is also present in :
(a) Chlorophyll (b) Vitamin B_{12} (c) *cis*-platin (d) Haemoglobin

220. Select incorrect statement
(a) *cis* - $[Pt(NH_3)_2Cl_2]$ is an anticancer compound
(b) Cobalt cation is present in Vitamin B_{12}
(c) Mn cation is present in chlorophyll
(d) $EDTA^{4-}$ is used to estimate Ca^{2+} and Mg^{2+} cation

221. Incorrect match is :
(a) $EDTA^{4-}$: Estimation of Hardness of water
(b) DMG : Analysis of $Ni^{2+}(aq)$
(c) Na_2H_2EDTA : Lead poisoning
(d) $[RhCl(PPh_3)_3]$: Wilkinson's catalyst

222. Metal cation present in Haemoglobin is also present in :
(a) Chlorophyll (b) Vitamin B_{12}
(c) *cis*-platin (d) Sodium Nitroprusside

223. Select correct statement.
(a) Lead poisoning is removed by carbon mono oxide by complex formation
(b) Hardness of water is estimated by $EDTA^{4-}$
(c) Ag^+ does not form cyano complex with excess KCN
(d) $TiCl_3(aq)$ is colourless while $TiCl_4(aq)$ is coloured

224. Incorrect match is :
(a) $[Rh(PPh_3)_3Cl]$: Wilkinson's catalyst
(b) $[Co(CO)_4]^-$: Bond order of Co — CO bond is greater than one
(c) $[Zn(NH_3)_4][Be(OH)_4]$: colorless complex
(d) $[Cr(CN)_6]^{3-}$: Inner orbital low spin complex

Level 2

Synergic Bonding

1. Which of the following ligand does not as π-acid ligand ?

(a) N_2 (b) CO (c) C_2H_4 (d) O_2^{2-}

2. The π-acid ligand which uses its *d*-orbital during synergic bonding in its complex compound.

(a) CN^- (b) PR_3 (c) NO (d) N_2

3. The IR stretching frequencies of free CO, and CO in $[V(CO)_6]^-$, $[Cr(CO)_6]^-$ and $[Mn(CO)_6]^-$ are 2143 cm^{-1}, 1860 cm^{-1}, 2000 cm^{-1} and 2090 cm^{-1}, respectively. Then correct statement about metal carbonyls is :

(a) 'C—O' bond is strongest in the cation and weakest in the anion.

(b) 'C—O' bond is weakest in the cation and strongest in the anion.

(c) 'C—O' bond is longer in the cation than in the anion.

(d) 'M—C' pi bonding is higher in the cation.

4. The π-acid ligand which uses its *d*-orbital during synergic bonding in its complex compound:

(a) NO^+ (b) PR_3 (c) C_6H_6 (d) CO

5. Correct sequence of CO bond order in given compounds is :

(P) $Fe(CO)_5$ (Q) CO (R) $H_3B \leftarrow CO$ (S) $[Mn(CO)_5]^-$

(a) P>R>S>Q (b) S>P>R>Q (c) Q>S>P>R (d) R>Q>P>S

Sidwick's Rule of EAN

6. Consider the complex $[Co(NH_3)_4CO_3]ClO_4$, in which coordination number, oxidation number and number of *d*-electrons on the metal are respectively.

(a) 6, 3, 6 (b) 6, 2, 7 (c) 5, 3, 6 (d) 5, 3, 7

7. If E.A.N.of central metal cation M^{2+} in a non-chelating complex is 36 and atomic no. of metal *M* is 26, then the number of monodentate ligand is in this complex are :

(a) 5 (b) 4 (c) 6 (d) None of these

8. $[Mn(CO)_4NO]$ is diamagnetic because :

(a) Mn metal is diamagnetic in free state

(b) Mn is in +1 oxidation state in this complex

(c) NO is present as positive ligand

(d) All of the above

9. Choose the correct option regarding the following complex compound which follows (F) and does not follow (NF) the Sidgwick EAN rule :

(I) $[(Ph_3P)_2PdCl_2PdCl_2]$ (II) $[NiBrCl(en)]$

(III) $Na_4[Fe(CN)_5NOS]$ (IV) $Cr(CO)_3(NO)_2$

	(I)	(II)	(III)	(IV)		(I)	(II)	(III)	(IV)
(a)	NF	NF	NF	NF	(b)	F	F	NF	F
(c)	NF	NF	F	F	(d)	NF	NF	F	NF

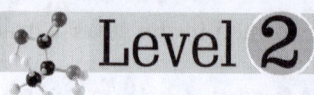

10. If CO ligands are substituted by NO in respective neutral carbonyl compounds then which of the following will not be correct formula ?

(a) $Cr(CO)_3(NO)_2$ (b) $Fe(CO)_2(NO)_2$
(c) $Cr(NO)_4$ (d) $Ni(CO)_2(NO)_2$

11. Which of the following species can act as reducing agent ?

(a) $[Co(CO)_4]^-$ (b) $Mn(CO)_6$
(c) $Mn(CO)_5$ (d) $Cr(CO)_6$

IUPAC Name

12. A complex whose IUPAC name is not correctly written is :

	Complex	**Name**
(a)	$Fe(\sigma - C_5H_5)_2$	Bis(η^5-cyclopentadienyl)iron(0)
(b)	$Cr(C_6H_6)_2$	Bis(η^6-benzene)chromium(0)
(c)	$[CoCl_2(H_2O)_4]Cl.2H_2O$	Tetraaquadichlorocobalt (III)chloride-2-water
(d)	$[Zn(NCS)_4]^{2-}$	Tetrathiocyanato-*N*-zincate (II) ion

13. Which of the following is correct IUPAC name of any complex compound?

(a) Tris(acetylacetonato)iron(III)chloride
(b) Hexachloroplatinum(IV)tetraammine dicyano platinate(IV)
(c) Ammine bromochloro methylamine platinum(II)
(d) *cis*-dichloro (ethylenediamine) platinum (II)

14. Find out correct IUPAC name of complex compound .

(a) Triamminetricyanidochromium(III)hexanitrito-N-irridate(III)
(b) Pentaamminecyanidochromium(III)hexanitrito-N-irridium(III)
(c) Hexanitrito-N-irridium(III)pentaamminecyanidochromate(II)
(d) Pentaamminecyanidochromium(III)hexanitrito-N-irridate(III)

Valence Bond Theory

15. Select correct statement(s) regarding $[Ni(DMG)_2]$ complex compound :

(a) It acts as oxidising agent because Ni^{2+} cation is having E.A.N. 34.
(b) It is extra stabilized by hydrogen bonding
(c) It's IUPAC name is Bis(dimethylglyoximato)nickelate (II)
(d) It's ligand contains two different donar sites

16. In which of the following complex ion the value of magnetic moment (spin only) is $\sqrt{3}$ BM and outer *d*-orbitals is used in hybridization.

(a) $[Mn(CN)_6]^{4-}$ (b) $[Fe(NH_3)_6]^{3+}$
(c) $[Co(CO)_4]$ (d) $[Cu(H_2O)_6]^{2+}$

17. Hybridisation of which complex is correctly matched :

(a) $[Ni(NH_3)_6]^{2+} : d^2sp^3$ (b) $[Co(Ox)_3]^{3-} : sp^3d^2$
(c) $[RhCl(PPh_3)_3]^0 : dsp^2$ (d) $[Fe(NH_3)_6]^{2+} : d^2sp^3$

18. Select correct statement regarding $[Ni(DMG)_2]$ complex compound.

(a) It acts as oxidising agent because Ni^{2+} cation is having EAN 34.

(b) It is extra-stabilized by hydrogen bonding

(c) It's IUPAC name is Bis (dimethylglyoximato) nickelate (II)

(d) It's ligand contains two different donar sites

19. Which of the following is correctly matched?

(a) $[Fe(CN)_6]^{4-}$ and $[Fe(CN)_6]^{3-}$ — both are octahedral and diamagnetic with d^2sp^3-hybridisation

(b) $Ni(CO)_4$ and $[Ni(CN)_4]^{2-}$ — both are tetrahedral and diamagnetic with sp^3-hybridisation

(c) $Ni(CO)_4$ and $[Co(CO)_4]^-$ — both are tetrahedral and diamagnetic

(d) $[Co(H_2O)_6]^{3+}$ and $[Cr(H_2O)_6]^{3+}$ — both are paramagnetic and metal is d^2sp^3-hybridised

20. Match List-I with List-II and select the correct answer using the codes given below the lists :

List-I (Compound)	List-II (of Central atom)
(A) $[Ni(NH_3)_6]^{2+}$	(1) sp^3
(B) $[PtCl_4]^{2-}$	(2) sp^3d^2
(C) $[Ni(CO)_4]$	(3) dsp^2
(D) $[Co(ox)_3]^{3-}$	(4) d^2sp^3

	A	B	C	D		A	B	C	D
(a)	2	1	3	4	(b)	2	3	1	4
(c)	4	1	3	2	(d)	4	3	1	2

21. Match List-I (Species) with List-II (Hybrid orbitals used by the central atom in their formation) and select the correct answer :

List-I	List-II
(A) $Ni(CN)_5^{3-}$	(1) sp^3
(B) $CuCl_5^{3-}$	(2) dsp^2
(C) $AuCl_4^-$	(3) $sp^3d_{z^2}$
(D) ClO_4^-	(4) $d_{x^2-y^2}sp^3$

	A	B	C	D		A	B	C	D
(a)	1	3	2	4	(b)	3	4	2	1
(c)	4	2	1	3	(d)	4	3	2	1

22. Which of the following is correctly matched?

Column-I	Column-II	Column-III
(a) $[Cr(CO)_6]$	Paramagnetic	Octahedral, sp^3d^2
(b) $[Fe(CO)_5]$	Paramagnetic	Trigonal bipyramid, sp^3d
(c) $[Co(CO)_4]^-$	Diamagnetic	Tetrahedral, sp^3
(d) $[Ni(CO)_4]$	Diamagnetic	Square planar, dsp^2

23. The hybridization of the complex $[CrCl_2(NO_2)_2(NH_3)_2]^-$ is :

(a) sp^3d^2 (b) d^2sp^3
(c) sp^3d (d) cannot be predicted

24. Which of the following statement is not true for the reaction given below?

$$[Cu(H_2O)_4]^{2+} + 4NH_3 \rightleftharpoons [Cu(NH_3)_4]^{2+} + 4H_2O$$

(a) It is a ligand substitution reaction
(b) NH_3 is a relatively strong field ligand while H_2O is a weak field ligand
(c) During the reaction, there is a change in colour from light blue to dark blue
(d) $[Cu(NH_3)_4]^{2+}$, has a tetrahedral structure and is paramagnetic

25. Which of the following match is incorrect ?

Complex compounds		**Type of hybridization**
(a) $[V(NH_3)_6]^{3+}$	:	d^2sp^3
(b) $[CrCl_3(NMe_3)_3]$	:	d^2sp^3
(c) $[Cu(CN)(NO_2)(NH_3)(py)]$	:	dsp^2
(d) $K_3[Co(ox)_3]$	:	sp^3d^2

Crystal Field Theory

26. What is electronic arrangement of metal atom/ion in octahedral complex with d^4 configuration, if $\Delta_0 <$ pairing energy?

(a) $t_{2g}^4e_g^0$ (b) $e_g^4t_{2g}^0$ (c) $t_{2g}^3e_g^1$ (d) $e_g^2t_{2g}^2$

27. Which of the following statement is not correct?

(a) Bis(glycinatio)Zinc(II) is optically active
(b) $[NiCl_4]^{2-}$ and $[PtCl_4]^{2-}$ have different shape
(c) $[Ni(CN)_4]^{4-}$ is square planar complex
(d) $[Ni(CN)_4]^{2-}$ and $[Ni(CO)_4]$ have the same magnetic moment

28. Give the correct of initials **T** or **F** for following statements. Use **T** if statement is true and **F** if it is false.

(I) Co(III) is stabilised in presence of weak field ligands, while Co(II) is stabilised in presence of strong field ligand.
(II) Four coordinated complexes of Pd(II) and Pt(II) are diamagnetic and square planar.
(III) $[Ni(CN)_4]^{4-}$ ion and $[Ni(CO)_4]$ are diamagnetic tetrahedral and square planar respectively.
(IV) Ni^{2+} ion does not form inner orbital octahedral complexes.

(a) TFTF (b) TTTF (c) TTFT (d) FTFT

29. Match List-I with List-II and select the correct answer using the codes given below :

List-I	List-II
(I) $[FeF_6]^{3-}$	(A) 1.73 BM
(II) $[Ti(H_2O)_6]^{3+}$	(B) 5.93 BM
(III) $[Cr(NH_3)_6]^{3+}$	(C) 0.00 BM
(IV) $[Ni(H_2O)_6]^{2+}$	(D) 2.83 BM
(V) $[Fe(CN)_6]^{4-}$	(E) 3.88 BM

	(I)	(II)	(III)	(IV)	(V)		(I)	(II)	(III)	(IV)	V
(a)	B	A	C	D	E	(b)	B	A	E	D	C
(c)	B	C	D	E	A	(d)	D	E	A	B	C

30. The value of 'spin only' magnetic moment for one of the following configuration is 2.84 BM. The correct one is :

(a) d^4 (in strong field ligand)
(b) d^2 (in weak field ligand)
(c) d^3 (in weak as well as in strong field ligand)
(d) d^5 (in strong field ligand)

31. The correct order of magnetic moments (spin values in BM) among is :

(a) $[Fe(CN)_6]^{4-} > [CoCl_4]^{2-} > [MnCl_4]^{2-}$ (b) $[MnCl_4]^{2-} > [Fe(CN)_6]^{4-} > [CoCl_4]^{2-}$
(c) $[Fe(CN)_6]^{4-} > [MnCl_4]^{2-} > [CoCl_4]^{2-}$ (d) $[MnCl_4]^{2-} > [CoCl_4]^{2-} > [Fe(CN)_6]^{4-}$

32. Which of the following statements is incorrect?

(a) The stability constant of $[Co(NH_3)_6]^{3+}$ is greater than that of $[Co(NH_3)_6]^{2+}$
(b) The cyano complexes are far more stable than those formed by halide ions
(c) The stability of halide complexes follows the order $I^- < Br^- < Cl^-$
(d) The stability constant of $[Cu(NH_3)_4]^{2+}$ is greater than that of $[Cu(en)_2]^{2+}$

33. Set of *d*-orbitals which is used by central metal during formation of MnO_4^- ?

(a) $d_{x^2-y^2}, d_{z^2}, d_{xy}$ (b) d_{xy}, d_{yz}, d_{xz} (c) $d_{x^2-y^2}, d_{xy}, d_{xz}$ (d) $d_{x^2-y^2}, d_{z^2}, d_{xz}$

34. $FeSO_4$ solution is a very good absorber for NO, the new compound formed by this process is found to contain number of unpaired electrons :

(a) 4 (b) 5 (c) 3 (d) 6

35. A $[M(H_2O)_6]^{2+}$ complex typically absorbs at around 600 nm. It is allowed to react with ammonia to form a new complex $[M(NH_3)_6]^{2+}$ that should have absorption at :

(a) 800 nm (b) 580 nm (c) 620 nm (d) 320 nm

36. An ion M^{2+}, forms the complexes $[M(H_2O)_6]^{2+}$, $[M(en)_3]^{2+}$ and $[MBr_6]^{4-}$, match the complex with the appropriate colour :

(a) Green, blue and red (b) Blue, red and green
(c) Green, red and blue (d) Red, blue and green

37. The CFSE for $[(CoCl)_6]^{4-}$ complex is 18000 cm^{-1}. The Δ for $[CoCl_4]^{2-}$ will be :
(a) 18000 cm^{-1} (b) 16000 cm^{-1} (c) 8000 cm^{-1} (d) 2000 cm^{-1}

38. MnO_4^- is of intense pink colour, though Mn is in (+7) oxidation state, it is due to :
(a) Oxygen gives colour to it
(b) Charge transfer when Mn(+7) gives its electron to oxygen and oxidise to Mn (+8) temporarily
(c) Charge transfer when oxygen gives its electron to Mn (+7) changing in Mn (+6)
(d) None is correct explanation

39. In which of the following complex ion the value of magnetic moment (spin only) is $\sqrt{3}$ B.M. and outer *d*-orbitals is used in hybridization:
(a) $[Fe(NH_3)_6]^{3+}$ (b) $[Mn(CN)_6]^{4-}$ (c) $[CuCl_5]^{3-}$ (d) $[Co(NH_3)_6]^{2+}$

40. Which of the following order of CFSE is incorrect ?
(a) $[Co(en)_3]^{3+} > [Co(NH_3)_6]^{3+} > [Co(H_2O)_6]^{3+}$
(b) $[PtCl_4]^{2-} > [PdCl_4]^{2-} > [NiCl_4]^{2-}$
(c) $[Ni(DMG)_2] < [Ni(en)_2]^{2+}$ (d) $[Co(ox)_3]^{3-} < [Co(en)_3]^{3+}$

41. For which of the following d^n configuration of octahedral complexes, can not exist in both high spin and low spin forms :
(I) d^3 (II) d^5 (III) d^6 (IV) d^8
(a) I, II & III (b) II, III & IV (c) I & IV (d) None of these

Isomerism

42. Select the correct code of TRUE and FALSE for given statements :
(a) Peroxide ion as well as dioxygen molecule both are paramagnetic species
(b) In set of isomers, $[Cr(H_2O)_6]Cl_3$ and $[CrCl(H_2O)_5]Cl_2 \cdot H_2O$, both compounds can easily loose water molecule on treatment with conc. H_2SO_4
(c) During transformation $NO \longrightarrow NO^+$, bond length and magnetic behaviour decreases
(d) An ether is more volatile than alcohol both having same molecular formula
(a) FFTT (b) FTFT (c) FTTT (d) TFFT

43. The total possible coordination isomers for the following compounds respectively are :
$[Co(en)_3][Cr(C_2O_4)_3]$
$[Cu(NH_3)_4][CuCl_4]$
$[Ni(en)_3][Co(NO_2)_6]$
(a) 4, 4, 4 (b) 2, 2, 2 (c) 2, 2, 4 (d) 4, 2, 3

44. Select the incorrect match :
(a) $[Co(NO_2)(H_2O)(en)_2]Cl_2$, $[CoCl(NO_2)(en)_2]Cl \cdot H_2O$: Hydrate isomerism
(b) $[Cu(NH_3)_4][PtCl_4]$, $[CuCl(NH_3)_3][PtCl_3(NH_3)]$: Co-ordination isomerism
(c) $[Ni(CN)(H_2O)(NH_3)_4]Cl$, $[NiCl(H_2O)(NH_3)_4]CN$: Ionization isomerism
(d) $[Cr(NO_2)(NH_3)_5][ZnCl_4]$, $[Cr(NO_3)(NH_3)_5][ZnCl_4]$: Linkage isomerism

45. Select incorrect statement about complex $[Cr(NO_2)(NH_3)_5][Zn(SCN)_4]$:
(a) It shows co-ordination isomerism
(b) It shows optical activity (c) It shows linkage isomerism
(d) IUPAC name of the compound is Pentaamminenitrito-N-chromium(III) tetrathiocyanato-S-zincate(II)

46. Complex compound(s) having even number of space (stereo) isomers is/are :
(where *AA*-symmetrical bidentate ligand and *a, b, c, d, e*-monodentate ligands)
(a) $[M(AA)_2b_2]^{n\pm}$ (b) $[Ma_3b_3]^{n\pm}$ (c) $[Ma_3bcd]^{n\pm}$ (d) $[Ma_2bcde]^{n\pm}$

47. Which of the following isomersm is not possible for complexes having molecular formulae :
(i) $Pt(SCN)_2 \cdot 3PEt_3$ (ii) $CoBr \cdot SO_4 \cdot 5NH_3$ (iii) $FeCl_2 \cdot 6H_2O$
(a) Optical (b) Linkage (c) Ionisation (d) Hydrate

48. Unmatched characteristic of complex $[PdCl_2(H_2O)_2(NH_3)_2]^{2+}$ is :
(a) Diamagnetic (b) Low spin
(c) Geometrical isomerism (d) Fac. and Mer. form

49. Which of the following has largest number of isomers ?
(a) $[Co(en)_2Cl_2]^+$ (b) $[Co(NH_3)_5Cl]^{2+}$
(c) $[Ir(PR_3)_2H(CO)]^{2+}$ (d) $[Ru(NH_3)_4Cl_2]^+$

50. Which one of the following complexes exhibit chirality?
(a) $[Cr(ox)_3]^3$ (b) $[PtCl_2(en)]$
(c) *cis*-$[RhCl_2(NH_3)_4]^+$ (d) $[Co(NO_2)_3(dien)]$

51. Consider the following isomerism :
(i) Ionization (ii) Hydrate (iii) Coordination (iv) Geometrical (v) Optical
Which of the above isomerisms are exhibited by $[Cr(NH_3)_2(OH)_2Cl_2]^-$?
(a) (i) and (v) (b) (ii) and (iii) (c) (iii), (ii) and (i) (d) (iv) and (v)

52. Which complex is likely to show optical activity?
(a) *trans*-$[Co(NH_3)_4Cl_2]^+$ (b) $[Cr(H_2O)_6]^{3+}$
(c) *cis*-$[Co(NH_3)_2(en)_2]$ (d) *trans*-$[Co(NH_3)_2(en)_2]^{3+}$

53. Which of the following statement is true ?
(a) In $[PtCl_2(NH_3)_2]^{2+}$ the *cis* form is optically inactive while *trans* form is optically active
(b) In $[Fe(C_2O_4)_3]^{3-}$, geometrical isomerism does not exist while optical isomerism exists
(c) In *Mabcd*, square planar complexes show both optical as well as geometrical isomerism
(d) In *Mabcd* tetrahedral complex, optical isomerism cannot be observed

54. The following complexes are given :
(1) *trans*-$[Co(NH_3)_4Cl_2]^+$ (2) *cis*-$[Co(NH_3)_2(en)_2]^{3+}$
(3) *trans*-$[Co(NH_3)_2(en)_2]^{3+}$ (4) $NiCl_4^{2-}$
(5) TiF_6^{2-} (6) CoF_6^{3-}
Choose the correct code :
(a) (1), (2) are optically active, (3) is optically inactive
(b) (2) is optically active; (1), (3) are optically inactive
(c) (4), (5) are coloured and (6) is colourless
(d) (4) is coloured and (5), (6) are colourless

55. Which of the following can show geometrical isomerism?
(a) $[Pt(NH_2—CH(CH_3)—CH(CH_3)—NH_2)_2]^{2+}$ (b) $[Co(en)_2NH_3Cl]^{2+}$
(c) Both (a) and (b) (d) None of these

56. Which of the following complex compound exhibits *cis-trans* isomerism?

(a) $[CoCl(NH_3)_4(H_2O)]$ (b) $[CoCl_3(NH_3)_3]$
(c) $[CoCl_2(NH_3)_4]$ (d) All of these

57. Which of the following will have three stereoisomeric forms?

(i) $[Cr(NO_3)_3(NH_3)_3]$ (ii) $K_3[Co(C_2O_4)_3]$
(iii) $K_3[CoCl_2(C_2O_4)_2]$ (iv) $[CoBrCl(en)_2]$

(a) (iii) and (iv) (b) (i), (iii) and (iv) (c) (iv) only (d) All four

58. A coordination complex of type MX_2Y_2 (M-metal ion; X, Y-monodentate ligands), can have either a tetrahedral or a square planar geometry. The total number of possible isomers in these two cases are respectively :

(a) 1 and 2 (b) 2 and 1 (c) 1 and 3 (d) 3 and 2

59. The ratio of *cis* and *trans*-isomers of the complex $[Ma_2bcde]^{n\pm}$ is :

(a) 5 : 3 (b) 2 : 1 (c) 7 : 3 (d) 3 : 1

60. $[PdCl_2(PMe_3)_2]$ is a diamagnetic complex of Pd(II). How many total isomers are possible of analogous paramagnetic complex of Ni(II)?

(a) Zero (b) 1 (c) 2 (d) 3

61. Complex compounds(s) which is optical active and does not depend upon the orientation of the ligands around metal cation :

(i) $[CoCl_3(NH_3)_3]$ (ii) $[Co(en)_3]Cl_3$
(iii) $[Co(C_2O_4)_2(NH_3)_2]^-$ (iv) $[CrCl_2(NH_3)_2(en)]^+$

(a) (ii), (iii) and (iv) (b) (i), (ii) and (iv) (c) (ii) and (iv) (d) only (ii)

62. Choose the correct code regarding, possible number of geometrical isomers exhibited by following complexes :

(I) $[CrCl_2(NO_2)_2(NH_3)_2]^-$ (II) $[Co(NO_2)_3(NH_3)_3]$
(III) $[PtCl(NO_2)(NH_3)(py)]$ (IV) $[PtBrCl(en)]$

	(I)	(II)	(III)	(IV)		(I)	(II)	(III)	(IV)
(a)	4	2	3	1	(b)	5	2	4	0
(c)	3	2	0	1	(d)	5	2	3	0

63. How many geometrical isomers are possible for complex $[Mab(AB)_2]^{n\pm}$?

(a) 5 (b) 4 (c) 3 (d) 6

64. $[CoCl_2(NH_3)_4]^+ + Cl^- \longrightarrow [CoCl_3(NH_3)_3] + NH_3$. If in this reaction two isomers of the product are obtained, which is true for the initial (reactant) complex :

(a) compound is in *cis*-form (b) compound is in *trans*-form
(c) compound is in both (*cis* and *trans*) form (d) can't be predicted

65. Select the correct statement about given square planar complex.

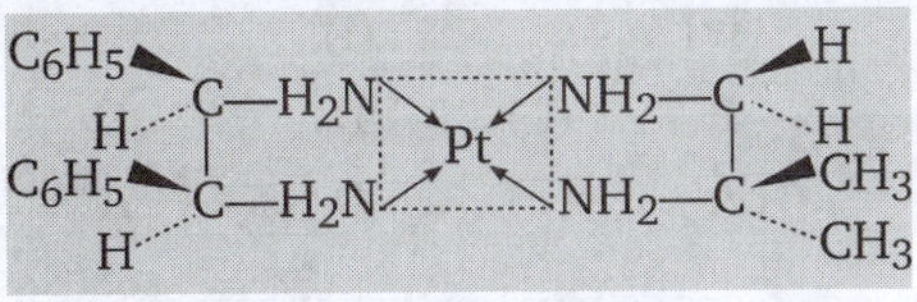

(a) It has no geometrical isomer
(b) It is optically active because it does not have plane of symmetry
(c) It is optically inactive because square planar complex have plane of symmetry
(d) It is optically active because it has symmetric carbon

66. Select the correct code regarding total number of space isomers for the following compounds :
(I) $[Ma_3b_2c]^{n\pm}$ (II) $[M(AB)_3]^{n\pm}$ (III) $[Ma_2b_2c_2]^{n\pm}$

	(I)	(II)	(III)		(I)	(II)	(III)
(a)	4	4	6	(b)	4	3	5
(c)	3	3	5	(d)	3	4	6

67. How many geometrical isomers are possible or $[Pd^{2+}(NH_2—CH(CH_3)—CO_2^-)_2]$
(a) 2 (b) 3 (c) 4 (d) 6

68. Total number of stereoisomers of $[Co(acac)_2BrCl)]^{\ominus}$ are :
(a) 4 (b) 3 (c) 6 (d) 2

69. Which of the following complex compound exhibits geometrical isomerism ?
(a) $[Fe(DMG)_2]$ (b) $[Be(gly)_2]$ (c) $[PdClBr(gly)]^-$ (d) $[Cd(NH_3)Cl(gly)]$

70. In which case racemic mixture is obtained on mixing its mirror images (*d* & *l* form) in 1 : 1 molar ratio?
(a) *trans* - $[Co(gly)_3]$ (b) $[Ni(DMG)_2]$
(c) *cis* - $[Cu(gly)_2]$ (d) $[Zn(en)(gly)]^+$

71. Which of the following compound show optical isomerism?
(a) *cis* - $[CrCl_3(NHl_3)_3]$ (b) *cis* - $[Co(NH_3)_4Cl_2]^+$
(c) $[Co(en)_3]^{3+}$ (d) *trans* - $[Co(en)_2Cl_2]^+$

72. The inner orbital complex which exhibits both geometrical as well as optical isomerism.
(a) $[Cr(en)_3]^{3+}$ (b) $[IrF_3(H_2O)_2(NH_3)]$
(c) $[NiCl_2(en)_2]$ (d) $[Co(CN)_2(ox)_2]^{3-}$

Application of Coordination Compounds

73. Match List-I with List-II and select the correct answer using the codes given below :

List-I (Ion involved)		List-II (agent)
(i)	Ni^{2+}	(A) Sodium thiosulphate
(ii)	Ag^+	(B) Sodium nitroprusside
(iii)	Cu^{2+}	(C) Ammonia
(iv)	S^{2-}	(D) Dimethylglyoxime

	(i)	(ii)	(iii)	(iv)		(i)	(ii)	(iii)	(iv)
(a)	C	A	D	B	(b)	D	C	A	B
(c)	D	C	B	A	(d)	D	A	C	B

Level 3

Passage 1

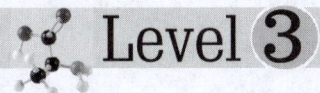

Magnetic moment, ionic conductance and colligative properties are useful in deciding structure/constitution of a given unknown complex compound.

1. If molar conductivity of complex is almost equal to that of NaCl and it does not exhibits stereoisomerism then the complex will be :
(a) $[Co(CO_3)(en)_2]Br$
(b) $[Co(CO_3)(H_2O)_2(NH_3)_2]Br$
(c) $[Co(CN)(NH_3)_5]Br_2$
(d) $[Co(CO_3)(NH_3)_4]Br$

2. A metal *M* having electronic configuration $(n-1)d^8ns^2$ forms complexes with co-ordination No. = 4 and 6, if it forms diamagnetic complexes then permissible oxidation states of metal cation and geometry is :
(a) +2, octahedral (b) +4, octahedral (c) +2, square planar (d) (b) and (c) both

3. The cyano complex that exhibit highest value of paramagnetism is :
(a) $[Mn(CN)_6]^{4-}$ (b) $[Co(CN)_6]^{3-}$ (c) $[Fe(CN)_6]^{3-}$ (d) $[Cr(CN)_6]^{3-}$

Passage 2

The crystal field theory assumes interaction between metal ion and the ligands as a purely electrostatic and ligands are supposed to be point charges.

1. Which of the following order of CFSE is incorrect ?
(a) $[Cr(NO_2)_6]^{3-} > [Cr(NH_3)_6]^{3+} > [Cr(H_2O)_6]^{3+}$
(b) $[PtF_4]^{2-} > [PdF_4]^{2-} > [NiF_4]^{2-}$
(c) $[Ni(DMG)_2] < [Ni(en)_2]^{2+}$
(d) $[Co(EDTA)]^{-} > [Co(en)_3]^{3+}$

2. Which of the following match are incorrect ?

Complex Compound	Magnetic Moment
(a) $[VCl_3(NMe_3)_3]$	$\sqrt{8}$ BM
(b) $[CrCl_3(NMe_3)_3]$	$\sqrt{15}$ BM
(c) $[Cu(CN)(NO_2)(NH_3)(Py)]$	$\sqrt{3}$ BM
(d) $[Co(ox)(H_2O)_4]^{+}$	$\sqrt{24}$ BM

3. Amongst the following complexes which has square planar geometry ?
(a) $[RhCl(CO)(PPh_3)_2]$
(b) $K_2[Cu(SCN)_4]$
(c) $K_2[Ni(PH_3)_2Cl_2]$
(d) MnO_4^{2-}

Passage 3

The magnetic property, dipole moment, plane of symmetry, colour and absorption band can be helpful in structure elucidation of complex compounds.

1. Which of the following complex ion is expected to absorb light in 4000 Å to 7800 Å region ?

(a) $[Ti(en)_3]^{4+}$ (b) $[Cr(H_2O)_6]^{3+}$

(c) $[Sc(NH_3)_4(H_2O)_2]^{3+}$ (d) $[Zn(en)_2(NH_3)_2]^{2+}$

2. Compound 'X' has molecular formula $CrCl_2Br \cdot 6H_2O$ can show type of isomerism.

(i) hydrate isomerism (ii) ionization isomerism

(iii) geometrical isomerism (iv) optical isomerism

(a) (i), (ii) and (iii) only (b) (i) and (ii) only

(c) (i), (ii), (iii) and (iv) (d) (i) and (iii) only

3. Complex compound(s) having even number of space (stereo) isomers is/are :
(Where *AA*-symmetrical bidentate ligand and *a*, *b*, *c*, *d* *e*-monodentate ligands)

(a) $[M(AA)_2b_2]^{n\pm}$ (b) $[Ma_3b_3]^{n\pm}$ (c) $[Ma_3bcd]^{n\pm}$ (d) $[Ma_2bcde]^{n\pm}$

Passage 4

Ligands are broadly classified into two classes classical and non-classical ligands, depending on their donor and acceptor ability. Classical ligands form classical complexes while non-classical ligands form non-classical complexes. Bonding mechanism in non-classical is called synergic bonding.

1. Synergic bonding is absent in :

(a) $[Mo(CO)_6]$ (b) $[Cr(CO)_3(B_3N_3H_6)]$

(c) $[Sc(CO)_6]^{3+}$ (d) $[Ni(CN)_4]^{4-}$

2. Which is not π-acceptor ligand ?

(a) 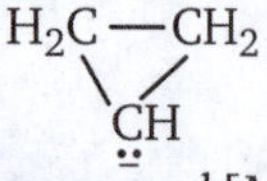

(b) $\sigma - C_5H_5^-$ (c) PH_3 (d) $B_3N_3H_6$

3. In compound $[M(CO)_n]^z$, the correct match for highest '*M*—C' bond length for given *M*, *n* and *z* respectively :

	M	*n*	*z*
(a)	Cr	6	0
(b)	V	6	–1
(c)	Ti	6	–2
(d)	Mn	6	+1

Passage 5

An isomer of the complex $CoBrCl_2(en)_2(H_2O)$, on reaction with concentrated H_2SO_4 (dehydrating agent), suffers no loss in weight and on reaction with $AgNO_3$ solution it gives only white precipitate, which is soluble in NH_3 solution.

1. The incorrect statement about complex is :
(a) It can show geometrical isomerism
(b) cis isomer is optically active
(c) Trans isomer is optically active
(d) It can exhibit solvate isomerism

2. The correct formula of the complex is :
(a) $[CoBrH_2O(en)_2]Cl_2$
(b) $[CoCl(en)_2H_2O]BrCl$
(c) $[CoBrCl(en)_2]Cl \cdot H_2O$
(d) $[CoCl_2(en)_2]Br \cdot H_2O$

Passage 6

Crystal field theory provides correct electronic distribution of central metal under surrounding ligand field, hence it clearly explains magnetic moment, colour of a complex.

1. Which of the following complex is high spin ?
(a) $K_4[Fe(CN)_6]$
(b) $[PtCl_4]^{2-}$
(c) $[CoF_6]^{3-}$
(d) $[Ni(NH_3)_6]^{2+}$

2. In which of the following complex transition of electron occurs from one shell to other shell of central metal.
(a) $[Fe(H_2O)_5(NO)]^{2+}$
(b) $[Co(H_2O)_6]^{2+}$
(c) $[Rh(NH_3)_6]^{2+}$
(d) $[Ni(CN)_6]^{4-}$

3. Which of the following hydrated complex ion has high intensity colour in aqueous solution.
(a) $[Mn(H_2O)_6]^{3+}$
(b) $[Co(H_2O)_6]^{2+}$
(c) $[Ni(H_2O)_6]^{2+}$
(d) $[Mn(H_2O)_6]^{2+}$

Passage 7

Two important physical evidences supporting the synergic bonding in non-classical complexes are bond lengths and vibrational spectra. Vibrational spectra is based on the fact that the compression and extension of a bond may be analogous to the behavior of a spring and obeys Hook's law.

$$\bar{\nu} = \frac{1}{2\pi c}\sqrt{\frac{k}{\mu}}\ \text{cm}^{-1}$$

where, k = force constant of the bond which is directly proportional to bond strength of CO
μ = reduced mass of ligand
$\bar{\nu}$ = stretching frequency of the CO bond
c = velocity of light

1. In which of the following complex stretching frequency for CO ligand is least as well as bond energy of *M*—C bond is higher .
(a) (dien) $Mo(CO)_3$
(b) $(Et_3P)_3Mo(CO)_3$
(c) $(F_3P)_3Mo(CO)_3$
(d) $(Cl_3P)_3Mo(CO)_3$

2. In $Mn_2(CO)_{10}$ carbonyl complex, the *d*-orbital of Mn-atom which can not be involved in synergic bonding between Mn and CO ligands :
(a) d_{xz}
(b) d_{xy}
(c) d_{yz}
(d) None of these

3. In which of the following ligand, σ-bond strength does not change during synergic bonding in their respective complexes :
(a) CO (b) N_2
(c) $CH_2=CH_2$ (d) PEt_3

Passage 8

Complex compounds that have the same molecular formula but have different structural/ space arrangements of ligands around central metal atom/ ion are called isomers, these are of two types namely structural and stereoisomers.

1. Which of the following is different among structural isomers?
(a) Oxidisation state (b) Co-ordination number
(c) IUPAC name (d) None of these

2. Types of isomerism exhibited by $[CrCl_2(NO_2)_2(NH_3)_2]^-$ complex ion are :
(a) ionisation, optical (b) hydrate, optical
(c) geometrical, optical (d) co-ordinate, geometrical

3. Complex species that exhibits isomerism is :
(a) $[Ag(NH_3)_2]^+$ (b) $[Co(NO_2)(NH_3)_5]^{2+}$ (c) $[PtCl_2(en)]$ (d) $[CoCl(NH_3)_5]^{2+}$

Passage 9

A complex compound of chromium contains five NH_3 molecules, one nitro group and two chloride ions for one Cr^{3+} cation. One molecule of this compound produces three ions in aq. solution, on reacting with excess of $AgNO_3$ solution, two moles of AgCl get precipitated.

1. The formula of the complex compound is :
(a) $[CrCl(NO_2)(NH_3)_4]NH_3 \cdot Cl$ (b) $[CrCl(NH_3)_5]Cl \cdot NO_2$
(c) $[Cr(NO_2)(NH_3)_5]Cl_2$ (d) $[Cr(NH_3)_5]NO_2 \cdot Cl_2$

2. The types of isomerism shown by the complex compound is:
(a) geometrical, ionization (b) ionization, linkage
(c) linkage, optical (d) geometrical, optical

3. Magnetic moment of complex compound is :
(a) 0 BM (b) $\sqrt{24}$ BM (c) $\sqrt{15}$ BM (d) $\sqrt{3}$ BM

Passage 10

According to C.F.T. , attraction between the central metal ion and ligands in a complex is purely electrostatic. The transition metal which forms the central atom cation in the complex is regarded as a positive ion. It is surrounded by negative ligands or neutral molecules which have a lone pair of electrons, if the ligand is a neutral molecule such as NH_3, the negative end of the dipole in the molecule is directed towards the metal cation. The electrons on the central metal ion are under repulsive forces from those on the ligands. Thus the electrons occupy the *d*-orbitals remain away from the direction of approach of ligands.

1. Correct relationship between pairing energy (P) and C.F.S.E (Δ_o) in complex ion $[Ir(H_2O)_6]^{3+}$ is :

(a) $\Delta_o < P$ (b) $\Delta_o > P$ (c) $\Delta_o = P$ (d) cannot comment

2. The crystal field-spliting order for Cr^{3+} cation is octahedral field for ligands CH_3COO^-, NH_3 H_2O, CN^- is :

(a) $CH_3COO^- < H_2O < NH_3 < CN^-$ (b) $CH_3COO^- < NH_3 < H_2O < CN^-$

(c) $H_2O < CH_3COO^- < NH_3 < CN^-$ (d) $NH_3 < CH_3COO^- < H_2O < CN^-$

3. The value of 'x' in the complex $H_x [Co(CO)_4]$ (on the basis of EAN rule) ; and geometry arround Co ion respectively is :

(a) 1, square planar (b) 2, tetrahedral (c) 1, tetrahedral (d) 2 , square planar

Passage 11

An isomer of the complex $Co(en)_2(H_2O)ICl_2$, on reaction with concentrated H_2SO_4 it suffers loss in weight and on reaction with $AgNO_3$ solution gives a yellow precipitate, which is insoluble in NH_3 solution .

1. If all the ligands in the co-ordination sphere of the above complex are replaced by CN^- ion, then the magnetic moment of the complex ion will be :

(a) 0.0 BM (b) 5.9 BM (c) 4.9 BM (d) 1.73 BM

2. If one mole of original complex is treated with excess $Pb(NO_3)_2$ solution, then the number of moles of white precipitate formed will be :

(a) 2.0 (b) 1.0 (c) 0.0 (d) 3.0

3. Total number of space isomers of the formula of the above complex is :

(a) 2 (b) 3 (c) 4 (d) 1

Passage 12

In complexes of weak field ligands, $\Delta_O < P$ (Pairing energy), the energy difference between t_{2g} and e_g sets is relatively less. Under the influence of strong field ligands, $\Delta_O > P$ (Pairing energy), the energy difference between t_{2g} and e_g sets is relatively high.

1. Which of the following is correct statement ?

(a) Complex $[Co(H_2O)_6]^{2+}$ is more stable than $[Co(H_2O)_6]^{3+}$

(b) All complexes of Ni (II) are bound to be outer *d*-orbital complexes.

(c) Stability constant for $[Ni(en)_3]^{2+}$ is greater than stability constant for $[Ni(NH_3)_6]^{2+}$

(d) Δ_{oct} for $[Cr(H_2O)_6]^{3+}$ is greater than Δ_{oct} for $[Cr(NH_3)_6]^{3+}$

2. Select the correct increasing order of 10 Dq. value for chromium complexes:

(1) $[Cr(en)_3]^{3+}$ (2) $[Cr(ox)_3]^{3-}$ (3) $[CrF_6]^{3-}$ (4) $[Cr(H_2O)_6]^{3+}$

(a) 4< 3< 1< 2 (b) 3< 4< 2< 1 (c) 4< 3< 2< 1 (d) 3< 4< 1< 2

3. Select the correct statement regarding $[Cr(en)_2Cl_2]^+$ and $[Co(C_2O_4)_2(NH_3)_2]^-$ complex ions:

(a) Both are equally stable complexes
(b) Both have equal number of stereoisomers
(c) Both are diamagnetic complexes
(d) (a) and (c) both

Passage 13

Complex compounds are molecular compounds which retain their identities even when dissolved in water. They do not give all the simple ions in solution but instead furnish complex ions. The complex compounds are often called coordination compounds because certain groups called ligands are attached to the central metal ion by coordinate or dative bonds. Coordination compounds exhibit isomerism, both structural and stereoisomerism. The structure, magnetic property, colour and electrical properties of complexes are explained by various theories.

1. Arrange the following compounds in order of their molar conductance :

(i) $K[Co(NO_2)_4(NH_3)_2]$
(ii) $[Cr(ONO)_3(NH_3)_3]$
(iii) $[Cr(NO_2)(NH_3)_5]_3[Co(NO_2)_6]_2$
(iv) $Mg[Cr(NO_2)_5(NH_3)]$

(a) (ii) < (i) < (iv) < (iii)
(b) (i) < (ii) < (iii) < (iv)
(c) (ii) < (i) < (iii) < (iv)(d) (iv) < (iii) < (ii) < (i)

2. The oxidation number, coordination number and magnetic moment in the following complex is :

$$[Cr(C_2O_4)_2(NH_3)_2]^-$$

(a) O.N. = +3, C.N. = 6, M.M. = $\sqrt{15}$ BM
(b) O.N. = −1, C.N. = 6, M.M. = $\sqrt{15}$ BM
(c) O.N. = +3, C.N. = 6, M.M. = $\sqrt{3}$ BM
(d) O.N. = +3, C.N. = 6, M.M. = $\sqrt{12}$ BM

3. In which of the following pairs, both the complexes have the same geometry?

(a) $[NiCl_4]^{2-}, [Ni(CN)_4]^{2-}$
(b) $[CoF_6]^{3-}, [Co(NH_3)_6]^{3+}$
(c) $[Ni(CO)_4], [Ni(CN)_4]^{2-}$
(d) $[Cu(NH_3)_4]^+, [Ni(NH_3)_4]^{2+}$

Passage 14

Recent X-ray work, IR and other spectroscopic methods have proved that Turnbull's blue is identical to Prussian blue.

1. What is the common formula of Turnbull's blue and Prussian blue?

(a) $Fe_3[Fe(CN)_6]_2$
(b) $Fe_4[Fe(CN)_6]_3$
(c) $KFe[Fe(CN)_6]$
(d) $KFe_2[Fe(CN)_6]$

2. Intense blue colour arises as a result of :

(a) electron transfer between Fe(II) and Fe(I)
(b) electron transfer between Fe(II) and Fe(III)
(c) *d-d* transition
(d) spin magnetic moment

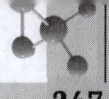

Passage 15

On the basis of stability of complex ion in the solution, complexes may be of two types, perfect and imperfect complexes. The stability depends upon the extent of dissociation which in turn depends upon the strength of metal-ligand bond. The stability of complex also depends upon charge on central metal atom, basic nature of ligand, chelation, and nature of metal ion and ligand according to HSAB principle.

1. Which one of the following does not follow EAN rule?
(a) $Fe(CO)_5$ (b) $V(CO)_6$ (c) $K_4[Fe(CN)_6]$ (d) $Mn_2(CO)_{10}$

2. Which complex is most stable?
(a) $[Cu(CN)_2]^- \ K_d = 1 \times 10^{-16}$ (b) $[Fe(CN)_6]^{4-} \ K_d = 1 \times 10^{-37}$
(c) $[Fe(CN)_6]^{3-} \ K_d = 1 \times 10^{-44}$ (d) $[Ag(CN)_2]^- \ K_d = 1 \times 10^{-20}$

Passage 16

When degenerate *d*-orbitals of an isolated atom/ion come under influence of magnetic field of ligands, the degeneracy is lost. The two set $t_{2g}(d_{xy}, d_{yz}, d_{xz})$ and $e_g(d_{z^2}, d_{x^2-y^2})$ are either stabilized or destabilized depending upon the nature of magnetic field. It can be expressed diagrammatically as :

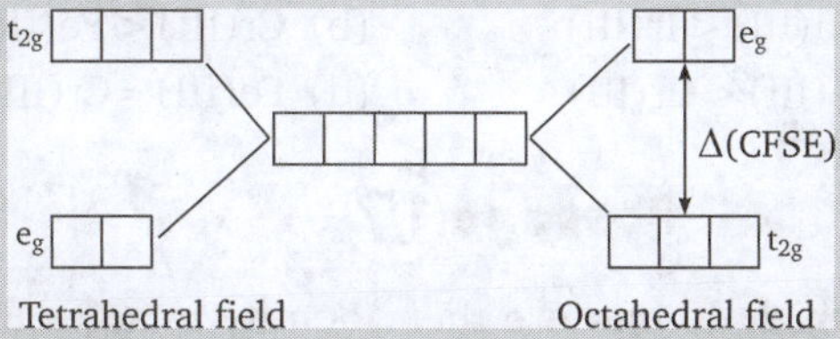

Value of CFSE depends upon nature of ligand and a spectrochemical series has been made experimentally, for tetrahedral complexes, Δ is about 4/9 times to Δ_0 (CFSE for octahedral complex). This energy lies in visible region and *i.e.,* why electronic transition are responsible for colour. Such transitions are not possible with d^0 and d^{10} configuration.

1. The value of CFSE (Δ_0) for complexes given below follow the order :
(I) $[Co(NH_3)_6]^{3+}$ (II) $[Rh(NH_3)_6]^{3+}$ (III) $[Ir(NH_3)_6]^{3+}$
(a) $I < II < III$ (b) $I > II > III$
(c) $I < II > III$ (d) $I = II = III$

2. Cr^{3+} form four complexes with four different ligands which are $[Cr(Cl)_6]^{3-}$, $[Cr(H_2O)_6]^{3+}$, $[Cr(NH_3)_6]^{3+}$ and $[Cr(CN)_6]^{3-}$. The order of CFSE (Δ_0) in these complexes is in the order :
(a) $[CrCl_6]^{3-} = [Cr(H_2O)_6]^{3+} = [Cr(NH_3)_6]^{3+} = [Cr(CN)_6]^{3-}$
(b) $[CrCl_6]^{3-} < [Cr(H_2O)_6]^{3+} < [Cr(NH_3)_6]^{3+} < [Cr(CN)_6]^{3-}$
(c) $[CrCl_6]^{3-} > [Cr(H_2O)_6]^{3+} > [Cr(NH_3)_6]^{3+} > [Cr(CN)_6]^{3-}$
(d) $[CrCl_6]^{3-} < [Cr(H_2O)_6]^{3+} = [Cr(NH_3)_6]^{3+} < [Cr(CN)_6]^{3-}$

3. The *d*-orbitals, which are stabilized in an octahedral field, are :
(a) d_{xy} and d_{z^2}
(b) $d_{x^2-y^2}$ and d_{z^2}
(c) d_{xy}, d_{xz} and d_{yz}
(d) d_{z^2} only

4. For an octahedral complex, which of the following *d*-electron configuration will give maximum CFSE?
(a) High spin d^6
(b) Low spin d^4
(c) Low spin d^5
(d) High spin d^7

5. Ti^{3+} (*aq.*) is purple while Ti^{4+} (*aq.*) is colourless because :
(a) There is no crystal field effect in Ti^{4+}
(b) The energy difference between t_{2g} and e_g Ti^{4+} is quite high and does not fall in the visible region
(c) Ti^{4+} has d^0 configuration
(d) Ti^{4+} is very small in comparison to Ti^{3+} and hence does not absorb any radiation

6. Which of the following is correct arrangement of ligand in terms of the Dq values of their complexes with any particular metal ion :
(a) $Cl^- < F^- < NCS^- < NH_3 < CN^-$
(b) $NH_3 < F^- < Cl^- < NCS^- < CN^-$
(c) $Cl^- < F^- < NCS^- < CN^- < NH_3$
(d) $NH_3 < CN^- < NCS^- < Cl^- < F^-$

7. The extent of crystal field splitting in octahedral complexes of the given metal with particular weak field ligand are :
(a) Fe(III) < Cr(III) < Rh(III) < Ir(III)
(b) Cr(III) < Fe(III) < Rh(III) < Ir(III)
(c) Ir(III) < Rh(III) < Fe(III) < Cr(III)
(d) Fe(III) = Cr(III) < Rh(III) < Ir(III)

Passage 17

Addition compounds which do not lose their identity in aqueous solution are called double salts and those lose their identity in aqueous solution are called complex salts, species which are directly linked with central metal atom/ion are called ligands. The ligands having two or more donor atoms are called polydentate or multidentate ligands.

1. Which of the following compound does not give precipitate with $BaCl_2$ solution ?
(a) Carnallite
(b) Potash alum
(c) Mohr's salt
(d) Chrome alum

2. Which of the following complex compound is non-ionisable in aqueous solution ?
(a) $PtCl_4 \cdot 3NH_3$
(b) $PtCl_4 \cdot 6NH_3$
(c) $PtCl_4 \cdot 2NH_3$
(d) $PtCl_4 \cdot 4NH_3$

3. (i) Complex (*P*) + $AgNO_3 \longrightarrow$ White precipitate
(ii) Complex (*Q*) + $BaCl_2 \longrightarrow$ White precipitate
(iii) Complex (*R*) + $Na_2SO_4 \longrightarrow$ White precipitate
Pick the most appropriate option
(a) Complex (*P*) may contain Cl^- in coordination sphere but not in ionisation shpere
(b) Complex (*Q*) may contain Ag^+ cation in coordination sphere but not in ionisation shpere
(c) Complex (*R*) may contain Ba^{2+} cation in ionisation sphere but not in coordination sphere
(d) Complex (*Q*) may contain SO_4^{2-} ion in coordination sphere but not in ionisation shpere

Passage 18

Formation of complex compounds is one of the most important properties of *d*-block metal cations. Among various theories of bonding of co-ordination compounds, two theories : Valence bond theory and crsytal field theory play very important roles in determining geometry of a complex ion/compound and electronic distribution of *d* orbitals of central metal atom/ion in presence of given ligands respectively. A very important property of complex ion/compound is to exhibit isomerism.

1. Which of the following complex ion(s) is/are inner orbital complex as well as low spin complex ion(s) ?

(a) $[Cu(NH_3)_4]^{2+}$ (b) $[IrF_6]^{3-}$ (c) $[Ag(S_2O_3)_2]^{3-}$ (d) $[Ni(CN)_5]^{3-}$

2. Which of the following complex compound(s) can exhibit at least two types of structural isomerism.

(a) $[PdBr(NO_2)(NH_3)_4](C_2O_4)$ (b) $[Co(SCN)(H_2O)_5]Br_2$

(c) $[Cr(NH_3)_6][Co(ONO)_6]$ (d) $K[Fe(CN)_2(H_2O)_4]$

Passage 19

The concept of co-ordination compounds arises from the complex formation tendency of transition elements. These compounds play a vital role in our lives, as chlorophyll of plants, vitamin B_{12} and haemoglobin of animal blood are the co-ordination compounds of Mg, Co and Fe respectively. The co-ordination compounds play important role in analytical chemistry, polymerisation reactions, metallurgy and refining of metals, photography, water purification etc. Co-ordination compounds also find many application in electroplating, textile dyeing and medicinal chemistry.

1. What is the IUPAC name of $[Co(en)_2(NCS)_2]NO_3$?

(a) Bis(ethylene diamine) dithiocyanato-N cobalt(II)Nitrate

(b) Bis(ethylene diamine)dithiocyanato-N cobalt(III)Nitrate

(c) Bis(ethylene diamine)dithiocyanato-N cobalt(IV)Nitrate

(d) Bis(ethylenediamine) dithiocyanato-N cobaltate(III)Nitrate

2. Which of the given ligand can show geometrical isomerism as well as optical isomerism in square planar homoleptic complex ?

(a) 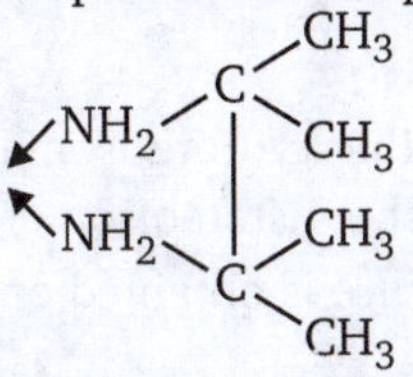

(b) 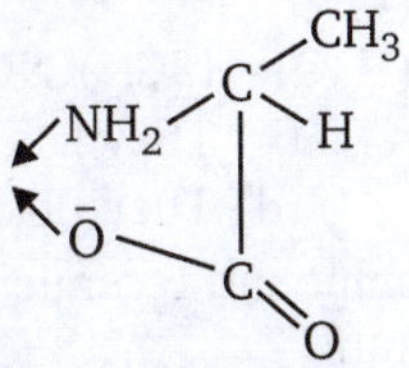

(c) 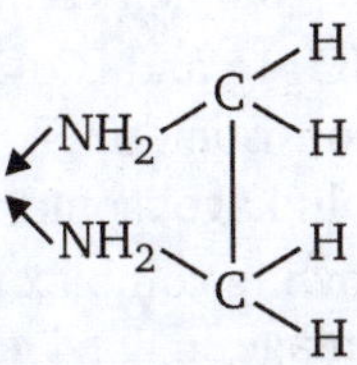

(d) 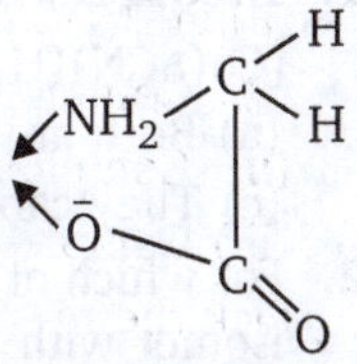

Passage 20

Complexes *X* (Red) and *Y* (Yellow) have same formula $Co \cdot 5NH_3 \cdot NO_2 \cdot Cl_2$.
1 moles of each *X* and *Y* both gives 2 moles of AgCl when react with excess of $AgNO_3$.

1. Select correct statement for *X* and *Y*
(a) Both *X* and *Y* contain NO_2^- as a ligand
(b) Both *X* and *Y* contain ONO^- as a ligand
(c) *X* contain NO_2^- while *Y* contain ONO^- as a ligand
(d) *X* contain ONO^- while *Y* contain NO_2^- as a ligand

2. *X* and *Y* both can show :
(a) Linkage isomerism
(b) Ionization isomerism
(c) Both linkage as well as ionization isomerism
(d) Geometrical isomerism

3. Select correct statement for *X* and *Y*.
(a) *X* and *Y* both are diamagnetic (b) *X* and *Y* both are paramagnetic
(c) *X* is paramagnetic while *Y* is diamagnetic (d) *X* is diamagnetic while *Y* is paramagnetic

Passage 21

According to valence bond theory strong ligands can change electronic distribution of central metal cation in a complex compound and in this new electronic distribution central metal atom/ion makes available number of empty atomic orbitals and co-ordinate covalent bond is formed with surrounding ligands.

1. For which of the following complex ion, $\mu_{eff} = 3.89$ B.M.
(a) $[Ni(en)_2]^{2+}$ (b) $[CoF_6]^{4-}$ (c) $[HgI_4]^{2-}$ (d) $[CuCl_5]^{3-}$

2. Which of the following complex ion is inner orbital complex and paramgnetic ?
(a) $[Fe(CN)_6]^{4-}$ (b) $[Cu(CN)_4]^{3-}$ (c) $[Ni(NH_3)_6]^{2+}$ (d) $[Cu(NO_2)_5]^{3-}$

Passage 22

One of the most important property of *d*-block metal cation is formation of co-ordination compounds. Among theories of bonding in co-ordination compound widely used theories are valence bond theory and crystal field theory.

1. Incorrect option for complex compounds.
$[Co(SCN)(H_2O)_5](NO_3)_2$ and $[Co(NO_3)(H_2O)_5](SCN)(NO_3)$ is :
(a) Both are ionization isomers. (b) They can exhibit hydrate isomerism.
(c) They can exhibit linkage isomerism. (d) They do not show stereoisomerism.

2. For which of the following complex ion/compound recemic mixture is obtained on mixing its isomer with mirror image in 1 : 1 molar ratio ?
(a) $[Ni(dmg)_2]$ (b) $[Co(ox)_3]^{3-}$
(c) *trans* $[CrBrCl(en)_2]$ (d) $[IrBr_3(H_2O)_2(NH_3)]$

3. The pair of complex ions which have same value of magnetic moment :
(a) $[Co(H_2O)_6]^{3+}, [NiF_6]^{2-}$ (b) $[Cr(H_2O)_6]^{3+}, [Fe(H_2O)_6]^{3+}$
(c) $[Mn(NH_3)_6]^{2+}, [Fe(CN)_6]^{3-}$ (d) $[CoCl_4]^{2-}, [NiCl_4]^{2-}$

ONE OR MORE ANSWERS IS/ARE CORRECT

1. Consider the following two reactions :

$Cd^{2+}(aq.) + 4CH_3NH_2 \xrightarrow{K_1} 'A', \Delta G_1^\circ$

$Cd^{2+}(aq.) + 2H_2NCH_2CH_2NH_2 \xrightarrow{K_2} 'B', \Delta G_2^\circ$

According to given information the correct statement(s) is/are :
(a) ΔG_2° is more negative than ΔG_1°
(b) Compound '*A*' is optically inactive
(c) Compound '*B*' is optically active
(d) Formation constant K_2 is greater than formation constant K_1

2. Complex compound $[Co(SCN)_2(NH_3)_4]Cl$ exhibits :
(a) Ionization isomerism
(b) Geometrical isomerism
(c) Optical isomerism
(d) Linkage isomerism

3. Which of the following compound has/have effective atomic number equal to the atomic number of a noble gas ?
(a) $K[Co(CO)_4]$
(b) $K_2[Fe(CO)_4]$
(c) $[Co(NH_3)_6]Cl_2$
(d) $[CoCl_3(H_2O)_3]$

4. Select correct statement(s) regarding octahedron complex having CFSE $= -1.2\Delta_0$.
(a) Compound is neither low spin nor high spin complex
(b) Type of hybridisation complex does not depend upon nature of ligands
(c) Magnetic moment of complex compounds is either $\sqrt{15}$ B.M. or $\sqrt{8}$ B.M.
(d) All are incorrect statements

5. Consider the following two carbonyl compounds
(i) $[Tc(CO)_6]^+$ and (ii) $[Nb(CO)_6]^-$
Select incorrect statement(s) for given carbonyl compounds.
(a) $[Tc(CO)_6]^+$ acts as reducing agent and $[Nb(CO)_6]^-$ acts as oxidizing agent
(b) $[Nb(CO)_6]^-$ acts as reducing agent and $[Tc(CO)_6]^+$ acts as oxidizing agent
(c) "Nb—C" bond order in $[Nb(CO)_6]^-$ is greater than "Tc—C" bond order in $[Tc(CO)_6]^+$
(d) "CO" bond order is greater in $[Nb(CO)_6]^-$ than in $[Tc(CO)_6]^+$

6. Which of the following ligand(s) can act as π-acid ligand. ?
(a) σ-cyclopentadienyl
(b) π-Allyl
(c) $B_3N_3H_6$
(d) π-cyclopentadienyl

7. Find out correct I.U.P.A.C. name of complex compound.
(a) Pentaamminecyanidochromium(II) hexanitrito-N-irridate(III)
(b) Triamminetricyanidochromium(III)hexanitrito-N-irridate(III)
(c) Hexanitrito-N-irridium(III)pentaamminecyanidochromate(II)
(d) Pentaamminecyanidochromium(III) hexanitrito-N-irridate(III)

8. Consider the following reactions of complex compounds A, B and C

(i) $CoCl_2Br \cdot 5NH_3$ + excess Ag^+ (aq.) $\longrightarrow$ $1AgCl(s) + 1AgBr(s)$
(Compound A)

(ii) $CoCl_2Br \cdot 5NH_3$ + excess Ag^+ (aq.) $\longrightarrow$ $2AgCl(s)$
(Compound B)

(iii) $CoCl_2Br \cdot 4NH_3$ + excess Ag^+ (aq.) $\longrightarrow$ $1AgCl(s)$
(Compound C)

Then according to the given information the correct statement(s) is/are :

(a) Compounds (A) and (B) are ionisation isomers
(b) Molar conductivity of compounds (A) and (B) are almost same
(c) Compounds (A), (B) and (C) do not exhibit geometrical isomerism
(d) Order of CFSE values : $\Delta_0(A) > \Delta_0(B) > \Delta_0(C)$

9. Which complex species does/do not exhibit geometrical isomerism and only have two stereoisomers.

(a) $[Co(EDTA)]^-$
(b) $[PtBrCl(gly)]^-$
(c) $[Co(acac)_2(en)]^+$
(d) $[Pd(NO_2)(ox)(gly)]$

10. Which of the following complex(s) can not exhibit both geometrical and optical isomerism ?

(a) $[Ru(en)_3]^{3+}$ (b) $[Co(H_2O)Cl_3]^-$ (c) $[PtBrCl(H_2O)NH_3]$ (d) $[FeBr_2(en)_2]^+$

11. Complex ions $[NiCl_6]^{4-}$, $[Ni(CN)_6]^{4-}$ similar in their given properties :

(a) oxidation state, geometry
(b) co-ordination number , EAN
(c) magnetic moment, geometry
(d) stability , colour

12. Select correct statement(s) regarding given complexes:

(a) $[Fe(CO)_5]$, the orbitals used for hybridization in Fe atom are $s, p_x, p_y, p_z, d_{z^2}$ and it is high spin complex
(b) $[Pt(NH_3)_2Cl_2]$, the orbitals used for hybridization on Pt atom are $s, p_x, p_y, d_{x^2-y^2}$ and it is low spin complex
(c) $[Cr(H_2O)_6]^{3+}$, the orbitals used for hybridization in Cr atom are $s, p_x, p_y, p_z, d_{z^2}, d_{x^2-y^2}$ and it is high spin complex
(d) $Ni(CO)_4$, the orbitals used for hybridization in Ni atom are, s, p_x, p_y, p_z, and it is low spin complex

13. Complex compound $[Co(SCN)_2(NH_3)_4]Cl$ exhibits :

(a) ionization isomerism
(b) geometrical isomerism
(c) optical isomerism
(d) linkage isomerism

14. Which of the following compound has/have effective atomic number equal to the atomic number of a noble gas ?

(a) $K[Co(CO)_4]$ (b) $K_2[Fe(CO)_4]$ (c) $[Co(NH_3)_6]Cl_2$ (d) $[CoCl_3(H_2O)_3]$

15. $K_2[Ni(CN)_4] \xrightarrow[NH_3]{\text{K in liq.}}$ 'X'

Regarding this reaction correct statement is/are:

(a) 'X' is $K_4[Ni(CN)_4]$
(b) The oxidation state of Ni changed +2 to zero

(c) The structure of 'X' is tetrahedral
(d) $[Ni(CN)_4]^{2-}$ is square planar complex

16. Which of the following statement(s) is/are correct?
(a) The oxidation state of iron in sodium nitro prusside $Na_2[Fe(CN)_5(NO)]$ is +II
(b) $[Ag(NH_3)_2]^+$ is linear in shape
(c) In $[Fe(H_2O)_6]^{3+}$, Fe is d^2sp^3 hybridized
(d) In $[Co(H_2O)_6]^{3+}$ complex ion, Co is d^2sp^3 hybridized

17. Which one of the following statement(s) is/are false?
(a) Weak ligands like F^-, Cl^- and OH^- usually form low spin complexes
(b) Strong ligand like CN^- and NO_2^-, generally form high spin complexes
(c) $[FeF_6]^{3-}$ is high spin complex
(d) $[Ni(CO)_4]$ is high spin complex

18. A *d*-block element forms octahedral complex but its magnetic moment remains same either in strong field or in weak field ligand. Which of the following is/are correct?
(a) Element always forms colourless compound
(b) Number of electrons in t_{2g} orbitals are higher than in e_g orbitals
(c) It can have either d^3 or d^8 configuration
(d) It can have either d^7 or d^8 configuration

19. For which of the following d^n configuration of octahedral complex(es), cannot exist in both high spin and low spin forms?
(a) d^3 (b) d^5 (c) d^6 (d) d^8

20. Which of the following pairs show coordination isomerism?
(a) $[Co(NH_3)_6][Cr(CN)_6]$ and $[Cr(NH_3)_6][Co(CN)_6]$
(b) $[Co(NH_3)_3(H_2O)_2Cl]Br_2$ and $[Co(NH_3)_3(H_2O)Cl\cdot Br]Br\cdot H_2O$
(c) $[Pt(NH_3)_4Cl_2]Br_2$ and $[Pt(NH_3)_3B_2]Cl_2$
(d) $[Co(NH_3)_6][Cr(C_2O_4)_3]$ and $[Cr(NH_3)_6][Co(C_2O_4)_3]$

21. Which of the following are coordination isomers of $[Co(NH_3)_6][Cr(CN)_6]$?
(a) $[Cr(NH_3)_6][Co(CN)_6]$ (b) $[Cr(NH_3)_4(CN)_2][Co(CN)_4(NH_3)_2]$
(c) $[Cr(NH_3)_3(CN)_3][Co(NH_3)_3(CN)_3]$ (d) None of these

22. Which of the following statements is not true about the complex ion $[CrCl(NO_2)(en)_2]^+$?
(a) It has two geometrical isomers *cis* and *trans*
(b) *cis* and *trans* forms are not diastereomers to each other
(c) Only the *cis* isomer displays optical activity
(d) It has three optically active isomers : *d*, *l* and *trans* forms

23. Which of the following statement(s) is/are incorrect?
(a) In $[CoBrCl(en)_2]^+$ geometrical isomerism exists, while optical isomerism does not exist
(b) Potassium aquadicyanosuperoxoperoxoperoxoch-romate(III) is IUPAC name $K_2[Cr(N)_2O_2(O_2)(H_2O)]$

(c) There are 3 geometrical and 15 stereoisomers possible for $[Pt(NO_2)(NH_3)(NH_2OH)(py)]^+$ and $[PtBrClI(NO_2)(NH_3)(py)]$ respectively

(d) *cis* and *trans* forms are not diastereomers to each other

24. Which of the following statement is true about the complex $[CrCl_3(OH)_2(NH_3)]^{2-}$ ion?

(a) It has three geometrical isomers

(b) Only one space isomers is optically active and remaining are inactive

(c) There are total four space isomers

(d) The magnetic moment of complex ion is 3.89 BM

25. Which of the following is correct about Tetraamminedithiocyanato-*s* cobalt (III) tris(oxalato)cobaltate(III)?

(a) Formula of the complex is $[Co(SCN)_2(NH_3)_4][Co(ox)_3]$

(b) It is a chelating complex and show linkage isomerism

(c) It shows optical isomerism

(d) It shows geometrical isomerism

26. Which of the following statement(s) is/are false?

(a) In $[PtCl_2(NH_3)_4]^{2+}$ complex ion, the *cis*-form is optically active, while *trans*-form is optically inactive

(b) In $[Fe(C_2O_4)_3]^{3-}$, geometrical isomerism does not exist, while optical isomerism exists

(c) In $[Mabcd]^{n\pm}$ tetrahedral complexes, optical isomerism cannot be observed

(d) In $[Mabcd]^{n\pm}$ square planar complexes, optical isomerism can be observed

27. Which of the following statement(s) is/are true?

(a) In metal carbonyl complexes d_{C-O} increases compared to that in CO molecule

(b) The pair of compounds $[Cr(H_2O)_6]Cl_3$ and $[CrCl_3(H_2O)_3]\cdot 3H_2O$ show hydrate isomerism

(c) d_{z^2} orbital of central metal atom/ion is used in dsp^2 hybridisation

(d) Facid and Meridional isomers associated with $[Ma_3b_3]^{n\pm}$ type complex compound, both are optically inactive

28. Select the correct statement :

(a) Chelation effect is maximum for five and six membered rings

(b) Greater the charge on the central metal cation, greater the value of Δ (CFSE)

(c) In complex ion $[CoF_6]^{3-}$, F^- is a weak field ligand, so that $\Delta_{oct} < P$ (Pairing energy) and it is low spin complex

(d) $[CoCl_2(NH_3)_2(en)]^{\oplus}$ complex ion will have four different isomers

29. Which of the following statement(s) is/are true?

(a) In ferrocyanide ion, the effective atomic number is 36

(b) Chelating ligands are atleast bidentate ligand

(c) $[CrCl_2(CN)_2(NH_3)_2]^{\ominus}$ and $[CrCl_3(NH_3)_3]$ both have d^2sp^3 hybridisation

(d) As the number of rings in complex increases, stability of complex (chelate) also increases

30. In test of NO_3^- ion, the dark brown ring complex is formed, which is true of this complex?

(a) The colour is due to charge transfer spectra
(b) Iron and NO both have +1 charge
(c) The complex species can be represented as $[Fe^{I}(H_2O)_5NO]^{2+}$
(d) Iron has +2 oxidation state and NO is neutral

31. The complex(es) which is/are blue in colour :

(a) $Fe_4[Fe(CN)_6]_3$ (b) $Zn_2[Fe(CN)_6]$
(c) $Cu_2[Fe(CN)_6]$ (d) $Fe_3[Fe(CN)_6]_2$

32. What is/are the coordination number(s) of Au in the complexes formed by Au?

(a) 6 (b) 4 (c) 5 (d) 2

33. The *d*-orbitals involved in sp^3d^2 or d^2sp^3 hybridisation of the central metal ion are :

(a) $d_{x^2-y^2}$ (b) d_{xy}
(c) d_{yz} (d) d_{z^2}

34. Which is not correctly matched ?

Complex compounds	IUPAC name
(a) $K[CrF_4O]$	Potassium tetrafluorooxo chromate (v)
(b) $Na[BH(OCH_3)_3]$	Sodium hydrido trimethoxy borate (III)
(c) $[Be(CH_3-CO-CH-CO-C_6H_5)_2]^0$	Bis (Benzoylacetonato beryllium (III)
(d) $H[AuCl_4]$	Hydrogen tetrachloro aurate (III)

35. Which of the following statement(s) is(are) correct?

(a) The complexes $[NiCl_4]^{2-}$ and $[NiCN_4]^{2-}$ differ in the magnetic properties
(b) The complexes $[NiCl_4]^{2-}$ and $[NiCN_4]^{2-}$ differ in the geometry
(c) The complexes $[NiCl_4]^{2-}$ and $[NiCN_4]^{2-}$ differ in primary valencies of nickel
(d) The complexes $[NiCl_4]^{2-}$ and $[NiCN_4]^{2-}$ differ in the state of hybridization of nickel

36. Which is correct statement(s)?

(a) $[Ag(NH_3)_2]^+$ is linear with *sp* hybridised Ag^+ ions
(b) $NiCl_4^{2-}$, CrO_4^{2-} and MnO_4^- have tetrahedral geometry
(c) $[Cu(NH_3)_4]^{2+}$, $[Pt(NH_3)_4]^{2+}$ and $[Ni(CN)_4]^{2-}$ have dsp^2 hybridisation of the metal ion
(d) $Fe(CO)_5$ has trigonal bipyramidal structure with $d_{z^2}sp^3$ hybridised ion

37. Select complex(s) with their correct IUPAC name :

(a) $Fe[Fe(CN)_6]$ Iron (III) hexacyanido ferrate (III)
(b) $Fe_2[Fe(CN)_6]$ Iron (II) hexacyanido ferrate (II)
(c) $Fe_3[Fe(CN)_6]_2$ Iron (II) hexacyanido ferrate (III)
(d) $Fe_4[Fe(CN)_6]_3$ Iron (III) hexacyanido ferrate (II)

38. Which can form square planar complex ?

(a) Pt(II), Pd(II) with strong and weak field ligand
(b) Au(III) with strong and weak field ligand

(c) Ni(II) with C.N. = 4 and strong field ligand
(d) Hg(II) with C.N. = 4 and strong field ligand

39. Pair(s) of co-ordination compounds which have different values of μ_{eff} (in B.M.)
(a) $[Co(NO_2)(H_2O)_5]^{2+}$, $[Co(ONO)(H_2O)_5]^{+}$
(b) Cis – $[PtCl_2(NH_3)_4]^{2+}$, Trans – $[PtCl_2(NH_3)_4]^{2+}$
(c) $[Ni(CN)_4]^{2-}$, $[Ni(NH_3)_6]^{2+}$
(d) $[Zn(NH_3)_4]^{2+}$, $[Fe(NH_3)_6]^{2+}$

40. In which of the following complex ion five atoms are lying in a line including metal ?
(a) $[Ag(SCN)_2]^-$ (b) $[Ag(CN)_2]^-$ (c) $[Zn(CN)_4]^{2-}$ (d) $[Pt(CN)_4]^{2-}$

41. In an aqueous solution of $NiCl_2$, if didentate ligand, ethane-1, 2-dien(en) is progressively added in molar ratios such as Ni : en :: 1 : 1, 1 : 2, 1 : 3 then three octahedron complexes x, y, z formed respectively. Select Correct statement(s) about x, y, z.
(a) Complex x has maximum value of absorbed wavelength
(b) Complex y expected to be coloured
(c) Complex z has maximum number of chelate rings
(d) Al three are paramagnetic outer orbital complexes

42. *d*-orbitals of metal lose their degeneracy in :
(a) Blue vitriol (b) Anhydrous $CuSO_4$
(c) Potassium ferrocyanide (d) Potassium ferricyanide

43. Which of the following pair of complex compound(s) has/have different colour ?
(a) $[CoBr(NO_2)(NH_3)_4]$ Br and $[CoBr_2(NH_3)_4](NO_2)$
(b) *Cis* - $[IrBr_2(en)_2]$Br and *Trans* - $[IrBr_2(en)_2]$Br
(c) *d* - $[Ni(en)_3]^{2+}$ and *l* - $[Ni(en)_3]^{2+}$
(d) $[Cr(ONO)_2(H_2O)_4]^+$ and $[Cr(NO_2)_2(H_2O)_4]^+$

44. Assume the complex $[Ni(PPh_3)_2(SCN)_2]$ is paramagnetic. The analogous complex of Pd(II) is diamagnetic. The isomerism shown by Pd(II) complex is/are :
(a) Linkage (b) Optical (c) Geometrical (d) Polymerization

45. Which of the following complex ion(s) exhibits geometrical isomerism but their all isomer(s) do not exhibit optically isomersm ?
(a) $[Co(en)_3]^{3+}$ (b) $[CoBr_3(H_2O)_2(NH_3)]$
(c) $[CrBr_4(en)]^-$ (d) $[PtBrCl(H_2O)(NH_3)]$

46. Complex $[Cr(NH_3)_4(NO_2)_2]$Cl can show :
(a) Ionization isomerism (b) Linkage isomerism
(c) Geometrical isomerism (d) Optical isomerism

MATCH THE COLUMN

Column-I and **Column-II** contains four entries each. Entries of Column-I are to be matched with one or more than one entries of Column-II. Each entry of Column-I may have the matching with one or more than one entries of Column-II.

1.

Column-I	Column-II
(A) Co^{2+} (aq.)	(P) Pink/Light Pink
(B) Mn^{2+} (aq.)	(Q) Purple
(C) V^{2+} (aq.)	(R) Outer orbital complex and M.M. $=\sqrt{15}$ B.M.
(D) Ti^{3+} (aq.)	(S) Iinner orbital complex and M.M. $=\sqrt{3}$ B.M.
	(T) Paramagnetic

2.

Column-I	Column-II (Characteristics of complex ion compound)
(A) $[Pt(NO_2)_2(en)]^{2+}$	(P) Stable according to E.A.N. rule
(B) $[Cr(\pi\text{-}C_6H_6)(NO)_2]$	(Q) Ligand acts as ambidentate
(C) $[Ir(SCN)(SO_4)(NH_3)_4]$	(R) Bond order of all *M*—*L* bond > 1.0
(D) $[Cr(C_2H_4)(CO)_5]$	(S) Bond order of all ligand decreases
	(T) Co-ordination number of central metal is six

3.

Column-I (Complex compounds)	Column-II (Characteristics of complex)
(A) $[PtBrCl(acac)(H_2O)_2]NO_3$	(P) Difference between optical isomers and optically active isomers is two
(B) $[IrBr_2(en)(H_2O)(NH_3)]Br$	(Q) Only *cis* configurations are optically active.
(C) $[CrCl_2(acac)(H_2O)_2]$	(R) Exhibit structural isomerism.
(D) $[Pt(ox)_2(NH_3)_2]$	(S) Two trans are optically inactive.
	(T) Optically active when both monodentate neutral ligands are at adjacent sites in cis configuration.

4.

Column-I	Column-II
(A) $[Cr(CN)_3(NO_2)_3]^{4-}$	(P) Outer orbital complex
(B) $[Co(C_2O_4)_3]^{3-}$	(Q) Inner orbital complex
(C) $[Fe(EDTA)]^-$	(R) $\mu = 2.83$ BM
(D) $[Ni(en)_3](NO_3)_2$	(S) Shows optical activity
	(T) $\mu = 0$

5.

Column-I (complex ion)	Column-II (CFSE and hybridisation)
(A) $[Cr(NH_3)_6]^{3+}$	(P) $0.0\ \Delta_o$, sp^3d^2-hybridisation
(B) $[Cu(NH_3)_6]^{2+}$	(Q) $-0.6\ \Delta_o$, sp^3d^2-hybridisation
(C) $[Fe(H_2O)_6]^{3+}$	(R) $-1.2\ \Delta_o$, d^2sp^3-hybridisation
(D) $[IrF_6]^{3-}$	(S) Diamagnetic
	(T) Paramagnetic

6.

Column-I	Column-II
(A) $[MnCl_4]^{2-}$	(P) sp^3hybridisation
(B) $[Ni(CN)_4]^{2-}$	(Q) Diamagnetic
(C) $[Ni(CO)_4]$	(R) Paramagnetic
(D) $[Cu(NH_3)_4]^{2+}$	(S) dsp^2 hybridisation

7.

Column-I	Column-II
(A) $[Fe(CN)_6]^{4-}$	(P) Paramagnetic
(B) $[Fe(H_2O)_6]^{2+}$	(Q) Diamagnetic
(C) $[Cu(NH_3)_6]^{2+}$	(R) Inner orbital complex
(D) $[Ni(CN)_6]^{4-}$	(S) Outer orbital complex

8.

Column-I	Column-II
(A) $[Ni(H_2O)_6]Cl_2$	(P) d^2sp^3 hybridisation
(B) $[Co(CN)_2(NH_3)_4]OC_2H_5$	(Q) Ionisation isomerism
(C) $[IrCl_6]^{3-}$	(R) $\mu = 2.83$ BM
(D) $[PtCl_2(NH_3)_4]Br_2$	(S) $\Delta_O < P$

9.

Column-I	Column-II
(A) $[Cr(gly)_3]^0$	(P) Low spin complex
(B) $[CoBr_2Cl_2(SCN)_2]^{3-}$	(Q) High spin complex
(C) $[Fe(NH_3)_6]^{3+}$	(R) Optical isomerism
(D) $Na[PtBrCl(NO_2)(NH_3)]$	(S) Geometrical isomerism

10.

Column-I	Column-II
(A) Sodium nitroprusside	(P) $\mu = 0$ BM
(B) Brown ring complex	(Q) Octahedral
(C) Complex of Ag formed during its extraction	(R) $\mu = \sqrt{15}$ BM
(D) Potassium ferrocyanide	(S) NO^+ ligand

11.

Column-I (Pair of complex compounds)	Column-II (Property which is different in given pair)
(A) $[Ni(CO)_4]$ and $K_2[Ni(CN)_4]$	(P) Magnetic moment
(B) $[Cu(NH_3)_4]SO_4$ and $K_3[Cu(CN)_4]$	(Q) Oxidation no. of central metal
(C) $K_2[NiCl_4]$ and $K_4[Ni(CN)_4]$	(R) Geometry
(D) $K_2[NiCl_4]$ and $K_2[PtCl_4]$	(S) EAN of central metal

12.

Column-I (Pair of complexes)	Column-II (Property which is similar in given pair)
(A) $[Fe(CN)_6]^{3-}$ and $[Co(NH_3)_6]^{2+}$	(P) Magnetic moment
(B) $[Fe(H_2O)_6]^{2+}$ and $[Fe(CN)_6]^{4-}$	(Q) Geometry
(C) $[Ni(CN)_4]^{4-}$ and $[Ni(CO)_4]$	(R) Hybridisation
(D) $[Ni(H_2O)_6]^{2+}$ and $[NiCl_4]^{2-}$	(S) Number of d-electrons

13.

Column-I (Coordination compound)	Column-II (Type of isomerism shown)
(A) $Na_2[Pt(SCN)_2(ox)_2]$	(P) Ionization isomerism
(B) $[CrCl_2(NH_3)_4]NO_3$	(Q) Linkage isomerism
(C) $[Pt(NO_2)(Gly)(NH_3)]$	(R) Geometrical isomerism
(D) $K_3[Fe(OH)_2(C_2O_4)_2]$	(S) Optical isomerism

14.

Column-I	Column-II
(A) $K_3[Fe(CN)_5(CO)]$	(P) Complex having lowest bond length of CO ligand
(B) $K[PtCl_3(C_2H_4)]$	(Q) Follow rule of EAN
(C) $Na[Co(CO)_4]$	(R) Complex involved in synergic bonding
(D) $V(CO)_6$	(S) Complex having highest bond length of CO ligand

15.

Column-I (Molar conductance at infinite dilution)	Column-II (Complex compound)
(A) 229	(P) $[Pt(NH_3)_5Cl]Cl_3$
(B) 0	(Q) $[Pt(NH_3)_2Cl_4]$
(C) 404	(R) $[Pt(NH_3)_4Cl_2]Cl_2$
(D) 523	(S) $[Pt(NH_3)_6]Cl_4$

16.

Column-I (Complex ions)	Column-II (Number of unpaired electrons)
(A) $[CrF_6]^{4-}$	(P) One
(B) $[MnF_6]^{4-}$	(Q) Two
(C) $[Cr(CN)_6]^{4-}$	(R) Three
(D) $[Mn(CN)_6]^{4-}$	(S) Four
	(T) Five

17.

Column-I (Complexes)	Column-II (Hybridization of central atom)
(A) $Ni(CO)_4$	(P) sp^3
(B) $[Ni(CN)_4]^{2-}$	(Q) dsp^2
(C) $[Fe(CN)_6]^{4-}$	(R) sp^3d^2
(D) $[MnF_6]^{4-}$	(S) d^2sp^3

18.

Column-I (Coordination compounds)	Column-II (Type of isomerism)
(A) $[Co(NH_3)_4Cl_2]$	(P) Optical isomerism
(B) $[Co(en)_3]Cl_2$	(Q) Ionization isomerism
(C) $[Co(en)_2(NO_2)Cl]SCN$	(R) Coordination isomerism
(D) $[Co(NH_3)_6][Cr(CN)_6]$	(S) Geometrical isomerism

19.

Column-I (pair of complexes)	Column-II (characteristics exhibited by pair of complexes
(A) $[Fe(H_2O)_2(NH_3)_4]Br_2$, $[NiBr(H_2O)(en)_2]NO_3$	(P) Structural isomerism
(B) $[Co(NO_2)_2(NH_3)_4]Cl$, $[Cd(SCN)_2(H_2O)_2]$	(Q) Geometrical isomerism
(C) $[Ir(NCS)_2(ox)_2]^{3-}$, $[Fe(CN)_2(en)_2]$	(R) Equal number of unpaired electrons
(D) $[PtBrCl(H_2O)_4]Br_2$, $[Rh(gly)_3]$	(S) Minimum two space isomers are coloured
	(T) Low spin complex

20.

Column-I (pair of complex compounds)	Column-II (property which is same in the given pair)
(A) $[Cr(NO_3)_2(H_2O)_4]Cl$, $[Ni(en)_2(H_2O)(NH_3)]Br_2$	(P) Magnetic moment
(B) $[Co(CO)_4]^-$, $[Zn(CN)_4]^{2-}$	(Q) Geometry
(C) $[Ni(CN)_2(NH_3)_2]$, $[Pt(gly)_2]$	(R) Inner orbital complex
(D) $[Co(CN)_2(NH_3)_4]Cl$; $[Fe(NO_2)_2(en)_2]$	(S) Structural isomerism
	(T) Geometrical isomerism

21.

Column-I	Column-II
(A) $[Sc(H_2O)_6]^{3+}$	(P) Paramagnetic complex
(B) $[Fe(H_2O)_6]^{3+}$	(Q) Diamagnetic complex
(C) $[Co(H_2O)_6]^{3+}$	(R) Coloured compelx
(D) $[Cr(H_2O)_6]^{3+}$	(S) Colourless complex
	(T) Inner orbital complex

22.

Column-I	Column-II
(A) $[M(NH_3)_6]^{n\pm}$	(P) If $M = Fe^{3+}$, then CFCE $= 0$
(B) $[M(H_2O)_6]^{n\pm}$	(Q) If $M = Cr^{3+}$, then CFCE $= -1.2\,\Delta_o$
(C) $[M(CN)_6]^{n\pm}$	(R) If $M = Mn^{3+}$, then CFSE $= -0.6\,\Delta_o$
(D) $[M(en)_3]^{n\pm}$	(S) If $M = Ni^{4+}$, then low spin complex
	(T) If $M = Co^{2+}$, then paramagnetic complex

ASSERTION-REASON TYPE QUESTIONS

These questions consist of two statements each, printed as assertion and reason, while answering these questions you are required to choose any one of the following responses :

(A) If assertion is true but the reason is false

(B) If assertion is false but reason is true

(C) If both assertion and reason are true and the reason is the correct explanation of assertion

(D) If both assertion and reason are true but reason is not the correct explanation of assertion

1. Assertion : In N_2 molecule, any N-atom can coordinate with central atom/ion.
Reason : N_2 molecule can also act as ambidentate ligand.

2. Assertion : In N_2H_4, any one N-atom can coordination with central metal cation in a coordination compound.
Reason : N_2H_4 can also act as ambidentate ligand.

3. Assertion : $[Ti(H_2O)_6]^{4+}$ is coloured while $[Sc(H_2O)_6]^{3+}$ is colourless.
Reason : d-d transition is not possible in $[Sc(H_2O)_6]^{3+}$.

4. Assertion : Acidified $[Cu(NH_3)_4]^{2+}$ and $[Cu(H_2O)_4]^{2+}$ both react with $K_4[Fe(CN)_6]$ to give brown ppt.
Reason : Both complexes are blue in colour of little different shade.

5. Assertion : $[Fe(EDTA)]^-$ complex is octahedral in shape.
Reason : EDTA is a hexadentate ligand and undergoing sp^3d^2 hybridisation.

6. Assertion : Tetrahedral complexes with chiral structure exhibit optical isomerism.
Reason : They lack plane of symmetry.

7. Assertion : Oxidation state of Fe in $Fe(CO)_5$ is zero.
Reason : Synergic bonding takes place in this metal carbonyl complex.

8. Assertion : Zeise's salt is a π-bonded organometallic compound.
Reason : Zeise's salt contain C_2H_4 molecules as one of the ligand.

9. Assertion : $[CoCl_3(NH_3)_3]$ does not give white precipitate with $AgNO_3$ solution.
Reason : $[CoCl_3(NH_3)_3]$ complex is optically inactive.

10. Assertion : Transition metal ion forming octahedral complexes undergo sp^3d^2 or d^2sp^3 hybridisation.
Reason : Strong field ligands force the unpaired electrons of central metal ion to pair up causing d^2sp^3 hybridisation whereas weak field ligands do not affect electronic configuration of the metal ion undergoes in sp^3d^2 hybridisation.

11. Assertion : Complex ion $[Co(NH_3)_6]^{2+}$ is readily oxidized to $[Co(NH_3)_6]^{3+}$.
Reason : Unpaired electron in complex ion $[Co(NH_3)_6]^{2+}$ is present in $4p$ orbital.

12. Assertion : Hydrazine is a neutral ligand.
Reason : It has two N as donor atoms and behaves as a chelating ligand.

13. Assertion : Complex anion $[Re_2Cl_8]^{2-}$ has one δ-bond, one sigma and one π-bond.
Reason : d_{z^2} orbital can never form δ-bond.

SUBJECTIVE PROBLEMS

1. Consider the following compounds with their regular geometries.

Compounds	Geometry
A	Square planar
B	Trigonal bipyramidal
C	Square pyramidal
D	Octahedral
E	Pentagonal bipyramidal

Calculate value of $(x + y - z)^2$, where x is total number of axial d-orbitals having zero nodal plane, y and z are total no. of non-axial and axial d-orbitals respectively each one having two nodal planes used in hybridization of central atoms of compounds A to E.

2. How many π-bonds are present in ferrocene?

3. Consider the following complex compounds
(i) $[Cu(NH_3)_4][Cu(NO_2)_4]$ (ii) $[Cr(py)_6][Cr(SCN)_6]$
(iii) $[Co(NH_3)_5(NO_2)][Pt(SCN)_4]$
If x_1, x_2, x_3 are more possible coordination isomers of given complex compounds respectively then calculate value of $x_1^2 + x_2^2 + x_3^2$.

4. Consider the following carbonyl complex compounds.
(i) $Mo(CO)_x$ (ii) $H_y[Cr(CO)_5]$ and (iii) $Co_2(CO)_z$
Then calculate value of $|x + y - z|$.

5. If x and y are total number of electrons which are present in non-axial and axial set of d-orbitals respectively in Ni cation of $[Ni(DMG)_2]$, then calculate value of $\frac{2x^2}{y}$.

6. Consider the following complex compounds :
(i) $[Pt(NH_3)_2(SCN)_2]$ (ii) $[Co(NH_3)_3(NO_2)_3]$
(iii) $[Pt(en)Cl_2]$ (iv) $[Cr(en)_2Br_2]^+$
(v) $[Rh(en)_3]^{3+}$ (vi) $[CoCl_2Br_2]^{2-}$
Then calculate sum of total number of geometrical isomers in all above complex compounds.

7. Consider the following transformation
$$Cr(CO)_x \longrightarrow Cr(CO)_y(NO)_z$$
If both reactant and product follow EAN rule, then calculate value of $x + z - y$ (where x, y and z are natural numbers).

8. Brown colour of the complex $[Fe(H_2O)_5(NO)]SO_4$ is due to C.T. spectrum which causes momentary change in oxidation state. Find out oxidation state of Fe in this complex.

9. Calculate |C.F.S.E.| (mod value) is term of Dq. for complex ion $[MnF_6]^{3-}$.

10. Total number of geometrical isomers of $[CoBrClI(CN)(H_2O)(NH_3)]^-$ complex ion, in which all halides are in *cis*-position.

11. What is CFSE of complex ion $[FeF_6]^{4-}$ in terms of Dq ?

12. How many more co-ordination isomers are possible of the compound $[Cu(NH_3)_4][PtCl_4]$?

13. Total number of space (stereo) isomers of complex ion $[Cr(gly)(en)_2]^{2+}$ are..................

14. Calculate CFSE of light pink compound formed, when $KMnO_4$ is reduced by acidified H_2S.

15. How many electrons are present in t_{2g} set of d-orbitals of central metal cation in $[Fe(H_2O)_5(NO)]SO_4$ brown ring complex ?

16. A (Light pink colour complex) $\xrightarrow[\Delta]{Pb_3O_4/dil.HNO_3}$ $HMnO_4$ $\xrightarrow{H_2S/H^+}$ A (Light pink colour complex).
Calculate CFSE value in light pink colour complex.

17. Calculate value of "$x \div y$" if x is the total number of σ bonds and y is total number of π bonds in ligand EDTA and phenanthrolene.
{EDTA = Ethylene diamine tetraacetate, phen = 1, 10 – N, N-Phenanthrolene}

18. Consider the following complex compounds.
(i) $[Pt(NH_3)_2(SCN)_2]$ (ii) $[Co(NH_3)_3(NO_2)_3]$
(iii) $[Pt(en)Cl_2]$ (iv) $[Cr(en)_2Br_2]^+$
(v) $[Rh(en)_3]^{3+}$ (vi) $[Co\,Cl_2\,Br_2]^{2-}$
Then calculate sum of total number of geometrical isomers in all above complex compounds.

19. Total number of complexes among the following which are optically active ?
(i) $[Cr(Ox)_3]^{3-}$ (ii) $[Pt(Cl_2)(en)]$
(iii) *cis*-$[Rh(Cl_2)(NH_3)_4]^+$ (iv) $[Ru(dipy)_3]^{3+}$
(v) *cis*-$[Co(NO_2)_3(dien)]$ (vi) *Trans*-$[Co(NO_2)_3(dien)]$
(vii) *cis*-$[Co(NO_2)_3(NH_3)_3]$

20. Consider the following complexes.
(i) $[Fe\,IF(CN)(H_2O)(en)]$ (ii) $[Mo\,Cl_2F_2(gly)]^{2-}$
Then, calculate value of $|x - y|$ (where x and y are total number of possible optically active isomers in (i) and (ii) complex respectively).

21. Consider the following ligands NH_2^-, acac, OH^-, Gly, O_2^-, Phen, DMG, NO_2^-, CO_3^{2-}, Cl^-, CH_3COO^-, en, SO_4^{2-}. Then calculate value of "$P + Q - R - S$"
Here
P : Total number of ligands which act as bridging as well as monodentate only.
Q : Total number of flexidentate ligands
R : Total number of bidentate ligands only
S : Total number of unsymmetrical bidentate ligands

22. $M(CO)_x(NO)_y \xrightarrow[-CO]{+NO} M(NO)_z$
Where EAN of metal (M) in both product and reactant is same and it is 54. Then calculate value of $(x + y - z)$. (where x, y and z are natural numbers and M belong to 6th group according to long form of periodic table)

23. 100 mL 0.15 M solution of $CoCl_3 \cdot xNH_3$ was treated with excess of $AgNO_3$ solution and 0.03 moles of AgCl was obtained, then find out value of x.

24. Find out total number of compound(s) in which at least half of Cl^- are ionizable
$CrCl_3 \cdot 6NH_3$, $CrCl_3 \cdot 5NH_3$, $CrCl_3 \cdot 4NH_3$, $CrCl_3 \cdot 3NH_3$, $PtCl_4 \cdot 6NH_3$, $PtCl_4 \cdot 5NH_3$, $PtCl_4 \cdot 4NH_3$, $PtCl_4 \cdot 3NH_3$, $PtCl_4 \cdot 2NH_3$

25. Find the value of n for diamagnetic complex $[Fe(en)_3]_n\,[Co(NH_3)_2(NO_2)_4]_2$

26. Find out total number of compound(s) which is/are paramagnetic in nature
Cl_2O, ClO_2, ClO_3, Cl_2O_7, $K_3[Co(ox)_3]$, $K_3[Cr(CN)_6]$, $K_2[NiCl_4]$, $K_2[PtCl_4]$, $K_2[NiF_6]$

27. For given reaction :
$$Co^{2+}(aq) + KNO_2 \text{ (excess)} \xrightarrow{\text{air}} \text{Coloured complex salt precipitated}$$
Find out total no. of unpaired electron(s) in *d*-orbitals of precipitated complex salt.

28. Maximum number of Nitrogen atoms that can lie in molecular plane of complex $[Pt(trien)]^{2+}$.

29. Find out value of expression $(x - y)$ for complex compound $[Zn(acac)_2]$
where, x = Total number of O — Zn — O bond angle(s) in the compound
y = Total number of sp^3 Hybridized atom(s) in the compound

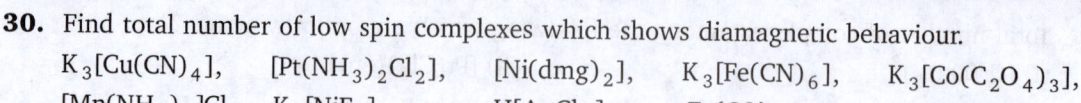

30. Find total number of low spin complexes which shows diamagnetic behaviour.
$K_3[Cu(CN)_4]$, $[Pt(NH_3)_2Cl_2]$, $[Ni(dmg)_2]$, $K_3[Fe(CN)_6]$, $K_3[Co(C_2O_4)_3]$, $[Mn(NH_3)_6]Cl_2$, $K_2[NiF_6]$, $H[AuCl_4]$, $Fe(CO)_5$

31. Find out maximum number of carbon atom(s) that can lie in a plane in $[Fe(dmg)_2]$.

32. Find out total number of paramagnetic inner orbital complex
$K_2[NiCl_4], K_3[Fe(CN)_6], K_3[Cr(CN)_6], K_2[PtCl_4], Na_2[Fe(CN)_5NO], [Fe(H_2O)NO]SO_4$, $K_3[Co(C_2O_4)_3], K_4[Co(CN)_6], [Cu(NH_3)_4]SO_4$.

33. Find out value of expression $|x-y|$, for complex compound, $[Ni(dmg)_2]$
where ; x = Maximum number of carbon atom(s) that can lie in a plane.
y = Number of carbon atom(s) which are sp^2 hybridized.

34. Find out total number of ionic species/compounds from following list in which central atom uses $d_{x^2-y^2}$ orbital in its hybridization.
$[Ni(CN)_4]^{2-}, Fe(CO)_5, [Cr(NH_3)_6]^{3+}, [XeF_5]^-, [Ni(CO)_4], MnO_4^-, [PtCl_2(NH_3)_2], ClF_5$, $[CuCl_5]^{3-}$

35. Find total number of inner orbital diamagnetic complexes.
$[Fe(CN)_6]^{3-}$, $[Co(H_2O)_6]^{2+}$, $[Cr(en)_3]^{3+}$, $[Fe(CN)_6]^{4-}$, $[Co(H_2O)_6]^{3+}$, $[Cr(CN)_6]^{3-}$, $[PtCl_6]^{2-}$, $[Ni(H_2O)_6]^{2+}$, $[Cr(CO)_6]$

36. Consider following transformation

$$[Co(H_2O)_x]^{2+}\text{(Pink complex)} \xrightarrow[\text{HCl}]{\text{Excess}} [CoCl_y]^{n-}\text{(Blue complex)}$$

Find the value of expression $\frac{x+y}{n}$

37. Given that crystal field stabilization energy for $[Co(H_2O)_6]^{2+}$ is 7200 cm^{-1}, pairing energy for Co^{2+} is 20,800 cm^{-1}, then calculate the value of $\frac{\Delta_o}{10^3}$ in cm^{-1}.

38. Find out total number of electrons of Co^{2+} ion which are present in non-axial *d*-orbitals in the complex compound : $[Co(dmg)_2]$

39. Find out number of electrons(s) in axial orbitals of inner shell of central metal cation in complex $[Co(NH_3)_6]^{2+}$.

40. Two stereoisomers of which of the following complexes are optically active :
$[Zn(gly)(en)]^+, [Pt(gly)_2], [Co(en)_3]^{3+}, [Ir(acac)(CN)_4]^{2-}, [PtBr_2(NO_2)_2(H_2O)_2]$, $[CrBr(NO_2)(H_2O)_4]^+, [Ru(acac)_2(NO_2)(NH_3)], [IrBr_2(SCN)(NH_3)_3], [Zn(gly)(NH_3)(H_2O)]^+$

41. Find total number of optically active isomers for complex compound having molecular formula $Pt \cdot x(en) \cdot Cl_4$ (where $x = 1, 2, 3$)

Answers

Level-1

1. (a)	2. (d)	3. (d)	4. (d)	5. (c)	6. (b)	7. (d)	8. (a)	9. (b)	10. (c)
11. (b)	12. (d)	13. (d)	14. (c)	15. (a)	16. (d)	17. (d)	18. (d)	19. (c)	20. (b)
21. (d)	22. (c)	23. (c)	24. (a)	25. (d)	26. (c)	27. (a)	28. (d)	29. (d)	30. (d)
31. (a)	32. (c)	33. (b)	34. (b)	35. (d)	36. (c)	37. (d)	38. (d)	39. (b)	40. (d)
41. (a)	42. (a)	43. (b)	44. (d)	45. (c)	46. (a)	47. (a)	48. (d)	49. (d)	50. (d)
51. (c)	52. (a)	53. (d)	54. (a)	55. (a)	56. (a)	57. (c)	58. (c)	59. (a)	60. (a)
61. (a)	62. (b)	63. (d)	64. (c)	65. (d)	66. (c)	67. (a)	68. (c)	69. (c)	70. (b)
71. (c)	72. (b)	73. (b)	74. (a)	75. (b)	76. (a)	77. (b)	78. (a)	79. (c)	80. (c)
81. (c)	82. (a)	83. (a)	84. (d)	85. (b)	86. (a)	87. (a)	88. (d)	89. (b)	90. (d)
91. (b)	92. (c)	93. (d)	94. (a)	95. (c)	96. (c)	97. (c)	98. (d)	99. (a)	100. (b)
101. (d)	102. (b)	103. (c)	104. (d)	105. (d)	106. (d)	107. (a)	108. (c)	109. (c)	110. (c)
111. (d)	112. (b)	113. (a)	114. (d)	115. (a)	116. (c)	117. (b)	118. (a)	119. (d)	120. (a)
121. (c)	122. (a)	123. (c)	124. (b)	125. (a)	126. (c)	127. (b)	128. (b)	129. (c)	130. (a)
131. (c)	132. (b)	133. (b)	134. (c)	135. (a)	136. (d)	137. (a)	138. (d)	139. (b)	140. (c)
141. (a)	142. (b)	143. (a)	144. (c)	145. (b)	146. (d)	147. (d)	148. (b)	149. (c)	150. (b)
151. (d)	152. (a)	153. (a)	154. (c)	155. (d)	156. (b)	157. (d)	158. (d)	159. (b)	160. (d)
161. (b)	162. (b)	163. (b)	164. (b)	165. (b)	166. (d)	167. (d)	168. (b)	169. (a)	170. (d)
171. (a)	172. (b)	173. (d)	174. (b)	175. (a)	176. (a)	177. (d)	178. (b)	179. (c)	180. (d)
181. (d)	182. (b)	183. (b)	184. (c)	185. (d)	186. (d)	187. (b)	188. (b)	189. (c)	190. (c)
191. (c)	192. (c)	193. (b)	194. (c)	195. (b)	196. (a)	197. (b)	198. (a)	199. (b)	200. (b)
201. (c)	202. (d)	203. (b)	204. (b)	205. (d)	206. (c)	207. (c)	208. (d)	209. (a)	210. (d)
211. (c)	212. (a)	213. (b)	214. (b)	215. (d)	216. (a)	217. (a)	218. (b)	219. (d)	220. (c)
221. (c)	222. (d)	223. (b)	224. (d)						

Level-2

1.	(d)	**2.**	(b)	**3.**	(a)	**4.**	(b)	**5.**	(d)	**6.**	(a)	**7.**	(c)	**8.**	(c)	**9.**	(c)	**10.**	(d)
11.	(b)	**12.**	(a)	**13.**	(c)	**14.**	(d)	**15.**	(b)	**16.**	(d)	**17.**	(c)	**18.**	(b)	**19.**	(c)	**20.**	(b)
21.	(d)	**22.**	(c)	**23.**	(b)	**24.**	(d)	**25.**	(d)	**26.**	(c)	**27.**	(c)	**28.**	(d)	**29.**	(b)	**30.**	(b)
31.	(d)	**32.**	(d)	**33.**	(b)	**34.**	(c)	**35.**	(b)	**36.**	(b)	**37.**	(c)	**38.**	(c)	**39.**	(c)	**40.**	(c)
41.	(c)	**42.**	(a)	**43.**	(d)	**44.**	(d)	**45.**	(b)	**46.**	(b)	**47.**	(a)	**48.**	(d)	**49.**	(a)	**50.**	(a)
51.	(d)	**52.**	(c)	**53.**	(b)	**54.**	(b)	**55.**	(c)	**56.**	(d)	**57.**	(a)	**58.**	(a)	**59.**	(b)	**60.**	(b)
61.	(d)	**62.**	(d)	**63.**	(d)	**64.**	(a)	**65.**	(b)	**66.**	(d)	**67.**	(c)	**68.**	(b)	**69.**	(c)	**70.**	(a)
71.	(c)	**72.**	(d)	**73.**	(d)														

Level-3

Passage–1	**1.**	(d)	**2.**	(d)	**3.**	(d)								
Passage–2	**1.**	(c)	**2.**	(d)	**3.**	(a)								
Passage–3	**1.**	(b)	**2.**	(a)	**3.**	(b)								
Passage–4	**1.**	(c)	**2.**	(a)	**3.**	(d)								
Passage–5	**1.**	(c)	**2.**	(a)										
Passage–6	**1.**	(c)	**2.**	(a,c)	**3.**	(a)								
Passage–7	**1.**	(a)	**2.**	(b)	**3.**	(d)								
Passage–8	**1.**	(c)	**2.**	(c)	**3.**	(b)								
Passage–9	**1.**	(c)	**2.**	(b)	**3.**	(c)								
Passage–10	**1.**	(b)	**2.**	(a)	**3.**	(c)								
Passage–11	**1.**	(a)	**2.**	(c)	**3.**	(b)								
Passage–12	**1.**	(c)	**2.**	(b)	**3.**	(b)								
Passage–13	**1.**	(a)	**2.**	(a)	**3.**	(b)								
Passage–14	**1.**	(c)	**2.**	(b)										
Passage–15	**1.**	(b)	**2.**	(c)										
Passage–16	**1.**	(a)	**2.**	(b)	**3.**	(c)	**4.**	(c)	**5.**	(c)	**6.**	(a)	**7.**	(a)
Passage–17	**1.**	(a)	**2.**	(c)	**3.**	(c)								
Passage–18	**1.**	(b,d)	**2.**	(a,b,c)										
Passage–19	**1.**	(b)	**2.**	(b)										
Passage–20	**1.**	(d)	**2.**	(c)	**3.**	(a)								
Passage–21	**1.**	(b)	**2.**	(d)										
Passage–22	**1.**	(c)	**2.**	(b)	**3.**	(a)								

One or More Answers is/are correct

1. (a,b,d)	**2.** (a,b,d)	**3.** (a,b,d)	**4.** (a,b,c)	**5.** (a,b,d)	**6.** (a,b,c,d)	**7.** (a,d)	**8.** (a,b,d)
9. (a,c)	**10.** (b)	**11.** (a,b,c)	**12.** (b,d)	**13.** (a,b,d)	**14.** (a,b,d)	**15.** (a,b,c,d)	**16.** (a,b,d)
17. (a,b,d)	**18.** (b,c)	**19.** (a,d)	**20.** (a,d)	**21.** (a,b)	**22.** (b,d)	**23.** (a,b,c,d)	**24.** (a,d)
25. (b,c,d)	**26.** (a,c)	**27.** (a,d)	**28.** (a,b,d)	**29.** (a,b,c,d)	**30.** (a,b,c)	**31.** (a, d)	**32.** (b,d)
33. (a,d)	**34.** (b,c,d)	**35.** (a,b,d)	**36.** (a,b,c,d)	**37.** (a,b,c,d)	**38.** (a,b,c)	**39.** (a,c,d)	**40.** (b,d)
41. (a,b,c,d)	**42.** (a,c,d)	**43.** (a,b,d)	**44.** (a,c,d)	**45.** (b,d)	**46.** (a,b,c)		

Match the Column

1. A → P, R, T;	B → P, T;	C → Q, T;	D → Q, S, T
2. A → P, T;	B → P, R, S;	C → P, Q, T;	D → P, R, S, T
3. A → P, Q,R,S, T;	B → P, Q, S, T;	C → P, Q, S, T;	D → Q, T
4. A → Q, R;	B → Q, S, T;	C → Q, S;	D → P, R, S
5. A → R, T;	B → Q, T;	C → P, T;	D → S
6. A → P, R;	B → Q, S;	C → P, Q;	D → R, S
7. A → Q, R;	B → P, S;	C → P, S;	D → P,S
8. A → R, S;	B → P,Q	C → P;	D → P, Q
9. A → R, S;	B → Q, R, S;	C → P;	D → P, S
10. A → P, Q, S;	B → Q, R, S;	C → P;	D → P, Q
11. A → Q, R, S;	B → P, Q, R,S;	C → P, Q, S;	D → P, R, S
12. A → P, Q, R;	B → Q, S;	C → P, Q, R, S;	D → P, S
13. A → Q, R, S;	B → P, R;	C → Q, R;	D → R, S
14. A → P, Q, R;	B → R;	C → Q, R, S;	D → R
15. A → R;	B → Q;	C → P;	D → S
16. A → S;	B → T;	C → Q;	D → P
17. A → P;	B → Q;	C → S;	D → R
18. A → S;	B → P;	C → P,Q,S;	D → R
19. A → P, Q, S;	B → P, R;	C → P, Q, R, S, T;	D → Q, R, S, T;
20. A → Q, S, T;	B → P, Q;	C → P, Q, R, T;	D → P, Q, R, S, T
21. A → Q, S, T;	B → P, R;	C → Q, R, T;	D → P, R,T
22. A → Q, S, T;	B → P, Q, R, S,T;	C → Q, S, T;	D → Q, S, T

Assertion-Reason Type Questions

1. (A)	**2.** (A)	**3.** (B)	**4.** (D)	**5.** (A)	**6.** (C)	**7.** (D)	**8.** (C)
9. (D)	**10.** (C)	**11.** (A)	**12.** (A)	**13.** (B)			

Subjective Problems

1. 0	**2.** 6	**3.** 41	**4.** 0	**5.** 36	**6.** 6	**7.** 5
8. 1	**9.** 6	**10.** 6	**11.** 4	**12.** 3	**13.** 2	**14.** 0
15. 5	**16.** 0	**17.** 5	**18.** 6	**19.** 2	**20.** 8	**21.** 1
22. 1	**23.** 5	**24.** 5	**25.** 1	**26.** 4	**27.** 0	**28.** 4
29. 1	**30.** 6	**31.** 8	**32.** 4	**33.** 4	**34.** 5	**35.** 4
36. 5	**37.** 9	**38.** 5	**39.** 0	**40.** 4	**41.** 4	

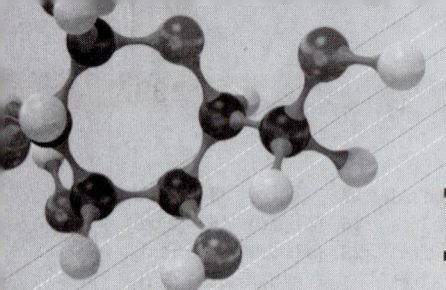

Hints and Solutions

Level 1

3. (d) $Cu^{2+}(aq) + 4NH_3 \underset{}{\overset{OH^-}{\rightleftharpoons}} [Cu(NH_3)_4]^{2+}$

$Cu^{2+}(aq) + 4NH_3 \overset{OH^+}{\rightleftharpoons} Cu^{2+} + 4NH_4^+$ (No complex formation)]

As NH_3 combines with H^+ of acid and changes to NH_4^+ which have no donor site.

4. (d) Alum is a "Double salt" and it's constituent ions do not loose their identity in aqueous solution.

6. (b) CO bond strength is reciprocal to the extent of back donation involved in synergic bonding

i.e., $M \rightleftharpoons CO$

7. (d) CO is called π-acid ligand. In metal carbonyl complexes, there is donation of an electron pair from carbon to the empty orbital of metal and then simultaneously a back π-bonding is formed by sideways overlap of a filled orbital on the metal with empty antibonding π^*_{2py} orbital of CO.

8. (a) C—O bond length : $(C—O)_{Cr(CO)_6} > (C—O)_{CO} > (C—O)_{CO^+}$

Bond order of CO in $Cr(CO)_6$ is less than three.

Bond order of CO = 3

Bond order of $CO^+ > 3$

9. (b) $[V(CO)_6]^-$:more will be negative charge on metal more will be extent of synergic bonding due to which C—O bond order decreases thus C—O bond length increases.

15. (a) $Mn(CO)_5 + \bar{e} \longrightarrow [Mn(CO)_5]^-$

less stable (O.A.) — more stable, as EAN of Mn = 36 (Kr)

18. (d)

Ligand (s)	One ligand donate e^-
π-C_5H_5	$6e^-$
π-C_3H_5	$4e^-$
CO	$2e^-$

If $[Fe(\pi\text{-}C_5H_5)_x(\pi\text{-}C_3H_5)_y(CO)_z]$

Complex compound following Sidewick's rule then

$$26-(2)+6(1)+4(1)+2(1)=36$$

$$x+y+z=1+1+1=3$$

19. (c) $[Mn^{+1}(CO)_x(\eta^y - C_5H_5)]$

$\eta^5 - C_5H_5^- = 6e^-$ donor

$$EAN = 25-1+3(2)+6\times 1 = 36$$

So, $x=3, y=5$

20. (b) E.A.N of Cr $= 36 = 24 + 2x + 6$

∴ $x = $ [illegible]

The value [illegible] E.A.N. of Cr = 36

21. (d) (a) $[Fe(CN)_6]^{3-}$ EAN = 35

$[Fe(NH_3)_6]^{3+}$ EAN = 35

(b) $[Cr(NH_3)_6]^{3+}$ EAN = 33

$[Cr(CN)_6]^{3-}$ EAN = 33

(c) $[FeF_6]^{3-}$ EAN = 35

$[Fe(CN)_6]^{3-}$ EAN = 35

(d) $[Ni(CO)_4]$ EAN = 36

$[Ni(CN)_4]^{2-}$ EAN = 34

23. (c) $[Ca(EDTA)]^{2-}$ $20-2+(6\times2)=30$

$[Cr(en)_3]^{3+}$ $24-3+(2\times2\times3)=33$

$[CoBrCl(trien)]^+$ $27-3+2+2+(4\times2)=36$

$[Ni(dmg)_2]$ $28-2+(4\times2)=34$

24. (a) $[\overset{*}{Ni}(CO)]_4$

$EAN = 28-0+2\times4 = 28+8 = 36$

$[\overset{*}{Fe}(CN)_6]^{4-}$

$EAN = 26-2+6\times2 = 26-2+12 = 36$

25. (d) The correct name is chlorobis(ethylenediamine)nitritocobalt (III).

30. (d) $H_2[PtCl_6]$ is an acid, not salt hence its name : Hexachloroplatinic(IV)acid.

34. (b) $NH_3 \longrightarrow$ ammine

en $\longrightarrow$ ethylene diamine

35. (d) $[\overset{+3}{Co}(NCS)(NH_3)_5][\overset{+2}{Zn}(CN)_4]$

Pentaamminethiocyanato-N-cobalt(III) tetracyanidozincate(II).

36. (c) Prussian Blue : $Fe_4[Fe(CN)_6]_3$ or $Fe^{3+}[Fe^{2+}(CN)_6]^{4-}$

Iron(III) hexacyanoferrate(II)

38. (d) In "Pentaaquacyanido Iron (III) trichloridotricyanido cobaltate (III)"

Complex cation is $[Fe^{III}(CN)(H_2O)_5]^{2+}$ and complex anion is $[Co^{III}Cl_3(CN)_3]^{3-}$

Therefore complex is $[Fe(CN)(H_2O)_5]_3[CoCl_3(CN)_3]_2$

39. (b) $K[Co(CH_5NH_2)_2Cl_4]$

Potassium tetrachloridodi(methylamine)cobaltate(III)

40. (d) $Na_2[Fe(CN)_5(NO^+)]$ = Sodiumpentacyanidonitrosyliumferrate(II)

41. (a) Wilkinson's catalyst : $[Rh(PPh_3)_3Cl]$

chloridotris (triphenyl phosphine) rhodium (I)

47. (a) Conductivity $\propto$ number of ions in aqueous medium

$[Cr(NH_3)_6]Cl_3 \rightarrow [Cr(NH_3)_6]^{3+} + 3Cl^-$

$[Cr(NH_3)_5Cl]Cl_2 \rightarrow [Cr(NH_3)_5Cl]^{2+} + 2Cl^-$

$[Cr(NH_3)_4Cl_2]Cl \rightarrow [Cr(NH_3)_4Cl_2]^+ + Cl^-$

$[Cr(NH_3)_3Cl_3] \rightarrow$ Does not ionize

49. (d) 100 mL of a 10 *M* solution of $AgNO_3$ = 1 mole $AgNO_3$

$$[Co(NH_3)_6]Cl_3 \xrightarrow[AgNO_3]{1\ mole} \text{One mole AgCl}$$

$$[CoCl\ (NH_3)_5]\ Cl_2 \xrightarrow[AgNO_3]{1\ mole} \text{One mole AgCl}$$

$$[CoCl_2(NH_3)_5]Cl_2 \xrightarrow[AgNO_3]{1\ mole} \text{One mole AgCl}$$

(Above reaction $AgNO_3$ is a limiting reagents)

50. (d) $PtBr_4 \cdot xNH_3 + AgNO_3$ solution $\longrightarrow$ $AgBr \downarrow$

0.01 mole Excess 0.03 moles

$\therefore$ The value of $x = 5$

i.e., complex is $[Pt\,Br(NH_3)_5]Br_3$

51. (c) $Cr \cdot 6NH_3 \cdot Cl_3 \longrightarrow [Cr(NH_3)_6]Cl_3$

Secondary valency '6' satisfied by only NH_3, all Cl^- satisfy only primary valency.

$$Cr \cdot 5NH_3 \cdot Cl_3 \longrightarrow [Cr(NH_3)_5Cl]Cl_2$$

Secondary valency '6' satiesfied by five NH_3 and one Cl^- while all three Cl^- satify primary valency.

58. (c) Fe^{2+} in $[Fe(H_2O)_6]^{2+}$

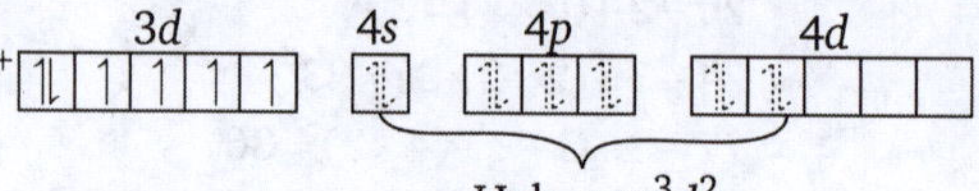

Hyb. : sp^3d^2

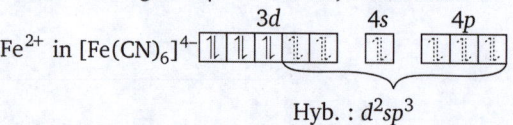

Colour : Pale green $\mu = 4.9$ B.M.; octahedral

Fe^{2+} in $[Fe(CN)_6]^{4-}$

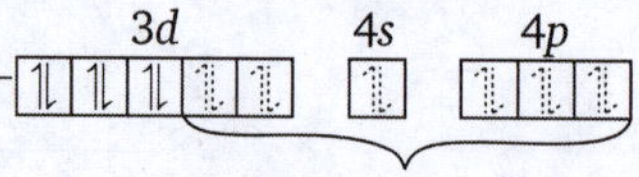

Hyb. : d^2sp^3

Colour : Yellow; $\mu = 0$; octahedral

65. (d)

$$Ni(CO)_4; \mu_{eff} = 0$$
$$[Co(NH_3)_4(NO_2)_2]^+; \mu_{eff} = 0$$
$$[Ag(CN)_2]; \mu_{eff} = 0$$
$$[CuBr_4]^{2-}; \mu_{eff} = 1.732 \text{ BM}$$

66. (c) Degenerate *d*-orbitals undergo splitting under ligand field created by strong, weak or mixed ligands.

71. (c) $[Mn(NH_3)_6]^{2+}$, NH_3 act as WFL for Mn^{2+} so d^5, WFL outer orbital complex.

$[Co(H_2O)_6]^{3+}$, H_2O act as SFL for Co^{3+} so d^6, SFL outer orbital complex.

$K_3[Cu(CN)_4]$, d^{10} always diamagnetic

73. (b) $[Cu(NH_3)_5]^{2+} \rightarrow$ geometry with C.N. = 5 is sq. pyramidal, dsp^3 hybridisation and $d_{x^2-y^2}$ orbital is used in hybridisation.

(a) $Fe(CO)_5 \rightarrow d_{z^2}sp^3$

(c) $[Co(NH_3)_6]^{2+} \rightarrow d^2sp^3$

(d) $[IrF_6]^{3-} \rightarrow d^2sp^3$

74. (a) $[Cr(CN)_6]^{3-}$ Cr^{3+} in strong ligand field $= t_{2g}^3\, e_g^0 = 3$ unpaired electron

$[Mn(CN)_6]^{3-}$ Mn^{3+} in strong ligand field $= t_{2g}^4\, e_g^0 = 2$ unpaired electron

$[Fe(CN)_6]^{3-}$ Fe^{3+} in strong ligand field $= t_{2g}^5\, e_g^0 = 1$ unpaired electron

$[Co(CN)_6]^{3-}$ Co^{3+} in strong ligand field $= t_{2g}^6 e_g^0 =$ Zero unpaired electron

75. (b) (I) $[Ni(CO)_4]$ $\vec{\mu} = 0$ BM

(II) $[Mn(CN)_6]^{4-}$ $\vec{\mu} = \sqrt{3}$ BM

(III) $[Cr(NH_3)_6]^{3+}$ $\vec{\mu} = \sqrt{15}$ BM

(IV) $[CoF_6]^{3-}$ $\vec{\mu} = \sqrt{24}$ BM

Order of magnetic moment : I < II < III < IV

76. (a) $\vec{\mu} = 2.83$ BM $\Rightarrow$ Number of unpaired e^- must be $= 2$

(a) $[V(H_2O)_6]^{3+}$ Number of unpaired $e^- = 2$
(b) $[Cr(H_2O)_6]^{3+}$ Number of unpaired $e^- = 3$
(c) $[Cu(CN)_4]^{2-}$ Number of unpaired $e^- = 1$
(d) $[MnCl_4]^{2-}$ Number of unpaired $e^- = 5$

77. (b) (I) $[Cu(CN)_4]^{3-}$ $\vec{\mu} = 0$ (Diamagnetic)
(II) $[Co(NH_3)_6]^{3+}$ $\vec{\mu} = 0$ (Diamagnetic)
(III) $[Ni(NH_3)_6]^{2+}$ $\vec{\mu} = \sqrt{8}$ BM (Paramagnetic)
(IV) $[Fe(CN)_6]^{3-}$ $\vec{\mu} = \sqrt{3}$ BM (Paramagnetic)

78. (a) (a) $[Ni(NH_3)_6]^{2+}$ Hyb. = sp^3d^2 (Outer orbital complex)
(b) $[Mn(CN)_6]^{4-}$ Hyb. = d^2sp^3 (Inner orbital complex)
(c) $[Co(NH_3)_6]^{3+}$ Hyb. = d^2sp^3 (Inner orbital complex)
(d) $[Fe(CN)_6]^{4-}$ Hyb. = d^2sp^3 (Inner orbital complex)

79. (c) (a) $[Co(CN)_6]^{4-}$ Number of unpaired $e^- = 1$
(b) $[Cr(H_2O)_6]^{3+}$ Number of unpaired $e^- = 3$
(c) $[FeCl_4]^{2-}$ Number of unpaired $e^- = 4$
(d) $[Fe(H_2O)_6]^{3+}$ Number of unpaired $e^- = 5$

80. (c) (a) Geometry of complexes $\rightarrow$ Both square planer
(b) Hybridisation of central metal cation $\rightarrow$ dsp^2
(c) Magnetic behaviour $[Cu(en)_2]^{2+}$ $\rightarrow$ Paramagnetic ; $[Ni(dmg)_2]$ $\rightarrow$ Diamagnetic
(d) Number of stereoisomers = 0.

81. (c)

	Comples species	Magnetic behaviour
(a)	$[NiCl_4]^{2-}$	Paramagnetic
(b)	$K_3[Fe(CN)_6]$	Paramagnetic
(c)	$[Ni(CO)_4]$	Diamagnetic
(d)	$[Co(CN)_6]^{4-}$	Paramagnetic

82. (a) $[Mn(NH_3)_6]Cl_2$

It is a outer orbital complex

$Mn^{2+}(d^5)$ | ↑ | ↑ | ↑ | ↑ | ↑ | sp^3d^2 – hyb^n

M.M. = $\sqrt{35}$ B.M.

83. (a) $Na_3[\overset{+3}{Co}(OX)_3]$ is a inner orbital complex having d^2sp^3 hybridization and diamagnetic.

84. (d) In $[Pt(NH_3)_4]Cl_2$, Pt^{2+} surrounded by four strong "NH_3" ligands.

85. (b) (a) $[Ni(PF_3)_4]$ Ni : sp^3 Hybridization
P : sp^3 Hybridization
(b) $[Fe(dmg)_2]$ Fe : dsp^2 Hybridization
N-atom of dmg : sp^2 Hybridization
(c) $[Zn(en)_2]^{2+}$ Zn : sp^3 Hybridization
N-atom of en : sp^3 Hybridization
(d) $[Ni(PMe_3)_4]^{2+}$ Ni : sp^3 Hybridization
P : sp^3 Hybridization

86. (a) $[Cr(C_2O_4)_2(NH_3)_2]^{-1}$

O.N.(Cr) = +3, C.N. = 6, M.M. = $\sqrt{15}$ BM

No. of unpaired electron = 3.

87. (a) (a) $[Ni(NH_3)_6]^{2+}$ Hyb. : sp^3d^2 (OOC)

(b) $[Mn(CN)_6]^{4-}$ Hyb. : d^2sp^3 (IOC)

(c) $[Co(NH_3)_6]^{3+}$ Hyb. : d^2sp^3 (IOC)

(d) $[Fe(CN)_6]^{4-}$ Hyb. : d^2sp^3 (IOC)

88. (d) $[Co(CN)_6]^{4-}$

Co^{2+}, d^7, SFL

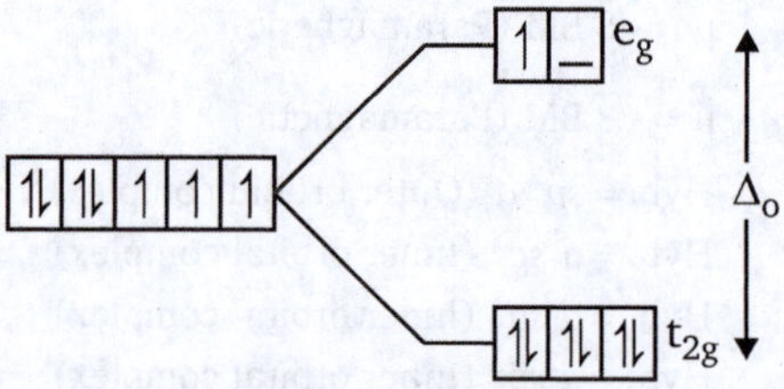

Unpaired e^- = 1

$[Cr(NH_3)_6]^{3+}$

Cr^{3+}, d^3, SFL

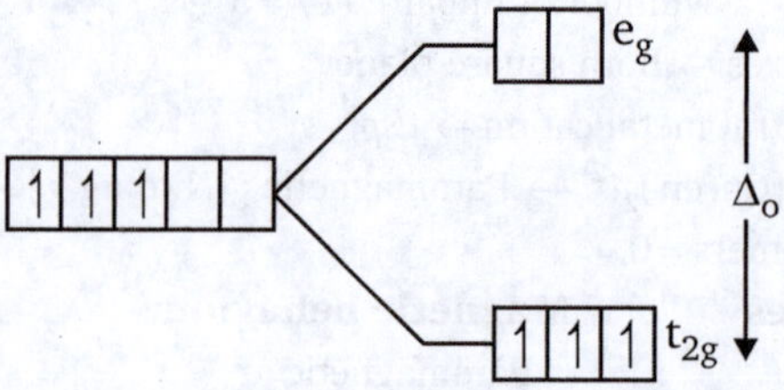

Unpaired e^- = 3

89. (b) (a) $[NiCl_4]^{2-}$, $[Ni(CN)_4]^{2-}$

Hybr. sp^3, dsp^2

Geometry-Tetrahedral, square planer

(b) $[CoF_6]^{3-}$, $[Co(NH_3)_6]^{3+}$

Hybr. sp^3d^2, d^2sp^3

Geometry-octahedral, octahedral.

(c) $[Cu(NH_3)_4]^+$, $[Ni(NH_3)_4]^{2+}$

Hybr. sp^3, dsp^2

Geometry-Tetrahedral, square planer.

(d) $[Ni(CO)_4]$, $[Ni(CN)_4]^{2-}$

Hybr. sp^3, dsp^2

Geometry-Tetrahedral, square planer.

91. (b)

	Complex ions	μ_{eff} **(in B.M.)**
(a)	$[Cr(NH_3)_6]^{2+}$	2.8
(b)	$[Fe(NH_3)_6]^{2+}$	4.9
(c)	$[Co(H_2O)_6]^{3+}$	0
(d)	$[NiF_6]^{2-}$	0

92. (c) $[Ni(NH_3)_6]Cl_2$ paramagnetic, outer orbital complex, sp^3d^2
$K_3[Fe(CN)_6]$ paramagnetic, inner orbital complex, d^2sp^3
$K_2[PtCl_6]$ diamagnetic, inner orbital complex, d^2sp^3
$[Cr(H_2O)_6]Cl_3$ paramagnetic, inner orbital, d^2sp^3

93. (c) $[NiF_6]^{4-} \rightarrow$ High and low spin not defined $[IrF_6]^{3-} \rightarrow$ low spin complex.
Both complex are dimagnetic, d^2sp^3 hybridised and have octahedral geometry.

94. (a)

	Number of unpaired electrons
(a) $[Fe(CN)_6]^{4-}$	$0\,(t_{2g}^6\, e_g^0)$
(b) $[Fe(CN)_6]^{3-}$	$1\,(t_{2g}^5\, e_g^0)$
(c) $[Mn(CN)_6]^{3-}$	$2\,(t_{2g}^4\, e_g^0)$
(d) $[Cr(CN)_6]^{3-}$	$3\,(t_{2g}^3\, e_g^0)$

95. (c) $[Co(CO)_4] \rightarrow$ Paramagnetic, dsp^2 (square planer)

107. (a) V^{3+} in $[V(H_2O)_6]^{3+}$

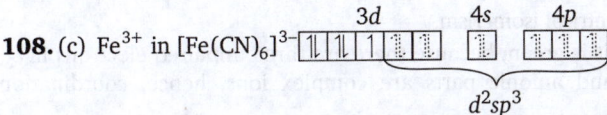

$\mu_{Exp} = \sqrt{2(2+2)} = 2.83$ BM 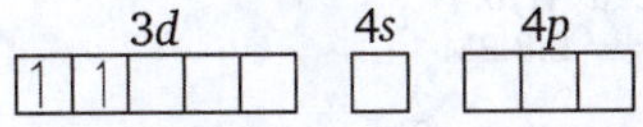

108. (c) Fe^{3+} in $[Fe(CN)_6]^{3-}$ 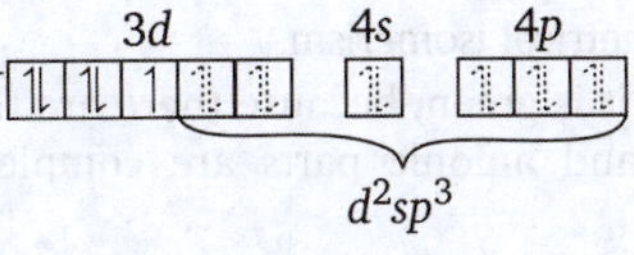

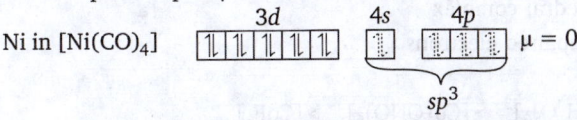

$\Rightarrow$ low spin complex $\mu = 1.732$ BM

Ni in $[Ni(CO)_4]$ 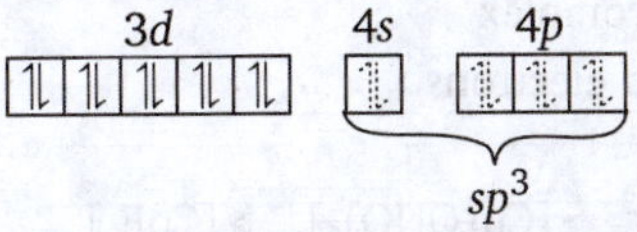 $\mu = 0$

Cr^{3+} in $[Cr(NH_3)_6]^{3+}$ 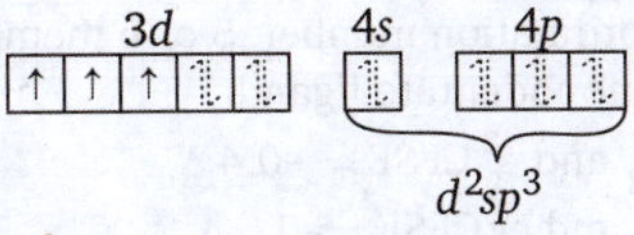

$\Rightarrow$ low and high spin complex is applicable for d^4 to d^7 configuration.

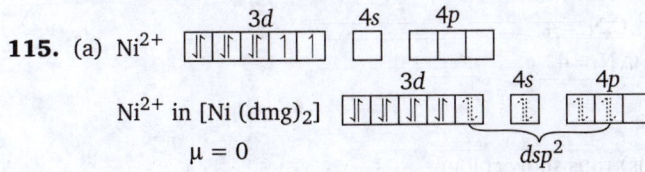

Mn^{2+} in $[Mn(CN)_6]^{4-}$ 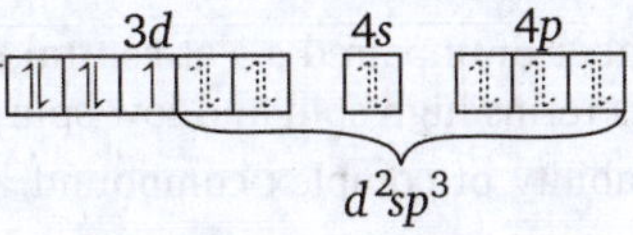

$\Rightarrow$ low spin complex $\mu = 1.732$ BM

114. (d) In complexes $[Rh(H_2O)_6]^{3+}$ and $[Co(H_2O)_6]^{3+}$, central metal cations have same oxidation state as well as same ligands and they fall in same group, but Δ_0 of $[Rh(H_2O)_6]^{3+} > \Delta_0$ of $[Co(H_2O)_6]^{3+}$ because Rh^{3+} has high Z_{eff} value than CO^{3+}.

115. (a) Ni^{2+} 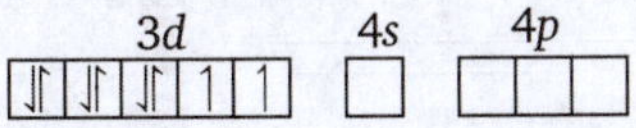

Ni^{2+} in $[Ni\ (dmg)_2]$ 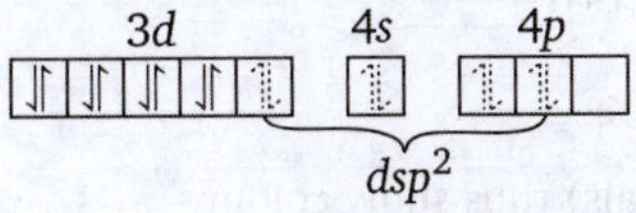

$\mu = 0$

116. (c) Number of unpaired electrons = 3

$\mu_{eff} = 3.9$ BM

type of hybridisation = sp^3d^2

117. (b) Increasing stability order :

(a) $[Cu(NH_3)_4]^{2+} < [Cu(en)_2]^{2+} < [Cu(trien)]^{2+}$

Their formation entropy increases in the same order, because denticity of ligand increases

(b) $[Fe(H_2O)_6]^{3+} < [Fe(NO_2)_6]^{3-} < [Fe(NH_3)_6]^{3+}$

NO_2^- is stronger ligand than NH_3

(c) $[Co(H_2O)_6]^{3+} < [Rh(H_2O)_6]^{3+} < [Ir(H_2O)_6]^{3+}$

Z_{eff} value increases from Co^{3+} to Ir^{3+}

(d) $[Cr(NH_3)_6]^{1+} < [Cr(NH_3)_6]^{2+} < [Cr(NH_3)_6]^{3+}$

Oxidation state of Cr atom increases from +1 to +3

118. (a) $[Ni(H_2O)_6]^{2+} + 6NH_2 \rightleftharpoons [Ni(NH_3)_6]^{2+} + 6H_2O$

sp^3d^2 Hyb. $\qquad sp^3d^2$ Hyb.

$\mu_{eff} = 2.8$ BM $\qquad \mu_{eff} = 2.8$ BM

120. (a) $[PtCl_2(NH_3)(OH)_2]$; Pt-oxidation state +2 ;

Valence configuration = $5d^8$

Complex is diamagnetic and exhibits geometrical isomerism.

123. (c) Due to the cationic part of the complex, it is green, because there are three unpaired electrons in t_{2g} orbitals of Cr^{3+} cation, both cationic and anionic parts are complex ions, hence, coordination isomerism will be exhibited by it.

127. (b) $[Ti(H_2O)_6]Cl_4$

Coordination number 6 $\Rightarrow$ octahedral complex

Ti is in +4 oxidations state $\Rightarrow$ no unpaired electrons

$\Rightarrow$ magnetic moment = 0 B.M.

128. (b) Stability order : $[Co(ox)_3]^{3-} > [Co(H_2O)_6]^{3+} > [Co(ONO)_6]^{3-} > [CoF_6]^{3-}$

For a given metal cation and fixed co-ordination number, 5 or 6 membered chelated complex is found to be more stable than complex with monodentate ligand.

129. (c) (a) High spin with d^6 configuration t_{2g}^4 and e_g^2 CFSE $= -0.4\,\Delta_o$

(b) Low spin with d^4 configuration t_{2g}^4 and e_g^0 CFSE $= -1.6\,\Delta_o$

(c) Low spin with d^5 configuration t_{2g}^5 and e_g^0 CFSE $= -2\,\Delta_o$

(d) High spin with d^7 configuration t_{2g}^5 and e_g^2 CFSE $= -0.8\,\Delta_o$

130. (a) In d^3 and d^8 octahedral complexes number of unpaired e^-s at central metal atom/ion never changes, therefore for such octahedral complexes terms high spin and low spin not used.

131. (c) As number of stable rings increases stability of complex compound also increases due to chelation effect.

Number of rings in $[Ni(en)_2]^{2+} = 2$

Number of rings in $[Ni(dmg)_2] = 4$

132. (b) $K_2[PtCl_4]$ Diamagnetic square planar d^8, SFL, C.N. = 4

$K_2[MnCl_4]$ Paramagnetic tetrahedral d^5, WFL, C.N. = 4

$K_2[ZnCl_4]$ Diamagnetic tetrahedral d^{10}, C.N. = 4

$K_2[HgI_4]$ Diamagnetic tetrahedral d^{10}, C.N. = 4

133. (b) Lowered in energy by $0.4\,\Delta_o$

134. (c) In $K_3[VF_6]$

${}_{23}V^{3+} = 3d^2$ (two electrons in *d*-robitals) thus show colour.

while others have d^0 and d^{10} configuration thus they are colourless.

135. (a) Stability constant (K_s) $\propto$ strength of ligand
strength of ligand N donor > Cl donor.

137. (a) Δ_o (splitting energy) $\propto \dfrac{1}{\lambda\,(\text{Absorbed})}$

Basic strength of ligand C > N > O > X (halogen) donor.

138. (d) $[Ni(NH_3)_6]^{2+} > [Ni(dmg)_2]$
$\Delta_o < \Delta_{sq.\,planar}$

139. (b)

Observed colour	Violet	Green
Absorbed complementory colour	Yellow	Red

$\Delta_{\text{Splitition energy}}$ of $[Co(H_2O)_6]Cl_3 > [Co(H_2O)_4Cl_2]Cl\cdot 2H_2O$

142. (b) d^5 configuration
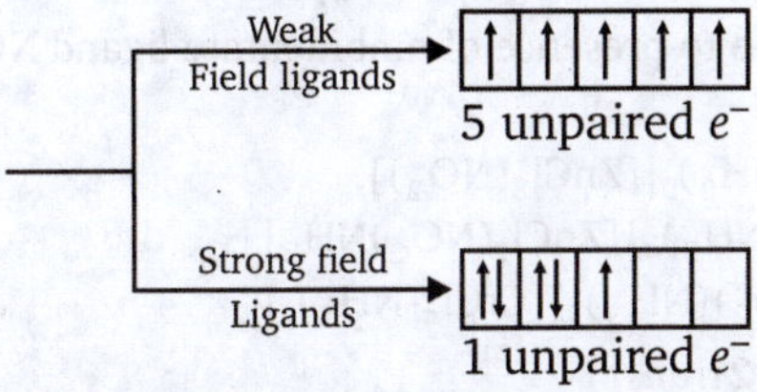

143. (a) $[Ni(CN)_4]^{2-}$ is square planar complex. Thus CFSE released in it is more than octahedral complex leading to more stability.

144. (c) $Na_2[CuCl_4]$ has $Cu^{2+} = 3d^9$ configuration while other compounds have d^{10} configuration.

145. (b) $[Fe(H_2O)_5(NO)]\,SO_4 \rightarrow$ Brown ring complex. [Due to charge transfer phenomenon]

146. (d) Correct order of Δ_o (splitting energy)
(a) $[Co(NH_3)_6]^{3+} < [Co(CN)_6]^{3-}$
(b) $[CoF_6]^{3-} < [Co(NH_3)_6]^{3+}$
(c) $[Co(H_2O)_6]^{2+} < [Co(H_2O)_6]^{3+}$
(d) $[Rh(H_2O)_6]^{3+} > [Co(H_2O)_6]^{3+}$

147. (d) $TiF_6^{2-} \rightarrow$ Colourless (d^0 configuration)
$CoF_6^{3-} \rightarrow$ Coloured (d^6 configuration)
$Cu_2Cl_2 \rightarrow$ Colourless (d^{10} configuration)
$NiCl_4^{2-} \rightarrow$ Coloured (d^8 configuration)

148. (b) $[Ir(H_2O)_6]^{3+}$: $\Delta_o > P$

149. (c) $[Ni(DMG)_2]$ contains four rings due to chelation effect of DMG and due to H-Bonding.

150. (b)
(a) High spin : $d^6 \Rightarrow t_{2g}^4 e_g^2$ CFSE $= -0.4\,\Delta_o$
(b) Low spin : $d^5 \Rightarrow t_{2g}^5 e_g^0$ CFSE $= -2.0\,\Delta_o$
(c) Low spin : $d^4 \Rightarrow t_{2g}^4 e_g^0$ CFSE $= -1.6\,\Delta_o$
(d) High spin : d^7 CFSE $= -0.8\,\Delta_o$

151. (d) Δ_o of $[Ni(en)_3]^{2+}$ is more w.r.t. $[Ni(H_2O)_2(en)_2]^{2+}$.
So $[Ni(en)_3]^{2+}$ absorb more frequency colour for $d-d$ transition. So possibly its colour is violet.

152. (a) Splitting energy $\propto \Delta_{abs} \propto \dfrac{1}{\lambda_{abs}}$

H_2O has more splitting energy than Cl^-, therefore $[Cr(H_2O)_6]Cl_3$ absorbs shorter wave length.

153. (a) CFSE $= -0.4\,\Delta_o\,(t_{2g}\ es^-) + 0.6\,\Delta_o\,(e_g\ es^-)$
For Brown ring complex $= -0.4\,\Delta_o(5) + 0.6\,\Delta_o(2) = -0.8\,\Delta_o$.

154. (c) $[Cr(NH_3)_6]^{3+}$ show colour due to partially filled *d*-orbital. While other complexes have d^0 configuration and thus they are colourless.

155. (d) $[Cu(NH_3)_4]^{2+}$ has square planar structure and is paramagnetic.

156. (b) Strongest the ligand, greater will be the stability constant.

157. (d) $[CoBr(NH_3)_5]SO_4 \rightleftharpoons [CoBr(NH_3)_5]^{2+} + SO_4^{2-}$; Total charges = 4

$[Co(SO_4)(NH_3)_5]Br \rightleftharpoons [Co(SO_4)(NH_3)_5]^+ + Br^-$; Total charges = 2

hence, both have different molar conductivities.

160. (d) Complexes $[Co(SO_4)(NH_3)_5]Br$ and $[Co(SO_4)(NH_3)_5]Cl$ are not any isomers to each other.

161. (b) (I) IUPAC name is Pentaamminenitrito-N-chromium(III) tetrachlorozincate (II)

(II) It does not exhibit geometrical isomerism

(III) It shows linkage isomerism due to presence of ambidentate ligand NO_2^-

(IV) Its coordination isomers are :

$[CrCl(NH_3)_5][ZnCl_3(NO_2)]$,

$[CrCl_2(NH_3)_4][ZnCl_2(NO_2)NH_3]$

$[Zn(NO_2)(NH_3)_3][CrCl_4(NH_3)_2]$

162. (b) $[M(AA)b_2c_2]^{n\pm}$; Total GI = 3 [1 *cis* + 2 *trans*]

$[Ma_3bcd]^{n\pm}$; Total GI = 4 [1 *cis* + 3 *trans*]

$[Ma_2b_2c_2]^{n\pm}$; Total GI = 5 [1 *cis* + 4 *trans*]

$[Ma_2bcde]^{n\pm}$; Total GI = 9 [6 *cis* + 3 *trans*]

163. (b) ⇒ The formula for complex compounds '*X*' and '*Y*' is

$[PtCl_2(NH_3)_2]$

⇒ As compound is neutral co-ordination compound therefore it does not exhibit ionization isomerism, solvate isomerism and co-ordination isomerism.

⇒ Complex compound exhibit geometrical isomerism.

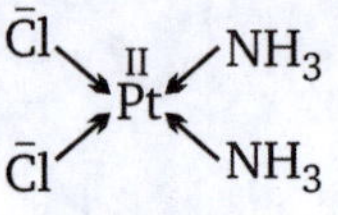

Cis (polar)

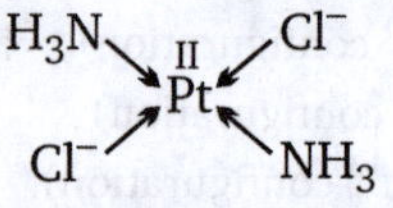

Trans (non-polar)

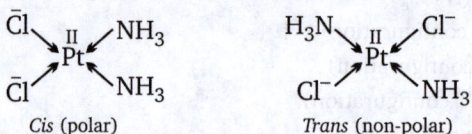

164. (b) $[CrBr_2(H_2O)(NH_3)_3]$; No. of stereoisomers = 3, *cis* = 1 *trans* = 2

$[Zn(gly)_2]$; No. of stereoisomers = 2, both are in *d* and *l* forms

$[PtBrCl(CN)(H_2O)]^-$; No. of stereoisomers = 3, all are geometrical isomers

$[Co(en)(NH_3)_4]^{3+}$; No. of stereoisomers = 0

165. (b) $[CrBrCl_2(H_2O)(NH_3)_2] \cdot H_2O$ is not hydrate isomer of the complex $[CrCl_2(H_2O)_2(NH_3)_2]Br$.

166. (d) ⇒ $[Co(ox)(H_2O)_3(NH_3)]Br$: Does not exhibit structural and optical isomerism but it can exhibit geometrical isomerism.

⇒ $[Cr(SCN)(H_2O)_3(en)](C_2O_4)$: It can exhibit linkage and geometrical isomerism.

⇒ $[ZnBr(CN)(SCN)(NH_3)]^-$: It exhibits optical isomerism.

⇒ $[Co(BrCl)(H_2O)_4][Ag(CN)_2]$: and $[CoCl(CN)(H_2O)_4][AgBr(CN)]$ are co-ordination isomers.

167. (d) ⇒ $[PdBrCl(NO_2)(NH_3)]^-$ Hyb. of Pd^{2+} : dsp^2, complex has plane of symmetry hence does not exhibit optical isomerism. But it exhibits geometrical isomerism and number of geometrical isomers = 3.

⇒ The complex : $[Zn(SCN)(H_2O)(gly)]$ exhibits optical isomerism

Number of stereoisomers = 2

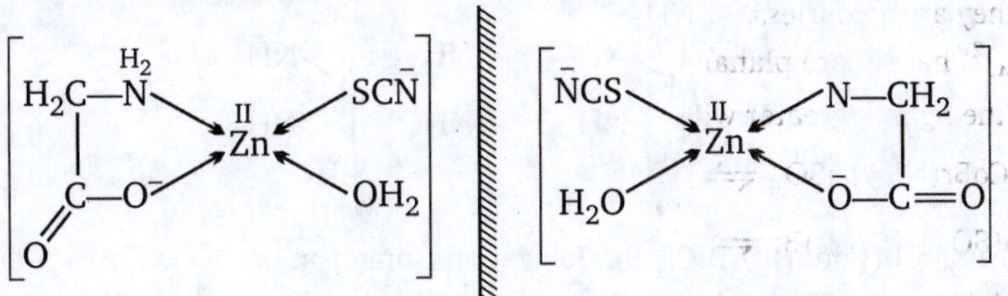

d-form *l*-form

Hybridization of zinc : sp^3

⇒ The complex : $[Co(acac)_3]$ exhibits optical isomerism

Number of stereoisomers = 2

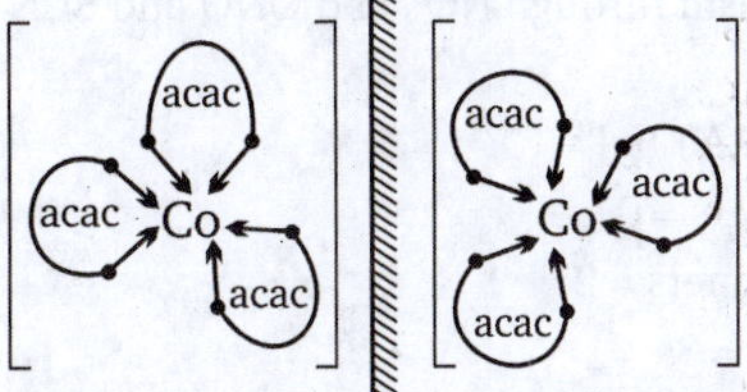

d l

⇒ The complex $[PtBr(H_2O)(en)]$ does not exhibit geometrical and optical isomerism, because it contains plane of symmetry.

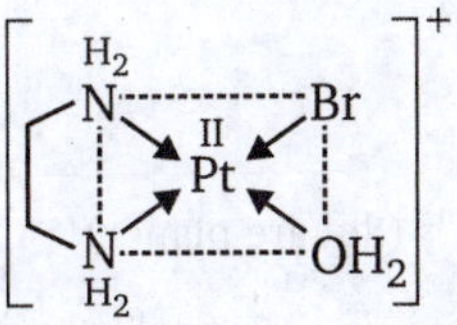

168. (b) $[Pt(NH_3)_4Cl_2]Br_2$

Ionization isomer

$[Pt(NH_3)_4ClBr]Cl \cdot Br$

Geometrical isomers

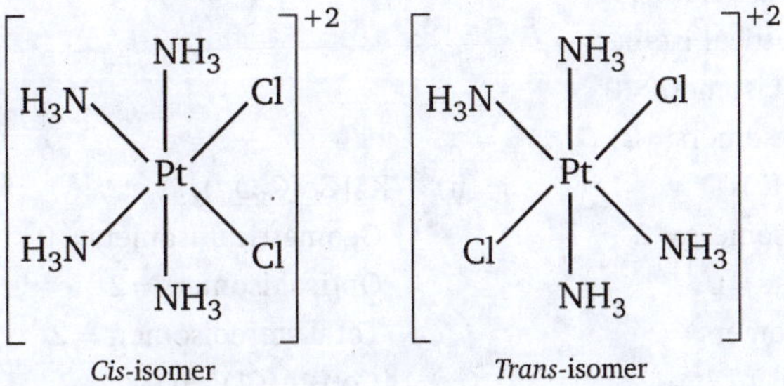

Cis-isomer *Trans*-isomer

169. (a) $[Co(H_2O)_3(NH_3)_2(NO_3)]Br_2 \rightarrow$ Cannot show linkage isomerism as it does not have ambidentate ligand.

170. (d) $[Cr(en)_3]^{3+}$ Geometrical isomer = 0, Optical isomers = 2

Total Stereo isomers = 2

171. (a) $[Co(NH_3)_4Br_2]Cl$: $[Ma_4b_2]^{\pm n}$

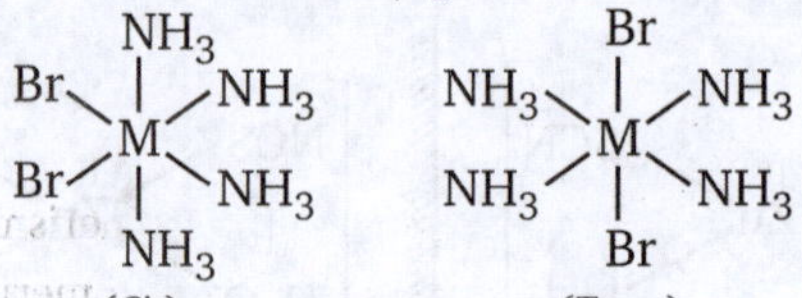

(Cis) (Trans)

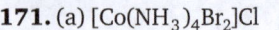

$[Co(NH_3)_4Br_2]\ Cl, [Co(NH_3)_4BrCl]\ Br$; Ionization Isomerism

172. (b) $[Cr(NH_3)_5(NO_2)][Zn(SCN)_4]$ cannot show optical isomerism.

$[Cr(NH_3)_5(NO_2)]^{+2} \Rightarrow [Ma_5b]^{\pm n}$

$[Zn(SCN)_4]^{-2} \Rightarrow [Ma_4]^{\pm n}$

173. (d) $[M(AA)_2]^{n\pm}$ does not show geometrical isomerism but can show optical isomerism.

174. (b) $[Cr(NO_2)_2(en)_2]^+, [Rh(SCN)(H_2O)(ox)_2]^{2-}$

Both exhibit linkage isomerism through NO_2 and ONO and SCN and NCS linkage respectively.

175. (a)

(a) $[Co(en)_2Cl_2]^+ \approx [M(AA)_2b_2]^{n\pm}$

Total structural isomers = 0

Total geometrical isomers = 2

Total optical isomers = 3

Total stereoisomers = 3

(b) $[Co(NH_3)_5Cl]^{2+} \approx [Ma_5b]^{\pm n}$

Total structural isomers = 0

Total geometrical isomers = 0

Total optical isomers = 0

Total stereoisomers = 0

(c) $[Ir(PR_3)H(CO)]^{2+} \approx [Ma_2bc]^{n\pm}$ (Square planer)

Total structural isomers = 0

Total geometrical isomers = 2

Total optical isomers = 0

Total stereoisomers = 2

(d) $[Ru(NH_3)_4Cl_2]^+ \approx [Ma_4b_2]^{\pm n}$

Total structural isomers = 0

Total geometrical isomers = 2

Total optical isomers = 0

Total stereoisomers = 2

176. (a) (i) $[Cr(NO_3)_3(NH_3)_3]$

Geometrical isomers = 2

Optical isomers = 0

Total stereoisomers = 2

(ii) $K_3[Co(C_2O_4)_3]$

Geometrical isomers = 0

Optical isomers = 2

Total stereoisomers = 2

(iii) $K_3[CoCl_2(C_2O_4)_2]$

Geometrical isomers = 2

Optical isomers = 3

Total stereoisomers = 3

(iv) $[Co(Br)(Cl)(en)_2]$

Geometrical isomers = 2

Optical isomers = 3

Total stereoisomers = 3

178. (b) $[Co(NH_3)_3(NO_2)_3]Cl_2$ complex exhibits geometrical isomerism (G.I.)
Geometrical isomers = 2 (1 *cis* + 1 *trans*)
Optical isomers = 0
Space isomers = 2
$[Co(NH_3)_5NO_2]Cl_2$ complex shows linkage and ionization isomerism.

179. (c) (a) Ionization isomerism (b) Co-ordination isomerism
(c) No isomerism (d) Linkage isomerism

180. (d)

	Complexes	No. of stereoisomers
(a)	$[Cd(gly)(H_2O)(NH_3)]^+$	2
(b)	$[PtBr_2(H_2O)_2]$	2
(c)	$[Cr(en)_3]^{3+}$	2
(d)	$[CoBr(NO_2)(en)_2]^+$	3

181. (d) (a) Square planar $[Pt(NH_3)_3Cl]Cl, Ma_3b$ does not show *cis trans* isomerism.
(b) $[Zn(NH_3)_2Cl_2]$, tetrahedral does not show *cis trans* isomerism.
(c) $K_3[Fe(C_2O_4)_3], M(AA)_3$ does not show *cis trans* isomerism.
(d) $Co(gly)_3$; $M(AB)_3$ show *cis trans* isomerism.

182. (b) $X = [Ni(en)(NH_3)_4]^{2+}$ neither G.I. nor OI
$Y = [Ni(en)_2(NH_3)_2]^{2+}$ G.I. as well as OI
$Z = [Ni(en)_3]^{2+}$ does not show G.I. while show OI

183. (b) When symmetrical bidentate ligand present in C.N. 4 it does not show SI.

184. (c) $[Co(ox)_3]^{3-}, [Zn(gly)_2]$: are diamagnetic
$[FeF_3(H_2O)_2(NH_3)]$: does not exhibit optical activity due to presence of plane of symmetry.
$[Ni(NH_3)_2(en)_2]^{2+}$: is paramagnetic and its *cis* form is optically active.

185. (d) $[Co(H_2O)Cl_3]$ do not show both geometrical and optical isomerism as it has plane of symmetry.

186. (d)

	Complexes	Hyd. of central metal cation	No. of stereoisomers
(a)	$[Cd(gly)(H_2O)(NH_3)]^+$	sp^3	2
(b)	$[PtBr_2(H_2O)_2]$	dsp^2	2
(c)	$[Cr (en)_3]^{3+}$	d^2sp^3	2
(d)	$[Co Br(NO_2)(en)_2]^+$	d^2sp^3	3

187. (b) $K_3[Cr(C_2O_4)_3] \Rightarrow [Cr(C_2O_4)_3]^{3-}$

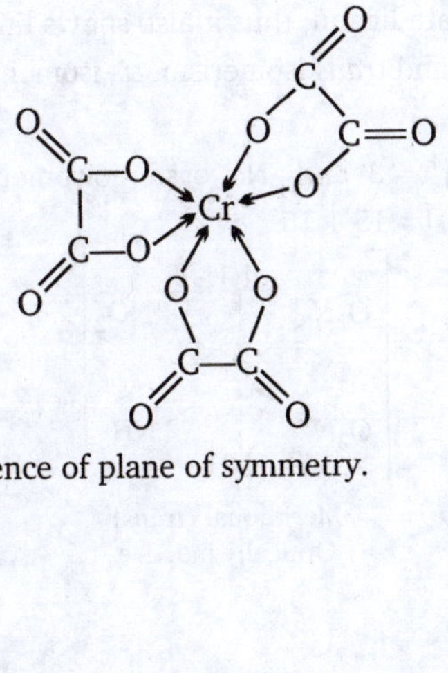

3 rings in different plane absence of plane of symmetry.
$\therefore$ optically active

188. (b) $Cd^{2+}(aq.) + 2\,en \xrightarrow{K_1} [Cd(en)_2]^{2+}$
Optically active ligand

$Cd^{2+}(aq.) + 2bn \xrightarrow{K_2} [Cd(bn)_2]^{2+}$
Optically active ligand

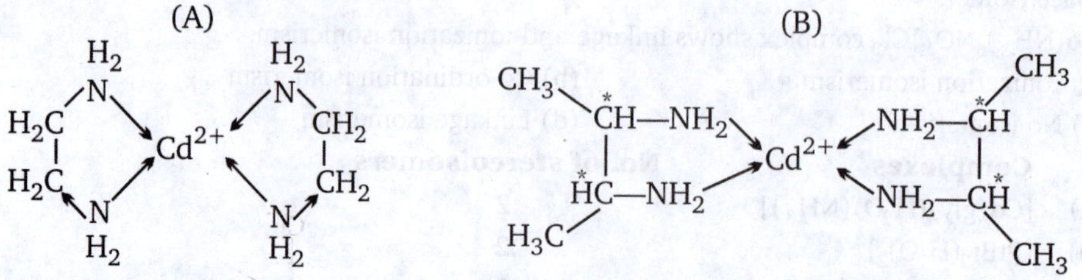

Symmetrical ligands (Optically inactive)   Symmetrical ligands (Optically active centre present)

190. (c) (a) $[Zn(bcac)(en)]^+$ Td geometry does not show O.I.
(b) $[PtBrCl(CN)(SCN)]^{2-}$ *sq.* planar does not show O.I.
(c) $[Ir(acac)_2(H_2O)(NH_3)]^+$ *cis* isomer will show O.I.
(d) $[CrCl_3(SCN)(H_2O)_2]^-$ does not show O.I.

191. (c) $a \rightarrow$ Cationic monodentate ligand
$b \rightarrow$ Neutral mondentate ligand
$c, e \rightarrow$ Anionic monodentate ligand
$d \rightarrow$ Ambidentate anionic ligand
[Mac]e shows ionization isomerism
$[Md_2]^-$ shows linkage isomerism
$[M(H_2O)a]c_2$ and $[Mac]c \cdot H_2O$ will show hydrate isomerism.

192. (c) $PtCl_4 \cdot 3NH_3 \longrightarrow [Pt(NH_3)_3Cl_3]Cl$
$PtCl_4 \cdot 6NH_3 \longrightarrow [Pt(NH_3)_6]Cl_4$
$PtCl_4 \cdot 2NH_3 \longrightarrow [Pt(NH_3)_2Cl_4]$
$PtCl_4 \cdot 4NH_3 \longrightarrow [Pt(NH_3)_4Cl_2]Cl_2$

193. (b) Ma_3b_3 is always optically in active.

194. (c) *cis*-$[M(AA)b_2c_2]$ is optically active as it do not have P.O.S. AA = symmetrical bidentate ligand.

195. (b) $Ni^{2+}(aq)$ with DMG (dimethylglyoxime) form square planar complex which is obtically inactive. While $[Co(EDTA)]^-$, $[Zn(gly)_2]^{2+}$ and $[Pt(en)_3]^{4+}$ are optically active as they do not have P.O.S.

196. (a) $[Co(en)_2(SCN)_2]^+$ has largest number of isomers. It shows *cis* and *trans* form and its *cis* form is optically active. Also SCN^- is ambidentate ligand, thus it also shows linkage isomerism.

197. (b) $[CrCl_2(OH)_2(NH_3)_2]$ show *cis* and *trans* isomerism, *cis* isomer is optically active.

200. (b) No. of geometrical isomers
$[Pt(NO_2)(NH_3)(NH_2OH)(Py)]^+ = 3$ and No. of stereoisomers for
$[Pt(Br)(Cl)(I)(NO_2)(NH_3)(Py)] = 15 + 15$

203. (b) (I)

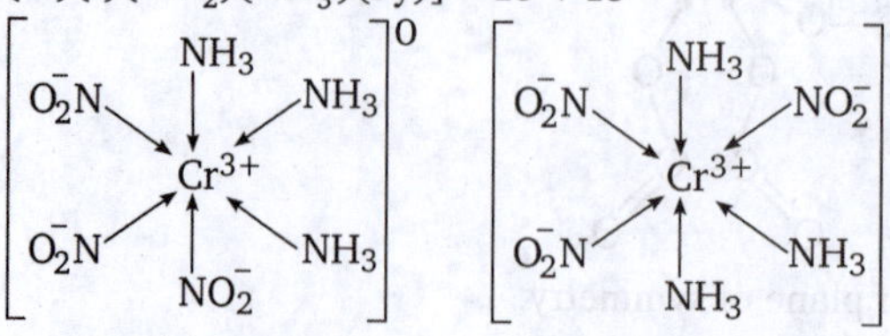

Facial (or *cis*) Optically inactive   Meridional (*trans*) Optically inactive

⇒ Two stereoisomers

(II) 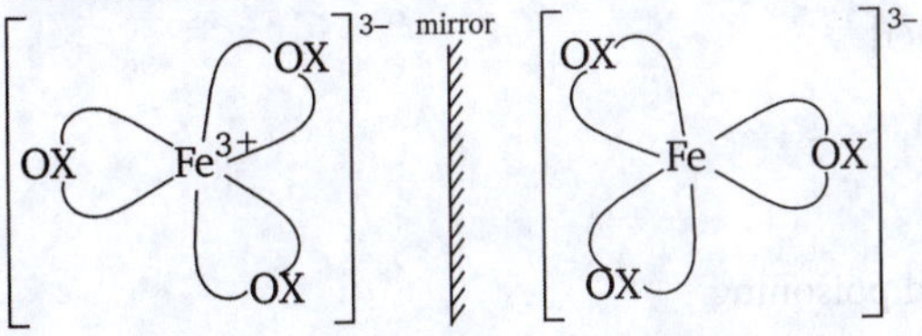

d-form *l*-form

⇒ Two stereoisomers

(III) 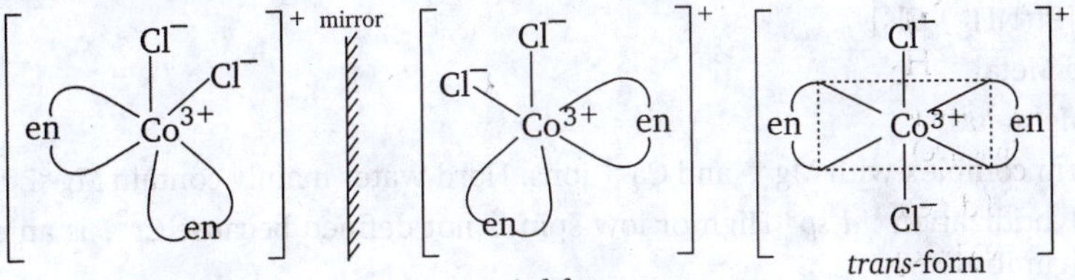

cis-d-form *cis-l*-form *trans*-form (*meso*-form)

⇒ Three stereoisomers

(IV) 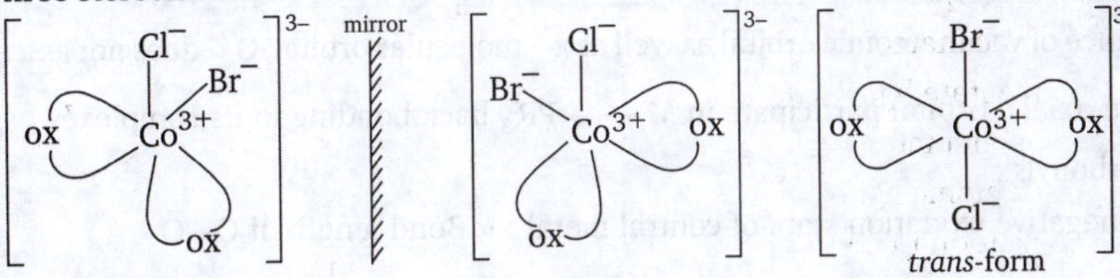

cis-d-form *cis-l*-form *trans*-form (*meso*-form)

⇒ Three stereoisomers

204. (b) II and III are geometrical isomers as II is *trans* while III is *cis* of the given complex.

205. (d) *Trans* complex is optically inactive.

211. (c) 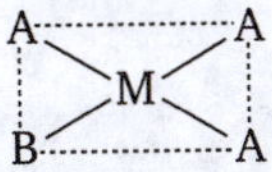

⇒ In this square planar complex, only one configuration is possible. Hence, geometrical isomerism is not observed.

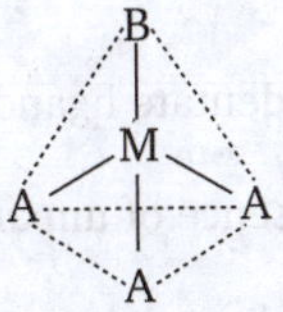

⇒ Tetrahedral complexes never show geometrical isomerism.

212. (a) (I) $[Pt(SCN)(3PEt_3)](SCN)$: Exhibits only linkage isomerism.

(II) $[CoBr(NH_3)_5]SO_4$: Exhibit only ionization isomerism.

(III) $[Fe(H_2O)_6]Cl_2$: Exhibits only hydrate isomerism.

213. (b) $[CoBr_3(H_2O)_3]$: It does not exhibit hydrate isomerism.

214. (b) $[Cr(H_2O)_4Cl_2]Cl \cdot 2H_2O$; hydrate isomer of complex $[Cr(H_2O)_6]Cl_3$ has lowest electrical conductivity, because it gives only two ions on ionisation in aqueous medium.

218. (b) (I) Mond's process for purification of Ni - $[Ni(CO)_4]$

(II) Removal of unreacted AgBr from photographic plate— $[Ag(S_2O_3)_2]^{3-}$

(III) Removal of lead poisoning from body—$[Pb(EDTA)]^{2-}$

219. (d) Haemoglobin contain metal Fe^{2+}

Sodium nitroprusside : $Na_2[Fe(CN)_5NO]$

cis platin : *cis* - $[Pt(NH_3)_2Cl_2]$

Vitamin B_{12} : Co Metal

Chlorophyll : Mg metal

221. (c) CaH_2 EDTA salt is used to remove lead poisoning

222. (d) Haemoglobin contain metal Fe^{2+}

Sodium nitroprusside : $Na_2[Fe(CN)_5NO]$

cis platin : *cis* - $[Pt(NH_3)_2Cl_2]$

Vitamin B_{12} : Co Metal

Chlorophyll : Mg metal

223. (b) $EDTA^{4-}$ can form complex with Mg^{2+} and Ca^{2+} ions. Hard water mainly contain Mg^{2+} and Ca^{2+} salt.

224. (d) $[Cr(CN)_6]^{3-}$: Hybridization : d^2sp^3 High or low spin is not defined because Cr^{3+} is an example of d^3 system of configuration.

Level 2

1. (d) Due to absence of vacant atomic orbital as well as π * molecular orbital, O_2^{2-} does not as π acid ligand.

2. (b) Vaccant non-axial *d*-orbital participate in $M \xrightarrow{\pi} PR_3$ back bonding in its complexes.

3. (a) In metal carbonyls :

Higher the negative oxidation state of central metal : $\propto$ Bond length of C—O

$$: \propto \frac{1}{\text{Bond order of CO}}$$

: Bond order of *M*—C bond

4. (b) In PR_3 there is vacant atomic *d*-orbital on P-atom, which can be involved in Synergic bonding.

5. (d) $$\text{CO bond order} \propto \frac{1}{\text{Extent of back bonding } (M \rightarrow CO)}$$

Correct sequence of CO bond order :

$$\underset{\text{(CO bond order > 3.0)}}{H_3B \leftarrow CO} > \underset{\text{B.O. = 3.0}}{CO} > \underset{\text{CO bond order <3.0}}{Fe(CO)_5} > \underset{\text{(CO bond order <3.0)}}{[Mn(CO)_5]^-}$$

6. (a) $[\overset{III}{Co}(NH_3)_4CO_3]^+ ClO_4^-$, CO_3^- is working as bidentate ligand, have coordination number of $\overset{III}{Co} = 6$.

8. (c) $[\overset{+1}{Mn}(CO)_4(NO^-)]$: Paramagnetic due to presence of unpaired e^-s in NO^-

$[\overset{-1}{Mn}(CO)_4(NO^+)]$: No unpaired e^- either on ligands or on $\overset{-1}{Mn}$ hence it is diamagnetic

9. (c) (I) $[(Ph_3P)_2PdCl_2PdCl_2]$; EAN of Pd $= 46 - 2 + 4 \times 2 = 52$

(II) [NiBrCl(en)]; EAN of Ni $= 28 - 2 + 8 = 34$

(III) $Na_4[Fe(CN)_5NOS]$;
EAN of Fe $= 26 - 2 + 5 \times 2 + 2 = 36$ [Kr]

(IV) $Cr(CO)_3(NO)_2$; EAN of
Cr $= 24 - 0 + 3 \times 2 + 3 \times 2 = 36$[Kr]

10. (d) Ligand NO is $3e^-$ donar hence three CO ligands can be substituted by two NO ligands.

11. (b) $Mn(CO)_6$ can act as reducing agent because the metal corbonyl is stable when EAN is equal to nearest noble gas configuration.

$$\underset{\substack{EAN = 37 \\ \text{(Less stable)}}}{[Mn(CO)_6]} \xrightarrow{-e^-} \underset{\substack{EAN = 36 \\ \text{(More stable)}}}{[Mn(CO)_6]^+}$$

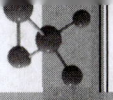

13. (c) Correct name of (a) : Tris(acetylacetonato)iron(III)
Correct name of (b) : Tetraammine dicyanoplatinum (IV)hexachloroplatinate(IV)
Correct name of (d) : Dichloro (ethylenediamine) platinum(II)

14. (d) The correct IUPAC name of complex compound is $[Cr(NH_3)_5(CN)]_3[Ir(NO_2)_6]_2$.
Pentaamminecyanidochromium(III)hexanitrito-N-irridate(III).

16. (d) $[\overset{II}{Mn}(CN)_6]^{4-}$: Hyb. : $d^2sp^3, \mu_{eff} = \sqrt{3}$ B.M.
$[\overset{III}{Fe}(NH_3)_6]^{3+}$: Hyb. : $d^2sp^3, \mu_{eff} = \sqrt{3}$ B.M.
$[Co(CO)_4]$: Hyb : $dsp^2, \mu_{eff} = \sqrt{3}$ B.M
$[Cu(H_2O)_6]^{2+}$: Hyb. : $sp^3d^2, \mu_{eff} = \sqrt{3}$ B.M

17. (c) $[RhCl(PPh_3)]^0$ or Wilkinson's catalyst have dsp^2 hybridisation of Rhodium.

20. (b) $C_2O_4^{2-}$ is a bidentate ligand, hence due to chelation Δ_0 is high, and $[Co(ox)_3]^{3-}$ is an inner-orbital complex having d^2sp^3-hybridization.

23. (b)

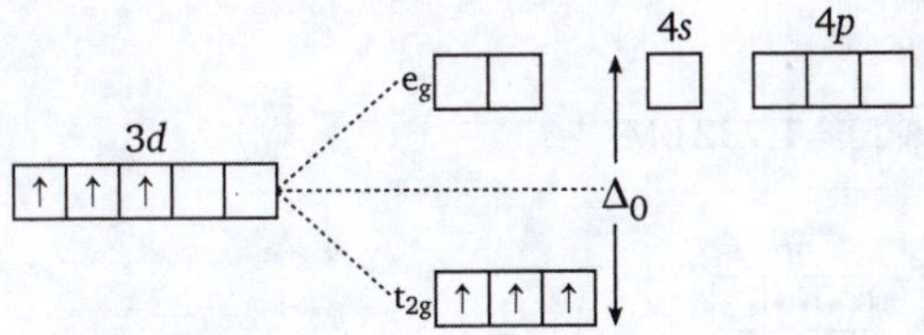

Hence, hybridization : d^2sp^3

24. (d) In $[Cu(NH_3)_4]^{2+}$, Cu^{2+} is dsp^2 hybridized, hence structure is square planar and complex is paramagnetic.

25. (d) $K_3[Co(ox)_3]$ is inner orbital complex with d^2sp^3-hybridisation.

26. (c)

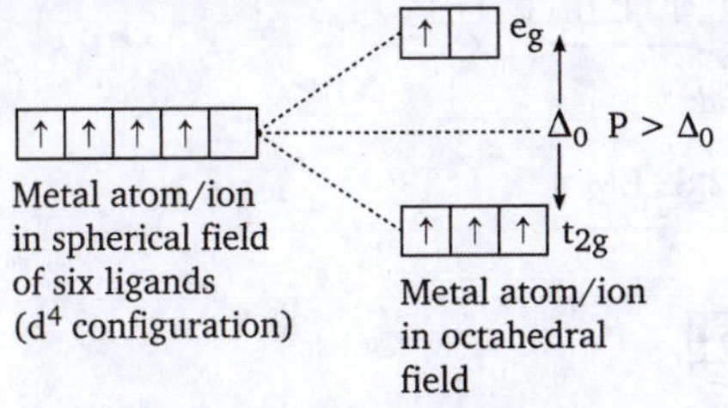

27. (c) $[Ni(CN)_4]^{4-}$; sp^3; Tetrahedral complex.

28. (d) (I) Both CO^{2+} and Co^{3+} are stabilized in the presence of strong field ligands due to higher CFSE values.
(II) Because of higher Z_{eff} value on the valence shell of Pd^{2+} and Pt^{2+} cations they, always from inner orbital complex.
(III) $[Ni(CO)_4]$; sp^3, tetrahedral, $\mu = 0$ BM
$[Ni(CN)_4]^{4-}$; sp^3, tetrahedral, $\mu = 0$ BM
(IV) Ni^{2+} in the octahedral field.

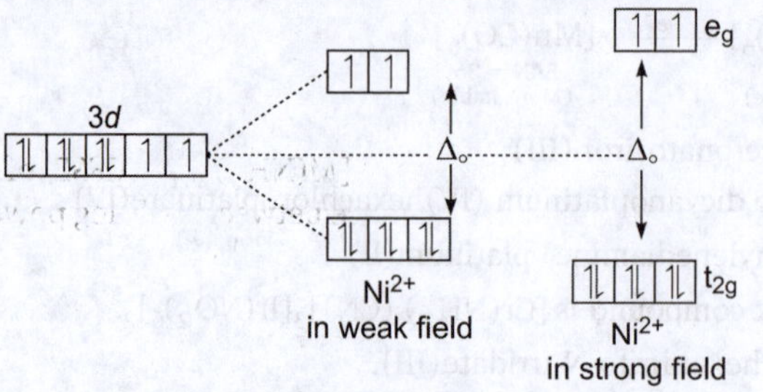

⇒ *i.e.*, electronic distribution remains unaffected.

29. (b) (I) Fe^{3+} in $[FeF_6]^{3-}$

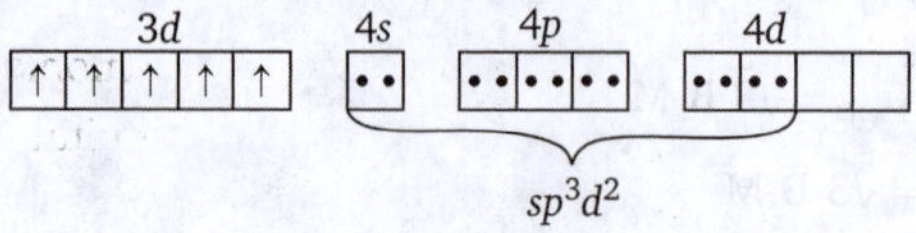

$$\mu = \sqrt{5(5+2)} = 5.93 \text{ BM}$$

(II) Ti^{3+} in $[Ti(H_2O)_6]^{3+}$

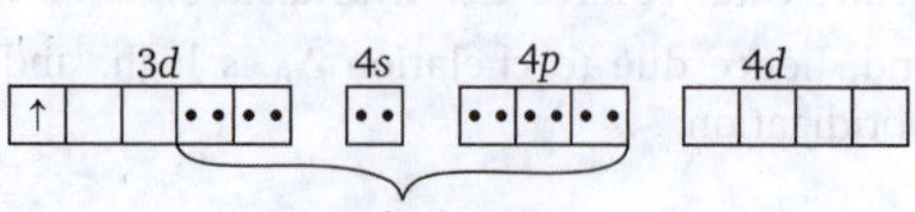

$$\mu = \sqrt{1(1+2)} = 1.732 \text{ BM}$$

(III) Cr^{3+} in $[Cr(NH_3)_6]^{3+}$

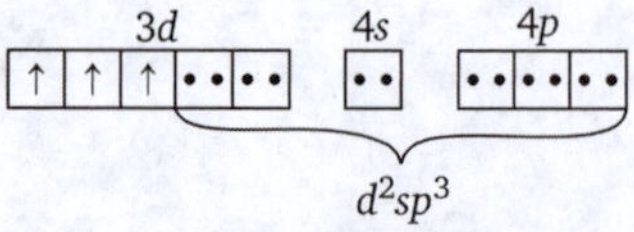

$$\mu = \sqrt{3(3+2)} = 3.88 \text{ BM}$$

(IV) Ni^{2+} in $[Ni(H_2O)_6]^{2+}$

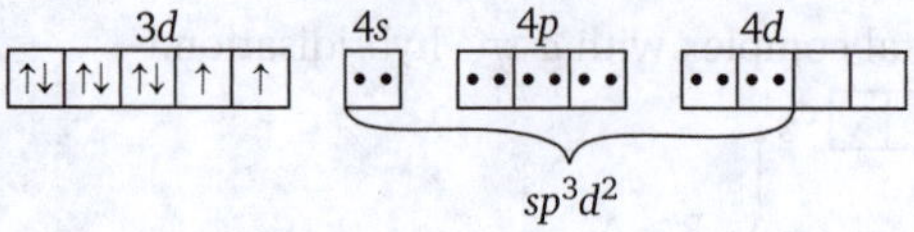

$$\mu = \sqrt{2(2+2)} = 2.83 \text{ BM}$$

(V) Fe^{2+} in $[Fe(CN)_6]^{4-}$

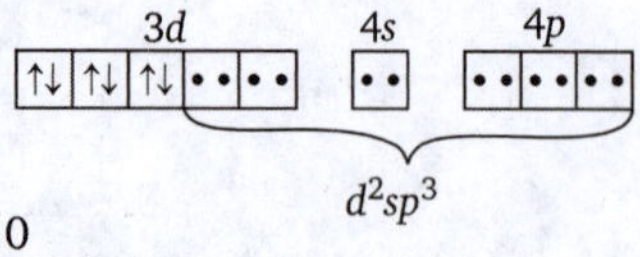

$\mu = 0$

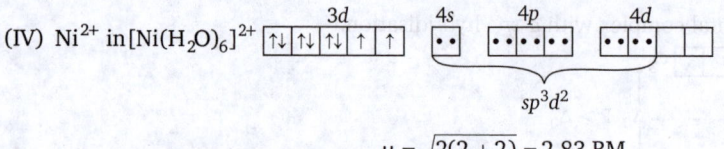

33. (b) Hybridisation of Mn in MnO_4^- : d^3s

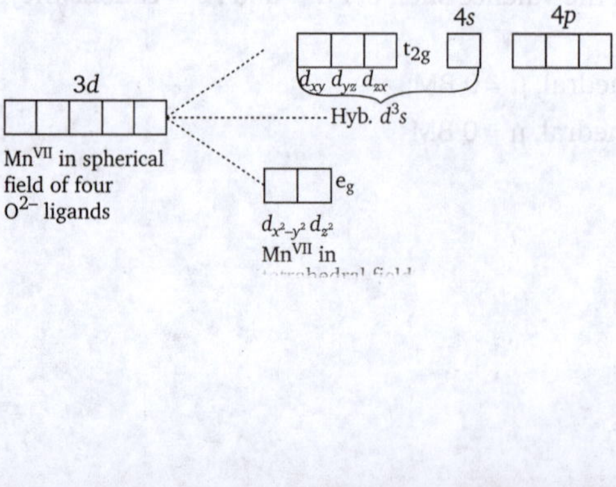

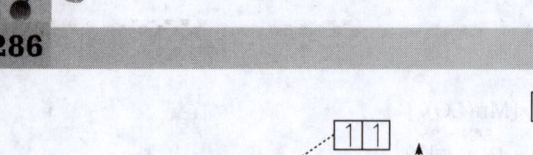

34. (c) $Fe^{2+}(aq) + NO + SO_4^{2-}(aq) \rightarrow [Fe(H_2O)_5(NO)]^{2+} + SO_4^{2-}$

$\mu_{eff} = 3.89$ BM

Hence, no. of unpaired electrons = 3

35. (b) As NH_3 is stronger ligand than H_2O, hence CFSE value for $[M(NH_3)_6]^{2+} >$ CFSE of $[M(H_2O)_6]^{2+}$ therefore, absorption shifts to smaller wavelength. Also difference between splitting power of NH_3 and H_2O is not very high.

37. (c) $\Delta_t = \frac{4}{9}\Delta_0$

$\therefore\ \Delta_t$ for $[CoCl_4]^{2-} = \frac{4}{9} \times 18000\ cm^{-1} = 8000\ cm^{-1}$

39. (c) $[CuCl_5]^{2-}$; sp^3d-hybridisation (outer orbital complex) (Magnetic moment = $\sqrt{3}$ B.M.)

$[Fe(NH_3)_6]^{3+}$, $[Mn(CN)_6]^{4-}$ and $[Co(NH_3)_6]^{2+}$ are inner orbital complexes and are also paramagnetic in nature having magnetic moment of $\sqrt{3}$ B.M.

40. (c) $[Ni(DMG)_2] < [Ni(en)_2]^{2+}$ is incorrect order of C.F.S.E. because stability of chelated complex is directly related to number of stable rings.

41. (c) Octahedral complexes having metal cation with d^3 and d^8 configuration can not be defined in terms of high and low spin complex.

42. (a) Peroxide ion is diamagnetic while dioxygen is paramagnetic.

Conc. H_2SO_4 can dehydrate water of crystallization from $[CrCl(H_2O)_5]Cl_2 \cdot H_2O$ but it can not remove those water molecules which are working as ligands.

43. (d) $[Co(en)_3][Cr(C_2O_4)_3]$, $[Co(C_2O_4)(en)_2][Cr(C_2O_4)_2(en)]$,

$[Cr(C_2O_4)(en)_2]$ $[Co(C_2O_4)_2(en)]$,

$[Cr(en)_3][Co(C_2O_4)_3]$, Total coordination isomers = 4

$[Cu(NH_3)_4][CuCl_4]$, $[CuCl(NH_3)_3][CuCl_3(NH_3)]$

Total coordination isomers = 2

$[Ni(en)_3][Co(NO_2)_6]$, $[Ni(NO_2)_2(en)_2][Co(NO_2)_4(en)]$,

$[Co(NO_2)_2(en)_2][Ni(NO_2)_4(en)]$, $[Co(en)_3][Ni(NO_2)_6]$

Total no. of coordination isomers = 4

44. (d) NO_3^- ion never acts as ambidentate ligand.

45. (b) Complex $[Cr(NO_2)(NH_3)_4][Zn(SCN)_4]$ can not shows optical activity.

47. (a) (i) $Pt(SCN)_2$

48. (d) $[PdCl_2(H_2O)_2(NH_3)_2]^{2+}$ $Pd^{4+} \rightarrow 4d^6 5s^0 5p^0$

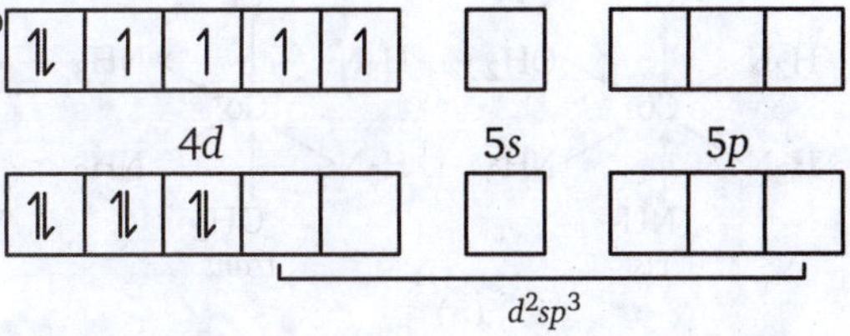

(a) m.m. = 0 B.M. (Diamagnetic)

(b) Low spin complex

(c) Show geometrical isomerism 5 geometrical isomer (1 *cis* + 4 *trans*)

(d) Ma_3b_3 type complex show fac and mer form and this complex is $Ma_2b_2c_2$ type, so does not show fac and mer form

53. (b)

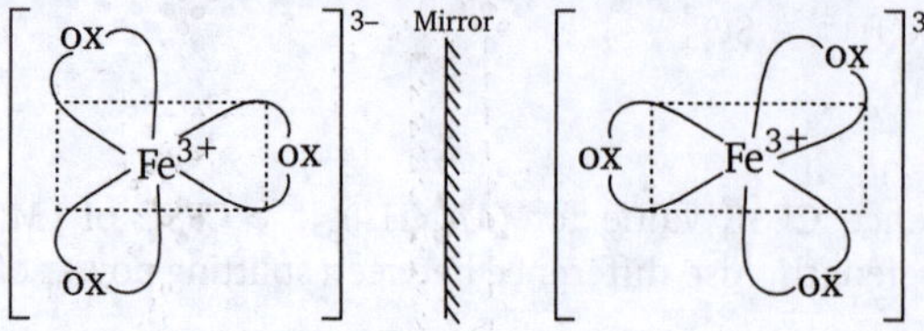

Above configuration is asymmetrical, hence optically active.

Mabcd square planar exhibits geometrical isomerism.

Mabcd tetrahedral complex is optically active.

54. (b)

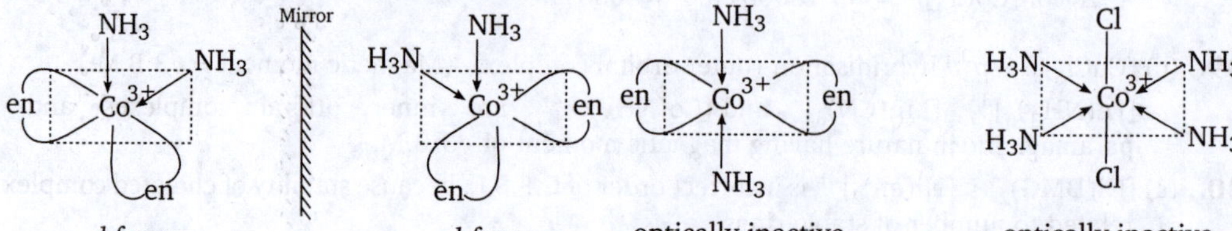

d-form *l*-form optically inactive optically inactive

55. (c)

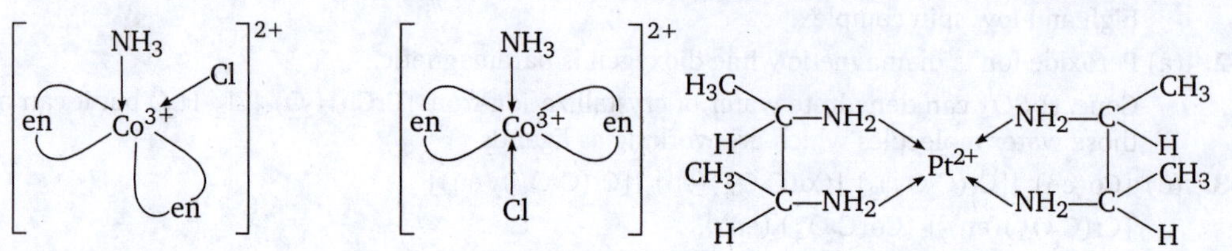

cis-form *trans*-form *cis*-form

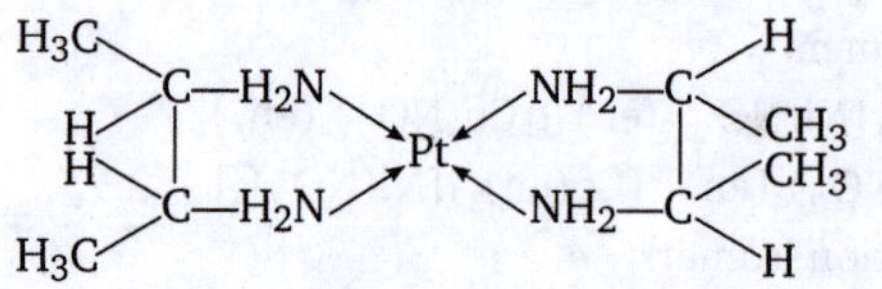

trans-form

56. (d)

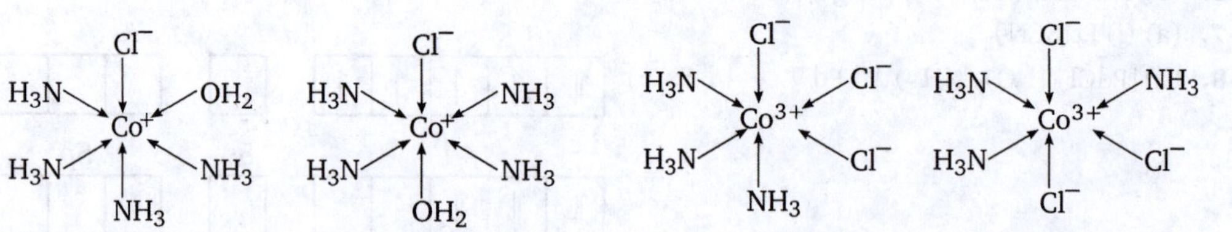

cis *trans* (a) *cis* *trans* (b)

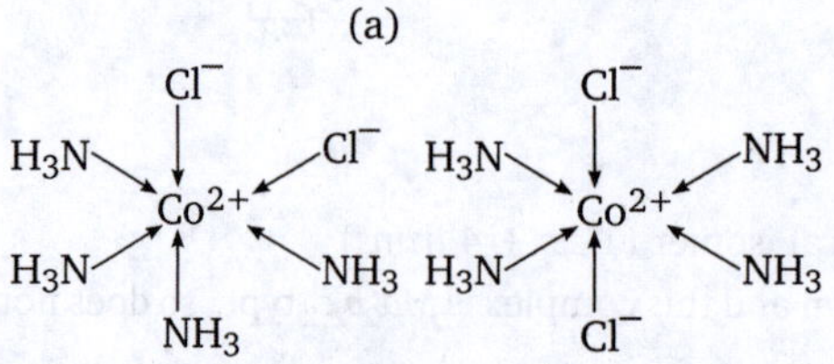

cis *trans*

(c)

57. (a)

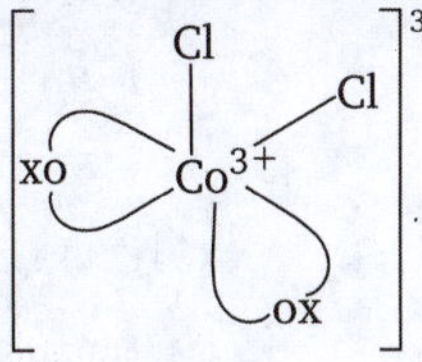

d-form

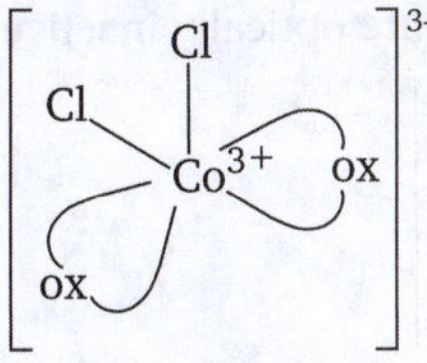

l-form

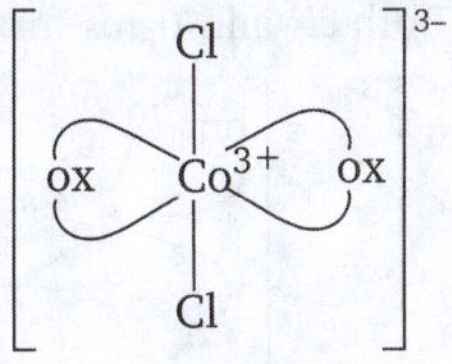

meso-form

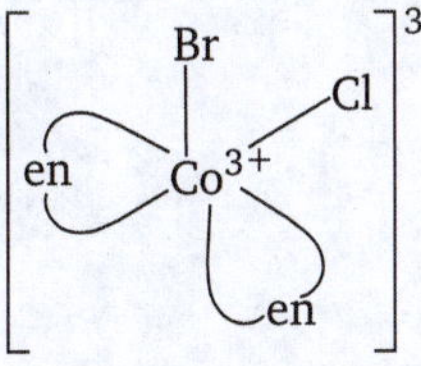

d-form

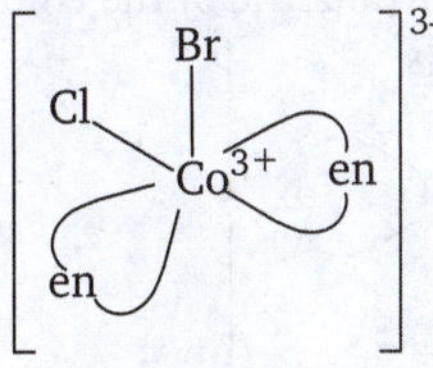

l-form

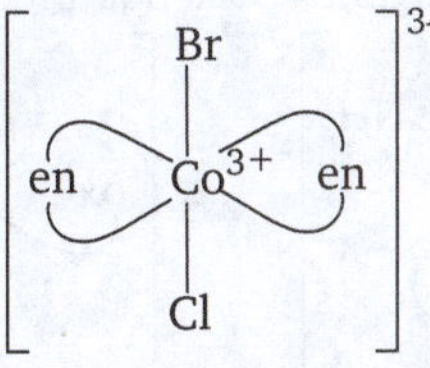

meso-form

58. (a) In tetrahedral all the position are adjacent to one another hence only one isomer is possible

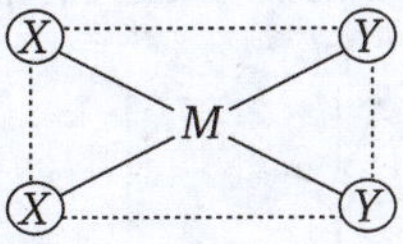

cis

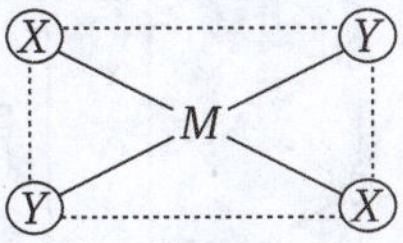

trans

⟶ Two isomers

59. (b)

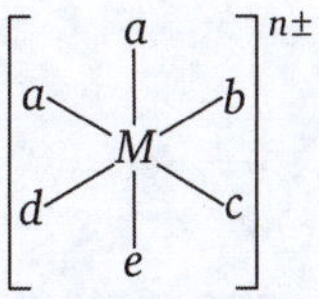
cis

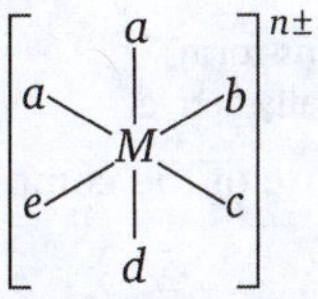
cis

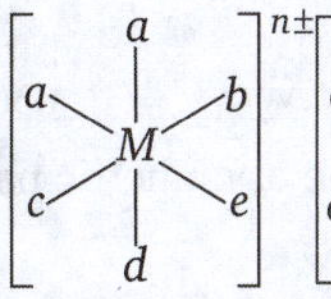
cis

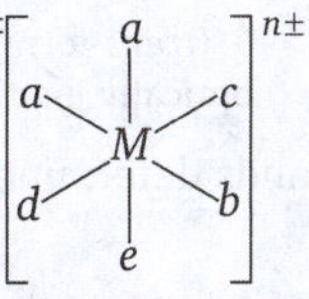
cis

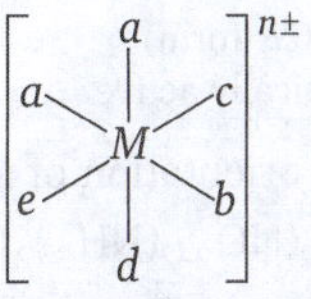
cis

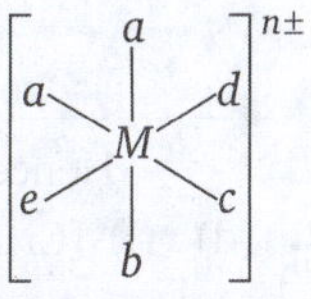
cis

No. of *cis*-isomers = 6

They are :

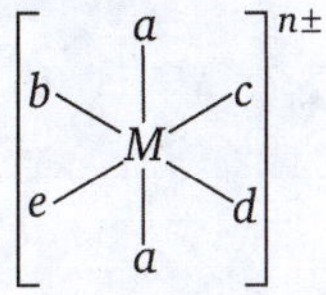
trans

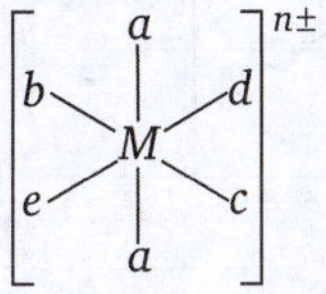
trans

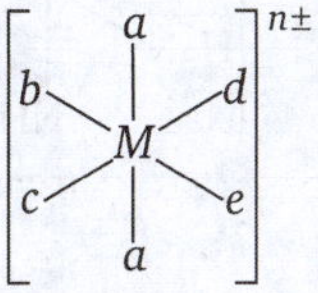
trans

No. of *trans*-isomers = 3

60. (b) $[NiCl_2(PMe_3)_2]$

Ni^{2+} in $[NiCl_2(PMe_3)_2]$

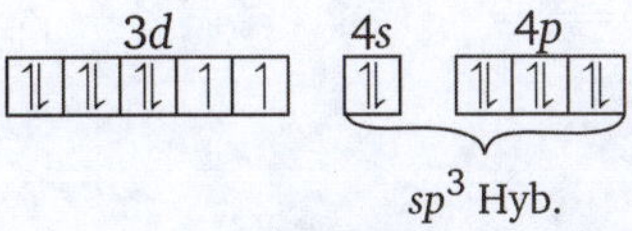

Structure : Tetrahedral

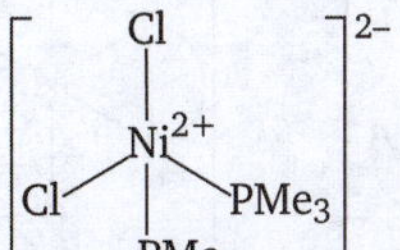

No isomer is possible.

61. (d) (i) $[CoCl_3(NH_3)_3]$: Both *cis* and *trans* forms are optically inactive

(ii)

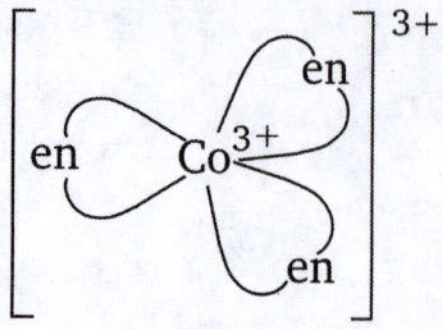

(*d*-form)

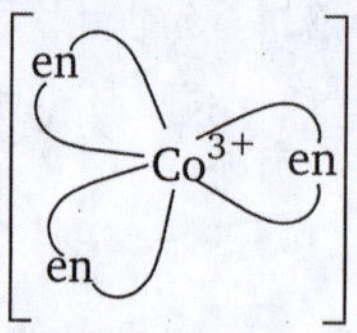

(*l*-form)

Orientation of the ligands does not affect asymmetric of the complex.

(iii)

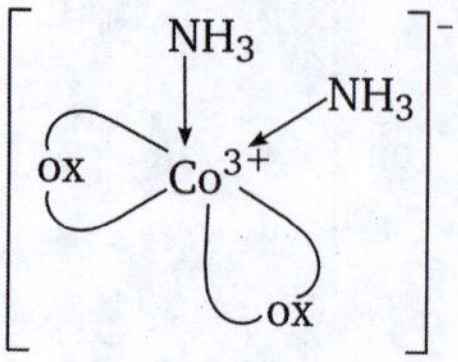

(*cis*-form)
optically active

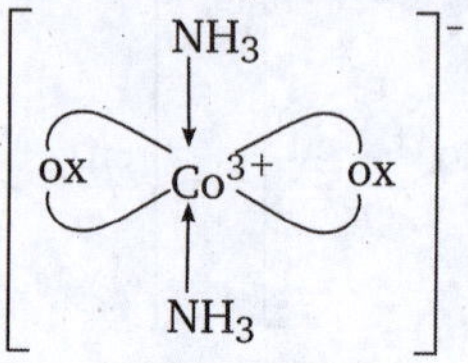

(*trans*-form)
optically inactive

Orientation of NH_3 molecules determine asymmetric character of the complex.

(iv)

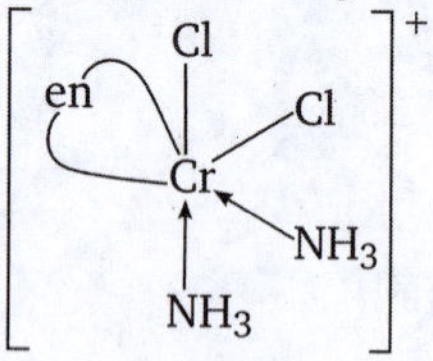

(*cis*-form)
optically active

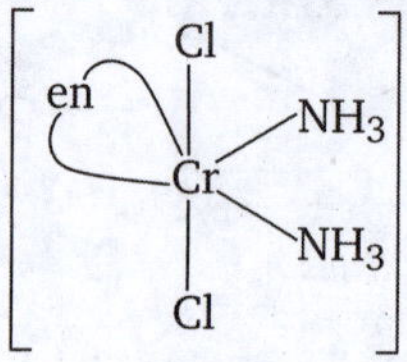

(*trans*-form)
optically inactive

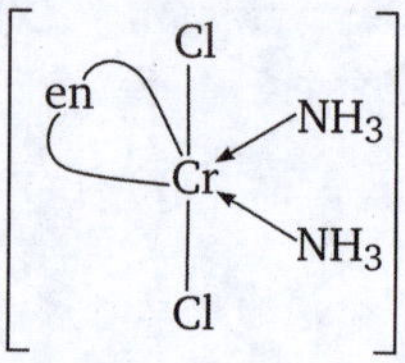

(*trans*-form)
optically active

Hence, orientation of ligands determine asymmetric nature of the complex.

62. (d) (I) $[CrCl_2(NO_2)_2(NH_3)_2]^-$

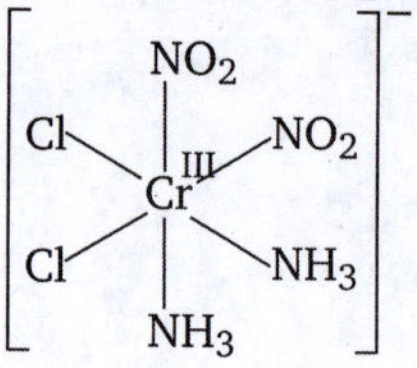

cis

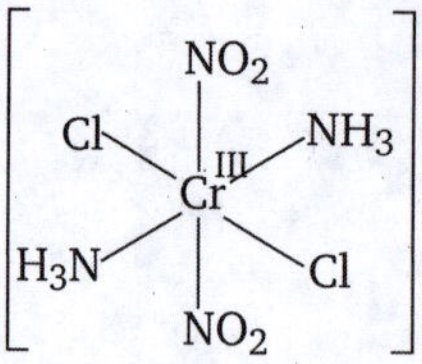

trans

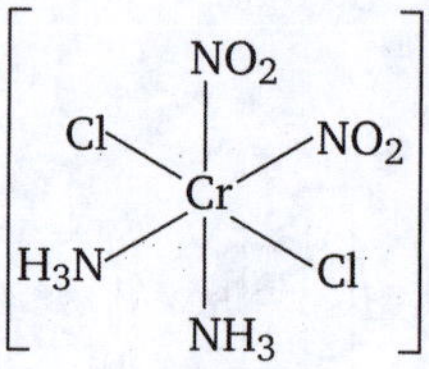

trans

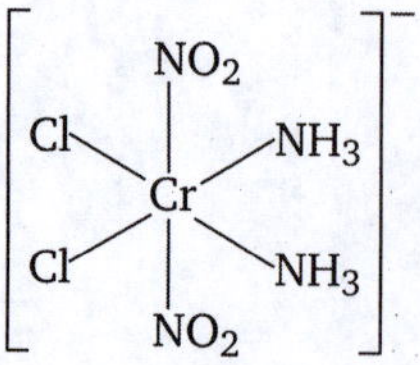

trans

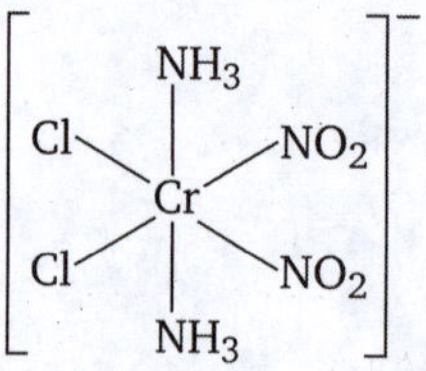

trans

⇒ No. of Geo. Iso.

63. (d)

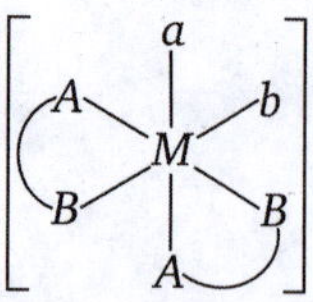

cis-form

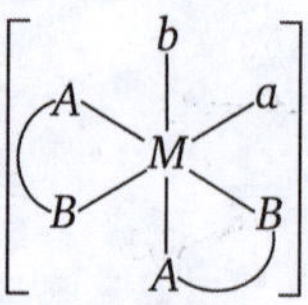

cis-form

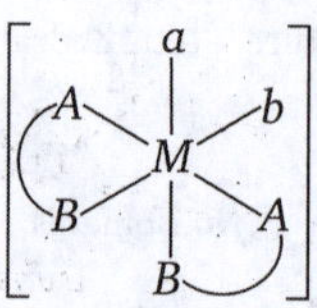

trans-form

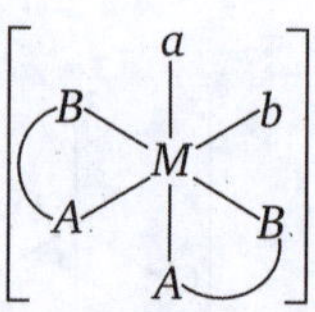

trans-form

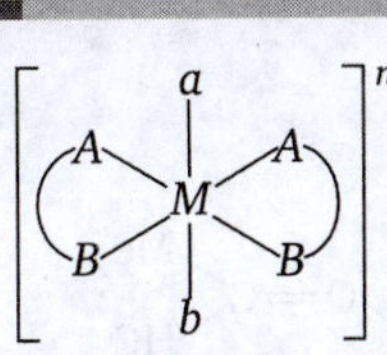

trans-form

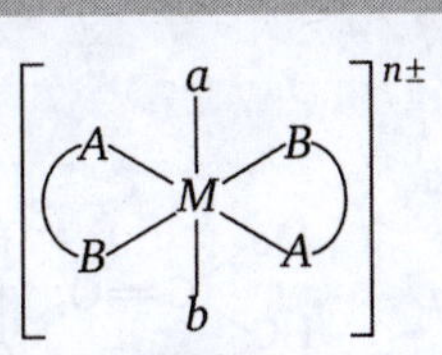

trans-form

64. (a)

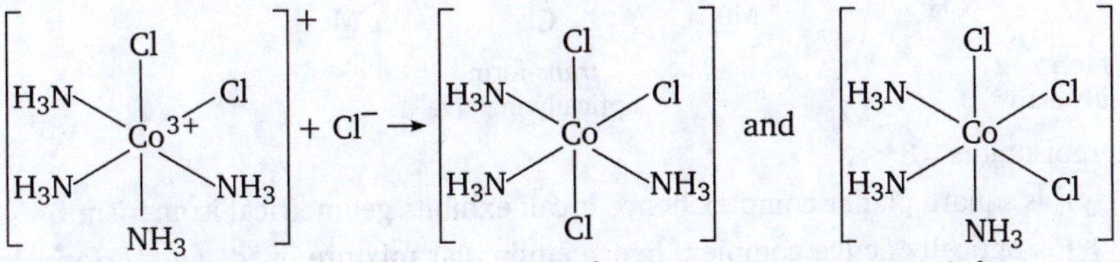

cis-form *trans*-form *cis*-form

65. (b) The complex does not contain any element of symmetry hence the configuration is asymmetric, therefore, it is optically active.

66. (d) (I)

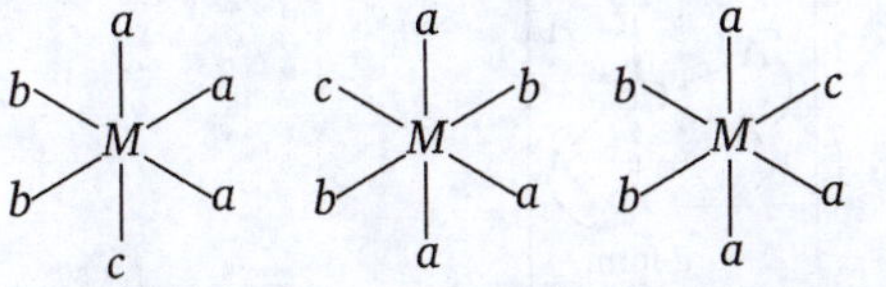

cis-form *trans*-form *trans*-form

⇒ All are optically inactive; No. of stereoisomers = 3

(II)

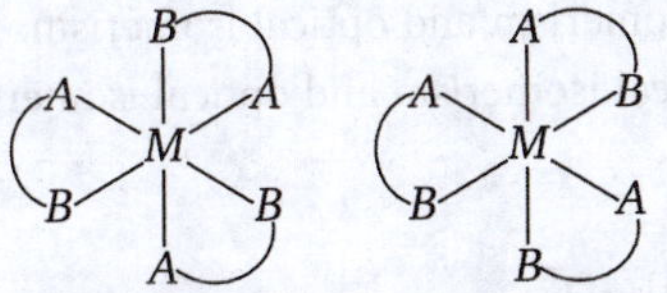

cis-form optically active *trans*-form optically active

⇒ Both are optically active; No. of stereoisomers = 4

(III)

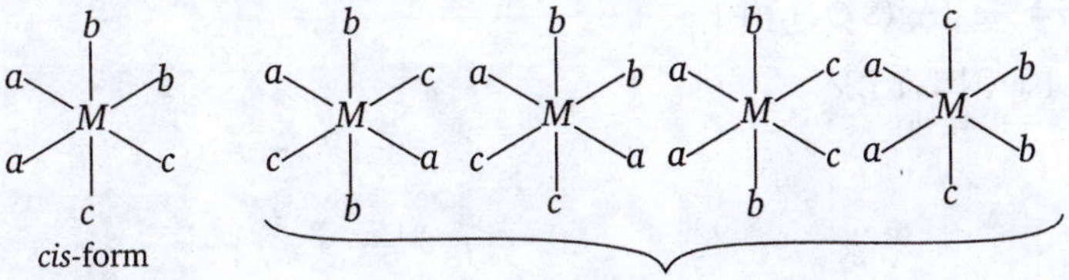

cis-form optically active

trans-form optically inactive

⇒ No. of stereoisomers = 6

67. (c)

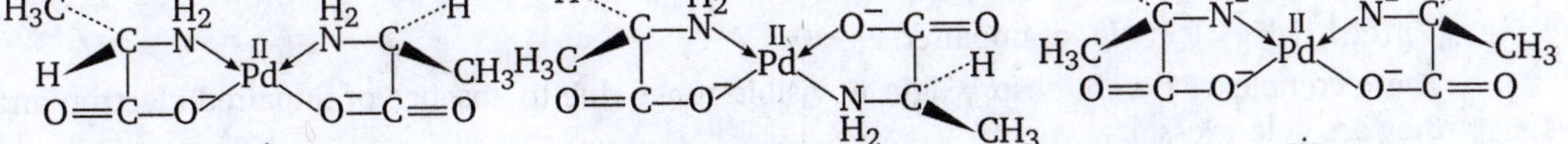

cis *trans* *cis*

68. (b)

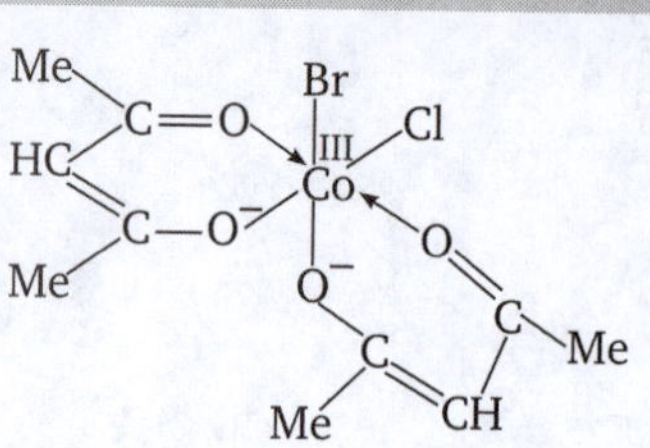

cis-form
optically active

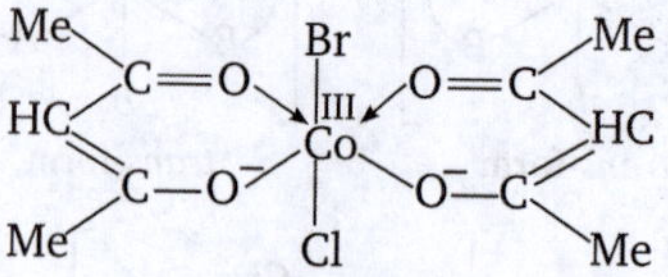

trans-form
optically inactive

∴ No. of stereoisomers = 3

69. (c) [Pd(Cl)(Br)(gly)] is square planer complex hence it can exhibits geometrical isomerism.

70. (a) *Trans* $[Co(gly)_3]$ is optically active complex, hence equimolar mixture of '*d*' and '*l*' form on mixing gives racemic mixture.

71. (c) Compound $[Co(en)_3]^{3+}$ can show optical isomerism.

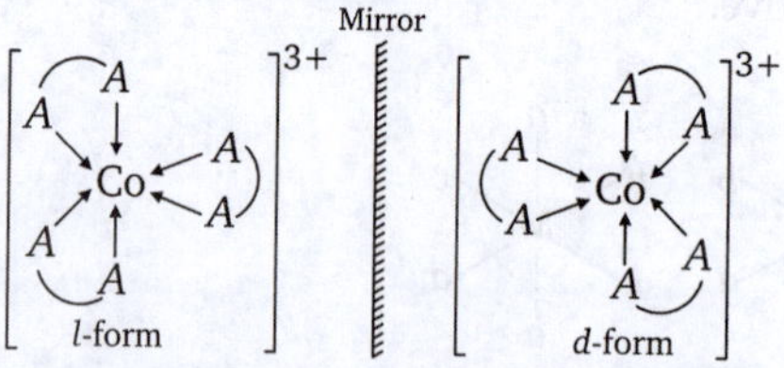

72. (d) $[Cr(en)_3]^{3+}$; Hyb. : d^2sp^3; does not exhibit geometrical isomerism but exhibits optical isomerism.

$[IrF_3(H_2O)_2(NH_3)]$; Hyb. : d^2sp^3; exhibits geometrical isomerism but does not exhibit optical isomerism.

$[NiCl_2(en)_2]$; Hyb. : sp^3d^2; exhibits both geometrical isomerism and optical isomerism.

$[Co(CN)_2(ox)_2]^{3-}$; Hyb. : d^2sp^3; exhibits both geometrical isomerism and optical isomerism.

73. (d) $\underset{\text{(Sod. nitroprusside)}}{Na_2[Fe(CN)_5NO]} + Na_2S \longrightarrow \underset{\text{(Purple)}}{Na_4[Fe(CN)_5(NOS)]}$

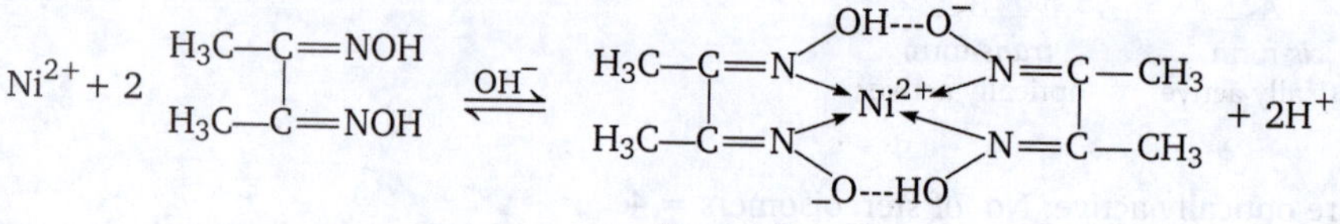

(Rosy red ppt.)

$Ag^+ + 2Na_2S_2O_3 \rightleftharpoons Na_3[Ag(S_2O_3)_2] + Na^+$

$Cu^{2+} + 4NH_3 \rightleftharpoons \underset{\text{(Deep blue)}}{[Cu(NH_3)_4]^{2+}}$

Level 3

Passage-3

1. (b) $[\overset{+IV}{Ti}(en)_3]^{4+}$: No. of unpaired $\bar{e}$s = 0

$[Sc(NH_3)_4(H_2O)_2]^{3+}$: No. of unpaired $\bar{e}$s = 0

$[Zn(en)_2(NH_3)_2]^{2+}$: No. of unpaired $\bar{e}$s = 0

These complexes do not absorb light in visible range due to absence of unpaired electron and hence they are colourless.

While, in complex $[Cr(H_2O)_6]^{3+}$ there are unpaired $\bar{e}$s and it is coloured due to absorption of light in visible range.

2. (a) From formula $CrCl_2Br \cdot 6H_2O$ following complexes can be derived
$[Cr(H_2O)_6]BrCl_2[CrBr(H_2O)_5]Cl_2 \cdot H_2O$
$[CrCl(H_2O)_5]BrCl \cdot H_2O[CrCl_2(H_2O)_4]Br \cdot 2H_2O$
$[CrBrCl(H_2O)_4]Cl \cdot 2H_2O$

3. (b) $[M(AA)_2b_2]^{n\pm}$: No. of space/stereoisomers = 3
$[Ma_3b_3]^{n\pm}$: No. of space/stereoisomers = 2
$[Ma_3bcd]^{n\pm}$: No. of space/stereoisomers = 5
$[Ma_2bcde]^{n\pm}$: No. of space/stereoisomers = 15

Passage-4

1. (c) $\overset{+III}{Sc}: 3d^{o}4s^{o}$, As *d*-orbitals at $\overset{+III}{Sc}$ are empty, hence, there is no synergic bonding in $[Sc(CO)_6]^{3+}$.

2. (a) No vacant '*d*' or π^* orbitals on 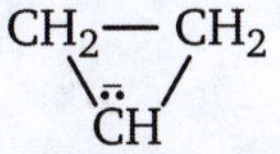

3. (d) Higher the positive oxidation state of metal, poor will be $M \xrightarrow{\pi} L$ hence $\overset{+1}{Mn}—C$ bond will longer among given complexes.

Passage-5

1. (c) $[CoBr(en)_2(H_2O)]Cl_2$: Its trans isomer is optically inactive.

2. (a) $[CoBr(en)_2(H_2O)]Cl_2$

Passage-6

1. (c) $K_4[Fe(CN)_6]$: Low spin complex : $P < \Delta_0$
$[PtCl_4]^{2-}$: Low spin complex : $P < \Delta_0$
$[CoF_6]^{3-}$: High spin complex : $P > \Delta_0$
$[Ni(NH_3)_6]^{2+}$: High spin or low spin not defined.

2. (a, c)

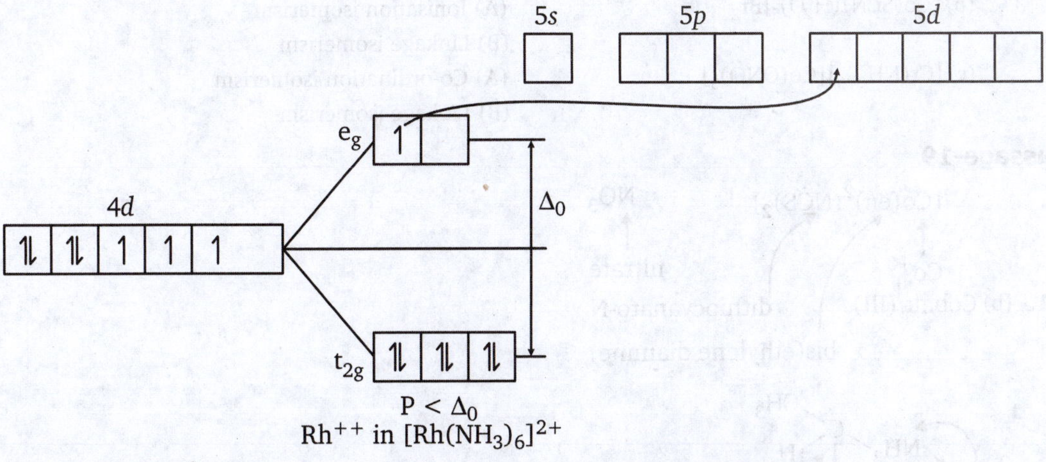

$P < \Delta_0$

Rh^{++} in $[Rh(NH_3)_6]^{2+}$

3. (a) In $[Mn(H_2O)_6]^{3+}$: Selection rule is followed due to unsymmetrical filling of e_g set of orbitals.

Passage-7

1. (a) dien is not π-acid ligend while PF_3, PCl_3, PEt_3 are π-acid ligands, therefore extent of $Mo \xrightarrow{\pi} CO$ back bonding in (dien) $Mo(CO)_3$ is maximum in order to disperse increased electron density at Mo; while in other complexes all ligands participate in $M \xrightarrow{\pi} L$ back bonding.

Extent of back bonding αMo—CO bond order $\propto \dfrac{1}{\text{stretching frequency of CO}}$

2. (b) As d_{xy} forms δ-bond in $Mn_2(CO)_{10}$

3. (d) As PEt_3 accepts $M \xrightarrow{\pi} L$ back bonding into non-axial d-orbital of phosphorus and it forms $M \xrightarrow{\pi} L$ bond using its non-bonding molecular orbital.

Passage-18

1. (b, d)

(b) $[IrF_6]^{3-}$, d^2sp^3 octahedral

Ir^{3+}, d^6, high nuclear charge on metal of lower transition series always forms low spin inner orbital complex irrespective of the nature of ligand.

(d) $[Ni(CN)_6]^{3-}$

Ni^{2+}, $3d^8$, SFL

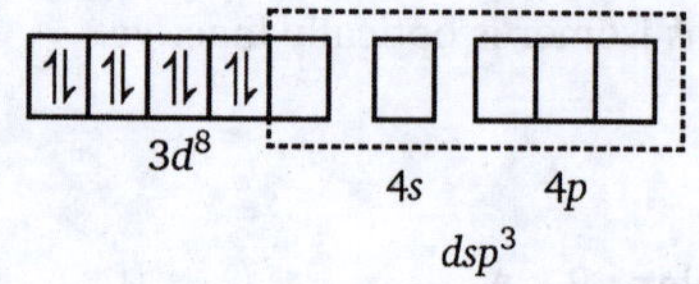

2. (a, b, c)

Complex	Isomerism
(a) $[PbBr(NO_2)(NH_3)_4](C_2O_4)$	(A) Ionization isomerism (B) Linkage isomerism
(b) $[Co(SCN)(H_2O)_5]Br_2$	(A) Ionisation isomerism (B) Linkage isomerism
(c) $[Cr(NH_3)_6][Co(ONO)_6]$	(A) Co-ordination isomerism (B) Linkage isomerism

Passage-19

1. (b)

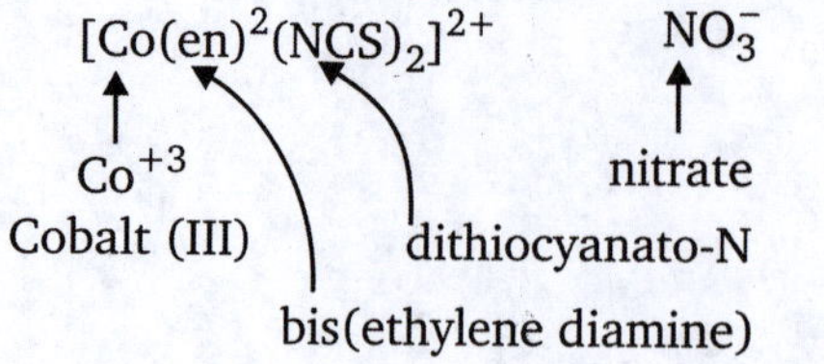

2. (b)

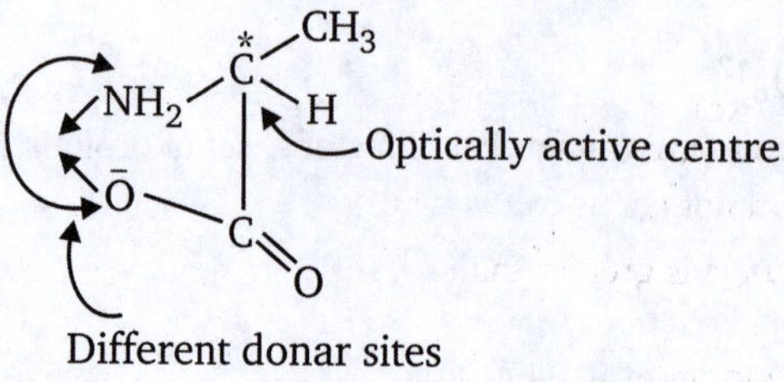

Passage-20

1. (d) Complex $X : [Co(NH_3)_5(ONO)]Cl_2$

$Y = [Co(NH_3)_5(NO_2)]Cl_2$

N is better (strong) doner than O, therefore complex Y absorbs at higher energy and gives yellow colour, where as complex X absorbs at lower energy and gives red colour.

2. (c) X, Y both show linkage and ionisation isomerism.

3. (a) Cobalt in (III) oxidation stable in both complexes.

d^6 configuration makes the complex diamagetic in the presence of strong field ligands.

Passage-21

1. (b)

Complexes	μ_{eff} (B.M.)
$[Ni(en)_2]^{2+}$	0
$[CoF_6]^{4-}$	3.89
$[HgI_4]^{2-}$	0
$[CuCl_5]^{3-}$	1.732

2. (d)

Complexes	Hybridization	μ_{eff} (in B.M.)
$[Fe(CN)_6]^{4-}$	d^2sp^3 (Inner orbital)	0
$[Cu(CN)_4]^{3-}$	sp^3	0
$[Ni(NH_3)_6]^{2+}$	sp^3d^2 (outer orbital)	2.8
$[Cu(NO_2)_5]^{3-}$	dsp^3 (Inner orbital)	1.732

Passage-22

1. (c) NO_3^- does not act as ambidentate ligand.

2. (b) $[Co(ox)_3]^{3-}$ exhibits optical activity due to absence of elements of symmetry.

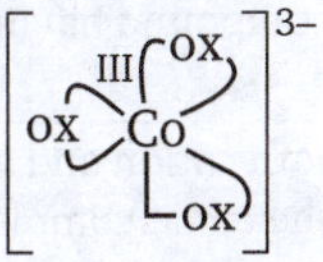

3. (a) Co^{3+} in $[Co(H_2O)_6]^{3+}$

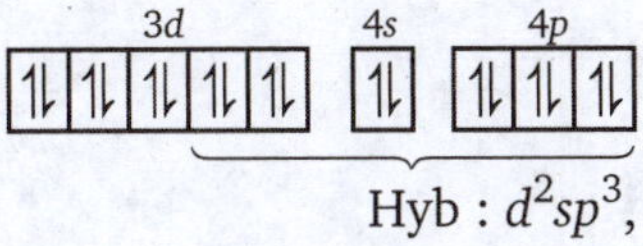

Hyb : d^2sp^3, $\mu_{eff} = 0$

Ni^{4+} in $[NiF_6]^{2-}$

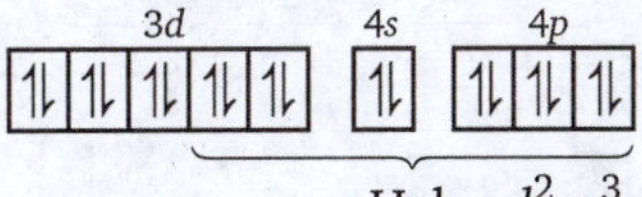

Hyb : d^2sp^3, $\mu_{eff} = 0$

ONE OR MORE ANSWERS IS/ARE CORRECT

5. (a,b,d)

$[Tc(CO)_6]^+$ E.A.N. of Tc = 43 – 1 + 6 × 2 = 54 (Xe)

$[Nb(CO)_6]^-$ E.A.N. of Nb = 41 + 1 + 6 × 2 = 54 (Xe)

Hence, both complexes are stable and they can not act as oxidizing or reducing agent.

Extent of $M \xrightarrow{\pi} CO$ back bonding in $[Nb(CO)_6]^-$ is greater than in $[Tc(CO)_6]^+$, hence

Bond order of Nb—C > bond order of Tc —C

Bond order of C—O in $[Tc(CO)_6]^+$ > C—O bond order in $[Nb(CO)_6]^-$

6. (a, b, c, d)

Given ligands accept $M \xrightarrow{\pi} L$ back bonding to disperse increased electron density at metal.

8. (a, b, d)

A : $[CoCl(NH_3)_5] \cdot BrCl$

B : $[CoBr(NH_3)_5] \cdot Cl_2$

C : $[CoBrCl(NH_3)_4] \cdot Cl$

9. (a, c)

$[PtBrCl(gly)]^-$ and $[Pd(NO_2)(ox)(gly)]$ exhibit geometrical isomerism.

10. (b)

$[Ru(en)_3]^{3+}$: Hyb. : d^2sp^3; does not exhibit geometrical isomerism but exhibits optical isomerism.

$[Co(H_2O)Cl_3]$: Hyb. : sp^3; does not exhibit both geometrical isomerism and optical isomerism.

$[PtBrCl(H_2O)NH_3]$: Hyb. : dsp^2; exhibit geometrical isomerism but does not exhibit optical isomerism.

$[FeBr_2(en)_2]^+$: Hyb. : d^2sp^3; exhibits both geometrical isomerism and optical isomerism.

17. (a,b,d)

F^-, Cl^- and OH^- are weak field ligands usually form high spin complexes.

CN^- and NO_2^- are strong field ligands usually form low spin complexes.

$[Ni(CO)_4]$ is low spin complex.

18. (b,c)

Irrespective of nature of ligand field, magnetic moment of octahedral complexes having metal ions in d^1, d^2, d^3, d^8, d^9 configuration, remains same.

Element may or may not form colourless complex.

19. (a, d)

Irrespective nature of ligand, complex compound having d^1 to d^3 configuration-inner orbital complex.

Irrespective nature of ligand, complex compound having d^8 to d^{10} configuration-outer orbital complex.

20. (a,d)

Coordination isomerism occurs when both cation and anion are complex, caused due to interchange of ligands between two complex ions of the same complex.

22. (b, d)

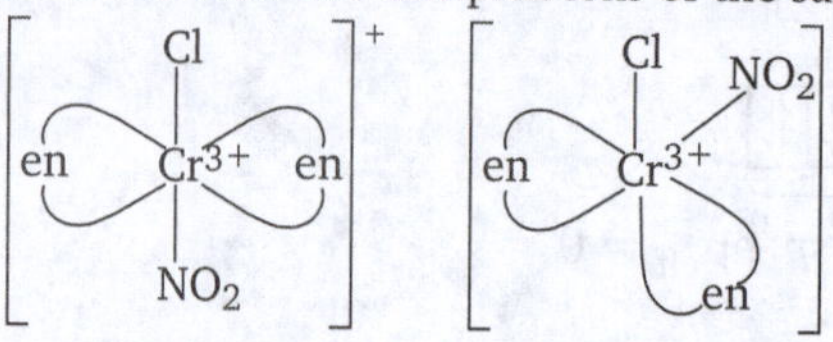

Trans-form (optically inactive) *cis*-form (optically active)

cis and *trans* are diastereomers to each other.

23. (a,b,c,d)

cis-$[CoBrCl(en)_2]^+$ will exhibit optical isomerism. No. of geometrical isomers of $[Pt(NO_2)(NH_3)(NH_2OH)py]^{3+}$ and space isomers for $[PtBrCl](NO_2)(NH_3)(py)$ are 30 *cis* and *trans* forms are diastereomers to each other.

24. (a, d)

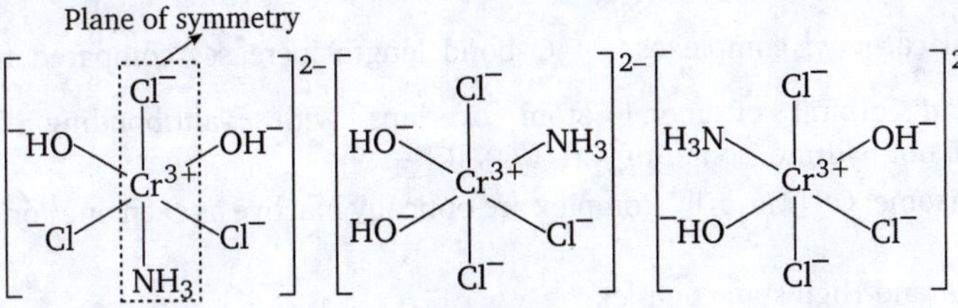

cis-form Optically inactive | *trans*-form Optically inactive | *trans*-form Optically inactive

Cr^{3+} in $[CrCl_3(OH)_2(NH_3)]^{2-}$

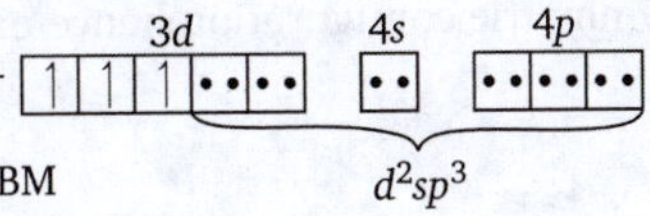

$\mu = 3.9$ BM

25. (b, c, d)

Formula of the complex $[Co^{III}(SCN_2)(NH_3)_4]_3[Co^{III}(ox)_3]$

Linkage isomerism is due to presence of SCN^-

Optical isomerism is exhibited due to presence of $[Co(ox)_3]^{3-}$ complex ion, which has asymmetric structure.

Geometrical isomerism is exhibited due to cationic part :

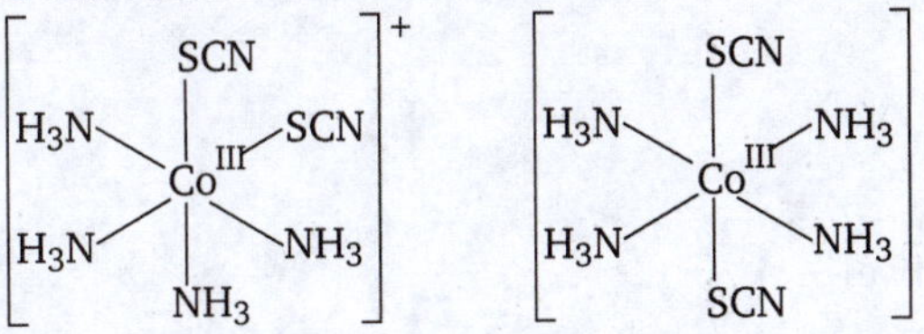

cis | *trans*

26. (a, c)

$[PtCl_2(NH_3)_4]^{2+}$ ⇒ both *cis* and *trans* forms are optically inactive

(b)

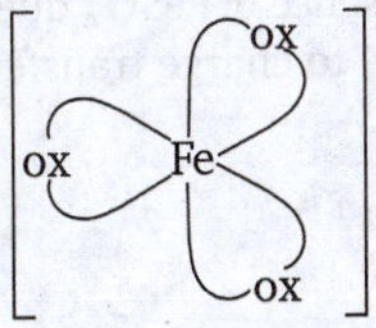

⇒ Due to asymmetrical configuration, it exhibits optical isomerism.

(c)

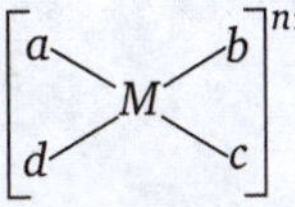

square planar

⇒ Due to plane of symmetry does not exhibit optical isomerism, but exhibits geometrical isomerism.

(d)

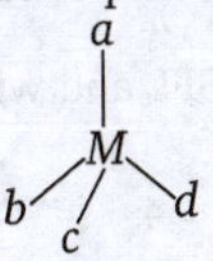

⇒ Tetrahedral complex, Asymmetric configuration, hence exhibits optical isomerisms.

27. (a, d) $M \underset{\sigma}{\overset{\pi}{\rightleftharpoons}} L$, In metal carbonyl complexes, C—O bond length increases compared to that in CO molecule as filled '*d*' orbital of metal atom overlaps with π-antibonding M.O. of CO
$[CrCl_3(H_2O)_3].3H_2O$ is not hydrate isomer of $[Cr(H_2O)_6]Cl_3$.
Facial and Meridional isomers of $[Ma_3b_3]^{n+}$ complex are optically inactive as each one contains plane of symmetry.

28. (a,b,d) $[CoF_6]^{3-}$: $\Delta_0 < P$ and High spin complex

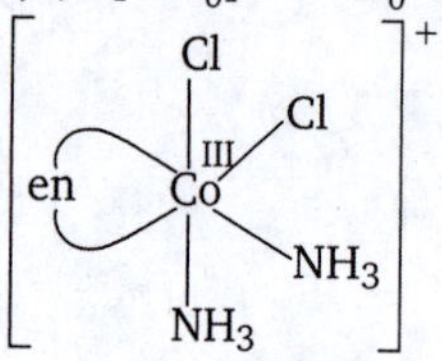

⇒ Asymmetric configuration hence exist in *d* and *l* forms

cis-form

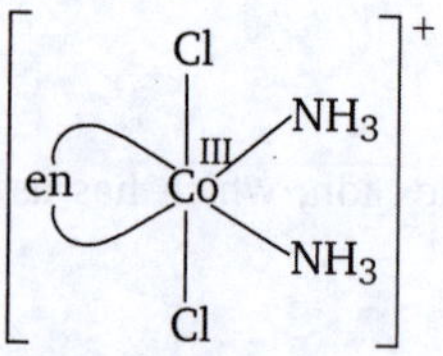

⇒ Optically inactive

trans-form

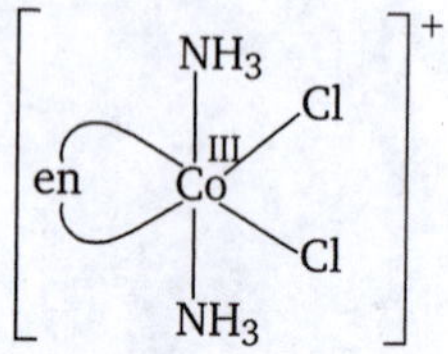

⇒ Optically inactive

trans-form

Total isomers = 4

30. (a,b,c) Nitrate ion gives a brown ring when reacts with conc. H_2SO_4 in presence of $FeSO_4$ due to formation of $[Fe(H_2O)_5NO]SO_4$ complex compound. Brown colour is just due to charge transfer spectra.

34. (b, c, d)
(b) Sodium hydridotrimethoxoborate(III)
(c) Bis (benzoyl acetaonate) beryllium(II)
(d) Tetrachloroauric(III)acid.

37. (a, b, c, d)
(a) $Fe^{+3}[Fe^{+3}(CN)_6]^{3-}$
(b) $Fe^{2+}[Fe^{2+}(CN)_6]^{4-}$
(c) $Fr^{2+}[Fe^{+3}(CN)_6]^{-3}$
(d) $Fe^{+3}[Fe^{2+}(CN)_6]^{4-}$

38. (a, b, c)
(a) (b) Pt^{+2}, Pd^{+2} and Au^{+3} form inner orbital complex (dsp^2 hyb.) with both SFL and with WFL when CN = 4.
(c) Ni^{+2} form inner orbital complex (dsp^2 hybridisation) with SFL when CN = 4.
(d) $Hg^{+2}(5d^{10})$ always form outer orbital complex with both SFL and WFL having sp^3 hybridisation and tetrahedral geometry with CN = 4.

39. (a, c, d)

$[Co(NO_2)(H_2O)_5]^{2+}$

$Co^{3+} = t_{2g}^6\, e_g^0\ \mu_{eff} = 0$ B.M.

$Co^{2+} = t_{2g}^5\, e_g^2 = \mu_{eff} = \sqrt{15}$ B.M.

Cis-$[PtCl_2(NH_3)_4]^{2+}$

Trans-$[PtCl_2(NH_3)_4]^{2+}$

Both are diamagnetic with $\mu = 0$ B.M.

$[Ni(CN)_4]^{2-}$	$\mu_{eff} = 0$ B.M.
$[Ni(NH_3)_6]^{2+}$	$\mu_{eff} = \sqrt{8}$ B.M.
$[Zn(NH_3)_4]^{2+}$	$\mu_{eff} = 0$ B.M.
$[Fe(NH_3)_6]^{2+}$	$\mu_{eff} = \sqrt{24}$ B.M.

41. (a, b, c, d)

	Complex	**no. of rings**
$x =$	$[Ni(en)(H_2O)_4]^{2+}$	1
$y =$	$[Ni(en)_2(H_2O)_2]^{2+}$	2
$z =$	$[Ni(en)_3]^{2+}$	3

Stability of complex $\propto$ number of chelate rings $\propto \Delta_{Absorbed} \propto \frac{1}{\lambda_{Absorbed}}$

All are paramagnetic outer orbital complexes and each having two unpaired electrons.

42. (a, c, d)

d-orbitals losses their degeneracy because of the formation of complexes.

(a) Blue vitrol —$CuSO_4 \cdot 5H_2O$

(c) Potassium ferrocyanide —$K_4[Fe(CN)_6]$

(d) Potassium ferricyanide —$K_3[Fe(CN)_6]$

43. (a, d)

Structural and geometrical isomers have different value of crystal field stabilization energy hence colour of these isomers vary.

44. (a, c, d)

$[Pd(PPh_3)_2(SCN)_2]^{2+}$

Hybr-dsp^2, square planer

— Shows linkage isomerism (presence of SCN^-, ambidentate ligand)

— Optically inactive (POS present)

— Shows Geometrical isomerism (*cis trans*)

— Shows Polymerisation. $[Pd(PPh_3)_4][Pd(SCN)_4]$

45. (b, d)

Complexes $[CoBr_3(H_2O)_2(NH_3)]$ and $[PtBrCl(H_2O)(NH_3)]$ exhibit geometrical isomerism but due to presence of plane of symmetry these geometrical isomers are optically inactive.

46. (a, b, c)

$[Cr(NH_3)_4(NO_2)_2]Cl$

Shows ionization isomerism $[Cr(NH_3)_4Cl(NO_2)]NO_2$

Shows linkage isomerism (ONO and NO_2)

Show GI (*cis/trans*). Ma_4b_2

MATCH THE COLUMN

2. $[Pt(NO_2)_2(en)]^{2+}$

→ E.A.N. = 78 – 4 + 12 = 86 ($_{86}Rn$)

→ Co-ordination number of Pt = 6

$[Cr(\pi\text{-}C_6H_6)(NO)_2]$

→ E.A.N. = 24 + 6 + 2 × 3 = 36 ($_{36}Kr$)

→ Synergic bonding is present hence, bond order of *M—L* bond > 1.0 and bond order of ligand decreases.

→ Co-ordination number for central metal not applicable.

$[Ir(SCN)(SO_4)(NH_3)_4]$

→ E.A.N = 77 – 3 + 12 = 86 ($_{86}Rn$)

→ SCN^-: Ambidentate ligand

→ Co-ordination number of central metal = 6

$[Cr(C_2H_4)(CO)_5]$

→ E.A.N. = 24 + 2 + 10 = 36 ($_{36}Kr$)

→ Synergic bonding is present hence, bond order of *M—L* bond > 1.0 and bond order of ligand decreases.

→ Co-ordination number of central metal = 6

3. (a) : $[Pt(acac)BrCl(H_2O)_2]NO_3$

⇒ *Cis* configurations = 2, both optically active; *Trans* configurations = 2, both optically inactive

⇒ Exhibits ionization isomerism

⇒ Total number of optical isomers = 6

Optically active isomers = 4

(b) : $[IrBr_2(en)(H_2O)(NH_3)]Br$:

⇒ *Cis* configurations = 2, both are optically active.

Trans configurations = 2, both are optically inactive.

⇒ Does not exhibit structural isomerism.

⇒ Total number of optical isomers = 6

Optically active isomers = 4

(c) : $[Cr(acac)Cl_2(H_2O)_2]$

⇒ *Cis* configuration = 1, which is optically active.

Trans configurations = 2, which are optically inactive.

⇒ Does not exhibit structural isomerism.

⇒ Total number of optical isomers = 4

Optically active isomers = 2

(d) : $[Pt(Ox)_2(NH_3)_2]$

⇒ *Cis* configuration = 1, which is optically active.

Trans configuration = 1, which is optically inactive.

⇒ Does not exhibit structural isomerism.

⇒ Total number of optical isomers = 3

Optically active isomers = 2.

7.

Complex	Oxidation state	Type	Magnetic property
$[Fe(CN)_6]^{4-}$	+2	d^2sp^3 (inner-orbital complex)	Diamagnetic
$[Fe(H_2O)_6]^{2+}$	+2	sp^3d^2 (outer-orbital complex)	Paramagnetic
$[Cu(NH_3)_6]^{2+}$	+2	sp^3d^2 (outer complex)	Paramagnetic
$[Ni(CN)_6]^{4-}$	+2	sp^3d^2 (outer complex)	Diamagnetic

8. (A) R, S

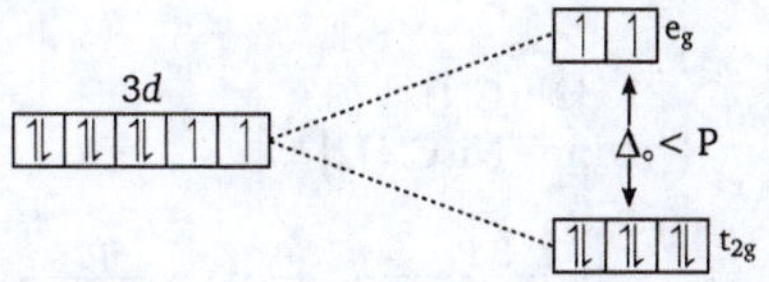

Ni^{2+} in
Octahedral field

$\mu = 2.8$ BM, Hyb. : sp^3d^2

(B) P, Q

$[Co(CN)_2(NH_3)_4]OC_2H_5$

Its ionization isomer $[Co(CN)(OC_2H_5)(NH_3)_4]CN$

Co^{3+}in$[Co(CN)_2(NH_3)_4]$

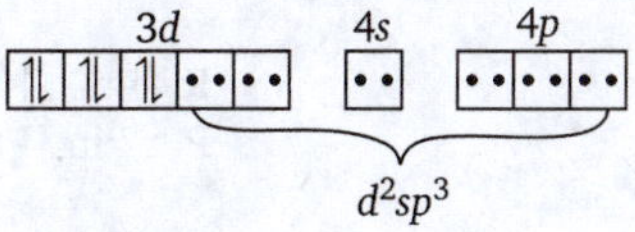

, $\mu = 0$

(C) P

$[IrCl_6]^{3-}$ Ir^{3+}in$[IrCl_6]^{3-}$

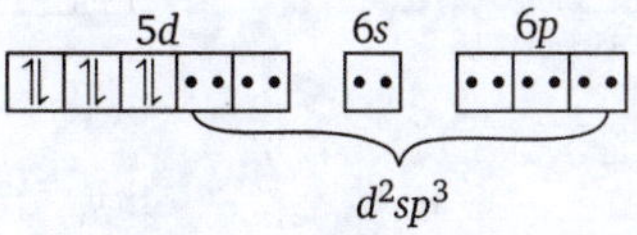

, $\mu = 0$

(D) P, Q

$[PtCl_2(NH_3)_4]Br_2$, d^2sp^3, octahedral , $\mu = 0$

There are two ionisation isomers : $[PtBrCl(NH_3)_4]BrCl$, $[PtBr_2(NH_3)_4]Cl_2$

10. Sodium nitroprusside—$Na_2[Fe(CN)_5NO]$

Hyb^n — d^2sp^3; $\mu = 0$; octahedral, NO^+ ligand

Brown ring $[\overset{+1}{Fe}(H_2O)_5NO]^{2+}$

Hyb^n.—sp^3d^2; octahedral, $m = 3.89$ BM, NO^+ ligand

Complex formed during extraction of Ag is $[Ag(CN)_2]^-$

Hyb^n—sp; linear, $\mu = 0$

Potassium ferrocyanide—$K_4[Fe(CN)_6]$

Hyb^n—d^2sp^3; octahedral, $\mu = 0$

11. (A) $[Ni(CO)_4]$

Ni in $[NI(CO)_4]$

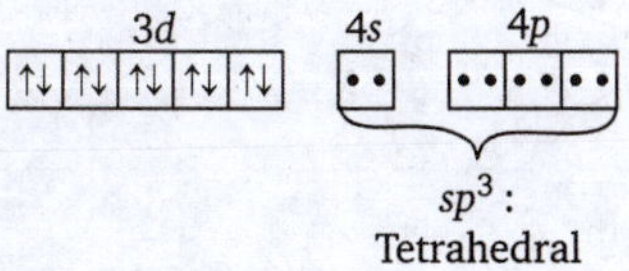

$\mu = 0$

EAN = 28 − 0 + 4 × 2 = 36

$K_2[Ni(CN)_4]$

Ni^{2+} in $[Ni(CN)_4]^{2-}$

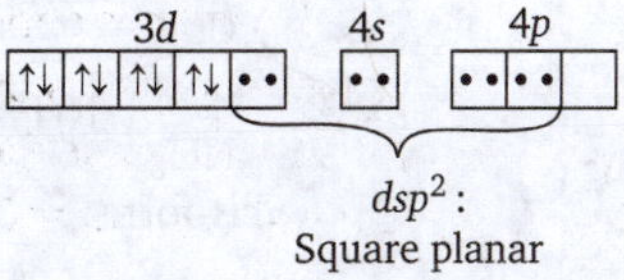

$\mu = 0$

EAN = 28 − 2 + 4 × 2 = 34

(B) $[Cu(NH_3)_4]SO_4$

Cu^{2+} in $[Cu(NH_3)_4]^{2+}$

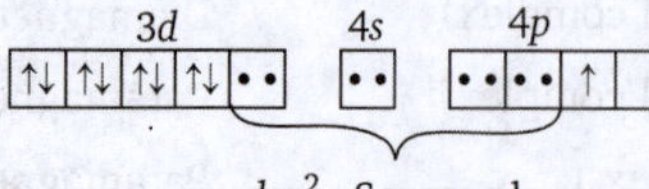

dsp^2 : Square planar

$\mu = 1.732$ BM

EAN = 29 − 2 + 4 × 2 = 35

$K_3[Cu(CN)_4]$

Cu^+ in $[Cu(CN)_4]^{3-}$

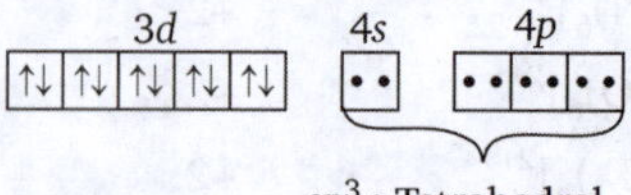

sp^3 : Tetrahedral

$\mu = 0$

EAN = 29 − 1 + 4 × 2 = 36

(C) $K_2[NiCl_4]$

Ni^{2+} in $[NiCl_4]^{2-}$

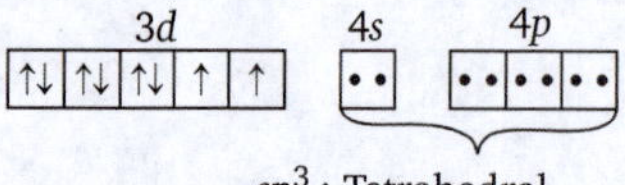

sp^3 : Tetrahedral

$\mu = 2.8$ BM

EAN = 28 − 2 + 4 × 2 = 34

$K_4[Ni(CN)_4]$

Ni in $[Ni(CN)_4]^{4-}$

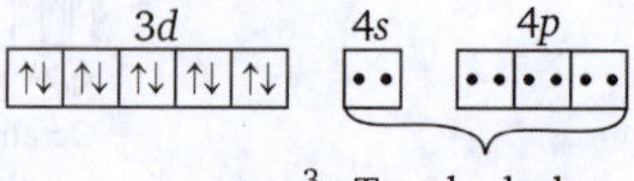

sp^3 : Tetrahedral

$\mu = 0$

EAN = 28 − 0 + 4 × 2 = 36

(D) $K_2[NiCl_4]$

Ni^{2+} in $[NiCl_4]^{2-}$

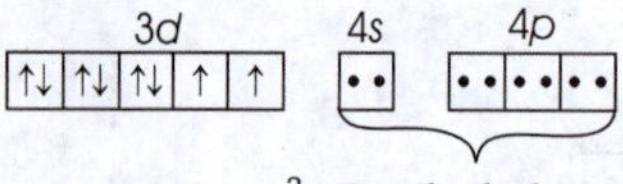

sp^3 : Tetrahedral

$\mu_{eff} = 2.8$ BM

EAN = 28 − 2 + 4 × 2 = 34

$K_2[PtCl_4]^{2-}$

Pt^{2+} in $[PtCl_4]^{2-}$

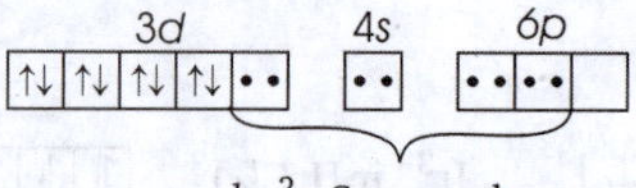

dsp^2 : Square planar

$\mu_{eff} = 0$

EAN = 78 − 2 + 4 × 2 = 84

13. (A) SCN^- is ambidentate ligand, therefore it shows linkage isomerism

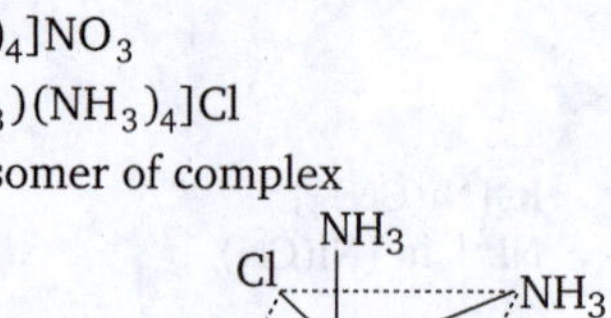

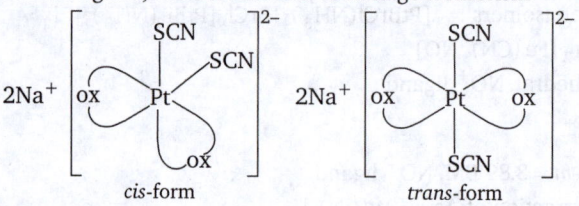

cis-form

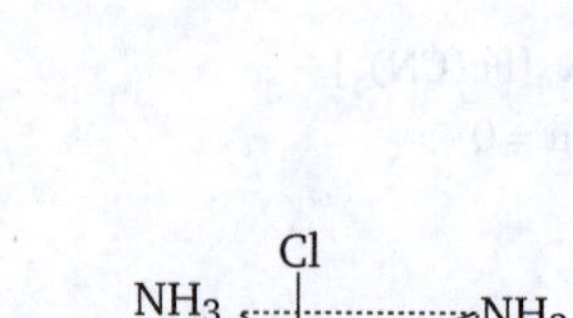

trans-form

cis-form is optically active.

(B) $[CrCl_2(NH_3)_4]NO_3$

$[Cr(Cl)(NO_3)(NH_3)_4]Cl$

Ionization isomer of complex

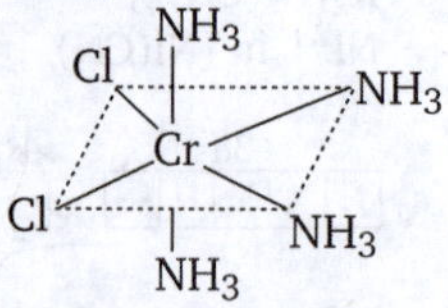

cis-form

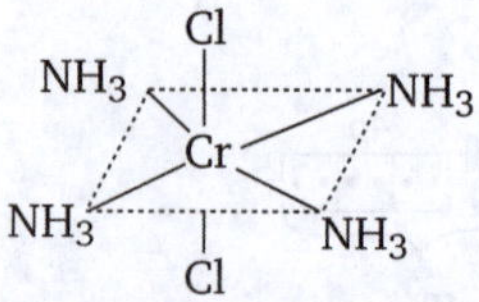

trans-form

Both *cis* and *trans*-form are optically inactive.

(C) 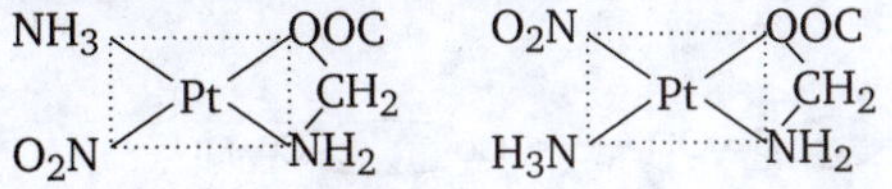

NO_2^- is ambidentate ligand so it also shows linakge isomerism. It is optically inactive square planar complex.

(D) $K_3[Fe(OH)_2(C_2O_4)_2]$

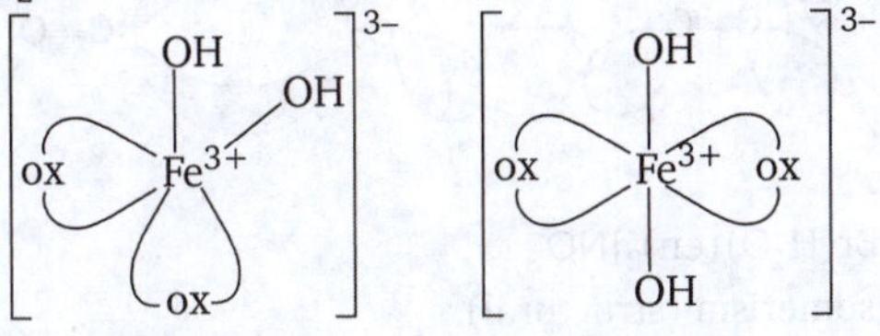

cis-form
Optically active

trans-form
Optically active

14. (A) $K_3[Fe(CN)_5(CO)]$

→ Due to +2 oxidation state of Fe extent of $d\pi(Fe^{II}) \longrightarrow \pi^*$ (CO) is poor, hence C—O bond length is not increased considerably as in $[Co(CO)_4]^-$ and $[V(CO)_6]$

→ EAN of Fe = 26 – 2 + 5 × 2 + 2 = 36 (Kr)

$\overset{II}{Fe} \underset{\sigma}{\overset{\pi}{\rightleftharpoons}} CO$, hence synergic bonding is present.

(B) $K[PtCl_3(CH_2{=}CH_2)]$

EAN of Pt = 78 – 2 + 3 × 2 + 2 = 84, (At. no. of Rn = 86)

$\overset{II}{Pt} \underset{\pi}{\overset{\pi}{\rightleftharpoons}} (CH_2{=}CH_2)$, synergic bonding is present.

$Pt \overset{\pi}{\longleftarrow} (CH_2{=}CH_2)$

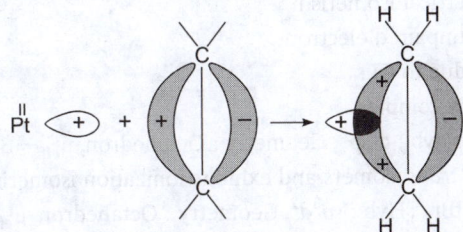

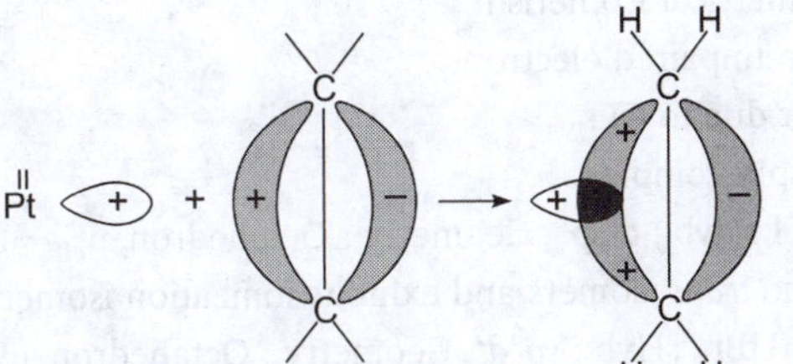

$Pt \overset{\pi}{\longrightarrow} (CH_2{=}CH_2)$

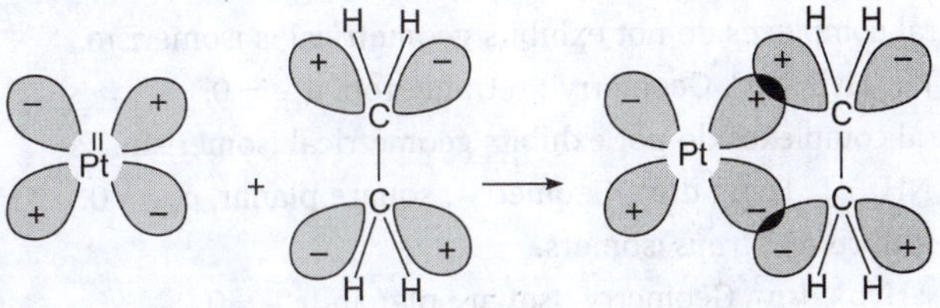

(C) $Na[CO(CO)_4]$

EAN of Co = 27 + 1 + 4 × 2 = 36 (Kr)

$Co \underset{\sigma}{\overset{\pi}{\rightleftharpoons}} CO$, synergic bonding takes place.

$Co \xleftarrow{\sigma} CO$

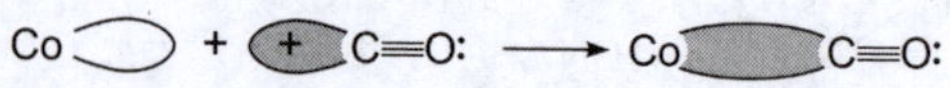

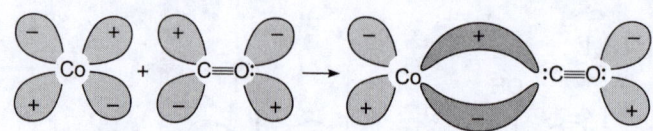

$Co \xrightarrow{\pi} CO$

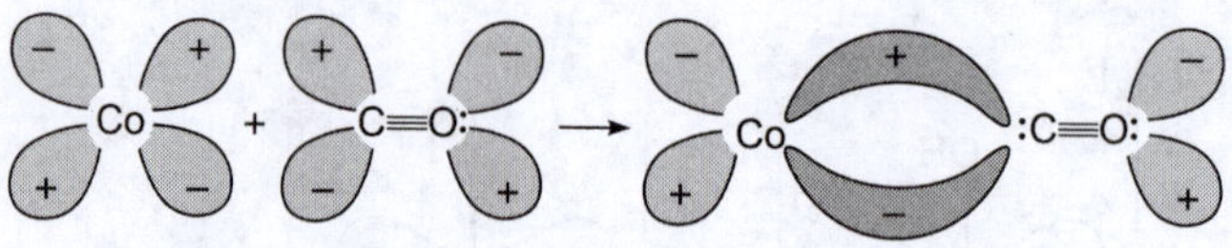

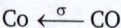

19. (A) $[Fe(H_2O)_2(NH_3)_4Br_2, [NiBr(H_2O)(en)_2]NO_3$
—both show ionisation isomerism (structural)
—both show *cis*/*trans* isomerism (geometrical)
—having 4 and 2 unpaired electrons respectively
—both show coloured due to GI.

(B) $[Co(NO_2)_2(NH_3)_4]Cl, [Cd(SCN)_2(H_2O)_2]$
—both show linkage isomerism (structural)
—both having zero unpaired electron

(C) $[Ir(NCS)_2(ox)_2]^{3-}, [Fe(CN)_2(en)_2]$
—both shows linkage isomerism (structural)
—both show geometrical isomerism
—both have no unpaired electrons
—both show coloured due to GI
—both forms low spin complexes

(D) $[PtBr(Cl(H_2O)_4]Br_2, [Rh(gly)_3]$
—both shows geometrical isomerism
—both having zero unpaired electrons
—both show colour due to GI
—both forms low spin complex.

20. (A) $[Cr(NO_3)_2(H_2O)_4]Cl$: Hyb : d^2sp^3, Geometry : Octahedron, $\mu_{eff} = 3.89$ B.M.
It can exist in *cis* and *trans* isomers and exhibits ionization isomerism.
$[Ni(en)_2(H_2O)(NH_3)]Br_2$: Hyb : sp^3d^2, Geometry : Octahedron, $\mu_{eff} = 2.8$ B.M.
It can exist in *cis* and *trans* isomers and exhibits ionization isomerism.

(B) $[Co(CO)_4]^-$: Hyb : sp^3, Geometry : tetrahedron, $\mu_{eff} = 0$.
Tetrahedral complexes do not exhibits geometrical is isomerism.
$[Zn(CN)_4]^{2-}$: Hyb : sp^3, Geometry : tetrahedron, $\mu_{eff} = 0$.
Tetrahedral complexes do not exhibits geometrical isomerism.

(C) $[Ni(CN)_2(NH_3)_2]$: Hyb : dsp^2, Geometry : square planar, $\mu_{eff} = 0$.
It can exist in *cis* and *trans* isomers.
$[Pt(gly)_2]$: Hyb : dsp^2, Geometry : square planar, $\mu_{eff} = 0$.
It can exist in *cis* and *trans* isomers.

(D) $[Co(CN)_2(NH_3)_4]Cl$: Htb : d^2sp^3, Geometry : Octahedron, $\mu_{eff} = 0$.
It can exist in *cis* and *trans* isomers and exhibits ionization isomerism.
$[Fe(NO_2)_2(en)_2]$: Htb : d^2sp^3, Geometry : Octahedron, $\mu_{eff} = 0$.
It can exist in *cis* and *trans* isomers and exhibits linkage isomerism.

21. (a) $[Sc(H_2O)_6]^{3+}$

Sc^{3+}, d^0 configuration, dimagnetic, colourless and forms inner orbital complex, d^2sp^3.

(b) $[Fe(H_2O)_6]^{3+}$

Fe^{3+}, d^5 configuration, paramagnetic coloured and forms outer orbital complex, sp^3d^2.

(c) $[Co(H_2O)_6]^{3+}$

Co^{3+}, d^6 configuration, diamagnetic (act as SFL) coloured, forms inner orbital complex, d^2sp^3.

(d) $[Cr(H_2O)_6]^{3+}$

Cr^{3+}, d^3 configuration, paramagnetic coloured, forms inner orbital complex, d^2sp^3.

ASSERTION-REASON TYPE QUESTIONS

2. (A) N_2H_4 can only act as monodentate ligand.

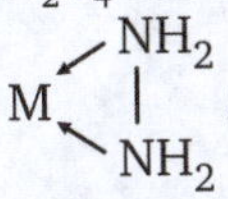

; Three membered (unstable) ring. Hence it acts as monodentate ligand only.

3. (B) Both $[Ti(H_2O)_6]^{4+}$ and $[Sc(H_2O)_6]^{3+}$ are colourless, due to absence of free electrons in 3*d* subshell.

5. (A) EDTA is hexadentate ligand. When it forms complex with a metal cation, the hybridisation of central atom will be d^2sp^3.

12. (A) $\ddot{N}H_2 - \ddot{N}H_2$ Neutral ligand

It does not act as bidentate because when it acts as bidentate, because when it acts as bidentate a three membered ring (chelat complex) will be formed, that will be highly strained.

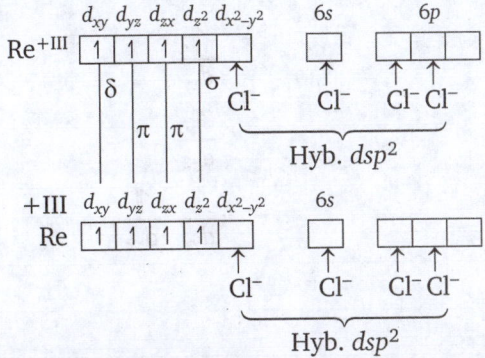

13. (B)

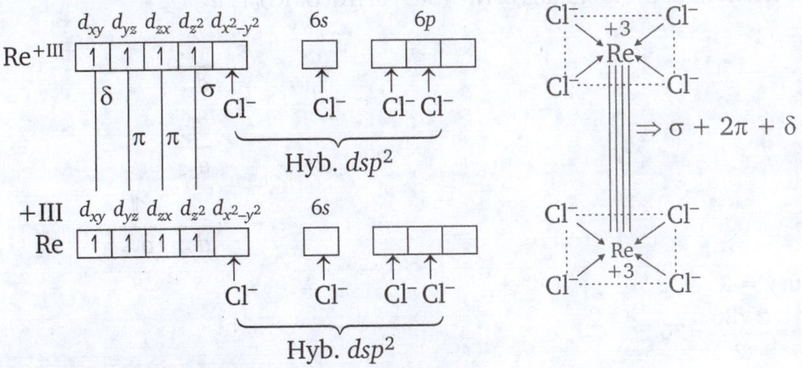

SUBJECTIVE PROBLEMS

1.

Compounds	Geometry	Hybridization	used *d*-orbital
A	Square planar	dsp^2	$d_{x^2-y^2}$
B	Trigonal bipyramidal	sp^3d	d_{z^2}
C	Square pyramidal	sp^3d	$d_{x^2-y^2}$
D	Octahedral	sp^3d^2	$d_{x^2-y^2}, d_{z^2}$
E	Pentgaonal bipyramidal	sp^3d^3	$d_{x^2-y^2}, d_{z^2}, d_{xy}$

$x = d_{z^2} = 3$

$y = d_{xy} = 1$; $(x+y-z)^2 = (3+1-4)^2 = 0$

$z = d_{x^2-y^2} = 4$

3. $[M_1^{2+}A_4]^{2+}[M_1^{2+}B_4]^{2-}$ $x_1 = 1$

$[M_2^{3+}A_6]^{3+}[M_2^{3+}B_6]^{3-}$ $x_2 = 2$

$[M_2^{3+}C(A)_5]^{2+}[M_1B_4]^{2-}$ $x_3 = 6$

$x_1^2 + x_2^2 + x_3^2 = 1^2 + 2^2 + 6^2 = 41$

4. The carbonyls in general obey the effective atomic number rule and their effective atomic number = atomic number of next noble gas

(i) $Mo(CO)_x \Rightarrow$ EAN '54'

$42 + 2x = 54$

$x = 6$

(ii) $H_yCr(CO)_5 \Rightarrow$ EAN '36'

$24 + (2 \times 5) + y = 36$

$y = 2$

(iii) $Co_2(CO)_z \Rightarrow$ EAN '36'

$27 + 1$ (from other Co-atom) $+ 2z = 36$

Then $x + y - z = 6 + 2 - 8 = 0$

5. $Ni^{2+}(aq) + DMG \xrightarrow{AqNH_3} [Ni(DMG)_2]\downarrow + 2H^+$

green — Rosy Red voluminous ppt.

Hyb. of Ni^{2+} : dsp^2

Distribution of electrons in the d-orbitals of $Ni^{2+}(3d^8)$ in $[Ni(DMG)_2]$:

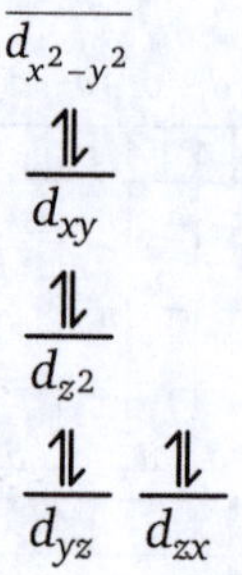

Hence $x = 6, y = 2$

$\therefore$ Value of $\frac{2x^2}{y} = \frac{2 \times 36}{2} = 36$

6.

Complexes	**No. of geometrical isomers**
(i) $[Pt(NH_3)_2(SCN)_2]$	2
(ii) $[Co(NO_2)_3(NH_3)_3]$	2
(iii) $[Pt(en)Cl_2]$	0
(iv) $[Cr(en)_2Br_2]^+$	2
(v) $[Rh(en)_3]^{3+}$	0
(vi) $[CoCl_2Br_2]^{2-}$	0

Hence, sum of total number of geometrical isomers = 6

7. $Cr(CO)_x \longrightarrow Cr(CO)_y(NO)_z$

$x = 6, y = 3, z = 2$

Hence, $x + z - y = 6 + 2 - 3 = 5$

8. $\overset{+1}{[Fe(H_2O)_5(NO)]SO_4}$

Experimental evidence : $\mu_{eff}(obs) = 3.89$

: Complex is highly unstable

9.

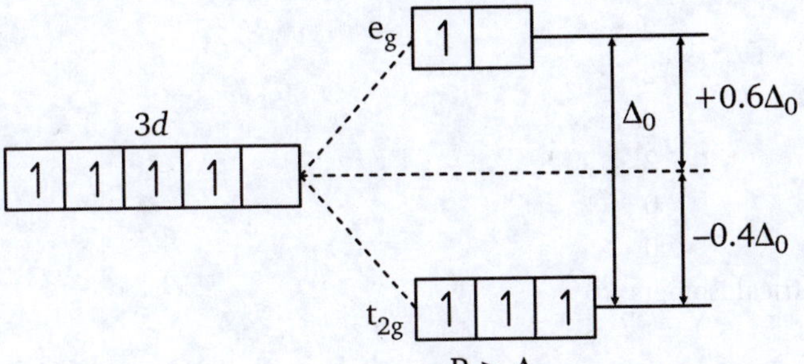

$P > \Delta_0$

$\overset{3+}{Mn}$ in $[MnF_6]^{3-}$

C.F.S.E. value $= -(3 \times 0.4\Delta_0) + (1 \times 0.6\Delta_0) = -0.6\Delta_0 = -6Dq$

$|CFSE| = 6Dq.$

10.

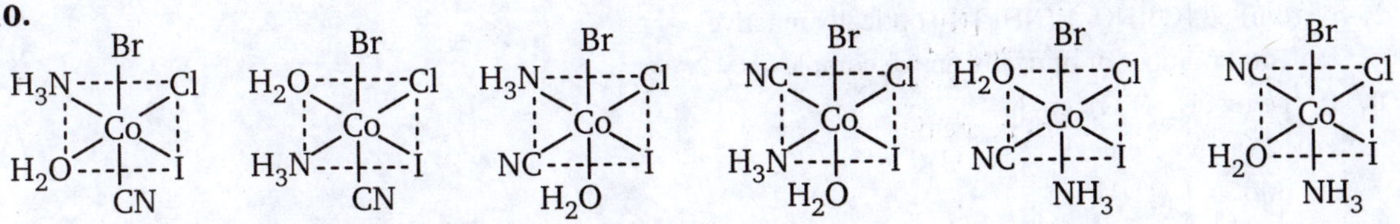

15. $\Rightarrow$ $[\overset{+I}{Fe}(H_2O)_5(NO)]^{2+}SO_4^{2-}$

$\overset{+I}{Fe}(3d^7)$ in $(\overset{+I}{Fe}(H_2O)_5(NO)]^{2+}$; $\Delta_0 < P$

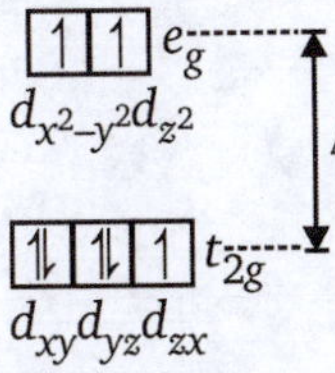

Number of electrons in t_{2g} set of d-orbitals = **5**

16. $\Rightarrow$ Pink colour complex : $[Mn(H_2O)_6]^{2+}$

$Mn^{2+}(3d^5)$ in $[Mn(H_2O)_6]^{++}$, $\Delta_0 < P$

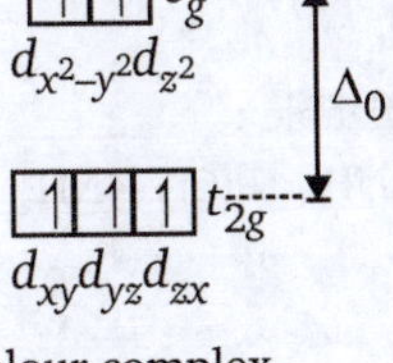

CFSE of pink colour complex

$$= 3 \times \left(-\frac{2}{5}\Delta_0\right) + 2 \times \left[\frac{3}{5}\Delta_0\right] = 0$$

17.

	EDTA		Phen		
σ bond	31	+	24	=	55
π bond	4	+	7	=	11

18.

	Complexes	No. of geometrical isomers
(i)	$[Pt(NH_3)_2(SCN)_2]$	2
(ii)	$[Co(NO_2)_3(NH_3)_3]$	2
(iii)	$[Pt(en)Cl_2]$	0
(iv)	$[Cr(en)_2Br_2]^+$	2
(v)	$[Rh(en)_3]^{3+}$	0
(vi)	$[CoCl_2Br_2]^{2-}$	0

Hence, sum of total number of geometrical isomers = 6

19. $\Rightarrow$ (i) $[Cr(ox)_3]^{3-}$: optically active.

(ii) $[Pt(Cl_2)(en)]$: optically inactive

(iii) *cis*-$[Rh(Cl_2)(NH_3)_4]$: optically inactive

(iv) $[Ru(dipy)_3]^{3+}$: optically active

(v) *cis*-$[Co(NO_2)_3(dien)]$: optically inactive

(vi) *Trans*-$[Co(NO_2)_3(dien)]$: optically inactive

(vii) *cis*-$[Co(NO_2)_3(NH_3)_3]$: optically inactive

$\Rightarrow$ Total number of optically active complexes = 2

20. (i) $[Fe\,IF(CN)(H_2O)(en)]$

$x = 12$ (active isomer)

(ii) $[MoCl_2\,F_2(gly)]^-$

$y = 4$ (active isomer)

$x - y = 12 - 4 \quad \Rightarrow 8$

21. $P = NH_2^-, O_2^-, OH^-, Cl^- = 4$

$Q = SO_4^{2-}, NO_2^-, CO_3^{2-}, CH_3COO^- = 4$

$R =$ en, acac, Phen, DMG, Gly $= 5$

$S =$ DMG, Gly $= 2$

$4 + 4 - 5 - 2 = 1$

22. Metal $(M) \Rightarrow$ Mo $(z = 42)$

$Mo(CO)_x(NO)_y \xrightarrow[-CO]{+NO} Mo(NO)_z$

If $y = 2$, then $x = 3$ and $z = 4$, hence $x + y - z = 3 + 2 - 4 = 1$

23. Moles of complex $= 0.15 \times \dfrac{100}{1000} = 0.015$

Moles of AgCl formed $= 0.030$, *i. e.*, twice the moles of complex. Hence, $2Cl^-$ ions must present in ionization sphere.

For octahedral Geometry, complex $= [Co(NH_3)_5Cl]Cl_2$; $\quad x = 5$

24. Total number of compound(s) in which at least half of Cl^- are ionizable :

$\Rightarrow CrCl_3 \cdot 6NH_3, CrCl_3 \cdot 5NH_3, PtCl_4 \cdot 6NH_3, PtCl_4 \cdot 5NH_3$; $PtCl_4 \cdot 4NH_3$

26. ClO_2 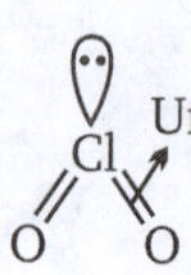

Unpaired e^- (paramagnetic)

ClO_3

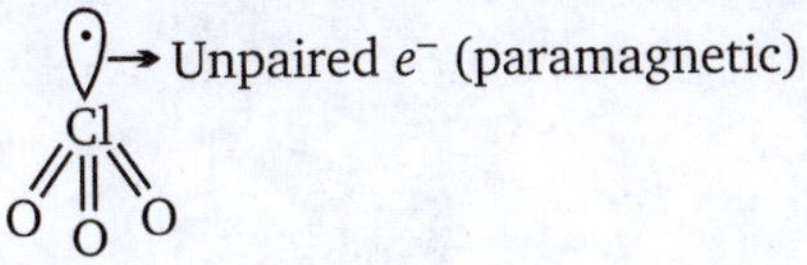

$K_3[Cr(CN)_6]$

$Cr^{3+} \Rightarrow 4s^0 3d^3$

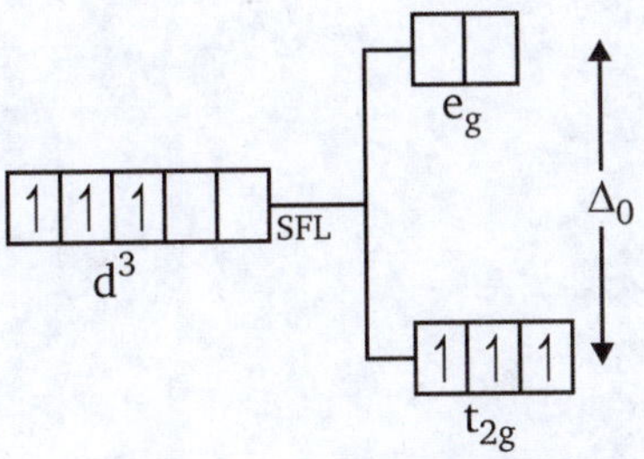

3 unpaired e⁻
(paramagnetic)

$K_2[NiCl_4]$

$Ni^{2+} \Rightarrow 4s^0 3d^8$

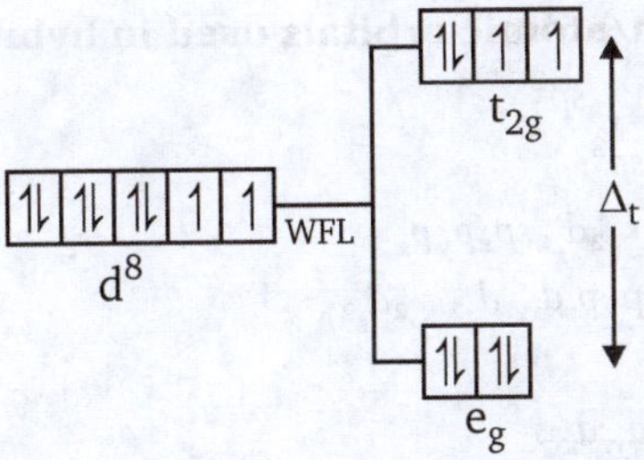

2 unpaired e⁻
(paramagnetic)

28. 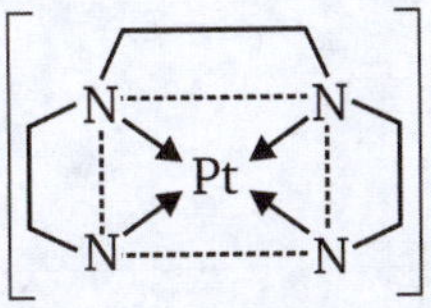

(Square planar complex)

Number of N-atom in a plane = 4

29. [Zn (acac)$_2$] is tetrachedral complex in which O — Zn — O bond angles are 6 and total no. of sp^3 hybridised atoms = 5.

∴ 6 − 5 = 1

31. 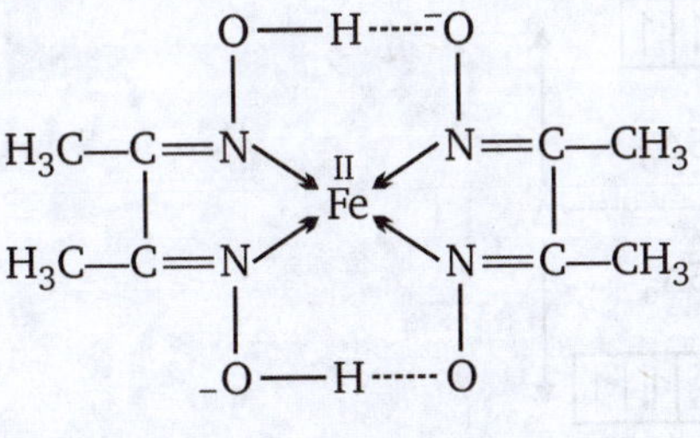

Hybridisation – dsp^2

sq. planar geometry

32.

$K_2[NiCl_4]$	sp^3 paramagnetic
$K_3[Fe(CN)_6]$	d^2sp^3 paramagnetic
$K_3[Cr(CN)_6]$	d^2sp^3 paramagnetic
$K_2[PtCl_4]$	dsp^2 diamagnetic
$Na_2[Fe(CN)_5NO]$	d^2sp^3 diamagnetic
$[Fe(H_2O)NO]SO_4$	sp^3d^2 paramagnetic
$K_3[Co(C_2O_4)_3]$	d^2sp^3 diamagnetic
$K_4[Co(CN)_6]$	d^2sp^3 paramagnetic
$[Cu(NH_3)_4]SO_4$	dsp^2 paramagnetic

33.

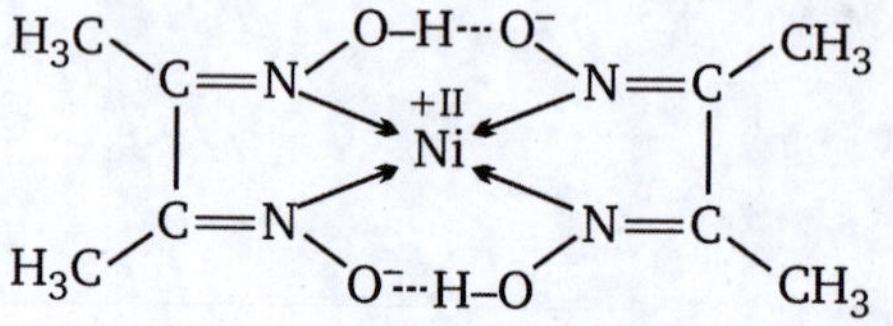

$x = 8, y = 4$

$8 - 4 = 4$

34.

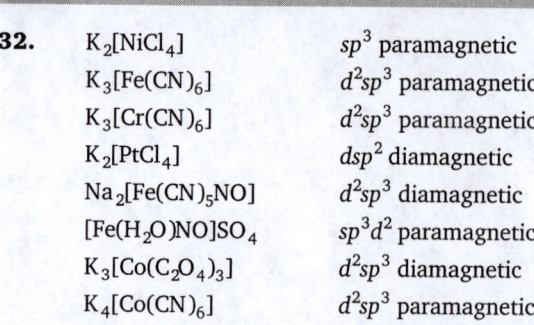

Compounds/ions	**Hybridization/atomic orbitals used in hybridization**
$[Ni(CN)_4]^{2-}$	$d_{x^2-y^2}sp^2$
$Fe(CO)_5$	$d_{z^2}sp^3$
$[Cr(NH_3)_6]^{3+}$	$d_{x^2-y^2}d_{z^2}sp_xp_yp_z$
XeF_5^-	$sp_xp_yp_zd_{xy}\,d_{x^2-y^2}d_{z^2}$
$[Ni(CO)_4]$	sp^3
MnO_4^-	$d_{xy}d_{yz}d_{zx}s$
$[PtCl_2(NH_3)_2]$	$d_{x^2-y^2}sp_xp_y$
ClF_5	$sp_xp_yp_z\,d_{x^2-y^2}d_{z^2}$
$[CuCl_5]^{3-}$	$sp_xp_yp_zd_{z^2}$

35. $[Fe(CN)_6]^{4-}, [Co(H_2O)_6]^{3+}, [PtCl_6]^{2-}, [Cr(CO)_6]$

36. $\underset{\text{(Pink complex)}}{[Co(H_2O)_x]^{2+}} \xrightarrow[\text{HCl}]{\text{Excess}} \underset{\text{(Blue complex)}}{[CoCl_y]^{n-}}$

$$x = 6, y = 4, n = 2$$

$$\frac{x+y}{n} = 5$$

37. $[Co(H_2O)_6]^{2+}, Co^{2+}, d^7$

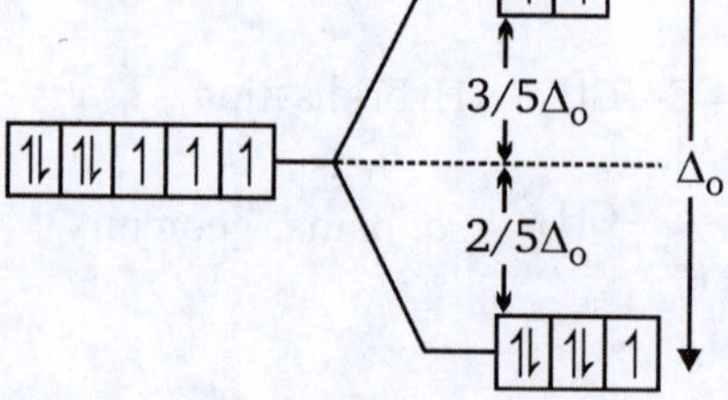

$CFSE$ = Splitting energy - Pairing energy

$7200 = (0.4\times5 - 0.6\times2)\Delta_o - 0$

$7200 = 0.8\,\Delta_o$

$\Delta_o = \frac{7200}{0.8}$

$\frac{\Delta_o}{10^3} = 9\text{ cm}^{-1}$

38. $[Co(dmg)_2]$: square planer geometry

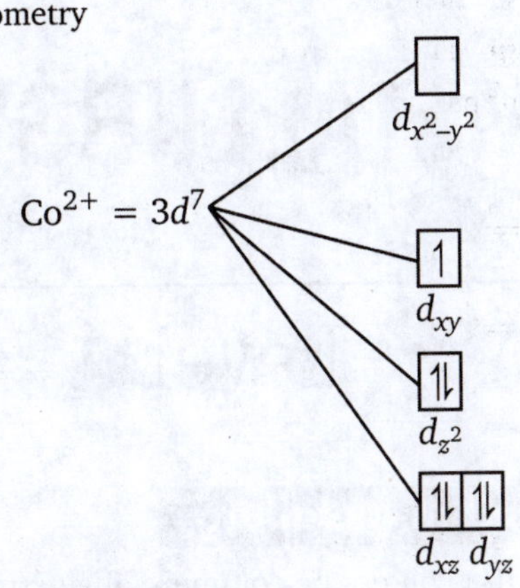

No. of e^- in non-axial d-orbitals $(d_{xy}, d_{yz}, d_{xz}) = 2+2+1 = 5$

39. Electronic distribution of Co^{2+} in complex $[Co(NH_3)_6]^{2+} = t_{2g}^6\, e_g^0$.

Unpaired electron migrates from inner shell e_g orbital to valence shell d-orbital.

41. $x = 1$ $Pt(en)Cl_4 \rightarrow [Pt(en)Cl_4]$

$x = 1$ $Pt_2(en)Cl_4 \rightarrow [Pt(en)_2Cl_2]Cl_2$

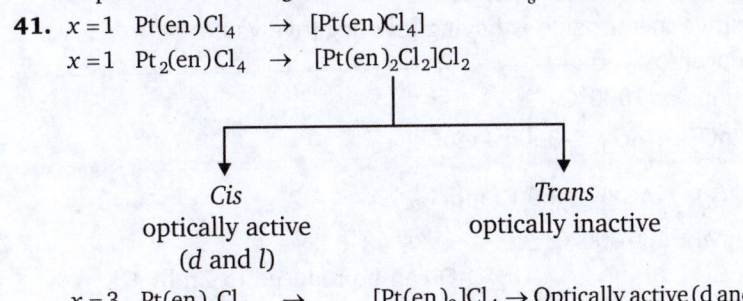

Cis — optically active (d and l)

Trans — optically inactive

$x = 3$ $Pt(en)_3Cl_4 \rightarrow [Pt(en)_3]Cl_4 \rightarrow$ Optically active (d and l)

5

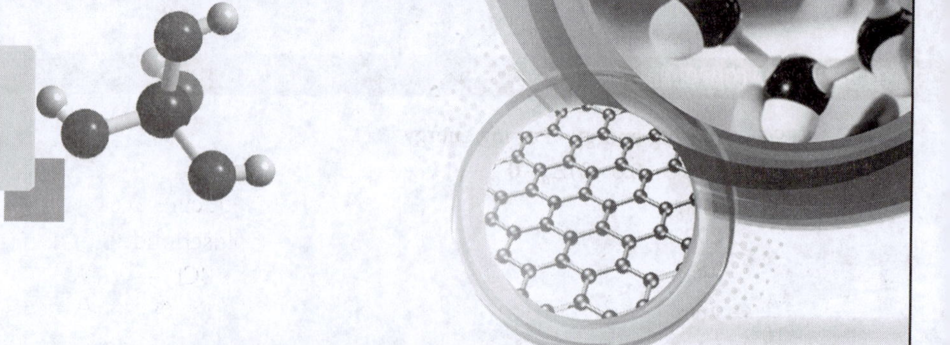

METALLURGY

Level 1

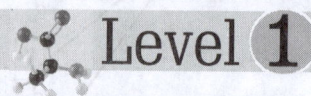

General Principle Involved in Metallurgy

1. Highly electropositive metal(s) can not be commercially extracted by carbon reduction process at high temperature because these :
(a) metals combine with carbon to form covalent carbide
(b) metals combine with carbon to form ionic carbide
(c) ΔG_f of highly electropositive metal oxide is having low negative value
(d) metal oxides are not reduced by carbon

2. Consider the following reactions at 1000°C.
(I) $Zn(s) + 1/2O_2(g) \xrightarrow{\Delta} ZnO(g)$; $\Delta G^o = -360$ kJ mol^{-1}
(II) $C(s) + 1/2O_2(g) \xrightarrow{\Delta} CO(g)$; $\Delta G^o = -460$ kJ mol^{-1}
and choose the correct statement at 1000°C.
(a) ZnO is more stable than CO
(b) ZnO can be reduced to Zn by C
(c) ZnO and CO are formed at equal rate
(d) ZnO can not be reduced to Zn by C

3. Which of the following pair of ores cannot be converted into corresponding metals by pyrometallurgy ?
(a) Ag_2S, ZnS
(b) Cu_2S, HgS
(c) MnO_2, SnO_2
(d) None of these

4. Ellingham diagram represents:
(a) change of ΔG with temperature
(b) change of ΔH with temperature
(c) change of ΔG with pressure
(d) change of $(\Delta G - T\Delta S)$ with temperature

5. The process of the isolation of a metal by dissolving the ore in a suitable chemical reagent followed by precipitation of the metal by a more electropositive metal is called:
(a) hydrometallurgy
(b) electrometallurgy
(c) zone refining
(d) electrorefining

6. The process of the isolation of a metal by dissolving the ore in a suitable chemical reagent followed by precipitation of the metal by a more electropositive metal is called :
(a) hydrometallurgy
(b) electrometallurgy
(c) zone refining
(d) electrorefining

7. In the alumino-thermite process, Al acts as :
(a) an oxidising agent (b) a flux
(c) solder (d) a reducing agent

8. Which of the following reaction forms the basis of Goldschmidt alumino-thermite process?
(a) $2Al + N_2 \rightarrow 2AlN$ (b) $2Al + 3Cl_2 \rightarrow 2AlCl_3$
(c) $2Al + 6HCl \rightarrow 2AlCl_3 + 3H_2$ (d) $2Al + Fe_2O_3 \rightarrow Al_2O_3 + 2Fe$

9. The extraction of zinc from zinc blende is achieved by :
(a) electrolytic reduction
(b) roasting followed by reduction with carbon
(c) roasting followed by reduction with another metal
(d) roasting followed by self-reduction

10. Thermite is a mixture of :
(a) Fe powder and Al_2O_3 (b) Al powder and Fe_2O_3
(c) Cu powder and Fe_2O_3 (d) Zn powder and Cr_2O_3

11. If a metal has low oxygen affinity then the purification of metal may be carried out by:
(a) liquation (b) distillation (c) zone refining (d) cupellation

12. Neutral refractory material used in furnaces is :
(a) Graphite (b) CaO (c) SiO_2 (d) MgO

Ores and their Concentration

13. Which of the following set of elements mostly occur as sulphide ores ?
(a) Zn, Cu, Na (b) Zn, Cu, Pb (c) Fe, Al, Ti (d) Cu, Ag, Au

14. Which one contains both Ca and Mg?
(a) Limestone (b) Dolomite (c) Chalk (d) Feldspar

15. Match Column-I with Column-II and select the correct answer using the codes given below:

Column-I (Metals)	Column-II (Ores)
(A) Tin	(1) Calamine
(B) Zinc	(2) Cassiterite
(C) Titanium	(3) Cerrusite
(D) Lead	(4) Rutile

	(A)	(B)	(C)	(D)
(a)	1	2	3	4
(b)	2	1	4	3
(c)	4	3	2	1
(d)	2	1	3	4

16. Which of the following is not an ore of magnesium?
(a) Carnallite (b) Magnesite
(c) Dolomite (d) Gypsum

17. Which one of the following is not an ore of aluminium?
(a) Bauxite (b) Corundum (c) Epsomite (d) Cryolite

18. Cinnabar is the ore of :
(a) Zn (b) Cd (c) Hg (d) Ag

19. Which of the following minerals does not contain iron?
(a) Magnetite (b) Magnesite (c) Haematite (d) Limonite

20. Which one of the following types of metals is expected to occur in the native state?
(a) The alkali metals (b) The alkaline earth metals
(c) The noble metals (d) The rare earth metals

21. Which one of the following elements is most abundant in earth crust?
(a) Aluminium (b) Silicon (c) Carbon (d) Oxygen

22. The two most abundant metals in the earth crust are :
(a) Al, Zn (b) Ag, Au (c) Fe, Cu (d) Fe, Al

23. A mineral is usually associated with a large amount of unwanted material called :
(a) Gangue (b) Flux (c) Slag (d) Ore

24. The metal which mainly occurs as oxide ore in nature is :
(a) Silver (b) Lead (c) Aluminium (d) Copper

25. Three most occurring elements into the earth crust are :
(a) O, Si, Al (b) Si, O, Fe (c) Fe, Ca, Al (d) Si, O, N

26. Froth floatation process for the concentration of sulphide ores is an illustration of the practical application of:
(a) adsorption (b) absorption (c) sedimentation (d) coagulation

27. Froth floatation process is used for the concentration of the ore of :
(a) Fe (b) Al (c) Cr (d) Cu

28. Haematite ore is concentrated by :
(a) gravity separation method (b) froth floatation process
(c) amalgamation (d) hand picking

29. Electromagnetic separation is used in the concentration of :
(a) Copper pyrite (b) Bauxite
(c) Cassiterite (d) Cinnabar

30. Which one of the following is not a method of concentration of ore?
(a) Electromagnetic separation (b) Smelting
(c) Gravity separation (d) Froth floatation process

31. Chemical leaching is useful in the concentration of :
(a) Copper pyrite (b) Bauxite (c) Cassiterite (d) Galena

32. The ore which is concentrated by wetting of oil is :
(a) oxide ore (b) sulphate ore
(c) carbonate ore (d) sulphide ore

33. Rutile is separated from chlorapatite by :
(a) Froth floatation method (b) Levigation
(c) Magnetic separation method (d) Electrostatic separation method

34. In the extraction of copper from its sulphide ore, the metal is formed by reduction of Cu_2O with:
(a) FeS (b) CO (c) Cu_2S (d) SO_2

35. Which of the following pair is incorrectly matched?
(a) van Arkel method — Zirconium (b) Kroll's process — Titanium
(c) Froth Floatation — Cerussite (d) Distillation — Zinc

36. Most abundant metal in earth crust is:
(a) Al (b) O (c) Fe (d) Si

Extraction of Metals

37. Consider the following reactions :

$2XS + 3O_2 \xrightarrow{\Delta} 2XO + 2SO_2$

$2XO + XS \xrightarrow{\Delta} 3\text{'}X\text{'} + SO_2$

Then 'X' can not be :

(a) Hg (b) Pb (c) Zn (d) None

38. In the alumino-thermite process, Al metal acts as :

(a) Oxidising agent (b) Reducing agent
(c) Catalyst (d) Flux

39. Extraction of aluminium from bauxite ore, reduction is carried out by:

(a) carbon (b) magnesium
(c) electrolysis (d) hydrogen

40. Chromium is obtained by reducing concentrated chromite ore with:

(a) red hot coke (b) gaseous hydrogen
(c) aluminium powder (d) carbon monoxide

41. The element which is recovered from electrolytic process is:

(a) iron (b) lead (c) aluminium (d) zinc

42. Magnesium is manufactured by electrolysing fused magnesium chloride using:

(a) a nickel cathode and a graphite anode
(b) the iron container as anode and a nickel cathode
(c) the iron container with coating as cathode graphite and anode graphite
(d) the nickel container as cathode and iron anode

43. Copper is extracted from sulphide ore using the method :

(a) carbon reduction (b) carbon monoxide reduction
(c) auto reduction (d) none of these

44. In the extraction of copper, metal is formed in the Bassemer converter due to reaction :

(a) $Cu_2S + 2Cu_2O \rightarrow 6Cu + SO_2$ (b) $Cu_2S \rightarrow 2Cu + S$
(c) $Fe + Cu_2O \rightarrow 2Cu + FeO$ (d) $2Cu_2O \rightarrow 4Cu + O_2$

45. Silica is added to roasted copper ore during extraction in order to remove :

(a) cuprous sulphide (b) ferrous oxide (c) ferrous sulphide (d) cuprous oxide

46. Calcium is extracted by the electrolysis of :

(a) Fused mixture of $CaCl_2$ and CaF_2 (b) $CaCl_2$ fused salt solution
(c) Used mixture of $CaCl_2$ and NaF (d) $Ca_3(PO_4)_2$ fused salt solution

47. Lead is mainly extracted by:

(a) Carbon reduction method
(b) Self-reduction method
(c) Electrolytic reduction
(d) Leaching with aqueous solution of NaCN followed by reduction

48. In which of the following metallurgy, no reducing agent is required from out side?

(a) Mercury from cinnabar (b) Zinc from zinc blende
(c) Iron from haematite (d) Aluminium from Bauxite

49. Aluminium is used as a reducing agent in the reduction of :
(a) Cr_2O_3 (b) SnO_2 (c) ZnO (d) HgO

50. Bessemerisation is carried out for:
(a) Fe, Cu (b) Cu, Al (c) Al, Ag (d) Fe, Al

51. Silver can be separated from commercial lead by :
(a) fractional crystallisation (b) amalgamation
(c) cupellation (d) addition of zinc (Parke's method)

52. A solution of Na_2SO_4 in water is electrolysed using inert electrodes. The products at cathode and anode are respectively:
(a) $O_2; H_2$ (b) O_2; Na (c) $H_2; O_2$ (d) $O_2; SO_2$

53. The metal *X* is prepared by the electrolysis of fused chloride. It reacts with hydrogen to form a colourless solid from which hydrogen gas is released on treatment with water. The metal is :
(a) Al (b) Ca (c) Cu (d) Zn

54. The function of fluorspar in the electrolytic reduction of alumina dissolved in fused cryolite (Na_3AlF_6) is :
(a) as a catalyst
(b) to lower the temperature of the melt and to make the fused mixture very conducting
(c) to decrease the rate of oxidation of carbon at the anode
(d) none of the above

55. In the extraction of copper from copper pyrites, iron is removed as :
(a) $FeSO_4$ (b) $FeSiO_3$ (c) Fe_3O_4 (d) Fe_2O_3

56. The material mixed before ore is subjected for smelting in the extraction of iron are :
(a) coke and silica (b) coke and limestone
(c) limestone and silica (d) coke, limestone and silica

57. The maximum temperature 1550°C is obtained in the .... region of the blast furnace used in the extraction of iron.
(a) reduction (b) fusion
(c) combustion (d) slag formation

58. The iron obtained from the blast furnace is called :
(a) pig iron (b) cast iron (c) wrought iron (d) steel

59. Which metal can not obtained by electrolysis of their aqueous salt solution?
(a) Silver (b) Magnesium
(c) Copper (d) Platinum

Refining of Metals

60. Impure aluminium is purified by :
(a) Baeyer's process (b) Hall's process
(c) Hoop's process (d) Serpeck's process

61. Which is not correctly matched :
(a) Spiegleisan : Mn + Fe + C
(b) Dow's sea water process : $Ca(OH)_2$
(c) Parke's process : Ag
(d) Liquation : spelter (Impure Zn)

62. Incorrect match is :
(a) Purification of Al metal : Baeyer's method
(b) Polling : Reduction of Cu_2O
(c) $FeCr_2O_4$ (chromite ore) : $NaOH/Na_2CO_3$
(d) Ag : Mac Arthur cyanide process

63. Refining of tin cannot be done by:
(a) cupellation
(b) liquation
(c) poling
(d) electrorefining

64. Which method is not correct given for refining of crude metals?
(a) Distillation : zinc and mercury
(b) Liquation : tin
(c) van Arkel : Zirconium
(d) Mond process : lead

65. Aluminium metal is purified by :
(a) Hoope's process
(b) Hall's process
(c) Serpeck's process
(d) Baeyer's process

66. High purity copper metal is obtained by :
(a) carbon reduction
(b) hydrogen reduction
(c) electrolytic reduction
(d) thermite reduction

67. Poling process is used for:
(a) The removal of Cu_2O from Cu
(b) The removal of Al_2O_3 from Al
(c) The removal of Fe_2O_3 from Fe
(d) All of these

68. In zone refining method, the molten zone :
(a) consists of impurities only
(b) contains more impurity than the original metal
(c) contains the purified metal only
(d) moves to either side

69. Which of the following pair is correctly matched?
(a) Copper — Oxidative refining
(b) Nickel — Kroll's process
(c) Mercury — Distillation
(d) Lead — van Arkel method

70. Formation of $Ni(CO)_4$ and subsequent its decomposition into Ni and CO makes basis of Mond's process ;

$Ni + 4CO \xrightarrow{T_1} Ni(CO)_4 \xrightarrow{T_2} Ni + 4CO$, T_1 and T_2 are :
(a) 100°C, 50°C
(b) 50°C, 100°C
(c) 50°C, 200°C
(d) 230°C, 50°C

71. In the electrolytic refining of copper, Ag and Au are found :
(a) on anode
(b) in electrolyte solution
(c) in anode mud
(d) in cathode mud

72. Electrolyte solution in electrolytic refining of lead contains :
(a) H_2SiF_6 only
(b) $PbSiF_6$ only
(c) H_2SiF_6 in presence of gelatin
(d) H_2SiF_6 and $PbSiF_6$ in presence of gelatin

73. Blister copper is :
(a) pure copper
(b) ore of copper
(c) alloy of copper
(d) impure copper

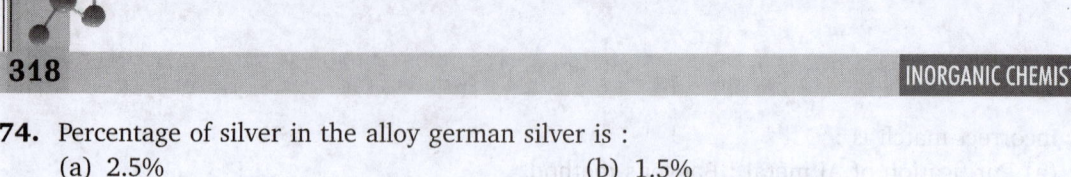

74. Percentage of silver in the alloy german silver is :
(a) 2.5% (b) 1.5%
(c) 10% (d) 0%

75. AgCl on fusion with sodium carbonate, gives :
(a) Ag_2CO_3 (b) Ag_2O
(c) Ag (d) Ag_2C_2

76. An alloy which does not contain copper is :
(a) bronze (b) magnalium
(c) brass (d) bell metal

77. Stainless steel contains iron and :
(a) Zn (b) Cu
(c) Al (d) Cr

78. Axles are made by heating rods of iron embedded in charcoal powder. The process is known as :
(a) tempering (b) annealing
(c) nitriding (d) case hardening

79. Nitriding is a process of heating steel in atmosphere of :
(a) ammonia (b) oxygen
(c) carbon dioxide (d) air

80. Bassemer converter is used in making of :
(a) pig iron (b) steel
(c) wrought iron (d) cast iron

81. Which of the following elements constitutes a major impurity in pig iron?
(a) Carbon (b) Oxygen
(c) Sulphur (d) Silicon

Level 2

General Principle Involved in Metallurgy

1. Which of the following pair of ores can not be converted into corresponding metals by pyrometallurgy ?
(a) Ag_2S, ZnS (b) Cu_2S, HgS
(c) MnO_2, SnO_2 (d) None

2. $XCl_2\text{(excess)} + YCl_2 \longrightarrow XCl_4 + Y\downarrow;$

$$YO \xrightarrow[>400°]{\Delta} \frac{1}{2}O_2 + Y,$$ Ore of Y would be :
(a) Siderite (b) Cinnabar
(c) Malachite (d) Hornsilver

3. A sulphide ore is first converted into its oxide before reduction. This is done because :
(a) a sulphide ore cannot be reduced to metal at all
(b) no reducing agent is found suitable for reducing a sulphide ore
(c) the enthalpy of formation of CO_2 is more than that of CS_2
(d) a metal oxide is generally less stable than the metal sulphide

4. Choose the correct code regarding Roasting process.
(I) It is the process of heating ore in air to obtain the oxide
(II) It is an exothermic process
(III) It is used for hydrated oxide and oxysalt ore
(IV) It is used after the concentration of ore
(a) I, II and III (b) I, II and IV
(c) I, III and IV (d) I, II, III and IV

5. Carbon cannot be used in the reduction of Al_2O_3 because :
(a) it is non-metal
(b) the heat of formation of CO_2 is more than that of Al_2O_3
(c) pure carbon is not easily available
(d) the heat of formation of Al_2O_3 is too high

6. On heating quick lime with coke in an electric furnace, we get :
(a) Ca and CO_2 (b) $CaCO_3$
(c) CaO (d) CaC_2

7. Boron can be obtained by various methods but not by :
(a) thermal decomposition of B_2H_6 (b) pyrolysis of BI_3 (van Arkel)
(c) reducing BCl_3 with H_2 (d) electrolysis of fused BCl_3

8. Select correct statement :
(a) The decomposition of an oxide into oxygen and metal in vapour phase entropy of reaction increases
(b) Decomposition of an oxide is an endothermic change
(c) To make $\Delta G°$ negative, temperature should be high enough so that $T\,\Delta S° > \Delta H°$
(d) All are correct statements

9. The oxide of a metal (R) can be reduced by the metal (P) and metal (R) can reduce the oxide of metal (Q). Then the decreasing order of the reactivity of metal (P), (Q) and (R) with oxygen is:

(a) $P > Q > R$ (b) $P > R > Q$

(c) $R > P > Q$ (d) $Q > P > R$

10. Consider the following metallurgical processes :

(I) Heating impure metal with CO and distilling the resulting volatile carbonyl (b.p. 43°C) and finally decomposition at 150°–200°C to get the pure metal

(II) Heating the sulphide ore in air until a part is converted to oxide and then further heating in the absence of air to let the oxide react with unchanged metal sulphide

(III) Electrolysis of the molten electrolyte containing approximately equal amounts of the metal chloride and NaCl to obtained the metal

The processes used for obtaining magnesium, nickel and copper are respectively :

(a) (I), (II) and (III) (b) (II), (III) and (I)

(c) (III), (I) and (II) (d) (II), (I) and (III)

11. When alumina is heated with carbon in nitrogen atmosphere, the products are :

(a) Al + CO (b) Al + CO_2

(c) Al + CO + CO_2 (d) AlN + CO

12. MgO is used as a refractory material because :

(a) It has high melting point (b) It is a good conductor of heat

(c) It is a good electrical insulator (d) All of these

Ores and their Concentration

13. Among the following statements, the incorrect statement is :

(a) calamine and cerrusite are carbonate ores

(b) rutile and cuprite are oxide ores

(c) zinc blende and pyrites are sulphide ores

(d) malachite and azurite are sulphate ores of Cu

14. Give the correct order of initials **T** or **F** for following statements. Use **T** if statement is true and **F** if it is false.

(i) Every mineral is an ore but every ore is not a mineral

(ii) Slag is product formed during extraction of metal by combination of flux and impurities.

(iii) Highly pure semi conductor can be obtained by zone refining.

(iv) Carnallite is an ore of magnesium and sodium.

(a) TTTF (b) FTTF

(c) FTTT (d) TFTF

15. Find the incorrectly matched pair?

Column-I (ores)	Column-II (metals)
(a) Sylvine	(1) Potassium
(b) Malachite	(2) Magnesium
(c) Cinnabar	(3) Mercury
(d) Fluorite (Flourspar)	(4) Calcium

16. Froth floatation process used for the concentration of sulphide ore :
(a) is based on the difference in wettability of different minerals
(b) uses sodium ethyl xanthate, $C_2H_5OCS_2Na$ as collector
(c) uses NaCN as depressant in the mixture of ZnS and PbS when ZnS forms soluble complex and PbS forms froth
(d) All are correct statements

17. When ZnS and PbS minerals are present together, then NaCN is added to separate them in the froth floatation process as a depressant, because :
(a) $Pb(CN)_2$ is precipitated while no effect on ZnS
(b) ZnS forms soluble complex $Na_2[Zn(CN)_4]$
(c) PbS forms soluble complex $Na_2[Pb(CN)_4]$
(d) They cannot be separated by adding NaCN

18. Leaching of Ag_2S is carried out by heating it with a dilute solution of :
(a) NaCN only (b) HCl
(c) NaOH (d) NaCN in presence of O_2

19. Leaching is commercially carried out in the concentration of :
(a) Galena (b) Argentite
(c) Copper pyrites (d) Tin stone

20. NaCN is sometimes added in the forth flotation process as depressant when ZnS and PbS minerals are expected because :
(a) $Pb(CN)_2$ is precipitated while no effect on ZnS
(b) ZnS forms soluble complex $Na_2[Zn(CN)_4]$ while PbS forms froth
(c) PbS forms soluble complex $Na_2[Pb(CN)_4]$ while ZnS forms froth
(d) NaCN is never added in froth floatation process

21. Which of the following substance acts as collector in froth floatation method ?
(a) Sodium xenate (b) Sodium pyrophosphate
(c) Sodium nitroprusside (d) Sodium ethyl xanthate

Extraction of Metals

22. In which of the following pair of metals, both are commercially extracted from their respective ores by carbon reduction method?
(a) Zn, Cu (b) Fe, Cu
(c) Sn, Zn (d) Al, Ag

23. Formation of metallic copper from the sulphide ore in the commercial metallurgical process involves.

(a) $Cu_2S + \frac{3}{2}O_2 \longrightarrow Cu_2O + SO_2$; $Cu_2O + C \longrightarrow 2Cu + CO$

(b) $Cu_2S + \frac{3}{2}O_2 \longrightarrow Cu_2O + SO_2$; $2Cu_2O + Cu_2S \longrightarrow 6Cu + SO_2$

(c) $Cu_2S + 2O_2 \longrightarrow CuSO_4$; $CuSO_4 + Cu_2S \longrightarrow 3Cu + 2SO_2$

(d) $Cu_2S + \frac{3}{2}O_2 \longrightarrow Cu_2O + SO_2$; $Cu_2O + CO \longrightarrow 2Cu + CO_2$

24. There are following extraction process of silver but not :
(a) as a side product in electrolytic refining of copper
(b) Parke's process in which Zn is used to extract silver by solvent extraction from molten lead
(c) by reaction of silver sulphide with KCN and then reaction of soluble complex with Zn
(d) by heating $Na[Ag(CN)_2]$

25. In the extraction of aluminium
Process X : applied for red bauxite to remove iron oxide (chief impurity)
Process Y : (Serpeck's process) : applied for white bauxite to remove Z (chief impurity) then, process X and impurity Z are :
(a) X = Hall and Heroult's process and $Y = SiO_2$
(b) X = Baeyer's process and $Y = SiO_2$
(c) X = Serpeck's process and Y = iron oxide
(d) X = Baeyer's process and Y = iron oxide

26. Give the correct order of initials **T** or **F** for following statements. Use **T** if statement is true and **F** if it is false.
(i) In Gold schmidt thermite process aluminium acts as a reducing agent.
(ii) Mg is extracted by electrolysis of aq. solution of $MgCl_2$
(iii) Extraction of Pb is possible by carbon reduction method
(iv) Red Bauxite is purified by Serpeck's process
(a) TTTF (b) TFFT (c) FTTT (d) TFTF

27. $FeCr_2O_4$ (chromite) is converted to Cr by following steps :
$$\text{Chromite} \xrightarrow{\text{I}} NaCrO_4 \xrightarrow{\text{II}} Cr_2O_3 \xrightarrow{\text{III}} Cr$$
Reagents in I, II and III step might be :

	I-Step	II-Step	III-Step
(a)	Na_2CO_3/air, Δ	C	C
(b)	NaOH/air, Δ	C, Δ	Al, Δ
(c)	Na_2CO_3/air, Δ	C, Δ	C, Δ
(d)	conc. H_2SO_4, Δ	NH_4Cl, Δ	C, Δ

28. The electrolysis of pure alumina is not feasible because :
(a) it is bad conductor of electricity and its fusion temperature is high
(b) it is volatile in nature
(c) it is decomposed when fused
(d) it is amphoteric

29. Which of the following reaction does not occur in Bessemer's converter?
(a) $2Cu_2S + 5O_2 \longrightarrow 2CuSO_4 + Cu_2O$
(b) $2Cu_2S + 3O_2 \longrightarrow 2Cu_2O + 2SO_2 \uparrow$
(c) $2CuFeS_2 + O_2 \longrightarrow Cu_2S + 2FeS + SO_2$
(d) $FeO + SiO_2 \longrightarrow FeSiO_3$

30. What products are formed during, the electrolysis of a concentrated aqueous solution of NaCl?
(I) $Cl_2(g)$ (II) $NaOH(aq)$ (III) $H_2(g)$
(a) I only (b) I and II only
(c) I and III only (d) I, II and III

31. During the electrolysis of carnallite, $MgCl_2$ is decomposed and not KCl. This is because of :
(a) lower decomposition voltage of $MgCl_2$ than that of KCl
(b) reverse reaction $MgCl_2 + 2K \longrightarrow Mg + 2KCl$ if KCl is decomposed under other experimental condition
(c) both (a) and (b)
(d) none of the above

32. The reduction of an oxide by aluminium is called :
(a) Beeyer's process
(b) Goldschmidt's aluminothermite process
(c) Hall's process
(d) van Arkel process

33. Incorrect statement in electrolysis of Al_2O_3 by Hall-Heroult process is :
(a) Cryolite $Na_3[AlF_6]$ lowers the m.pt. of Al_2O_3 and increases its electrical conductivity
(b) Al is obtained at cathode and CO_2 at anode
(c) Li_2CO_3 can be used in place of cryolite (Na_3AlF_6)
(d) None of these

Refining of Metals

34. In the leaching of Ag_2S with NaCN, a stream of air is also passed. It is because of :
(a) reversible nature of reaction between Ag_2S and NaCN
(b) to oxide Na_2S formed into Na_2SO_4 and sulphur
(c) both (a) and (b)
(d) none of the above

35. In van Arkel method, if I_2 is introduced at 700 K over impure metal, the product will be :
(a) Iodide of the metal
(b) No reaction takes place
(c) Impurities react with iodine
(d) None of these

36. The method of zone refining of metals is based on the principle of :
(a) Greater mobility of the pure metal than that of impurity
(b) Higher melting point of the impurity than that of the pure metal
(c) Greater noble character of the solid metal than that of the impurity
(d) Greater solubility of the impurity in the molten state than in the solid

37. Blister copper is refined by stirring molten impure metal with green logs of wood because such a wood liberates hydrocarbon gases (like CH_4). This process X is called .... and the metal contains impurities of Y is ....
(a) X = cupellation, $Y = CuO_2$
(b) X = polling, $Y = Cu_2O$
(c) X = polling, $Y = CuO$
(d) X = cupellation, $Y = CuO$

38. The anode mud in the electrolytic refining of silver contains :
(a) Zn, Cu, Ag, Au
(b) Zn, Ag, Au
(c) Cu, Ag, Au
(d) Au only

39. The method of electrolytic refining is not suitable with metal :
(a) Aluminium
(b) Copper
(c) Mercury
(d) Silver

40. Match Column-I with Column-II

Column-I	Column-II
(P) Nitriding	(I) Process of heating steel to redness and then cooling it very slowly
(Q) Annealing	(II) Process of heating steel in presence of NH_3 and producing hard coating of Iron Nitride on the surface of steel
(R) Tempering	(III) Process of heating steel to redness and then cooling it suddenly by plunging it into water or oil
(S) Quenching	(IV) Process of heating quenched steel to a temperature well below redness and then cooling it slowly

	P	Q	R	S
(a)	II	I	III	IV
(b)	II	I	IV	III
(c)	I	II	IV	III
(d)	I	II	III	IV

41. 'Softening of lead' means :
(a) conversion of lead to PbO
(b) conversion of lead to Pb_3O_4
(c) removal of impurities (metallic) from lead
(d) washing lead with HNO_3 followed by alkali solution

42. In the purification of impure nickel by Mond's process, metal is purified by :
(a) Electrolytic reduction
(b) Vapour phase thermal decomposition
(c) Thermite reduction
(d) Carbon reduction

43. Correct match is :
(a) Bayer's method — Na_2CO_3
(b) Matte — 98% Cu_2S + 2% FeS
(c) van Arkel method — AgI
(d) Thomas slag — Raw material for cement industry

Level 3

Passage 1

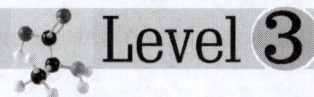

For a spontaneous reaction, the free energy change must be negative. $\Delta G = \Delta H - T\Delta S$, ΔH is the enthalpy change during the reaction. T is the absolute temperature, and ΔS is the change in entropy during the reaction. Consider a reaction such as the formation of an oxide

$$M + O_2 \longrightarrow MO$$

Dioxygen is used up in the course of this reaction. Gases have a more random structure (less ordered) than liquid or solids. Consequently gases have a higher entropy than liquids and solids. In this reaction S (entropy or randomness) decreases, hence ΔS is negative. Thus, if the temperature is raised then $T\Delta S$ becomes more negative. Since, $T\Delta S$ is substracted in the equation, then ΔG becomes less negative. Thus, the free energy change increases with the increase in temperature.

The free energy changes that occur when one mole of common reactant (in this case dioxygen) is used may be plotted graphically against temperature for a number of reactions of metals to their oxides. The following plot is called an Ellingham diagram for metal oxide. Understanding of Ellingham diagram is extremely important for the efficient extraction of metals.

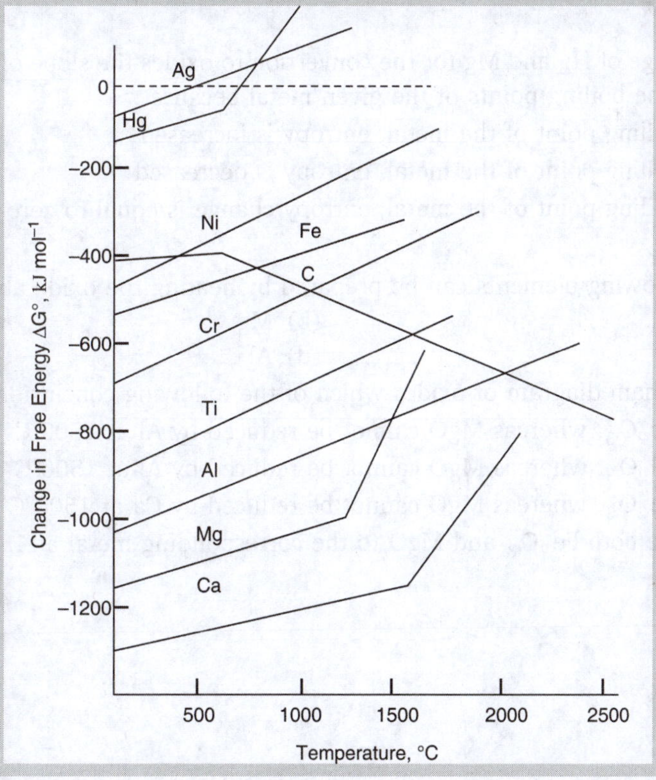

1. For the conversion of Ca(*s*) to CaO(*s*) which of the following represent the ΔG *vs.* T ?

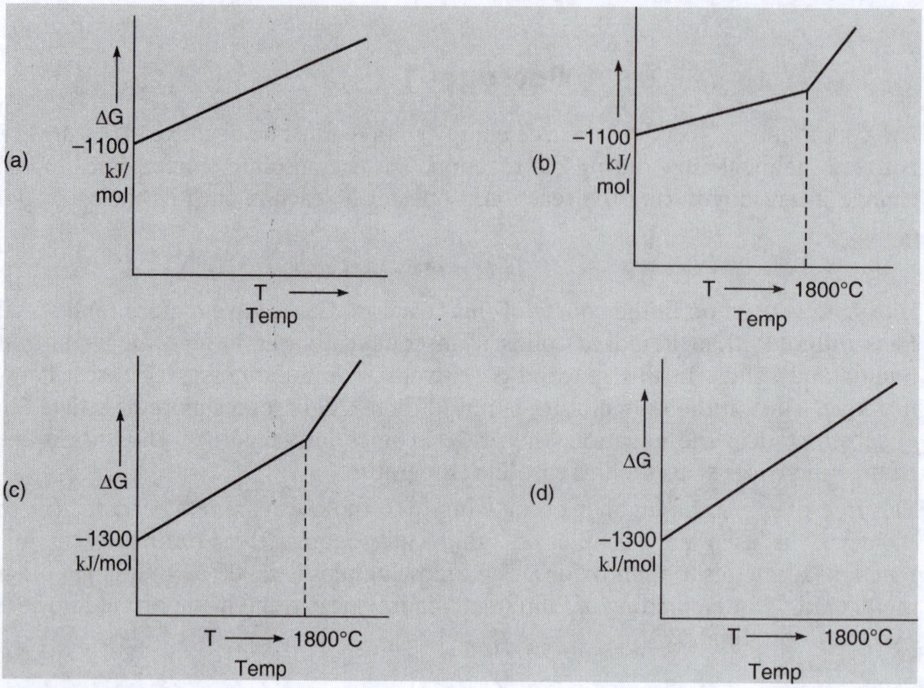

2. Free energy change of Hg and Mg for the convertion to oxides the slope of ΔG *vs.* T has been changed above the boiling points of the given metal because :

(a) above the boiling point of the metal, entropy is increased

(b) above the boiling point of the metal, entropy is decreased

(c) above the boiling point of the metal, entropy change is equal to zero

(d) All of these

3. Which of the following elements can be prepared by heating the oxide above 400°C?

(a) Hg (b) Mg

(c) Fe (d) Al

4. As per the Ellingham diagram of oxides which of the following conclusion is true?

(a) Al reduces Fe_2O_3, whereas MgO cannot be reduced by Al at 1500°C

(b) Fe reduces Al_2O_3, whereas MgO cannot be reduced by Al at 1500°C

(c) Al reduces Fe_2O_3, whereas MgO cannot be reduced by Ca at 1500°C

(d) Al can reduce both Fe_2O_3 and MgO to the corresponding metal at 1500°C

Passage 2

The Ellingham diagram for zinc, magnesium and carbon converting into corresponding oxides is shown below.

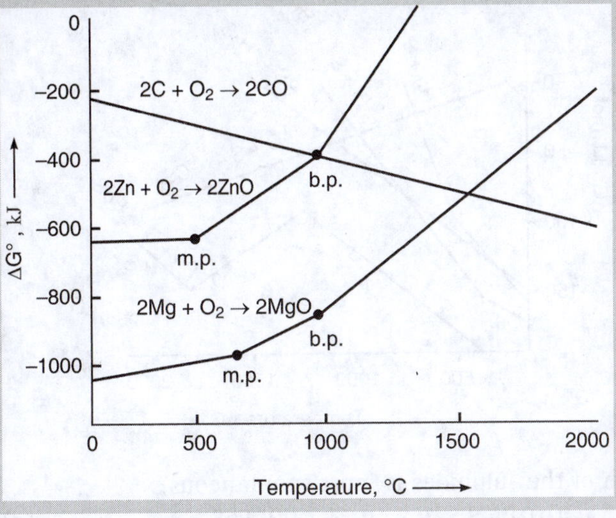

1. At what temperature, zinc and carbon have equal affinity for oxygen?

(a) 1000°C (b) 1500°C

(c) 500°C (d) 1200°C

2. To make the following reduction process spontaneous, temperature should be :

$$ZnO + C \longrightarrow Zn + CO$$

(a) 1000°C (b) > 1100°C

(c) < 500°C (d) < 1000°C

3. At 1100°C, which reaction is spontaneous to a maximum extent?

(a) $MgO + C \longrightarrow Mg + CO$

(b) $ZnO + C \longrightarrow Zn + CO$

(c) $MgO + Zn \longrightarrow Mg + ZnO$

(d) $ZnO + Mg \longrightarrow MgO + Zn$

Passage 3

The Ellingham diagram for a number of metallic sulphides is shown below.

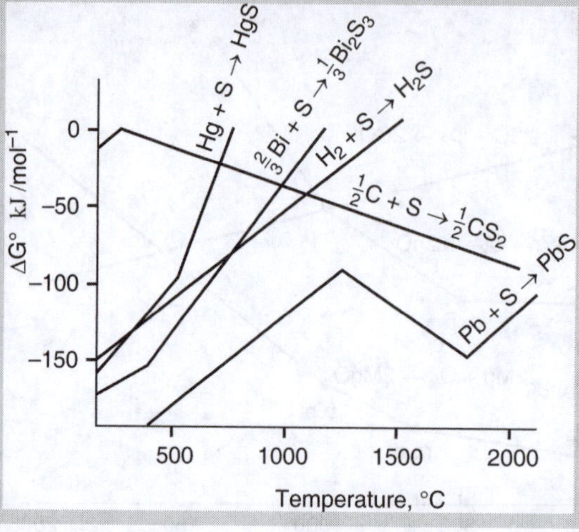

1. Formation of which of the sulphides is most spontaneous?
(a) HgS (b) Bi_2S_3 (c) PbS (d) CS_2

2. Which sulphide occurs to minimum extent in nature?
(a) HgS (b) H_2S (c) Bi_2S_3 (d) CS_2

3. Which of the following sulphides can not be reduced to metal by H_2 at about 1000°C ?
(a) HgS (b) PbS (c) Bi_2S_3 (d) all of these

Passage 4

Magnesium is a valuable, light weight metal used as a structural material as well as in alloys, batteries, and in chemical synthesis. Although magnesium is plentiful in Earth's crust, it is mainly found in the sea water (after sodium). There is about 1.3 g of magnesium in every kilogram of sea water. The process for obtaining magnesium from sea water employs all three types of reactions, *i.e.*, precipitation, acid-base, and redox-reactions.

1. Precipitation reaction involves formation of :
(a) insoluble $MgCO_3$ by adding Na_2CO_3
(b) insoluble $Mg(OH)_2$ by adding $Ca(OH)_2$
(c) insoluble in $MgSO_4$ by adding Na_2SO_4
(d) insoluble $MgCl_2$ by adding NaCl

2. Acid-base reaction involves reaction between :
(a) $MgCO_3$ and HCl
(b) $Mg(OH)_2$ and H_2SO_4
(c) $Mg(OH)_2$ and HCl
(d) $MgCO_3$ and H_2SO_4

3. Redox reaction takes place (in the extraction of Mg) :
(a) in the electrolytic cell when fused $MgCl_2$ is subjected to electrolysis
(b) when fused $MgCO_3$ is heated
(c) when fused $MgCO_3$ is strongly heated
(d) none of the above

Passage 5

Dow's process of extraction of Mg involves extraction of Mg from sea water. Sea water is concentrated in sun-light and is then treated with slaked lime. Magnesium hydroxide is heated in a stream of HCl to give $MgCl_2$ which is electrolysed to discharge Mg. The mixture is in the ratio 35% $MgCl_2$ + 50% NaCl + 15% $CaCl_2$. NaCl and $CaCl_2$ are added to lower the fusion temperature and to increases the conductance.

$$Mg^{2+} + Ca(OH)_2 \longrightarrow Mg(OH)_2 + Ca^{2+}$$

$$Mg(OH)_2 + 2HCl \longrightarrow MgCl_2 + 2H_2O(l)$$

Electrolysis of fused $MgCl_2 \rightleftharpoons Mg^{2+} + 2Cl$

$$Mg^{2+} + 2e^- \longrightarrow Mg \text{ (At Cathode)}$$

$$2Cl^- \longrightarrow Cl_2 + 2e^- \text{ (At Anode)}$$

Mg electrolysed is protected from atmospheric oxidation by a blanket of inert gases.

1. In the hydrated chloride of Mg the value of x is :
(a) 6 (b) 4 (c) 8 (d) 10

2. Molten mixture contains Mg^{2+}, Na^+ and Ca^{2+} but at cathode only Mg^{2+} is discharged because :
(a) Standard reduction potential of Mg^{2+} is least among the three
(b) Standard oxidation potential of Mg is the least among the three
(c) Discharge potential of Mg^{2+} is highest
(d) None of these

3. Molten mixture of NaCl and $CaCl_2$ is added to the heated $MgCl_2$ because:
(a) $MgCl_2 \cdot xH_2O + \text{dry HCl} \xrightarrow{973\text{–}1223\text{ K}}$ Partially dehydrated $MgCl_2$ and molten mixture (NaCl + $CaCl_2$) makes it fully dehydrated
(b) $CaCl_2$ is dehydrating agent
(c) ($CaCl_2$ + NaCl) lowers the melting point of $MgCl_2$
(d) None of these

Passage 6

$$FeCr_2O_4 + NaOH + air \longrightarrow (A) + Fe_2O_3$$

$$(A) + (B) \longrightarrow Na_2Cr_2O_7$$

$$Na_2Cr_2O_7 + X \xrightarrow{\Delta} Cr_2O_3$$

$$Cr_2O_3 + Y \xrightarrow{\Delta} Cr$$

1. Compound (A) and (B) are :
(a) Na_2CrO_4, H_2SO_4 (b) $Na_2Cr_2O_7$, HCl
(c) Na_2CrO_5, H_2SO_4 (d) $Na_4[Fe(OH)_6], H_2SO_4$

2. (*X*) and (*Y*) are respectively :
(a) C and Al (b) Al and C (c) C in both (d) Al in both

3. Na_2CrO_4 and Fe_2O_3 are separated by :
(a) dissolving in conc. H_2SO_4 (b) dissolving in NH_3
(c) dissolving in H_2O (d) dissolving in dil. HCl

Passage 7

Electrolysis is an important technique for extraction of metals, and each ion of the solution needs a minimum voltage to get discharged and this value is expressed in terms of discharge potential. For some metal ions the discharge potentials follow the order given below :

$Li^+ > K^+ > Ca^{2+} > Na^+ > Mg^{2+} > Al^{3+} > Zn^{2+} > Fe^{2+} > Ni^{2+} > H_3O^+ > Cu^{2+} > Hg_2^{2+} > Ag^+ > Au^{3+}$

For some anions the discharge potentials are in the order :

$SO_4^{2-} > NO_3^- > OH^- > Br^- > I^-$

1. When aqueous solution of cupric bromide is electrolyzed the product obtained at cathode will be:
(a) Cu (b) H_2 (c) Br_2 (d) O_2

2. The product formed at anode and cathode, when dilute H_2SO_4 is electrolysed are :
(a) SO_2, H_2 (b) SO_3, H_2 (c) $H_2S_2O_8, H_2$ (d) O_2, H_2

3. A mixture containing chlorides of sodium, calcium and zinc is electrolysed in presence of water. The product obtained at cathode will be :
(a) Na (b) H_2 (c) Ca (d) Cl_2

4. When conc. H_2SO_4 is electrolysed with high current using Pt electrodes, the product obtained at anode is :
(a) SO_2 (b) SO_3 (c) O_2 (d) $H_2S_2O_8$

ONE OR MORE ANSWERS IS/ARE CORRECT

1. Which of the following metal(s) is/are commercially extracted by self reduction method from their corresponding ore ?
(a) Cu (b) Fe (c) Pb (d) Hg

2. Which of the following process makes the ore porous?
(a) Roasting (b) Calcination (c) Reduction (d) Distillation

3. Which of the following ores is/are oxide ore(s)?
(a) Tinstone (b) Bauxite (c) Cryolite (d) Carnallite

4. Roasting of copper pyrites is done :
(a) to remove moisture (b) to oxidise free sulphur
(c) to decompose pyrite into Cu_2S and FeS (d) to remove volatile organic impurities

5. Which of the following is a correct statement?
(a) Calamine is the ore of zinc (b) Pyrolusite is the ore of manganese
(c) Cassiterite is the ore of tin (d) Calcite is the ore of calcium

6. In which of the following pairs, both the minerals are oxides?
(a) Sylvine, saltpetre
(b) Casseterite, litharge
(c) Siderite, corundum
(d) Cuprite, tinstone

7. Which of the following mineral does not contain sodium?
(a) Trona
(b) Borax
(c) Epsomite
(d) Cerrusite

8. Which of the following pair consists of ore of the same metal?
(a) Bauxite, Limonite
(b) Haematite, Siderite
(c) Cinnabar, Cassiterite
(d) Galena, Cerrusite

9. The process(es) by which lighter earthy particles are freed from the heavier particles using water is/are :
(a) Gravity separation
(b) Levigation
(c) Hydraulic washing
(d) Leaching

10. Roasting is carried out to :
(a) convert sulphide to oxide and sulphate
(b) remove water of hydration
(c) melt the ore
(d) remove arsenic and sulphur impurities

11. The chemical treatment of the ore for commercial concentration is done in the case of :
(a) aluminium
(b) silver
(c) copper
(d) gold

12. Froth floatation :
(a) is a physical method of separating mineral from the gangue
(b) is a method to concentrate the ore depending on the difference in wetability of gangue and the ore
(c) is used for the sulphide ores
(d) is a method in which impurities sink to the bottom

13. Which of the following reaction(s) occur during calcination?
(a) $CaCO_3 \longrightarrow CaO + CO_2$
(b) $4FeS_2 + 11O_2 \longrightarrow 2Fe_2O_3 + 8SO_2$
(c) $2Al(OH)_3 \longrightarrow Al_2O_3 + 3H_2O$
(d) $CuS + CuSO_4 \longrightarrow 2Cu + 2SO_2$

14. Amphoteric nature of aluminium oxide is employed in which of the following process ?
(a) Baeyer's process
(b) Hall's process
(c) Serpek's process
(d) Dow's process

15. Which of the following is true for calcination of a metal ore?
(a) It makes the ore more porous
(b) The ore is heated to a temperature when fusion just begins
(c) Hydrated salts lose their water of crystallisation
(d) Impurities of S, As and Sb are removed in the form of their volatile oxides

16. The difference(s) between roasting and calcination is/are :
(a) roasting is highly endothermic while calcination is not
(b) partial fusion occurs in calcination but not in roasting
(c) calcination is performed in limited amount of air but roasting employs excess air
(d) combustion reaction occur in roasting but not in calcination

17. The extraction of metals from oxide ores involve :
(a) Reduction with carbon
(b) Reduction with aluminium
(c) Electrolytic reduction
(d) Reduction with CO

18. Metals which can be extracted by smelting process are :
(a) Pb (b) Fe (c) Zn (d) Al

19. Of the following reduction processes, correct processes are :
(a) $Fe_2O_3 + C \longrightarrow Fe$ (b) $ZnO + C \longrightarrow Zn$
(c) $Ca_3(PO_4)_2 + C \longrightarrow P$ (d) $PbO + C \longrightarrow Pb$

20. In the extraction of aluminium metal, one of the process is summarised as follows :

$$\underset{\text{Impure}}{\underset{\text{(bauxite)}}{Al_2O_3 \cdot 3H_2O}} \xrightarrow[\text{concentrated 'A'}]{\text{hot}} \underset{\text{(aqueous soln.)}}{\text{Product 'B'}} \xrightarrow[\text{to change pH}]{\text{bubble gas 'C'}} \text{Pure } Al_2O_3 \cdot 3H_2O$$

$$\text{Pure } Al_2O_3 \cdot 3H_2O \xrightarrow{\text{mix with 'D', melt at } 1000^\circ \text{ C}} \xrightarrow[\text{with carbon electrodes}]{\text{electrolyse molten material}} \text{Aluminium at 'E'}$$

Which of the following entries correctly summarises reagents, electrodes & products of the process?

	I	II	III	IV	V
(a)	NaOH	Al^{3+}	HF	Na_3AlF_6	Cathode
(b)	NaOH	$NaAlO_2$	CO_2	NaF	Anode
(c)	H_2SO_4	$Al_2(SO_4)_3$	NH_3	Na_3AlF_6	Cathode
(d)	NaOH	$NaAlO_2$	CO_2	Na_3AlF_6	Cathode

21. During the production of iron and steel.
(a) The oxide ore is primarily reduced to iron by solid coke according to the reaction

$$2Fe_2O_3 + 3C \longrightarrow 4Fe + 3CO_2$$

(b) The oxide ore is reduced by the carbon monoxide according to the reaction

$$Fe_2O_3 + 3CO \longrightarrow 2Fe + 3CO_2$$

(c) Major silica impurities are removed as calcium silicate slag by addition of a fluxing agent limestone
(d) The silicate slag is used in manufacturing cement

22. The smelting of iron in a blast furnace involves the following processes :
(a) combustion (b) reduction (c) slag formation (d) sublimation

23. Which one of the following metals can be extracted by aluminothermic process?
(a) Manganese (b) Iron (c) Chromium (d) Magnesium

24. For which of the following metal, the carbon reduction cannot be used?
(a) Lead (b) Manganese (c) Tungsten (d) Iron

25. The advantage(s) of using carbon to reduce a number of oxides and other compounds are :
(a) easy availability of coke
(b) low cost of carbon
(c) tendency of carbon to show catenation
(d) presence of carbon lowers the melting point of the oxides

26. Carbon reduction method can not be used with highly electro positive metal:
(a) high temperature needed which is expensive and requires the use of a blast furnace
(b) metals combine with carbon forming carbides

(c) carbon combines with oxygen to form poisonous CO
(d) All of these

27. Which of the following metals are extracted from its ore by using self-reduction method?
(a) Copper (b) Mercury (c) Lead (d) Silver

28. Which of the following is/are correctly matched?

Column-I (Metals)	Column-II (Process used for reduction)
(a) Titanium	Kroll process
(b) Aluminium	Baeyer process
(c) Chromium	Thermite process
(d) Silver	Mac-Arthur cyanide process

29. The function of adding cryolite in the electrolytic reduction of alumina by Hall-Heroult process is to :
(a) dissolve alumina
(b) lower the melting point of alumina
(c) lower the fuel bill
(d) increase the electrical conductivity of alumina

30. Which of the following reduction reactions are actually employed in commercial extraction of metals?
(a) $Fe_2O_3 + 2Al \longrightarrow Al_2O_3 + 2Fe$
(b) $Cr_2O_3 + 2Al \longrightarrow Al_2O_3 + 2Cr$
(c) $2Na[Au(CN)_2] + Zn \longrightarrow Na_2[Zn(CN)_4] + 2Au$
(d) $Cu_2S + Pb \longrightarrow Cu + PbS\downarrow$

31. The chief reaction(s) occurring in blast furnace during extraction of iron from haematite is/are :
(a) $Fe_2O_3 + 3CO \longrightarrow 2Fe + 3CO_2$ (b) $FeO + SiO_2 \longrightarrow FeSiO_3$
(c) $Fe_2O_3 + C \longrightarrow 2Fe + 3CO$ (d) $CaO + SiO_2 \longrightarrow CaSiO_3$

32. Which of the following are true for electrolytic extraction of aluminium?
(a) Cathode material contains graphite
(b) Anode material contains graphite
(c) Cathode reacts away forming CO_2
(d) Anode reacts away forming CO_2

33. Select correct statement regarding silver extraction process.
(a) When the lead-silver alloy is rich in silver, lead is removed by the cupellation process
(b) When the lead-silver alloy is rich in lead, lead is removed by parke's or pattinson's process
(c) Zinc forms an alloy with lead, from which lead is separated by distillation
(d) Zinc forms an alloy with silver, from which zinc is separated by distillation

34. Aluminothermy used for the spot welding of large iron structures is based upon the fact that :
(a) As compared to iron, aluminium has greater affinity for oxygen
(b) As compared to aluminium, iron has greater affinity for oxygen
(c) Reaction between aluminium and oxygen is endothermic
(d) Reaction between iron oxide and aluminium is exothermic

35. Highly electropositive metals can not be extracted by carbon reduction process because these :

(a) Metals combine with carbon to form carbides
(b) Metals do not react with carbon
(c) Metal oxides are not reduced by carbon
(d) Loss of metal is more by vaporisation

36. Which of the following reaction in the blast furnace is/are endothermic?

(a) $C(s) + O_2(g) \rightleftharpoons CO_2(g)$
(b) $CO_2(g) + C(s) \rightleftharpoons 2CO(g)$
(c) $CaCO_3(s) \rightleftharpoons CaO(s) + CO_2(g)$
(d) $Fe_2O_3(s) + 3CO(g) \rightleftharpoons 2Fe(l) + 3CO_2(g)$

37. The furnace lining in steel manufacture consists of :

(a) CaO (b) SiO_2
(c) MgO (d) $CaCO_3$

38. Pick up the correct statement(s) :

(a) All minerals are ores
(b) All minerals cannot be an ore
(c) All ores are minerals
(d) The minerals from which metals can be extracted profitably are called ores

MATCH THE COLUMN

Column-I and **Column-II** contains four entries each. Entries of column-I are to be matched with some entries of column-II. Each entry of column-I may have the matching with one or more than one entries of column-II.

1.

Column-I (Main ore of metal)	Column-II (Process involved in commercial extraction pure metal)
(A) Cinnabar	(P) Froth floatation method
(B) Chalcopyrite	(Q) Roasting
(C) Bauxite	(R) Distillation
(D) Argentite	(S) Leaching
	(T) Calcination

2.

Column-I (Statements)	Column-II (Corresponding metals)
(A) Hydrometallurgy applied in commercial extraction of metal	(P) Ag
(B) Carbon reduction applied in commercial extraction in metal	(Q) Zn
(C) Aqueous salt solution is used in electrolytic Refining method	(R) Sn
(D) Metal present in anode mud of refining of crude copper	(S) Au
	(T) Cu

3.

Column-I	Column-II
(A) Haematite	(P) Self reduction
(B) Copper pyrites	(Q) Roasting
(C) Carnalite	(R) Electrolytic reduction
(D) Bauxite	(S) Calcination
	(T) Reduction by carbon monoxide (mainly) as well as carbon at different temperature.

4.

Column-I	Column-II
(A) Ca	(P) Found as its native state
(B) Zn	(Q) Found as its sulphide
(C) Cr	(R) Found as its carbonate
(D) Ag	(S) Found as its oxide

5.

Column-I	Column-II
(A) Ilmentie	(P) Iron
(B) Dolomite	(Q) Magnesium
(C) Carnallite	(R) Potassium
(D) Chromite	(S) Titanium
	(T) Calcium

6.

Column-I	Column-II
(A) Cuprite	(P) Sulphate ore
(B) Cerussite	(Q) Carbonate ore
(C) Kainite	(R) Oxide ore
(D) Calamine	(S) Chloride ore

7.

Column-I	Column-II
(A) Poling	(P) Titanium
(B) Cupellation	(Q) Copper
(C) Electro-refining	(R) Silver
(D) van Arkel method	(S) Tin

8.

Column-I	Column-II
(A) Metal which occur in the native state in nature is	(P) Hg
(B) The oxides of metal that can be commercially reduced by Aluminothermic reduction process is	(Q) Ti
(C) van Arkel method is used for preparing ultrapure metal of	(R) Cr
(D) Auto reduction process is employed for the sulphide ore of	(S) Ag

9.

Column-I	Column-II
(A) Mond's process	(P) $Cr_2O_3 + 2Al \xrightarrow{\Delta} 2Cr + Al_2O_3$
(B) van Arkel process	(Q) $TiCl_4 + 2Mg \xrightarrow{\Delta} Ti + 2MgCl_2$
(C) Thermite process	(R) $Ni(CO)_4 \xrightarrow{\Delta} Ni + 4CO$
(D) Kroll's process	(S) $ZrI_4 \xrightarrow{\Delta} Zr + 2I_2$

10.

Column-I (Metal)	Column-II (Process involved in commercial extraction from their ore)
(A) Pb	(P) Bessemerisation
(B) Cu	(Q) Roasting
(C) Zn	(R) Pyrometallurgy
(D) Fe (Steel)	(S) Self-reduction method

ASSERTION-REASON TYPE QUESTIONS

The questions given below consist of "Assertion" and their "Reason". Use the following key to choose the appropriate answer.

(A) If both assertion and reason are CORRECT, and reason is the CORRECT explanation of the assertion

(B) If both assertion and reason are CORRECT, but reason is NOT the CORRECT explanation of the assertion

(C) If assertion is CORRECT but reason is INCORRECT

(D) If assertion is INCORRECT but reason is CORRECT

1. **Assertion** : $PbSiF_6 + H_2SiF_6$ + gelatine is taken as electrolyte in electrolytic refining of lead.
   Reason : Discharge potential of Pb^{2+} is less than H^+.
2. **Assertion** : Nitriding is the process of heating steel in presence of N_2 to form iron nitrides.
   Reason : The surface of steel becomes hard after nitriding process.
3. **Assertion** : Ores are generally converted into oxides, prior to reduction.
   Reason : Metal oxides can be easily reduced.
4. **Assertion** : In the extraction of Ag, complex $Na[Ag(CN)_2]$ is reacted with Zn.
   Reason : Zn is *d*-block transition metal.
5. **Assertion** : Thermite mixture Fe_2O_3 + Al (powder) is used in the welding.
   Reason : Al is a good reductant.
6. **Assertion** : In froth floatation process sodium ethyl xanthate is used as collector.
   Reason : Sulphide ores are water soluble.
7. **Assertion** : Cryolite is used in electrolytic extraction of Al from alumina.
   Reason : It dissolves alumina.
8. **Assertion** : $CuFeS_2$ is concentrated by froth floatation method.
   Reason : $CuFeS_2$ is main ore of copper.
9. **Assertion** : In the electrolytic reduction of Al_2O_3, cryolite is used.
   Reason : Cryolite is an ore of aluminium.
10. **Assertion** : Wrought iron is more malleable and ductile than steel.
    Reason : It contains slightly less percentage of carbon.
11. **Assertion** : Lead, tin and bismuth are purified by liquation method.
    Reason : Lead, tin and bismuth have low m.p. as compared to impurities.
12. **Assertion** : Al_2O_3 can be converted into Al by reduction with carbon at high temp.
    Reason : Carbon has greater affinity for oxygen than aluminium at room temperature.
13. **Assertion** : Reduction of ZnO with carbon is done at 1100°C.
    Reason : $\Delta G°$ is negative at this temperature thus, process is spontaneous.
14. **Assertion** : Desilverisation of lead is done by Parke's method.
    Reason : When lead-silver alloy is poor in silver, zinc is added to molten ore.
15. **Assertion** : All the ores are mineral.
    Reason : Ores contains metals in combined state.

Answers

Level-1

1. (b)	2. (b)	3. (a)	4. (a)	5. (a)	6. (a)	7. (d)	8. (d)	9. (b)	10. (b)
11. (d)	12. (a)	13. (b)	14. (b)	15. (b)	16. (d)	17. (c)	18. (c)	19. (b)	20. (c)
21. (d)	22. (d)	23. (a)	24. (c)	25. (a)	26. (a)	27. (d)	28. (a)	29. (c)	30. (b)
31. (b)	32. (d)	33. (c)	34. (c)	35. (c)	36. (a)	37. (c)	38. (b)	39. (c)	40. (c)
41. (c)	42. (c)	43. (c)	44. (a)	45. (b)	46. (a)	47. (b)	48. (a)	49. (a)	50. (a)
51. (d)	52. (c)	53. (b)	54. (b)	55. (b)	56. (b)	57. (c)	58. (a)	59. (b)	60. (c)
61. (d)	62. (a)	63. (a)	64. (d)	65. (a)	66. (c)	67. (a)	68. (b)	69. (c)	70. (c)
71. (c)	72. (d)	73. (d)	74 (d)	75. (c)	76. (b)	77. (d)	78. (d)	79. (a)	80. (b)
81. (a)									

Level-2

1. (a)	2. (b)	3. (d)	4. (b)	5. (d)	6. (d)	7. (d)	8. (d)	9. (b)	10. (c)
11. (d)	12. (d)	13. (d)	14. (b)	15. (b)	16. (d)	17. (b)	18. (d)	19. (b)	20. (b)
21. (d)	22. (c)	23. (b)	24. (d)	25. (b)	26. (d)	27. (b)	28. (a)	29. (c)	30. (d)
31. (c)	32. (b)	33. (d)	34. (c)	35. (a)	36. (d)	37. (b)	38. (d)	39. (c)	40. (b)
41. (c)	42. (b)	43. (b)							

Level-3

Passage–1	1. (c)	2. (a)	3. (a)	4. (a)
Passage–2	1. (a)	2. (b)	3. (d)	
Passage–3	1. (c)	2. (d)	3. (b)	
Passage–4	1. (b)	2. (c)	3. (a)	
Passage–5	1. (a)	2. (b)	3. (c)	

Passage–6	**1.** (a)	**2.** (a)	**3.** (c)	
Passage–7	**1.** (a)	**2.** (d)	**3.** (b)	**4.** (d)

One or More Answers is/are correct

1.	(a,c,d)	**2.**	(a,b)	**3.**	(a,b)	**4.**	(a,b,c,d)	**5.**	(a,b,c,d)	**6.**	(b,d)
7.	(c,d)	**8.**	(b,d)	**9.**	(a,b,c)	**10.**	(a,b,d)	**11.**	(a,b,d)	**12.**	(a,b,c,d)
13.	(a,c)	**14.**	(a,b)	**15.**	(a,c)	**16.**	(c,d)	**17.**	(a,b,c,d)	**18.**	(a,b,c)
19.	(a,b,d)	**20.**	(d)	**21.**	(b,c,d)	**22.**	(a,b,c)	**23.**	(a,b,c)	**24.**	(b,c)
25.	(a,b)	**26.**	(d)	**27.**	(a,b,c)	**28.**	(a,c,d)	**29.**	(a,b,c,d)	**30.**	(b,c)
31.	(a,d)	**32.**	(a,b,d)	**33.**	(a,b,d)	**34.**	(a,d)	**35.**	(a,d)	**36.**	(b,c)
37.	(a,c)	**38.**	(b,c,d)								

Match the Column

1. A → P, Q, R;	B → P, Q;	C → S, T;	D → P, S	
2. A → P, S;	B → Q, R;	C → P, Q, R, S, T;		D → P, S
3. A → Q, S, T;	B → P, Q;	C → R, S;	D → R, S	
4. A → R;	B → Q, R, S;	C → S;	D → P, Q	
5. A → P, S;	B → Q, T;	C → Q, R;	D → P	
6. A → R;	B → Q;	C → P, S;	D → Q	
7. A → Q, S;	B → R;	C → Q, R, S;	D → P	
8. A → S;	B → R,	C → Q;	D → P	
9. A → R;	B → S;	C → P;	D → Q	
10. A → Q, R, S;	B → P, Q, R, S;	C → Q, R;	D → P, Q, R	

Assertion-Reason Type Questions

1. (C)	**2.** (D)	**3.** (A)	**4.** (C)	**5.** (B)	**6.** (C)	**7.** (A)	**8.** (B)	**9.** (B)	**10.** (A)
11. (A)	**12.** (C)	**13.** (A)	**14.** (A)	**15.** (C)					

Hints and Solutions

Level 1

2. (b) From given reactions, Free energy of the reaction : $ZnO(g) + C(s) \xrightarrow[1000^\circ C]{\Delta} Zn(g) + CO(g)$, is negative.

37. (c) Zn is extracted from its sulphide ore by roasting followed by carbon reduction
Hg, Pb and Cu are extracted by self reduction from their sulphide ores.

40. (c) Cr metal is commercially extracted by Al-reduction method.

61. (d) From spelter pure zinc is obtained either by distillation or by electrolytic refining.

62. (a) Purification of Al metal : Hoop's Method

65. (a) Others are purification methods of bauxite ore.

67. (a) When impure metal has impurity of its own metal oxide, then Poling process is used, *e.g.*, impure Cu and Sn are purified by this method.

75. (c) $2AgCl + Na_2CO_3 \longrightarrow 2NaCl + Ag_2CO_3 \xrightarrow{\Delta} 2Ag + \frac{1}{2}O_2 + CO_2 \uparrow$

Level 2

2. (b) $\underset{(XCl_2)}{SnCl_2} + \underset{(YCl_2)}{HgCl_2} \longrightarrow \underset{(XCl_4)}{SnCl_4} + \underset{(Y)}{Hg}$

$HgO \xrightarrow[>400^\circ C]{\Delta} Hg + \frac{1}{2}O_2$

HgS : Cinnabar

8. (d) See Ellingham diagram.

10. (c) (I) $\underset{\text{(impure)}}{Ni} + 4CO \xrightarrow{50^\circ C} \underset{\text{(volatile)}}{[Ni(CO_4)]} \xrightarrow{230^\circ C} \underset{\text{(pure)}}{Ni} + 4CO \uparrow$

(II) $Cu_2S + \frac{3}{2}O_2 \xrightarrow{\Delta} Cu_2O + SO_2$

$Cu_2S + 2Cu_2O \xrightarrow[\text{temp.}]{\text{high}} 6Cu + SO_2$

(III) $MgCl_2(s) \xrightarrow{\text{electrolysis}} Mg^{2+}(l) + 2Cl^-(l)$

At cathode : $Mg^{2+} + 2e^- \longrightarrow Mg(s)$

At anode : $2Cl^-(l) \longrightarrow Cl_2(g) + 2e^-$

17. (b) $ZnS + 4NaCN \rightleftharpoons 4Na^+ + \underset{\text{water soluble}}{[Zn(CN)_4]^{2-}} + S^{2-}$

18. (d) $Ag_2S + 4NaCN \xrightarrow{\text{Air}} 2Na[Ag(CN)_2] + Na_2S$

$2Na[Ag(CN)_2] + \begin{pmatrix} \text{Zn} \\ \text{dust} \end{pmatrix} \longrightarrow Na_2[Zn(CN)_4] + 2Ag \downarrow$

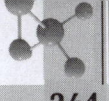

19. (b) Leaching is carried out for the concentration of argentite (Ag_2S).

(i) $$Ag_2S + 4NaCN \xrightarrow{Air} 2Na[Ag(CN)_2]^- + Na_2S \xrightarrow{Air} Na_2SO_4 + S$$

20. (b) Depressant is a substance that is added to suppress the floating characteristic of metal sulphide present as an impurity.

$$PbS + \underset{(Impurity)}{ZnS} \xrightarrow{4NaCN} \underset{\text{Soluble complex}}{Na_2[Zn(CN)_4]} + PbS$$

21. (d) Sodium ethyl xanthate acts as collector for sulphide ore.

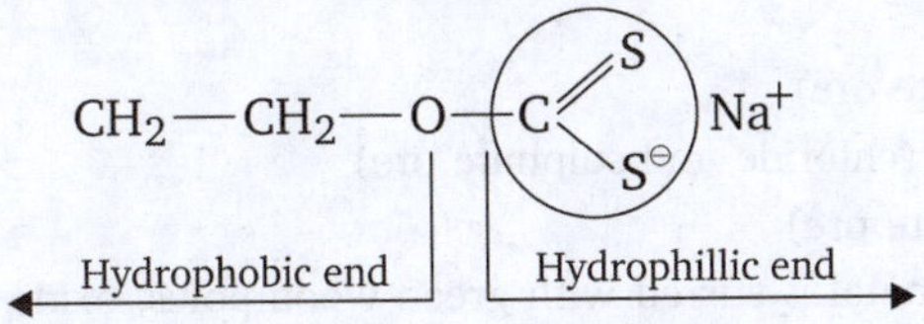

26. (d) (i) $Cr_2O_3 + 2Al\ (R.A.) \xrightarrow{\Delta} Al_2O_3 + 2Cr;\ \Delta H = -ve$

(ii) Mg is extracted by electrolysis of fused $MgCl_2$ and NaCl

(iii) $PbS + \frac{3}{2}O_2 \longrightarrow PbO + SO_2$

$PbO + C \longrightarrow Pb + CO$

(iv) Red Bauxite is purified by Baeyer's process

27. (b) Chromite $\xrightarrow{NaOH/air,\ \Delta} NaCrO_4 \xrightarrow{C,\ \Delta} Cr_2O_3 \xrightarrow{Al,\ \Delta} Cr$

32. (b) The reduction of metal oxides by aluminium powder is called Gold schmidt's aluminothermite process.

$$\underbrace{\underset{(3\ part)}{Cr_2O_3} + \underset{(1\ part)}{Al\ powder}}_{\text{Thermite mixture}} \xrightarrow[\text{Ignition mixture}]{Mg\ powder + BaO_2} \underset{(Molten)}{2Cr} + Al_2O_3 + Heat$$

38. (d) Metals, which are less reactive than Ag, remain in anode mud, and metals which are more reactive than Ag metal will be in electrolyte solution.

42. (b) $\underset{(Impure)}{Ni} + 4CO \xrightarrow{50° \text{ to } 60°C} \underset{\text{Volatile compound}}{[Ni(CO)_4]\uparrow} \xrightarrow[\text{Thermal decompotion}]{200 \text{ to } 230°C} \underset{Pure}{Ni} + 4CO\uparrow$

43. (b) Roasted mass obtained from roasting step is called **matte**. (98% Cu_2S + 2% FeS)

Level 3

ONE OR MORE ANSWERS IS/ARE CORRECT

21. (b, c, d)

The oxide ore (Fe_2O_3) is primarily reduced to iron by carbon monoxide

$$SiO_2 + CaO \longrightarrow CaSiO_3\ (Slag)$$

31. (a, d)

In extraction of Fe, Fe_2O_3 is primary reduced by CO below 710°C and acidic impurity of SiO_2 is removed in the form of $CaSiO_3$ (slag).

MATCH THE COLUMN

5. Ilmenite $FeTiO_3$ or $FeO \cdot TiO_2$
Dolomite $CaCO_3 \cdot MgCO_3$
Carnaollite $KCl \cdot MgCl_2 \cdot 6H_2O$
Chromite $FeCr_2O_4$ or $FeO \cdot Cr_2O_3$

6. Cuprite Cu_2O (oxide ore)
Cerussite $PbCO_3$ (carbonate ore)
Kainite $KCl \cdot MgSO_4 \cdot 3H_2O$ (chloride and sulphate ore)
Calamine $ZnCO_3$ (carbonate ore)

7. **Poling :** Impure molten metal is stirred with green wood poles, oxide impurities are removed, mainly used for Cu and Sn.
Cupellation is used when impurities are of other metals, mainly used for silver.
Electro-refining : Cu, Ag, Au, Cr, Zn, Ni, etc., are mainly purified by removing insoluble impurities as anode mud.
van Arkel method : (vapour phase refining) Metals like titanium, zirconium, thorium and uranium are purified by this method.

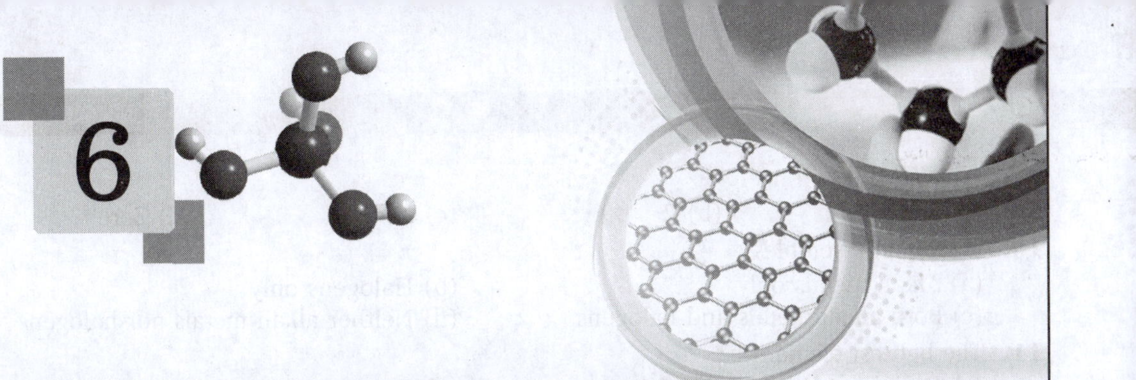

6 HYDROGEN AND ITS COMPOUNDS

Level 1

Dihydrogen

1. The sum number of neutrons and protons in radioactive isotopes of hydrogen is:
(a) 3 (b) 4 (c) 5 (d) 6

2. The most abundant isotope of hydrogen is:
(a) Tritium (b) Deuterium (c) Protium (d) Para hydrogen

3. Ordinary hydrogen at room temperature is a mixture of:
(a) 75% *o*-Hydrogen + 25% *p*-Hydrogen
(b) 25% *o*-Hydrogen + 75% *p*-Hydrogen
(c) 50% *o*-Hydrogen + 50% *p*-Hydrogen
(d) 1% *o*-Hydrogen + 99% *p*-Hydrogen

4. Hydrogen is:
(a) Electropositive element
(b) Electronegative element
(c) Both electropositive as well as electronegative element
(d) Neither electropositive nor electronegative element

5. Para hydrogen is:
(a) Less stable than ortho hydrogen
(b) More stable than ortho hydrogen
(c) As stable as ortho hydrogen
(d) None of these

6. Ratio of $o\text{-}H_2$ and $p\text{-}H_2$ at room temperature is:
(a) 1 : 1 (b) 3 : 1 (c) 1 : 3 (d) 2 : 5

7. Like halogens, hydrogen:
(a) shown +1 oxidation state
(b) liberated at anode
(c) metallic
(d) none of these

8. The catalyst used in process of manufacture of H_2 from water gas is:
(a) Finely divided Ni
(b) V_2O_5
(c) Pb
(d) $Fe_2O_3 + Cr_2O_3$

9. The n/p ratio for ${}_1H^1$ is:
(a) 1 (b) 2 (c) 3 (d) Zero

10. Hydrogen resembles:
(a) Alkali metals only (b) Halogens only
(c) Both alkali metals and halogens (d) Neither alkali metals nor halogens

11. The lightest element is:
(a) Nitrogen (b) Helium (c) Lithium (d) Hydrogen

12. Atomic hydrogen is obtained by:
(a) Electrolysis of heavy water
(b) Reaction of water with heavy metals
(c) Thermal decomposition of water
(d) Passing silent electric discharge through hydrogen at low pressure

13. Which of the following produces hydrolith with dihydrogen ?
(a) Mg (b) Al (c) Cu (d) Ca

14. Hydrogen economy refers to:
(a) economical use of hydrogen (b) use of hydrogen as fuel
(c) earning foreign currency (d) hydrogen dependent economy

15. Hydrogen cannot be placed with alkali metals because:
(a) it shows +1 oxidation state (b) it is liberated at cathode
(c) it has reducing properties (d) it is diatomic and non-metallic

16. Ionic hydrides react with water to give:
(a) Acidic solutions (b) Basic solutions (c) Hydride ion (d) Protons

17. Deuterium, an isotope of hydrogen is:
(a) Radioactive (b) Non-radioactive
(c) Heaviest (d) Lightest

Water (H_2O)

18. Both temporary and permanent hardness is removed on boiling water with:
(a) $Ca(OH)_2$ (b) Na_2CO_3 (c) $CaCO_3$ (d) CaO

19. High boiling point of water is due to:
(a) Its high specific heat (b) Hydrogen bonding
(c) High dielectric constant (d) Low dissociation constant

20. Temporary hardness is caused due to the presence of:
(a) $CaSO_4$ (b) $CaCl_2$ (c) $CaCO_3$ (d) $Ca(HCO_3)_2$

21. Density of ice is:
(a) less than water (b) more than water
(c) same as water (d) cannot be said

22. H — O — H bond angle is:
(a) 109° (b) 102° (c) 104.5° (d) 90°

23. Calgon, a water softner is:
(a) Sodium aluminosilicate (b) Sodium hexametaphosphate
(c) Sodium zeolite (d) Sodium bicarbonate

Hydrogen Peroxide (H_2O_2)

24. The bleaching properties of H_2O_2 are due to its:
(a) Reducing properties (b) Oxidising properties
(c) Unstable nature (d) Acidic nature

25. Hydrogen peroxide is manufactured by the auto-oxidation of:
(a) 2-ethylanthraquinol (b) Anthraquinone
(c) Naphthalene (d) Anthracene

26. Decomposition of H_2O_2 is retarded by:
(a) Acetanilide (b) MnO_2
(c) Zinc (d) Finely divided metals

27. H_2O_2 is prepared in the laboratory when:
(a) MnO_2 is added to dilute cold H_2SO_4
(b) BaO_2 is added to CO_2 bubbling through cold water
(c) PbO_2 is added to an acidified solution of $KMnO_4$
(d) Na_2O_2 is added to boiling water

28. Hydrogen peroxide has a:
(a) Linear structure (b) Pyramidal structure
(c) Closed book type structure (d) Half open book type structure

29. Which of the following is a true structure of H_2O_2?

(a) 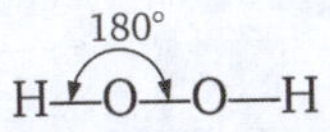

(b) 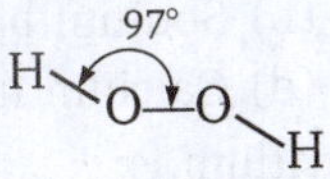

(c) 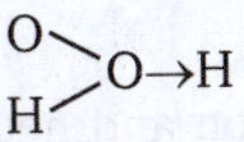

(d) 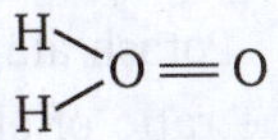

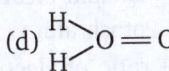

30. H_2O_2 is stored in:
(a) Iron container after addition of stabilizer
(b) Glass container after addition of stabilizer
(c) Plastic container after addition of stabilizer
(d) None

Level 2

1. Select correct order of boiling point:
(a) $H_2O > D_2O$ (b) $H_2 > T_2 > D_2$ (c) $H_2O_2 > H_2O$ (d) $(CH_3)_2O > H_2O$

2. Which set of properties has same value for D_2 and H_2?
(I) Bond length (II) Bond energy (III) Boiling point
(a) Only I (b) Only I and II (c) Only II, III (d) Only (II)

3. Gas that can not be collected over water is:
(a) N_2 (b) O_2 (c) SO_2 (d) PH_3

4. Zeolites are extensively used in:
(a) Softening of water and catalyst (b) Preparing heavy water
(c) Increasing the hardness of water (d) Mond's process

5. Ortho and Para hydrogen differ:
(a) In the number of protons (b) In the molecular mass
(c) In the nature of spins of protons (d) In the nature of spins of electrons

6. In Bosch's process which gas is utilised for the production of hydrogen:
(a) Producer gas (b) Water gas (c) Coal gas (d) Natural gas

7. Water softening by Clark's process uses:
(a) Calcium bicarbonate (b) Sodium bicarbonate
(c) Potash alum (d) Calcium hydroxide

8. The ratio of electron, proton and neutron in tritium is:
(a) 1 : 1 : 1 (b) 1 : 1 : 2 (c) 2 : 1 : 1 (d) 1 : 2 : 1

9. The adsorption of hydrogen by metals is called:
(a) Dehydrogenation (b) Hydrogenation (c) Occlusion (d) Adsorption

10. Water is said to be permanently hard when it contains:
(a) Sulphates of Mg and Ca
(b) Bicarbonates of Mg and Ca
(c) Sulphates of Cu and Hg
(d) Carbonates and bicarbonates of Mg and Ca

11. Which method can not be used to remove hardness of water?
(a) Clark's method (b) By adding washing soda
(c) Calgon process (d) Filtration

12. Which is not a water softener?
(a) Calgon (b) Permutit (c) Na_2CO_3 (d) Na_2SO_4

13. A molten ionic hydride on electrolysis gives:
(a) H^+ ions moving towards the cathode (b) H^+ ion moving towards the anode
(c) H_2 is liberated at anode (d) H_2 is liberated at cathode

14. Hardness of water is due to dissolved impurities of:
(a) Calcium and magnesium salts (b) Barium and magnesium salts
(c) Calcium and strontium salts (d) Sodium and potassium salts

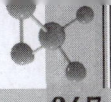

15. Calgon is an industrial name given to:
(a) Normal sodium phosphate (b) Sodium meta-aluminate
(c) Sodium hexametaphosphate (d) Hydrated sodium aluminium silicate

16. Permutit is:
(a) Hydrated sodium aluminium silicate (b) Sodium hexametaphosphate
(c) Sodium silicate (d) Sodium meta-aluminate

17. When zeolite, which is hydrated sodium aluminium silicate, is treated with hard water the sodium ions are exchanged with:
(a) H^+ ions (b) Ca^{2+} ions (c) SO_4^{2-} ions (d) OH^- ions

18. The gas used in the hydrogenation of oils in presence of nickel as a catalyst is:
(a) Methane (b) Ethane (c) Ozone (d) Hydrogen

19. The nuclei of tritium (H^3) atom would contain neutrons:
(a) 1 (b) 2 (c) 3 (d) 4

20. Ionic hydrides are usually:
(a) Good electrical conductors when solid (b) Easily reduced
(c) Good reducing agents (d) Liquid at room temperature

21. Which is poorest reducing agent?
(a) Nascent hydrogen (b) Atomic hydrogen
(c) Dihydrogen (d) All have same reducing strength

22. Hydrogen can be prepared by mixing steam and water gas at 500°C in the presence of Fe_2O_3 and Cr_2O_3. This process is called:
(a) Nelson process (b) Serpeck's process (c) Bosch process (d) Parke's process

23. Ortho hydrogen and para hydrogen resembles in which of the following property?
(a) Thermal conductivity (b) Magnetic properties
(c) Chemical properties (d) Heat capacity

24. Nascent hydrogen consists of:
(a) Hydrogen ions in the excited state (b) Hydrogen molecules with excess energy
(c) Solvated protons (d) Hydrogen atoms with excess energy

25. H_2 molecule has two electrons and two nuclei. In which form of hydrogen the spin of electrons and also the spin of nuclei in opposite directions?
(a) Ortho hydrogen (b) Para hydrogen (c) Meta hydrogen (d) β-hydrogen

26. Pure H_2O_2 is:
(a) Semi-solid (b) Liquid (c) Solid (d) Gas

27. The molecule of ortho hydrogen is distinguished from para hydrogen:
(a) Two electrons moving in opposite directions
(b) Two electrons moving in the same direction
(c) Two protons revolving in opposite directions
(d) Two protons revolving in the same direction

28. Ionic hydrides is:
(a) NH_3 (b) BeH_2 (c) MgH_2 (d) CaH_2

29. Hydrogen peroxide is now generally prepared on industrial scale by the:
(a) Action of H_2SO_4 on barium peroxide (b) Action of H_2SO_4 on sodium peroxide
(c) Electrolysis of 50% H_2SO_4 (d) Burning hydrogen in excess of oxygen

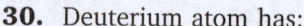

30. Deuterium atom has:
(a) One neutron and one proton
(b) One neutron and two protons
(c) Two neutrons and two protons
(d) None of these

31. H_2O_2 restores the colour of old lead paintings, blackened by the action of H_2S gas by:
(a) Converting PbO_2 to Pb
(b) By oxidising PbS to $PbSO_4$
(c) Converting $PbCO_3$ to Pb
(d) Oxidising $PbSO_3$ to $PbSO_4$

32. At absolute zero:
(a) Only para hydrogen exists
(b) Only ortho hydrogen exists
(c) Both para and ortho hydrogen exist
(d) None

33. Metals like platinum and palladium can adsorb large volumes of hydrogen under special conditions. Such adsorbed hydrogen by the metal is known as:
(a) Adsorbed hydrogen
(b) Occluded hydrogen
(c) Reactive hydrogen
(d) Atomic hydrogen

34. Correct order of occlusion property is:
(a) Pd > Pt > Au > Colloidal Pd > Pt
(b) Colloidal Pd > Pd > Pt > Au > Ni
(c) Ni < Au > Pt > Pd > Colloidal Pd
(d) Au > Pt > Pd > Ni > Colloidal Pd

Level 3

ONE OR MORE ANSWERS IS/ARE CORRECT

1. Which of the following statements concerning protium, deuterium and tritium is/are true?
(a) They are isotopes of each other
(b) They have similar electronic configurations
(c) They exist in the nature in the ratio of 1 : 2 : 3
(d) Their mass numbers are in the ratio of 1 : 2 : 3

2. Select **correct** statement for saline hydrides :
(a) Their aqueous solution is alkaline.
(b) Electrolysis of molten saline hydrides produces hydrogen gas at cathode.
(c) They produce hydrogen gas on reaction with water.
(d) They can be used for preparation of diborane.

3. Select **correct** statement for hydrogen peroxide:
(a) It is industrially prepared by air oxidation of 2-ethylanthraquinone.
(b) It is concentrated by distillation under reduced pressure.
(c) It is oxidized into oxygen by HOCl.
(d) It is used in the treatment of domestic and industrial effluents to reduce water pollution.

4. Which of the following statement is/are incorrect ?
(a) Hydrogen has same ionisation potential as sodium
(b) H has same electronegativity as halogens
(c) It can not be liberated at anode
(d) H has oxidation state +1 and −1

5. Which of the following is/are true?
(a) Hardness of water is shown by its behaviour towards soap
(b) The temporary hardness is due to the presence of Ca and Mg bicarbonates
(c) Permanent hardness is due to the presence of soluble Ca and Mg sulphates and chloride
(d) Permanent hardness can be removed by boiling the water

6. Hydrogen peroxide is:
(a) A reducing agent
(b) An oxidising agent
(c) A dehydrating agent
(d) A bleaching agent

7. What is/are the true about Lane's process?
(a) Method is used for manufacture of dihydrogen
(b) It involves the oxidation of iron by steam
(c) It involves the reduction of steam by iron
(d) It involves the oxidation of water gas

8. Which statement is/are correct?
(a) Ordinary hydrogen is an equilibrium mixture of ortho and para hydrogen
(b) In ortho hydrogen spin of two nuclei is in same direction

(c) Ortho and para forms do not resemble in their chemical properties
(d) In para hydrogen spin of two nuclei is in opposite direction

9. Incorrect statement is/are:
(a) Reaction of H_2 with Cl_2 is 13 times faster than deuterium
(b) D_2 is more readily adsorbed than H_2
(c) D_2 radioactive isotope
(d) D_2 is heaviest among all isotopes.

10. $MnO_4^- \xrightarrow{(x)} Mn^{2+} \xrightarrow{(y)} Mn^{4+}$

$MnO_4^- \xrightarrow{(z)} MnO_2$

In the above reaction x, y, z are respectively:
(a) $H_2O_2/H^+, H_2O_2/OH^-, H_2O_2/OH^-$
(b) $H_2O_2/OH^-, H_2O_2/OH^-, H_2O_2/H^+$
(c) $H_2O_2/OH^-, H_2O_2/H^+, H_2O_2/H^+$
(d) $H_2O_2/H^+, H_2O_2/H^+, H_2O_2/OH^-$

11. The reaction $H_2S + H_2O \longrightarrow S + 2H_2O$ shows:
(a) Acidic nature of H_2O_2
(b) Alkaline of H_2O_2
(c) Oxidising nature of H_2O_2
(d) Reducing nature of H_2O_2

12. Which can adsorb largest volumes of hydrogen gas?
(a) Colloidal solution of palladium
(b) Finely divided nickel
(c) Colloidal ferric hydroxide
(d) Finely divided platinum

13. H_2O_2 reduces $K_3[Fe(CN)_6]$ in:
(a) Neutral solution (b) Acidic solution (c) Alkaline solution (d) Non-polar medium

14. The exhausted permutit is generally regenerated by percolating through it in a solution of:
(a) Sodium chloride
(b) Calcium chloride
(c) Magnesium chloride
(d) Potassium chloride

15. Permanent hardness of water can be removed by adding calgon $(NaPO_3)_n$. This is an example of:
(a) Adsorption
(b) Exchange of ion
(c) Precipitation
(d) None of these

16. H_2O_2 can be prepared by:
(a) Oxidation of 2-ethylanthraquinol
(b) Passing CO_2 in paste of BaO_2 in water
(c) Electrolysis of concentrated H_2SO_4
(d) All of these

17. The difference between ortho and para hydrogen is:
(a) Ortho is more stable than para
(b) Conductivity of ortho is more than para
(c) Magnetic moment of ortho is zero
(d) All of these

MATCH THE COLUMN

1. Match Column I with Column II and select the correct answer using the codes given below the Columns:

Column-I	Column-II
(A) Heavy water	(P) Bicarbonates of Mg and Ca in water
(B) Temporary hardness	(Q) lather with soap water
(C) Soft water	(R) D_2O
(D) Permanent hardness	(S) Sulphates and chloride of Mg and Ca

ASSERTION-REASON TYPE QUESTIONS

These questions consist of two statements each, printed as assertion and reason, while answering these questions you are required to choose any one of the following responses.

(A) If both assertion and reason are true and the reason is the correct explanation of assertion

(B) If both assertion and reason are true but reason is not the correct explanation of assertion

(C) If assertion is true but the reason is false

(D) If assertion is false but the reason is true

1. **Assertion** : o-H_2 and p-H_2 can be considered allotropes of hydrogen.
   Reason : o-H_2 and p-H_2 resemble in chemical proportion but differ in physical properties.
2. **Assertion** : Hydrides of *d* block elements have metallic lusture.
   Reason : Hydrogen occupies some interstitial spaces.
3. **Assertion** : Temporary hardness can be removed by boiling.
   Reason : Mg^{2+} and Ca^{2+} are precipitated in form of carbonates due to boiling.
4. **Assertion** : BeH_2 and MgH_2 are covalent in nature.
   Reason : *p*-block elements form covalent hydrides.

SUBJECTIVE PROBLEMS

1. Which of the following combinations produce H_2 gas?

(i) Zn + dilute HCl, (ii) Zn + dilute H_2SO_4,

(iii) $Al + KOH + H_2O$, (iv) $NaH + H_2O$,

(v) $NH_3 + H_2O$ (vi) $K_2Cr_2O_7/H^+ + H_2O_2$,

(vii) $BaO_2 + H_2SO_4$ (dilute) (viii) $BaCO_3 + H_2SO_4$ (conc.)

Answers

Level-1

1. (a)	2. (c)	3. (a)	4. (c)	5. (a)	6. (b)	7. (b)	8. (d)	9. (d)	10. (c)
11. (d)	12. (d)	13. (d)	14. (b)	15. (d)	16. (b)	17. (b)	18. (b)	19. (b)	20. (d)
21. (a)	22. (c)	23. (b)	24. (b)	25. (a)	26. (a)	27. (b)	28. (d)	29. (b)	30. (c)

Level-2

1. (c)	2. (a)	3. (c)	4. (a)	5. (c)	6. (b)	7. (d)	8. (b)	9. (c)	10. (a)
11. (d)	12. (d)	13. (c)	14. (a)	15. (c)	16. (a)	17. (b)	18. (d)	19. (b)	20. (c)
21. (c)	22. (c)	23. (c)	24. (d)	25. (b)	26. (b)	27. (d)	28. (d)	29. (c)	30. (a)
31. (b)	32. (a)	33. (b)	34. (b)						

Level-3

One or More Answers is/are correct

1. (a,b,d)	2. (a, c, d)	3. (b, c, d)	4. (a, b, c)	5. (a, b, c)	6. (a, b, d)
7. (a, b, c)	8. (a, b, d)	9. (b, c, d)	10. (a)	11. (c)	12. (a)
13. (c)	14. (a)	15. (b)	16. (d)	17. (a)	

Match the Column

1. $A \rightarrow R$; $B \rightarrow P$; $C \rightarrow Q$; $D \rightarrow S$

Assertion-Reason Type Questions

1. (a) 2. (a) 3. (a) 4. (b)

Subjective Problems

1. (4)

Hints and Solutions

Level 1

16. *s*-block elements form ionic hydrides which form basic hydroxide with water. Ex— NaOH

17. For, ${}_1D^2$, the $\frac{n}{p} = \frac{1}{1} = 1$. Hence, it is a stable nucleus.

23. Calgon removes Ca and Mg ions from hard water by forming a soluble complex.

$$\underset{\text{Hard water}}{2Ca^{2+}} + \underset{\text{Calgon}}{Na_2[Na_4(PO_3)_6]} \longrightarrow \underset{\text{Soluble complex}}{Na_2[Ca_2(PO_3)_6]} + 2Na^+$$

Level 3

ONE OR MORE ANSWERS IS/ARE CORRECT

2. Electrolysis of molten saline hydrides produces hydrogen gas at anode.

3. It is industrially prepared by air oxidation of 2-ethylanthraquinol.

10.

$$MnO_4^- \xrightarrow{H_2O_2/H^+} Mn^{2+} \xrightarrow{H_2O_2/OH^-} Mn^{4+}$$

$$MnO_4^- \xrightarrow{H_2O_2/OH^-} MnO_2$$

11. H_2O_2 oxidises H_2S to sulphur, it shows its oxidising nature.

12. Amount to hydrogen occluded metal in decreasing order are:

Colloidal Pd > Pd > Pt > Au > Ni

13. $2K_3[Fe(CN)_6] + 2KOH + H_2O_2 \longrightarrow 2K_4[Fe(CN)_6)] + 2H_2O + O_2$

14. $CaZ + 2NaCl \longrightarrow Na_2Z + CaCl_2$

15. $(NaPO_3)_n$ is used in calgon process, it forms soluble complex with Ca^{2+} and Mg^{2+} ions.

16. All methods are suitable for preparation of H_2O_2.

17. At room temp. ratio of *o*-H_2 and *p*-H_2 is 3 : 1.

SUBJECTIVE PROBLEMS

1. Zn + dilute HCl, Zn + dilute H_2SO_4,

$Al + KOH + H_2O$, $NaH + H_2O$ will produce H_2 gas.

7

s-BLOCK ELEMENTS

Level 1

Alkali Metals

1. Sodium bicarbonate has :

(a) Ionic bond (b) Covalent bond (c) Hydrogen bond (d) All of these

2. Which of the following metal on burning in moist air does not give smell of ammonia ?

(a) Mg (b) Ca (c) K (d) Li

3. For the alkali metals, which of the following increases with increasing atomic number?

(a) First ionization energy (b) Electronegativity

(c) Hydration energy of the univalent ion (d) Atomic radius

4. Among the carbonates of alkali metals which one has highest thermal stability?

(a) Cs_2CO_3 (b) Rb_2CO_3 (c) K_2CO_3 (d) Na_2CO_3

5. Which of the following is most soluble in water?

(a) $CsClO_4$ (b) $NaClO_4$ (c) $KClO_4$ (d) $LiClO_4$

6. A solution of sodium in liquid ammonia is blue in colour due to :

(a) the presence of ions Na^+ (b) the presence of ammoniated electron

(c) the formation of $NaNH_2$ (d) the formation of sodium hydride

7. The basicity of the hydroxides of the following alkali metals is of the order :

(a) Li > Na > Rb > Cs (b) Na > Li > Rb > Cs

(c) Cs > Rb > Na > Li (d) Rb > Cs > Na > Li

8. The metallic lustre exhibited by sodium is explained by :

(a) diffusion of Na^+ ions (b) oscillation of loose electrons

(c) excitation of free protons (d) existence of body-centered cubic lattice

9. Soda lime is made from :

(a) $Na + CaO + H_2O$ (b) $CaO + NaOH(aq)$

(c) $NaOH + CaCO_3$ (d) $NaHCO_3 + CaO$

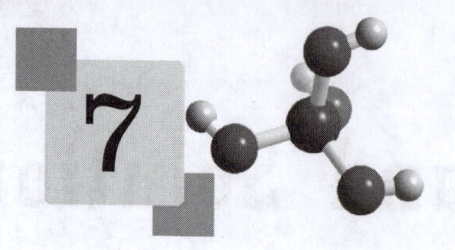

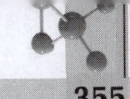

10. The compound called microcosmic salt is :
(a) $Na_2HPO_4 \cdot 2H_2O$ (b) $Na(NH_4)HPO_4 \cdot 4H_2O$
(c) $Na_2NH_4PO_4 \cdot 2H_2O$ (d) $(NH_4)_2HPO_4 \cdot 2H_2O$

11. Potassium when heated strongly in oxygen, it forms :
(a) K_2O (b) KO_2 (c) K_2O_2 (d) KO_3

12. When a concentrated solution of ammonia is saturated with sodium chloride in the presence of pieces of dry ice, a water cloud forms. This is due to the :
(a) precipitation of sodium carbonate from the reaction mixture
(b) precipitation of sodium hydrogen carbonate from the reaction mixture
(c) precipitation of ammonium hydrogen carbonate from the mixture
(d) precipitation of ammonium carbonate

13. The compound formed on heating sodium metal in a current of dry ammonia gas, is :
(a) sodium imide (b) sodium nitrite (c) sodium amide (d) sodium azide

14. Which of the following compounds is not obtained when the products obtained from the electrolysis of brine are mixed?
(a) NaCl (b) H_2 (c) NaOCl (d) Cl_2

15. When dry ammonia gas is passed over heated sodium (in absence of air) the product formed is :
(a) sodium hydride (b) sodium nitride
(c) sodamide (d) sodium cyanamide

16. Which of the following compounds liberate(s) oxygen on heating?
(a) Li_2CO_3 (b) LiOH
(c) $LiNO_3$ (d) NaOH

17. Sodium peroxide is used to purify the air in submarines and confined spaces because :
(a) it removes CO_2 and produces O_2
(b) it decomposes to form Na_2O
(c) it reacts with oxygen to form sodium superoxide
(d) none of these

18. Which of the following salt is known as washing soda?
(a) Na_2CO_3 (b) $Na_2CO_3 \cdot H_2O$
(c) $Na_2CO_3 \cdot 10H_2O$ (d) $Na_2CO_3 \cdot 5H_2O$

19. Which of the following compounds is formed when sodium burns in excess supply of air?
(a) Sodium suboxide (b) Sodium oxide
(c) Sodium peroxide (d) Sodium superoxide

20. Glauber's salt is :
(a) Na_2SO_4 (b) $Na_2SO_4 \cdot H_2O$
(c) $Na_2SO_4 \cdot 5H_2O$ (d) $Na_2SO_4 \cdot 10H_2O$

21. Sodium hydroxide is produced on a large scale :
(a) by the hydrolysis of Na_2CO_3
(b) by the electrolysis of an aqueous solution of NaCl
(c) by adding water to sodium oxide
(d) by reacting sodium with water

22. Which of the following metal is used in flash bulbs?
(a) Be (b) Mg
(c) Ca (d) Ba

23. The pairs of compounds which cannot exist together in aqueous solution are :
(I) NaH_2PO_4 and Na_2HCO_3 (II) Na_2CO_3 and $NaHCO_3$
(III) NaOH and NaH_2PO_4 (IV) $NaHCO_3$ and NaOH
(a) I, II, III (b) III, IV
(c) I, IV (d) II, III

24. Which one on reaction with NaOH solution gives inflammable gas?
(a) S (b) Zn
(c) NH_4Cl (d) I_2

25. In the reaction $LiH + AlH_3 \rightarrow LiAlH_4$, AlH_3 and LiH acts as :
(a) Lewis acid and Lewis base (b) Lewis base and Lewis acid
(c) Bronsted base and Bronsted acid (d) None of these

26. Which of the following is the most important factor in making lithium metal, the strongest reducing agent?
(a) Ionisation energy (b) Hydration energy (c) Heat of sublimation (d) None of these

27. Which set of compounds in the following pair of ionic compounds has the higher lattice energy ?
(i) KCl and MgO (ii) LiF and LiBr (iii) Mg_3N_2 and NaCl
(a) KCl, LiBr, Mg_2N_2 (b) MgO, LiBr, Mg_3N_2
(c) MgO, LiF, NaCl (d) MgO, LiF, Mg_3N_2

28. Sodium bicarbonate has:
(a) ionic bond (b) covalent bond
(c) hydrogen bond (d) all of these

29. Compound having lowest melting point:
(a) LiCl (b) CsCl
(c) RbCl (d) KCl

30. Incorrect statement is :
(a) $NaHCO_3$ and $KHCO_3$ have same crystal structure
(b) On heating $LiNO_3$ decomposes into Li_2O and NO_2
(c) Among alkali metals, Li metal impart red colour to flame
(d) Li_2SO_4 does not form alum

31. The solubility of metal halides depends on their nature, lattice enthalpy and hydration enthalpy of the individual ions. Amongst fluorides of alkali metals, the lowest solubility of LiF in water is due to :
(a) Ionic nature of lithium fluoride (b) High lattice enthalpy
(c) High hydration enthalpy of lithium ion (d) Low ionisation enthalpy of lithium atom

32. The reducing power of a metal depends on various factors. Suggest the factor which makes Li metal the strongest reducing agent in aqueous solution :
(a) Sublimation enthalpy (b) Ionisation enthalpy
(c) Hydration enthalpy (d) Electron-gain enthalpy

Alkaline Earth Metals

33. Mg_2C_3 reacts with water forming propyne gas. C_3^{4-} ions has :

(a) two sigma and two pi bonds (b) three sigma and one pi bond
(c) two sigma and one pi bond (d) two sigma and three pi bonds

34. The fluoride which is most soluble in water is :

(a) CaF_2 (b) BaF_2 (c) SrF_2 (d) BeF_2

35. The highest occupied energy level of the group 2 elements radius is $7s^2$, which of these statements is likely to be incorrect?

(a) The element will show an oxidation state of +II in all its compounds
(b) The element will decompose water, liberating hydrogen
(c) Hydroxide of the element will be amphoteric
(d) Metal carbonate is relative stable at higher temperature than calcium carbonate

36. Amongst the following hydroxides, the one which has the highest value of K_{sp} at ordinary temperature is :

(a) $Mg(OH)_2$ (b) $Ca(OH)_2$ (c) $Sr(OH)_2$ (d) $Ba(OH)_2$

37. Which of the following alkaline earth metal hydroxides is the least soluble in water?

(a) $Be(OH)_2$ (b) $Mg(OH)_2$
(c) $Ca(OH)_2$ (d) $Ba(OH)_2$

38. The thermal stability of $BaCO_3, CaCO_3, SrCO_3$ and $MgCO_3$ decreases in the order :

(a) $BaCO_3 > SrCO_3 > MgCO_3 > CaCO_3$ (b) $CaCO_3 > SrCO_3 > MgCO_3 > BaCO_3$
(c) $MgCO_3 > CaCO_3 > SrCO_3 > BaCO_3$ (d) $BaCO_3 > SrCO_3 > CaCO_3 > MgCO_3$

39. Magnesium cation has polarising power close to that of :

(a) Li^+ (b) Na^+ (c) K^+ (d) Cs^+

40. Which of the following salt does not impart colour to the flame?

(a) $MgCl_2$ (b) $SrCl_2$ (c) $BaCl_2$ (d) LiCl

41. Mortar is mixture of :

(a) $Ca(OH)_2$, silica and water (b) $CaCO_3$ and SiO_2
(c) CaO and silica (d) $CaCO_3, SiO_2$ and water

42. When $MgCl_2 \cdot 6H_2O$ is strongly heated, then it forms :

(a) MgO (b) $Mg(OH)_2$
(c) Mg(OH)Cl (d) $MgCl_2$

43. A piece of magnesium ribbon is heated to redness in an atmosphere of nitrogen and on cooling with water, the evolved gas is :

(a) ammonia (b) hydrogen
(c) nitrogen (d) oxygen

44. Plaster of Paris when mixed with the correct amount of water sets into a solid mass due to the formation of :

(a) $CaSO_4$ (b) $(CaSO_4)_2 \cdot H_2O$
(c) $CaSO_4 \cdot 2H_2O$ (d) CaO

45. Plaster of Paris is :

(a) $CaSO_4$ (b) $CaSO_4 \cdot 7H_2O$
(c) $2CaSO_4 \cdot H_2O$ (d) $CaSO_4 \cdot 2H_2O$

46. Magnesium liberates H_2 on reaction with :
(a) dil. HCl (b) dil. H_2SO_4
(c) very dil. HNO_3 (d) all of these

47. At high temperature, nitrogen combines with CaC_2 to give :
(a) calcium cyanide (b) calcium cyanamide
(c) calcium carbonate (d) calcium nitride

48. Calcium hydride on hydrolysis forms?
(a) $CaO + H_2$ (b) $Ca(OH)_2$ only
(c) $Ca(OH)_2 + H_2$ (d) only CaO

49. Magnesium wire is heated in the atmosphere of CO_2 then :
(a) magnesium acts as an oxidising agent
(b) magnesium has two electrons in the outermost shell
(c) magnesium acts as a reducing agent and removes oxygen from CO_2
(d) none of the above

50. Na and Li are placed in dry air, we get:
(a) NaOH, Na_2O, Li_2O (b) Na_2O, Li_2O
(c) Na_2O, Li_2O, Li_3N, NH_3 (d) Na_2O, Li_3N, Li_2O

51. Amongst LiCl, RbCl, $BeCl_2$, $MgCl_2$, the compounds with greatest and least ionic character respectively are :
(a) LiCl and RbCl (b) RbCl and $BeCl_2$
(c) RbCl and $MgCl_2$ (d) $MgCl_2$ and $BeCl_2$

52. Coloured compound is obtained on heating which of the following metal in excess oxygen:
(a) Li (b) Al
(c) Mg (d) K

53. By adding gypsum to cement :
(a) Setting time of cement becomes less (b) Setting time of cement increases
(c) Colour of cement becomes light (d) Shining surface is obtained

54. A compound (*A*) is used in preparation of washing soda to recover ammonia in Solvay's process. When CO_2 is bubbled through an aqueous solution of (*A*), the solution turns milky. It is used in white washing due to disinfectant nature. What is the chemical formula of *A*?
(a) $Ca(HCO_3)_2$ (b) CaO
(c) $Ca(OH)_2$ (d) $CaCO_3$

55. Select incorrect statement for hydrides of *s*-block metals:
(a) Most of *s*-block metals from saline or ionic hydrides
(b) Significant covalent character is found in LiH, BeH_2, MgH_2
(c) Saline hydrides are crystalline, non volatile and nonconducting in solid state
(d) Presence of H^- ion in saline hydrides is confirmed by liberation of hydrogen gas at cathode on electrolysis of their melts

Level 2

Alkali Metals

1. $KO_2 + CO_2(\text{excess}) + H_2O \longrightarrow [X] + [Y]$
Products [X] and [Y] are respectively :
(a) K_2CO_3, O_2 (b) $KHCO_3, O_2$ (c) KOH, K_2CO_3 (d) $KHCO_3, H_2O$

2. The correct order of increasing solubility in water is :
(a) KF < NaF < LiF (b) $NaHCO_3 < KHCO_3 < RbHCO_3$
(c) $K_2CO_3 < Na_2CO_3 < Li_2CO_3$ (d) $LiNO_3 < NaNO_3 < KNO_3$

3. Which of the following carbonate salt is soluble due to high entropy change ?
(a) K_2CO_3 (b) Li_2CO_3 (c) $(NH_4)_2CO_3$ (d) Na_2CO_3

4. Oxygen gas is not produced by thermal decomposition of :
(a) $Mg(NO_3)_2$ (b) Na_2CO_3 (c) H_2O_2 (d) PbO_2

5. Li does not resemble with other alkali metals in following properties :
(a) Li_2CO_3 decomposes into oxides while other alkali metal carbonates are thermally stable
(b) LiCl is predominantly covalent
(c) Li_3N is formed, when Li metal is heated with N_2 gas
(d) all are correct

6. Which of the following statement about the sulphate of alkali metal is correct?
(a) Except Li_2SO_4 all sulphate of other alkali metals are soluble in water
(b) All sulphate salts of alkali metals except lithium sulphate forms alum.
(c) All sulphate salts of alkali metals except lithium sulphate do not decompose at high temperature
(d) All of the above

7. Alkali metals possess metallic lustre when freshly cut because :
(a) they have a hard surface and light is reflected back
(b) their crystal structure contains ordered arrangement of constituent atoms
(c) they contain loosely bound electrons which absorb the photons and then re-emit
(d) they are obtained from the minerals on which light has been falling for years

8. Select incorrect statement :
(a) Li_2CO_3 is only sparingly soluble in water and no $LiHCO_3$ has been isolated
(b) K_2CO_3 can not be made by a method similar to the solvey process
(c) Li_2CO_3 and $MgCO_3$ both are thermally stable
(d) $Na_2CO_3{\cdot}NaHCO_3{\cdot}2H_2O$ is a mineral called trona

9. Melting point of a mixture of $Na_2CO_3 + K_2CO_3$, mixture is :
(a) higher than that of Na_2CO_3
(b) higher than that of K_2CO_3
(c) lower than that of both Na_2CO_3 and K_2CO_3
(d) lower than that of K_2CO_3 only

10. Select **incorrect** statement :
(a) Stability of peroxides and superoxides of alkali metals increases with increases in size of the metal ion
(b) NaOH does not absorb water from atmosphere

(c) Increases in stability in (a) is due to stabilisation of large anions by larger cations through lattice energy effects
(d) The low solubility of LiF is due to its high lattice energy whereas low solubility of CsI is due to smaller hydration energy

11. The alkali metals dissolve in liquid NH_3, it is found that :
(a) the dilute solution are blue but the colour changes to bronze with increasing concentration
(b) the blue colour is due to the presence of solvated electrons
(c) the blue solutions are paramagnetic but the bronze coloured solutions are diamagnetic
(d) all the facts given above are found

12. Among the nitrate of alkali metals which one can be decomposed to its oxide on strong heating?
(a) $NaNO_3$ (b) KNO_3 (c) $LiNO_3$ (d) All of these

13. When a standard solution of NaOH is left in air for a few hours :
(a) a precipitate will form
(b) strength of solution will decrease
(c) the strength of solution will increase
(d) the concentration of Na^+ ion in solution will remains same

14. Addition of Na_2CO_3 to a solution of an oxide in water produces CO_2. This experiment indicates that :
(a) the oxide is basic (b) the oxide is amphoteric
(c) the oxide is that of a metal (d) the oxide is that of a non-metal

15. Salt $A + S \longrightarrow B \xrightarrow{BaCl_2}$ White ppt.
A is paramagnetic in nature and contains about 55% K. Thus, A is :
(a) K_2O (b) K_2O_2 (c) KO_2 (d) K_2SO_4

16. Baking powder used to make cake is a mixture of starch, $NaHCO_3$ and $Ca(H_2PO_4)_2$. The function of $Ca(H_2PO_4)_2$ is :
(a) to show down the release of CO_2 gas
(b) being acidic in nature and gives CO_2 when moistened with $NaHCO_3$
(c) to act as a filler
(d) None of the above

17. To an acidified dichromate solution, a pinch of Na_2O_2 is added and shaken. What is observed?
(a) Blue colour (b) Orange colour changing to green directly
(c) Copious evolution of oxygen (d) Bluish-green precipitate

18. Select incorrect statement for alkali metals:
(a) Their pure dilute solutions in liquid NH_3 have same colour.
(b) They all form basic carbonates.
(c) Superoxides of K, Rb and cs act better oxidants than their respective peroxides.
(d) Their chlorides exist in anhydrous state except that of lithium.

19. Which of the following statements is incorrect?
(a) Sodium and potassium are soft and silvery white metals
(b) Sodium and potassium in air get tarnished due to the formation of a layer of oxide or carbonates

(c) Sodium and potassium burn in dry oxygen (excess) giving peroxides
(d) Sodium and potassium are kept under kerosene to avoid the contact with air and moisture

20. Nitrogen dioxide cannot be obtained from :
(a) $Cu(NO_3)_2$ (b) $Hg(NO_3)_2$ (c) $NaNO_3$ (d) $AgNO_3$

21. $'A' + H_2O \longrightarrow NaOH$; $'A' \xrightarrow[400°C]{O_2} B \xrightarrow[at\ 25°C]{H_2O} NaOH + O_2$

B is used for oxygenating in submarine. *A* and *B* are :
(a) Na_2O_2 and Na_2O (b) Na_2O and Na_2O_2
(c) Na_2O_2 and O_2 (d) Na_2O and O_2

22. $CaCl_2$ is preferred over NaCl for clearing ice on roads particularly in very cold countries. This is because :
(a) $CaCl_2$ is less soluble in H_2O than NaCl
(b) $CaCl_2$ is hygroscopic but NaCl is not
(c) Eutectic mixture of $CaCl_2/H_2O$ freezes at –55°C while that of $NaCl/H_2O$ freezes at –18°C
(d) NaCl makes the road slipperty but $CaCl_2$ does not

23. A metal which does not react with nitrogen is :
(a) Li (b) K (c) Ca (d) Mg

24. The pair of compounds which cannot exist together in aqueous solution is :
(I) NaH_2PO_4 and $NaHCO_3$ (II) Na_2CO_3 and $NaHCO_3$
(III) NaOH and NaH_2PO_2 (IV) $NaHCO_3$ and NaOH
(a) I, II, III (b) II, III (c) III, IV (d) only IV

Alkaline Earth Metals

25. The incorrect order of solubility in water is :
(a) $Ca(OH)_2 < Sr(OH)_2 < Ba(OH)_2$ (b) $Li_2CO_3 < Na_2CO_3 < K_2CO_3$
(c) $CsNO_3 < RbNO_3 < KNO_3$ (d) $BaS_2O_3 < MgS_2O_3 < CaS_2O_3$

26. Which metal bicarbonates does not exist in solid state?
(i) $LiHCO_3$ (ii) $Ca(HCO_3)_2$ (iii) $Zn(HCO_3)_2$ (iv) $AgHCO_3$
(a) i, ii, iii, iv (b) i, ii, iii (c) i, ii, iv (d) ii, iii, iv

27. Which of the following order is correct ?
(a) $K^+ < Ca^{2+} < P^{3-} < S^{2-}$: Ionic size
(b) $Na^+_{(aq.)} > K^+_{(aq.)} > Rb^+_{(aq.)} > Cs^+_{(aq.)}$: Electrical conductance
(c) $Al^{3+}_{(aq.)} > Mg^{2+}_{(aq.)} > Na^+_{(aq.)}$: Hydrated size
(d) $I^-_{(aq.)} < Br^-_{(aq.)} < Cl^-_{(aq.)} < F^-_{(aq.)}$: Ionic mobility

28. Metal M + air $\xrightarrow{\Delta} A \xrightarrow{H_2O} B \xrightarrow{HCl}$ White fumes; Metal *M* can be :
(a) Li, Mg (b) Li, Al or K
(c) Na, K or Mg (d) Li, Na or K

29. *X* and *Y* are two metals. When burnt in air, *X* forms only oxide while *Y* forms oxide and nitride. The metals *X* and *Y* may be :
(a) Ca and Mg (b) Na and Mg
(c) Li and Na (d) Na and K

30. Which is incorrect statement?

(a) The heats of hydration of the dipositive alkaline earth metal ions decrease with an increase in their ionic size

(b) $NaNO_3$ forms Na_2O_2 on heating

(c) Hydration of alkali metal ion is less than that of IIA group

(d) Alkaline earth metal ions, because of their much larger charge to size ratio, exert a much stronger electrostatic attraction on the oxygen of water molecule surrounding them

31. Which of the following statement is not related to similarties between beryllium and aluminium?

(a) Both Be^{2+} and Al^{3+} ions can form fluorido complex ion.

(b) Both beryllium and aluminium become passive in presence of concentrated HNO_3.

(c) Both beryllium and aluminium from ionic fluorides.

(d) Both beryllium and aluminium from polymeric chlorides.

32. Thermal stability of MCO_3 is in order :

(a) $BeCO_3 < MgCO_3 < CaCO_3 < SrCO_3 < BaCO_3$

(b) $MgCO_3 < BeCO_3 < CaCO_3 < SrCO_3 < BaCO_3$

(c) $CaCO_3 < SrCO_3 < BaCO_3 < BeCO_3 < MgCO_3$

(d) $BaCO_3 < SrCO_3 < CaCO_3 < MgCO_3 < BeCO_3$

33. Select incorrect statement about alkaline earth metals :

(a) Solubility of sulphates decreases down the group

(b) Solubility of hydroxides decreases down the group

(c) Thermal stability of carbonates increases down the group

(d) Basic nature increases down the group

34. In polymeric $(BeCl_2)_n$, there are :

(a) three centre four-electron bonds (b) three centre three-electron bonds

(c) two centre three-electron bonds (d) two centre two-electron bonds

35. A metal is burnt in air and the ash on moistening smells of NH_3. The metal is :

(a) Na (b) Fe (c) Mg (d) Al

36. Which is not obtained when metal carbides react with H_2O?

(a) $Al_4C_3 + H_2O \longrightarrow CH{\equiv}CH$ (b) $CaC_2 + H_2O \longrightarrow CH{\equiv}CH$

(c) $Mg_4C_3 + H_2O \longrightarrow CH_3C{\equiv}CH$ (d) $Be_2C + H_2O \longrightarrow CH_4$

37. Choose incorrect statement :

(a) $BeCO_3$ is kept in the atmosphere of CO_2 since, it is least thermally stable

(b) Be dissolves in alkali forming $[Be(OH)_4]^{2-}$

(c) BeF_2 forms complex ion with NaF in which Be goes with cation

(d) BeF_2 forms complex ion with NaF in which Be goes with anion

38. II A (alkaline earth metals) and II B (zinc family) resemble :

(a) $MgSO_4 \cdot 7H_2O$ is isomorphous with $ZnSO_4 \cdot 7H_2O$

(b) II A and II B cations are not precipitated by H_2S in acidic medium

(c) both (a) and (b)

(d) none of the above

39. Select the correct statement :
(a) Be and Al show diagonal relationship
(b) Be forms tetrahedral complexes $[Be(C_2O_4)_2]^{2-}$
(c) Al forms AlF_6^{3-} , an octahedral complex
(d) All are correct statements

40. Calcium imide on hydrolysis gives gas (*B*) which on oxidation by bleaching powder gives gas (*C*). Gas (*C*) on reaction with magnesium give compound (*D*) which on hydrolysis gives again gas (*B*). Identify (*B*), (*C*) and (*D*).
(a) NH_3, N_2, Mg_3N_2
(b) $N_2, NH_3, MgNH$
(c) $N_2, N_2O_5, Mg(NO_3)_2$
(d) $NH_3, NO_2, Mg(NO_2)_2$

41. A compound *X* on heating gives a colourless gas. The residue is dissolved in water to obtain *Y*. Excess CO_2 is bubbled through aqueous solution of *Y* and *Z* is formed. *Z* on gentle heating gives back *X*. The *X* is :
(a) $CaCO_3$
(b) $Ca(HCO_3)_2$
(c) Na_2CO_3
(d) $NaHCO_3$

42. Which of the following statement is false?
(a) The milk of magnesia used as antacid is chemically $MgO + MgCl_2$
(b) Stability of alkali metal peroxides increases with increase in atomic number
(c) Hydration energy of AgF is higher than its lattice energy
(d) Anhydrous $MgCl_2$ cannot be prepared by direct heating of $MgCl_2 \cdot 6H_2O$

43. The more commonly used baking powder contains about 30% $NaHCO_3$, 20% $NaAl(SO_4)_2$, 10% $Ca(H_2PO_4)_2$ and 40% starch. Which of the following statements is/are correct?
(a) $Ca(H_2PO_4)_2$ is acidic and when moistened it reacts with $NaHCO_3$ evolving CO_2 gas
(b) $NaAl(SO_4)_2$ slows down the decomposition reaction of $NaHCO_3$ so that CO_2 is evolved more slowly
(c) $NaAl(SO_4)_2$ is acidic and when moistened it reacts with $NaHCO_3$ evolving CO_2
(d) Both (a) and (b)

Level 3

Passage 1

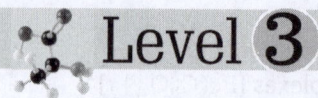

All alkali metals dissolve in anhydrous liquid ammonia to give blue colour solution. It is the ammoniated electron which is responsible for the blue colour of the solution, and the electrical conductivity is due to the ammoniated cation, $[M(NH_3)_x]^+$ as well as the ammoniated electron, $[e(NH_3)_y]^-$, values of x and y depend on the extent of solvation by NH_3. Dilute solutions are paramagnetic due to free ammoniated electrons.

1. What happens if more alkali metals is allowed to react with concentrated liquid ammonia?
(a) Paramagnetic character of solvated electrons is retained
(b) Solvated electrons associate to form electron-pairs and paramagnetic character decreases
(c) Reducing character is increased
(d) Reducing character is not affected

2. Which of the following statement about solution of alkali metals in liquid ammonia is correct?
(a) The solution have strong oxidizing properties
(b) Both the dil. solutions as well as conc. solution are equally paramagnetic in nature
(c) Charge transfer is responsible for the colour of the solution
(d) None of these

3. Ammoniated solutions of alkali metals are reducing agents due to the presence of free ammoniated or solvated electrons that can reduce :
(I) O_2 to O_2^{2-} (II) $K_2[Ni(CN)_4]$ to $K_4[Ni(CN)_4]$
(III) Aromatic ring (IV) Non-terminal alkyne
Choose the correct code :
(a) III and IV (b) II and III (c) I, II, III and IV (d) I, III and IV

Passage 2

$$Na \xrightarrow{H_2O} A \xrightarrow{CO_2} B \xrightarrow{SO_2} C \xrightarrow[\Delta]{Na_2S/I_2} D \xrightarrow{Ag^+/\text{salt}} E\text{ (complex)}$$

1. The compound B and C are :
(a) Na_2CO_3, Na_2SO_4 (b) $NaHCO_3, Na_2SO_4$
(c) Na_2CO_3, Na_2SO_3 (d) None of these

2. The compound D is :
(a) Na_2SO_4 (b) $Na_2S_4O_6$ (c) $Na_2S_2O_5$ (d) $Na_2S_2O_3$

3. Oxidation number of each 'S' atom in compound D :
(a) +2, +2 (b) +4, 0 (c) +6, –2 (d) +5, –1

Passage 3

$$\text{Metal} + \text{dil. HCl} \longrightarrow A \xrightarrow[NH_4OH]{Na_2HPO_4} B \text{ (white ppt.)}$$

$$A \xrightarrow{HCl(g) \text{ Heated}} C$$

$$C \xrightarrow[\text{presence of NaCl}]{\text{Electrolysis in}} \text{Metal } (M)$$

1. The compound A is :
(a) $CaCl_2 \cdot 2H_2O$
(b) $MgCl_2 \cdot 6H_2O$
(c) $Na_2SO_4 \cdot 10H_2O$
(d) $CaSO_4 \cdot 2H_2O$

2. The compound B is :
(a) $Mg(NH_4)PO_4$
(b) $Ca_3(PO_4)_2 + NH_3$
(c) $Na(NH_4)HPO_4$
(d) both (a) and (b)

3. The compound C and metal M are :
(a) NaCl, Na (b) $CaCl_2$, Ca (c) $MgCl_2$, Mg (d) $BeCl_2$, Be

Passage 4

Calcium sulphate is found in nature in two forms, anhydrous calcium sulphate and hydrated calcium sulphate. When anhydrous calcium sulphate is heated with coke, sulphur dioxide gas is obtained. When hydrated calcium sulphate is heated to 200°C, it forms anhydrous salt.

1. The anhydrous calcium sulphate is called :
(a) gypsum (b) anhydrite (c) plaster of Paris (d) lime

2. When calcium sulphate is mixed with conc. HCl and the paste is formed. What colour is obtained when a pinch of this paste is brought near the flame?
(a) golden yellow (b) brick red (c) crimson red (d) apple green

3. What is the product formed when hydrated $CaSO_4$ is heated to 125°C instead of 200°C?
(a) $(CaSO_4)_2H_2O$ (b) $CaSO_4 \frac{3}{4}H_2O$ (c) $CaSO_4$ (d) $CaO + SO_3$

Passage 5

Sodium sulphite (Na_2SO_3) is added to meat as a preservative. The presence of Na_2SO_3 can be detected by adding dil. H_2SO_4 when the pungent smelling gas evolved turns the lime water milky. The gas evolved was detected as sulphur dioxide. The SO_2 evolved was dissolved in water and it requires I_2 solution in order to oxidize SO_2 to SO_4^{2-} in titration.

$$SO_2 + 2H_2O + I_2 \longrightarrow 4H^+ + SO_4^{2-} + 2I^-$$

In order to check the results of titration, excess barium chloride is added to the final solution. The resulting precipitate is collected and weighed.

1. SO_2 and CO_2 both turns lime water milky. Which of the following reagent can be used to distinguish these two gases?

(I) $K_2Cr_2O_7/H_2SO_4$ (II) $KMnO_4/H^+$ (III) I_2 solution

(a) I, II, III correct (b) I, III only correct
(c) II, III only correct (d) III only correct

2. SO_2 gas is used as a bleaching agent. Its bleaching action is :

(a) temporary and due to its oxidizing nature
(b) temporary and due to its reducing action
(c) permanent and due to its oxidizing action
(d) permanent and due to its reducing action

3. Which of the following compounds is formed, when Na_2SO_3 is boiled with sulphur.

(a) Na_2SO_4 (b) $Na_2S_2O_5$ (c) $Na_2S_2O_6$ (d) $Na_2S_2O_3$

Passage 6

On treatment with cold water, an element (*A*) reacts readily liberating a colourless, odourless gas (*B*) and a solution (*C*). Lithium is reacted with (*B*) yielding a solid product (*D*) which effervesce with water to give a strongly basic solution (*E*). When CO_2 gas is bubbled through solution (*C*), a white ppt. (*F*) is formed but this redissolved forming solution (*G*) when more CO_2 is passed. Precipitate (*F*) effervesced when moistened with conc. HCl and give deep red colouration to a Bunsen burner flame. (*F*) on heating with excess of carbon at 2000°C give (*H*).

Answer the following questions on the basis of above passage.

1. Metal (*A*) may be :

(a) Be (b) Ca (c) Mg (d) Ba

2. Solution (*G*) contains a salt which :

(i) causes permanent hardness of water
(ii) can not be obtained in solid state
(iii) causes temporary hardness of water
(iv) can be obtained in solid state

Select the correct statements :

(a) (i) and (ii) (b) (i) and (iv)
(c) (ii) and (iii) (d) (ii) and (iv)

3. Solid (*H*) on hydrolysis gives a gas, which on passing through ammoniacal $AgNO_3$ solution, yields :

(a) white ppt. (b) red ppt. (c) no ppt. (d) brown ppt.

Passage 7

Lithium only forms monoxide when heated in oxygen. Sodium forms monoxide and peroxide in excess of oxygen. Other alkali metals form superoxide with oxygen, *i.e.*, MO_2. The abnormal behaviour of lithium is due to small size. The larger size of higher alkali metals also decides the role in formation of superoxides. All the three anions abstract proton from water. The three anions are related to each other as follows :

$$\underset{\text{Oxide ion}}{O^{2-}} \xrightarrow{\frac{1}{2}O_2} \underset{\text{Peroxide ion}}{O_2^{2-}} \xrightarrow{O_2} \underset{\text{Superoxide ion}}{2O_2^-}$$

1. Consider the following reaction :

$$\underset{(M = \text{alkali metal})}{M + O_2} \longrightarrow \underset{\text{(stable superoxide)}}{MO_2}$$

(a) M can not be Li and Na (b) M can not be Cs and Rb
(c) M can not be Li and Rb (d) None of these

2. Which anion is stable towards water :
(a) O^{2-} (b) O_2^{2-} (c) O_2^- (d) None of these

3. Which compound will liberate oxygen when reacts with ice cold water?
(a) Na_2O_2 (b) KO_2 (c) Na_2O (d) Cs_2O_2

4. In hydrolysis, the alkali metal oxides, peroxides and superoxides act as :
(a) Bronsted acid (b) Bronsted base
(c) Lewis acid (d) Lewis base

Passage 8

Most metal oxides are thermally stable at temperatures upto 1000°C but the oxide of metals below hydrogen in the electrochemical series decompose fairly easily. Thus HgO and Ag_2O decompose on heating.

1. Which of the following salt does not give NO_2 gas on heating ?
(a) $Pb(NO_3)_2$ (b) $Zn(NO_3)_2$ (c) $AgNO_3$ (d) KNO_3

2. Which of the following compound cannot be thermally decomposed even at high temperature?
(a) $CsHCO_3$ (b) Rb_2CO_3 (c) Li_2CO_3 (d) $(NH_4)_2CO_3$

3. Correct code for following thermal decomposition reaction(s) evolving gas having equal number of σ- and π- bonds is :

(i) $BeCO_3 \xrightarrow{\Delta}$ (ii) $ZnSO_4 \xrightarrow[T<800°C]{\Delta}$

(iii) $FeSO_4 \xrightarrow{300°C}$ (iv) $(NH_4)_2Cr_2O_7 \xrightarrow{\Delta}$

(a) I, II (b) I, III, IV (c) I, II, III (d) All of these

ONE OR MORE ANSWERS IS/ARE CORRECT

1. The correct statement(s) is/are:

(a) Thermal stability of alkaline earth metal chloride decreases with increasing molecular mass but reverse order is true for their melting point

(b) Thermal stability of boron halides increases with decreasing molecular mass but reverse order is true for their melting point

(c) Thermal stability of beryllium halides increases with decreasing molecular mass and same order is also true for their melting point

(d) Thermal stability of hydra acids of halogens increases with decreasing molecular mass but reverse order is true for their melting point.

2. Consider the following two graphs between atomic number of element and hydration enthalpies (at 25°C) of corresponding ion.
(M = Alkali metal and X = halogens)

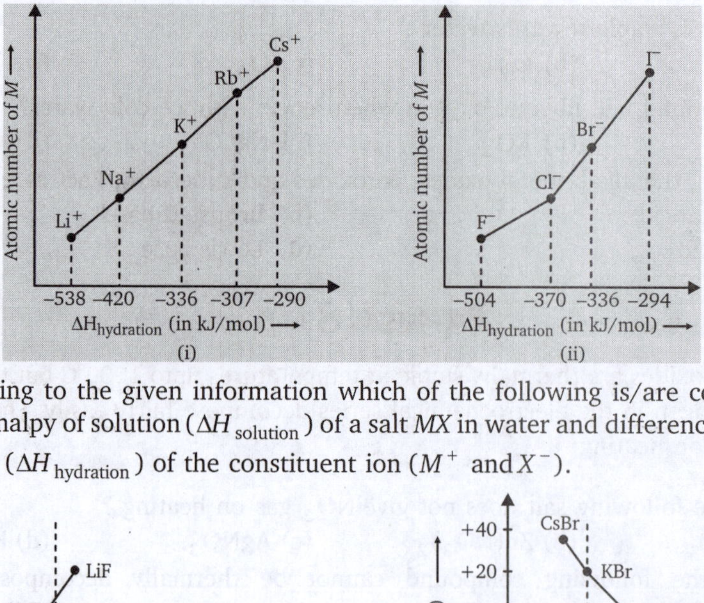

Then according to the given information which of the following is/are correct relationship between enthalpy of solution ($\Delta H_{\text{solution}}$) of a salt MX in water and difference of the enthalpies of hydration ($\Delta H_{\text{hydration}}$) of the constituent ion (M^+ and X^-).

(a) 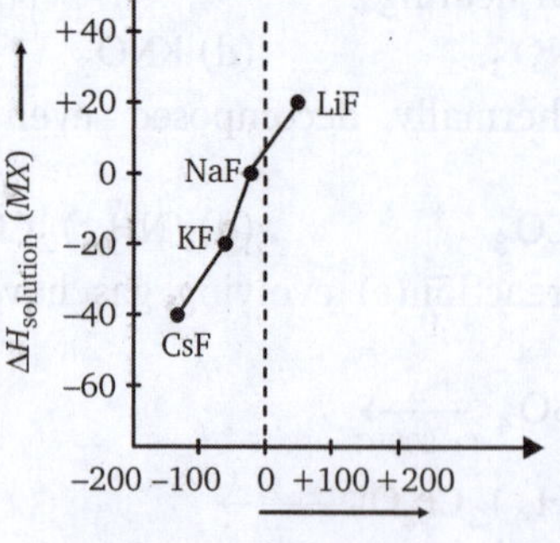

(b) 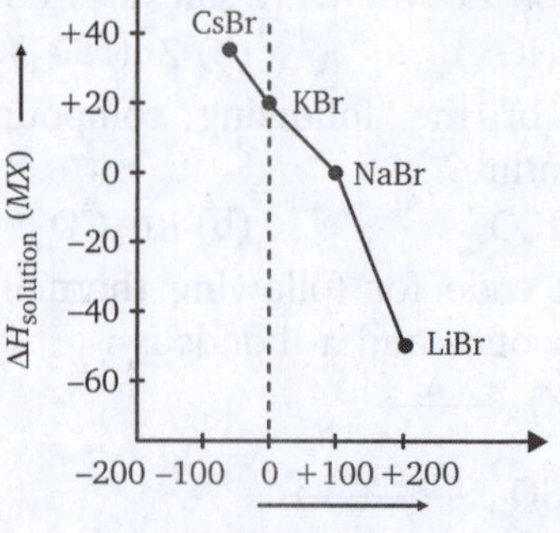

(c) 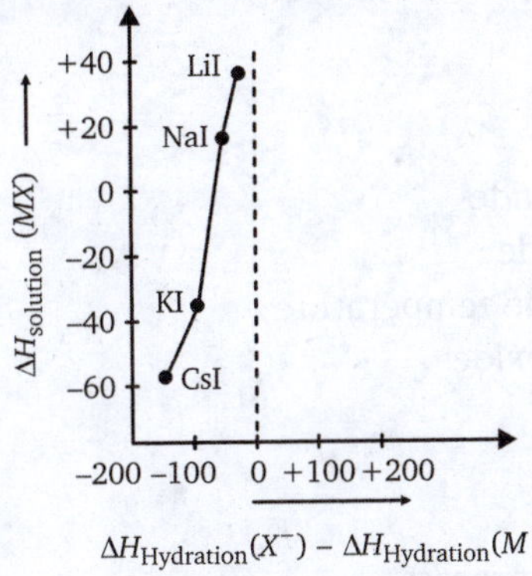

(d) none of these

3. Which of the following metal(s) in liquid NH_3 with low conc. is not paramagnetic ?
(a) Cs (b) Be (c) K (d) Mg

4. Which of the following substances can be used directly as fertilizer ?
(a) $(NH_4)_2SO_4$ (b) $Ca_3(PO_4)_2$ (c) $Ca(H_2PO_4)_2$ (d) $CaCN_2 + C$

5. Which of the following will release CO_2 when heated to 1000°C?
(a) $KHCO_3$ (b) Li_2CO_3
(c) K_2CO_3 (d) $PbCO_3$

6. Which of the following properties show a similar trend on moving from Li to Cs within the group?
(a) Ionic mobility in aqueous solution (b) Reactivity towards water
(c) Solubility of bromide salt (d) Thermal stability of carbonate salt

7. The alkali metals :
(a) form salt like ionic hydrides (b) possess low ionisation potential
(c) have high affinity for non-metals (d) have low density

8. On heating $NaNO_3$ gives :
(a) O_2 (b) NO_2
(c) $O_2 + NO_2$ (d) $NaNO_2$

9. Which of the following statements is/are true?
(a) All alkali metals are soft and can be cut with knife
(b) Alkali metals do not occur in free state in nature
(c) Alkali metals are highly electropositive elements
(d) Alkali metal hydrides are covalent in character

10. Nitrogen dioxide cannot be obtained by heating :
(a) KNO_3 (b) $LiNO_3$ (c) $Pb(NO_3)_2$ (d) $NaNO_3$

11. Select the incorrect statement(s) :
(a) Cs^+ is more hydrated than the other alkali metal ions
(b) Among the alkali metals Li, Na, K and Rb, lithium has the highest melting point
(c) Ionic mobility of Li^+ is maximum among alkali metal cations
(d) Ionisation potential of Li is lower than that of Na

12. Select the correct statement(s) :
(a) Sodium can be prepared by electrolysing aqueous solution of NaCl
(b) Sodium can be prepared by electrolysing fused NaCl

(c) Sodium is a strong oxidising agent
(d) Sodium is soluble in liquid ammonia

13. Identify the correct statement(s) :
(a) Sodium carbonate on heating evolves carbon dioxide
(b) Sodium nitrate on heating evolves nitrogen dioxide
(c) Sodium hydroxide decomposes on heating at flame temperature
(d) Sodium bicarbonate on heating evolve carbon dioxide

14. Which statements are false?
(a) Manufacture of NaOH is done by Solvay process
(b) Manufacture of K_2CO_3 is done by Solvay process
(c) Manufacture of NaOH is done by Castner Kellner process
(d) Manufacture of $NaHCO_3$ is done by Solvay process

15. Sulphates salt gives metal oxide and SO_3 (or $SO_2 + \frac{1}{2}O_2$) on heating :
(a) K_2SO_4 (b) $CaSO_4$
(c) $MgSO_4$ (d) $(NH_4)_2SO_4$

16. The correct statements about sodium and its compounds would include that :
(a) Sodium forms an ionic hydride NaH
(b) Sodium nitrate decomposes to the nitrite on heating
(c) Sodium is a hard metal
(d) Sodium carbonate decomposes readily on heating

17. NaH reacts with water to give :
(a) alkaline solution (b) acidic solution
(c) neutral solution (d) hydrogen gas

18. Which of the following statement(s) is/are incorrect?
(a) Magnesium may be extracted by self reduction method
(b) Down's cell process is used to extract magnesium from sea water
(c) Magnalium is an alloy of magnesium
(d) Formula of Epsom salt is $MgSO_4 \cdot 6H_2O$

19. Identify the incorrect statement(s) :
(a) Density of Mg is less than Ca
(b) The atomic radius of Mg is greater than that of Ca
(c) Mg alloys are used in the construction of air crafts
(d) Mg is used as a reducing agent

20. Which of the following properties of the elements of group II (alkaline earth metals) increase(s) with increasing atomic number?
(a) Stability of carbonate (b) Solubility of hydroxide
(c) Reactivity with water (d) First ionization energy

21. Select the wrong statement(s) :
(a) CaF_2 is soluble in water (b) $BaSO_4$ is soluble in water
(c) $Ba(OH)_2$ is soluble in water (d) $MgSO_4$ is soluble in water

22. Which of the following statements about the elements, Mg, Ca, Sr and Ba and their compounds is true?
(a) Solubility of the hydroxides in water increases with increasing atomic number

(b) Thermal stability of the carbonates increases with increasing atomic number
(c) All given elements react with water or steam to give hydrogen
(d) Metal chlorides are all liquids at room temperature

23. Which of the following does/do not impart characteristic colour to the flame?
(a) $MgSO_4$
(b) $CaCl_2$
(c) $Sr(NO_3)_2$
(d) $BeCl_2$

24. Which statement is correct regarding the diagonal relationship between the Al and Be?
(a) BeO and Al_2O_3 are amphoteric in nature
(b) Both carbide on hydrolysis produce same gas
(c) Both can form complex
(d) Both have nearly close m.p.

25. Which of the following metals on treatment with alkali will liberate H_2 gas?
(a) Be
(b) Sn
(c) Ga
(d) In

26. Choose the correct statement(s) :
(a) $BeCO_3$ is kept in the atmosphere of CO_2 since, it is least thermally stable
(b) Be dissolves in an alkali solution forming $[Be(OH)_4]^{2-}$
(c) BeF_2 forms complex ion with NaF in which Be goes with cation
(d) BeF_2 forms complex ion with NaF in which Be goes with anion

27. Select the incorrect statement(s) :
(a) Magnesium can be burnt in the atmosphere of CO_2 and SO_2
(b) Magnesium reacts with alkyl halides to form Grignard's reagent
(c) Out of Mg and Ca, only Mg reacts with N_2 to form magnesium nitride
(d) Calcium is less reactive than magnesium

28. Which of the following statement(s) is/are correct?
(a) Sodium bicarbonate is more soluble than sodium carbonate
(b) Sodium hydroxide is known as caustic soda
(c) Sodium bicarbonate is used as antacid
(d) Sodium nitrate is used in the manufacture of soaps

29. Select the incorrect statement(s) :
(a) KOH is a weaker base than NaOH
(b) Milk of magnesia is an aqueous solution of $Mg(OH)_2$
(c) Mg^{2+} ions are precipitated with the addition of NH_4OH in the presence of NH_4Cl
(d) CaO_2 is less stable than MgO_2

30. Which of the following statement regarding the oxides of alkali and alkaline metals is correct?
(a) The reactivity of K_2O towards water is more than that of Na_2O
(b) The oxides of alkaline earth metals are more basic than those of alkali metals
(c) MgO is used as a refractory material for lining of electric furnaces
(d) The milk of lime and lime water are two different solutions

31. The pair of compounds which can not exist together in aqueous solution is :
(a) Na_2CO_3 and $NaHCO_3$
(b) $NaHCO_3$ and NaOH
(c) NaOH and NaH_2PO_4
(d) $NaOH + Na_2HPO_3$

32. Which of the following are soluble in water?
(a) Na_2CO_3
(b) BaC_2O_4
(c) $MgCO_3$
(d) $Ca(NO_3)_2$

33. Which of the following salts exist(s) as decahydrated crystals?
(a) Washing soda (b) Glauber's salt (c) Epsom salt (d) Gypsum salt

34. Which of the statements are true?
(a) $NaHCO_3$ and $KHCO_3$ have same crystal structure
(b) On heating Li_2CO_3 gives Li_2O and CO_2
(c) Among alkali metals, Li metal has high I.E. and impart no colour to flame
(d) Li_2SO_4 does not form alum

35. Saturated hydrocarbon gas is evolved by carbide(s) is/are :
(a) CaC_2 (b) Al_4C_3 (c) Mg_2C_3 (d) Be_2C

MATCH THE COLUMN

Entries of Column-I are to be matched with entries of Column-II. Each entry of Column-I may have the matching with one or more than one entries of Column-II.

1.

Column-I (Prop. of metals)	Column-II (Metals)
(A) Yellow flame colour	(P) Ca
(B) Most reactive with water	(Q) Mg
(C) Gives carbide with 'C'	(R) Na
(D) Metal nitrate $\xrightarrow{\Delta}$ metal oxide $+ NO_2 + O_2$	(S) Li

2.

Column-I	Column-II
(A) Product in Solvay process	(P) NaCl
(B) Evolve $CO_2 \uparrow$ on heating	(Q) Na_2O_2
(C) aq. soln. is neutral towards litmus	(R) $NaHCO_3$
(D) Oxone	(S) Na_2CO_3

3.

Column-I (Chemical Prop.)	Column-II (Metals)
(A) Metal sulphate $\xrightarrow{\Delta}$ metal oxide $+ SO_2 + O_2$	(P) Ba
(B) Metal cation $+ K_2CrO_4 \longrightarrow$ yellow ppt.	(Q) Sr
(C) Metal $+ NH_3 \xrightarrow{\text{(liquid)}}$ blue solution	(R) Na
(D) $MCl_2 +$ conc. $H_2SO_4 \longrightarrow$ white ppt.	(S) Mg

4.

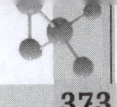

Column-I (Chemical eq. related to compounds)	Column-II (Compound in excess amount)
(A) $S \longrightarrow S_2O_3^{2+} + S^{2-}$	(P) $Na_2S_2O_3$
(B) Ag^+ salt $\longrightarrow$ soluble complex	(Q) NaOH
(C) $Fe^{3+} \longrightarrow Fe(OH)_3$	(R) KOH
(D) $FeCl_3 \longrightarrow FeCl_2$	(S) Na_2SO_3

5.

Column-I	Column-II
(A) Most negative standard electrode potential an element in the periodic table	(P) Solvated electrons
(B) Alkali metal carbonate which decomposes on heating	(Q) Mg_2C_3
(C) Na/liq. NH_3 is blue colour solution which conducts electricity	(R) Al_4C_3
(D) Metal carbide which gives methane on hydrolysis	(S) Magnesium
(E) Metal carbide which on hydrolysis gives propyne	(T) Li_2CO_3
(F) Metal used in flash bulbs	(U) Lithium

6.

Column-I (Compounds)	Column-II (Use of compounds)
(A) Magnesium hydroxide	(P) As a purgative
(B) Barium sulphate	(Q) As a fertilizer
(C) Magnesium sulphate	(R) As a constituent of sorrel cement
(D) Calcium cyanamide	(S) As a constituent of lithopone

7.

Column-I (Compound)	Column-II
(A) B_4C	(P) Propyne preparation
(B) Al_4C_3	(Q) Abrasive
(C) Mg_2C_3	(R) Methane preparation
(D) WC	(S) Interstitial carbides

8.

Column-I	Column-II
(A) $BaF_2 < SrF_2 < CaF_2 < MgF_2 < BeF_2$	(P) Lattice energy
(B) $LiBr < NaBr < KBr < RbBr < CsBr$	(Q) Solubility in water
(C) $Be(OH)_2 < Mg(OH)_2 < Ca(OH)_2 < Sr(OH)_2 < Ba(OH)_2$	(R) Thermal stability
(D) $BeCO_3 < MgCO_3 < CaCO_3 < SrCO_3 < BaCO_3$	(S) % ionic character

ASSERTION-REASON TYPE QUESTIONS

These questions consist of two statements each, printed as assertion and reason, while answering these questions you are required to choose any one of the following responses.

(A) If both assertion and reason are true and the reason is the correct explanation of assertion

(B) If both assertion and reason are true but reason is not the correct explanation of assertion

(C) If assertion is true but the reason is false

(D) If assertion is false but the reason is true

1. **Assertion :** Li_2SO_4 does not form double salt like alum.
Reason : Li reacts with NH_3 gas to form $LiNH_2$.
2. **Assertion :** $BeCl_2$ cannot be easily hydrolysed.
Reason : $BeCl_2$ is electron deficient compound.
3. **Assertion :** K^+ and NH_4^+ ions have many similarities in their test.
Reason : Radius of K^+ is almost equal to radius of NH_4^+.
4. **Assertion :** Alums are crystalline double salts, which are soluble in water.
Reason : The aq. solutions of alums have acidic character due to hydrolysis.
5. **Assertion :** Mg gets oxidised, when heated in CO_2 atmosphere.
Reason : Mg has a strongly affinity for oxygen.
6. **Assertion :** $Mg^{2+} + ZnSO_4 \longrightarrow MgSO_4 + Zn^{2+}$
Reason : More active metal can displace less active metal from its salt solution.
7. **Assertion :** Li resembles with Mg in properties.
Reason : Li^+ has almost same polarising power as Mg^{2+}.
8. **Assertion :** $Be(OH)_2$ dissolves in excess NaOH solution.
Reason : $Be(OH)_2$ is an acidic compound.
9. **Assertion :** SO_4^{2-} is estimated as $BaSO_4$ but not as $MgSO_4$.
Reason : Ionic radius of Mg^{2+} is smaller than that of Ba^{2+}.
10. **Assertion :** Alkali earth metals have lower densities than alkali metals.
Reason : Atomic radii of alkaline earth metals are smaller than that of corresponding alkali metals.
11. **Assertion :** Magnesium does not impart characteristic colour to the bunsen-burner flame.
Reason : Ionisation energy of Mg is very high.
12. **Assertion :** Among hydroxides of alkali metals, LiOH is the weakest base.
Reason : Among alkali metals, lithium has the highest ionisation energy.
13. **Assertion :** $BaSO_4$ is insoluble in water.
Reason : Lattice energy of $BaSO_4$ is higher than its hydration energy.
14. **Assertion :** CsI is sparingly soluble in water.
Reason : Hydration energy of Cs^+ and I^- ions are higher than lattice energy.
15. **Assertion :** Potassium is not obtained by the electrolysis of fused KCl.
Reason : Potassium vapourises at the melting point of KCl.

16. Assertion : M.P. of $BeCl_2$ is less than that of $MgCl_2$, but reverse is true for their thermal stability.

Reason : M.P. and thermal stability of both compounds depend upon their lattice energy.

17. Assertion : Li is most strong reducing agent among alkali metals.

Reason : Hydration energy of Li^+ is maximum among the alkali metals.

SUBJECTIVE PROBLEMS

1. $Na_2O_2 \xrightarrow[0°C]{\text{Water}} P + Q$

$Na_2O_2 \xrightarrow[25°C]{\text{Water}} P + R\uparrow + S$

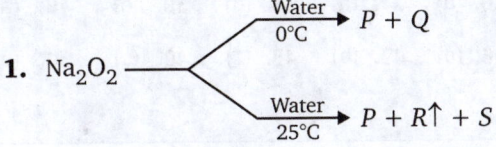

Calculate sum of bond order between same bonded atoms in Q and R compounds.

2. If five moles of gypsom salt are heated at 393 K then how many moles of H_2O molecules will be released.

Answers

Level-1

1. (d)	2. (c)	3. (d)	4. (a)	5. (d)	6. (b)	7. (c)	8. (b)	9. (b)	10. (b)
11. (b)	12. (b)	13. (c)	14. (d)	15. (c)	16. (c)	17. (a)	18. (c)	19. (c)	20. (d)
21. (b)	22. (b)	23. (b)	24. (b)	25. (a)	26. (b)	27. (d)	28. (d)	29. (a)	30. (a)
31. (b)	32. (c)	33. (a)	34. (d)	35. (c)	36. (d)	37. (a)	38. (d)	39. (a)	40. (a)
41. (a)	42. (a)	43. (a)	44. (c)	45. (c)	46. (d)	47. (b)	48. (c)	49. (c)	50. (d)
51. (b)	52. (d)	53. (b)	54. (c)	55. (d)					

Level-2

1. (b)	2. (b)	3. (c)	4. (b)	5. (d)	6. (d)	7. (c)	8. (c)	9. (c)	10. (b)
11. (d)	12. (d)	13. (b)	14. (d)	15. (c)	16. (b)	17. (a,c)	18. (b)	19. (c)	20. (c)
21. (b)	22. (c)	23. (b)	24. (d)	25. (d)	26. (a)	27. (c)	28. (a)	29. (b)	30. (b)
31. (c)	32. (a)	33. (b)	34. (a)	35. (c)	36. (a)	37. (c)	38. (a)	39. (d)	40. (a)
41. (a)	42. (a)	43. (d)							

Level-3

Passage–1	1. (b)	2. (d)	3. (c)	
Passage–2	1. (c)	2. (d)	3. (c)	
Passage–3	1. (b)	2. (a)	3. (c)	
Passage–4	1. (b)	2. (b)	3. (a)	
Passage–5	1. (a)	2. (b)	3. (d)	
Passage–6	1. (b)	2. (c)	3. (a)	
Passage–7	1. (a)	2. (d)	3. (b)	4. (b)
Passage–8	1. (d)	2. (b)	3. (c)	

One or More Answers is/are Correct

1. (b) **2.** (a) **3.** (b,d) **4.** (a,c,d) **5.** (a,b,d) **6.** (a,b,d) **7.** (a,b,c,d) **8.** (a,d)
9. (a,b,c) **10.** (a,d) **11.** (a,c,d) **12.** (b,d) **13.** (d) **14.** (a,b) **15.** (b,c) **16.** (a,b)
17. (a,d) **18.** (a,b,d) **19.** (a,b) **20.** (a,b,c) **21.** (a,b) **22.** (a,b,c) **23.** (a,d) **24.** (a,b,c)
25. (a,b,c) **26.** (a,b,d) **27.** (c,d) **28.** (b,c) **29.** (a,c,d) **30.** (a,c,d) **31.** (b,c) **32.** (a,d)
33. (a,b) **34.** (b,d) **35.** (b,d)

Match the Column

1. A→ R; B→ R, C→ P, Q, S; D→ P, Q, S
2. A→ R, S; B→ R; C→ P; D→ Q
3. A→ P, Q, S; B→ P, Q; C→ P, Q, R; D→ P, Q
4. A→ Q, R; B→ P, S; C→ Q, R; D→ P, S
5. A→ U; B→ T; C→ P; D→ R; E → Q; F → S
6. A→ R; B→ S; C→ P; D→ Q
7. A→ Q; B→ R; C→ P; D→ S
8. A→ P, R; B→ S; C→ Q, R, S; D→ R, S

Assertion-Reason Type Questions

1. (C) **2.** (D) **3.** (A) **4.** (B) **5.** (A) **6.** (D) **7.** (A) **8.** (C) **9.** (B) **10.** (D)
11. (A) **12.** (B) **13.** (A) **14.** (C) **15.** (A) **16.** (C) **17.** (A)

Subjective Problems

1. 3 **2.** 7.5

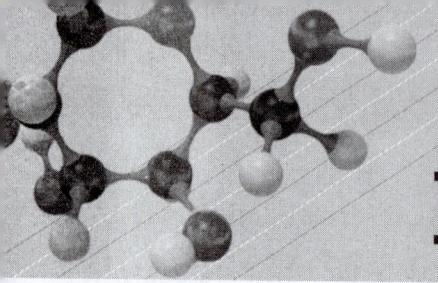

Hints and Solutions

Level 1

2. (c) In I group only Li form nitride and all II group metals form nitride.

$$Mg + N_2 \rightarrow Mg_3N_2 \xrightarrow{H_2O(moist)} Mg(OH)_2 + NH_3$$

$$Ca + N_2 \rightarrow Ca_3N_2 \xrightarrow{H_2O(moist)} Ca(OH)_2 + NH_3$$

$$Li + N_2 \rightarrow Li_3N \xrightarrow{H_2O(moist)} LiOH + NH_3$$

$$K + N_2 \rightarrow \text{no reaction}$$

4. (a) It is due to more ionic character of Cs_2CO_3.

29. (a) In general order of melting point.

$$\underbrace{LiX}_{\substack{\text{Predominantly}\\ \text{covalent}}} < \underbrace{CsX < RbX < KX < NaX}_{\substack{\text{Predominantly ionic}\\ \text{(M.P.} \propto \text{Lattice energy)}}} \qquad [X = Cl,\ Br,\ I]$$

LiX being predominantly covalent have low m.pt.

30. (a) Li metal imparts carmine red colour to flame due to emission spectrum.

31. (b) Due to strong packing of Li^+ and F^- ion, lattice energy of LiF is higher than its hydration energy.

32. (c) Due to high hydration energy of Li^+ cation, the standard reduction potential of Li^+ is more negative among all alkali metal cations hence Li acts as strong reducing agent in water.

52. (d) On heating 'K' into excess oxygen KO_2 is formed which is yellow coloured.

53. (b) By adding gypsum the setting time and strength of cement increases.

54. (c) $NH_3 \uparrow \xleftarrow[\text{Solvay's process}]{NH_4Cl} \underset{(A)}{Ca(OH)_2} \xrightarrow{CO_2} CaCO_3$

55. (d) Presence of H^- ion in saline hydrides is confirmed by liberation of hydrogen gas at anode on electrolysis of their melts.

Level 2

2. (b) Order of solubility in water

$LiF < NaF < KF$

$LiNO_3 > NaNO_3 > KNO_3$

$Li_2CO_3 < Na_2CO_3 < K_2CO_3$

3. (c) ΔH_{sol} of ammonium salts are found to be positive but they are highly soluble due to high positive entropy change it makes ΔG_{sol} more negative according to equation $\Delta G_{sol} = \Delta H_{sol} - T\Delta S_{sol}$

4. (b) Carbonates of Na^+, K^+, Rb^+, Cs^+ do not decompose, but on heating they melt.

6. (d) All are facts.

13. (b) NaOH being deliquescent absorb water from atmosphere therefore strength of solution will decrease.

18. (b) As their hydroxides are water soluble, hence they do not form basic carbonate.

20. (c) $NaNO_3 \xrightarrow[500°C]{\text{below}} NaNO_2 + \frac{1}{2}O_2$ $\qquad Cu(NO_3)_2 \xrightarrow{\Delta} CuO + 2NO_2\uparrow + \frac{1}{2}O_2\uparrow$

$Hg(NO_3)_2 \xrightarrow{\Delta} Hg\downarrow + 2NO_2\uparrow + O_2\uparrow$ $\qquad AgNO_3 \xrightarrow{\Delta} Ag + NO_2\uparrow + \frac{1}{2}O_2\uparrow$

22. (c) Due to much lower freezing point of eutectic mixture of $CaCl_2/H_2O$.

26. (a) Only bicarbonate salt of alkali metals are found in solid state.

27. (c)

(a) $Ca^{2+} < K^+ < S^{2-} < P^{3-}$: Ionic size

(b) $Na^+_{(aq.)} > K^+_{(aq.)} > Rb^+_{(aq.)} > Cs^+_{(aq.)}$: Electrical conductance

(d) $I^-_{(aq.)} < Br^-_{(aq.)} < Cl^-_{(aq.)} < F^-_{(aq.)}$: Ionic mobility

31. (c) Beryllium forms covalent fluoride while aluminium forms ionic fluoride.

40. (a)

$$Ca(NH) + 2H_2O \longrightarrow Ca(OH)_2 + \underset{(B)}{NH_3(g)}$$

$$\underset{(B)}{2NH_3} + 3CaOCl_3 \longrightarrow \underset{(C)}{N_2(g)} + 3CaCl_2 + 3H_2O$$

$$\underset{(C)}{N_2(g)} + 3Mg \longrightarrow \underset{(D)}{Mg_3N_2}$$

$$\underset{(D)}{Mg_3N_2} + 6H_2O \longrightarrow 3Mg(OH)_2 + \underset{(B)}{2NH_3}$$

42. (a) Milk of magnesia is a suspension of $MgO + H_2O$.

Level 3

Passage-1

2. (d) All are wrong. The solution has strong reducing nature and coloured due to ammoniated electron.

3. (c) $M(s) + \underset{\text{excess}}{NH_3(l)} \longrightarrow M^+(NH_3)_x + \bar{e}(NH_3)_y$

Ammoniated $\bar{e}$ responsible for blue colour and reducing character.

If conc. of solution is increased, then association of solvated electrons get started hence, paramagnetism decreases and solution changes to bronze colour.

Passage-6

1. (b,c)

$$\underset{(A)}{Ca} \xrightarrow{H_2O} \underset{(B)}{H_2} + \underset{(C)}{Ca(OH)_2(aq.)} \xrightarrow{CO_2\uparrow} \underset{(F)}{CaCO_3} \xrightarrow{2000°C} \underset{(H)}{CaC_2} \xrightarrow{CO_2\uparrow} \underset{(F)}{CaCO_3} \xrightarrow{2000°C} \underset{(H)}{CaC_2}$$

$$\underset{(B)}{H_2} \xrightarrow{Li} \underset{(D)}{LiH} \xrightarrow{H_2O} \underset{(E)}{LiOH} + H_2\uparrow$$

$$\underset{(F)}{CaCO_3} \xrightarrow{CO_2\ (Excess)} \underset{(G)}{Ca(HCO_3)_2}$$

2. (c) It is $CaHCO_3$, which can not be obtained in solid state and causes temporary hardness.

3. (a) It is acetylene gas and gives white ppt. of silver acetylide.

Passage-7

1. (a) Li and Na do not form stable superoxide.

2. (d) All the three O^{2-}, O_2^{2-} and O_2^- are unstable in presence of water and abstract proton from water.

3. (b) All superoxides liberate oxygen with water :

$$2O_2^- + 2H_2O(l) \longrightarrow 2OH^-(aq) + H_2O_2(l) + O_2(g)$$

4. (b) All abstract proton from water so they are Bronsted base.

ONE OR MORE ANSWERS IS/ARE CORRECT

1. (b)

(d) $\Rightarrow$ Thermal stability of Hydra acids HF > HCl > HBr > HI $\Rightarrow$ Melting point : HI > HF > HBr > HCl

3. (b, d)

Due to high ionization energy and metallic lattice energy Be and Mg do not dissolve into liquid NH_3; hence their solution in liquid NH_3 is not paramagnetic.

4. (a, c, d)

$Ca_3(PO_4)_2$: It is a tertiary phosphate and not soluble in water hence it is of no use for plants.

19. (a,b) Magnesium is more dense than calcium.

Magnalium is an alloy of magnesium which is used in the construction of air crafts.

25. (a,b,c) Be, Sn and Ga are amphoteric metals.

26. (a,b,d) $BeF_2 + 2NaF \longrightarrow Na_2[BeF_4]$

ASSERTION-REASON TYPE QUESTIONS

1. (C) Among sulphate salt of alkali metals only Li_2SO_4 does not forms alum, as Li^+ has very small size.

$$2LiI + NH_3(g) \xrightarrow{\Delta} Li_2NH + H_2\uparrow$$

2. (D) $BeCl_2$ can be easily hydrolysed due to its e^- deficient nature

$$BeCl_2 + 2H_2O \longrightarrow Be(OH)_2 + 2HCl\uparrow$$

3. (A) Ionic radius of NH_4^+ is almost equal to ionic radius of K^+.

4. (B) Alums are $M'_2(SO_4)\, M'''_2(SO_4)_3 \cdot 24H_2O$

These are soluble in water. Their aqueous solution are acidic in nature both the statements are true but it is not the correct explanation.

5. (A) $2Mg + CO_2 \xrightarrow{\Delta} 2MgO + C$

Mg is a strong reducing agent and have great affinity for O_2 at high temperature.

6. (D) $Mg^{2+} + Zn^{2+} + SO_4^{2-} \longrightarrow Mg^{2+} + SO_4^{2-} + Zn^{2+}$ (no reaction)

8. (C) $Be(OH)_2$ is amphoteric in nature.

SUBJECTIVE PROBLEMS

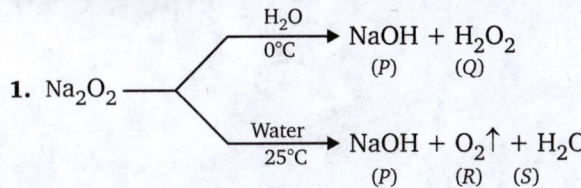

1. $Na_2O_2 \xrightarrow[0°C]{H_2O} \underset{(P)}{NaOH} + \underset{(Q)}{H_2O_2}$

$Na_2O_2 \xrightarrow[25°C]{Water} \underset{(P)}{NaOH} + \underset{(R)}{O_2\uparrow} + \underset{(S)}{H_2O}$

Bond order of [O – O] in $H_2O_2 = 1.0$

Bond order of [O – O] in $O_2 = 2.0$

Sum of bond order between same bonded atoms in Q and R compounds $= 1 + 2.0 = 3.0$

2. $[CaSO_4 \cdot 2H_2O \xrightarrow{393\,K} CaSO_4 \frac{1}{2} H_2O + \frac{3}{2} H_2O] \times 5$

8

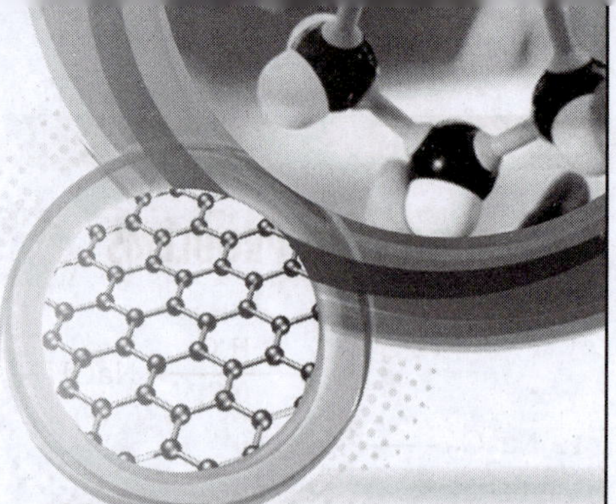

p-BLOCK ELEMENTS

Level 1

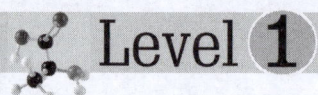

Boron Family and their Compounds (13 gp.)

1. Which of the following metal oxide form blue coloured compound on fusion with B_2O_3:

(a) ZnO (b) CoO (c) FeO (d) Cr_2O_3

2. Al_4C_3 is an ionic carbide, named as:

(a) Acetylide (b) Methanide

(c) Allylide (d) Alloy

3. Which of the following compounds is formed by addition of mineral acid to an aqueous solution of borax?

(a) Boron oxide (b) Orthoboric acid

(c) Metaboric acid (d) Pyroboric acid

4. $AlCl_3$ on hydrolysis gives:

(a) $Al_2O_3 \cdot H_2O$ (b) $Al(OH)_3$

(c) Al_2O_3 (d) $AlCl_3 \cdot 6H_2O$

5. Alumina is insoluble in water because:

(a) It is a covalent compound

(b) It has high lattice energy and low heat of hydration

(c) It has low lattice energy and high heat of hydration

(d) Al^{3+} and O^{2-} ions are not excessively hydrated

6. Which of the following is an electron deficient molecule?

(a) LiH (b) B_2H_6

(c) $LiBH_4$ (d) $B_3N_3H_6$

7. Anhydrous aluminium chloride fumes in moist air owing to the formation of:

(a) gaseous aluminium chloride (b) chlorine

(c) chlorine dioxide (d) hydrogen chloride

8. Colour of the bead in borax bead test is mainly due to the formation of:
(a) metal oxides
(b) boron oxide
(c) metal metaborates
(d) elemental boron

9. The possible oxidation state of Tl are:
(a) +1 and + 2
(b) +2 and + 3
(c) +1 and – 1
(d) +1 and + 3

10. Which of the following sublimes on heating?
(a) Al_2O_3
(b) $Al(OH)_3$
(c) $(AlH_3)_n$
(d) $(AlCl_3)_n$

11. The gaseous product(s) expected at room temperature by reaction of sodium borohydride and boron trifluoride under anhydrous conditions is/are:
(a) H_2
(b) B_2H_6 and H_2
(c) B_2H_6
(d) BH_2F and H_2

Carbon Family and their Compounds (14 gp.)

12. Silicate having one monovalent corner oxygen atom in each tetrahedron unit is :
(a) sheet silicate
(b) cyclic silicate
(c) single chain silicate
(d) double chain silicate

13. PbI_4 does not exist because:
(a) iodine is not a reactive
(b) Pb(IV) is oxidizing and I^- is strong reducing agent
(c) Pb(IV) is less stable than Pb(II)
(d) Pb^{4+} is not easily formed

14. The silicate anion in the mineral kinoite is a chain of three SiO_4 tetrahedra, that share corners with adjacent tetrahedra. The change of the silicate anion is:
(a) –4
(b) –8
(c) –6
(d) –2

15. The gaseous product of the reaction between Sn and conc. H_2SO_4 is:
(a) H_2
(b) SO_2
(c) SnH_4
(d) SO_3

16. The dehydration of malonic acid $CH_2(COOH)_2$ with P_4O_{10} gives:
(a) carbon monoxide
(b) carbon suboxide
(c) carbon dioxide
(d) all three

17. Which of the following structural features of graphite best accounts for its use as a lubricant?
(a) Delocalized electrons
(b) Strong covalent bonds between carbon atoms
(c) van der Waals' forces between layers
(d) limited three covalency of carbon

18. Which of the following is sparingly soluble in cold water and fairly soluble in hot water?
(a) $Pb(NO_3)_2$
(b) $PbCl_2$
(c) $PbSO_4$
(d) $PbCrO_4$

19. The structural of silicon(IV) oxide belongs to the type:
(a) ionic lattice
(b) macromolecular, with a layer structure

(c) molecular lattice, with van der Waals' forces among the molecules
(d) macromolecular, with a non-layer structure

20. Silicon dissolves in excess of HF due to formation of:
(a) SiF_4 (b) SiH_4 (c) H_2SiF_6 (d) H_2SiF_4

21. Which of the following halides does not hydrolyse at room temperature?
(a) $PbCl_4$ (b) $SiCl_4$ (c) CCl_4 (d) $SnCl_4$

22. $SiCl_4$ on hydrolysis gives:
(a) silica (b) silicic acid
(c) silicone (d) silicate

23. Which substance is having molecular solid:
(a) graphite (b) C_{60} (c) gold (d) $Ca_3(PO_4)_2$

24. A cyclic skeleton of silicon and oxygen can constructed by the silicate ion composition:
(a) $Si_2O_7^{4-}$ (b) $Si_2O_5^{2-}$ (c) SiO_3^{2-} (d) SiO_4^{4-}

25. Which of the following is an organo silicon polymer?
(a) Silica (b) Silicone
(c) Silicon carbide (d) Silicic acid

26. $SnCl_2$ acts as a reducing agent because:
(a) $SnCl_2$ can accept electrons readily
(b) Sn^{2+} is more stable than Sn^{4+}
(c) Sn^{4+} is more stable than Sn^{2+}
(d) Sn^{2+} can be easily converted to metallic tin

27. The correct order of decreasing ionic nature of lead dihalides is:
(a) $PbF_2 > PbCl_2 > PbBr_2 > PbI_2$ (b) $PbF_2 > PbBr_2 > PbCl_2 > PbI_2$
(c) $PbF_2 < PbCl_2 > PbBr_2 < PbI_2$ (d) $PbI_2 < PbBr_2 < PbCl_2 < PbF_2$

28. Carborundum is a:
(a) molecular solid (b) covalent solid
(c) ionic solid (d) amorphous solid

29. The plague of tin is the:
(a) conversion of stannous to stannic
(b) conversion to white tin to grey tin
(c) emission of sound while bending a tin rod
(d) atmospheric oxidation of tin

30. The butter of tin is represent by:
(a) $SnCl_2{\cdot}5H_2O$ (b) $SnCl_2$ (c) $SnCl_4$ (d) $SnCl_4{\cdot}5H_2O$

31. $H_2C_2O_4(B) \xrightarrow{\Delta} \text{gas}\,(A) + \text{gas}\,(B) + \text{liquid}\,(C)$.
Gas (A) burns with a blue flame and is oxidised to gas (B)

$$\text{Gas}\,(A) + Cl_2 \longrightarrow (D) \xrightarrow{NH_3,\,\Delta} (E)$$

A, B, C and E are:
(a) $CO_2, CO, H_2O, HCONH_2$ (b) $CO, CO_2, COCl_2, HCONH_2$
(c) $CO, CO_2, H_2O, NH_2CONH_2$ (d) $CO, CO_2, H_2O, COCl_2$

32. $Si_2O_7^{6-}$ anion is obtained when:
(a) no oxygen of a SiO_4 tetrahedron is shared with another SiO_4 tetrahedron
(b) one oxygen of a SiO_4 tetrahedron is shared with another SiO_4 tetrahedron
(c) two oxygen of a SiO_4 tetrahedron are shared with another SiO_4 tetrahedron
(d) three or all four oxygen of a tetrahedron are shared with other SiO_4 tetrahedron

Nitrogen Family and their Compounds (15 gp.)

33. Trisilyamine $(SiH_3)_3N$ is:
(a) trigonal pyramidal and acidic
(b) trigonal pyramidal and basic
(c) trigonal pyramidal and neutral
(d) trigonal planar and weakly basic

34. The mixed anhydride of nitrogen is:
(a) N_2O_2 (2NO)
(b) N_2O_4 ($2NO_2$)
(c) N_2O_5
(d) N_2O_3

35. Among NH_3, PH_3, AsH_3 and SbH_3 which one is a stronger reducing agent?
(a) NH_3
(b) PH_3
(c) AsH_3
(d) SbH_3

36. When zinc reacts with very dilute HNO_3, the oxidation state of nitrogen changes from:
(a) +5 to +1
(b) +5 to −3
(c) +5 to +4
(d) +5 to +3

37. Which of the following orders regarding thermal stability of hydrides MH_3 of group 15 is correct?
(a) $NH_3 > PH_3 > AsH_3$
(b) $NH_3 < PH_3 < AsH_3$
(c) $NH_3 > PH_3 < AsH_3$
(d) $NH_3 < PH_3 > AsH_3$

38. The products formed by complete hydrolysis of PCl_3 are:
(a) H_3PO_3 and HCl
(b) $POCl_3$ and HCl
(c) H_3PO_4 and HCl
(d) $H_4P_2O_7$ and HCl

39. When a sample of NO_2 is placed in a container, this equilibrium is rapidly established.

$$2NO_2(g) \rightleftharpoons N_2O_4(g)$$

If this equilibrium mixture is a darker colour at high temperatures and at low pressure, which of these statements about the reaction is true?
(a) The reaction is exothermic and NO_2 is darker in colour than N_2O_4
(b) The reaction is exothermic and N_2O_4 is darker in colour than NO_2
(c) The reaction is endothermic and NO_2 is darker in colour than N_2O_4
(d) The reaction is endothermic and N_2O_4 is darker in colour than NO_2

40. Heating of ammonium dichromate produces:
(a) NH_3, Cr_2O_3 and H_2O
(b) N_2, Cr_2O_3 and H_2O
(c) NO, CrO_3 and H_2O
(d) N_2O, CrO_3 and H_2O

41. Which of the following halide undergoes in hydrolysis *via* S_{N^1} reaction ?
(a) BCl_3
(b) NF_3
(c) NCl_3
(d) $AsCl_3$

42. Which of the following compound does not give oxyacid of central atom on hydrolysis?
(a) $SiCl_4$
(b) NCl_3
(c) PCl_3
(d) PCl_5

43. In which process does the nitrogen undergo oxidation?
(a) $N_2 \rightarrow 2NH_3$
(b) $N_2O_4 \rightarrow 2NO_2$
(c) $NO_3^- \rightarrow N_2O_5$
(d) $NO_2^- \rightarrow NO_3^-$

44. For which element would XH_3 be a stable species :
(a) C (b) Si (c) P (d) S

Oxygen Family and their Compounds (16 gp.)

45. S—O bond length is maximum in :
(a) $SOBr_2$ (b) $SOCl_2$
(c) SOF_2 (d) $SO(CH_3)_2$

46. In case of hydride of oxygen family, which of the following physical property change regularly on moving down the group.
(a) Melting point (b) Thermal stability
(c) Boiling point (d) Critical temperature

47. When $KHSO_4$ is added into a concentrated solution of H_2SO_4, the acidity of the solution:
(a) increases (b) decreases
(c) remains constant (d) can't be predicted

48. Hydrolysis of one mole of peroxodi-sulphuric acid produces:
(a) two moles of sulphuric acid
(b) two moles of peroxomono-sulphuric acid
(c) one mole of sulphuric acid, one mole of peroxomono-sulphuric acid
(d) one mole of sulphuric acid, onle mole of peroxomono-sulphuric acid and one mole of hydrogen peroxide

49. In trimer form of sulphur trioxide, each sulphur atom is bonded with:
(a) four oxygen atoms (b) three oxygen atoms
(c) two oxygen atoms (d) two sulphur atoms

50. Sodium thiosulphate is formed when:
(a) SO_2 is boiled into Na_2S
(b) Na_2SO_3 is boiled with elemental sulphur
(c) $H_2S_2O_3$ is neutralised by NaOH
(d) Na_2SO_4 is reduced by zinc dust

51. $K_4[Fe(CN)_6]$ reacts with ozone to give:
(a) Fe_2O_3 (b) $Fe(OH)_2$
(c) $K_3[Fe(CN)_6]$ (d) KNO_3

52. The dipole moment of H_2O_2 is more than that of H_2O but H_2O_2 is not a good solvent because:
(a) It has a very high dielectric constant so that ionic compounds cannot be dissolved in it
(b) It does not act as an oxidising agent
(c) It acts as a reducing agent
(d) It dissociates easily and acts as an oxidising agent in chemical reactions

53. In which of the following reaction hydrogen peroxide acts as reducing agent:
(a) $SO_3^{2-}(aq.) + H_2O_2 \longrightarrow$ Products
(b) $HOCl + H_2O_2 \longrightarrow$ Products
(c) $Mn^{2+}(aq.) + H_2O_2 + OH^-(aq.) \longrightarrow$ Products
(d) $Fe^{2+}(aq.) + H^+(aq.) + H_2O_2 \longrightarrow$ Products

Halogen Family and their Compounds (17 gp.)

54. In which case, the order of acidic strength is not correct ?
(a) $HI > HBr > HCl$ (b) $HIO_4 > HBrO_4 > HClO_4$
(c) $HClO_4 > HClO_3 > HClO_2$ (d) $HF > H_2O > NH_3$

55. Concentrated nitric acid reacts with iodine to give:
(a) HOI (b) HI
(c) $HOIO_2$ (d) $HOIO_3$

56. Thermally most stable compound is:
(a) $HOClO_3$ (b) $HOClO_2$
(c) HOCl (d) HOClO

57. Which of the following halogen oxide is used for estimation of carbon monoxide in automobile exhaust gases?
(a) Cl_2O_7 (b) I_2O_5 (c) ClO_2 (d) BrO_3

58. The interhalogen which does not exist is:
(a) IF_5 (b) ClF_3 (c) BrCl (d) ICl_4

59. Which of the following halogen disproportionates in water?
(a) F_2 (b) Cl_2 (c) I_2 (d) All three

60. Which of the following is correct statement?
(a) F_2 has higher dissociation energy than Cl_2
(b) F has higher electron affinity than Cl
(c) HF is stronger acid than HCl
(d) Boiling point increases down the group in halogens

61. Only iodine forms hepta-fluoride IF_7, but chlorine and bromine give penta-fluorides. The reason for this is:
(a) low electron affinity of iodine
(b) unusual pentagonal bipyramidal structure of IF_7
(c) that the larger iodine atom can accommodate more number of smaller fluorine atom around it
(d) low chemical reactivity of IF_7

62. Acid used for making permanent marking on the glass surface is:
(a) HNO_3 (b) HF
(c) HIO_3 (d) H_2SO_4

63. The unfavourable electrochemical reaction among the following is:
(a) $Zn + H_2SO_4 \longrightarrow ZnSO_4 + H_2$ (b) $KI + Cl_2 \longrightarrow KCl + I_2$
(c) $KCl + I_2 \longrightarrow KI + ICl$ (d) $Al + 3HCl \longrightarrow AlCl_3 + \frac{3}{2}H_2$

64. Which anion can undergo both oxidation and reduction?
(a) $Cr_2O_7^{2-}$ (b) NO_3^- (c) OCl^- (d) S^{2-}

65. In the series HCl, HBr and HI, the boiling point increases in the order HCl < HBr< HI. This is due to :
(a) HI is the strongest acid among the series
(b) HI is the strongest reducing agent among the series
(c) higher van der waals' forces of attraction in HI
(d) intermolecular H-bonding in HI

Noble Gases and Xenon Compounds (18 gp.)

66. Which factor is most responsible for the increase in boiling points of noble gases from He to Xe?
(a) Decrease in I.E.
(b) Monoatomic nature
(c) Decrease in polarisability
(d) Increase in polarisability

67. The compound that cannot be formed by xenon is:
(a) XeO_3
(b) XeF_4
(c) $XeCl_4$
(d) XeO_2F_2

68. The noble gases can be separated by:
(a) passing them through suitable solution
(b) electrolysis of their fluorides
(c) adsorption and desorption on charcoal
(d) adsorption and desorption on activated hydrogen

69. Which of the following xenon compound has the same number of lone pairs as in I_3^-?
(a) XeO_4
(b) XeF_4
(c) XeF_2
(d) XeO_3

Level 2

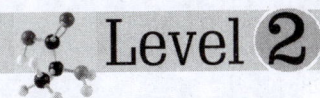

Boron Family and their Compounds (13 gp.)

1. $BX_3 + NH_3 \xrightarrow{R.T.} BX_3 \cdot NH_3$ + Heat of adduct formation (ΔH)

The numerical value of ΔH is found to be maximum for :

(a) BF_3 (b) BCl_3 (c) BBr_3 (d) BI_3

2. Which of the following properties describes the diagonal relationship between boron and silicon?

(a) BCl_3 is not hydrolysed while $SiCl_4$ can be hydrolysed

(b) Both form oxides B_2O_3 is amphoteric and SiO_2 is acidic

(c) Both dissolve in cold and dilute nitric acid

(d) Silicide and boride salts are hydrolysed by water

3. Anhydrous $AlCl_3$ is covalent however, when it is dissolved in water hydrated ionic species are formed. This transformation is owing to:

(a) the trivalent state of Al (b) the large hydration energy of Al^{3+}

(c) the low hydration energy of Al^{3+} (d) the polar nature of water

4. Borax in its crystal possess:

(a) 3 tetrahedral unit

(b) 2 tetrahedral and 2 planar triangular units

(c) 3 tetrahedral and 2 planar triangular units

(d) all tetrahedral units

5. Consider the following statements for diborane:

1. Boron is approximately sp^3 hybridized
2. B—H—B angle is 180°
3. There are two terminal B—H bonds for each boron atom
4. There are only 12 bonding electrons available

Of these statements:

(a) 1, 3 and 4 are correct (b) 1, 2 and 3 are correct

(c) 2, 3 and 4 are correct (d) 1, 2 and 4 are correct

6. Aluminium vessels should not be washed with materials containing washing soda because:

(a) washing soda reacts with aluminium to form soluble aluminate

(b) washing soda is expensive

(c) washing soda is easily decomposed

(d) washing soda reacts with aluminium to form insoluble aluminium oxide

7. Which of the following statements about anhydrous aluminium chloride is correct?

(a) It can exist as $AlCl_3$ molecule in vapour

(b) It is a strong Lewis base

(c) It sublimes at 180°C under vacuum

(d) It is not easily hydrolysed

8. $Na_2B_4O_7 \cdot 10H_2O \xrightarrow{\text{Heat}} X + NaBO_2 + H_2O$, $X + Cr_2O_3 \xrightarrow{\text{Heat}} \underset{\text{(Green coloured)}}{Y}$

X and *Y* are :

(a) Na_3BO_3 and $Cr(BO_2)_3$ (b) $Na_2B_4O_7$ and $Cr(BO_2)_3$
(c) B_2O_3 and $Cr(BO_2)_3$ (d) B_2O_3 and $CrBO_3$

9. Borax is converted into crystalline boron by the following steps:

$$\text{Borax} \xrightarrow{X} H_3BO_3 \xrightarrow{\Delta} B_2O_3 \xrightarrow[\Delta]{Y} B$$

X and *Y* are respectively:

(a) HCl, Mg (b) HCl, C (c) C, Al (d) HCl, Al

10. The dissolution of $Al(OH)_3$ by a solution of NaOH results in the formation of:

(a) $[Al(H_2O)_4(OH)_2]^+$ (b) $[Al(H_2O)_3(OH)_3]$
(c) $[Al(H_2O)_2(OH)_4]^-$ (d) $[Al(H_2O)_6(OH)_3]$

11. Choose the correct sequence for the geometry of the given molecules Borazone, Borazole, $B_3O_6^{3-}$, Fe_2Cl_6, trimer of FCN.

['P' stands for planar and 'NP' stands for non-planar]

(a) NP,, NP, NP, P, P (b) P, P, NP, NP, P
(c) NP, NP, NP, P, NP (d) NP, P, P, NP, P

12. Which is not true about borax?

(a) It is a useful primary standard for titrating against acids
(b) One mole of borax contains 4 B — O — B bonds
(c) Aqueous solution of borax can be used as buffer
(d) It is made up of two triangular BO_3 units and two tetrahedral BO_4 units

13. $B(OH)_3 + NaOH \longrightarrow NaBO_2 + Na[B(OH)_4] + H_2O$

How can this reaction is made to proceed in forward direction?

(a) addition of *cis*1,2 diol (b) addition of borax
(c) addition of *trans*1,2 diol (d) addition of Na_2HPO_4

14. Which of the following cation can not give borax bead test ?

(a) Cr^{3+} (b) Co^{2+}
(c) Ag^+ (d) Mn^{2+}

15. Al Metal

$$Al \xrightarrow{HCl_{(aq.)}} 'X' + \text{Gas } 'P'$$
$$Al \xrightarrow[+H_2O]{NaOH_{(aq.)}} 'Y' + \text{Gas } 'Q'$$

The incorrect statement regarding above reactions is :

(a) Al shows amphoteric character (b) Gas '*P*' and '*Q*' are different
(c) Both *X* and *Y* are water soluble (d) Gas *Q* is inflammable

16. The incorrect statement regarding '*X*' in given reaction is :

$$BF_3 + LiAlH_4 \xrightarrow{\text{Ether}} (X) + LiF + AlF_3$$

(a) Twelve electrons are involved in bonding
(b) Four, two centre-two electron bonds

(c) Two, three centre-two electron bonds
(d) X does not react with NH_3

17. The incorrect stability order of +3 and +1 states of 13th group elements (boron family) is :
(a) $Ga^{3+} < In^{3+} < Tl^{3+}$
(b) $Tl^{+} > Tl^{3+}$
(c) $Ga^{+} < In^{+} < Tl^{+}$
(d) $Ga^{3+} > Ga^{+}$

Carbon Family and their Compounds (14 gp.)

18. Consider the following route of reactions:

$$R_2SiCl_2 + \text{Water} \longrightarrow (A) \xrightarrow{\text{Polymerisation}} (B)$$

Compound(B) in above reaction is :
(a) Dimer silicone
(b) Linear silicone
(c) Cross linked silicone
(d) Polymerisation of (A) does not occur

19. The most basic oxide of elements in group 14 of the periodic table is:
(a) SiO_2 (b) GrO (c) SnO_2 (d) PbO

20. $(Si_2O_5)_n^{2n-}$ anion is obtained when:
(a) no oxygen of a SiO_4^{4-} tetrahedron is shared with another SiO_4^{4-} tetrahedron
(b) one oxygen of a SiO_4^{4-} tetrahedron is shared with another SiO_4^{4-} tetrahedron
(c) two oxygen of a SiO_4^{4-} tetrahedron are shared with another SiO_4^{4-} tetrahedron
(d) three oxygen of a SiO_4^{4-} tetrahedron are shared with another SiO_4^{4-} tetrahedron

21. Amphibole silicate structure has 'x' number of corner shared per tetrahedron. The value of 'x' is:
(a) 2 (b) $2\frac{1}{2}$ (c) 3 (d) 4

22. The silicate anion in the mineral kinoite is a chain of three SiO_4 tetrahedra that share corners with adjacent tetrahedra. The mineral also contains Ca^{2+} ions, Cu^{2+} ions, and water molecules in a 1 : 1 : 1 ratio mineral is represented as:
(a) $CaCuSi_3O_{10} \cdot H_2O$
(b) $CaCuSi_3O_{10} \cdot 2H_2O$
(c) $Ca_2Cu_2Si_3O_{10} \cdot 2H_2O$
(d) none of these

23. Choose the correct order of C — C bond length in the given compounds:
(a) Acetylene < ethylene < graphite < benzene < ethane
(b) Acetylene < ethylene < benzene < graphite < ethane
(c) Acetylene < graphite < ethylene < benzene < ethane
(d) Acetylene < benzene < graphite < ethylene < ethane

24. Silicate having one monovalent corner oxygen atom in each tetrahedron unit is:
(a) sheet silicate
(b) cyclic silicate
(c) single chain silicate
(d) double chain silicate

25. In which of the following silicates, only two corners per tetrahedron are shared ?
(i) Pyro silicate
(ii) Cyclic silicate
(iii) Double chain silicate
(iv) Single chain silicate
(v) 3D silicate
(vi) Sheet silicate
(a) (i), (ii) and (v)
(b) (iv) and (vi) only
(c) (i) and (vi) only
(d) (ii) and (iv) only

26. The correct code for stability, of oxidation states for given cations is :
(i) $Pb^{2+} > Pb^{4+}$, $Tl^{+} < Tl^{3+}$
(ii) $Bi^{3+} < Sb^{3+}$, $Sn^{2+} < Sn^{4+}$
(iii) $Pb^{2+} > Pb^{4+}$, $Bi^{3+} > Bi^{5+}$
(iv) $Tl^{3+} < In^{3+}$, $Sn^{2+} > Sn^{4+}$
(v) $Sn^{2+} < Pb^{2+}$, $Sn^{4+} > Pb^{4+}$
(vi) $Sn^{2+} < Pb^{2+}$, $Sn^{4+} < Pb^{4+}$
(a) (v) and (vi)
(b) (i), (iii) and (vi)
(c) (iii) and (v)
(d) (ii) and (iv)

Nitrogen Family and their Compounds (15 gp.)

27. Nitrogen gas is liberated by thermal decomposition of :
(a) NH_4NO_2
(b) NaN_3
(c) $(NH_4)_2Cr_2O_7$
(d) All

28. Two oxides of nitrogen, NO and NO_2 are allowed to react together at 243° K and form a coloured compound of nitrogen (*X*). When compound (*X*) reacts with water to yield another compound of nitrogen (*Y*). The shape of the anion of (*Y*) molecule is :
(a) triangular planar
(b) triangular pyramidal
(c) tetrahedron
(d) square planar

29. Consider the following sequence of reaction.

$$Na + NH_3(g) \longrightarrow [X] \xrightarrow{N_2O} [Y] \xrightarrow{\text{Heat}} \underset{\text{Gas Pure}}{[Z]}$$

Identify [*Z*] gas :
(a) N_2
(b) NH_3
(c) O_2
(d) H_2

30. Which of the following oxyacid contains both P—H and P—P bond simultaneously ?
(a) $H_4P_2O_5$
(b) $H_4P_2O_7$
(c) $H_4P_2O_6$
(d) None

31. Among the following statement which one is true?
(a) NH_3 is less soluble than PH_3 in water
(b) NH_3 is stronger base and stronger reducing agent than PH_3
(c) NH_3 has higher boiling point than PH_3 and has lower melting point than PH_3
(d) PH_3 is stronger reducing agent than NH_3 and it has lower critical temperature than NH_3

32. Which of the following statements regarding N_2O_4 is not correct?
(a) It is a planar molecule
(b) It is used as non-aqueous solvent
(c) It involves N—N bond which is larger than the N—N bond in hydrazine
(d) Ammonium nitrate in N_2O_4 acts as a base

33. Which of the following on heating produces NO_2?
(a) $NaNO_3$
(b) $AgNO_3$
(c) NH_4NO_3
(d) NH_4NO_2

34. Which of the following equation is incorrectly written?
(a) $P_4 + 20HNO_3 \longrightarrow 4H_3PO_4 + 20NO_2 + 4H_2O$
(b) $I_2 + 10HNO_3 \longrightarrow 2HIO_4 + 10NO_2 + 4H_2O$
(c) $S + 6HNO_3 \longrightarrow H_2SO_4 + 6NO_2 + 2H_2O$
(d) None of the above

35. The cyclotrimetaphosphoric acid is:
(a) $(HPO_3)_3$ and contains 9 σ-bonds
(b) $H_3P_3O_6$ and contains 12 σ-bonds
(c) $(HPO_3)_3$ and contains 15 σ-bonds
(d) $H_3P_3O_9$ and contains 18 σ-bonds

36. $A + H_2O \longrightarrow B + HCl$
$B + H_2O \longrightarrow C + HCl$
Compound (*A*), (*B*) and (*C*) will be respectively:
(a) $PCl_5, POCl_3, H_3PO_3$
(b) $PCl_5, POCl_3, H_3PO_4$
(c) $SOCl_2, POCl_3, H_3PO_3$
(d) $PCl_3, POCl_3, H_3PO_4$

37. It is recommended that liquor ammonia bottle should be opened after cooling it in ice for sometime. This is because liquor ammonia:
(a) brings tears in the eyes
(b) is a corrosive liquid
(c) is a mild explosive
(d) generates high vapour pressure

38. Which of the following statements are correct about the reaction between the copper metal and dilute HNO_3?
(I) The principal reducing product is NO gas
(II) Cu metal is oxidised to Cu^{2+} (*aq.*) ion which is blue in colour.
(III) NO is paramagnetic and has one unpaired electron in antibonding molecular orbital
(IV) NO reacts with O_2 to produce NO_2 which is linear in shape
Choose the correct statements:
(a) I, II, III
(b) I, III
(c) II, IV
(d) All the above

39. In which of the following acids, P—P bonds is present?
(a) Tetra poly phosphoric acid ($H_6P_4O_{13}$)
(b) Pyrophosphoric acid ($H_4P_2O_7$)
(c) Hypophosphoric acid ($H_4P_2O_6$)
(d) Polymetaphosphoric acid $(HPO_3)_n$

40. $NH_3 + O_2 \xrightarrow[\Delta]{Pt} A + H_2O;$
$A + O_2 \longrightarrow B;$
$B + O_2 + H_2O \longrightarrow C$
A, *B* and *C* are:
(a) N_2O, NO_2 and HNO_3
(b) NO, NO_2 and HNO_3
(c) NO_2, NO and HNO_3
(d) N_2O, NO and HNO_3

41. The formation of PH_4^+ is difficult compared to NH_4^+ because:
(a) lone pair of phosphorus is optically inert
(b) lone pair of phosphorus resides in almost pure *p*-orbital
(c) lone pair of phosphorus resides at sp^3 orbital
(d) lone pair of phosphorus resides in almost pure *s*-orbital

42. Nitrogen(I) oxide is produced by:
(a) thermal decomposition of sodium nitrite at low temperature
(b) thermal decomposition of ammonium nitrite
(c) disproportionation of N_2O_4
(d) interaction of hydroxyl amine and excess nitrous acid

43. Amongst the following compounds
(I) $H_5P_3O_{10}$ (II) $H_6P_4O_{13}$
(III) $H_5P_5O_{15}$ (IV) $H_7P_5O_{16}$
non-cyclic phosphates are:
(a) I, III (b) I, II, III
(c) I, II, IV (d) I, II, III, IV

44. Match List-I with List-II and select the correct answer using the codes given below the lists:

List-I (Compounds)		**List-II (used in)**	
(A)	$BaSO_4 + ZnS$	(1)	Explosive
(B)	NI_3	(2)	Oxidiser in rocket propellants
(C)	N_2O_4	(3)	Space capsule
(D)	KO_2	(4)	Pigment

	(A)	(B)	(C)	(D)		(A)	(B)	(C)	(D)
(a)	3	1	4	2	(b)	4	1	2	3
(c)	3	4	1	2	(d)	4	3	2	1

45. Which is the correct sequence in the following properties? For the correct order mark (**T**) and for the incorrect order mark (**F**):
(a) Lewis acidity order : $SiF_4 < SiCl_4 < SiBr_4 < SiI_4$
(b) Melting point : $NH_3 > SbH_3 > AsH_3 > PH_3$
(c) Boiling point : $NH_3 > SbH_3 > AsH_3 > PH_3$
(d) Bond dipole order : $NH_3 > SbH_3 > AsH_3 > PH_3$
(a) FTFT (b) TFTF (c) FFTT (d) FFTF

46. An orange solid (X) on heating gives a colourless gas (Y) and only a green residue (Z). Gas (Y) on treatment with Mg produces a white solid substance:
(a) Mg_3N_2 (b) MgO (c) Mg_2O_3 (d) $MgCl_2$

47. Calcium imide on hydrolysis will give gas (B) which on oxidation by bleaching powder given gas (C). Gas (C) on reaction with magnesium gives compound (D). (D) on hydrolysis gives again gas (B). (B), (C) and (D) are:
(a) NH_3, N_2, Mg_3N_2 (b) $N_2, NH_3, MgNH$
(c) $N_2, N_2O_5, Mg(NO_3)_2$ (d) $NH_3, NO_2, Mg(NO_2)_2$

48. Among the following compounds, which on heating do not produce N_2?
(a) $(NH_4)_2Cr_2O_7$ (b) $NH_4Cl + NaNO_2$
(c) $NH_4Cl + CaO$ (d) $Ba(N_3)_2$

49. In which of the following compounds hydrolysis takes place through $S_{N}1$ and $S_{N}2$ mechanism respectively?
(a) NF_3, NCl_3
(b) P_4O_{10}, $SiCl_4$
(c) SF_4, TeF_6
(d) $SiCl_4$, SiF_4

50. Incorrect statement about PH_3 is :
(a) It is produced by hydrolysis of Ca_3P_2
(b) It gives black ppt. (Cu_3P_2) with $CuSO_4$ solution
(c) Spontaneously burns in presence of P_2H_4
(d) It does not react with B_2H_6

51. Which of the following compound does not produce oxyacid of central atom on hydrolysis?
(a) BF_3
(b) NCl_3
(c) SF_4
(d) PCl_5

52. The incorrect statement regarding 15th group hydrides (EH_3). [E = N, P, As, Sb, Bi]
(a) $NH_3 > PH_3 > AsH_3 > SbH_3 > BiH_3$: Thermal stability
(b) N—H > P—H > As—H > Sb—H > Bi—H : E—H bond dissociation enthalpy
(c) $NH_3 > PH_3 > AsH_3 > SbH_3 > BiH_3$: Reducing character
(d) $NH_3 > PH_3 > AsH_3 > SbH_3 > BiH_3$: Basicity

53. Calculate $x + y + z$ for H_3PO_3 acid, where x is number of lone pairs, y is number of σ-bonds and z is number of π-bonds :
(a) 5
(b) 14
(c) 13
(d) 12

54. A non-metal M forms MCl_3, M_2O_5 and Mg_3M_2 but does not form MI_5. Then incorrect statement regarding non-metal M is :
(a) M can form multiple bond
(b) M is of second period element
(c) Atomicity of non-metal is 4
(d) The range of oxidation number for M is +5 to −3

55. The incorrect order is :
(a) Thermal stability : $HF > HCl > HBr$
(b) Lewis basic character: $PF_3 < PCl_3 < PBr_3$
(c) % p-character : $NO_2^+ > NO_3^- > NH_4^+$
(d) Bond angle : $NH_3 > PH_3 > AsH_3$

Oxygen Family and their Compounds (16 gp.)

56. The correct order of S—S bond length in following oxyanions is :
(I) $S_2O_4^{2-}$ (II) $S_2O_5^{2-}$ (III) $S_2O_6^{2-}$
(a) I > II > III
(b) I > III > II
(c) III > II > I
(d) III > I > II

57. In which of the following reaction product does not contain 'Peroxy' linkage?
(a) $2OF \xrightarrow{\text{Dimerisation}}$
(b) $H_4P_2O_8 \xrightarrow{+H_2O}$
(c) $2Na \xrightarrow[\Delta]{\text{excess } O_2}$
(d) None of these

58. Consider the following statements in respect of oxides of sulphur.
(1) In gas phase SO_2 molecule is V-shape.

(2) In gas phase SO_3 molecule is planar.
(3) γ - SO_3 is cyclic trimer.
Which of the above statements are correct ?
(a) 1 and 2 only (b) 2 and 3 only
(c) 1 and 3 only (d) 1, 2 and 3

59. Gas that can not be collected over water is :
(a) N_2 (b) O_2 (c) SO_2 (d) PH_3

60. In thiosulphuric acid:
(a) each sulphur atom is in identical oxidation state
(b) there is a S=S linkage present
(c) one S atom is in +2 and other sulphur atom is in +4 oxidation state
(d) there is only one replaceable hydrogen atom

61. One gas bleaches the colour of flowers by reduction, while the other by oxidation, the two gases respectively are:
(a) CO and Cl_2 (b) H_2S and Br_2
(c) NH_3 and SO_3 (d) SO_2 and Cl_2

62. Which of the following halides cannot be hydrolysed at room temperature?
(I) TeF_6 (II) SF_6 (III) NCl_3 (IV) NF_3
Choose the correct code:
(a) III and IV (b) I, II and III
(c) I, II and IV (d) II and IV

63. By which of the following methods, H_2O_2 can't be synthesised?
(a) Lewis addition of ice cold H_2SO_4 on BaO_2
(b) Addition of ice cold H_2SO_4 on PbO_2
(c) Aerial oxidation of 2-ethyl anthraquinol
(d) Electrolysis of $(NH_4)_2SO_4$ at a high current density

64. Give the correct order of initials **T** or **F** for following statements. Use **T** if statement is true and **F** if it is false.
(I) Number of S—S bonds in $H_2S_nO_6$ are $(n+1)$
(II) When F_2 reacts with water gives HF, O_2 and O_3
(III) $LiNO_3$ and $BaCl_2$ compounds are used in fire works
(IV) Be and Mg hydrides are ionic and polymeric
(a) FTTF (b) FTTT (c) TFTT (d) TTFF

65. Which of the following parent oxy acid does not have its hypo acid ?
(a) H_2SO_3 (b) HNO_2 (c) H_3PO_3 (d) $HClO_3$

66. Which pair of elements can from multiple bond with itself and oxygen?
(a) F, N (b) N, Cl
(c) N, P (d) N, C

67. Consider the following reactions :
(i) $PCl_3 + 3H_2O \longrightarrow H_3PO_3 + 3HCl$ (ii) $SF_4 + 3H_2O \longrightarrow H_3SO_3 + 4HF$
(iii) $BCl_3 + 3H_2O \longrightarrow H_3BO_3 + 3HCl$ (iv) $XeF_6 + 3H_2O \longrightarrow XeO_3 + 6HF$
Then according to given information the incorrect statement is :

(a) During the (i) reaction the hybridisation of 15th group element does not change
(b) During the (ii) reaction the hybridisation of 16th group element has been changed
(c) During the (iii) reaction the hybridisation of 13th group element does not change
(d) During the (iv) reaction the hybridisation of 18th group element does not change

Halogen Family and their Compounds (17 gp.)

68. Consider the oxy acids $HClO_n$ series, here value of n is 1 to 4. Then incorrect statement regarding these oxy acids is :
(a) Acidic character of oxy acids increases with increasing value of n.
(b) oxidising power of oxy acids increases with decreasing value of n.
(c) Thermal stability of oxy acids decreases with increasing value of n.
(d) 'Cl—O' bond order decreases with decreasing value of n

69. The correct statement regarding ClO_n^- molecular ion is :
(a) On decreasing value of 'n', 'Cl—O' bond order increases
(b) On increasing value of 'n', 'Cl—O' bond length increases
(c) On increasing value of n, oxidation number of central atom increases
(d) On increasing value of n, hybrid orbitals on central atom increase

70. In, $Cl_2O_6(l) + HF \longrightarrow P + Q$
If H^+ of acid HF is with Q, then correct option for hybridization of Cl-atom and ∠OClO in the P and Q :
(a) $P : sp^2; > 120°$ (b) $Q: sp^3; 109°28'$
(c) $P: sp^2; < 109°28'$ (d) $Q: sp^3; > 109°28'$

71. Bromine is commercially prepared from sea water by displacement reaction

$$Cl_2 + 2Br^-(aq) \longrightarrow 2Cl^-(aq) + Br_2$$

Br_2 gas thus formed is dissolved into solution of Na_2CO_3 and then pure Br_2 is obtained by treatment of the solution with :
(a) $Ca(OH)_2$ (b) NaOH (c) H_2SO_4 (d) HI

72. Which of the following properties of halogens increase with increasing atomic number?
(I) Ionization energy (II) Ionic radius
(III) Bond energy of the X_2 molecule (IV) Enthalpy of vaporisation
(a) I, II, III (b) I, III
(c) II, IV (d) IV

73. Predict the correct product when Cl_2 passed through $H—\overset{18}{O}—\overset{18}{O}—H$ dilute solution.
(a) $H^+ + Cl^- + O_2$ (both oxygen having 18)
(b) HOCl and $HClO_2$ (all oxygen having 18)
(c) $HClO_4$ and HCl (all oxygen having 18)
(d) Cl_2O and H_2O (all oxygen having 18)

74. $Cl_2(g) + Ba(OH)_2 \xrightarrow{\text{Hot}} X(aq.) + BaCl_2 + H_2O$

$$X + H_2SO_4 \longrightarrow Y + BaSO_4$$

$$Y \xrightarrow[\Delta > 365\text{ K}]{\Delta} Z + H_2O + HClO_4$$

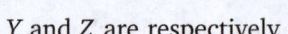

Y and *Z* are respectively :

(a) $HClO_4, ClO_2$ (b) $HClO_3, ClO_2$

(c) $HClO_3, ClO_6$ (d) $HClO_4, Cl_2O_7$

75. Heating of bleaching powder gives:

(a) calcium chlorate (b) calcium chloride

(c) calcium hypochlorite (d) both (a) and (b)

76. Which is incorrectly matched?

(a) $I_4O_9 \rightleftharpoons I^{3+} + 3IO_3^-$ (b) $I_2O_4 \rightleftharpoons IO^+ + IO_3^-$

(c) $CsBr_3 \rightleftharpoons Cs^+ + Br_3^-$ (d) None of these

77. The three elements X, Y and Z with electronic configurations shown below all form hydrides:

Element	Electronic configuration
X	$1s^2 2s^2 2p^2$
Y	$1s^2 2s^2 2p^6 3s^1$
Z	$1s^2 2s^2 2p^6 3s^2 3p^6 3d^{10} 4s^2 4p^5$

Which set of properties match correctly with properties of the hydrides of these elements:

	Hydride of X	Hydride of Y	Hydride of Z
(a)	Colourless gas insoluble in H_2O	Silver/grey solid reacts with H_2O to form an alkali	Colourless gas forms a strong acid in H_2O
(b)	Colourless liquid, no reaction with H_2O	Silver/grey solid forms H_2 and H_2O	Ionic solid with formula *ZH*
(c)	Non-polar compound reacts with Cl_2 in light	Silver/grey ionic solid with formula YH_2	Forms when water is added to phosphorus and elemental *Z*.
(d)	Colourless gas which burns with air	Silver/grey solid which reacts violently with acids	Colourless, corrosive liquid at STP

78. The incorrect order is :

(a) HF < HCl < HBr < HI : Acidic strength

(b) HF > HCl > HBr > HI : Thermal stability

(c) HF > HCl > HBr > HI : Boiling point

(d) HF > HCl > HBr > HI : Bond dissociation enthalpy

Noble Gases and Xenon Compounds (18 gp.)

79. The correct statement regarding perxenate ion (XeO_6^{4-}) is :

(a) It is polar species

(b) It is a planar species

(c) 'Xe—O' bond order is 1.33

(d) Molecular ion has only one type of bond angle

80. XeF_2 and XeF_6 are separately hydrolysed then;
(a) both give out O_2
(b) XeF_6 gives O_2 and XeF_2 does not
(c) XeF_2 alone gives O_2
(d) Neither of them gives HF

81. $MF + XeF_4 \longrightarrow$ 'A' (M^+ = Alkali metal cation)

The state of hybridisation of the central atom in 'A' and shape of the species are:
(a) sp^3d, TBP
(b) sp^3d^3, distorted octahedral
(c) sp^3d^3, pentagonal planar
(d) No compound formed at all

82. Xenon tetrafluoride, XeF_4 is:
(a) tetrahedral and acts as a fluoride donor with SbF_5
(b) square planar and acts as a fluoride donor with PF_5
(c) square planar and acts as fluoride donor with NaF
(d) see-saw shape and acts as a fluoride donor with AsF_5

83. XeF_6 dissolves in anhydrous HF to give a good conducting solution which contains:
(a) H^+ and XeF_7^- ion
(b) HF_2^- and XeF_5^+ ions
(c) $HXeF_6^+$ and F^- ions
(d) none of these

84. Which of the following is not true about helium?
(a) It has the lowest boiling point
(b) It has the highest first ionization energy
(c) It can diffuse through rubber and plastic material
(d) It can form clathrate compounds

85. SbF_5 reacts with XeF_4 to form an adduct. The shapes of cation and anion in the adduct are respectively:
(a) square planar, trigonal bipyramidal
(b) T-shaped, octahedral
(c) square pyramidal, octahedral
(d) square planar, octahedral

86. Consider the following transformations:

(I) $XeF_6 + NaF \longrightarrow Na^+[XeF_7]^-$
(II) $2PCl_5(s) \longrightarrow [PCl_4]^+[PCl_6]^-$
(III) $[Al(H_2O)_6]^{3+} + H_2O \longrightarrow [Al(H_2O)_5OH]^{2+} + H_3O^+$

Possible transformations are:
(a) I, II, III
(b) I, III
(c) I, II
(d) II, III

87. Which of the following is an uncommon hydrolysis product of XeF_2 and XeF_4?
(a) Xe
(b) XeO_3
(c) HF
(d) O_2

88. Incorrect statement regarding following reactions is :

$$XeF_6 \xrightarrow{+\text{Excess } H_2O} \text{'}X\text{'} + HF$$

$$XeF_6 \xrightarrow{+2H_2O} \text{'}Y\text{'} + HF$$

(a) '*X*' is explosive

(b) '*Y*' is an oxyacid of xenon

(c) Both are example of non-redox reaction

(d) XeF_6 can undergo partial hydrolysis

89. Which of the following noble gas does not form clathrate compound?

(a) Kr (b) Ne

(c) Xe (d) Ar

Level 3

Passage 1

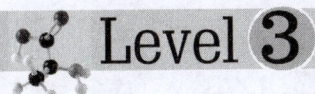

Each oxy-acid contains at least one *X*—OH unit (*X* is non-metal). The H-atom of *X*—OH unit is ionisable and the number of —OH groups directly attach to non-metal decides the basicity of oxy-acid.

1. Which of the following oxy-acid does not have its peroxy form having two central atoms ?
(a) H_2SO_4
(b) HNO_3
(c) H_3PO_4
(d) None

2. Which of the following hypoform of oxy-acid can exhibit tautomerism ?
(a) $H_2N_2O_2$
(b) $H_4P_2O_6$
(c) $H_2S_2O_6$
(d) H_3PO_3

3. Which of the following oxyanion of Pyro acid has different oxidation state of central atom ?
(a) $S_3O_6^{2-}$
(b) $Si_2O_7^{6-}$
(c) $S_2O_5^{2-}$
(d) None

Passage 2

Formation of a bridge bond is best explained by molecular orbital theory. According to which a bridge bond is formed by filling electrons into molecular orbital which spread over three nuclei hence such bonds are specified as three centered bond.

1. In which of the following dimer empty atomic orbital of central atom of monomer does not involve in hybridization:
(a) Ga_2H_6
(b) Al_2Br_6
(c) Be_2H_4
(d) Cl_2O_6

2. In which of the following compound hybridization of bridging atom is different from hybridisation of central atom :
(a) $Al_2(NH_2)_6$
(b) I_2Cl_6
(c) Solid $BeCl_2$
(d) $Al_2(OH)_6$

3. Which of the following compound is having maximum number of atoms in same plane ?
(a) Al_2Me_6
(b) B_2H_6
(c) Be_2H_4
(d) C_3H_4

Passage 3

Question No. 1 to 3 (3 questions)

(i) $P + C(\text{carbon}) + Cl_2 \longrightarrow Q + CO\uparrow$ (ii) $Q + H_2O \longrightarrow R + HCl$

(iii) $BN + H_2O \longrightarrow R + NH_3\uparrow$ (iv) $Q + LiAlH_4 \longrightarrow S + LiCl + AlCl_3$

(v) $S + H_2O \longrightarrow R + H_2\uparrow$ (vi) $S + NaH \longrightarrow T$

(*P*, *Q*, *R*, *S* and *T* do not represent their chemical symbols)

1. Compound *Q* has:

(I) zero dipole moment (II) a planar trigonal structure

(III) an electron deficient compound (IV) a Lewis base

Choose the correct code:

(a) I, IV (b) I, II, IV (c) I, II, III (d) I, II, III, IV

2. Compound *T* is used as a/an:

(a) oxidising agent (b) complexing agent (c) bleaching agent (d) reducing agent

3. Compound *S* is:

(I) an odd-e^- compound (II) $(2c - 3e^-)$ compound

(III) a electron deficient compound (IV) a sp^2 hybridized compound

Choose the correct code:

(a) III (b) I, III

(c) II, III, IV (d) I, II, IV

Passage 4

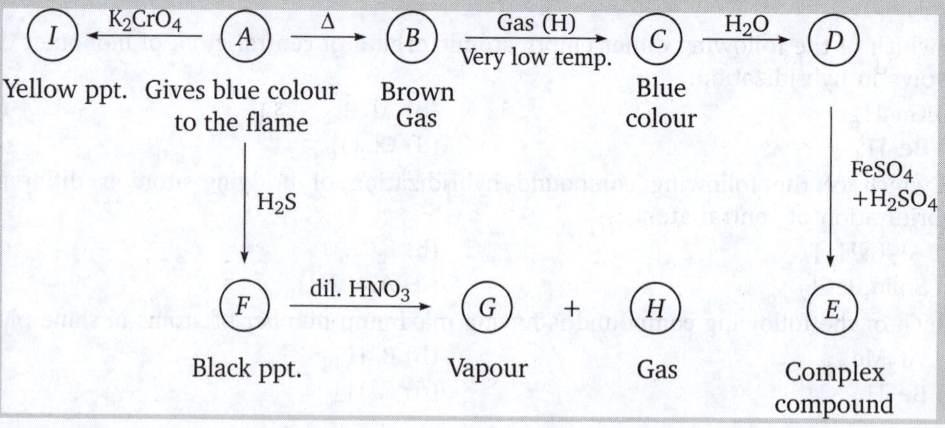

1. Compound $(D) + I^- + H^+ \longrightarrow$ Gas

Evolved gas is similar to:

(a) Gas-*B* (b) Gas-*G* (c) Gas-*H* (d) None

2. Yellow ppt. of compound (*I*) is insoluble in:

(a) NaOH (b) CH_3COOH

(c) dil. HNO_3 (d) none

3. Type of hybridization of complex (*E*) is:

(a) sp^3d^2 (b) d^2sp^3

(c) sp^3 (d) dsp^2

4. Type of hybridization of central atom of gas (B) is:

(a) sp (b) sp^2

(c) sp^3 (d) no hybridization

Passage 5

The following flow diagram represent the industrial preparation of nitric acid from ammonia:

$$\underset{}{NH_3} + \underset{\text{(excess air)}}{O_2} \xrightarrow[900°C]{(X)} NO \xrightarrow[\text{air}]{(Y)} (Z) \xrightarrow{\text{water}} HNO_3 + NO$$

Answer the questions given below:

1. Which line of entry describes the undefined reagents, products and reaction conditions?

	X	*Y*	*Z*
(a)	Pt	cool (−25° C)	NO_2
(b)	Ni	cool (−25° C)	N_2O
(c)	Fe	cool (−11° C)	NO_2
(d)	Pd	high pressure	N_2O_3

2. When (*Z*) is dissolved in H_2O then formation of HNO_3 takes place through various reactions. Select the reaction not observed in this step:

(a) $NO_2 + H_2O \longrightarrow HNO_3 + HNO_2$

(b) $HNO_2 \longrightarrow H_2O + NO + NO_2$

(c) $NO_2 + H_2O \longrightarrow HNO_3 + NO$

(d) none of these

Passage 6

Species having *X* — O — H linkage (*X* = non-metal with positive oxidation state) are called oxy acids and parent acid of a non-metal may exist in two form (a) –ic form of parent oxy acid (b) –us form of parent oxy acid.

1. Number of P—O bond(s) having bond order = 2, in $P_2O_6^{4-}$ ion is :

(a) 0 (b) 2

(c) 3 (d) 6

2. Which of the following parent oxy acid does not have its pyro-oxy acid ?

(a) H_2SO_3 (b) HNO_3

(c) H_3PO_3 (d) H_4SiO_4

3. $X — O — X$ bond (where X = central atom) is not present in species.

(a) Cl_2O_7 (b) $H_2N_2O_2$

(c) N_2O_5 (d) $H_2S_2O_7$

Passage 7

Consider the following sequence of reactions, if *A* is sulphuric acid, then give the answer of following questions.

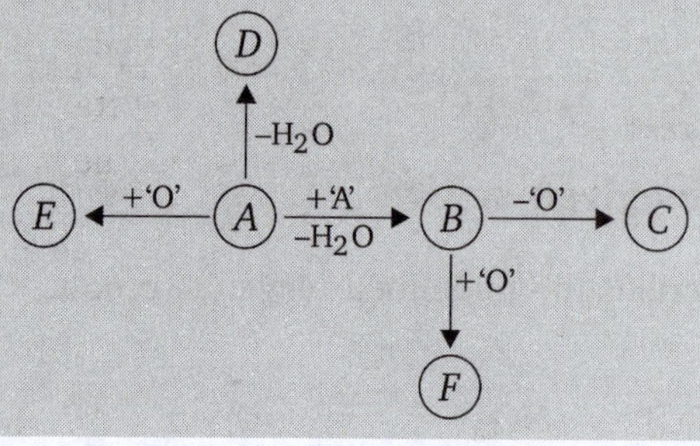

1. Which of the following oxy acid does not have peroxy (—O—O—) linkage ?

(a) *F* (b) *C*

(c) *E* (d) None of these

2. In which of the following compound S-atom is sp^2-hybridised :

(a) *C* (b) *E*

(c) *D* (d) *B*

3. Which of the following oxy acid is having S—O—S linkage ?

(a) *B* (b) *C*

(c) *F* (d) None of these

ONE OR MORE ANSWERS IS/ARE CORRECT

1. Select **correct** characteristic of noble gases:
   (a) Noble gases are coloured and have specific odour
   (b) Their solubility in water increases with increase in their atomic number
   (c) $Xe[PtF_6]$ is the first compound of noble gas
   (d) All noble gases except He and Ne form clathrate compound with ice
2. Which of the following is V-shaped :
   (a) S_3^{2-} (b) I_3^- (c) N_3^- (d) I_3^+
3. $X + 3H_2O \longrightarrow Y + 6HF$
   $X + H_2O \longrightarrow Z + 2HF$
   If X is xenon hexafluoride than correct statement is:
   (a) Compound Y is XeO_3 which is explosive solid
   (b) Both compound Y and Z have same number of lone pair(s) at central atom
   (c) Z is a partially hydrolysed product of compound X
   (d) X act as fluoride donor when it reacts with alkali metal fluoride.
4. Which of the following oxy anion(s) contain(s) P—O bond order equal to 1.5 ?
   (a) $H_2P_2O_6^{2-}$ (b) $H_2PO_3^-$ (c) $H_2PO_4^-$ (d) $H_2PO_2^-$
5. Which of the following order is correct ?
   (a) $N_2 > F_2 > O_2$: Ionisation energy
   (b) $H_2Te > H_2Se > H_2S > H_2O$: Reducing nature
   (c) $H_2O > H_2Te > H_2Se > H_2S$: Boiling point
   (d) $HClO_4 > HClO_3 > HClO_2 > HClO$: Oxidising nature
6. Consider the following sequence of reaction

$$SOCl_2 \xrightarrow[-2HCl]{+H_2O} \text{'A'} \xrightarrow[-\text{'B'}]{+PCl_5} SOCl_2$$

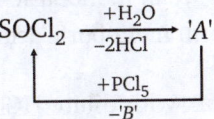

   Then according to given information the **correct** statement(s) is/are :
   (a) Compound 'A' has $p\pi$-$p\pi$ bond
   (b) Central atom of compound B is sp^3-hybridized
   (c) Compound 'B' has plane of symmetry
   (d) Compound 'A' is polar and B is non-polar
7. Correct statement(s) about hydrolysis of $H_5P_3O_{10}$ is/are :
   (a) $H_4P_2O_6$ can be formed by its partial hydrolysis
   (b) Hydrolysis is proceeded by SN_{AE} mechanism
   (c) Complete hydrolysis produces H_3PO_4
   (d) $H_5P_3O_{10}$ is obtained by hydrolysis of $H_3P_3O_9$
8. The species which react with silica/glass in presence of moisture :
   (a) HF (b) XeF_2 (c) XeF_4 (d) XeF_6

9. In which of the following compound(s) terminal $(2C - 2e^-)$ bond and bridge bonds are lying in same plane :

(a) I_2Cl_6 (b) Fe_2Cl_4
(c) Solid $BeCl_2$ (d) Ga_2H_6

10. The correct statement(s) regarding diborane (B_2H_6) is/are :

(a) Maximum six hydrogen atoms can lie in a plane
(b) Maximum six atoms can lie in a plane.
(c) Bridging $H_b — B — H_b$ bond is stronger than terminal $B — H_t$ bond
(d) Terminal $H_t — \hat{B} — H_t$ bond angle is greater than bridging $H_b — \hat{B} — H_b$ bond angle

11. In which of the compounds oxygen does not exhibit oxidation state (–2) ?

(a) CsO_2 (b) K_2O_2 (c) OF_2 (d) Cl_2O

12. Aqueous solution of boric acid is treated with salicylic acid. Which of the following statements is/are incorrect for the product formed in the above reaction?

(a) no product will be formed because both are acid
(b) product is 4-coordinated complex and optically resolvable
(c) product is 4-coordinated complex and optically non-resolvable
(d) there are two ring only which are five membered

13. Borazine is called 'inorganic benzene' min view of its ring structure with alternate BH and NH groups. Which of the following statements is correct about borazine?

(a) Each B and N atom is sp^2 hybridised
(b) Borazine satisfies the $(4n + 2)$ Huckel's rule
(c) Like organic benzene, borazine does not give addition product with HCl
(d) Borazine contains dative $p\pi - p\pi$ bond

14. Identify the correct statement about orthoboric acid:

(a) It has a layer structure in which planar BO_3 units are joined by hydrogen bonds
(b) Orthoboric acid (H_3BO_3) is a weak monobasic Lewis acid
(c) On heating ortho-boric acid form meta-boric acid and on further heating to red hot, forms boric oxide anhydride
(d) It is obtained by reacting borax with dilute HCl using phenolphthalein as an indicator

15. Which of the following methods can be used for the preparation of anhydrous aluminium chloride?

(a) Heating $AlCl_3 \cdot 6H_2O$
(b) Heating a mixture of alumina and coke in a current of dry chlorine
(c) Passing dry HCl gas over heated aluminium powder
(d) Passing dry chlorine over heated aluminium

16. Identify the correct statements regarding structure of diborane:

(a) There are two bridging hydrogen atoms
(b) Each boron atom forms four bonds
(c) The hydrogen atoms are not in the same plane
(d) each boron atom is in sp^3 hybridized state

17. Heating of oxalic acid with conc. H_2SO_4 evolves:

(a) CO (b) SO_2 (c) CO_2 (d) SO_3

18. Which of the following is/are correct for group 14 elements?
(a) The stability of dihalides are in the order $CX_2 + SiX_2 < GeX_2 < SnX_2 < PbX_2$
(b) The ability to form $p\pi$-$p\pi$ multiple bonds among themselves increases down the group
(c) The tendency for catenation decreases down the group
(d) They all form oxides with the formula MO_2

19. Select the correct statement about silicates:
(a) Cyclic silicate having three Si atoms contains six Si—O—Si linkages.
(b) $2\frac{1}{2}$ over oxygen atoms of per tetrahedron unit are shared in double chain silicate
(c) $(Si_2O_5)_n^{2n-}$ is formula of double chain silicate
(d) SiO_4^{4-} units polymerize to form silicate because Si atom has less tendency to form π-bond with oxygen

20. SiO_2 reacts with:
(a) Na_2CO_3 (b) CO_2 (c) HF (d) HCl

21. Which of the following statement(s) is/are true?
(a) The lattice structure of diamond and graphite are different
(b) Graphite is an impure form of carbon while diamond is a pure form
(c) Graphite is harder than diamond
(d) Graphite is thermally more stable than diamond

22. On strong heating $Pb(NO_3)_2$ gives:
(a) PbO (b) NO_2
(c) O_2 (d) NO

23. PbO_2 is:
(a) acidic in character (b) basic in character
(c) reducing agent (d) oxidising agent

24. Which of the following is true for allotropes of phosphorus?
(a) Yellow phosphorus is soluble in CS_2 while red phosphorus is not
(b) P—P—P bond angle is 60° in red phosphorus
(c) On heating in air, white phosphorus changes to red
(d) White phosphorus slowly changes to red phosphorus at ordinary temperatures

25. Which of the following statements are true about P_4O_6 and P_4O_{10}?
(a) Both these oxides have a closed cage like structure
(b) Each oxide requires 6 water molecules for complete hydrolysis to form their respective oxoacids
(c) Both these oxides contain 12 equivalent P—O bonds
(d) P_4O_6 and P_4O_{10} both contains $p\pi - d\pi$ bonds

26. Which of the following, when dissolved in water, will liberated ammonia?
(a) $NaNO_3$ (b) $NaNO_2$
(c) $NaNH_2$ (d) Na_3N

27. PH_3 can be obtained by:
(a) heating hypophosphorus acid
(b) heating orthophosphorus acid
(c) reacting white phosphorus with hot conc. NaOH
(d) hydrolysis of calcium phosphide

28. Which of the following are used as fertilizers?
(a) $Ca_3(PO_4)_2$
(b) $Ca(H_2PO_4)_2$
(c) CaNCN
(d) CaC_2

29. Which of the following statement(s) regarding nitrogen sesquioxide (N_2O_3) is/are correct?
(a) Nitrogen sesquioxide is stable only in the liquid state. It dissociates in the vapour state
(b) Nitrogen sesquioxide is a neutral oxide
(c) Nitrogen sesquioxide contains a weak N—N bond
(d) Nitrogen sesquioxide exists in two different forms

30. Photochemical decomposition of HNO_3 produces:
(a) N_2
(b) N_2O
(c) NO_2
(d) O_2

31. Identify the correct statement(s):
(a) P_4O_{10} is used as a drying agent
(b) P_4O_{10} contains $p\pi$-$d\pi$ back bonding
(c) in P_4O_{10} each P atom is bonded to three oxygen atoms
(d) P_4O_{10} hydrolyse in water forming phosphorus acid

32. Which of the following will be formed when HNO_2 disproportionates in aqueous medium?
(a) NH_3
(b) N_2
(c) NO
(d) HNO_3

33. Which of the following species is/are formed when conc. HNO_3 is added to conc. sulphuric acid?
(a) NO_3^-
(b) NO_2^+
(c) NO^+
(d) HSO_4^-

34. The correct order of reducing power of MH_3 is:
(a) $NH_3 < PH_3 < SbH_3 < BiH_3$
(b) $PH_3 < AsH_3 < BiH_3 < SbH_3$
(c) $BiH_3 < SbH_3 < PH_3 < NH_3$
(d) $PH_3 < AsH_3 < SbH_3 < BiH_3$

35. Select **correct** characteristic of fullerenes:
(a) They are cage like molecules
(b) They contain odd number of carbon atoms
(c) Thermodynamically they are less stable crystalline allotrope than diamond and graphite
(d) They exhibit aromatic character

36. Metal(s) M in the following equation is/are

$$M + N_2 \xrightarrow{\Delta} \text{Metal nitride}$$

(a) Na
(b) Li
(c) Cs
(d) Mg

37. Which of the following compound(s) is/are explosive(s)?
(a) NF_3
(b) NCl_3
(c) NBr_3
(d) NI_3

38. The compounds obtained by heating of orthophosphoric acid are:
(a) metaphosphoric acid
(b) pyrophosphoric acid
(c) P_4O_6
(d) P_4O_{10}

39. At high temperatures, nitrogen directly combines with:
(a) Zn (b) Mg
(c) Al (d) Fe

40. Phosphine is obtained by the reaction when:
(a) White phosphorus is heated with NaOH
(b) Ca_3P_2 reacts with water
(c) red phosphorus is heated with NaOH
(d) phosphorus is heated in current of hydrogen

41. Predict product(s) in the following reaction,

$$P_4 + OH^- \longrightarrow \text{Product(s)}$$

(a) PH_3 (b) PO_4^{2-} (c) $H_2PO_2^-$ (d) PO_2^-

42. Which of the following statements is/are correct?
(a) NO_2 is a paramagnetic substance (b) Solid is brown in colour
(c) NO_2 dimerizes to N_2O_4 (d) NO_2 is a mixed anhydride

43. Which is true about N_2O_5?
(a) It is anhydride of HNO_3
(b) In solid state it exists as $NO_2^+NO_3^-$
(c) It is structurally similar to P_2O_5
(d) It can be prepared by heating HNO_3 over P_2O_5

44. Consider a reaction in which excess dry chlorine gas is passed over heated white phosphorus and select **correct** characteristic of product X:

$$P_4(s) + Cl_2 \text{ (excess)} \xrightarrow{\Delta} X$$

(a) All P — Cl bonds in a molecule of X are not equivalent
(b) Compound X exists in cation-anion pair form in solid state
(c) X does not react with C_2H_5OH
(d) $POCl_3$ can be obtained by hydrolysis reaction of with heavy water

45. Orthophosphoric acid $\xrightarrow[220°C]{\text{gentle heat}} X$

What is/are correct about X?
(a) It is a tetrabasic acid
(b) It contains one P—O—P bond
(c) It is a dibasic acid
(d) On hydrolysis it produces metaphosphoric acid

46. Which of the following act as an oxidising as well as a reducing agent?
(a) HNO_2 (b) H_2O_2 (c) H_2S (d) SO_2

47. Which of the following statements are correct about SF_4?
(a) It is prepared by reacting sulphur directly with fluorine
(b) Sulphur tetrafluoride hydrolysed by water to give SO_2 and HF
(c) SF_4 has a square planar shape with S having two lone pair of electrons
(d) S-atom has a expanded octet

48. Nitrating mixture is obtained by mixing conc. HNO_3 and conc. H_2SO_4. Role of H_2SO_4 in nitration is:
(a) to force HNO_3 to behave as a base
(b) to supress the dissociation of HNO_3
(c) to produce NO_2^+ ions
(d) to remove the colour NO_2 produced during nitration

49. Drops of nitric acid reacts with P_4O_{10} to gives:
(a) NO (b) NO_2 (c) N_2O_5 (d) HPO_3

50. Which of the following statement(s) is/are correct?
(a) Rhombic sulphur is stable at room temperature
(b) Monoclinic sulphur is stable at room temperature
(c) Both rhombic and monoclinic sulphur has the molecular formula S_8
(d) Both rhombic and monoclinic sulphur are soluble in CS_2

51. Which of the following statements are true about sodium thiosulphate, $Na_2S_2O_3$?
(a) It is used in the estimation of iodine
(b) It can give a black precipitate with $AgNO_3$
(c) It is used to remove the unexposed AgBr from photographic films
(d) It contains ionic, covalent and coordinate covalent bonds

52. Peroxy acids of sulphur are:
(a) $H_2S_2O_8$ (b) H_2SO_5 (c) $H_2S_2O_7$ (d) $H_2S_2O_3$

53. Sulphur dioxide can be used as:
(a) bleaching agent (b) antichlor (c) disinfectant (d) none of these

54. Which statements are correct for ozone?
(a) It is obtained by silent electric discharge on oxygen
(b) It can be obtained by the action of ultraviolet rays on oxygen (modified)
(c) It is regarded as an allotrope of oxygen
(d) Ozone molecules is paramagnetic like oxygen molecule

55. Concentrated sulphuric acid is:
(a) efflorescent (b) hygroscopic
(c) oxidising agent (d) sulphonating agent

56. The reaction of sodium thiosulphate with I_2 gives:
(a) sodium sulphite (b) sodium sulphate
(c) sodium iodide (d) sodium tetrathionate

57. Identify the correct statement(s):
(a) Ozone is a powerful oxidising agent as compared to O_2
(b) Ozone reacts with KOH and gives an orange coloured solid KO_3
(c) There is a decrease in volume when ozone decomposed to form O_2
(d) The decomposition of O_3 to O_2 is exothermic

58. Oxygen is not evolved when:
(a) potassium chlorate is heated with MnO_2 catalyst
(b) sodium peroxide reacts with water
(c) ammonium nitrate is heated
(d) zinc oxide is treated with NaOH

59. Identify the correct statements:
(a) Fluorine is a super halogen (b) Iodine shows Lewis basic nature
(c) AgF is insoluble in water (d) SCN^- is a pseudohalide

60. Which of the following properties of the elements chlorine, bromine and iodine increase with increasing atomic number?
(a) Ionization energy (b) Ionic radius
(c) Bond energy of the molecule X_2 (d) Enthalpy of vaporization

61. Which of the following statement(s) is/are correct?
(a) Chlorine dioxide (ClO_2) is powerful oxidising agent but bleaching action is lower than Cl_2
(b) ClO_2 in alkaline solution undergoes disproportionation
(c) ClO_2 is diamagnetic in nature
(d) ClO_2 is a yellow gas but deep red liquid

62. Which of the following statement is true about NO_2 and ClO_2?
(a) Both are paramagnetic
(b) Both have a bent structure
(c) On cooling, both undergoes dimerisation
(d) In both oxides, the central atom has an oxidation state +4

63. $Cl_2O_6 + NaOH \longrightarrow ?$
(a) $NaClO_4$ (b) $NaOCl$ (c) $NaClO_2$ (d) $NaClO_3$

64. Predict product(s) in the following reaction,

$$Cl_2 + OH^- \xrightarrow{\text{hot}} ?$$

(a) Cl^- (b) ClO_2 (c) OCl^- (d) ClO_3^-

65. In the isolation of fluorine a number of difficulties were encountered. Which statements are correct:
(a) Fluorine reacts with moist glass vessels
(b) Fluorine has great affinity for hydrogen
(c) Electrolysis of aqueous HF gives oxygen
(d) The potential required for the discharge of the fluoride ions lowest

66. Iodine is formed when potassium iodide reacts with:
(a) $ZnSO_4$ (b) $CuSO_4$ (c) Cl_2 (d) Br_2

67. Available chlorine is liberated from bleaching powder when it:
(a) is heated (b) reacts with acid
(c) reacts with H_2O (d) reacts with CO_2

68. Which reactions are used for the preparation of the halogen acid?
(a) $2KBr + \underset{\text{(conc.)}}{H_2SO_4} \longrightarrow K_2SO_4 + 2HBr$ (b) $CaF_2 + \underset{\text{(conc.)}}{H_2SO_4} \longrightarrow CaSO_4 + 2HF$
(c) $NaCl + \underset{\text{(conc.)}}{H_2SO_4} \longrightarrow NaHSO_4 + HCl$ (d) $2KI + \underset{\text{(conc.)}}{H_2SO_4} \longrightarrow K_2SO_4 + 2HI$

69. Which of the following statement(s) is/are correct for Halogens.
(a) Halogen which is liquid at room temperature is bromine
(b) The most electronegative element is fluorine
(c) The most reactive halogen is fruorine
(d) The strongest oxidising agent is iodine

70. What are products in the following equation,

$$S + OH^- \longrightarrow ?$$

(a) H_2S (b) S^{2-} (c) $S_2O_3^{2-}$ (d) SO_3^{2-}

71. Correct statements about the hydrogen halides include that:
(a) they are all coloured
(b) the thermal stability decreases with increasing atomic number of halogen
(c) they all form soluble silver salts
(d) they all donate protons to water

72. Which of the following statement(s) is/are not correct?
(a) The covalency of N in HNO_3 is +5
(b) HNO_3 in the gaseous state has a trigonal planar structure
(c) The oxidation state of N in HNO_3 is +4
(d) Gold dissolves in HNO_3 to form gold nitrate

73. Which of the substances react with water?
(a) Chlorine (b) Phosphorus trichloride
(c) Silicon tetrachloride (d) Tetrachloro methane

74. Which of the following substances are soluble in NaOH solution?
(a) $Sn(OH)_2$ (b) $Al(OH)_3$
(c) $Bi(OH)_3$ (d) $Pb(OH)_2$

75. Which of the following molecules have a dative bonding ($p\pi - d\pi$)?
(a) P_4O_{10} (b) $(SiH_3)_3N$ (c) P_4O_6 (d) N_2O_5

76. Which of the following will give N_2 when heated?
(a) NaN_3 (b) NH_4NO_2
(c) NH_4NO_3 (d) $(NH_4)_2Cr_2O_7$

77. Which of the following will give NO_2 when heated?
(a) $LiNO_3$ (b) $NaNO_3$ (c) $Al(NO_3)_2$ (d) $AgNO_3$

78. Identify the correct statements:
(a) Calcium cyanamide on treatment with steam under pressure gives NH_3 and $CaCO_3$
(b) PCl_5 is kept in well stopped bottle because it reacts readily with moisture
(c) Ammonium nitrite on heating gives ammonia and nitrous acid
(d) Cane sugar reacts with conc. HNO_3 to form oxalic acid

79. Select the correct statement(s):
(a) When Al is added to potassium hydroxide solution, hydrogen gas is evolved
(b) H_2SiF_6 is formed when silica reacts with hydrogen fluoride followed by hydrolysis
(c) Phosphine gas is formed when red phosphorus is heated with NaOH
(d) $(NH_4)_2SO_4 \cdot FeSO_4 \cdot 6H_2O$ is called alums

80. Which of the following gases on dissolution in water make the solution acidic?
(a) CO (b) CO_2 (c) SO_3 (d) PH_3

81. Which of the following oxides is/are neutral?
(a) N_2O (b) CO (c) Al_2O_3 (d) NO

82. Which of the following statement(s) is/are incorrect about borazine (inorganic benzene)?
(a) It contains pπ - dπ back bond

(b) It does not give addition product with HCl like organic benzene
(c) Each boron and nitrogen atom is sp^2-hybridised
(d) Its disubstituted derivatives gives equal no. of ortho, meta and para derivatives like disubstituted organic benzene

83. What is true about NO and ClO_2 ?
(a) Both molecules have fractional bond order
(b) Both oxides are neutral in nature
(c) Both have odd e^- bond in their structures
(d) Both are paramagnetic in nature

84. Select the correct statement(s) regarding structure of $Al_2(CH_3)_6$:
(a) All carbon atoms of $—CH_3$ groups do not lie in the same plane
(b) One vacant orbital of each Al-atom is involved in sp^3-hybridisation
(c) There are only 8 sp^3-hybridised atoms are present
(d) There are total 48 bonding electrons are available

85. Which of the following statement(s) is/are correct about SF_4 molecule?
(a) It has a square planar shape with S-atom having two lone pairs
(b) It is hydrolysed by water to give H_2SO_3 and HF as final products
(c) During hydrolysis, S-atom in transition state is sp^3d^2 hybridised
(d) All S—F bond lengths are equal

86. Which of the given compound(s) can act as Lewis acid in both monomer and dimer form ?
(a) BH_3 (b) $BeCl_2$
(c) BeH_2 (d) $AlCl_3$

87. Which of the following parent acid(s) does/do not have corresponding hypo-oxyacid?
(a) HNO_3 (b) H_3PO_4
(c) H_2SO_4 (d) $HClO_3$

88. Oxy anion(s) containing (6,2) pair of equivalent X—O linkages (where X-central atom) is/are:
(a) $S_2O_8^{2-}$ (b) $P_2O_6^{4-}$
(c) $P_2O_7^{4-}$ (d) $P_2O_8^{4-}$

89. Which of the following reactions of xenon compounds in not feasible ?
(a) $XeF_2 + HF \longrightarrow H[XeF_3]$
(b) $XeF_6 + RbF \longrightarrow [XeF_5][RbF_2]$
(c) $XeF_4 + PF_5 \longrightarrow [XeF_3][PF_6]$
(d) $3XeF_4 + 6H_2O \longrightarrow 2Xe + XeO_3 + 12HF + 1.5O_2$

90. Select the incorrect statement(s):
(a) NF_3 has a highest dipole moment among CO, NH_3 and NF_3
(b) HF has a highest boiling point among CH_4, NH_3 and HF
(c) Cl_2 has a lowest boiling point among Cl_2, Br_2 and I_2
(d) $HClO_3$ is weakest acid among HIO_3, $HBrO_3$ and $HClO_3$

91. The possible product (s) formed in the following reaction is/are:

$$IF_5 + H_2O \longrightarrow ?$$

(a) HIO_3 (b) HIO (c) HIO_4 (d) HF

92. Which of the following species does/do not exist ?

(a) OF_4 (b) NH_2^- (c) NCl_5 (d) ICl_3^+

93. Consider the following table :

Compound	**Enthalpy of formation (kJ mol^{-1})**	**Bond angle (H—C.A.—H)**	**Boiling point (°C)**
H_2O	x_1	y_1	z_1
H_2S	x_2	y_2	z_2
H_2Se	x_3	y_3	z_3
H_2Te	x_4	y_4	z_4

According to given information the correct order is/are :

(a) $x_1 > x_2 > x_3 > x_4$ (b) $y_1 > y_2 > y_3 > y_4$

(c) $z_1 > z_4 > z_3 > z_2$ (d) $x_1 > x_4 > x_3 > x_2$

94. $2P \xrightarrow{-H_2O} Q \xrightarrow{-[O]} R$

If P is parent phosphoric acid then according to given information the correct statement is/are:

(a) Q is pyro form and R is hypo form of given present oxy acid P

(b) Number of H-atoms present in each given oxy acid is equal to its basicity

(c) In P, Q, R oxy acids, oxidation state of central atom remains same.

(d) All given oxy acids have $p\pi - d\pi$ bond(s) in their structure

95. The correct statement(s) regarding PCl_5 is/are :

(a) In solid phase, hybridisation of P-atom in cation is sp^3

(b) In vapour phase, all P — Cl bond lengths are equal

(c) In vapour and solid phase, central atom has no lone pair

(d) In solid phase, anion has only one type of bond angle

96. Correct order(s) is/are :

(a) Thermal stability : $H_2O > H_2S > H_2Se > H_2Te$

(b) Bond dissociation energy : $Cl_2 > Br_2 > F_2 > I_2$

(c) Melting point : $NH_3 > SbH_3 > AsH_3 > PH_3$

(d) $X — \hat{C} — X$ bond angle : $COCl_2 > COF_2$

97. Which of the following reaction(s) do/does not give an oxo-acid ?

(a) Two moles of Nitric acid $\xrightarrow{-H_2O}$ (b) One mole of Sulphurus acid $\xrightarrow{-H_2O}$

(c) Two moles of Chloric acid $\xrightarrow{-H_2O}$ (d) Two moles of Sulphuric acid $\xrightarrow{-H_2O}$

MATCH THE COLUMN

Entries of Column-I are to be matched with entries of Column-II. Each entry of Column-I may have the matching with one or more than one entries of Column-II.

1.

Column-I (Decreasing order)	**Column-II (Property)**
(A) $NH_3 > PH_3 > AsH_3 > SbH_3$	(P) Melting point
(B) $H_2O > H_2S > H_2Se > H_2Te$	(Q) Lewis acid character
(C) $AlCl_3 > AlBr_3 > AlI_3$	(R) Thermal stability
(D) $BI_3 > BBr_3 > BCl_3 > BF_3$	(S) Lewis basic character

2.

Column-I	**Column-II**
(A) Does not neutralise dil. HNO_3	(P) SiO_2
(B) Reaction with HF acid	(Q) PbO_2
(C) Solid at room temperature	(R) CO
(D) May acts as reducing agent	(S) SnO
	(T) NO

3.

Column-I (Hydrolysed Products)	**Column-II(Compounds that undergo hydrolysis)**
(A) H_2 gas is evolved	(P) CaH_2
(B) Proton donor oxyacid is formed	(Q) $POCl_3$
(C) Halogen acid is formed	(R) NCl_3
(D) Back bonding is present in formed oxyacid	(S) B_2H_6
	(T) R_2SiCl_2

4.

Column-I	Column-II
(A) $POCl_3$	(P) Oxyacid formed during hydrolysis undergoes Tautomeric change
(B) SOF_2	(Q) Oxidation state of central atom does not change during hydrolysis
(C) $XeOF_4$	(R) Complete as well as partial hydrolysis is possible
(D) $H_2S_2O_8$	(S) Hydrolysed product reacts with glass
	(T) Hybridization of central atom in the final product remains same as in the substrate on hydrolysis

5.

Column-I (Complete hydrolysis)	Column-II (Characteristics of any hydrolysed product/hydrolysis)
(A) $HNCl_3 \xrightarrow{H_2O}$	(P) Dibasic acid
(B) $NO_2 \xrightarrow{H_2O}$	(Q) Can act as flexidentate ligand
(C) $H_2S_2O_8 \xrightarrow{H_2O}$	(R) Can act as both oxidising and reducing agent
(D) $SF_4 \xrightarrow{H_2O}$	(S) Can act as monodentate ligand
	(T) Non-redox hydrolysis

6.

Column-I	Column-II
(A) Disproportionation in alkaline medium/heating	(P) Cl_2
(B) Oxidizing agent	(Q) NO_2
(C) Reacts with water/hydrolysis	(R) XeF_6
(D) Basic gas evolves on heating	(S) NaH_2PO_3
	(T) $(NH_4)_2S$

7. Match the Column-I with the graph of Column-II which is most close to the answer.

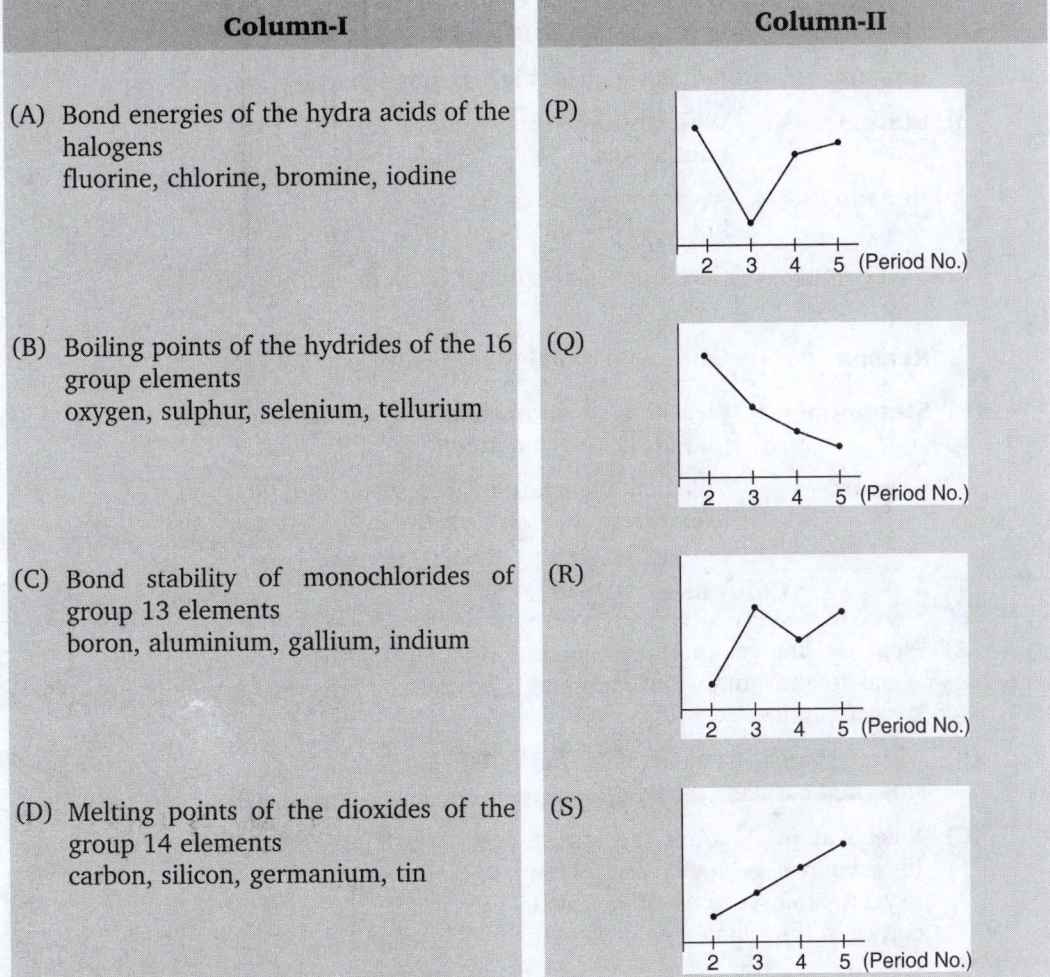

Column-I	Column-II
(A) Bond energies of the hydra acids of the halogens fluorine, chlorine, bromine, iodine	(P) 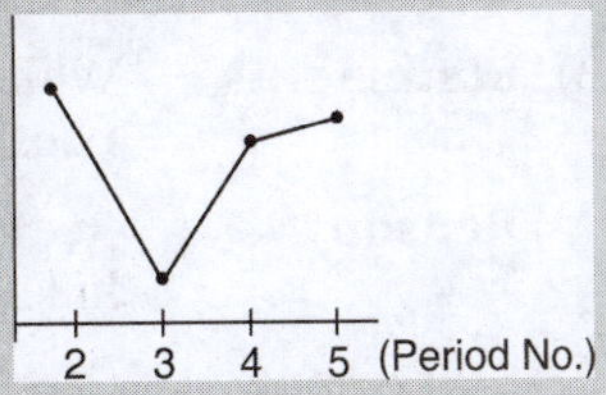
(B) Boiling points of the hydrides of the 16 group elements oxygen, sulphur, selenium, tellurium	(Q) 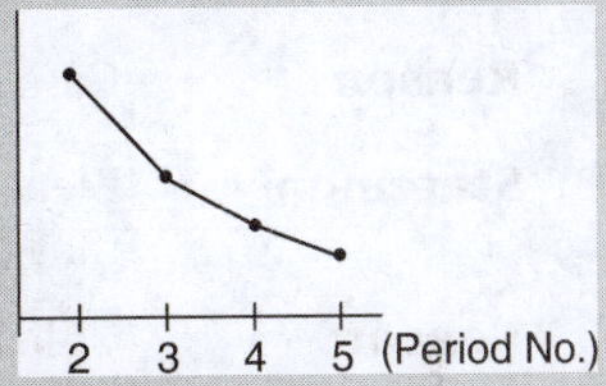
(C) Bond stability of monochlorides of group 13 elements boron, aluminium, gallium, indium	(R) 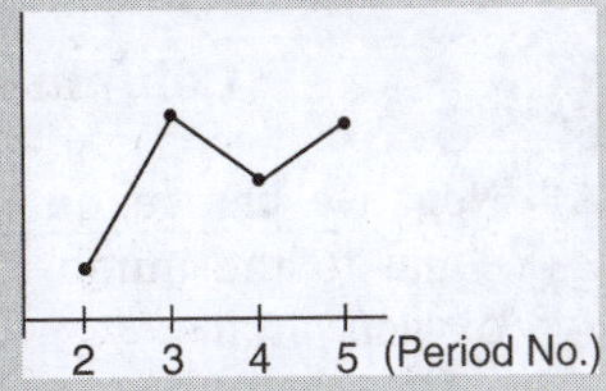
(D) Melting points of the dioxides of the group 14 elements carbon, silicon, germanium, tin	(S) 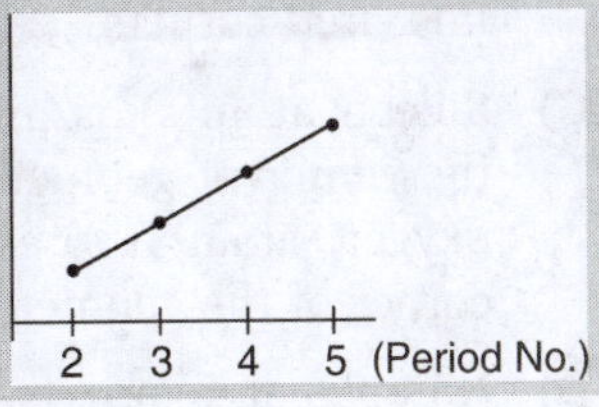

8. Column-I contains four statements following reason and Column-II consists of four options P, Q, R, S.

Answer the following :

P → If both statement and reason are true and reason is correct explanation of statement.

Q → If both statement and reason are true and reason is not correct explanation of statement.

R → If statement is correct and reason is incorrect.

S → If both statement and reason are incorrect.

Column-I			Column-II
(A)	**Statements** :	PbI_4 is a stable compound	P
	Reason :	Iodide stabilizes higher oxidation state.	
(B)	**Statements** :	White phosphorus is more reactive than red phosphorus.	Q
	Reason :	Red phosphorus consists of P_4 tetrahedral units linked to one another to form linear chains.	
(C)	**Statement** :	Caro's acid has sulphur atom in sp^3 hybridized state.	R
	Reason :	Caro's acid contains one peroxy O_2^{2-} linkage.	
(D)	**Statement** :	Bleaching action of chlorine is permanent while that of SO_2 is temporary.	S
	Reason :	Chlorine bleaches by reduction and SO_2 by oxidation.	

9.

Column-I	Column-II
(A) Negative charge on the anion is equal to the number of terminal oxygen atoms	(P) $Si_4O_{13}^{10-}$
(B) Three shared corners and ten unshared corners	(Q) SiO_4^{4-}
(C) Silicon atom(s) is/are present at the center of geometry and every oxygen atom is present at each corner of the geometry	(R) $Si_4O_{12}^{8-}$
(D) Non-planar geometry	(S) $Si_2O_7^{6-}$

10.

List-I (Mixtures)	List-II (Solution used for separation)
(A) N_2 and CO	(P) Water
(B) N_2 and O_2	(Q) H_2SO_4 acid
(C) N_2 and NH_3	(R) Ammonical CuCl
(D) PH_3 and NH_3	(S) Pyrogallol

11.

Column-I (Metal with HNO_3)	Column-II (Main product)
(A) Mg + very dil. HNO_3	(P) NO
(B) Zn + dil. HNO_3	(Q) H_2
(C) Sn + dil. HNO_3	(R) N_2O
(D) Pb + dil. HNO_3	(S) NH_4NO_3

12.

Column-I	Column-II
(A) Moissan method	(P) Purification of bauxite
(B) Ostwald process	(Q) Manufacture of Cl_2
(C) Deacon process	(R) Manufacture of HNO_3
(D) Baeyer process	(S) Isolation of F_2

13.

Column-I (Oxy acid)	Column-II (Acid anhydride)
(A) $HOCl$	(P) N_2O_5
(B) HNO_3	(Q) Cl_2O_7
(C) H_3PO_4	(R) Cl_2O
(D) $HClO_4$	(S) NO_2
	(T) P_4O_{10}

14.

Column-I	Column-II
(A) Maximum solubility in water	(P) F_2
(B) Corrosive liquid	(Q) Cl_2
(C) Maximum interatomic distance	(R) Br_2
(D) Maximum enthalpy of dissociation	(S) I_2

15.

Column-I	Column-II
(A) Borax $\xrightarrow{\Delta}$	(P) BN
(B) $B_2H_6 + H_2O \longrightarrow$	(Q) B_2H_6
(C) $B_2H_6 + NH_3$(excess) $\xrightarrow{\Delta}$	(R) H_3BO_3
(D) $BCl_3 + LiAlH_4 \longrightarrow$	(S) $NaBO_2 + B_2O_3$

16.

Column-I (Catalyst involved in process)	Column-II (Process)
(A) Platinum	(P) Decomposition of bleaching powder
(B) V_2O_5	(Q) Manufacturing of HNO_3
(C) Iron	(R) Manufacturing of H_2SO_4
(D) Cobalt chloride	(S) Manufacturing of NH_3
	(T) Hydrogenation

17.

Column-I	Column-II
(A) Hypo phosphoric acid	(P) All hydrogen are ionizable in water
(B) Pyro phosphoric acid	(Q) Lewis acid
(C) Boric acid	(R) Monobasic in water
(D) Hypo phosphorus acid	(S) sp^3 hybridized central atom

18.

Column-I	Column-II
(A) CO_2	(P) Acidic oxide
(B) SO_2	(Q) Colourless
(C) NO_2	(R) Paramagnetic
(D) N_2O	(S) Coloured

19.

Column-I	Column-II
(A) $Na_2B_4O_7 \cdot 10H_2O$	(P) Basic solution
(B) Na_2CO_3	(Q) Acidic solution
(C) $K_2SO_4 \cdot Al_2(SO_4)_3 \cdot 24H_2O$	(R) can react with NaOH
(D) NH_4Cl	(S) Swells up on heating

20.

Column-I	Column-II
(A) SiO_2	(P) React with HF
(B) CN^-	(Q) Pseudo halide
(C) I^-	(R) Gives compound with Cu^{2+} via redox Rxn
(D) SnO_2	(S) Can dissolves in alkali

21.

Column-I	Column-II
(A) Sheet silicate	(P) $(SiO_3)_n^{2n-}$
(B) Pyroxene chain	(Q) $(Si_4O_{11})_n^{6n-}$
(C) Pyro silicate	(R) 3-corner oxygen atom are shared
(D) Amphibole chain	(S) Non-planar

22.

Column-I	Column-II
(A) Br_2	(P) Liquid at room temperature
(B) O_2	(Q) Used in estimation of CO
(C) ClO_2	(R) Paramagnetic
(D) I_2O_5	(S) Powerful bleaching agent

23.

Column-I	Column-II
(A) $NH_3 > PH_3 > AsH_3 > SbH_3$	(P) Reducing property
(B) $KF > KCl > KBr > KI$	(Q) Heat of fusion (M.P.)
(C) $H_2O > H_2S > H_2Se > H_2Te$	(R) Thermal stability
(D) $CH_4 < SiH_4 < GeH_4 < SnH_4$	(S) Lewis basic character

24.

Column-I (Catalyst involved in process)	Column-II (Process)
(A) SF_4	(P) Central atom can act as Lewis acid as well as Lewis base
(B) AsH_3	(Q) Central atom belongs to 16th or 17th group
(C) ClO_4^-	(R) Non-axial set of *d*-orbitals do not use in bonding
(D) $SbCl_4^-$	(S) Only one type bond angle
	(T) Oxidation state of central atom is +4 or greater than +4

ASSERTION-REASON TYPE QUESTIONS

Questions given below consists of two statements each printed as Assertion (A) and Reason (R); while answering these questions you are required to choose any one of the following four responses:
(A) If both (A) and (R) are true and (R) is the correct explanation of (A)
(B) If both (A) and (R) are true but (R) is not correct explanation of (A)
(C) If (A) is true but (R) is false
(D) If (A) is false but (R) is true

1. **Assertion** : $Al(OH)_3$ is amphoteric in nature.
   Reason : $Al(OH)_3$ is H^+ donar acid as well as OH^- donar base.
2. **Assertion** : BF_3 is weaker lewis acid than BCl_3.
   Reason : $BF_3$is less electron deficient than BCl_3.
3. **Assertion** : Compound having *X*—O—H linkage (*X*=non-metal) always acts as Arrhenius acid.
   Reason : Bond polarity of O—H bond is higher than that of *X*—O bond.
4. **Assertion** : When two gaseous OF molecules are allowed to cool, then they undergo dimerisation through O-atom.
   Reason : Dimer form of OF molecule (*i.e.,*O_2F_2) is having one peroxy linkage in its structure.
5. **Assertion** : Bond dissociation energy of N—F bond in NF_3 molecule is lower than that of in NCl_3 molecule.
   Reason : Inter electronic repulsion exists between small size N and F atoms in N—F bond of NF_3 molecule.
6. **Assertion** : $KAlF_4$ salt can not be formed by combining $AlF_3$with KF.
   Reason : AlF_3being predominantly ionic compound never acts as Lewis acid.
7. **Assertion** : $NaBO_3/OH^-$ can be used for oxidation of Cr^{3+} to Cr^{6+}
   Reason : In alkaline medium $NaBO_3$ produces H_2O_2
8. **Assertion** : Aluminium and zinc metal evolve H_2 gas from NaOH solution.
   Reason : Several non-metals such as P, S, Cl, etc. yield a hydride instead of H_2 gas from NaOH.
9. **Assertion** : There is a very little difference in acidic strengths of H_3PO_4, H_3PO_3 and H_3PO_2.
   Reason : Number of unprotonated oxygen (=O) responsible for increase of acidic strength due to inductive effect remains the same.
10. **Assertion** : PCl_5 and $PbCl_4$ are thermally unstable.
    Reason : They produce same gas on thermal decomposition.
11. **Assertion** : Conc. H_2SO_4 cannot be used to prepare pure HBr from NaBr.
    Reason : It reacts slowly with NaBr.

12. **Assertion** : Oxygen is more electronegative than sulphur, yet H_2S is acidic, while H_2O is neutral.
    Reason : H—S bond is weaker than O—H bond.
13. **Assertion** : Liquid IF_5 conducts electricity.
    Reason : Liquid IF_5 conducts as, $2IF_5 \rightleftharpoons IF_4^+ + IF_6^-$.
14. **Assertion** : Red phosphorus is less volatile then white phosphorus.
    Reason : Red phosphorus has a discrete tetrahedral structure.
15. **Assertion** : $Al(OH)_3$ is amphoteric in nature.
    Reason : It cannot be used as an antacid.
16. **Assertion** : Chlorine gas disproportionates in hot and conc. NaOH solution.
    Reason : NaCl and NaOCl are formed in the above reaction.
17. **Assertion** : Silicones are very inert polymers.
    Reason : Both Si—O and Si—C bond energies are very high.
18. **Assertion** : AgI does not dissolve in NH_3.
    Reason : Due to ionic character of AgI.
19. **Assertion** : Anhydrous $AlCl_3$ is covalent while hydrated $AlCl_3$ is ionic.
    Reason : In water $AlCl_3$ is present as $Al^{3+}_{(aq.)}$ and $Cl^-_{(aq.)}$ ion.
20. **Assertion** : Boron reacts with HNO_3.
    Reason : Boron reacts with all acids.
21. **Assertion** : H_2SO_4 is a weaker acid than $HClO_4$.
    Reason : SO_4^{2-} is more stable than ClO_4^- in solution.
22. **Assertion** : HF forms two series of salts but HCl does not.
    Reason : F atom is more electronegative than Cl atom.

23. **Assertion** : PCl_3 on hydrolysis gives

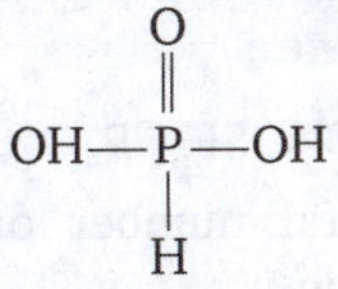

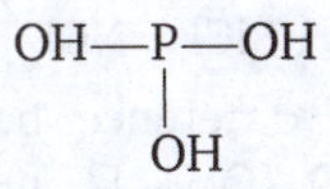

$$OH-\overset{\overset{\displaystyle O}{\|}}{\underset{\underset{\displaystyle H}{|}}{P}}-OH \text{ and not } OH-\underset{\underset{\displaystyle OH}{|}}{P}-OH \text{ as major}$$

product.

   Reason : H_3PO_3 exists in two tautomeric forms : 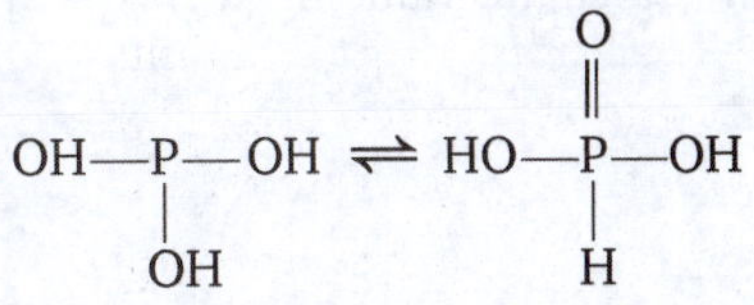

$$OH-\underset{\underset{\displaystyle OH}{|}}{P}-OH \rightleftharpoons HO-\overset{\overset{\displaystyle O}{\|}}{\underset{\underset{\displaystyle H}{|}}{P}}-OH$$

24. **Assertion** : BiI_3 with triiodide (I_3^-) ion never exists.
    Reason : Intramolecular redox reaction takes place between bismuth cation and tri-iodide ion.
25. **Assertion** : SnO is more reactive towards acid than SnO_2.
    Reason : Both SnO and SnO_2 are amphoteric oxides.

26. Assertion : Bond dissociation energy of F_2 molecule is less than that of Cl_2 molecule.
Reason : Due to inter-electronic repulsion between F atom, F — F bond length in F_2 molecule is higher than Cl—Cl bond length in Cl_2 molecule.

27. Assertion : In H_3PO_3, basicity of the oxy acid is two.
Reason : One H-atom is non-ionizable in more stable tautomeric form of H_3PO_3.

SUBJECTIVE PROBLEMS

1. In phosphorus acid, if X is number of non-bonding electron pairs. Y is number of σ-bonds and Z is number of π-bonds. Then calculate value of "$Y \times Z - X$".
2. Consider reaction between thionyl chloride and white phosphorus:
$$P_4 + SOCl_2 \xrightarrow{\Delta} X + Y + SO_2(g)$$
and find out algebraic sum of oxidation numbers of phosphorus and sulphur in compounds X and Y respectively.
3. For oxyacid $HClO_x$, if $x = y = z$ (x, y and z are natural numbers), then calculate the value of $|x+y+z|$. Where x = Number of 'O' atoms
y = Total number of lone pairs at central atom
z = Total number of pi(π) electrons in the oxyacid.
4. Consider the following representation of oxy-acid, $H_{n_1}S_2O_{n_2}$, (where S is central sulphur atom and n_1 and n_2 are natural numbers). If there are two possible oxy-acid of sulphur A and B contains ratio of $n_2 : n_1$ are 2 and 4 respectively, then sum of oxidation state of 'S' atom in both oxy-acid will be :
5. Total number of molecules which hydrolysed at room temperature and hybridization of central atom is sp^3d in transition state :
CCl_4, $SiCl_4$, NCl_3, PCl_3, $AsCl_3$, SF_6, P_4O_6, P_4O_{10}, SeF_6
6. The difference between total number of lone pairs and total number of σ-bonds in $[B_3O_3(OH)_6]^{3-}$ molecular ion is :
7. Calculate value of $|x + y - z|$ for the following silicate $[Si_xO_{y+z}]^{z-}$ anion.

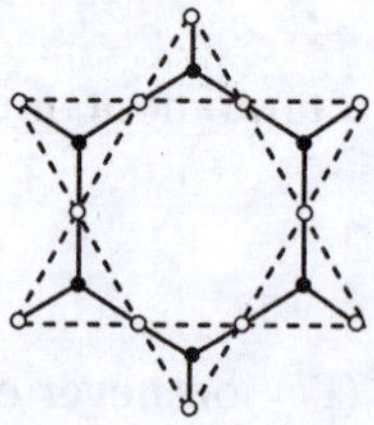

8. The general formula of polythionate ion is $S_{n+2}O_6^{2-}$. if average oxidation state of 'S' atom in any polythionate ion is equal to bond order of 'S—O' bond. Then calculate the value of 'n' for the corresponding polythionate ion.
9. Total number of Boron atoms in anionic part of borax which participate in back bonding.

10. Choose total number of correct reactions.

(i) When $CuSO_4$ solution reacts with NH_3, complex is formed.

(ii) When $CuSO_4$ solution react with PH_3, complex is formed.

(iii) $C_{12}H_{22}O_{11} \xrightarrow{\text{conc. } H_2SO_4} 2C + 11H_2O$

(iv) $\underset{\text{(excess)}}{NH_3} + Cl_2 \xrightarrow{\Delta} NH_4Cl + N_2$

(v) $NH_3 + \underset{\text{(excess)}}{Cl_2} \xrightarrow{\Delta} NCl_3 + HCl$

(vi) $HNO_3 + P_4O_{10} \xrightarrow{\Delta} HPO_3 + N_2O_5$

(vii) $S + H_2SO_4 \xrightarrow{\Delta} SO_2 + H_2O$

(viii) $SbF_5 + XeF_4 \rightarrow [SbF_4][XeF_5]$

(ix) $XeF_4 + O_2F_2 \rightarrow XeF_6 + O_2$

11. Consider the following orders :

(1) $H_2SO_4 > H_2SO_3$: Boiling point

(2) $H_2O > HF$: Extent of H-bond

(3) $H_2O > H_2O_2$: Strength of H-bond

(4) HF > HCl > HBr : Melting point

(5) para-dichlorobenzene > ortho-dichlorobenzene : Boiling point

(6) Ethylene glycol > Phenol : Viscosity

(7) 1, 3-Dichlorobenzene > 1, 3, 5-Trichlorobenzene : Strength of molecular force

(8) ortho-Hydroxy benzoic acid > para-Hydroxy benzoic acid : Solubility in water.

Then calculate value of $|x^2|$ (where 'x' is total number of correct orders.)

12. How many monovalent oxygen atoms are present in the mineral kinoite ($\overset{+2}{Ca_2}\overset{+2}{Cu_2}Si_3O_{10} \cdot 2H_2O$)?

13. How many moles of given compound are decomposed in the following decomposition in the following decomposition reaction?

$$NaOCl \xrightarrow{\Delta} NaClO_3 + NaCl$$

14. How many moles of NaOH are required to react with one mole of solid N_2O_5?

15. How many moles of hypophosphorous acid are involved in its thermal decomposition reaction when one mole of each product is formed.

16. Consider the structure of Al_2Me_6 compound and find the value of $\frac{x-y}{z}$.

Where x = Maximum number of atoms that can lie in plane having terminal (Al – Me) bonds.

y = Total number of $3c - 2e^-$ bonds.

z = Total number of atoms that are sp^3 hybridized.

17. Sum of oxidation state of nitrogen atom in hyponitrous acid, nitric acid and nitrous acid.

18. Find the value of x in the tremolite asbestos :

$$Ca_2Mg_x(Si_4O_{11})_2(OH)_2$$

19. Consider the following silicates

(a) $BaTi(Si_3O_9)$ (b) $ZnCa_2Si_2O_7$

Then calculate $X \div Y$, where X and Y are total number of monovalent and divalent oxygen atoms in both silicates respectively.

20. Atomicity of white or yellow phosphorus is 4 and it is represented as P_4 molecule

Calculate the value of expression $\frac{x \cdot y}{z}$ regarding this molecule.

Where x : Total number of vertex angles in P_4 molecule

y : Total number of lone pairs in P_4 molecule

z : Total number of P – P bonds in P_4 molecule

21. Marshall's acid $\xrightarrow{H_2O} A + B$

$A \xrightarrow{H_2O} B + C$

If P and Q represent maximum number of atoms that can lie in a plane of compound A and C respectively. Then, find out value of $(P - Q)$.

22. Find out numerical value of expression $\left|\frac{x^2}{y}\right|$ for B_2H_6 molecule:

Where; x = maximum number of atoms that can lie in a plane of B_2H_6 molecule.

y = maximum number of bonds that can lie in a plane of B_2H_6 molecule.

23. If following molecules undergo dimerization then find the value of $\frac{YZ}{X}$:

(i) ClO_3 (ii) OF (iii) GaH_3 (iv) $AlCl_3$

(v) ICl_3 (vi) BeH_2 (vii) NO_2

Where : X = Number of molecules which are hypervalent in dimeric form.

Y = Number of molecules which complete octet in dimer form

Z = Number of molecules which are hypovalent in dimeric form

24. Consider $Al_2(OH)_6$ compound and calculate the value of $(X + Y) \div Z$

Where X = Total number of $(2c - 2e^-)$ bond.

Y = Total number of $(3c - 2e^-)$ bond

Z = Total number of $(3c - 4e^-)$ bond

25. Consider the following covalent compounds in their solid state and find the value of expression $(X + Y + Z)$.

N_2O_5, Cl_2O_6, PCl_5, I_2Cl_6, XeF_6, PBr_5

Where X = Total number of compounds in which central atom of cationic or anionic part is sp^3 hybridized

Y = Total number of compounds having 90° bond angle either in cationic or anionic part.

Z = Total number of compounds having 109°28′ bond angle either in cationic or anionic part.

26. Consider following compounds A to E.

(A) XeF_n (B) $XeF^+_{(n+1)}$ (C) $XeF^-_{(n+1)}$ (D) $XeF_{(n+2)}$

(E) $XeF^{2-}_{(n+4)}$,

If value of n is 4, then calculate value of "$p \div q$" here, 'p' is total number of bond pair and 'q' is total number of lone pair on central atoms of compounds A to E.

27. When B_2H_6 is allowed to react with following lewis bases, then how many given lewis bases form adduct through symmetrical cleavage of B_2H_6 ?
NH_3, $MeNH_2$, Pyridine, CO, T.H.F., PH_3, PF_3, Me_3N, Me_2NH

28. What is covalency of chlorine atom in second excited state ?

29. Consider the following molecule :

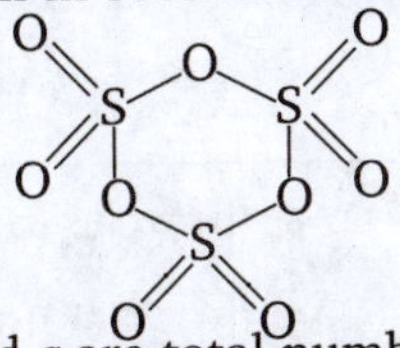

Calculate value of $p \div q$, here p and q are total number of $d\pi - p\pi$ bonds and total number of sp^3-hybridised atoms respectively in given molecule.

30. Consider the following structures and calculate value of $(P^2 - Q^2)$
Where P = Total number of correct structure representation.
Q = Total number of incorrect structure representation.

(i) 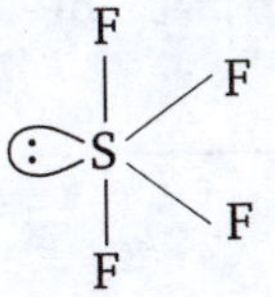
(ii) 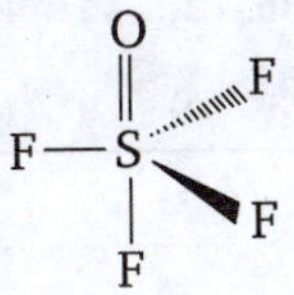
(iii) 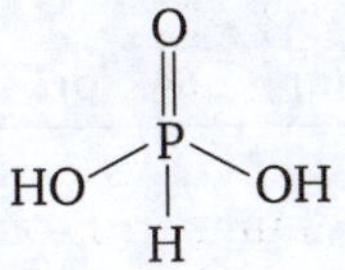
(iv) 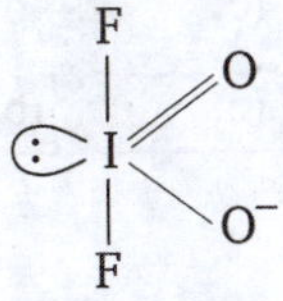
(v) 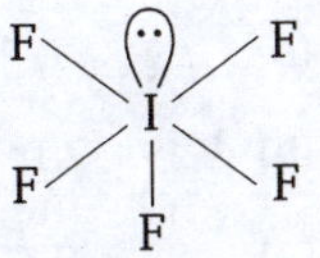
(vi) 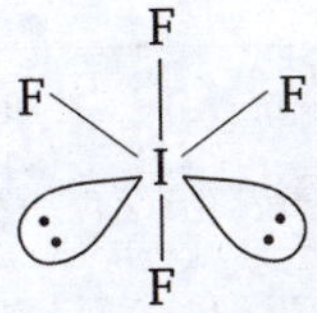
(vii) 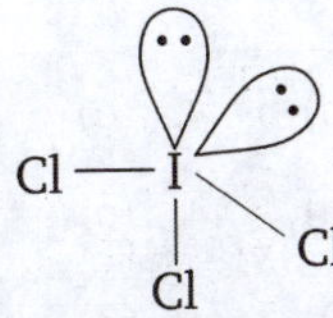

31. Calculate the value of "$x + y - z$" here, x, y and z are total number of non-bonded electron pair(s), pie(π) bond(s) and sigma bonds in hydrogen phosphite ion respectively.

32. Consider the following species :

(i) CH_3^+ (ii) $(C_3H_5)_3Al$ (iii) HCHO (iv) CH_4
(v) $(C_2H_5)_3N$ (vi) $TiCl_4$ (vii) CO_2 (viii) $SiCl_4$
(ix) BF_3

The find out total number of species which can act as Lewis acid.

33. Consider the following species CF_4, GeH_4, BCl_3, $AlBr_3$, H_2O, PH_3, PCl_5, CO_2, CH_4 and calculate value of $(x - y)^2$:
Where, x: Total number of species which act as only Lewis acid.
y: Total number of species which act as Lewis acid as well as Lewis base.

34. If X, Y and Z are total number of π-bond(s) in $H_2S_2O_6$, H_2SO_3 and $H_2S_2O_7$ respectively then calculate value of expression $|X + Y - Z|$.

35. Calculate value of "$x \div y$" for "hypophosphoric acid", where x is total number of lone pair(s) and y is total number π-bond(s) in given oxo-acids.

36. Atomicity of white or yellow phosphorus is 4 and it is represented as P_4 molecule.
Calculate the value of expression $\dfrac{X \cdot Y}{Z}$ regarding this molecule.

Where X: Total number of vertex angles in P_4 molecule
Y: Total number of lone pairs in P_4 molecule
Z: Total number of P—P bonds in P_4 molecule

Answers

Level-1

1. (b)	2. (b)	3. (b)	4. (b)	5. (b)	6. (b)	7. (d)	8. (c)	9. (d)	10. (d)
11. (c)	12. (a)	13. (b)	14. (b)	15. (b)	16. (b)	17. (c)	18. (b)	19. (d)	20. (c)
21. (c)	22. (b)	23. (b)	24. (c)	25. (b)	26. (c)	27. (a)	28. (b)	29. (b)	30. (d)
31. (c)	32. (b)	33. (d)	34. (b)	35. (d)	36. (b)	37. (a)	38. (a)	39. (a)	40. (b)
41. (b)	42. (b)	43. (d)	44. (c)	45. (d)	46. (b)	47. (b)	48. (c)	49. (a)	50. (b,c)
51. (c)	52. (d)	53. (b)	54. (b)	55. (c)	56. (a)	57. (b)	58. (d)	59. (b)	60. (d)
61. (c)	62. (b)	63. (c)	64. (c)	65. (c)	66. (d)	67. (c)	68. (c)	69. (c)	

Level-2

1. (d)	2. (d)	3. (b)	4. (b)	5. (a)	6. (a)	7. (a,c)	8. (c)	9. (d)	10. (c)
11. (d)	12. (b)	13. (a)	14. (c)	15. (b)	16. (d)	17. (a)	18. (b)	19. (d)	20. (d)
21. (b)	22. (c)	23. (b)	24. (a)	25. (d)	26. (c)	27. (d)	28. (a)	29. (a)	30. (d)
31. (d)	32. (c)	33. (b)	34. (b)	35. (c)	36. (b)	37. (d)	38. (a)	39. (c)	40. (b)
41. (d)	42. (d)	43. (c)	44. (b)	45. (a)	46. (a)	47. (a)	48. (c)	49. (a)	50. (d)
51. (b)	52. (c)	53. (c)	54. (c)	55. (c)	56. (a)	57. (a)	58. (d)	59. (c)	60. (b)
61. (d)	62. (d)	63. (b)	64. (a)	65. (d)	66. (d)	67. (d)	68. (c)	69. (c)	70. (d)
71. (c)	72. (c)	73. (a)	74. (b)	75. (d)	76. (d)	77. (a)	78. (c)	79. (c)	80. (c)
81. (c)	82. (b)	83. (b)	84. (d)	85. (b)	86. (a)	87. (b)	88. (b)	89. (b)	

Level-3

Passage–1	**1.**	(b)	**2.**	(a)	**3.**	(c)		
Passage–2	**1.**	(d)	**2.**	(b)	**3.**	(a)		
Passage–3	**1.**	(c)	**2.**	(d)	**3.**	(a)		
Passage–4	**1.**	(c)	**2.**	(b)	**3.**	(a)	**4.**	(b)
Passage–5	**1.**	(a)	**2.**	(d)				
Passage–6	**1.**	(a)	**2.**	(b)	**3.**	(b)		
Passage–7	**1.**	(b)	**2.**	(c)	**3.**	(a)		

One Or More Answers is/are correct

1. (b,c,d) **2.** (a,d) **3.** (a,b,c) **4.** (a,b,c,d) **5.** (a,b,c) **6.** (a,b,c) **7.** (b,c,d) **8.** (a,b,c,d)
9. (a,b) **10.** (b,c,d) **11.** (a,b,c) **12.** (a,c,d) **13.** (a,b,d) **14.** (a,b,c) **15.** (b,c,d) **16.** (a,b,c,d)
17. (a,c) **18.** (a,c,d) **19.** (b,d) **20.** (a,c) **21.** (a,d) **22.** (a,b,c) **23.** (a,b,d) **24.** (a)
25. (a,b,c) **26.** (c, d) **27.** (a,b,c,d) **28.** (b,c) **29.** (c,d) **30.** (c,d) **31.** (a,b) **32.** (c,d)
33. (b,d) **34.** (a,d) **35.** (a,c,d) **36.** (b,d) **37.** (b,c,d) **38.** (a,b,d) **39.** (b,c) **40.** (a,b,d)
41. (a,c) **42.** (a,c,d) **43.** (a,b,d) **44.** (a,b,d) **45.** (a,b) **46.** (a,b,d) **47.** (a,d) **48.** (a,b,c)
49. (c,d) **50.** (a,c,d) **51.** (a,b,c) **52.** (a,b) **53.** (a,b,c) **54.** (a,b,c) **55.** (b,c,d) **56.** (c,d)
57. (a,b,d) **58.** (c,d) **59.** (a,d) **60.** (b,d) **61.** (b,d) **62.** (a,b,d) **63.** (a,d) **64.** (a,d)
65. (a,b,c) **66.** (b,c,d) **67.** (b,d) **68.** (b,c) **69.** (a,b,c) **70.** (b,c) **71.** (b,d) **72.** (a,c,d)
73. (a,b,c) **74.** (a,b,d) **75.** (a,b) **76.** (a,b,d) **77.** (a,c,d) **78.** (a,b,d) **79.** (a,b) **80.** (b,c)
81. (a,b,d) **82.** (a,b,d) **83.** (a,c,d) **84.** (a,b,c,d) **85.** (b,c) **86.** (a,b,c,d) **87.** (a,d) **88.** (a,c,d)
89. (a,b) **90.** (a,d) **91.** (a,d) **92.** (a,c,d) **93.** (a,b,c) **94.** (a,b,d) **95.** (a,c) **96.** (a,b,c,d)
97. (a,b,c)

Match the Column

1. A→ R, S;	B→ R, S;	C→ Q, R;	D→ P, Q
2. A→ P, Q, R, T;	B→ P, S;	C→ P, Q, S;	D→ R, S, T
3. A→ P, S;	B→ Q, R;	C→ Q, T;	D→ R, S
4. A→ Q, T;	B→ P, Q, S, T;	C→ Q, R, S;	D→ Q, R, T
5. A→ R, S, T;	B→ Q, R, S;	C→ P,Q,R,S,T;	D→ P,Q,R,S,T
6. A→ P, Q, R, S;	B→ P,Q,R;	C→ P,Q,R,S,T;	D→ S,T
7. A→ Q;	B→ P;	C→ S;	D→ R
8. A→ S;	B→ P;	C→ Q;	D→ R
9. A→ P, Q, R, S;	B→ P;	C→ P, Q, R, S;	D→ P, Q, R, S
10. A→ R;	B→ S;	C→ Q;	D→ P
11. A→ Q;	B→ R;	C→ S;	D→ P
12. A→ S;	B→ R;	C→ Q;	D→ P
13. A→ R;	B→ P;	C→ S;	D→ Q
14. A→ P;	B→ R;	C→ S;	D→ Q
15. A→ S;	B→ R;	C→ P;	D→ Q
16. A→ Q, T;	B→ R;	C→ S;	D→ P
17. A→ P, Q, S;	B→ P, Q, S;	C→ Q, R;	D→ Q, R, S
18. A→ P, Q;	B→ P, Q;	C→ P, R, S;	D→ Q
19. A→ P, S;	B→ P;	C→ Q, R, S;	D→ Q, R
20. A→ P, S;	B→ P, Q, R;	C→ R;	D→ S
21. A→ R, S;	B→ P, S;	C→ S;	D→ Q, R, S
22. A→ P;	B→ R;	C→ R, S;	D→ Q
23. A→ R, S;	B→ Q,R, S;	C→ R, S;	D→ P, Q
24. A→ P, Q, R, T;	B→ P, R, S;	C→ Q, S, T;	D→ P, R

Assertion-Reason Type Questions

1. (C) **2.** (A) **3.** (D) **4.** (C) **5.** (D) **6.** (D) **7.** (A) **8.** (B) **9.** (A) **10.** (B)
11. (C) **12.** (A) **13.** (A) **14.** (C) **15.** (C) **16.** (C) **17.** (A) **18.** (C) **19.** (B) **20.** (C)
21. (C) **22.** (A) **23.** (A) **24.** (C) **25.** (B) **26.** (C) **27.** (A)

Subjective Problems

1. 0 **2.** 4 **3.** 6 **4.** 9 **5.** 5 **6.** 0 **7.** 0
8. 4 **9.** 2 **10.** 7 **11.** 16 **12.** 08 **13.** 03 **14.** 02
15. 2 **16.** 1 **17.** 9 **18.** 5 **19.** 3 **20.** 8 **21.** 2
22. 9 **23.** 3 **24.** 5 **25.** 9 **26.** 4 **27.** 6 **28.** 5
29. 1 **30.** 7 **31.** 3 **32.** 7 **33.** 16 **34.** 1 **35.** 6
36. 8

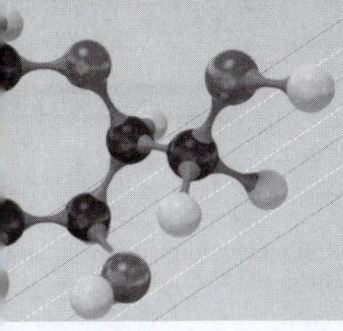

Hints and Solutions

Level 1

1. (b) $CoO(s) + B_2O_3(s) \xrightarrow{\Delta} \underset{\text{Blue}}{Co(BO_2)_2}$

14. (b)

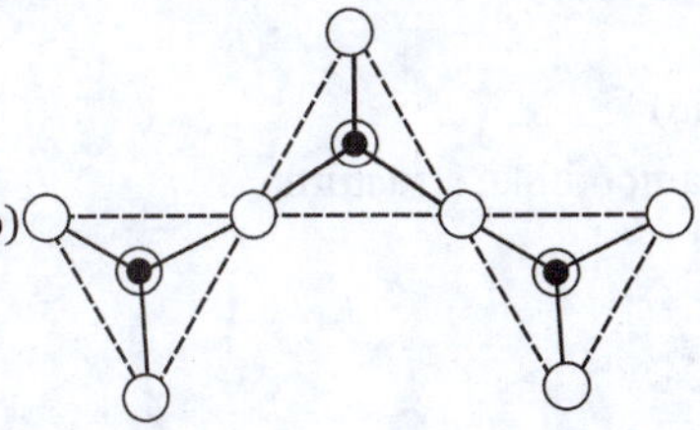

Formula: $Si_3O_{10}^{8-}$

43. (d) $\overset{+3}{N}O_2^- \xrightarrow{\text{Oxidation}} \overset{+5}{N}O_3^-$

44. (c) PH_3 stable species.

46. (b) Order of M.P. or B.P. or critical temperature : $H_2O > H_2Te > H_2Se > H_2S$

48. (c) $HO-S(=O)_2-O-O-S(=O)_2-OH + H_2O \longrightarrow HO-S(=O)_2-OH + H-O-O-S(=O)_2-O-H$

(Sulphuric acid) (Peroxomono-sulphuric acid)

52. (d) H_2O_2 is thermally unstable and it decomposes easily.

$$H_2O_2(l) \longrightarrow H_2O(l) + \frac{1}{2}O_2(g)$$

Its decomposition is catalysed by alkali metals present in traces in the glass of the vessel.

53. (b) $HOCl + H_2O_2 \longrightarrow Cl^-(aq.) + O_2(g) + H_2O$

54. (b) $HClO_4 > HBrO_4 > HIO_4 \Rightarrow$ acidic strength has been decided on the basis of electronegativity or charge density on central atom.

55. (c) $I_2 + 10HNO_3 \longrightarrow 2HIO_3 + 10NO_2 + 4H_2O$

56. (a) Decreasing order of thermal stability of oxy acids of chlorine.

$HOClO_3; HOClO_2; HOClO; HOCl$

In $HOClO_3$, chlorine is in +7 oxidation state.

57. (b) $5CO + I_2O_5 \longrightarrow 5CO_2 + I_2$

$I_2 + 2Na_2S_2O_3 \longrightarrow 2NaI + Na_2S_4O_6$

60. (d)

(a) — Bond dissociation energy of F_2 is less than that of Cl_2

(b) — Cl has higher E.A. than fluorine.

(c) — HF is weaker acid than HCl, due to higher bond energy

61. (c) Due to larger size of iodine atom it can accommodate upto seven small fluorine atoms around, it while due to smaller sizes of chlorine and bromine atoms do not accommodate seven fluorine atoms, *i.e.*, steric factor dominate in case of chlorine and bromine.

Level 2

1. (d) Lewis acidic strength : $BF_3 < BCl_3 < BBr_3 < BI_3$

As BI_3 is strongest lewis acid among all boron halides therefore, heat of adduct formation will be maximum numerically, for BI_3.

9. (d) $B_2O_3 \xrightarrow[\Delta]{Al} B(\text{crystalline})$

$B_2O_3 \xrightarrow[\Delta]{Mg} B\ (\text{Amorphous})$

10. (c) $Al(OH)_3$ dissolves in NaOH solution to give $Al(OH)_4^-$ ion which is supposed to have the octahedral complex species $[Al(OH)_4(H_2O)_2]^-$ in aqueous solution.

$Al(OH)_3 + NaOH(aq) \longrightarrow [Al(OH)_4(H_2O)_2]^-(aq) + Na^+(aq)$

11. (d) Borazone : A crystalline form of boron nitride which has diamond like structure. (Non-planar)

Borazole : Inorganic benzene : $B_3N_3H_6$ (planar)

$B_3O_6^{3-}$:

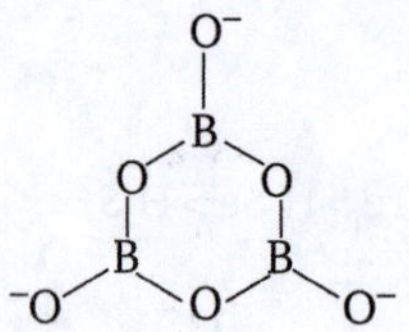

planar

Fe_2Cl_6 :

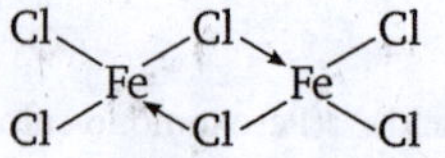

non planar

FCN :

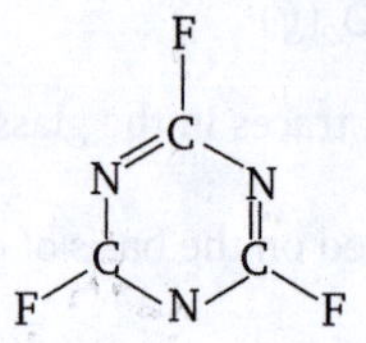

planar

12. (b) In borax ($Na_2B_4O_7 \cdot 10H_2O$), among 10 water molecules 2 molecules are part of structure, *i.e.*, exists $Na_2[B_4O_5(OH)_4] \cdot 8H_2O$

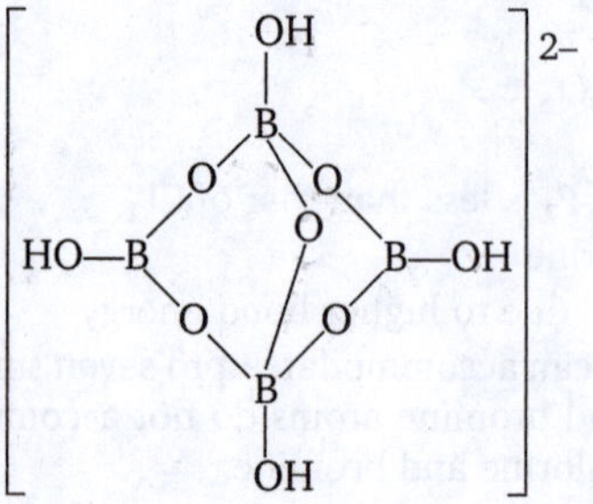

$Na_2[B_4O_5(OH)_4]{\cdot}8H_2O + 2HCl \longrightarrow 2NaCl + 4H_3BO_3 + 5H_2O$

Methyl orange (pH = 3.7) is used to detect end point. Aq. solution of borax acts as buffer, as borax is salt of strong base NaOH and weak acid H_3BO_3.

13. (a) H_3BO_3 acts are weak monobasic Lewis acid.

(i) $B(OH)_3 + NaOH \longrightarrow Na[B(OH)_4]$

On addition of *cis* 1, 2 diol in H_3BO_3 solution, acidic strength of H_3BO_3 increases due to chelation effect.

14. (c) Ag^+ ion can not give borax bead test because formed silver metaborate $AgBO_2$ is white/ colourless.

15. (b) Al Metal $\xrightarrow{HCl_{(aq.)}} \underset{(P)}{AlCl_3 + H_2\uparrow}$

Al Metal $\xrightarrow[+H_2O]{NaOH_{(aq.)}} \underset{(Q)}{Na[Al(OH)_4] + H_2\uparrow}$

16. (d) $BF_3 + LiAlH_4 \xrightarrow{\text{Ether}} \underset{(X)}{B_2H_6} + LiF + AlF_3$

NH_3 can react with B_2H_6.

$B_2H_6 + 2NH_3 \xrightarrow{\text{warm}} [BH_2{\cdot}2NH_3]^+{\cdot}[BH_4]^- \xrightarrow{200°C} B_3N_3H_6$ (Inorganic benzene)

20. (d)

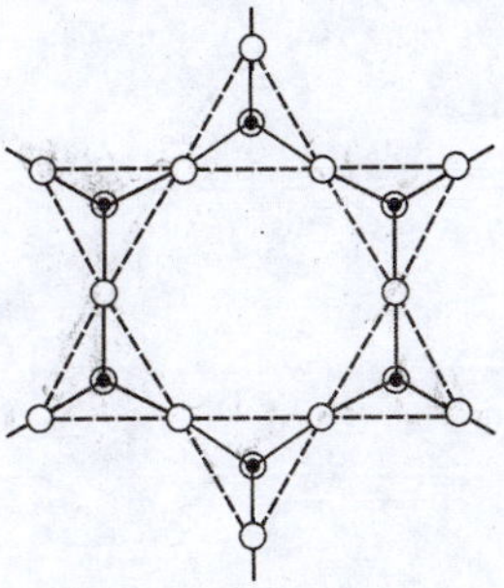

Total No. of oxygen atoms per silicon atom $= \frac{1}{2} + \frac{1}{2} + \frac{1}{2} + 1 = 2.5$

$\therefore$ Formula $Si_2O_5^{2-}$.

21. (b)

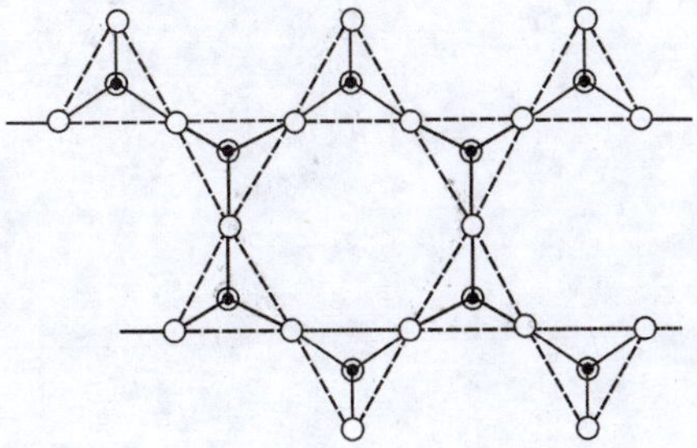

One tetrahedral shares three corners while other adjacent one shares only two corners hence average shared corners $= \frac{3+2}{2} = 2\frac{1}{2}$

25. (d) (i) Pyro silicates : (1 corner O-atom per tetrahedron is shared)
(ii) Cyclic silicates : (2 corner O-atom per tetrahedron is shared)
(iii) Double chain silicates (One unit shares two corner O-atom while one unit shares three corner O-atom)
(iv) Single chain silicate : (2 corner O-atom are shared)
(v) 3D silicate : (4 corner O-atom are shared)
(vi) Sheet silicates : (3 corner O-atom are shared)

26. (c) Due to inert effect the stability of lower oxidation state gradually increases while stability of higher oxidation state gradually decreases down the group in elements of group 13th to 15th. So correct orders are :
(iii) $Pb^{2+} > Pb^{4+}$, $Bi^{3+} > Bi^{5+}$
(iv) $Sn^{2+} < Pb^{2+}$, $Sn^{4+} > Pb^{4+}$

27. (d) $[\overset{-III}{N}H_4\overset{+III}{N}O_2] \xrightarrow{\Delta} N_2\uparrow + 2H_2O\uparrow$

$$NaN_3 \xrightarrow{\Delta} Na + \frac{3}{2}N_2\uparrow$$

$$(NH_4)_2Cr_2O_7 \xrightarrow{\Delta} N_2\uparrow + \underset{\text{(green)}}{Cr_2O_3(s)} + 4H_2O\uparrow$$

28. (a) $NO(g) + NO_2(g) \xrightarrow{243\,K} \underset{\substack{(X)\\ \text{(Blue coloured solid)}}}{N_2O_3} \xrightarrow{H_2O} \underset{(Y)}{HNO_2}$

Anion of $HNO_2 : NO_2^-$

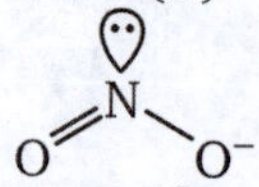

Hyb. sp^2
shape : Triangular planar

29. (a) $Na + NH_3(g) \xrightarrow{\Delta} \underset{[X]}{NaNH_2} \xrightarrow{N_2O} \underset{[Y]}{NaN_3} \xrightarrow{\Delta} \underset{[Z]}{N_2\uparrow}$

30. (d) (a) $H_4P_2O_5$

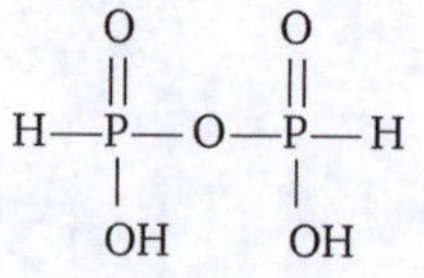

(b) $H_4P_2O_7$

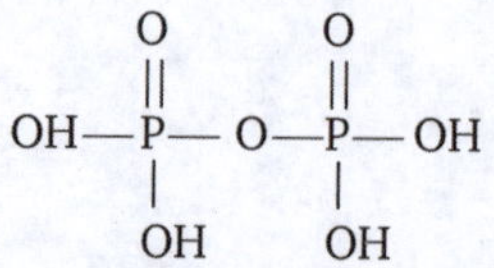

(c) $H_4P_2O_6$

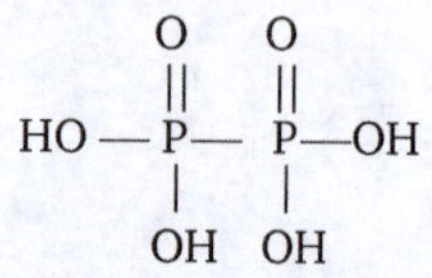

31. (d) NH_3 is a weak reducing agent than PH_3, because X—H bond strength decreases down the group. Due to absence of H-bonding, only weak van der Waals force of attraction exists in PH_3, it has lower critical temperature than NH_3.

33. (b) $AgNO_3 \longrightarrow Ag + \frac{1}{2}O_2 + NO_2$

$$2NaNO_3 \xrightarrow{500°C} 2NaNO_2 + O_2$$

$$4NaNO_3 \xrightarrow{800°C} 2Na_2O + 5O_2 + 2N_2$$

36. (b) $\underset{(A)}{PCl_5} + H_2O \longrightarrow \underset{(B)}{POCl_3} + 2HCl$

$$\underset{(B)}{POCl_3} + 3H_2O \longrightarrow \underset{(C)}{H_3PO_4} + 3HCl$$

41. (d) $\ddot{P}H_3 + H^+ \longrightarrow PH_4^+$

According to Drago's rule lone pair on phosphorus resides in almost pure *s*-orbital, hence due to non-directional nature, its overlapping tendency is greatly reduced in comparison to a lone pair present in hybrid orbital, which is directional as present in $\ddot{N}H_3$.

45. (a) (F); As the size of halogen atom increases crowding on Si atom will increase, hence, tendency of attack of Lewise base decreases.

(b) (T); M.P. of NH_3 is highest due to intermolecular H-bonding in it.

Next lower M.P. will be of SbH_3 followed by AsH_3 due to high mol. wt. of SbH_3.

(c) (F); M.P. and B.P. of increase from PH_3 to SbH_3 via AsH_3 due to increase in mol. wt. NH_3 does not follow this trend due to inter molecular H-bonding.

Increasing B.P. order : $PH_3 < AsH_3 < NH_3 < SbH_3$

(d) (T); Value of bond moment decreases.

48. (c) $NH_4Cl + NaNO_2 \longrightarrow NH_4NO_2 + NaCl$

$$NH_4NO_2 \xrightarrow{\Delta} N_2\uparrow + 2H_2O$$

$$Ba(N_3)_2 \longrightarrow Ba + 3N_2\downarrow$$

$$2NH_4Cl + CaO \longrightarrow CaCl_2 + 2NH_3\uparrow + H_2O$$

49. (a) $NF_3 + H_2O \longrightarrow S_{N^1}$ $\quad NCl_3 + H_2O \longrightarrow S_{N^2}$

(b) $P_4O_{10} \longrightarrow S_{N\,AE}$ $\quad SiCl_4 \longrightarrow S_{N^2}$

(c) SF_4, $TeF_6 \longrightarrow$ Both S_{N^2}

(d) $SiCl_4$, $SiF_4 \longrightarrow$ Both S_{N^2}

50. (d) PH_3 (Lewis base) can react with B_2H_6 (Lewis acid).

51. (b) In NCl_3 molecule, H_2O molecule attacks on less electronegative Cl-atom rather than central N-atom.

$$NCl_3 + 3H_2O \longrightarrow NH_3 + 3HOCl$$

52. (c) Reducing character $\propto \dfrac{1}{\text{'}E—H\text{' bond dissociation enthalpy}}$

Hence, correct reducing character is $NH_3 < PH_3 < AsH_3 < SbH_3 < BiH_3$.

54. (c) M exhibits two oxidation states +3 and +5 but covalency can not be 5; hence M can not expand its valence shell. Therefore, M will be nitrogen having atomicity two.

56. (a) 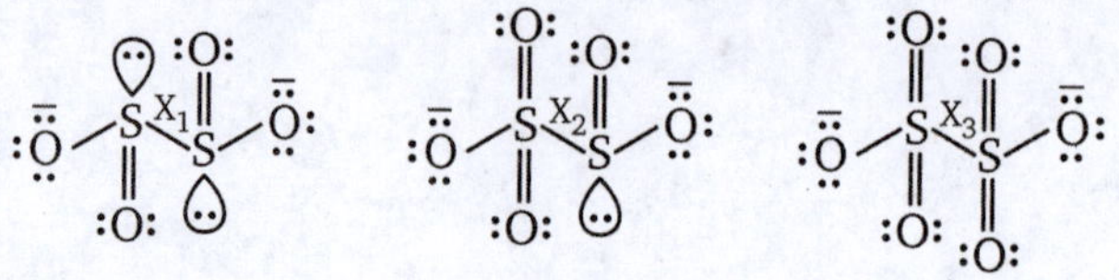

According to Bents rule $x_1 > x_2 > x_3$.

57. (a) a : $2OF \xrightarrow{\text{Dimerisation}} F-\overset{-I}{O}-\overset{-I}{O}-F$

b : $H_4P_2O_8 \xrightarrow{+H_2O} 2H_3PO_4 + H-\overset{-I}{O}-\overset{-I}{O}-H$

c : $2Na \xrightarrow[\Delta]{\text{excess } O_2} Na^+O^- - O^-Na^+$

58. (d) 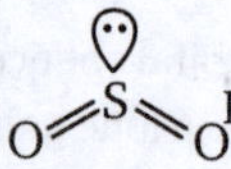 Hyb. : sp^2, structure : V-shape, planar

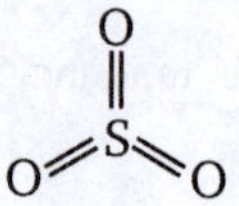 Hyb. : sp^2, structure : Triangular planar

$\gamma-SO_3$: Cyclic trimer : 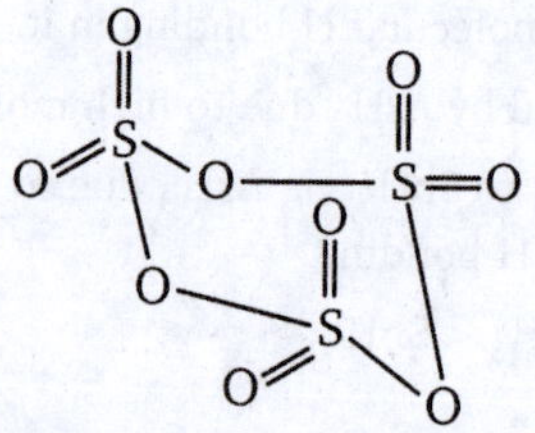

59. (c) SO_2 soluble in water. So can not be collected over water.

$$SO_2 + H_2O \longrightarrow H_2SO_4$$

61. (d) Aqueous solution of SO_2 acts as a reducing agent

$$SO_2 + 2H_2O \longrightarrow H_2SO_4 + \underset{\text{nascent hydrogen}}{2H}$$

Thus, SO_2 in presence of moisture is used as bleaching agent. This is due to the reducing nature of SO_2. For delicate articles

$$\text{Coloured matter} + H \longrightarrow \text{Colourless matter}$$

Similarly, Cl_2 acts as bleaching agent in presence of moisture

$$Cl_2 + H_2O \longrightarrow 2HCl + [O]$$

$$\text{Coloured matter} + [O] \longrightarrow \text{Colourless matter}$$

62. (d) In SF_6, S sterically hindered by six fluorine atoms hence, attack of H_2O molecule will not occur. NF_3 is not hydrolysed due to absence of vacant orbital either on N of F atom.

TeF_6 is hydrolysed due to large size of Te.

63. (b) $H_2SO_4 + PbO_2 \longrightarrow PbSO_4\downarrow + \frac{1}{2}O_2 + H_2O$ (PbO_2 is not peroxy compound)

$H_2SO_4 + BaO_2 \longrightarrow BaSO_4\downarrow + H_2O_2$

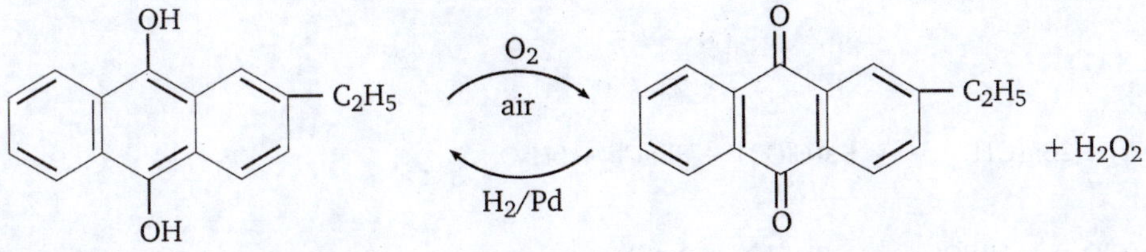

$(NH_4)_2SO_4 \rightleftharpoons 2NH_4^+ + SO_4^{2-}$

At anode : $2SO_4^{2-} \xrightarrow{\text{Electrolysis}} S_2O_8^{2-} + 2e^-$

Peroxo sulphate on hydrolysis, produces H_2O_2.

64. (a) → Number of S—S bonds in $H_2S_nO_6$ are $(n-1)$

→ $LiNO_3$ produces crimson red while $BaCl_2$ produces green colour in fire works

→ Hydrides of Be and Mg are covalent and polymeric

65. (d) Hypo form of '–ic' acid is derived from its pyro form, and $HClO_3$ does not have its pyro form therefore its hypo form is not possible.

67. (d) $PCl_3(sp^3)$, $H_3PO_3(sp^3)$

$SF_4(sp^3d)$, $H_2SO_3(sp^3)$

$BCl_3(sp^2)$, $H_3BO_3(sp^2)$

$XeF_6(sp^3d^2)$, $XeO_3(sp^3)$

68. (c) Acidic character : $HOCl < HClO_2 < HClO_3 < HClO_4$

Oxidising power : $HOCl > HClO_2 > HClO_3 > HClO_4$

Thermal stability : $HOCl < HClO_2 < HClO_3 < HClO_4$

'Cl—O' bond order : $HOCl < HClO_2 < HClO_3 < HClO_4$

69. (c) ⇒

	$\overset{+I}{ClO^-}$	$\overset{+III}{ClO_2^-}$	$\overset{+V}{ClO_3^-}$	$\overset{+VII}{ClO_4^-}$
B.O.	1.0	1.5	1.67	1.75
Hyb. of Cl	sp^3	sp^3	sp^3	sp^3

70. (b) $Cl_2O_6 + HF \longrightarrow \underset{(P)}{[\overset{+}{Cl}O_2]F^-} + \underset{(Q)}{HClO_4}$

$\overset{+}{Cl}O_2$: 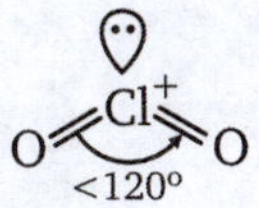 Hyb. : sp^2;

ClO_4^-: 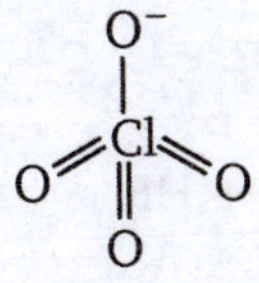 Hyb. : sp^3

$\angle OClO = 109°28'$

71. (c) $\underset{\text{(impure)}}{3Br_2} + \underset{\text{(Hot Aq. Sol.)}}{3Na_2CO_3} \longrightarrow 5NaBr + NaBrO_3 + 3CO_2\uparrow$

$$\xrightarrow{\Delta,\ H_2SO_4} \underset{\text{(Pure)}}{3Br_2\uparrow} + Na_2SO_4$$

74. (b) $6Cl_2 + 2Ba(OH)_2 \longrightarrow \underset{(X)}{Ba(ClO_3)_2} + 5BaCl_2 + 6H_2O$

$$Ba(ClO_3)_2 + H_2SO_4 \longrightarrow \underset{(Y)}{2HClO_3} + BaSO_4\downarrow$$

$$2HClO_3 \xrightarrow[\Delta > 365\text{ K}]{\Delta} 2ClO_2 + H_2O + \frac{1}{2}O_2$$

75. (d) $6CaOCl_2 \xrightarrow[\text{oxidation}]{\text{Auto}} Ca(ClO_3)_2 + 5CaCl_2$

77. (a) $X = CH_4$, $Y = NaH$, $Z = HBr$

78. (c) Correct order b.pt.

$$\underbrace{HF}_{\text{H-bonding}} > \underbrace{HI > HBr > HCl}_{\text{Dipole-dipole attraction (V.W. forces)}}$$

In case of same type of van der Waals' forces of attraction b.pt. $\propto$ molecular mass.

80. (c) $XeF_2 + H_2O \xrightarrow{\text{R.T.}} Xe + 2HF + \frac{1}{2}O_2\uparrow$

$$XeF_6 + 3H_2O \xrightarrow{\text{R.T.}} XeO_3 + 6HF$$

81. (c) $MF + XeF_4 \longrightarrow M^+[XeF_5^-]$

sp^3d^3, Pentagonal planar

83. (b) $HF + XeF_6 \longrightarrow XeF_5^+ + HF_2^-$

84. (d) Due to small size of He, it escapes from interstitial spaces/voids of molecular lattice of quinols.

85. (b) $XeF_4 + SbF_5 \longrightarrow [XeF_3]^+ [SbF_6]^- \longrightarrow \underset{\substack{sp^3d \\ \text{bent T-shape}}}{[XeF_3]^+} + \underset{\substack{sp^3d^2 \\ \text{octahedral}}}{[SbF_6]^-}$

87. (b) The compound XeO_3 is an uncommon hydrolysis product between XeF_2 and XeF_4.

(i) $XeF_2 + H_2O \longrightarrow Xe + \frac{1}{2}O_2 + 2HF$

(ii) $3XeF_4 + 6H_2O \longrightarrow XeO_3 + 2Xe + \frac{3}{2}O_2 + 12HF$

88. (b) $XeF_6 \xrightarrow{+\text{Excess } H_2O} \underset{(X)}{XeO_3} + HF$

$XeF_6 \xrightarrow{+2H_2O} \underset{(Y)}{XeO_2F_2} + HF$

Y is not an oxyacid of xenon.

89. (b) Both He and Ne do not form clathrate compound due to their small size.

Level 3

Passage-1

1. (b) As HNO_3 can not form its pyro oxyacid hence its peroxy form having two central atoms is not possible.

2. (a)

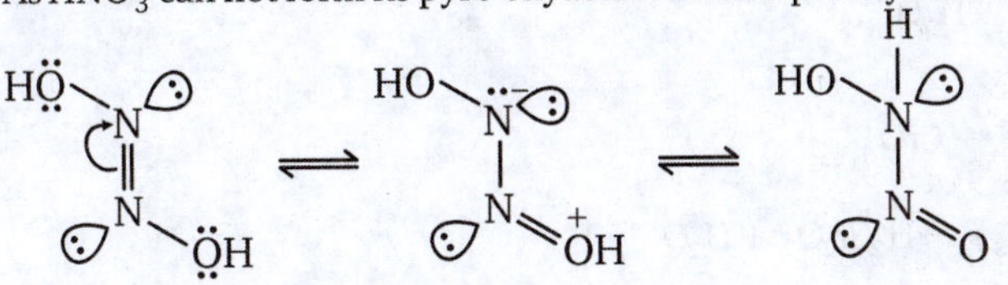

3. (c)

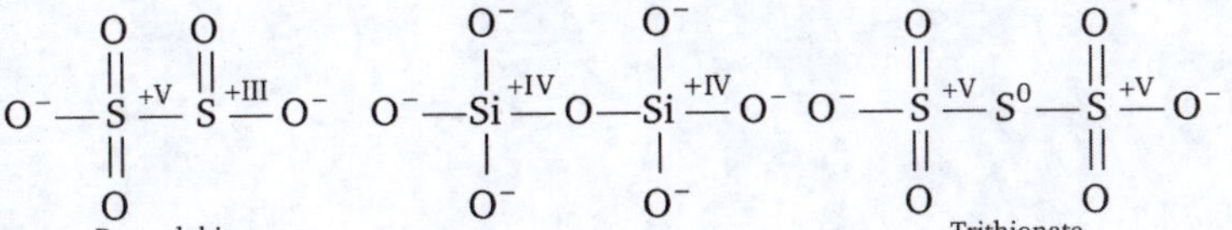

Pyrosulphite Pyrosilicate Trithionate

Passage-3

1-3. (i) $\underset{(P)}{B_2O_3} + 3C + 3Cl_2 \longrightarrow \underset{(Q)}{2BCl_3} + 3CO\uparrow$

(ii) $\underset{(Q)}{BCl_3} + 3H_2O \longrightarrow \underset{(R)}{H_3BO_3} + 3HCl$

(iii) $BN + 3H_2O \longrightarrow \underset{(R)}{H_3BO_3} + 3HCl$

(iv) $\underset{(Q)}{4BCl_3} + 3LiAlH_4 \longrightarrow \underset{(S)}{2B_2H_6} + 3LiCl + 3AlCl_3$

(v) $\underset{(S)}{B_2H_6} + 6H_2O \longrightarrow \underset{(R)}{2H_3BO_3} + 6H_2\uparrow$

(vi) $\underset{(S)}{B_2H_6} + 2NaH \longrightarrow \underset{(T)}{2NaBH_4}$

Passage-4

$2Pb(NO_3)_2 \longrightarrow 2PbO + 4NO_2\uparrow + O_2\uparrow$

$\underset{(B)}{NO_2} + \underset{(H)}{NO} \xrightarrow[\text{temp.}]{\text{low}} \underset{\text{(Blue colour liquid)}}{N_2O_3}$

$\underset{(C)}{N_2O_3} + H_2O \longrightarrow \underset{(D)}{2HNO_2}$

$2HNO_2 + 2FeSO_4 + H_2SO_4 \longrightarrow Fe(SO_3)_3 + 2NO + 2H_2O$

$FeSO_4(aq) + NO \longrightarrow \underset{\substack{(E)\\ \text{(Brown ring)}}}{[Fe(H_2O)_5NO]SO_4}$

$Pb(NO_3)_2 + H_2S \longrightarrow \underset{\substack{(G)\\ \text{Black ppt.}}}{PbS\downarrow} \longrightarrow Pb(NO_3)_2 + S + \underset{(H)}{NO\uparrow} + \underset{(G)}{H_2O}$

$$Pb(NO_3)_2 + K_2CrO_4 \longrightarrow \underset{\text{(yellow ppt.)}}{\underset{\text{(I)}}{PbCrO_4\downarrow}} + 2K^+ + 2NO_3^-$$

1. $$\underset{(D)}{NO_2^-} + 2H^+ + I^- \longrightarrow I_2\uparrow + \underset{\text{(gas)}}{NO\uparrow} + H_2O$$

2. $$PbCrO_4 + 4OH^- \longrightarrow \underset{\text{soluble}}{[Pb(OH)_4]^{2-}} + CrO_4^-$$

$$2PbCrO_4 + 4HNO_3 \longrightarrow 2Pb(NO_3)_2 + H_2Cr_2O_7 + H_2O$$

4. 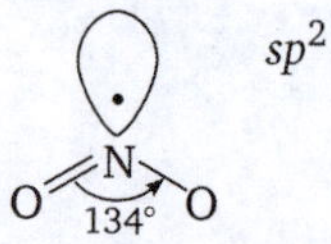

Passage-6

Inert pair effect phenomenon is exclusively applicable to sixth period elements belonging to 13, 14 and 15th group elements.

Due to inert pair effect Pb^{2+} is more stable than Pb^{4+}

$$Pb^{2+} \longrightarrow Pb^{4+} + 2e^-$$

$$\underset{\text{(More stable)}}{[Xe]4f^{14}5d^{10}6s^2} \qquad \underset{\text{(Less stable)}}{[Xe]4f^{14}5d^{10}}$$

$$Sn^{2+} \longrightarrow Sn^{4+} + 2e^-$$

$$\underset{\text{(Less stable)}}{[Kr]4d^{10}5s^2} \qquad \underset{\text{(More stable)}}{[Kr]4d^{10}}$$

$$Tl^{+} \longrightarrow Tl^{3+} + 2e^-$$

$$\underset{\text{(More stable)}}{[Xe]4f^{14}5d^{10}6s^2} \qquad \underset{\text{(Less stable)}}{[Xe]4f^{14}5d^{10}}$$

Hence, Tl^+ does not act as reducing agent.

$$In^{+} \longrightarrow In^{3+} + 2e^-$$

$$\underset{\text{(Less stable)}}{[Kr]4d^{10}6s^2} \qquad \underset{\text{(More stable)}}{[Kr]4s^{10}}$$

Hence, In^+ can act as stronger reducing agent than Tl^+.

Passage-7

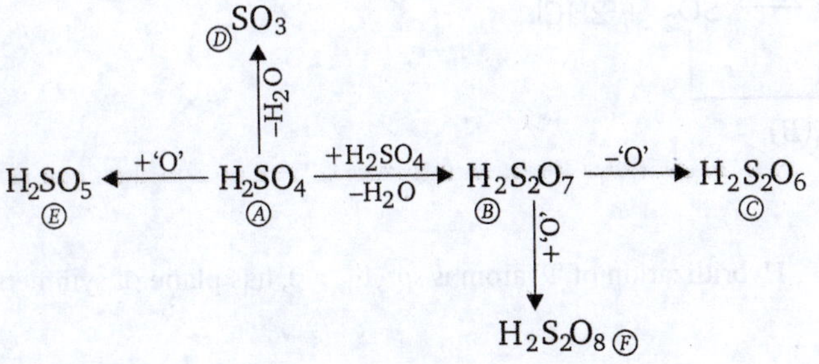

1. (b)

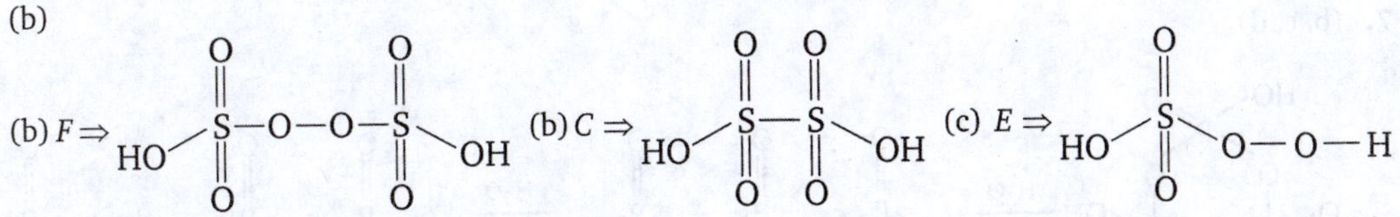

2. (c) In $SO_3(D)$, S is sp^2-hybridised.

3. (a)

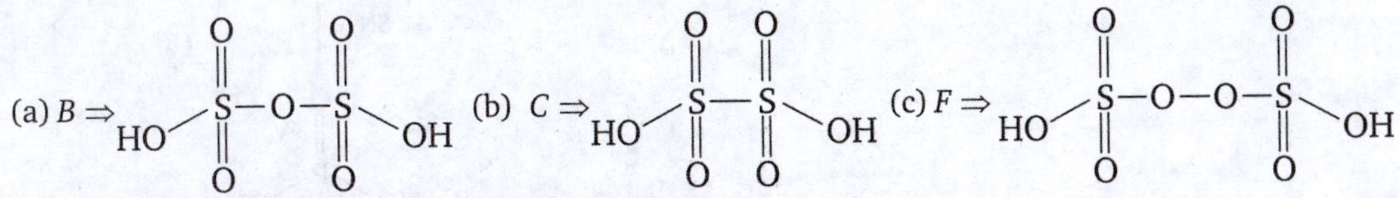

ONE OR MORE ANSWERS IS/ARE CORRECT

1. (b, c, d)

All Noble gases are colourless and odourless.

3. (a, b, c)

$XeF_6 + 6H_2O \xrightarrow[-6]{} XeO_3 + 6HF$

$XeF_6 + H_2O \xrightarrow[-2]{} XeOF_4 + 2HF$

XeF_6 act as fluoride donor when it reacts with non-metal fluoride.

4. (a, b, c, d)

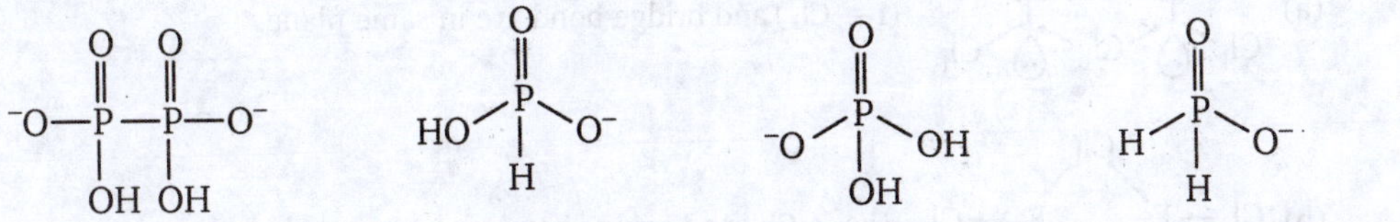

P—O Bond order = 1.5 P—O Bond order = 1.5 P—O Bond order = 1.5 P—O Bond order = 1.5

6. (a, b, c)

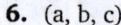

$$SOCl_2 + H_2O \longrightarrow SO_2 + 2HCl$$

$$SO_2 \xrightarrow{+PCl_5} SOCl_2$$

$POCl_3(B)$

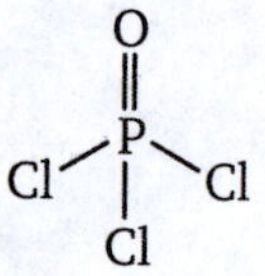

Hybridization of 'P' atom is $sp^3, \mu_D \neq 0$, has plane of symmetry.

7. (b, c, d)

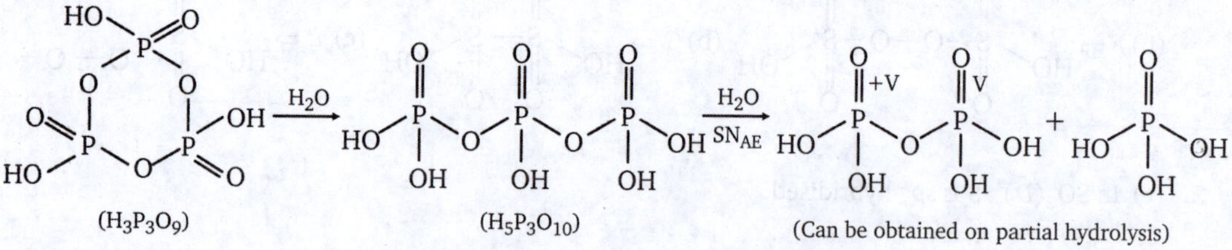

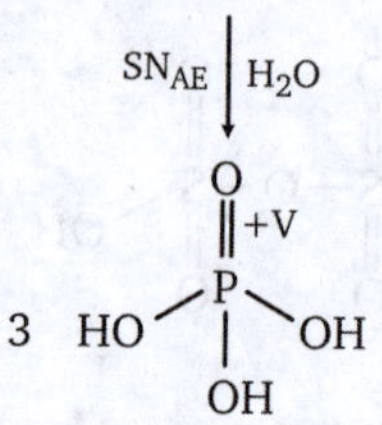

8. (a, b, c, d)

$$2XeF_2 + 2H_2O \xrightarrow{\text{R.T.}} 2Xe + 4HF + O_2$$

$$6XeF_4 + 12H_2O \xrightarrow{\text{R.T.}} 4Xe + 2XeO_3 + 24HF + 3O_2\uparrow$$

$$XeF_6 + 3H_2O \xrightarrow{\text{R.T.}} XeO_3 + 6HF$$

$$4HF + \underset{\text{Silica}}{SiO_2} \xrightarrow{\text{R.T.}} \underset{\text{P}}{SiF_4\uparrow} + 2H_2O$$

$$6HF + \underset{\text{glass}}{Na_2SiO_3} \xrightarrow{\text{R.T.}} 2NaF + SiF_4\uparrow + 3H_2O$$

9. (a, b)

(a) $(I—Cl_t)$ and bridge bond are in same plane.

(b) 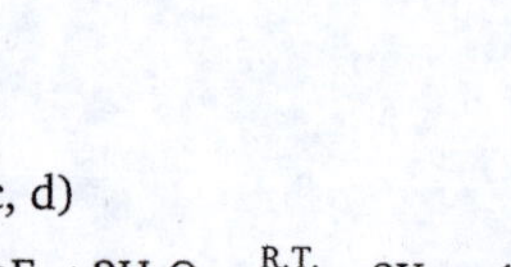 $(Fe—Cl_t)$ and bridge bond are in same plane.

10. (b, c, d)

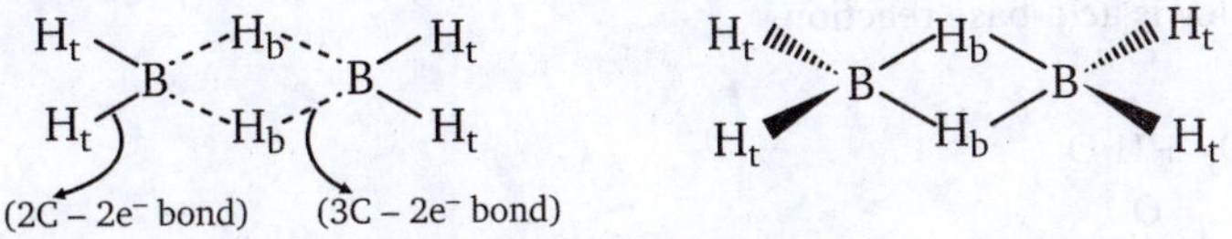

(a) Maximum Cl—H -atom can lie in a plane.

(b) Maximum 6-atom can lie in a plane $(H_t, H_t, B, H_t, H_t, B)$

(c) Bond strength $(B---H_b---B) > (B—H_t)$

(d) $(H_t—\hat{B}—H_t) > (H_b---\hat{B}---H_b)$

12. (a, c, d)

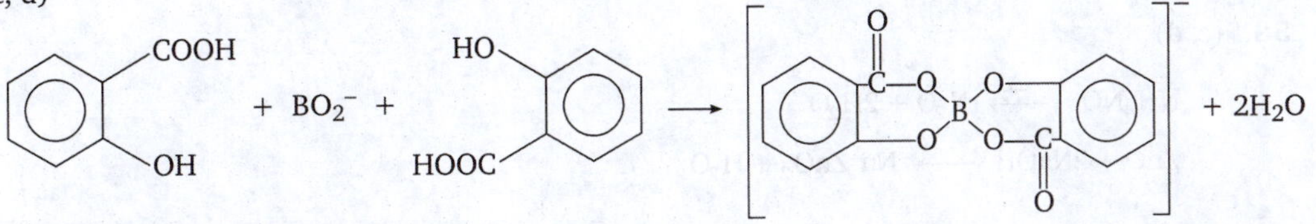

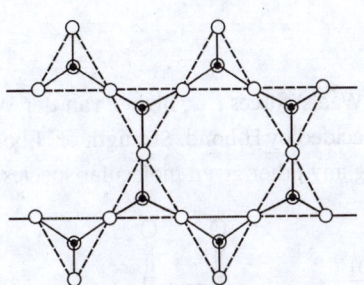

$$B(OH)_3 + H_2O \rightleftharpoons [B(OH)_4]^- + H^+$$
$$\updownarrow$$
$$BO_2^- + 2H_2O$$

⟶Opically resolvable due to asymmetric structure

⟶Two six membered rings.

18. (a, c, d)

Phenomenon of inert effect increases downward.

19. (b, d)

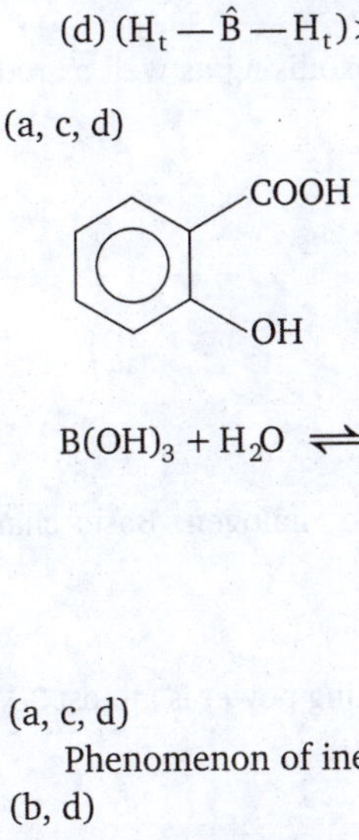

Cyclic silicate having three Si atoms $(Si_3O_9^{6-})$ contains three Si—O—Si linkage

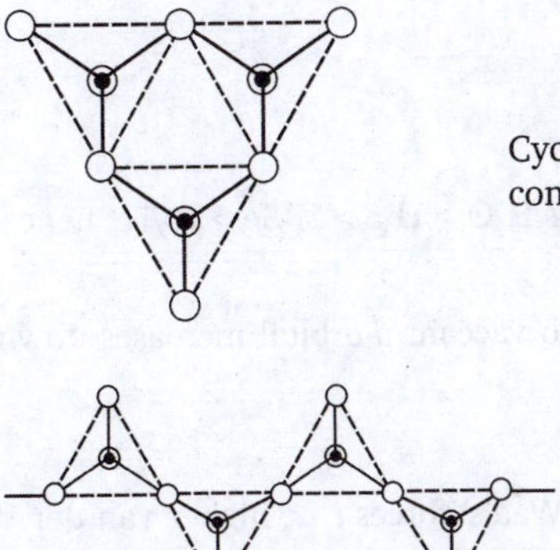

One tetrahedron shares three oxygen atoms while other share two oxygen atoms and these two tetrahedrons constitute one unit. Therefore, no. of oxygen atoms shared per tetrahedron or Si atom

$$= \frac{3+2}{2} = 2\frac{1}{2}$$

⇒ General formula of double chain silicates : $(Si_4O_{11})_n^{6n-}$

⇒ As the tendency of formation of multiple bond increases the extent of polymerization decreases. Silicon has large size hence, it forms less effective $p\pi$-$p\pi$ overlapping with oxygen.

35. (a, c, d)

They contain even number of carbon atoms.

44. (a,b, d)

X reacts with C_2H_5OH by lewis acid-base reaction.

45. (a, b)

$$2H_3PO_4 \xrightarrow{220°C} H_4P_2O_7 + H_2O$$

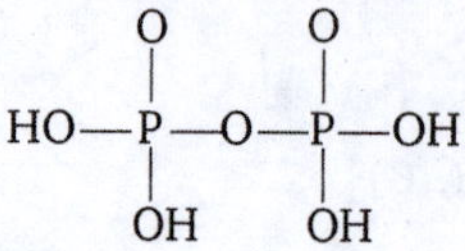

46. (a, b, d)

Only H_2S acts as a reducing agent while HNO_2, H_2O_2 and SO_2 act boh oxodising as well as reducing agents.

58. (c, d)

$$NH_4NO_3 \xrightarrow{\Delta} N_2O + 2H_2O$$

$$ZnO + 2NaOH \longrightarrow Na_2ZnO_2 + H_2O$$

59. (a, b, d)

Fluorine is the most reactive among all halongens hence, called super halogen. Basic character increases downward.

61. (b, d)

ClO_2 is powerful oxidising agent, also strong chlorinating agent. Its bleaching power is almost 30 times stronger than Cl_2. IN alkaline solution undergoes disproportionation

$$2ClO_2 + 2NaOH \longrightarrow NaClO + NaClO_3 + H_2O$$

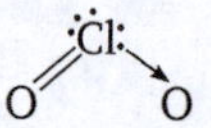
unpaired electron that's why paramagnetic.

93. (a, b, c)

As trend for decreasing bond energy in the given hydrides is $H_2O > H_2S > H_2Se > H_2Te$, hence their enthalpy of formation also varies in the same trend.

As extent of delocalization of lone pair on central atom into vaccant *d*-orbital increases downward hence bond angle decreases from H_2O to H_2Te.

Order of B.P. $H_2O > H_2Te > H_2Se > H_2S$

Boiling point of H_2Te, H_2Se and H_2S is decided by van der Waals' forces *i. e.*, higher van der Waals' force among molecules more will be B.P. But B.P. of H_2O is decided by H-bond. Strength of H-bond in H_2O is greater than van der Waals' forces of attraction among any other given molecular species.

94. (a, b, d)

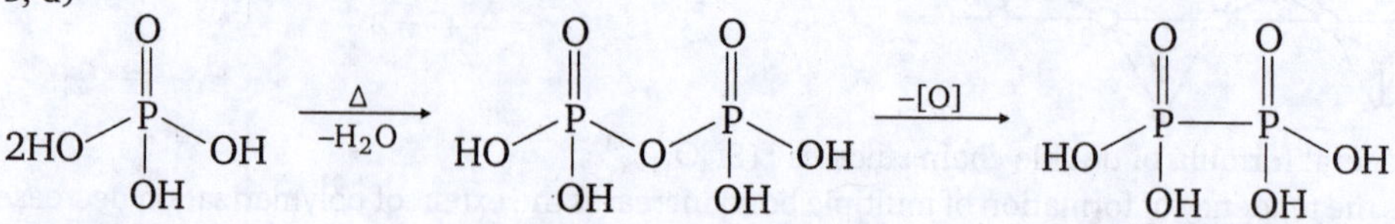

Phosphoric acid (*P*) Pyrophosphoric acid (*Q*) Hypophosphoric acid (*R*)

95. (a, c)

In gaseous or vapour phase PCl_5 exists as discrete molecule.

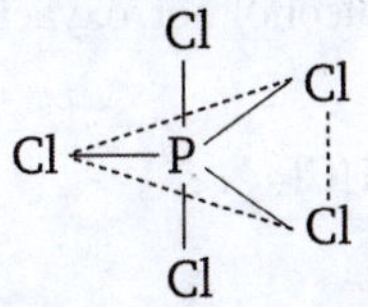

(In vapour state)

$d_{(P—Cl)}$ axial > $d_{(P—Cl)}$ equatorial

Whereas in solid state it exists as $[PCl_4]^+[PCl_6]^-$

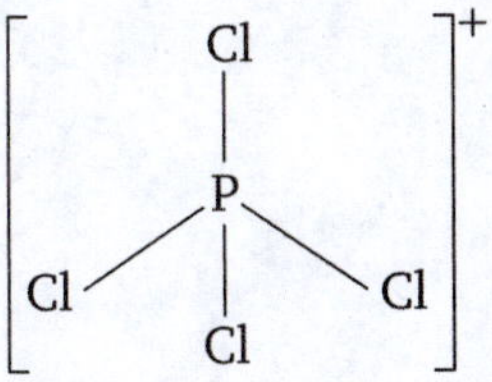

Hybridisation of P: sp^3

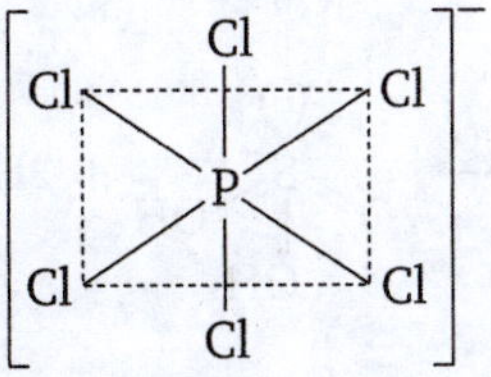

Hybridisation of P: sp^3d^2

Bond angle : 90° & 180°

96. (a, b, c, d)

(a) Thermal stability : $H_2O > H_2S > H_2Se > H_2Te$

(b) Bond dissociation energy : $Cl_2 > Br_2 > F_2 > I_2$

(c) Melting point : $NH_3 > SbH_3 > AsH_3 > PH_3$

(d) $X — \hat{C} — X$ bond angle : $COCl_2 > COF_2$

97. (a, b, c)

(a) $2HNO_3 \xrightarrow{-H_2O} N_2O_5$ (oxide of nitrogen)

(b) $H_2SO_4 \xrightarrow{-H_2O} SO_3$ (oxide of sulphur)

(c) $2HClO_4 \xrightarrow{-H_2O} Cl_2O_7$ (oxide of chlorine)

(d) $2H_2SO_4 \xrightarrow{-H_2O} H_2S_2O_7$ (oxo-acid)

(a), (b) and (c) are oxides and not oxo-acids.

MATCH THE COLUMN

3. $CaH_2 + 2H_2O \xrightarrow{R.T.} Ca(OH)_2 + H_2\uparrow$

$POCl_3 + 3H_2O \xrightarrow{R.T.} H_3PO_4 + 3HCl$

Proton donor oxyacid

No back bonding

$NCl_3 + 3H_2O \xrightarrow{R.T.} NH_3\uparrow + 3HOCl$

Proton donor oxyacid

$p\pi$-$d\pi$ back bonding

$B_2H_6 + 6H_2O \xrightarrow{R.T.} 2H_3BO_3 + 6H_2\uparrow$

does not furnish proton

$p\pi$-$d\pi$ back bonding

$$R_2SiCl_2 + 2H_2O \xrightarrow{R.T.} R_2Si(OH)_2 + 2HCl$$

Silanol an alcohol not oxyacid

4. (a) 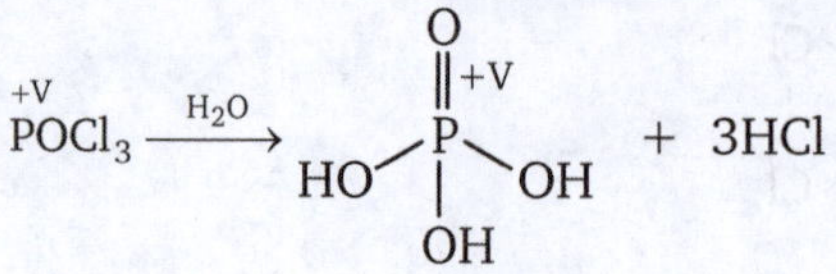

⇒ Complete hydrolysis

⇒ Hybridization of P in $POCl_3$: sp^3

⇒ Hybridization of P in H_3PO_4 : sp^3

⇒ H_3PO_4 does not undergo Tautomeric change due to absence of lone pair at P-atom.

(b) 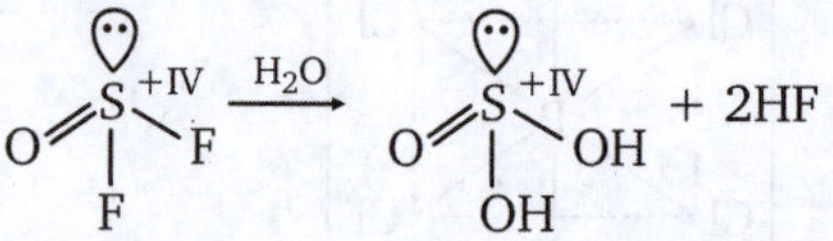

⇒ Complete hydrolysis

⇒ 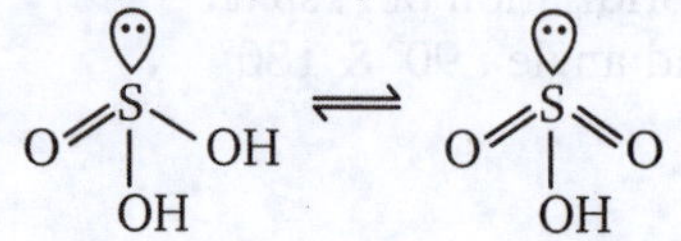 : Tautomeric change

(major) (very low)

⇒ Complete hydrolysis

⇒ HF reacts with glass

$$SiO_2 + 4HF \longrightarrow SiF_4 + 2H_2O$$

⇒ Hybridization of S-atom remains sp^3

(c) $\overset{+VI}{XeOF_4} \xrightarrow[-2HF]{H_2O} XeO_2F_2 \xrightarrow{H_2O} \overset{+VI}{XeO_3} + 2HF$

⇒ $XeOF_4$ can be partially hydrolysed to XeO_2F_2

⇒ HF forms which reacts with glass

⇒ Hybridization Xe in $XeOF_4$ is sp^3d^2 while in XeO_3 it is sp^3

(d) $\overset{+VI}{H_2S_2O_8} \xrightarrow{H_2O} \overset{+VI}{H_2SO_5} + \overset{+VI}{H_2SO_4} \xrightarrow{H_2O} \overset{+VI}{2H_2SO_4} + H—O—O—H$

⇒ $H_2S_2O_8$ can be partially hydrolysed to H_2SO_5

⇒ Hybridization S-atom in $H_2S_2O_8$ as well as in H_2SO_4 remains : sp^3

5. (a) $NCl_3 + 3H_2O \xrightarrow{R.T.} \overset{-III}{NH_3} + 3HO\overset{+I}{Cl}$

→ Non-redox hydrolysis

→ HOCl can act as both oxidizing and reducing agent.

→ NH_3: Monodentate ligand

(b) $NO_2 + H_2O \xrightarrow{R.T.} \overset{+III}{HNO_2} + \overset{+V}{HNO_3}$

→ NO_2^-, NO_3^- can act as flexidentate ligand.

→ HNO_2 can act as both oxidizing and reducing agent

→ NO_2^-, NO_3^- can act as monodentate ligand.

(c) $H_2S_2O_8 + 2H_2O \xrightarrow{R.T.} 2H_2\overset{-VI}{SO_4} + H_2\overset{-I}{O_2}$

→ H_2SO_4: Dibasic acid

→ SO_4^{--} can act as flexidentate ligand

→ H_2O_2 can act as both oxidizing and reducing agent

→ SO_4^{--} can act as monodentate ligand.

→ Non-redox reaction

(d) $SF_4 + 3H_2O \xrightarrow{R.T.} H_2SO_3 + 4HF$

→ H_2SO_3: Dibasic acid

→ SO_3^{--} can act as flexidentate ligand

→ H_2SO_3 can act as both oxidizing and reducing agent

→ SO_3^{--} can act as monodentate ligand

T → : Non-redox hydrolysis

6. (a) Disproportionation in alkaline medium/heating

$$Cl_2 \xrightarrow{\text{alkaline medium}} \bar{O}Cl + Cl^-$$

$$NO_2 \xrightarrow{\text{alkaline medium}} NO_2^- + NO_3^-$$

$$NaH_2PO_3 \xrightarrow{\Delta} Na_2HPO_4 + PH_3$$

(b) Oxidizing agent : Cl_2, NO_2, XeF_6

(c)

$$Cl_2 + H_2O \rightarrow HOCl + HCl$$

$$2NO_2 + H_2O \rightarrow HNO_3 + HNO_2$$

$$XeF_6 + H_2O \rightarrow XeOF_4 + 2HF \xrightarrow{H_2O} XeO_2F_2 + 2HF \xrightarrow{H_2O} XeO_3 + 2HF$$

$$NaH_2PO_3 + H_2O \rightarrow NaOH + H_3PO_3$$

$$(NH_4)_2S + H_2O \rightarrow NH_4OH + H_2S$$

(d)

$$NaH_2PO_3 \xrightarrow{\Delta} Na_2HPO_4 + PH_3 \uparrow$$

$$(NH_4)_2S \rightarrow \underset{\text{(acidic)}}{H_2S} + NH_3 \text{ (basic gas)}$$

7. A → Q, B → P, C → S, D → R

8. A → S, B → P, C → Q, D → R

PbI_4 is unstable compound Pb^{4+} is highly oxidising and I^- is a reducing agent.

Chlorine bleaches by oxidation and SO_2 by reduction.

9. P :

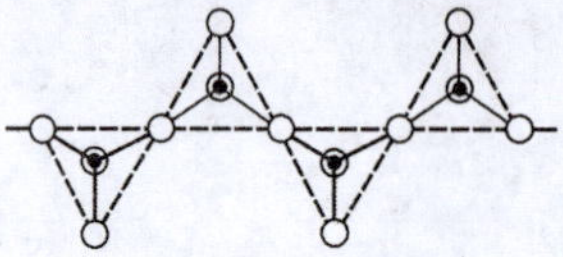

→ No. of terminal oxygen atoms = 10
→ Total no. of shared corners = 3
→ Silicon atom is present at the centre of geometry and oxygen atoms are present at corner of tetrahedron.
→ Non-planar

Q :

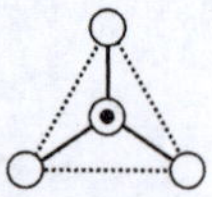

→ No. of terminal oxygen atoms = 4
→ Silicon atom is present at the centre of tetrahedron and oxygen atoms are present at the corner of tetrahedron.
→ Non-planar

R :

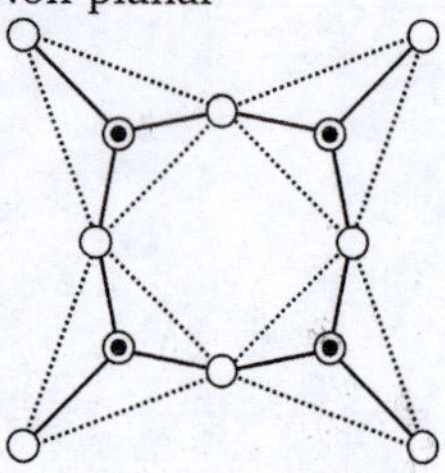

→ No. of terminal oxygen atoms = 8
→ Silicon atom is present at the centre of tetrahedron atoms are present at the corner of tetrahedron.
→ Non-planar geometry.

S :

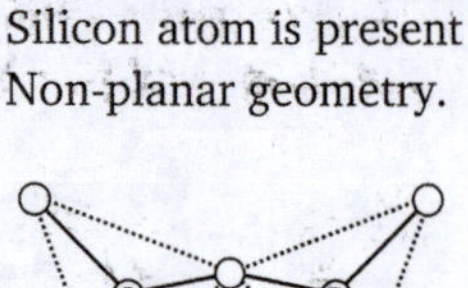

→ No. of terminal oxygen atoms = 7
→ Silicon atom is present at the centre of tetrahedron and oxygen atoms are present at the corner of tetrahedron.
→ Non-planar.

10. A → R, B → S, C → Q, D → P

(A) N_2 and CO : $\underset{\text{ammonical}}{CuCl} + 2CO \xrightarrow[\text{pressure}]{\text{high}} CuCl \cdot 2CO$

(B) N_2 and O_2 : O_2 is absorbed in alkaline pyrogallol.

(C) N_2 and NH_3 : $\underset{\text{base}}{2NH_3} + H_2SO_4 \longrightarrow (NH_4)_2SO_4$, while N_2 is a neutral gas.

(D) PH_3 and NH_3 : NH_3 is highly soluble in water and PH_3 is least soluble in water so can be separated by use of water.

$$NH_3 + H_2O \longrightarrow NH_4OH \rightleftharpoons NH_4^+ + OH^-$$

11. A → Q; B → R; C → S; D → P

(A) $Mg + 2HNO_3 \longrightarrow Mg(NO_3)_2 + H_2\uparrow$
very dil.

(B) $4Zn + 10HNO_3 \longrightarrow 4Zn(NO_3)_2 + N_2O\uparrow + 5H_2O$

(C) $4Sn + 10HNO_3 \longrightarrow 4Sn(NO_3)_2 + NH_4NO_3 + 3H_2O$

(D) $3Pb + 8HNO_3 \longrightarrow 3Pb(NO_3)_2 + 2NO\uparrow + 4H_2O$

12. A → S; B → R; C → Q; D → P

13. A → R, B → P, C → S, D → Q

14. A → P, B → R, C → P, D → Q

Halogen being non-polar is nature does not dissolve readily in water (polar solvent)
Solubility decreases : $F_2 > Cl_2 > Br_2 > I_2$
F_2 and Cl_2 are gases : Br_2-corrosive liquid; I_2-volatile solid
due to dense electronic arrangement two molecules arrange at maximum disstance in the case of fluorine. Moreover, F_2 has least and I_2 has maximum van der Waals' force thats why F_2 has maximum van der Waals' radius. Bond dissociation energy for Cl_2 is maximum and F_2 has less because of interelectronic repulsion.

15. A → S; B → R; C → P; D → Q

16. A → Q, T; B → R; C → S; D → P

17. A → P, Q, S; B → P, Q, S; C → Q, R; D → Q, R, S

(A) Hypophosphoric acid ($H_4P_2O_6$)

(P) 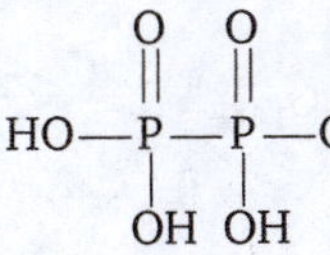 ; Basicity = 4

sp^3 *sp*^{3}

(B) Pyrophosphoric acid ($H_4P_2O_5$)

(Q) 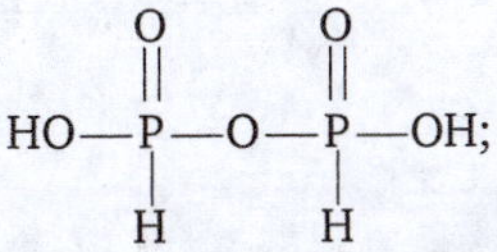 ; Basicity 2

(C) Boric acid (H_3BO_3)

(R) H_3BO_3 + OH ⇌ $[B(OH)_4]^-$
(L.B.) (L.B.) borate ion

(D) Hypophosphorus acid (H_3PO_2)

(S) 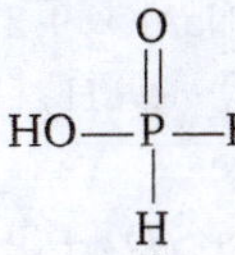 ; Basicity = 1

sp^3

18. A → P, Q; B → P, Q; C → P, R, S; D → Q

19. A → P, S; B → P; C → Q, R, S; D → Q, R

20. A → P, S; B → P, Q, R; C → R; D → S

21. A → R, S; B → P, S; C → S; D → Q, R, S

(A) Sheet silicate :

General formula = $(Si_2O_5)^{2-}$

Non-planar

3-corner oxygen atoms are shared

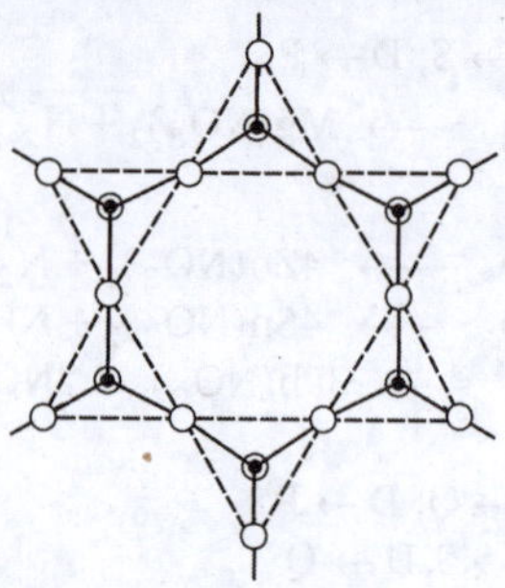

(B) Pyroxenes :

General formula = $(SiO_3)_n^{2n-}$

Non-planar

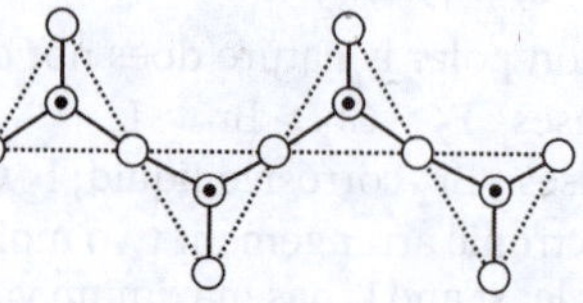

(C) Pyrosilicate :

General formula = $Si_2O_7^{6-}$

Non-planar

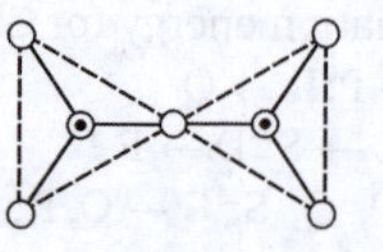

(D) Amphibole :

General formula = $(Si_4O_{11})_n^{6n}$

Non-planar

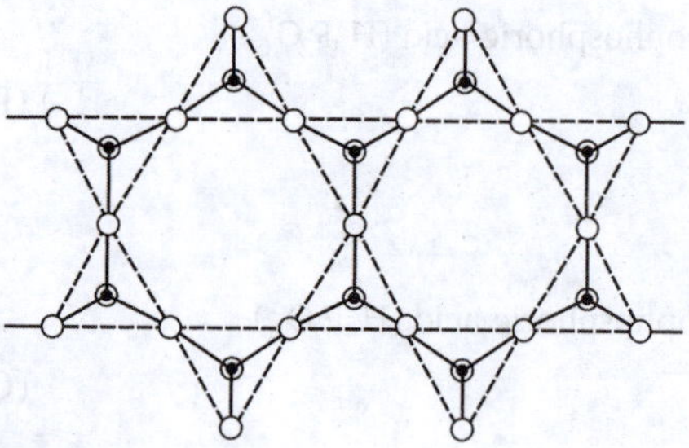

ASSERTION-REASON TYPE QUESTIONS

8. $2Al + 2NaOH + 2H_2O \longrightarrow 2NaAlO_2 + 3H_2\uparrow$

$Zn + 2NaOH \longrightarrow \underset{\text{sod. zincate}}{Na_2ZnO_2} + H_2\uparrow$

$4S + 6NaOH \longrightarrow 2Na_2S + Na_2S_2O_3 + 3H_2O$

$P_4 + 3NaOH + 3H_2O \longrightarrow \underset{\text{sod. hypophosphite}}{3NaH_2PO_2} + PH_3\uparrow$

$Cl_2 + 2NaOH \longrightarrow NaClO + H_2O$

9. Reason is the correct explanation of the assertion.

10. $PCl_5 \xrightarrow{\Delta} PCl_3 + Cl_2$

PCl_5 decomposes into PCl_3 and Cl_2 as in its structure two P—Cl axial bonds are longer than other three P—Cl equatorial bonds.

11. First, HBr is released, being reducing in character, it is oxidised into Br_2 by conc. H_2SO_4

$$NaBr + H_2SO_4 \longrightarrow NaHSO_4 + HBr$$

$$2HBr + H_2SO_4 \longrightarrow Br_2\uparrow + SO_2\uparrow + 2H_2O$$

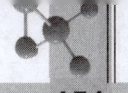

12. H—S bond is weaker than H—O bond hence, H_2S is more acidic than H_2O.

13. Due to dissociation of IF_5 into IF_4^+ and IF_6^-, the liquid IF_5 conducts electricity.

14. Red phosphorus is less volatile than white phosphorus because it exists in linked tetrahedral structures

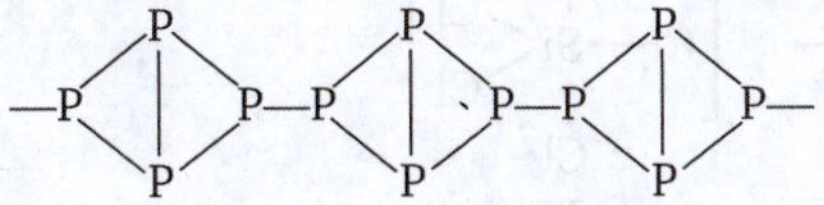

15. As $Al(OH)_3$ is amphoteric in nature hence, it can act as an antacid.

$$Al(OH)_3 + 3H^+ \longrightarrow Al^{3+} + 3H_2O$$

16. $$\underset{\text{(hot)}}{3Cl_2 + 6NaOH} \longrightarrow 5NaCl + NaClO_3 + 3H_2O$$

$$\underset{\text{(cold)}}{Cl_2 + 2NaOH} \longrightarrow NaCl + NaClO + H_2O$$

27.

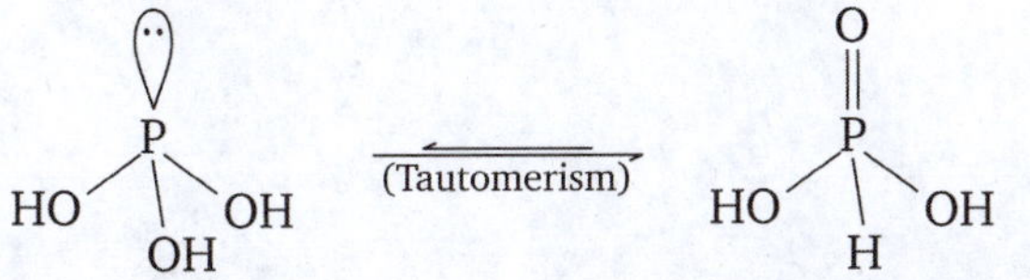

(A) Less stable form (B) More stable form

In more stable structure (B) one H-atom is non-ionizable hence its basicity is 2.

SUBJECTIVE PROBLEMS

1.

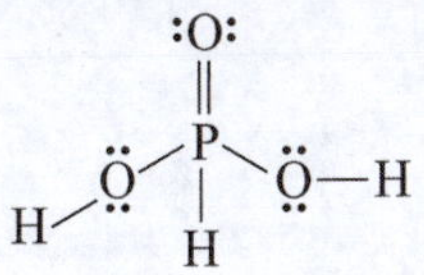

$X = 6$

$Y = 6$

$Z = 1 \qquad \therefore \quad Y \times Z - X = 6 \times 1 - 6 = 0$

2. $P_4 + 8SOCl_2 \xrightarrow{\Delta} 4PCl_3 + 2S_2Cl_2 + 4SO_2$

3. $HClO_2$

$x = y = z = 2$

$x + y + z = 6$

4. For any oxyacid of sulphur number of H-atoms = 2; $H_{n_1}S_2O_{n_2}$, $H_2S_2O_3$, $H_2S_2O_4$, $H_2S_2O_5$, $H_2S_2O_6$, $H_2S_2O_7$, $H_2S_2O_8$.

For $H_2S_2O_4$; $\frac{n_2}{n_1} = 2$; ⇒ Oxidation state of sulphur atom = +3

For $H_2S_2O_6$; $\frac{n_2}{n_1} = 4$; ⇒ Oxidation state of sulphur atom = +6

Sum of oxidation state = 3 + 6 = 9

5. Species are : $SiCl_4$, PCl_3, $AsCl_3$, P_4O_6, P_4O_{10}

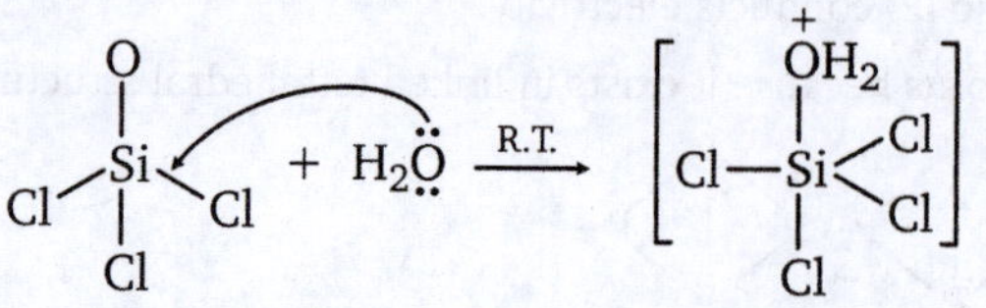

T.S.

Hybridization of Si : sp^2d

6. 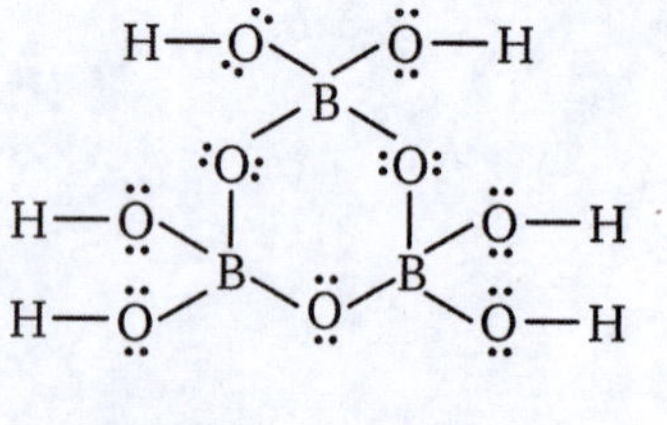

Total number of σ-bonds = 18

Total number of lone pairs = 18

7. $x = 6$

$y = 6$

$z = 12$

8. 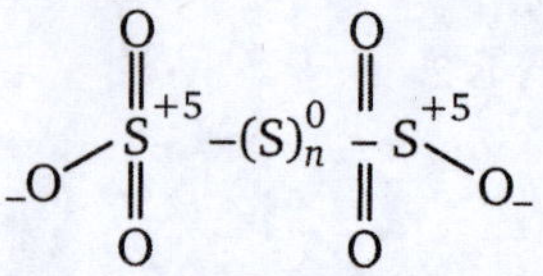

Bond order of 'S—O' bond is 1.66 (5/3) average oxidation state of 'S' atom is :

$\frac{10}{2+n} = \frac{5}{3}$

(or) $\frac{10}{2+n} = \frac{10}{6} \Rightarrow 2+n=6 \Rightarrow n = 4$

9. Borax : $2Na^+[B_4O_5(OH)_4]^{2-} \cdot 8H_2O$

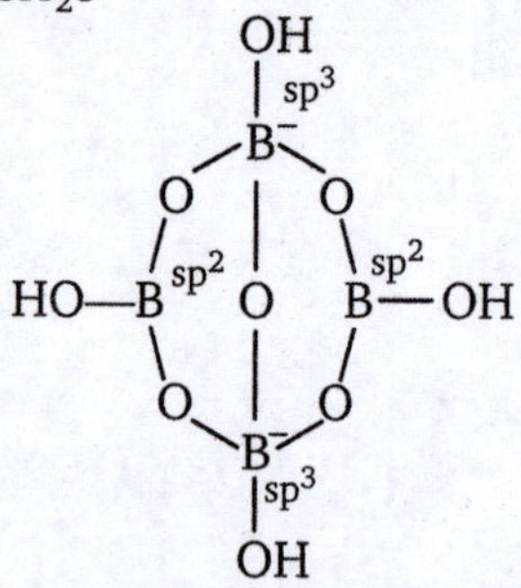

sp^2-hybridized Boron atoms only participate in $p\pi$-$p\pi$ back bonding.

10. (ii) $CuSO_4 + PH_3 \rightarrow \underset{\text{(Black)}}{Cu_3P_2}$

(iii) $SbF_5 + XeF_4 \rightarrow [XeF_3]^+[SbF_6]^-$

11. Correct order is :

(1) $H_2SO_4 > H_2SO_3$: Boiling point

(2) $H_2O > HF$: Extent of H-bond

(6) Ethylene glycol > Phenol : Viscosity

(7) 1, 3-Dichlorobenzene > 1, 3, 5-Trichlorobenzene : Strength of molecular force

15. $\Rightarrow 2H_3\overset{+I}{P}O_2 \xrightarrow{\Delta} H_3\overset{+V}{P}O_4 + \overset{-III}{P}H_3$

16. $x = 10, y = 2, z = 8$

$\frac{10-2}{8} = 1$

17. $1 + 5 + 3 = 9$

20. $x = 12$ $y = 4$ $z = 6$

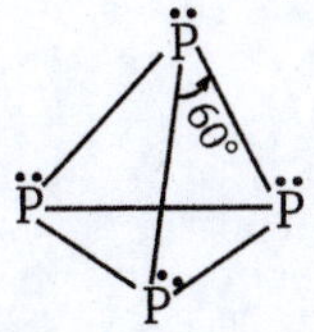

The value of $\frac{x.y}{z} = \frac{12 \times 4}{6} = 8$

21. $\underset{\text{Marshall's acid}}{H_2S_2O_8} + H_2O \longrightarrow \underset{(A)}{H_2SO_5} + \underset{(B)}{H_2SO_4}$

$\underset{(A)}{H_2SO_5} + H_2O \longrightarrow \underset{(C)}{H_2O_2} + \underset{(B)}{H_2SO_4}$

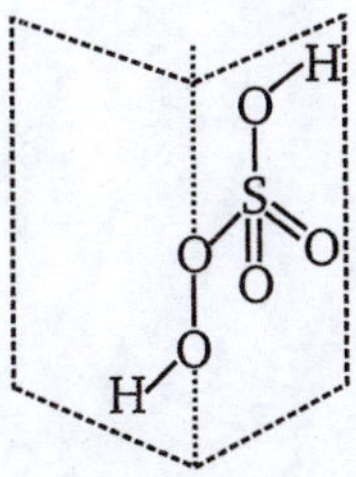

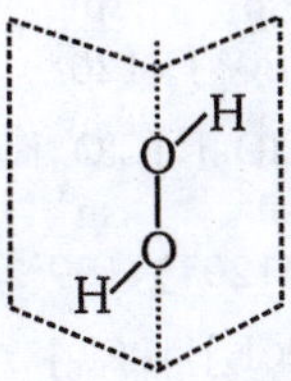

$P = 5$ $Q = 3$ $P - Q = 5 - 3 = 2$

22. $9\ (x = 6,\ y = 4)$

23. $2\,ClO_3 \xrightarrow[\text{dimerization}]{\text{cool}}$ 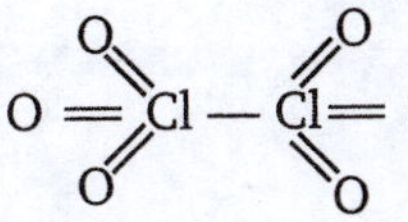 Hypervalent

$2\,OF \xrightarrow[\text{dimerization}]{\text{cool}}$ 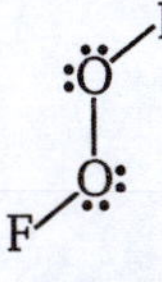 Completion of octet

$2\,GaH_3 \xrightarrow[\text{dimerization}]{\text{cool}}$ 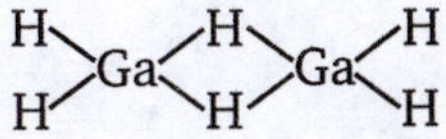 Hypovalent

$2AlCl_3 \xrightarrow[\text{dimerization}]{\text{cool}}$ 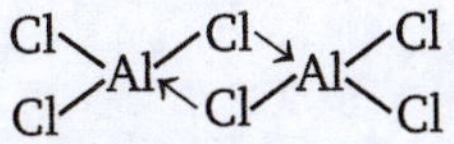 Completion of octet

$2ICl_3 \xrightarrow[\text{dimerization}]{\text{cool}}$ 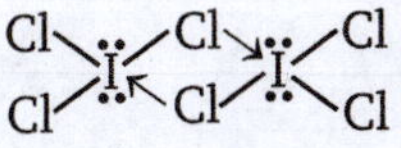 Hypervalent

$2BeH_2 \xrightarrow[\text{dimerization}]{\text{cool}}$ 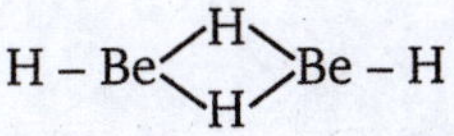 Hypovalent

$2NO_2 \xrightarrow[\text{dimerization}]{\text{cool}}$ 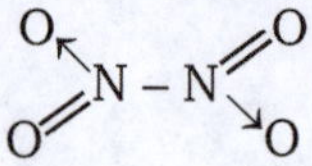 Completion of octet value of $\frac{yz}{x} = \frac{3\times2}{2} = 3$

24. X = Total number of $(2c-2e^-)$ bond $= 10$
Y = Total number of $(3c-2e^-)$ bond $= 0$
Z = Total number of $(3c-4e^-)$ bond $= 2$

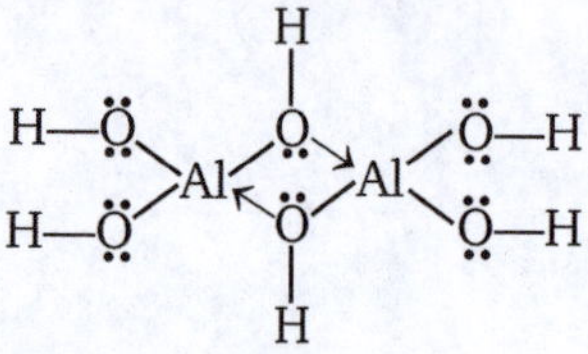

$(10+0)\div2 = 5$

25.

Compound	**Solid sate**
N_2O_5	$[NO_2]^+[NO_3]^-$ sp sp^2 $(180°)$ $(120°)$
Cl_2O_6	$[ClO_2]^+[ClO_4]^-$ sp^2 sp^3 $(<120°)$ $(109°28')$
PCl_5	$[PCl_4]^+[PCl_6]^-$ sp^3 sp^3d^2 $(109°28')$ $(90°)$
I_2Cl_6	$[ICl_2]^+[ICl_4]^-$ sp^3 sp^3d^2 $(<109°28')$ $(90°)$
XeF_6	$[XeF_5]^+F^-$ sp^3d^2 $(<90°)$
PBr_5	$[PBr_4]^+Br^-$ sp^3 $(109°28')$

$x = 1+1+1+1 = 4$
$y = 1+1 = 2$
$z = 1+1+1 = 3$
$x+y+z = 4+2+3 = 9$

26.

	b.p.	**l.p.**
(A) XeF_4	4	2
(B) XeF_5^+	5	1
(C) XeF_5^-	5	2
(D) XeF_6	6	1
(E) XeF_8^{2-}	8	1
	28	**7**

29.

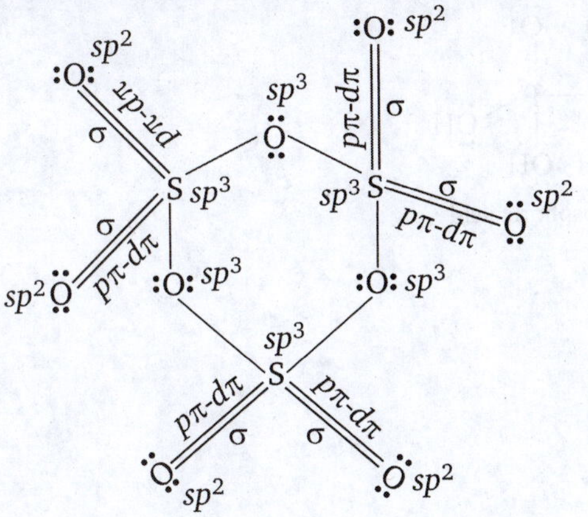

$p = 6,\ q = 6;\ \dfrac{p}{q} = \dfrac{6}{6} = 1$

30.

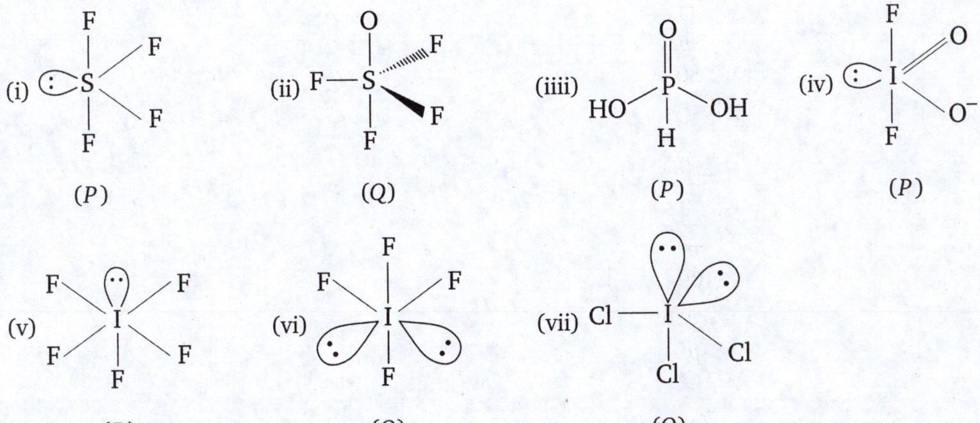

$P = 4,\quad Q = 3$

Hence $(P^2 - Q^2) = 16 - 9 = 7$

31.

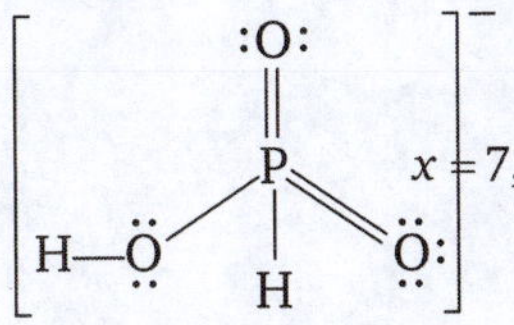

$x = 7,\quad y = 1,\quad z = 5$

$x + y - z = 7 + 1 - 5 = 3$

32. CH_3^+, $(C_3H_5)_3Al$, HCHO, $TiCl_4$, CO_2, $SiCl_4$, BF_3

33. $x = GeH_4$, BCl_3, $AlBr_3$, PCl_5, CO_2; $\quad y = PH_3$, $\quad (5 - 1)^2 = \mathbf{16}$

35. $\underset{\text{Phosphoric acid}}{2H_3PO_4} \xrightarrow{-H_2O} \underset{\text{Pyrophosphoric acid}}{H_4P_2O_7} \xrightarrow{-O}$ 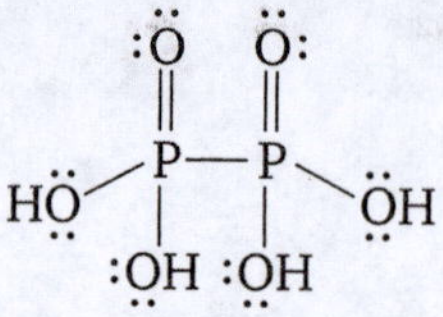

Hypophosphoric acid

$x = 12\,; \qquad y = 2$

$\therefore \quad \dfrac{x}{y} = \dfrac{12}{2} = 6$

36. $x = 12, \quad y = 4, \quad z = 6$

The value of $\dfrac{XY}{Z} = \dfrac{12 \times 4}{6} = 8$

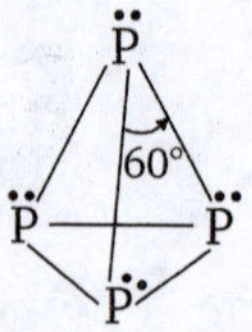

9

d AND *f*-BLOCK ELEMENTS

Level 1

1. CrO_4^{2-} (yellow) changes to $Cr_2O_7^{2-}$ (orange) in pH = x and vice-versa in pH = y. Hence, x and y are :

(a) 6, 8 (b) 6, 5 (c) 8, 6 (d) 7, 7

2. Manganese ions (Mn^{2+}) can be oxidised by Persulphate ions $S_2O_8^{2-}$ according to the following half-equations,

$$S_2O_8^{2-} + 2e^- \longrightarrow 2SO_4^{2-}$$

$$Mn^{2+} + 4H_2O \longrightarrow MnO_4^- + 8H^+ + 5e^-$$

How many moles of $S_2O_8^{2-}$ are required to oxidise 1 mole of Mn^{2+}?

(a) 2.5 (b) 2.0 (c) 11.0 (d) 0.4

3. AgCl on fusion with Na_2CO_3 forms :

(a) Ag_2CO_3 (b) Ag_2O (c) Ag (d) Ag_2C_2

4. Formula of Rust is :

(a) Fe_2O_3 (b) $FeO \cdot xH_2O$ (c) $Fe_2O_3 \cdot xH_2O$ (d) $Fe_3O_4 \cdot xH_2O$

5. CrO_3 dissolves in aqueous NaOH to give :

(a) $Cr_2O_7^{2-}$ (b) CrO_4^{2-} (c) $Cr(OH)_3$ (d) $Cr(OH)_2$

6. Chemically philosopher of wool is :

(a) ZnO (b) BaO (c) HgCl (d) Hg_2Cl_2

7. Boiling $CuCl_2$ with Cu in conc. HCl gives :

(a) CuCl (b) $CuCl_2$ (c) $H[CuCl_2]$ (d) Cu_2Cl

8. Thermal decomposition of zinc nitrate give :

(a) Zn (b) ZnO (c) $Zn(NO_3)_2$ (d) NO

9. Malachite and azurite are used respectively are :

(a) Blue and green pigment (b) Red and green pigment

(c) Green and blue pigment (d) Green and red pigment

10. Mercury is transported in the containers made of :
(a) Ag (b) Pb (c) Al (d) Fe

11. The higher oxidation states of transition elements are found to be in the combination with *A* and *B*, which are :
(a) F, O (b) O, N (c) O, S (d) F, Cl

12. White vitriol is :
(a) ZnS (b) $ZnSO_4$ (c) $ZnSO_4 \cdot 7H_2O$ (d) $ZnCO_3$

13. Among the following metals, the most dense is :
(a) osmium (b) chromium (c) platinum (d) gold

14. Silver nitrate is usually kept in coloured bottles because it is :
(a) oxidised in air (b) decomposes in sunlight
(c) explodes in sunlight (d) reacts with air in sunlight

15. Which of the following is arranged in order of increasing melting point?
(a) Zn < Cu < Ni < Fe (b) Fe < Ni < Cu < Zn
(c) Ni < Fe < Zn < Cu (d) Cu < Zn < Fe < Ni

16. Calomel is the name of :
(a) $HgCl_2$ (b) Hg_2Cl_2 (c) $HgCl_2 + Hg$ (d) $Hg_2Cl_2 + Hg$

17. The iron salt used in blue prints is :
(a) FeC_2O_4 (b) $Fe_2(C_2O_4)_3$ (c) $K_4Fe(CN)_6$ (d) $FeSO_4$

18. Percentage of gold in 14 carat gold is :
(a) 58 (b) 80 (c) 40 (d) 14

19. The maximum and minimum melting point of first and second transition series elements respectively are obtained with :
(a) Cr and Zn (b) Cr and Hg (c) Cr and Cd (d) Mo and Cd

20. ZnO shows yellow colour on Heating due to :
(a) *d-d* transition (b) *C-T* spectra
(c) Higher polarisation caused by Zn^{2+} ion (d) F-centres

21. When steam is passed over red hot iron, the substances formed are :
(a) $Fe_2O_3 + H_2$ (b) $Fe_3O_4 + H_2$ (c) $FeO + H_2$ (d) $FeO + H_2 + O_2$

22. Verdigris is :
(a) Basic copper acetate (b) Basic lead acetate
(c) Basic lead (d) None

23. Corrosive sublimate is :
(a) $HgCl_2$ (b) Hg_2Cl_2 (c) Hg_2Cl (d) Hg_2Cl_3

24. The product of I^- with MnO_4^- in alkaline medium is :
(a) I_2 (b) IO_3^- (c) IO^- (d) IO_4^-

25. Which of the following is the correct formula for a compound of scandium and oxygen?
(a) Sc_2O (b) ScO (c) Sc_3O_2 (d) Sc_2O_3

26. Mercury on heating with aqua-regia gives :
(a) $Hg(NO_3)_2$ (b) $HgCl_2$ (c) $Hg(NO_2)_2$ (d) Hg_2Cl_2

27. Chloroplatinic acid is :
(a) monobasic (b) dibasic (c) tribasic (d) tetrabasic

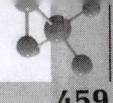

28. Which of the following statements is incorrect?
(a) Mercurous ion exists as Hg^+
(b) Mercurous ion is diamagnetic and exists as dimer Hg_2^{2+}
(c) Mercurous ion is colourless
(d) There is a metallic bond between two Hg^+ ions

29. Fe is made passive by :
(a) dil. H_2SO_4 (b) dil. HCl
(c) conc. HNO_3 (d) conc. H_2SO_4

30. Zn and Cd metals do not show variable valency because :
(a) They have only two electrons in the outermost subshells
(b) Their *d*-subshells are completely filled
(c) Their *d*-subshells are partially filled
(d) They are relatively soft metals

31. Ferrous sulphate on heating gives :
(a) SO_2 and SO_3 (b) SO_2 only
(c) SO_3 only (d) H_2S only

32. Photographic films or plates have .... as an essential ingredient.
(a) silver oxide (b) silver bromide
(c) silver thiosulphate (d) silver nitrate

33. In comparison of ferrous salts, ferric salts are :
(a) more stable (b) less stable
(c) equally stable (d) none of these

34. Chrome yellow is chemically known as :
(a) lead chromate (b) lead sulphate
(c) lead iodide (d) basic lead acetate

35. The property, which is not characteristic of transition metals :
(a) variable oxidation states (b) tendency to form complexes
(c) formation of coloured compounds (d) none of these

36. Iron is protected by coating it with a thin layer of :
(a) Cu (b) Zn (c) Pb (d) Mg

37. An oxide of copper which is red in colour has the formula :
(a) CuO (b) Cu_2O (c) CuO_2 (d) Cu_2O_2

38. In a transition series, as the atomic number increases, paramagnetism :
(a) increases gradually
(b) decreases gradually
(c) first increases to a maximum and then decreases
(d) first decreases to a minimum and then increases

39. The formula of azurite is :
(a) $CuCO_3 \cdot Cu(OH)_2$ (b) $2CuCO_3 \cdot Cu(OH)_2$
(c) $CuCO_3 \cdot 2Cu(OH)_2$ (d) $CuSO_4 \cdot Cu(OH)_2$

40. Oxide of metal cation which is not amphoteric?
(a) Al^{3+} (b) Cr^{3+} (c) Fe^{3+} (d) Zn^{2+}

41. The most abundant transition metal in earth crust is :
(a) Zn (b) Fe (c) Hg (d) Au

42. $CuSO_4$ solution + lime is called :
(a) Luca's reagent (b) Barfoed's reagent
(c) Fehling solution A (d) Bordeaux mixture

43. Preparation of looking mirrors involves the use of :
(a) red lead (b) ammonical silver nitrate
(c) ammonical $AgNO_3$ + red lead (d) ammonical $AgNO_3$ + red lead + HCHO

44. When ammonia is added to a cupric salt solution, the deep blue colour is observed it is due to the formation of :
(a) $[Cu(OH)_4]^{2-}$ (b) $[Cu(NH_3)_4]^{2+}$ (c) $[Cu(H_2O)_2(NH_3)_2]^{2+}$ (d) $[Cu(H_2O)_4]^{2+}$

45. Philosopher's wool when heated with BaO at 1100°C gives the compound :
(a) $BaCdO_2$ (b) $Ba + ZnO_2$ (c) $BaO_2 + Zn$ (d) $BaZnO_2$

46. The electrons which take part in order to exhibit variable oxidation states by transition metals are :
(a) *ns* only (b) $(n-1)$ *d* only
(c) *ns* and $(n-1)$ *d* only but not *np* (d) $(n-1)$ *d* and *np* only but not *ns*

47. On heating $ZnCl_2 \cdot 2H_2O$, the compound obtained is :
(a) $ZnCl_2$ (b) $Zn(OH)_2$ (c) ZnO (d) ZnH_2

48. During estimation of oxalic acid *Vs* $KMnO_4$, self indicator is :
(a) $KMnO_4$ (b) oxalic acid (c) K_2SO_4 (d) $MnSO_4$

49. Iron is rendered passive by treatment with :
(a) H_2SO_4 (dil.) (b) H_2PO_4 (c) conc. HNO_3 (d) HCl

50. When $KMnO_4$ solution is added to hot oxalic acid solution, the decolorisation is slow in the beginning but becomes instantaneous after some time. This is because :
(a) Mn^{2+} acts as auto catalyst (b) CO_2 is formed
(c) Reaction is exothermic (d) MnO_4^- catalysis the reaction

51. Gold dissolves in a aqua-regia forming :
(a) Auric chloride (b) Aurous chloride
(c) Chloroauric acid (d) Aurous nitrate

52. The solubility of silver bromide in hypo solution is due to the formation of :
(a) Ag_2SO_3 (b) $Ag_2S_2O_3$ (c) $[Ag(S_2O_3)]^-$ (d) $[Ag(S_2O_3)_2]^{3-}$

53. Metal used for making joints in jewellery is :
(a) Zn (b) Cu (c) Ag (d) Cd

54. Zn and Cd metals do not show variable valency because:
(a) they have only two electrons in the outermost subshells
(b) their *d*-subshells are completely filled
(c) their *d*-subshells are partially filled
(d) they are relatively soft metals

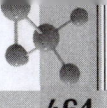

55. Which of the following transition element(s) do/does not exhibit variable oxidation state?

(i) Sc (ii) Ti (iii) Cu (iv) Zn

(a) (i) (b) (i) and (iv)

(c) (i), (ii) and (iv) (d) (iv)

[Zn does not consider as transition element]

56. The transition metals and their compounds are known for their catalytic activity due to having their:

(a) Variable oxidation state (b) Complex forming tendency

(c) Provide a solid surface to the reactant (d) All are correct

57. Which of the following metal of 3*d*-series does not liberate H_2 from acids in normal condition?

(a) Ti (b) Cr (c) Cu (d) Zn

58. The highest positive oxidation state can be shown by the following first transition series element:

(a) Cr (b) Mn (c) Ti (d) V

59. Consider the following reaction

$$2Cu^{2+} + 4X^- \longrightarrow Cu_2X_2(s) + X_2$$

Then X^- can be:

(a) F^- (b) Cl^- (c) Br^- (d) I^-

60. Lanthanide contraction is due to increase in:

(a) Shielding by 4*f*-electrons (b) Atomic number

(c) Effective nuclear charge (d) Size of 4*f*-orbital

61. Lanthanoid contraction implies:

(a) Decrease in density (b) Decrease in mass

(c) Decrease in ionic radii (d) Decrease in radioactivity

62. The common oxidation state of the elements of lanthanide series is:

(a) +2 (b) +3 (c) +4 (d) +1

63. In the lanthanide series, the basic strength of the lanthanide hydroxides:

(a) Increases (b) Decreases

(c) First increase and then decrease (d) First decrease and then increases

64. Which of the following statement is not correct?

(a) $La(OH)_2$ is less basic than $Lu(OH)_3$

(b) In lanthanide series, ionic radius of Ln^{3+} ions decreases

(c) La is actually an element of transition series rather than lanthanide series

(d) Atomic radii of Zr and Hf are same because of lanthanide contraction.

65. The reason for the stability of Gd^{3+} ion is:

(a) 4*f* subshell-half filled

(b) 4*f* subshell-completely filled

(c) Possesses the outer electronic configuration of noble gases

(d) 4*f* subshell empty

66. Lanthanoid contraction is caused due to:
(a) the same effective nuclear charge from Ce to Lu
(b) the imperfect shielding on outer electrons by $4f$-electrons from the nuclear charge
(c) the appreciable shielding on outer electrons by $4f$-electrons from the nuclear charge
(d) the appreciable shielding on outer electrons by $5d$-electrons from the nuclear charge

67. Identify the incorrect statement among the following:
(a) d-block elements show irregular and erratic chemical properties among themselves
(b) La and Lu have partially filled d-orbitals and no other partially filled orbitals
(c) The chemistry of various lanthanoids is very similar
(d) $4f$ and $5f$-orbitals are equally shielded

68. The actinoids exhibits more number of oxidation states in general than the lanthanoids. This is because:
(a) The $5f$-orbitals are more buried than the $4f$-orbitals
(b) There is a similarity between $4f$-and-$5f$ in their angular part of the wave function
(c) The actinoids are more reactive than the lanthanoids
(d) The $5f$-orbitals extend further from the nucleus than the $4f$-orbitals

69. Knowing that the Chemistry of lanthanoids (Ln) is dominated by its +3 oxidation state, which of the following statements is incorrect?
(a) The ionic sizes of Ln (III) decrease in general with increasing atomic number.
(b) Ln (III) compounds are generally colourless.
(c) Ln (III) hydroxides are mainly basic in character.
(d) Because of the large size of the Ln (III) ions the bonding in its compounds is predominantly ionic in character.

70. Which is not the correct statement?
(At. nos. Ce = 58, Lu = 71, La = 57, Yb = 70)
(a) Colour of Yb^{3+} ion is pink. (b) La^{3+} is diamagnetic.
(c) Ce^{4+} has f^0 configuration. (d) Lu^{3+} had f^{14} configuration.

71. Magnetic moment of Gd^{3+} ion ($Z = 64$) is:
(a) 3.62 BM (b) 9.72 BM (c) 7.9 BM (d) 10.60 BM

72. Which of the following forms stable + 4 oxidation state?
(a) La ($Z = 57$) (b) Eu ($Z = 63$) (c) Ce ($Z = 58$) (d) Gd ($Z = 64$)

73. The number of unpaired electrons in Gadolinium [$Z = 64$] is:
(a) 3 (b) 8 (c) 6 (d) 2

74. The effect of lanthanoid contraction in the lanthanoid series of elements by and large means :
(a) increase in both atomic and ionic radii
(b) decrease in both atomic and ionic radii
(c) decrease in atomic radii and increase in ionic radii
(d) increase in atomic radii and decrease in ionic radii

75. The electronic configurations of bivalent europium and trivalent cerium are :
(atomic number : Xe = 54, Ce = 58, Eu = 63)
(a) [Xe] $4f^7$ and [Xe] $4f^1$ (b) [Xe] $4f^7 6s^2$ and [Xe] $4f^2 6s^2$
(c) [Xe] $4f^2$ and [Xe] $4f^7$ (d) [Xe] $4f^4$ and [Xe] $4f^9$

Level 2

1. Which of the following is called Wilkinson's catalyst ?
(a) $[Ph_3P)_3RhCl]$ (b) $TiCl_4 + (C_2H_5)_3Al$
(c) $(C_2H_5)_4Pb$ (d) $[PtCl_2(NH_3)_2]$

2. Which of the following is not a consequence of the Lanthanoid contraction?
(a) 5*d* series elements have a higher IE_1 than 3*d* or 4*d* series
(b) Zr and Hf have a comparable size
(c) Zr and Hf occurs together in the earth crust in their minerals
(d) High density of the sixth period elements

3. A metal *M* and its compound can give the following observable changes in a consequence of reactions

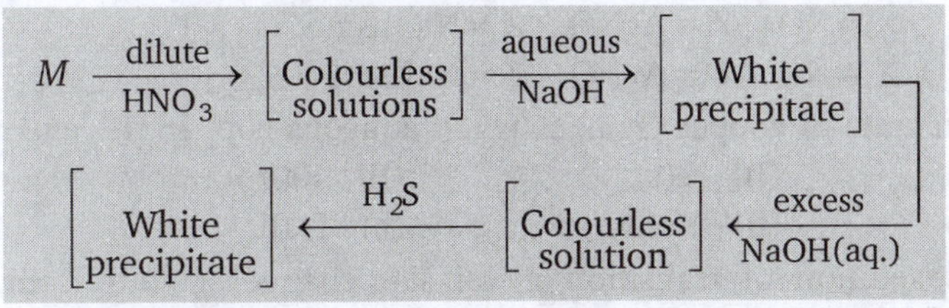

(a) Mg (b) Pb (c) Zn (d) Sn

4. Sodium thiosulphate is used to remove the unexposed AgBr from photographic films by forming a complex. In this complex of silver, the coordination number of silver is :
(a) 2 (b) 4 (c) 6 (d) 8

5. Each of the following ion contains vanadium the +V oxidation state except :
(a) VO_2^+ (b) $V(OH)_4^+$ (c) VO^{2+} (d) $[VO_3 \cdot OH]^{2-}$

6. Mercury (II) chloride solution on reaction with gaseous ammonia forms :
(a) $Hg(NH_2)Cl \cdot HgO$ (b) $Hg(NH_3)_2Cl_2$ (c) $[Hg(NH_3)_4]Cl_2$ (d) $[Hg(NH_3)_2]Cl$

7. Copper sulphate is prepared by blowing a current of air through copper scrap and dilute H_2SO_4. Dilute HNO_3 is also added :
(a) to oxidise copper to Cu^{2+} which then form $CuSO_4$ with dilute H_2SO_4
(b) to oxidise Fe^{2+} to iron (III) sulphate, which remains in solution after crystallisation of $CuSO_4$
(c) to speed up the ionisation of H_2SO_4 to give SO_4^{2-} ions
(d) which combines with H_2SO_4 to give a very strong oxidising mixture and oxidises Cu to Cu^{2+}

8. Which two sets of reactants best represent the amphoteric character of $Zn(OH)_2$?
Set 1 : $Zn(OH)_2(s)$ and $OH^-(aq)$
Set 2 : $Zn(OH)_2(s)$ and $H_2O(l)$
Set 3 : $Zn(OH)_2(s)$ and $H^+(aq)$
Set 4 : $Zn(OH)_2(s)$ and $NH_3(aq)$
(a) 1 and 2 (b) 1 and 3 (c) 2 and 4 (d) 3 and 4

9. The false statement about iron (III) hydroxide is that :
(a) it is a weaker base than $Fe(OH)_2$
(b) with concentrated KOH, it forms a complex $K_3[Fe(OH)_6]$
(c) it gradually loses water and transforms into Fe_2O_3
(d) it exhibits amphoteric properties with its predominating acidic nature

10. $AgNO_3 \xrightarrow{\Delta} (W) + (X) + O_2$
$(X) + H_2O \longrightarrow HNO_2 + HNO_3$
$(W) + HNO_3 \longrightarrow Y + NO + H_2O$
$(Y) + Na_2S_2O_3(\text{excess}) \longrightarrow (Z) + NaNO_3$
Identify (*W*) to (*Z*).
(a) $W = Ag$ $X = N_2O$ $Y = AgNO_3$ $Z = Na_2[Ag(S_2O_3)_2]$
(b) $W = Ag_2O$ $X = NO$ $Y = AgNO_3$ $Z = Na_3[Ag(S_2O_3)_2]$
(c) $W = Ag$ $X = NO_2$ $Y = AgNO_3$ $Z = Na_3[Ag(S_2O_3)_2]$
(d) $W = Ag_2O$ $X = N_2$ $Y = AgNO_3$ $Z = Na[Ag(S_2O_3)_2]$

11. The oxidation state of copper changes when aqueous copper (II) ions react with :
(I) NaOH(*aq*) (II) Fe(*s*) (III) KI(*aq*)
(a) I, II, III (b) II only (c) II, III (d) I only

12. The aqueous solution of transition metal salt changes colour from pink to blue, when concentrated hydrochloric acid is added to it. The change in colour is due to :
(a) evolution of hydrogen that changes the oxidation state of the metal ion
(b) change in the coordination number of the metal ion from 6 to 4 and formation of new species in solution
(c) formation of a coordination complex of the metal ion with hydrochloric acid
(d) protonation of the metal ion

13. Limestone is present in the blast furnace production of iron in order to :
(I) provide a source of CaO
(II) remove some impurities
(III) supply CO_2
(a) I, II, III (b) I, II (c) II, III (d) I only

14. Paramagnetism is not exhibited by :
(a) $CuSO_4 \cdot 5H_2O$ (b) $CuCl_2 \cdot 5H_2O$
(c) CuI (d) $NiSO_4 \cdot 6H_2O$

15. Which of the comparison regarding Zn, Cd, Hg is/are incorrect ?
(I) $ZnCl_2$ is ionic whereas $CdCl_2$ and $HgCl_2$ are covalent
(II) Zn and Cd dissolves in dilute acid (HCl) liberating H_2 but Hg can not
(III) Zn and Cd forming white ppt. of $Zn(OH)_2$ and $Cd(OH)_2$ but Hg forms coloured ppt. of $Hg(OH)_2$
(IV) all form A_2^{2+} type ion
(a) only III (b) I, III, IV (c) I and III (d) all of these

16. The oxoanion in which the oxidation state of the central atom is same as its group number in the periodic table is :
(a) SO_4^{2-} (b) VO_2^- (c) MnO_4^{2-} (d) $Cr_2O_7^{2-}$

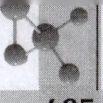

17. Which compound is formed when iron reacts with carbon?
(a) FeC_2 (b) Fe_3C (c) FeC_3 (d) Fe_2C

18. Which of the following compound can produce Riemann's green with $Co(NO_3)_2$ solution?
(a) ZnO (b) $3Zn(OH)_2 \cdot ZnCO_3$
(c) $ZnSO_4$ (d) All of these

19. Which of the following electronic configuration is associated with the highest stable oxidation state?
(a) $[Ar]3d^1 4s^2$ (b) $[Ar]3d^5 4s^1$ (c) $[Ar]3d^5 4s^2$ (d) $[Ar]3d^6 4s^2$

20. A blood red colour is obtained when ferric chloride solution reacts with :
(a) KCN (b) KSCN (c) $K_4[Fe(CN)_6]$ (d) $K_3[Fe(CN)_6]$

21. Metal-metal bonding is more frequent in 4*d* or 5*d* series than in 3*d* series due to :
(a) their greater enthalpies of atomisation
(b) the large size of the orbitals which participates in the metal-metal bond formation
(c) their ability to involve both *ns* and $(n-1)$ *d* electrons in the bond formation
(d) the comparable size of 4*d* and 5*d* series elements

22. The maximum and minimum m.p. of I[st] transition and 2nd transition series respectively are obtained with :
(a) Cr and Zn (b) Cr and Cd (c) Cr and Hg (d) Mo and Cd

23. When an aqueous solution of copper (II) sulphate is saturated with ammonia, the blue compound crystallises on evaporation. The formula of this blue compound is :
(a) $[Cu(NH_3)_4]SO_4 \cdot H_2O$ (square planar) (b) $[Cu(NH_3)_4]SO_4$ (Tetrahedral)
(c) $[Cu(NH_3)_6]SO_4$ (Octahedral) (d) $[Cu(SO_4)(NH_3)_5]$ (Octahedral)

24. In the extraction of copper, metal is formed in the Bessemer converter due to the reaction :
(a) $2Cu_2O \longrightarrow 4Cu + O_2$ (b) $2CuO + CuS \longrightarrow 3Cu + SO_2$
(c) $Cu_2S + 2Cu_2O \longrightarrow 6Cu + SO_2$ (d) $Fe + Cu_2O \longrightarrow FeO + 2Cu$

25. The compound in which nickel has the lowest oxidation state is :
(a) $Ni(CO)_4$ (b) $(CH_3COO)_2Ni$ (c) NiO (d) $NiCl_2(PPh_3)_2$

26. A metal *M* which is not affected by strong acids like conc. HNO_3, conc. H_2SO_4 and conc. solution of alkalies like NaOH, KOH forms MCl_3, which finds use for tanning in photography? The metal *M* is :
(a) Ag (b) Hg (c) Au (d) Cu

27. Copper (II) ions gives reddish brown precipitate with potassium ferrocyanide. The formula of the precipitate is :
(a) $Cu_4[Fe(CN)_6]$ (b) $Cu_2[Fe(CN)_6]$ (c) $Cu_3[Fe(CN)_6]$ (d) $Cu_3[Fe(CN)_6]_2$

28. Which of the following electronic configuration would be associated with the highest magnetic moment?
(a) $[Ar]3d^8$ (b) $[Ar]3d^3$ (c) $[Ar]3d^6$ (d) $[Ar]3d^7$

29. The correct statement about iron includes
(I) the highest oxidation state of iron is +6 in K_2FeO_4
(II) that the iron shows +2 oxidation state with six electrons in the 3*d* orbitals
(III) the common oxidation state of iron is +3 with five unpaired electrons in the 3*d* orbital
(a) I, II, III (b) I, II (c) II, III (d) I only

30. Many transition metals form interstitial compounds. The characteristics of these interstitial compounds are :

(I) They have high melting points, higher than those of pure metals
(II) They are very hard
(III) They retain metallic conductivity
(IV) They are chemically more reactive than the pure metals

(a) I, II, III (b) I, III (c) II, IV (d) IV only

31. Technetium, the element below manganese in the Periodic Table, would be expected to have high values for its :

(I) melting point (II) boiling point (III) density

(a) I, II, III (b) I, II (c) II, III (d) I only

32. All Zn(+II) compounds are white because :

(a) Zn^{2+} has a d^{10} configuration and the *d*-subshell is full
(b) Zn^{2+} shows *d-d* transition
(c) Zn^{2+} has no electron in the 4*s*-subshell
(d) Zn is not a transition element

33. Identify the wrong statement regarding copper sulphate :

(a) It reacts with KI to give I_2
(b) It reacts with KCl to give Cl_2
(c) It's tartarate complex reacts with NaOH and glucose to give Cu_2O
(d) It gives CuO on heating in air

34. The transition metals exhibit higher enthalpies of atomisation due to :

(a) their ability to show variable oxidation states
(b) the presence of incompletely filled *d*-subshell
(c) their ability to exist in the solid state with unpaired electrons
(d) strong interatomic interaction aries because of having large number of unpaired electrons in their atoms

35. Which of the following statements are correct about Zn, Cd and Hg?

(I) they exhibit high enthalpies of atomisation as the *d*-subshell is full
(II) Zn and Cd do not show variable oxidation states while Hg shows +I and +II
(III) Compound of Zn, Cd and Hg are paramagnetic in nature
(IV) Zn, Cd and Hg are called soft metals

(a) I, II, III (b) I, III (c) II, IV (d) IV only

36. When mercury (II) chloride is treated with excess of stannous chloride, the products obtained are :

(a) liquid Hg and $SnCl_4$ (b) Hg_2Cl_2 and $SnCl_4$
(c) Hg_2Cl_2 and $[SnCl_4]^{2-}$ (d) Liquid Hg and $[SnCl_4]^{2-}$

37. Which of the following is NOT a characteristic of the transition elements in the series from scandium to zinc?

(a) The formation of coloured cations
(b) The presence of at least one unpaired electron in a *d*-orbital of a cation
(c) The ability to form complex ions
(d) The possession of an oxidation state of +1

38. Spiegeleisen is an alloy of :
(a) Cu + Zn + Ni (b) Ni + Cr (c) Mn + Fe + C (d) Fe + Cr + Ni

39. The treatment of zinc with very dilute nitric acid produces :
(a) NO (b) N_2O (c) NO_2 (d) NH_4^+

40. Sodium chromate, Na_2CrO_4 is made commercially by :
(a) heating mixture of Cr_2O_3 and Na_2CO_3
(b) heating mixture of chromite ore and sodium carbonate in the presence of oxygen
(c) heating sodium dichromate with sodium carbonate
(d) reacting NaOH with chromic acid

41. Anhydrous mercurous chloride can be prepared by :
(a) the reduction of $HgCl_2$ with $SnCl_2$ solution
(b) the reaction of $HgCl_2$ with Hg
(c) the reaction of Hg with excess amount of Cl_2
(d) the reaction of Hg with concentrated HCl

42. When aqueous sodium hydroxide is added to an aqueous solution of chromium (III) ions, a green blue precipitate is first formed which re-dissolves to give a green solution. This green colour is due to :
(a) $[Cr(H_2O)_6]^{3+}$ (b) CrO_4^{2-}
(c) $[Cr(OH)_4]^-$ (d) $[Cr(OH)_3(H_2O)_3]$

43. $HgCl_2$ is a covalent compound, sparingly soluble in water, the solubility increases by the addition of chloride ions due to :
(a) common ion effect (b) formation of complex $[HgCl_4]^{2-}$
(c) weakening of Hg—Cl bonds (d) strong ion–dipole forces

44. Amongst TiF_6^{2-}, CoF_6^{3-}, Cu_2Cl_2 and $NiCl_4^{2-}$ the colourless species are :
(a) CoF_6^{3-} and $NiCl_4^{2-}$ (b) TiF_6^{2-} and CoF_6^{3-}
(c) Cu_2Cl_2 and $NiCl_4^{2-}$ (d) TiF_6^{2-} and Cu_2Cl_2

45. Which of the following complex ion has a magnetic moment same as $[Cr(H_2O)_6]^{3+}$?
(a) $[Mn(H_2O)_6]^{4+}$ (b) $[Mn(H_2O)_6]^{3+}$ (c) $[Fe(H_2O)_6]^{3+}$ (d) $[Cu(H_3N)_4]^{2+}$

46. Silver nitrate solution is kept in brown bottles in laboratory because :
(a) it reacts with ordinary white bottles
(b) brown bottles cut the passage of light through
(c) brown bottles do not react with it
(d) ordinary bottles catalyse its decomposition

47. $K_3[Fe(CN)_6]$ gives green ppt. with :
(a) Ag^+ *(aq)* (b) Cu^{2+} *(aq)* (c) Fe^{3+} *(aq)* (d) Fe^{2+} *(aq)*

48. Aqueous solution of which of the following compound is more acidic.
(a) $AlCl_3$ (b) NaCl (c) $MgCl_2$ (d) $FeCl_3$

49. Pure O_2 instead of air is used to oxidise the pig iron because :
(a) Molten metal took up small amount of nitrogen which makes the steel brittle
(b) Air is not as efficient to oxidise all the impurities to their respective oxides
(c) Air contains moisture and will precipitate iron as Fe_2O_3
(d) Iron reacts with air to form $FeCO_3$

50. Give the correct order of initials **T** or **F** for following statements. Use **T** if statement is true and **F** if it is false.

(I) Sulphide ions reacts with $Na_2[Fe(CN)_5(NO)]$ to form a purple coloured compound $Na_4[Fe(CN)_5(NOS)]$. In the reaction, the oxidation state of iron changes

(II) Pt(IV) compounds are relatively more stable than NI(IV) compounds

(III) The welding of magnesium can be done in the atmosphere of Helium

(IV) $LiAlH_4$ on hydrolysis will give H_2

(a) FFTT (b) FTTT (c) TFTF (d) TFTT

51. $(X) + K_2CO_3 + \text{Air} \xrightarrow{\text{heat}} (Y)$

$(Y) + Cl_2 \longrightarrow (Z)$ Pink

Which of the following is correct ?

(a) $X = \text{black}, MnO_2, Y = \text{Blue}, K_2CrO_4, Z = KMnO_4$

(b) $X = \text{green}, Cr_2O_3, Y = \text{Yellow}, K_2CrO_4, Z = K_2Cr_2O_7$

(c) $X = \text{black}, MnO_2, Y = \text{green}, K_2MnO_4, Z = KMnO_4$

(d) $X = \text{black}; Bi_2O_3, Y = \text{colourless } KBiO_2, Z = KBiO_3$

52. Sodium thiosulphate, $Na_2S_2O_3 \cdot 5H_2O$ is used in photography to :

(a) Reduce the silver bromide to metallic silver

(b) Convert the metallic silver to silver salt

(c) remove undecomposed AgBr as soluble silver thiosulphate complex

(d) remove reduced silver

53. The advantage(s) of using O_2 rather than air in the steel industry is(are)

(I) there is a faster conversion, so a given plant can produce more steel in a day

(II) larger quantities can be handled

(III) it gives a pure product, and the surface is free from nitrides

(a) I only (b) II and III only

(c) II only (d) I, II and III

54. When $AgNO_3$ comes in contact with skin, it leaves a black stain. This is because of :

(a) HNO_3 produced by hydrolysis of $AgNO_3$

(b) AgOH produced by hydrolysis of $AgNO_3$

(c) Its reduction of silver

(d) Its oxidation to silver oxide

55. The aqueous solution of copper(II) sulphate is slowly hydrolysed forming basic copper sulphate whose chemical composition is :

(a) $CuSO_4 \cdot Cu(OH)_2$ (b) $CuSO_4 \cdot CuO$

(c) $CuSO_4 \cdot Cu(OH)_2 \cdot CuO$ (d) $[Cu(H_2O)_4]SO_4 \cdot H_2O$

56. Which of the following compound, when reacts with conc. H_2SO_4 then at least two properties of conc. H_2SO_4 are used in the reaction?

(a) $Na_2B_4O_7$ (b) FeS

(c) CaF_2 (d) $Ca_3(PO_4)_2$

57. Zinc carbonate is precipitated from zinc sulphate solution by the addition of :

(a) Na_2CO_3 (b) $CaCO_3$

(c) $MgCO_3$ (d) $NaHCO_3$

58. Mark the correct statements :
(a) Hg forms an amalgam with iron
(b) Hg vapour is non-poisonous
(c) Hg is mono atomic and monovalent in mercurous compound
(d) Oxysalts of mercury are thermally unstable

59. Mercury is the only metal which is liquid at 0°C. This is due to its :
(a) Very high ionisation energy and weak metallic bond
(b) Low ionisation potential
(c) High atomic weight
(d) High vapour pressure

60. A white precipitate of AgCl dissolves in excess of :
(I) $NH_3(aq)$ (II) $Na_2S_2O_3$ (III) NaCN
(a) III only (b) I, II, III (c) I, II (d) I only

61. In context of the lanthanoids, which of the following statements is not correct?
(a) Availability of 4f electrons results in the formation of compounds in +4 state for all the members of the series
(b) There is a gradual decrease in the radii of the members with increasing atomic number in the series
(c) All the members exhibit +3 oxidation state
(d) Because of similar properties the separation of lanthanoids is not easy

62. Which of the following cation is not satisfying the given reaction?
$M^{+x} + KI(aq) \longrightarrow MI_x + I_2$
(a) Cu^{2+} (b) Pb^{4+} (c) Fe^{3+} (d) Bi^{3+}

63. Which of the following process is not associated with steel making?
(a) Bessemer process (b) Open-Hearth process
(c) Kaldo process (d) Auto-oxidation

64. Oxygen in absorbed by molten Ag, which is evolved on cooling and the silver particles are scattered, this phenomenon is known as :
(a) silvering of mirror (b) spitting of silver
(c) frosting of silver (d) hairing of silver

65. Which of the following is weaker oxidising agent than MnO_4^-/H^+?
(a) $NaBiO_3/H^+$ (b) $S_2O_8^{2-}/H^+$
(c) MnO_4^-/OH^- (d) PbO_2/H^+

66. Zinc (II) ion on reaction with NaOH first give a white precipitate which dissolves in excess of NaOH due to the formation of :
(a) ZnO (b) $Zn(OH)_2$
(c) $[Zn(OH)_4]^{2-}$ (d) $[Zn(H_2O)_4]^{2+}$

67. The conversion of pig iron to steel frequently requires the addition of :
(I) oxygen or iron oxide (II) transition elements
(III) inner transition elements (IV) silica
(a) I, II, III (b) I, II
(c) II, III (d) I only

68. Dilute nitric acid on reaction with silver liberates :

(a) NO gas
(b) NO_2 gas
(c) N_2 gas
(d) O_2 gas

69. Which of the following double salt does not exist?

(a) $(NH_4)_2SO_4 \cdot CuSO_4 \cdot 6H_2O$
(b) $(NH_4)_2SO_4 \cdot FeSO_4 \cdot 6H_2O$
(c) $(NH_4)_2SO_4 \cdot ZnSO_4 \cdot 6H_2O$
(d) $(NH_4)_2SO_4 \cdot NiSO_4 \cdot 6H_2O$

70. When steam is passed over red hot iron, the substances formed are :

(a) $Fe_2O_3 + H_2$
(b) $H_2 + FeO$
(c) $Fe_3O_4 + H_2$
(d) $Fe_3O_4 + H_2O$

71. The oxoanion which contains all equivalent M—O bond is :

(I) CrO_4^{2-} (II) MnO_4^- (III) $Cr_2O_7^{2-}$

(a) III only
(b) I, II, III
(c) I, II
(d) I only

72. $K_3[Fe(CN)_6] + M^{x+}(aq) \longrightarrow$ ppt. of complex salt.

Which of the following cation **does not** respond above reaction?

(a) $Cu^{2+}(aq)$
(b) $Fe^{2+}(aq)$
(c) $Zn^{2+}(aq)$
(d) None of these

73. $FeCr_2O_4 + Na_2CO_3 + O_2 \xrightarrow{\text{Fusion}} [X] \xrightarrow[H_2O]{H^+} [Y] \xrightarrow[\text{org. layer}]{H_2O_2/H^+} [Z]$

Which of the following statement is true for the compounds [X], [Y] and [Z] ?

(a) In all three compounds, the chromium is in +6 oxidation state
(b) [Z] is a deep blue-violet coloured compound which decomposes rapidly in aqueous solution into Cr^{+3} and dioxygen
(c) Saturated solution of [Y] gives bright orange compound, chromic anhydride, with concentrated H_2SO_4
(d) All of these

74. $CuSO_4$ soln. $\xrightarrow{H_2S\uparrow} M\downarrow \xrightarrow[\text{of KCN}]{\text{Excess}} N + O$

Then final products N and O are respectively.

(a) $[Cu(CN)_4]^{3-}$, $(CN)_2$
(b) CuCN, $(CN)_2$
(c) $[Cu(CN)_4]^{2-}$, $(CN)_2$
(d) $Cu(CN)_2$, K_2S

75. Consider the following transformation :

$$2CuX_2 \xrightarrow{\text{Room temperature}} 2CuX + X_2\uparrow$$

Then X^- can be :

(a) F^-, Br^-
(b) Cl^-, Br^-
(c) CN^-, I^-
(d) Cl^-, F^-

76. Acidified permanganate solution does not oxidize :

(a) $C_2O_4^{2-}$ *(aq.)*
(b) NO_3^- *(aq.)*
(c) S^{2-} *(aq.)*
(d) F^-*(aq.)*

77. Which of the following solid salt on heating with solid $K_2Cr_2O_7$ and conc. H_2SO_4 orange red vapours are evolved which turn aqueous NaOH solution yellow ?
(a) NaBr (b) NaCl
(c) $NaNO_3$ (d) NaI

78. K_2MnO_4 **does not** undergo disproportionation in the presence of:
(a) CO_2 gas (b) conc.KOH solution
(c) H_3PO_4 (d) excess water

79. $M_2(SO_4)_n$ salt soln. + $BaCl_2 \longrightarrow \underset{\text{White}}{N\downarrow} + \underset{\text{(coloured solution)}}{P}$

When KI is added into '*P*', its colour changes and precipitate is not formed, then M^{n+} cation of salt is:
(a) $Cu^{2+}(aq)$ (b) $Fe^{3+}(aq)$ (c) $Hg^{2+}(aq)$ (d) $Cr^{3+}(aq)$

80. Which of the following ion is oxidized by $Cu^{2+}(aq)$ as well as $Fe^{3+}(aq)$ cations?
(a) Cl^- (b) CN^- (c) SCN^- (d) $S_2O_3^{2-}$

81. Which of the following reaction gives observable change?
(a) $KCl(s) + \text{conc. } H_2SO_4 + K_2Cr_2O_7(s) \longrightarrow$ (b) $Na_2[Fe(CN)_5NO] + H_2S + HCl \longrightarrow$
(c) $K_2HgI_4 + NH_4Cl \longrightarrow$ (d) $FeSO_4 + \text{ dil. } H_2SO_4 + NaNO_3 \longrightarrow$

82. Which reagent can dissolve AgCl as well as Ag_2S separately?
(a) dil. HNO_3 (b) NH_4OH (c) KCN (d) $Na_2S_2O_3$

83. A solid mixture of AgCl and $K_2Cr_2O_7$ is heated with conc. H_2SO_4 and produces:
(a) Greenish yellow gas (b) Colourless gas
(c) Red coloured gas (d) No gas

84. Which does not produce H_2 gas when react with dil. HCl?
(a) Ti^{2+} (b) V^{2+} (c) Cr^{2+} (d) Fe^{2+}

85. Colour of $CrO_4^{2-}(aq)$ is not changed by:
(a) Dilute HCl (b) NH_3 solution
(c) CH_3COOH (d) NO_2 gas

86. $CuSO_4(aq) + ZnCl_2(aq) \longrightarrow (P)$ solution, **Colour** of '*P*' solution is:
(a) Yellow (b) Blue (c) White turbidity (d) Green

87. Which of the following molecular species exists in a solution having pH < 6?
(a) CrO_4^{2-} (b) $Cu(OH)_2$ (c) $Cr_2O_7^{2-}$ (d) $CaCO_3$

88. Select **incorrect** statement:
(a) In first series of *d*-block metals, enthalpy of atomization of zinc is highest.
(b) Scandium does not exhibit variable oxidation state.
(c) Highest oxidation state of transition metal is exhibited in its oxide form.
(d) Some transition metals can exhibit negative oxidation state in their carbonyl compounds.

89. Silver metal is **not** obtained by reaction of which of the following substance with aqueous solution of silver nitrate:
(a) $H_2(g)$ (b) H_3PO_2 (c) $CN^-(aq)$ (d) $Cr^{2+}(aq)$

90. Which of the following metal **does not** form *MO* type of oxide?

(a) Fe (b) Cu (c) Sc (d) Cd

91. Which of the following combination of reactants is **not** proceeded by redox reaction?

(a) $Sn^{2+}(aq) + Au^{3+}(aq)$ (b) $Au(s) + Pb^{2+}(aq)$

(c) $Fe^{3+}(aq) + 3I^{-}(aq)$ (d) $Sn^{2+}(aq) + Cr_2O_7^{2-}(aq) + H^{+}(aq)$

92. Which of the following combination of reactants **does not** react at room temperature?

(a) $AuCl_3(aq) + SnCl_2$ (b) $Fe^{3+}(aq) + KI$

(c) $Bi^{3+}(aq) + Sn^{2+}(aq)$ (d) $Hg + SnCl_2$

Level 3

Passage 1

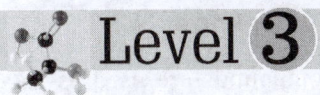

In salts of polyatomic anion, as polarising power of cation increases, thermal stability of the salt decreases and decomposed species may further undergo redox reaction.

1. Which of the following species undergoes non-redox thermal decomposition reaction on heating?

(a) $FeSO_4$ (b) $SnSO_4$
(c) $H_2C_2O_4$ (d) Na_2HPO_4

2. Water soluble salt (*x*) was heated into three products *A*, *B* and *C* and *B* and *C* are two different paramagnetic gases. *A* is yellow in hot condition, then salt (*x*) is :

(a) $Hg(NO_3)_2$ (b) FeC_2O_4
(c) $ZnSO_4$ (d) $Pb(NO_3)_2$

Passage 2

$$\text{Light green (Compound 'A')} \xrightarrow{\Delta} \text{White Residue (B)} \xrightarrow[\text{Temp.}]{\text{High}} C + D + E$$

(i) 'D' and 'E' are two acidic gas.
(ii) 'D' is passed through $HgCl_2$ solution to give yellow ppt.
(iii) 'E' is passed through water first and then H_2S is passed, white turbidity is obtained.
(iv) A is water soluble and addition of $HgCl_2$ in it, yellow ppt is obtained but white ppt does not turn into grey on addition of excess solution of 'A'.

1. 'D' and 'E' are respectively.

(a) SO_2 and SO_3 (b) SO_3 and SO_2
(c) SO_2 and CO_2 (d) CO_2 and CO

2. Yellow ppt in the above observation is :

(a) Mercuric oxide (b) Basic mercury (II) sulphite
(c) Basic mercury (II) sulphate (d) Mercuric iodide

3. The no. of water of crystallisation in 'A' is :

(a) 0 (b) 2
(c) 7 (d) 5

Passage 3

Transition metal and their compounds are used as catalysts in industry and in biological system. For example, in the Contact Process, vanadium compounds in the +5 state (V_2O_5 or VO_3^-) are used to oxidise SO_2 to SO_3 :

$$SO_2 + \frac{1}{2}O_2 \xrightarrow{V_2O_5} SO_3$$

It is thought that the actual oxidation process takes place in two stages. In the first step, V^{5+} in the presence of oxide ions converts SO_2 to SO_3. At the same time, V^{5+} is reduced to V^{4+}.

$$2V^{5+} + O^{2-} + SO_2 \longrightarrow 2V^{4+} + SO_3$$

In the second step, V^{5+} is regenerated from V^{4+} by oxygen :

$$2V^{4+} + \frac{1}{2}O_2 \longrightarrow 2V^{5+} + O^{2-}$$

The overall process is, of course, the sum of these two steps :

$$SO_2 + \frac{1}{2}O_2 \longrightarrow SO_3$$

1. Transition metals and their compounds catalyse reactions because :
(a) they have completely filled *s*-subshell
(b) they have a comparable size due to poor shielding of *d*-subshell
(c) they introduce an entirely new reaction mechanism with a lower activation energy
(d) they have variable oxidation states differ by two units

2. During the course of the reaction :
(a) catalyst undergoes changes in oxidation state
(b) catalyst increases the rate constant
(c) catalyst is regenerated in its original form when the reactants form the products
(d) all are correct

3. Catalytic activity of transition metals depends on :
(a) their ability to exist in different oxidation states
(b) the size of the metal atoms
(c) the number of empty atomic orbitals available
(d) none of these

4. Which of the following ion involved in the above process will show paramagnetism?
(a) V^{5+} (b) V^{4+} (c) O^{2-} (d) VO_3^-

Passage 4

MnO_2 is the most important oxide of manganese. MnO_2 occurs naturally as the black coloured mineral pyrolusite. It is an oxidising agent, and decomposes to Mn_3O_4 on heating to 530°C. It is used in the preparation of potassium permanaganate and in the production of Cl_2 gas. Over half a million tonnes per year of MnO_2 is used in dry batteries.

1. In the laboratory, MnO_2 is made by :
(a) heating Mn in O_2
(b) oxidising Mn^{2+} in air
(c) electrolytic oxidation of $MnSO_4$
(d) precipitating MnO_2 from solution when performing titration of $KMnO_4$ in alkaline medium

2. When MnO_2 is fused with KOH in the presence of air, the product formed is :
(a) purple colour $KMnO_4$
(b) green colour K_2MnO_4
(c) colourless MnO_4^-
(d) purple colour K_2MnO_4

3. MnO_2 dissolves in concentrated HCl to form :
(a) Mn^{4+} ion and Cl_2
(b) Mn^{2+} ion and Cl_2
(c) $[MnCl_4]^{2-}$ and Cl_2
(d) only $[MnCl_4]^{2-}$

4. In which of the following species, the colour is due to charge transfer?
(I) $[Mn(OH)_4]^{2-}$ (II) MnO_4^{2-} (III) MnO_2 (IV) $KMnO_4$
(a) I, II, III correct
(b) II, IV correct
(c) I, III correct
(d) only IV correct

Passage 5

Iron (+II) is one of the most important oxidation states, and salts are called ferrous salts. Most of the Fe (+II) salts are pale green and contain $[Fe(H_2O)_6]^{2+}$ ion. Fe(+II) compounds are easily oxidised by air and so are difficult to obtain pure Fe^{2+} form many complexes like $K_4[Fe(CN)_6]$.

1. Anhydrous $FeCl_2$ is made by :
(a) heating Fe with dilute HCl
(b) heating Fe with gaseous HCl
(c) reacting Fe with conc. HCl
(d) heating Fe with excess Cl_2 gas

2. $K_3[Fe(CN)_6]$ is used in the detection of Fe^{2+} ion with which it gives a deep blue colour. This colour is due to the formation of :
(a) $K_2Fe[Fe(CN)_6]$
(b) $Fe_4[Fe(CN)_6]_3$
(c) $Fe[Fe(CN)_6]$
(d) $Fe_3[Fe(CN)_6]_2$

3. $FeSO_4$ is used in brown ring test for nitrates and nitrites. In this test, a freshly prepared $FeSO_4$ solution is mixed with solution containing NO_2^- or NO_3^- and the conc. H_2SO_4 is run down the side of the test tube. If the mixture gets hot or is shaken,
(I) the brown colour disappear
(II) NO is evolved
(III) a yellow solution of $Fe_2(SO_4)_3$ is formed
(a) I, II, III correct
(b) I, III correct
(c) II, III correct
(d) only I correct

Passage 6

Iron forms iron halide salts by reacting the metal directly with halogen. FeI_3 does not exist. FeF_3 is white solid inspite of five unpaired electrons with d^5 configuration. $FeCl_3$ is soluble in water and is used as a mordant in dyeing industry.

1. FeI_3 does not exist because :
(a) of large size
(b) Fe^{3+} oxidises I^- to I_2
(c) of low lattice energy
(d) iodine is not highly electronegative enough to oxidise Fe to Fe^{3+}

2. Anhydrous $FeCl_3$ can be prepared by reaction of :
(a) Fe with dry chlorine
(b) Fe with dil. HCl in the presence of O_2
(c) $Fe(OH)_3$ with conc. HCl
(d) Fe_2O_3 with conc. HCl

3. $FeCl_3$ solution added to $K_4[Fe(CN)_6]$ gives A while with KSCN gives B. A and B respectively are :
(a) $Fe_3[Fe(CN)_6]_2, Fe(CNS)_3$
(b) $Fe_4[Fe(CN)_6]_3, KFe(CNS)_3$
(c) $Fe_4[Fe(CN)_6]_3, K_3[Fe(CNS)_6]$
(d) $Fe_4[Fe(CN)_6]_3, K_3[Fe(SCN)_6]$

Passage 7

The enthalpy of atomisation is an important factor in determining the standard electrode potential of a transition metals, metals with very high enthalpy of atomisation tend to be noble in their reactions.

1. The incorrect order of melting points of transition elements is:
(a) W > Re > Os
(b) Mo > Ru > Tc
(c) Cr > Fe > Mn
(d) Mo > Rh > Ru

2. The incorrect statement is:
(a) The metals of the second and third transition series have greater enthalpies of atomisation than the corresponding elements of the first series.
(b) Greater the unpaired electron in *d*-orbitals favourable for strong interatomic interaction.
(c) Zn, Cd, Hg and Mn have one or more typical metallic structures at normal temperatures.
(d) The melting and boiling point of transition elements regularly increases with the atomic number increases.

3. Which of the following reaction has least negative value of standard electrode potential.
(a) $Ti^{2+} + 2e^- \longrightarrow Ti$
(b) $V^{2+} + 2e^- \longrightarrow V$
(c) $Cr^{2+} + 2e^- \longrightarrow Cr$
(d) $Mn^{2+} + 2e^- \longrightarrow Mn$

Passage 8

$$4\text{ "Chromite ore"} + 8(P) + 7O_2 \longrightarrow 8(Q) + 2Fe_2O_3 + 8CO_2 \uparrow$$

$$2(Q) \underset{2OH^-}{\overset{2H^+}{\rightleftharpoons}} (R) + 2Na^+ + H_2O$$

$$(R) + 2KCl \longrightarrow \underset{\text{(Orange)}}{(S)} + 2NaCl$$

1. The incorrect statement is:
(a) oxidation number of transition metal ion is same in compound Q and R.
(b) (P) is carbonate salt.
(c) (Q) is dichromate salt.
(d) Chromite ore is $FeCr_2O_4$

2. Compound 'P' is:
(a) Na_2CO_3 (b) Na_2O (c) K_2CO_3 (d) none

3. Compound 'S' is:
(a) K_2CrO_4 (b) $K_2Cr_2O_7$ (c) Cr_2O_3 (d) $KHCrO_4$

Passage 9

$$2Mn^{2+} + 5S_2O_8^{2-} + 8H_2O \longrightarrow 2\text{ '}A\text{'} + 10\text{ '}B\text{'} + 16H^+$$

$$\text{'}A\text{'} \xrightarrow{KCl} 2C\ \text{(Purple)}$$

$$\uparrow O_2 + E + \underset{\text{(Black)}}{D} \xleftarrow[513\text{ K}]{\Delta} \underset{\text{(Purple)}}{2C}$$

1. The incorrect statement is:
(a) C is isostructural with $KClO_4$
(b) C is diamagnetic
(c) D is paramagnetic
(d) Colour of compound C is due to $d-d$ transition.

2. The correct match for compound/species is:

	(A)	(B)	(D)	(E)
(a)	MnO_4^-	SO_4^{2-}	K_2MnO_4	MnO_2
(b)	MnO_4^-	SO_3^{2-}	K_2MnO_4	Mn_2O_3
(c)	MnO_4^{2-}	SO_4^{2-}	$KMnO_4$	MnO_2
(d)	MnO_4^{2-}	SO_3^{2-}	$KMnO_4$	Mn_2O_3

3. Acidified permanganate solution can be oxidises:
(a) Oxalates to carbon dioxide (b) Nitrites to nitrates
(c) Iodide ion to free iodine (d) All

ONE OR MORE ANSWERS IS/ARE CORRECT

1. What changes occur when acidified CrO_4^{2-} ion reacts with H_2O_2 solution in presence of ether solvent ?
(a) Orange colour of solution turns blue
(b) Oxidation state of Cr-atom decreases
(c) Oxidation state of Cr-atom remains constant
(d) Orange colour of solution turns green

2. Mercury is a liquid at 0°C because of :
(a) very high ionisation energy
(b) weak metallic bonds
(c) high heat of hydration
(d) high heat of sublimation

3. Choose **correct** statement for lanthanoids and actinoids:
(a) Earlier members of actinoids have relatively long half lives than latter ones
(b) Stable oxidation state of both cerium and thorium is +4
(c) Actinoid contraction is greater from element to element than lanthanoid contraction.
(d) Ionization enthalpies of actinoids are higher than those of lanthanoids in respective groups.

4. The metal oxide which decomposes on heating is/are :
(a) ZnO
(b) Al_2O_3
(c) Ag_2O
(d) HgO

5. Which of the following acids attack(s) on copper and silver?
(a) dilute HNO_3
(b) dilute HCl
(c) conc. H_2SO_4
(d) aqua regia

6. Which of the following statements are true for Mohr's salt?
(a) it decolourizes $KMnO_4$ solution
(b) it is a double salt
(c) it is colourless salt
(d) it is a primary standard substance

7. Which of the following statement(s) is/are correct?
(a) The chief ore of zinc is cinnabar
(b) Mac-Arther's process is used to extract silver
(c) $Na_2S_2O_3$ is used to remove the unexposed AgBr from the photographic films
(d) Nessler's reagent is a complex of zinc in +2 oxidation state

8. Roasting of copper pyrites is done :
(a) to remove moisture and volatile impurities
(b) to oxidise free sulphur
(c) to decompose pyrites into Cu_2S and FeS
(d) to decompose Cu_2S into blister copper

9. Identify the correct statements :
(a) Iron belongs to first transition series of the periodic table
(b) The purest form of commercial iron is wrought iron
(c) Anhydrous ferrous sulphate is called as yellow vitriol
(d) Iron is the most abundant transition metal

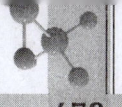

10. Which statements about mercury are correct?
(a) Hg is a liquid metal at room temperature
(b) Hg forms two series of salts
(c) Hg forms no amalgam with iron and platinum
(d) Hg does not show variable valency

11. Which statements about corrosive sublimate ($HgCl_2$) are correct?
(a) It sublimes on heating
(b) It oxidises stannous chloride
(c) It is highly poisonous
(d) It is prepared by heating mercury in excess chlorine

12. Which statements are correct regarding copper sulphate?
(a) It reacts with NaOH and glucose to give Cu_2O
(b) It reacts with KCl to give Cu_2O
(c) It gives CuO on heating in air
(d) It reacts with excess KI to give brown colouration

13. To an acidified dichromate solution, a pinch of Na_2O_2 is added and shaken. What is observed ?
(a) Blue colour (b) Orange colour changing to green
(c) Copious evolution of oxygen (d) Bluish-green precipitate

14. Pick out the correct statement(s) :
(a) MnO_2 dissolves in conc. HCl, but does not form Mn^{4+} ions
(b) Decomposition of acidic $KMnO_4$ is not catalysed by sunlight
(c) MnO_4^{2-} is strongly oxidising and stable only in very strong alkali. In dilute alkali, water or acidic solutions it disproportionates
(d) $KMnO_4$ does not act as oxidising agent in alkaline medium

15. The species that undergoes disproportionation in an alkaline medium are :
(a) Cl_2 (b) MnO_4^{2-} (c) NO_2 (d) ClO_4^-

16. Which of the following statements regarding *d*-block elements are true?
(a) the colour of anhydrous $CuSO_4$ is blue
(b) "splitting of silver" can be prevented by covering the surface of molten silver with charcoal
(c) Iodine liberated in a reaction can be estimated by titration against a standard thiosulphate solution
(d) Lanthanum is first element of third transition series

17. Which is/are insoluble in NH_3 solution?
(a) AgCl (b) AgBr (c) AgI (d) Ag_2S

18. Order of paramagnetic character among following elements is/are:
(a) Mn>Fe>Cr (b) Fe>Zn>Cr (c) Cr>Fe>Zn (d) Cr>Mn>Fe

19. Choose correct statement(s) regarding the following reaction.

$$Cr_2O_7^{2-}(aq) + 3SO_3^{2-}(aq) + 8H^+ \longrightarrow 2Cr^{3+}(aq) + 3SO_4^{2-}(aq) + 4H_2O$$

(a) $Cr_2O_7^{2-}$ is oxidising agent
(b) SO_3^{2-} is reducing agent
(c) The oxidation number of per 'S' atom in $3SO_3^{2-}$ is increase by two
(d) The oxidation number of per 'Cr' atom in $Cr_2O_7^{2-}$ is decreased by three

20. Mercuric chloride is converted into mercury by :
(a) placing copper metal in aqueous solution of $HgCl_2$
(b) treating aqueous solution of $HgCl_2$ with excess of stannous chloride
(c) treating aqueous solution of $HgCl_2$ with $PbCl_4$ solution
(d) none of these

21. What changes occur when acidified CrO_4^{2-} ion reacts with H_2O_2 solution in presence of ether solvent?
(a) Orange colour of solution turns blue
(b) Oxidation state of Cr-atom decreases
(c) Oxidation state of Cr-atom remains constant
(d) Orange colour of solution turns green

22. Choose correct statement(s) regarding the following reaction :
$Cr_2O^{2-}_{7(aq.)} + 3SO^{2-}_{3(aq.)} + 8H^+ \longrightarrow 2Cr^{3+}_{(aq.)} + 3SO^{2-}_{4(aq.)} + 4H_2O$
(a) $Cr_2O_7^{2-}$ is oxidising agent
(b) SO_3^{2-} is reducing agent
(c) The oxidation number of per S-atom in $3SO_3^{2-}$ is increased by two
(d) The oxidation number of per Cr-atom in $Cr_2O^{2-}_{7(aq.)}$ is decreased by three

23. Which of the following reaction(s) has/have been mentioned with incorrect products?
(a) $CrSO_4(s) \xrightarrow[\text{Heating}]{\text{Normal}} CrO(s) + SO_2(g) + SO_3(g)$
(b) $Fe^{3+}(aq) + 3CN^-(aq) \xrightarrow{\text{Room temp.}} Fe(CN)_2 + \frac{1}{2}(CN)_2\uparrow$
(c) $AuCl_3 + SnCl_2(\text{excess}) \xrightarrow{\text{Room temp.}} Au + SnCl_4$
(d) $Cu(OH)_2 \cdot CuCO_3(s) \xrightarrow[\text{Heating}]{\text{Normal}} Cu + CO_2(g) + H_2O + O_2(g)$

24. Which of the following metal cation does not produces gaseous product when reacts with KCN solution?
(a) $Cu^{2+}(aq)$
(b) $Ag^+(aq)$
(c) $Cd^{2+}(aq)$
(d) $Pb^{2+}(aq)$

25. Which of the following can act as oxidising agent in acidic as well as in alkaline medium?
(a) $KMnO_4$
(b) $K_2Cr_2O_7$
(c) H_2O_2
(d) Cl_2

26. Consider the following thermal decomposition reactions.
$x \xrightarrow{\Delta}$ element with highest % in air
$y \xrightarrow{\Delta}$ element with highest % in earth crust
then compounds, x and y are respectively.
(a) $(NH_4)_2Cr_2O_7$, $K_2Cr_2O_7$
(b) $(NH_4)_2CO_3$, K_2CO_3
(c) NH_4MnO_4, $KMnO_4$
(d) $(NH_4)_3PO_4$, K_3PO_4

27. Common properties of products obtained by heating of $KMnO_4$ and $K_2Cr_2O_7$ is/are:
(a) Paramagnetic gas
(b) Amphoteric oxide
(c) Colourless gas
(d) Salt does not exist in acidic medium

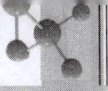

28. The correct statement(s) regarding transition elements is/are:
(a) The last electron goes to the *d*-orbitals of the penultimate energy level.
(b) These elements may have d^{10} configuration in their stable oxidation state.
(c) These elements shows variable oxidation state and formation of coloured ions.
(d) These elements form complex compound and have catalytic property.

29. Which of the following statement(s) is/are correct about interstitial compounds of transition metal?
(a) They have high melting points than pure metals.
(b) They are chemically inert.
(c) They are very hard
(d) They retain metallic conductivity

30. Consider the reaction, $3MnO_4^{2-} + 4H^+ \longrightarrow$

Then the correct statement(s) regarding this reaction is/are:
(a) This is a disproportionation reaction.
(b) MnO_2 is one of the product of this reaction.
(c) MnO_4^- is one of the product of this reaction
(d) Mn_2O_3 is one of the product of this reaction.

MATCH THE COLUMN

Entries of Column-I are to be matched with entries of Column-II. Each entry of Column-I may have the matching with one or more than one entries of Column-II.

1. **Column-I** contains four statements following reason and **Column-II** consists of four options P, Q, R, S

Answer the following :

P → If both statement and reason are true and reason is correct explanation of statement.

Q → If both statement and reason are true and reason is not correct explanation of statement.

R → If statement is correct and reason is incorrect.

S → If both statement and reason are incorrect.

Column-I	Column-II
(A) **Statement :** The reaction of oxalic acid with acidified $KMnO_4$ is first slow and then speeds up by itself. **Reason :** $KMnO_4$ decomposes into MnO_2 in sunlight.	(P)
(B) **Statement :** Anh. $ZnCl_2$ can't be made by heating $ZnCl_2 \cdot 2H_2O$. **Reason :** It undergoes hydrolysis to produce $Zn(OH)_2$ and HCl.	(Q)

(C) **Statement :** $KMnO_4$ is not used as a primary standard substance. **Reason :** It is deliquescent in nature.	(R)
(D) **Statement :** $K_2Cr_2O_7$ has orange colour due to polarisation. **Reason :** In dichromate ion all Cr—O bonds are identical.	(S)

2.

Column-I	Column-II
(A) Kipp's apparatus waste	(P) $(NH_4)_2SO_4 \cdot FeSO_4 \cdot 6H_2O$
(B) Green coloured compound	(Q) $Cu(OH)_2 \cdot CuCO_3$
(C) leave(s) brown residue on heating	(R) $FeSO_4 \cdot 7H_2O$
(D) leave(s) black residue on heating	(S) $CuCl_2 \cdot 2H_2O$

3.

Column-I	Column-II w x y z
(A) $\mathbf{w}MnO_4^-(aq) + xIO_3^-(aq) + H_2O(l) \longrightarrow yMnO_2(s) + zIO_4^-(aq) + 2OH^-(aq)$	(P) 1, 2, 1, 2
(B) $\mathbf{w}Cu(OH)_2(s) + xN_2H_4(aq) \longrightarrow \mathbf{y}\,Cu(s) + zH_2O(l) + N_2(g)$	(Q) 3, 4, 3, 1
(C) $CrO_4^{2-}(aq) + wFe(OH)_2(s) + xH_2O(l) \longrightarrow \mathbf{y}Fe(OH)_3(s) + zCr(OH)_4^-(aq) + OH^-(aq)$	(R) 2, 1, 2, 4
(D) $\mathbf{w}ClO_4^-(aq) + xH_2O_2(aq) \longrightarrow \mathbf{y}\,ClO_2^-(aq) + zH_2O(l) + 2O_2(g)$	(S) 2, 3, 2, 3
	(T) 2, 1, 1, 3

4.

Column-I	Column-II
(A) $Co^{2+}(aq)$	(P) Pink / light pink
(B) $Mn^{2+}(aq)$	(Q) Purple
(C) $V^{2+}(aq)$	(R) Outer orbital complex and magnetic moment $= \sqrt{15}$ BM.
(D) $Ti^{3+}(aq)$	(S) Inner orbital complex and magnetic moment $= \sqrt{3}$ BM.
	(T) Paramagnetic

5.

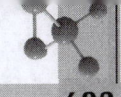

Column-I (Aqueous solution of salt)	Column-II (Reagents)
(A) $Fe_2(SO_4)_3$	(P) Formation of complex ion with excess $Na_2S_2O_3$
(B) $CuSO_4$	(Q) Formation of precipitate of basic carbonate with Na_2CO_3
(C) $Hg(NO_3)_2$	(R) Formation of precipitate with $(NH_4)_2S$ in non-redox reaction
(D) AgF	(S) Redox reaction with KI
	(T) Formation of precipitate with $BaCl_2$

6.

Column-I (Aqueous solution of following metal ions)	Column-II (Colour of aqueous solution)
(A) $Sc^{3+}(aq)$	(P) Light pink
(B) $Mn^{2+}(aq)$	(Q) Blue
(C) $Fe^{2+}(aq)$	(R) Green
(D) $Cu^{2+}(aq)$	(S) Colourless

ASSERTION-REASON TYPE QUESTIONS

These questions consists of two statements each, printed as assertion and reason, while answering these questions you are required to choose any one of the following responses.

(A) If both assertion and reason are true and the reason is a correct explanation of assertion

(B) If both assertion and reason are true but reason is not a correct explanation of assertion

(C) If assertion is true but the reason is false

(D) If assertion is false but the reason is true

1. Assertion : Melting point of Mn is more than that of Fe.

Reason : Mn has higher number of unpaired e^- than Fe in atomic state.

2. Assertion : $Cu^{+}_{(aq.)}$ is less stable than $Cu^{2+}_{(aq.)}$ but $Fe^{3+}_{(aq.)}$ is more stable than $Fe^{2+}_{(aq.)}$.

Reason : Half filled and completely filled subshells are more stable.

3. Assertion : Zn gives H_2 gas with dil. HCl and also with dil. H_2SO_4.

Reason : NO_3^- ion is reduced in preference to hydronium ion.

4. Assertion : $KMnO_4$ has different equivalent weights in acid, neutral or alkaline medium.

Reason : In different medium, change in oxidation number shown by manganese is altogether different.

5. Assertion : $Cu^{2+}_{(aq.)}$ is more stable than $Cu^{+}_{(aq.)}$.

Reason : Electrode potential is more important in determining stable oxidation state than electronic configuration.

6. Assertion : Concentrated aqueous solution of $CuCl_2$ is green in colour.

Reason : The solution contains two complex ions i.e. $[Cu(H_2O)_4]^{2+}$ and $[CuCl_4]^{2-}$ in equilibrium.

7. Assertion : $KMnO_4$ is purple in colour due to charge transfer.

Reason : There is no electron present in *d*-orbitals of manganese in MnO_4^-.

8. Assertion : CrO_3 reacts with HCl to form chromyl chloride gas.

Reason : Chromyl chloride (CrO_2Cl_2) has tetrahedral shape.

9. Assertion : Hg is the only metal which is liquid at 0°C.

Reason : It has very high I.P. and weak metallic bond.

10. Assertion : $CuSO_4 \cdot 5H_2O$ and $FeSO_4 \cdot 7H_2O$ are blue and green colour compounds respectively.

Reason : Both compounds have their specific colour due to phenomenon of polarisation of anion.

11. Assertion : $FeSO_4$ and $Fe_2(SO_4)_3$ undergo intramolecular redox reaction on thermal decomposition.

Reason : Both salts give brown solid of Fe_2O_3 after decomposition.

12. Assertion : $Zn(OH)_2$ is dissolved in both NH_4OH and NaOH solution.

Reason : Both NaOH and NH_4OH being basic can dissolve amphoteric $Zn(OH)_2$.

13. Assertion : Increasing order of covalent character among the given compounds is $HgCl_2 < CdCl_2 < ZnCl_2$.

Reason : Order of size of cations is $Zn^{2+} < Cd^{2+} < Hg^{2+}$.

14. Assertion : $AgNO_3$ reacts with KCN to form white ppt. of AgCN. This white ppt. disappears when excess KCN is added.

Reason : AgCN decomposes to form silver-carbide and evolve N_2 gas.

15. Assertion : Zero and negative oxidation state of *d*-block metal ion is possible in their complex compound.

Reason : Low oxidation state of metal ions are found when a complex compound has ligands capable of π-acceptor character in addition to the σ-bonding.

16. Assertion : Aquated copper (I) cation undergoes disproportionation as :

$$2Cu^{+}_{(aq.)} \rightarrow Cu^{2+}_{(aq.)} + Cu$$

Reason : Hydration energy of Cu^{2+} is higher than that of Cu^{+} which compensates second ionisation energy of Cu.

17. Assertion : Zinc, cadmium and mercury are not considered as transition metals.

Reason : A transition element is defined as the one which has incompletely filled *d*-orbitals in its ground state or in any one of its common oxidation state.

18. Assertion : In the first *d*-series (Sc to Zn), zinc has the lowest enthalpy of atomisation.

Reason : Zn does not have any unpaired electrons in its ground state.

19. Assertion : Cr(VI) ion in the form of dichromate in acidic medium is a strong oxidising agent, whereas MoO_3 and WO_3 are not.

Reason : Mo(VI) ion and W(VI) ion are found to be more stable than Cr(VI) ion.

20. Assertion : Zero and negative oxidation state of *d*-block metal ion are not possible in their complex compound.

Reason : Low oxidation state of metal ions are found when a complex compound has ligands capable of π-acceptor character in addition to the σ-bonding.

21. Assertion : Cr^{2+} and Mn^{3+} have better reducing and oxidising tendency respectively whenever both have d^4 configuration.

Reason : $Cr^{3+}(d^3)$ is more stable than $Cr^{2+}(d^4)$ configuration due to having a half-filled t_{2g} level, on the other hand $Mn^{2+}(d^5)$ is more stable than $Mn^{3+}(d^4)$.

22. Assertion : Copper (I) compounds are unstable in aqueous solution and undergo disproportionation.

$$2Cu^+(aq) \longrightarrow Cu^{2+}(aq) + Cu$$

Reason : The more stability of $Cu^{2+}(aq)$ rather than $Cu^+(aq)$ is due to the much more negative $\Delta H_{\text{Hydration}}$ of $Cu^{2+}(aq)$ than $Cu^+(aq)$ which compensates for the second ionisation enthalpy of Cu.

23. Assertion : The highest Mn fluoride is MnF_4 whereas the highest oxide is Mn_2O_7.

Reason : Ability of oxygen to form multiple bonds to metal ions, oxygen stabilise high oxidation state of metal ion than that of fluorine.

24. Assertion : Transition metals have tendency to form alloy.

Reason : They have almost similar radii and other similar characteristics.

SUBJECTIVE PROBLEMS

1. Addition of dilute H_2SO_4 into K_2MnO_4 is expressed chemically as :

$$MnO_4^{2-} + H^+(aq) \longrightarrow P(aq) + Q\downarrow + H_2O$$

If '*P*' is water soluble purple coloured anionic species and '*Q*' is water insoluble black oxide, then find out value of expression $\left|\frac{x}{y}\right|$.

Where, $x =$ Oxidation state of manganese in anionic species '*P*'

$y =$ Oxidation state of manganese in black oxide '*Q*'

2. Select the number of colourless species.

$Sc^{3+}(aq), Cr^{3+}(aq), CrO_4^{2-}(aq), Fe^{2+}(aq), Cu^{2+}(aq), CuF_2, Fe^{3+}(aq), Pb^{2+}(aq), PbS, Cd^{2+}(aq), CdS$

3. Consider reaction of dropwise addition of 2-3% H_2O_2 into acidified K_2CrO_4 solution in the presence of pyridine layer:

$$CrO_4^{2-}(aq) + H_2O_2(2-3\%) + H^+(aq) \xrightarrow{\text{Pyridine}} \underbrace{\text{'}P\text{'}}_{\substack{\text{Deep blue}\\ \text{layer}}} + H_2O$$

For pyridine solvated chromium compound '*P*', find out numerical value of expression $\left[\frac{x}{y}\right]$

where, x = Oxidation number of chromium in '*P*'

y = Number of chromium-oxygen single bond(s) in 'P'

4. Find out total number of reagents which can dissolve copper turning.

dil. HNO_3, conc. HNO_3, dil. H_2SO_4, conc. H_2SO_4, dil. HCl, conc. HCl, NaOH, H_3PO_4, H_2CO_3.

5. Calculate the magnetic moment of a high-spin octahedral complex that has six electrons in 3*d* -orbitals

6. How many π-bonds are present in ferrocene ?

7. The magnetic moment of a transition metal ion is found to be 3.87 Bohr Magneton (BM). The number of unpaired electrons present in it is :

Answers

Level-1

1. (a)	2. (a)	3. (c)	4. (c)	5. (b)	6. (a)	7. (a)	8. (b)	9. (c)	10. (d)
11. (a)	12. (c)	13. (a)	14. (b)	15. (a)	16. (b)	17. (b)	18. (a)	19. (c)	20. (d)
21. (b)	22. (a)	23. (a)	24. (b)	25. (d)	26. (b)	27. (b)	28. (a)	29. (c)	30. (b)
31. (a)	32. (b)	33. (b)	34. (a)	35. (d)	36. (b)	37. (b)	38. (c)	39. (b)	40. (c)
41. (b)	42. (d)	43. (d)	44. (b)	45. (d)	46. (c)	47. (c)	48. (a)	49. (c)	50. (a)
51. (c)	52. (d)	53. (d)	54. (b)	55. (b)	56. (d)	57. (c)	58. (b)	59. (d)	60. (c)
61. (c)	62. (b)	63. (b)	64. (a)	65. (a)	66. (b)	67. (d)	68. (d)	69. (b)	70. (a)
71. (c)	72. (c)	73. (b)	74. (b)	75. (a)					

Level-2

1. (a)	2. (d)	3. (c)	4. (b)	5. (c)	6. (a)	7. (a)	8. (b)	9. (b,d)	10. (c)
11. (c)	12. (b)	13. (b)	14. (c)	15. (b)	16. (d)	17. (b)	18. (d)	19. (c)	20. (b)
21. (a)	22. (b)	23. (a)	24. (c)	25. (a)	26. (c)	27. (b)	28. (c)	29. (a)	30. (a)
31. (a)	32. (a)	33. (b)	34. (d)	35. (c)	36. (a)	37. (a,d)	38. (c)	39. (d)	40. (b)
41. (b)	42. (c)	43. (b)	44. (d)	45. (a)	46. (b)	47. (b)	48. (d)	49. (a)	50. (b)
51. (c)	52. (c)	53. (d)	54. (c)	55. (a)	56. (b)	57. (d)	58. (d)	59. (a)	60. (b)
61. (a)	62. (d)	63. (d)	64. (b)	65. (c)	66. (c)	67. (b)	68. (a)	69. (a)	70. (c)
71. (c)	72. (c)	73. (d)	74. (a)	75. (c)	76. (b,d)	77. (b)	78. (b)	89. (b)	80. (d)
81. (a)	82. (c)	83. (d)	84. (d)	85. (b)	86. (b)	87. (c)	88. (a)	89. (c)	90. (c)
91. (b)	92. (d)								

Level-3

Passage–1	1. (d)	2. (d)		
Passage–2	1. (b)	2. (c)	3. (c)	
Passage–3	1. (c)	2. (d)	3. (a)	4. (b)
Passage–4	1. (d)	2. (b)	3. (b)	4. (d)
Passage–5	1. (b)	2. (d)	3. (a)	
Passage–6	1. (b)	2. (a)	3. (d)	

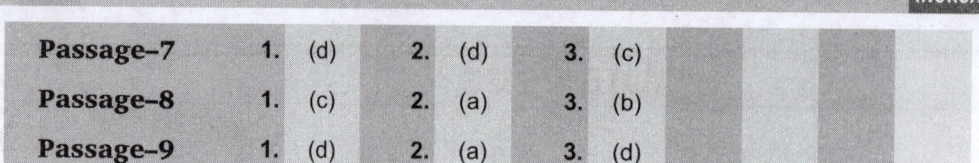

Passage–7	**1.**	(d)	**2.**	(d)	**3.**	(c)
Passage–8	**1.**	(c)	**2.**	(a)	**3.**	(b)
Passage–9	**1.**	(d)	**2.**	(a)	**3.**	(d)

One or More Answers is/are correct

1. (a,c) **2.** (a,b) **3.** (a,b,c) **4.** (c,d) **5.** (a,c,d) **6.** (a,b,d) **7.** (b,c) **8.** (a,b,c)
9. (a,b,d) **10.** (a,b,c,d) **11.** (a,b,c,d) **12.** (a,c,d) **13.** (a,c) **14.** (a,c) **15.** (a,b,c) **16.** (b,c,d)
17. (c,d) **18.** (c,d) **19.** (a,b,c,d) **20.** (a,b) **21.** (a,c) **22.** (a,b,c,d) **23.** (a,b,d) **24.** (b,c,d)
25. (a,c) **26.** (a,c) **27.** (a,b,c,d) **28.** (a,c,d) **29.** (a,b,c,d) **30.** (a,b,c)

Match the Column

1. A→ Q; B→ P; C→ R; D→ S
2. A→ R; B→ P,Q,R,S; C→ P,R; D→ Q, S
3. A→ S; B→ R; C→ Q; D→ P
4. A→ P, R, T; B→ P, T; C→ Q, T; D→ Q, S, T;
5. A→ P, S, T; B→ P,Q,R,S,T; C→ P,Q,R; D→ P, R, T;
6. A→ S; B→ P; C→ R; D→ Q;

Assertion-Reason Type Questions

1. (D) **2.** (B) **3.** (B) **4.** (A) **5.** (A) **6.** (A) **7.** (B) **8.** (B) **9.** (A)
10. (C) **11.** (D) **12.** (C) **13.** (D) **14.** (C) **15.** (A) **16.** (A) **17.** (A) **18.** (A)
19. (A) **20.** (D) **21.** (A) **22.** (A) **23.** (A) **24.** (A)

Subjective Problems

1. 01.75 **2.** 3 **3.** 1.50 **4.** 3
5. 4.9 ≈ 5 **6.** 6 **7.** 3

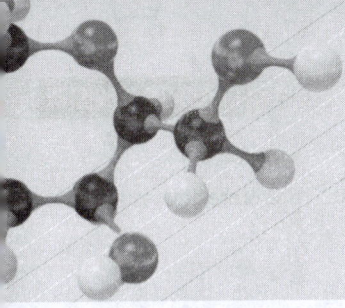

Hints and Solutions

Level 1

1. (a) $2CrO_4^{2-} + 2H^+ \longrightarrow Cr_2O_7^{2-} + H_2O$

$Cr_2O_7^{2-} + 2OH^- \longrightarrow 2CrO_4^{2-} + H_2O$

16. (b) $\underset{\text{Acid}}{Zn(OH)_2} + \underset{\text{Base}}{2OH^-} \longrightarrow \underset{\text{Salt}}{ZnO_2^{2-}} + \underset{\text{Water}}{2H_2O}$

$\underset{\text{Base}}{Zn(OH)_2} + \underset{\text{Acid}}{2H^+} \longrightarrow \underset{\text{Salt}}{Zn^{2+}} + \underset{\text{Water}}{2H_2O}$

17. (a) $2CrO_4^{2-} + 2H^+ \longrightarrow Cr_2O_7^{2-} + H_2O$

$Cr_2O_7^{2-} + 2\,OH^- \longrightarrow 2\,CrO_4^{2-} + H_2O$

21. (c) Among *d*-block elements

Max M.P. of first transition series = Cr

Min. M.P. of second transition series = Cd

26. (b) $MnO_4^- + I^- + H_2O \longrightarrow 2MnO_2 + IO_3^- + 2\,OH^-$

29. (b) Chloroplatinic acid is $H_2[PtCl_6]$, which is dibasic.

Level 2

1. (a) Wilkinson's catalyst is $[RhCl(PPh_3)_3]$, Red-violet in colour and has square planar structure. It is used for selective hydrogenation of organic molecules at room temperature and pressure.

$TiCl_4 + (C_2H_5)_3Al$ is Zeigler Natta catalyst.

$(C_2H_5)_4Pb$ is an anti-knocking agent.

cis-platin is used as an anti-cancer agent]

3. (c) $\underset{(M)}{Zn} \xrightarrow{\text{dil.}HNO_3} \underset{\substack{\text{Colourless}\\ \text{Solution}}}{Zn(ZO_3)_2} \xrightarrow[\text{NaOH}]{\text{Aq}} \underset{\text{Whit ppt.}}{Zn(OH)_2} \xrightarrow[\text{NaOH}]{\text{Excess}} \underset{\text{Soluble}}{Na_2[Zn(OH)_4]} \xrightarrow{H_2S} \underset{\text{Whiteppt.}}{ZnS}$

8. (b) $\underset{\text{Acid}}{Zn(OH)_2} + \underset{\text{Base}}{2OH^-} \longrightarrow \underset{\text{Salt}}{ZnO_2^{2-}} + \underset{\text{Water}}{2H_2O}$

$\underset{\text{Base}}{Zn(OH)_2} + \underset{\text{Acid}}{2H^+} \longrightarrow \underset{\text{Salt}}{Zn^{2+}} + \underset{\text{Water}}{2H_2O}$

17. (b) Interstitial compound Fe_3C (cementide) is formed.

47. (b) $K_3[Fe(CN)_6] + Cu^{2+}(aq) \longrightarrow \underset{\text{Green ppt.}}{Cu_3[Fe(CN)_6]_2}\downarrow$

48. (d) $Fe^{3+}(aq) \rightleftharpoons [Fe(OH)(H_2O)_5]^{2+} + H_3O^+$

due to higher $z_{eff.}$ value of Fe^{3+}, it forms stable complex ion with H_2O than Al^{3+}, therefore aqueous solution of $FeCl_3$ is more acidic due to higher $z_{eff.}$ value of Fe^{3+}.

50. (b) $Na_2[\overset{II}{Fe}(NO)(CN)_5] + Na_2S \longrightarrow Na_4[\overset{II}{Fe}(CN)_5(NOS)]$

51. (c) $\underset{(X)}{2MnO_2} + 2K_2CO_3 + \underset{(air)}{O_2} \xrightarrow{\Delta} \underset{\substack{green\\(Y)}}{2K_2MnO_4} + 2CO_2\uparrow$

$\underset{(Y)}{2K_2MnO_4} + Cl_2 \longrightarrow \underset{(Z)\ Pink}{2KMnO_4} + 2KCl$

56. (b) $FeS + H_2SO_4(conc.) \longrightarrow Fe_2(SO_4)_3 + SO_2(g)$

62. (d) $Cu^{2+} + KI \longrightarrow CuI\downarrow + I_2$

$Pb^{4+} + KI \longrightarrow PbI_2\downarrow + I_2$

$Fe^{3+} + KI \longrightarrow Fe^{2+} + I_2$ (No ppt.)

$Bi^{3+} + KI \longrightarrow BiI_3\downarrow$ (No redox)

65. (c) MnO_4^- is weak oxidising agent in basic medium than acidic medium.

72. (c) $K_3[\overset{III}{Fe}(CN)_6]$

$\xrightarrow{Cu^{2+}(aq)} \underset{(Green\ ppt.)}{Cu_3[Fe(CN)_6]_2\downarrow}$

$\xrightarrow{Fe^{2+}(aq)} \underset{(Turn\ Bull's\ blue\ ppt.)}{\overset{II}{Fe_3}[\overset{III}{Fe}(CN)_6]_2\downarrow}$

$\xrightarrow{Zn^{2+}(aq)}$ No ppt.

74. (a) $CuSO_{4(aq.)} \xrightarrow{H_2S} \underset{\substack{Black\ ppt.\\(M)}}{2CuS} \xrightarrow[Excess]{KCN} \underset{(N)}{[Cu(CN)_4]^{3-}} + \underset{(O)}{(CN)_2\uparrow}$

75. (c) $Cu(CN)_2$ and CuI_2 being unstable spontaneously decomposes into $CuCN\downarrow$ and $CuI\downarrow$ respectively at room temperature.

76. (d) Practically F^- ion being very weak R.A. has no reducing property.

77. (b) $NaCl_{(s)} + K_2Cr_2O_{7(s)} + H_2SO_4(few\ drops) \xrightarrow[reaction]{Non\text{-}redox} \underset{(orange\ red\ vapours)}{CrO_2Cl_2\uparrow} + HO$

$CrO_2Cl_2 + OH^-_{(aq.)} \rightarrow \underset{Yellow\ solution}{CrO^{2-}_{4(aq.)}} + Cl^- + 2H_2O$

78. (b) K_2MnO_4 does not undergo disproportionation in strong alkali medium, which is provided by conc. KOH solution.

79. (b) $Fe_2(SO_4)_3 + BaCl_2 \longrightarrow \underset{White\ ppt.}{BaSO_4\downarrow} + \underset{(P)\ Coloured\ solution}{FeCl_3}$

$\underset{\substack{(Yellow)\\(P)}}{FeCl_3} + KI \longrightarrow FeI_3 \xrightarrow{R.T.} \underset{Water\ soluble}{FeI_2} + \frac{1}{2}I_2$

80. (d) (a) $Cu^{2+} + 2Cl^- \longrightarrow CuCl_2$

$Fe^{3+} + Cl^- \longrightarrow FeCl_3$

(b) $Cu^{2+} + 2CN^- \longrightarrow CuCN + \frac{1}{2}(CN)_2$

$Fe^{3+} + 3CN^- \longrightarrow Fe(CN)_3 \downarrow$

(c) $Cu^{2+} + 2SCN^- \longrightarrow Cu(SCN) + \frac{1}{2}(SCN)_2$

$Fe^{3+} + 3SCN^- \longrightarrow Fe(SCN)_3$ (Blood red solution)

(d) $Cu^{2+} + S_2O_3^{2-} \longrightarrow Cu^+ + S_4O_6^{2-}$

$Fe^{3+} + S_2O_3^{2-} \longrightarrow Fe^{2+} + S_4O_6^{2-}$

81. (a) $KCl(s) + \text{conc. } H_2SO_4 + K_2Cr_2O_7(s) \longrightarrow CrO_2Cl_2$ reddish brown fumes (chromyl chloride test).

82. (c) AgCl is insoluble in dil. HNO_3, but soluble in NH_4OH, KCN, $Na_2S_2O_3$.

Ag_2S is soluble in dil. HNO_3 and KCN but insoluble in NH_4OH and $Na_2S_2O_3$.

83. (d) AgCl is predominantly covalent and does not give Cl^- ion easily, hence it gives –ve chromyl chloride test.

84. (d) Fe^{2+} does not undergoes redox reaction with dil. HCl.

85. (b) In acidic medium CrO_4^{2-} ion changes to $Cr_2O_7^{2-}$ ion having orange colour. But NH_3 produce alkali medium so colour does not changes.

86. (b) There is no reaction take place between $CuSO_4(aq)$ and $ZnCl_2(aq)$, solution will remain same and exhibit its original colour *i. e.*, blue due to $Cu^{2+}(aq)$.

87. (c) $2CrO_4^{2-}(aq) + 2H^+(aq) \longrightarrow Cr_2O_7^{2-}(aq) + H_2O$

$Cu(OH)_2$ and $CaCO_3$ dissolve in dilute HCl.

88. (a) In first series of *d*-block metals, enthalpy of atomization of zinc is lowest.

89. (c) $AgNO_3(aq) + CN^-(aq) \longrightarrow AgCN \downarrow + NO_3^- + NO_3^-(aq)$

90. (c) Sc exhibits only +3 oxidation state, hence its oxide is Sc_2O_3.

91. (b) $Sn^{2+}(aq) + Au^{3+}(aq) \longrightarrow Au + Sn^{4+}(aq)$

$Au(s) + Pb^{2+}(aq) \longrightarrow$ No reaction

$Fe^{3+}(aq) + 3I^-(aq) \longrightarrow FeI_2 + I_3^-$

$Sn^{2+}(aq) + Cr_2O_7^{2-}(aq) + H^+(aq) \longrightarrow Cr^{3+}(aq) + Sn^{4+}(aq)$

92. (d) $AuCl_3(aq) + SnCl_2 \longrightarrow Au + SnCl_4$

$Fe^{3+}(aq) + KI \longrightarrow FeI_2 + KI_3$

$Bi^{3+}(aq) + Sn^{2+}(aq) \longrightarrow Sn^{4+}(aq) + Bi \downarrow$

$Hg + SnCl_2 \longrightarrow$ No reaction

Level 3

Passage-1

1. (d) $2FeSO_4 \xrightarrow{\Delta} Fe_2O_3 + SO_2\uparrow + SO_3\uparrow$

$SnSO_4 \xrightarrow{\Delta} SnO_2 + SO_2\uparrow$

$H_2C_2O_4 \xrightarrow{\Delta} CO\uparrow + CO_2\uparrow + H_2O$

$2Na_2HPO_4 \xrightarrow{\Delta} Na_4P_2O_7 + H_2O$

2. (d) $Pb(NO_3)_2 \xrightarrow{\Delta} \underset{\substack{\text{Red in hot}\\ \text{(Litharge)}}}{PbO} + \underbrace{2NO_2\uparrow + \frac{1}{2}O_3}_{\substack{\text{Two different}\\ \text{Paramagnetic gases}}}$

$\Rightarrow \quad Hg(NO_3)_2 \xrightarrow{\Delta} Hg + 2NO_2\uparrow + O_2\uparrow$

$\Rightarrow \quad FeC_2O_4 \xrightarrow{\Delta} FeO + CO\uparrow + CO_2\uparrow$

$\Rightarrow \quad ZnSO_4 \xrightarrow{>800^\circ C} ZnO + SO_2\uparrow + \frac{1}{2}O_2\uparrow$

ONE OR MORE ANSWERS IS/ARE CORRECT

3. (a,b,c)

Ionization enthalpies of early actinoids are lower than those of early lanthanoids in respective groups.

13. (a,c) $\underset{\text{(Orange)}}{Cr_2O_7^{2-}} + 10H^+ + 4Na_2O_2 \longrightarrow$ 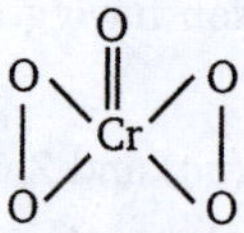 $+ 8Na^+ + 5H_2O$

(blue colour)

In the absence of ether or amyl alcohol, CrO_5 in acidic medium decomposes to Cr^{3+} with evolution of oxygen.

4 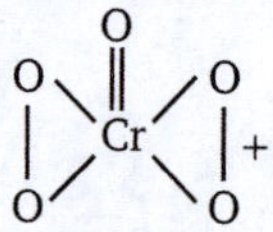 $+ 12H^+ \longrightarrow \underset{\text{(green)}}{4Cr^{3+}} + 7O_2 + 6H_2O$

(blue colour)

14. (a, c)

(a) $MnO_2 + 4HCl \longrightarrow MnCl_2 + Cl_2 + 2H_2O$

(b) Decomposition of acidic $KMnO_4$ is catalysed by sunlight

$$4MnO_4^- + 4H^+ \longrightarrow 4MnO_2 + 2H_2O + 3O_2$$

(c) $\underset{\text{green}}{3K_2MnO_4} + 2H_2O \longrightarrow \underset{\text{purple}}{2KMnO_4^-} + \underset{\text{dark brown}}{MnO_2\downarrow} + 4KOH$

(d) $KMnO_4$ also acts as an oxidizing agent in alkaline medium :

$$MnO_4^- + 2H_2O + 3e^- \longrightarrow MnO_2 + 4OH^-;\ E^\circ = +1.23\ \text{volt}$$

15. (a, b, c)

MnO_4^{2-}, Cl_2 and NO_2 undergo disproportionation, oxidation and reduction simultaneously take place in the alkaline medium.

$$Cl_2 + 2NaOH \longrightarrow NaCl + NaOCl + H_2O$$

$$2NO_2 + 2NaOH \longrightarrow NaNO_2 + NaNO_3 + H_2O$$

MnO_4^{2-} is stable in strong alkali solution and disproportionates into MnO_4^- and MnO_2 is less basic, Acidic and Neutral medium.

23. (a, b, d)

(a) $2CrSO_4(s) \xrightarrow[\text{Heating}]{\text{Normal}} Cr_2O_3 + SO_2(g) + SO_3(g)$

(b) $Fe^{3+}(aq) + 3CN^-(aq) \xrightarrow{\text{Room temp.}} Fe(CN)_3 \downarrow (\text{ppt.})$

(d) $Cu(OH)_2 \cdot CuCO_3 \xrightarrow[\text{Heating}]{\text{Normal}} 2CuO + CO_2 + H_2O$

24. (b, c, d)

(a) $Cu^{2+} + KCN \xrightarrow{aq.} CuCN \downarrow + \frac{1}{2}(CN)_2 \uparrow$

(b) $Ag^+ + KCN \xrightarrow{aq.} AgCN \downarrow$

(c) $Cd^{2+} + KCN \xrightarrow{aq.} Cd(CN)_2 \downarrow$

(d) $Pb^{2+} + KCN \xrightarrow{aq.} Pb(CN)_2 \downarrow$

25. (a, c) $K_2Cr_2O_7$ is oxidising agent only in acidic medium.

26. (a, c) Element with highest % in air $= N_2$

Element with highest % in earth crust $= O_2$

$(NH_4)_2Cr_2O_7 \xrightarrow{\Delta} N_2 + Cr_2O_3 + H_2O$

$K_2Cr_2O_7 \xrightarrow{\Delta} K_2CrO_4 + Cr_2O_3 + O_2$

$(NH_4)_2CO_3 \xrightarrow{\Delta} NH_3 + CO_2 + H_2O$

$K_2CO_3 \xrightarrow{\Delta} x$

$NH_4MnO_4 \xrightarrow{\Delta} N_2 + MnO_2 + H_2O$

$KMnO_4 \xrightarrow{\Delta} K_2MnO_4 + MnO_2 + O_2$

$(NH_4)_3PO_4 \xrightarrow{\Delta} NH_3 + H_3PO_4$

$K_3PO_4 \xrightarrow{\Delta} x$

27. (a, b, c, d)

$KMnO_4 \xrightarrow{\Delta} K_2MnO_4 + MnO_2 + O_2$

$K_2Cr_2O_7 \xrightarrow{\Delta} K_2CrO_4 + Cr_2O_3 + O_2$

K_2MnO_4 and $K_2CrO_4 \longrightarrow$ They are unstable in acidic medium

MnO_2 and $Cr_2O_3 \longrightarrow$ Amphoteric oxide

$O_2 \longrightarrow$ Colourless paramagnetic gas

MATCH THE COLUMN

5. $Fe_2(SO_4)_3$

$\xrightarrow[\text{Excess}]{Na_2S_2O_3} [Fe(S_2O_3)_2]^-$

$\xrightarrow{Na_2CO_3} Fe(OH)_3 \downarrow$

$\xrightarrow{(NH_4)_2S} FeS \downarrow$

$\xrightarrow{\text{KI (aq)}} Fe^{2+}(aq) + I_3^-$

$\xrightarrow{BaCl_2} BaSO_4 \downarrow$

$CuSO_4 \xrightarrow[\text{Excess}]{Na_2S_2O_3} Na_4[Cu_6(S_2O_3)_5]$

$CuSO_4 \xrightarrow{Na_2CO_3} Cu(OH)_2 \cdot CuCO_3$

$CuSO_4 \xrightarrow{(NH_4)_2S} CuS$

$CuSO_4 \xrightarrow{\text{KI (aq)}} CuI + I_2$

$CuSO_4 \xrightarrow{BaCl_2} BaSO_4$

$Hg(NO_3)_2 \xrightarrow[\text{Excess}]{Na_2S_2O_3} [Hg(S_2O_3)_2]^{2-}$

$Hg(NO_3)_2 \xrightarrow{Na_2CO_3} 3HgO \cdot HgCO_3$

$Hg(NO_3)_2 \xrightarrow{(NH_4)_2S} HgS$

$Hg(NO_3)_2 \xrightarrow{\text{KI (aq)}} \underset{\text{Red}}{HgI_2} \downarrow \xrightarrow[\text{KI}]{\text{Excess}} [HgI_4]^{2-}$

$Hg(NO_3)_2 \xrightarrow{BaCl_2} \text{No ppt.}$

$AgF \xrightarrow[\text{Excess}]{Na_2S_2O_3} [Ag(S_2O_3)_2]^{3-}$

$AgF \xrightarrow{Na_2CO_3} Ag_2CO_3 \downarrow$

$AgF \xrightarrow{(NH_4)_2S} Ag_2S \downarrow$

$AgF \xrightarrow{\text{KI (aq)}} AgI \downarrow$

$AgF \xrightarrow{BaCl_2} AgCl \downarrow$

ASSERTION-REASON TYPE QUESTIONS

3. (B) $Zn + \underset{\text{dil.}}{2HCl} \longrightarrow ZnCl_2 + H_2 \uparrow$

$Zn + \underset{\text{dil.}}{H_2SO_4} \longrightarrow ZnSO_4 + H_2 \uparrow$

$4Zn + \underset{\text{(dil.)}}{10HNO_3} \longrightarrow 4Zn(NO_3)_2 + N_2O + 5H_2O$

4. (A) $\underset{\text{(pink)}}{\overset{+7}{KMnO_4}} \xrightarrow{\text{(R.A.)}}$

- $\xrightarrow{\text{Acidic medium}} Mn^{2+}$ (colourless)
- $\xrightarrow{\text{Alakaline medium}} MnO_4^{2-}$ (green)
- $\xrightarrow{\text{Neutral medium}} MnO_2$ (brown)

15. (A) In case of π-acceptor ligands (like CO, NO) zero and negative oxidation state of *d*-block metal ion is possible due to phenomenon of Synergic bonding.

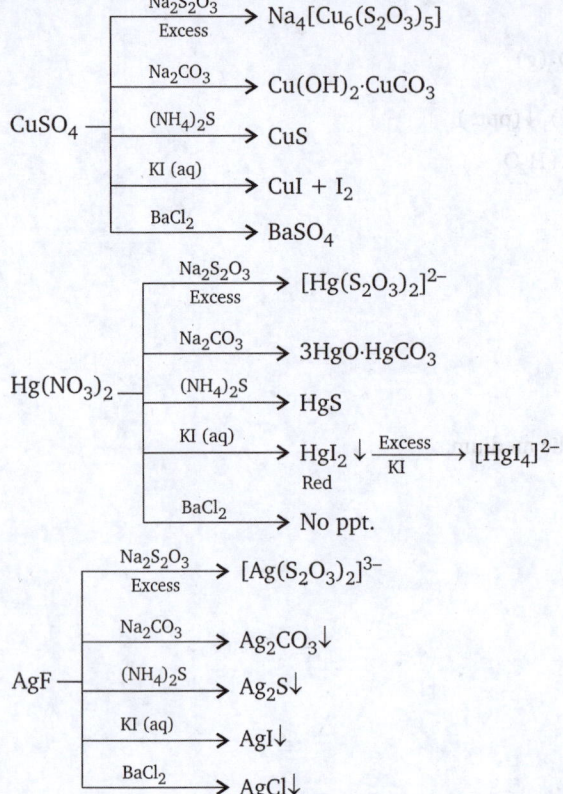

SUBJECTIVE PROBLEMS

1. $MnO_4^{2-} + H^+(aq) \longrightarrow MnO_4^-(aq) + MnO_2\downarrow + H_2O$
2. $Sc^{3+}, Pb^{2+}, Cd^{2+}$ (aq. solution are colourless)
3. $CrO_4^{2-}(aq) + H_2O_2(2-3\%) + H^+(aq) \longrightarrow$ 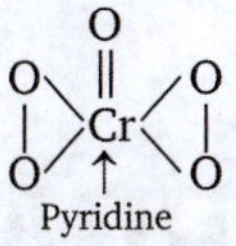 $+ H_2O$

   $x = 6,\ y = 4$

4. Reactivity of Cu is less than H_2. So it dissolves only in dil. HNO_3, con. HNO_3, con. H_2SO_4 (oxidising acids).
7. $\mu_{eff} = 3.87\ \text{B.M.} = \sqrt{n(n+2)}$

   Hence value of *n i.e.*, no. of unpaired electrons = 3

10

QUALITATIVE INORGANIC ANALYSIS (SALT ANALYSIS)

Level 1

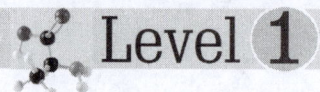

1. $Fe(OH)_3$ can be separated from $Al(OH)_3$ by addition of :

(a) $BaCl_2$ (b) Dil. HCl (c) NaOH solution (d) NH_4Cl & NH_4OH

2. Cations present in slightly acidic solution are Al^{3+}, Zn^{2+} and Cu^{2+}. The reagent which when added in excess to this solution would identity and separate Cu^{2+} in one step is :

(a) HCl acid (b) NH_3 solution (c) NaOH solution (d) Na_2CO_3 solution

3. When a KI solution is added to a metal nitrate, a black precipitate is produced which dissolves in an excess of KI to give an orange solution. The metal ion is:

(a) Hg^{2+} (b) Bi^{3+} (c) Cu^{2+} (d) Pb^{2+}

4. Which is not easily precipitated from aqueous solution?

(a) Cl^- (b) SO_4^{2-} (c) NO_3^- (d) CO_3^{2-}

5. Soda extract is useful when given mixture has any insoluble salt, it is prepared by:

(a) fusing soda and mixture and then extracting with water

(b) dissolving $NaHCO_3$ and mixture in dil. HCl

(c) boiling Na_2CO_3 and mixture in dil. HCl

(d) boiling Na_2CO_3 and mixture in distilled water

6. An aqueous solution of a substance, on treatment with dilute HCl, gives a white precipitate soluble in hot water. When H_2S is passed through the hot acidic solution, a black precipitate is formed. The substance is:

(a) Hg_2^{2+} salt (b) Cu^{2+} salt (c) Ag^+ salt (d) Pb^{2+} salt

7.

$$CrCl_3 \xrightarrow[NH_4OH]{NH_4Cl} (A) \xrightarrow[H_2O]{Na_2O_2} (B) \xrightarrow[\text{acetate}]{\text{Lead}} (C)$$

In this reaction sequence, the compound (*C*) is:

(a) Na_2CrO_4 (b) $Na_2Cr_2O_7$

(c) $Cr(OH)_3$ (d) $PbCrO_4$

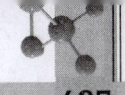

8. Identify the correct order of solubility of Na_2S, CuS and ZnS:
(a) $CuS > ZnS > Na_2S$ (b) $ZnS > Na_2S > CuS$
(c) $Na_2S > CuS > ZnS$ (d) $Na_2S > ZnS > CuS$

9. $2Cu^{2+} + 5I^- \longrightarrow 2CuI\downarrow + [X]$
$[X] + 2S_2O_3^{2-} \longrightarrow 3[Y] + S_4O_6^{2-}$; X and Y are:
(a) I_3^- and I^- (b) I_2 and I_3^- (c) I_2 and I^- (d) I_3^- and I_2

10. In Nessler's reagent, the ion present is:
(a) HgI^{2-} (b) HgI_4^{2-} (c) Hg^+ (d) Hg^2

11. A reddish pink substance on heating gives off a vapour which condenses on the sides of the test tube and the substance turns blue. It on cooling water is added to the residue it turns to its original colour. The substance is:
(a) Iodine crystals (b) Copper sulphate crystals
(c) Cobalt chloride crystals (d) Zinc oxide

12. Oxalate + MnO_2 + Dil. $H_2SO_4 \longrightarrow$ Gas
The gas evolved is:
(a) CO_2 (b) CO (c) SO_2 (d) O_2

13. Which of the following reagents can be used to identify bromide and iodide salt in the presence of organic layer?
(a) Chlorine water (b) Silver nitrate solution
(c) Starch solution (d) Dilute sulphuric acid

14. To avoid the precipitation of hydroxides of Ni^{2+}, Co^{2+}, Zn^{2+} and Mn^{2+} along with those of Fe^{3+}, Al^{3+} and Cr^{3+} the third group solution should be:
(a) Heated with a few drops of conc. HNO_3 (b) Treated with excess of NH_4Cl
(c) Concentrated (d) None of these

15. Which set gives yellow ppt.?
(a) KO_3, Sb_2S_3, CdS (b) Sb_2S_3, CdS, $PbCrO_4$
(c) $PbCrO_4, As_2S_3, SnS_2$ (d) $SnS_2, As_2S_3, PbCrO_4$, PbO

16. Which of the following reagents can separate a mixture of AgCl and AgI?
(a) KCN (b) $Na_2S_2O_3$ (c) HNO_3 (d) NH_3

17. Black ppt. (*A*) dissolve in HNO_3 gives (*B*) which gives white ppt. (*C*) with NH_4OH. (*C*) on reaction with HCl gives solution (*D*) gives white turbidity on addition of water. What is turbidity?
(a) $Ca(OH)_2$ (b) $Bi(OH)_3$ (c) BiOCl (d) $Bi(NO_3)_3$

18. Which nitrate on decomposition will give metal?
(a) $Hg_2(NO_3)_2$ (b) $NaNO_3$ (c) KNO_3 (d) $AgNO_3$

19. Which of the following compounds does not exist?
(a) CrO_2Br_2 (b) CrO_2Cl_2 (c) $POCl_3$ (d) BiOCl

20. Which one among the following pairs of ions cannot be separated by H_2S in dilute HCl?
(a) Bi^{3+}, Sn^{2+} (b) Al^{3+}, Hg^{2+} (c) Zn^{2+}, Cu^{2+} (d) Ni^{2+}, Cu^{2+}

21. Salt (*A*) gives brick red fumes (*B*) with conc. H_2SO_4 and $K_2Cr_2O_7$ which gives yellow solution (*C*) with NaOH and it gives yellow ppt. (*D*) with acetic acid and lead acetate. What is (*C*)?
(a) Na_2CrO_4 (b) CrO_2Cl_2 (c) $PbCrO_4$ (d) NaCl

22. When a nitrate is warmed with zinc powder and an NaOH solution, a gas is evolved. Which of the following reagents will be turned brown by the gas?
(a) Sodium nitroprusside (b) Sodium cobaltinitrite
(c) Nessler's reagent (d) Barium chloride

23. To avoid the precipitation of hydroxides of Ni^{2+}, Co^{2+}, Zn^{2+} and Mn^{2+} along with those of Fe^{3+}, Al^{3+} and Cr^{3+} the third group solution should be:
(a) Heated with a few drops of conc. HNO_3 (b) Treated with excess of NH_4Cl
(c) H_2S gas is passed into solution (d) None of these

24. Brown ppt. (*A*) dissolve in HNO_3 gives (*B*) which gives white ppt. (*C*) with NH_4OH. (*C*) on reaction with HCl gives solution (*D*) which gives white turbidity on addition of water. What is (*D*)?
(a) $BiCl_3$ (b) $Bi(OH)_3$ (c) BiOCl (d) $Bi(NO_3)_3$

25. $FeSO_4$ is used in the brown ring test for a nitrate. What is the oxidation state of Fe in the compound responsible for the brown colour of the ring?
(a) 0 (b) 1 (c) +2 (d) +3

26. On adding KI solution in excess to a solution of $CuSO_4$ we get a precipitate '*P*' and another liquor '*M*'. Select the correct pairs:
(a) *P* is CuI and *M* is I_2 solution (b) *P* is CuI_2 and *M* is I_2 solution
(c) *P* is CuI and *M* is KI_3 solution (d) *P* is CuI_2 and *M* is KI_3 solution

27. On heating a mixture of NaBr and conc. H_2SO_4 we obtain:
(a) HOBr (b) HBr (c) Br_2 (d) $HBrO_3$

28. Which of the following ions is responsible for the brown colour in the ring test for a nitrate?
(a) $[Fe(H_2O)_5NO]^{2+}$ (b) $[Fe(CN)_5NO]^{2-}$ (c) $[Fe(NO_2)_6]^{4-}$ (d) $[Fe(H_2O)_5NO_2]^+$

29. There is mixture of Cu(II) chloride and Fe(II) sulphate. The best way to separate the metal ions from this mixture in qualitative analysis is:
(a) hydrogen sulphide in acidic medium, where only Cu(II) sulphide will be precipitated
(b) ammonium hydroxide buffer, where only Fe(II) hydroxide will be precipitated
(c) hydrogen sulphide in acidic medium, where only Fe(II) sulphide will be precipitated
(d) ammonium hydroxide buffer, where only Cu(II) hydroxide will be precipitated

30. Which of the following reagents can be used to distinguish between a sulphite and a sulphate in solution?
(a) $FeSO_4$ (b) $Na_2[Fe(CN)_5NO]$
(c) $BaCl_2$ + dil.HCl (d) $Na_3[Co(NO_2)_6]$

31. A doctor by mistake administers a $Ba(NO_3)_2$ solution to a patient for radiography investigations. Which of the following should be given as the best to prevent the absorption of soluble barium?
(a) NaCl (b) Na_2SO_4 (c) Na_2CO_3 (d) NH_4Cl

32. A colourless water soluble solid '*X*' on heating gives equimolar quantities of *Y* and *Z*. *Y* gives dense white fumes HCl and *Z* does so with NH_3. *Y* gives brown precipitate with Nessler's reagent and *Z* gives white precipitate with nitrates of Ag^+, Pb^{2+} and Hg^+. '*X*' is:
(a) NH_4Cl (b) NH_4NO_3 (c) NH_4NO_2 (d) $FeSO_4$

33. The colour of the iodine solution is discharged by shaking with:
(a) sodium sulphate (b) hydrogen sulphide
(c) aqueous sulphur dioxide (d) sodium bromide

34. Three separate samples of a solution of a single salt gave these results. One formed a white precipitate with excess ammonia solution, one formed a white precipitate with dil. NaCl solution and one formed a black precipitate with H_2S. The salt could be:
(a) $AgNO_3$ (b) $Pb(NO_3)_2$ (c) $Hg(NO_3)_2$ (d) $MnSO_4$

35. In an alkaline solution, sodium nitroprusside gives a violet colour with:
(a) S^{2-} (b) SO_3^{2-} (c) SO_4^{2-} (d) NO_2^-

36. A pale yellow precipitate and a gas with pungent odour are formed on warming dilute hydrochloric acid with an aqueous solution containing:
(a) sulphate ion (b) sulphide ion
(c) thiosulphate ion (d) sulphite ion

37. $AgNO_3 \xrightarrow{\Delta} (W) + (X) + O_2$
$(X) + H_2O \longrightarrow HNO_2 + HNO_3$
$(W) + HNO_3 \longrightarrow Y + NO + H_2O$
$(Y) + Na_2S_2O_3 \text{ (excess)} \longrightarrow (Z) + NaNO_3$
Identify (W) to (Z):
(a) $W = Ag$, $X = N_2O$, $Y = AgNO_3$, $Z = Na_2[Ag(S_2O_3)_2]$
(b) $W = Ag_2O$, $X = NO$, $Y = AgNO_3$, $Z = Na_3[Ag(S_2O_3)_2]$
(c) $W = Ag$, $X = NO_2$, $Y = AgNO_3$, $Z = Na_3[Ag(S_2O_3)_2]$
(d) $W = Ag_2O$, $X = N_2$, $Y = AgNO_3$, $Z = Na[Ag(S_2O_3)_2]$

38. Consider the following sequence of tests,
$M^{n+} + HCl \longrightarrow \text{white precipitate} \xrightarrow{\Delta} \text{water soluble}$
The metal ion (M^{n+}) would be:
(a) Hg^{2+} (b) Ag^+ (c) Pb^{2+} (d) Sn^{2+}

39. The brown ring test for NO_3^- is due to the formation of the complex ion with formula:
(a) $[Fe(H_2O)_6]^{2+}$ (b) $Fe[NO(CN)_5]^{2-}$
(c) $[Fe(H_2O)_5NO]^{2+}$ (d) $[Fe(H_2O)(NO)_5]^{2+}$

40. Which of the following compounds does magnesium precipitate when you test for it?
(a) $MgCO_3 \cdot MgO$ (b) $MgCO_3$ (c) $Mg(OH)_2$ (d) $MgNH_4PO_4 \cdot 6H_2O$

41. $MgCO_3$ is not precipitated with the carbonates of Vth group radicals in presence of NH_4Cl and NH_4OH because:
(a) $MgCO_3$ is soluble in NH_4OH
(b) $MgCO_3$ is not precipitated in presence of NH_4Cl
(c) $MgCO_3$ is soluble in water
(d) $MgCO_3$ is soluble in $(NH_4)_2CO_3$

42. Which of the following salt gives green colour mass in cobalt nitrate charcoal cavity test?
(a) Zn salts (b) Al salts (c) Alums (d) Copper salts

43. Yellow coloured compound is:
(a) NH_4CNS (b) $PbCrO_4$ (c) NaOH (d) $K_4[Fe(CN)_6]$

44. Which of the following tests can you identify K^+ in a salt?
(a) Flame test (violet) and precipitation (yellow) with sodium cobaltinitrite
(b) Flame test (violet) and precipitation (violet) with sodium nitroprusside
(c) Flame test (crimson) and precipitation (yellow) with sodium cobaltinitrite
(d) Flame test (golden yellow) and precipitation (violet) with sodium nitroprusside

45. A chloride salt on addition of alkali solution gives gas *B* which gives brown ppt. with Nessler's reagent. What is *A, B* and *C*?
(a) NH_4Cl, NH_3 and $HgO{\cdot}Hg(NH_2)(NO_3)$
(b) NH_4Cl, NH_3 and $Hg(NH_2)Cl$
(c) NH_4Cl, NH_3 and $HgO{\cdot}Hg(NH_2)Cl$
(d) NH_4Cl, NH_3 and $HgO{\cdot}Hg(NH_2)I$

46. An inorganic salt is strongly heated. The residue is yellow when hot and white when cold. The salt contains:
(a) Pb^{2+} (b) Zn^{2+} (c) Hg^{2+} (d) NH_4^+

47. Which of the following sulphides is white ?
(a) CdS (b) PbS (c) ZnS (d) SnS

48. The gas evolved in which of the following reactions forms the iodide of Millon's base on being passed through a solution of $[HgI_4]^{2-}$ in KOH?
(a) $CaSO_4$ treated with dilute HCl
(b) NH_4Cl boiled with NaOH
(c) ZnS treated with dilute H_2SO_4
(d) $MgCO_3$ heated alone

49. A white, sublimable inorganic substance gives a brown precipitate on treatment with Nessler's reagent and a white precipitate (soluble in NH_3) with an $AgNO_3$ solution. The substance is:
(a) Hg_2Cl_2 (b) $HgCl_2$ (c) As_2O_3 (d) NH_4Cl

50. A white sublimable substance, that turns black on treatment with an NH_3 solution can be:
(a) Hg_2Cl_2 (b) $HgCl_2$ (c) As_2O_3 (d) NH_4Cl

51. Rinmann's green is:
(a) $[Ni(NH_3)_6]SO_4$ (b) $FeSO_4{\cdot}7H_2O$ (c) $CoZnO_2$ (d) $Fe(BO_2)_2$

52. A white crystalline salt imparts a violet colour to a Bunsen flame, and with hot concentrated H_2SO_4, forms a pungent gas. On treatment with an $AgNO_3$ solution, this gas forms a white precipitate readily soluble in NH_3. The white crystalline salt may be:
(a) Na_2SO_4 (b) KCl (c) $CaCl_2$ (d) $SrCl_2$

53. A white solid gives a green residue on being subjected to the cobalt nitrate test. On being warmed with concentrated H_2SO_4, the solid gives a brown gas, which evolves vigorously on the addition of Cu turnings. The solid may be:
(a) $Zn(NO_3)_2$ (b) $Al(NO_3)_2$ (c) $ZnBr_2$ (d) $Mg(NO_3)_2$

54. Which of the following is blue?
(a) $Co[Hg(SCN)_4]$ (b) $Ni(dmg)_2$ (c) $Cu_2[Fe(CN)_6]$ (d) $Fe(SCN)_3$

55. Which of the following pairs of cations cannot be separated by using an NH_3 solution ?
(a) Pb^{2+}, Zn^{2+} (b) Pb^{2+}, Cu^{2+} (c) Zn^{2+}, Cu^{2+} (d) Al^{3+}, Ag^+

56. Which of the following pairs of cations can be separated by adding NH_4Cl and NH_4OH to the mixture?
(a) Fe^{3+}, Al^{3+} (b) Cr^{3+}, Ni^{2+} (c) Al^{3+}, Cr^{3+} (d) Fe^{3+}, Cr^{3+}

57. Which of the following pairs of cations cannot be separated by adding NH_4Cl and NH_4OH to the mixture and then passing H_2S through it?
(a) Co^{2+}, Ca^{2+} (b) Ni^{2+}, Sr^{2+} (c) Co^{2+}, Ni^{2+} (d) Zn^{2+}, Ba^{2+}

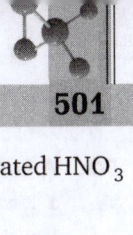

58. Before adding the reagents of group III, the solution is heated with some concentrated HNO_3 in order to:
(a) oxidise Fe^{2+} to Fe^{3+}
(b) oxidise Cr^{3+} to $Cr_2O_7^{2-}$
(c) lower than pH
(d) increase the NO_3^-

59. Which of the following pairs of sulphides are insoluble in dilute HCl?
(a) CoS and NiS
(b) CoS and MnS
(c) NiS and MnS
(d) NiS and ZnS

60. If a solution containing Al^{3+}, Ni^{2+} and Mg^{2+} is first treated with NH_4Cl and then with NH_4OH, which of the following will precipitate?
(a) $Al(OH)_3$
(b) Ni(OH)
(c) $Mg(OH)_2$
(d) $Al(OH)_3$, $Ni(OH)_3$ and $Mg(OH)_2$

61. Which of the following leaves a black residue on the addition of NH_3?
(a) AgCl
(b) $PbCl_2$
(c) Hg_2Cl_2
(d) $HgCl_2$

62. Which of the following is not soluble in hot and conc. HNO_3?
(a) PbS
(b) NiS
(c) CuS
(d) HgS

63. Which of the following cations will form an insoluble red-brown compound with $[Fe(CN)_6]^{4-}$?
(a) Hg^{2+}
(b) Pb^{2+}
(c) Cu^{2+}
(d) Cd^{2+}

64. Which of the following, on treatment with KCN, will give cyanogen gas?
(a) $[Ag(NH_3)_2]^+$
(b) $[Cu(NH_3)_4]^{2+}$
(c) $[Cd(NH_3)_4]^{2+}$
(d) $[Zn(NH_3)_4]^{2+}$

65. Which of the following is insoluble in yellow ammonium polysulphide?
(a) CuS
(b) As_2S_3
(c) Sb_2S_3
(d) SnS

66. Which of the following is formed when As_2S_3 is warmed with NH_4OH and H_2O_2?
(a) $As(OH)_3$
(b) AsO_4^{3-}
(c) AsO_3^{3-}
(d) $[As(NH_3)_6]^{5+}$

67. The role of NH_4Cl in the precipitation of the hydroxides of group III cations is to:
(a) increase the Cl^-
(b) facilitate the dissociation of NH_4OH
(c) suppress the dissociation of NH_4OH by the common ion effect
(d) render the solution weakly acidic

68. Which of the following pairs of cations can be separated by using on adding NaOH solution?
(a) Cu^{2+}, Zn^{2+}
(b) Pb^{2+}, Al^{3+}
(c) Sn^{2+}, Pb^{2+}
(d) Zn^{2+}, Pb^{2+}

69. On heating, a salt gives a gas which turns lime water milky and an acidified dichromate solution green. The salt may be:
(a) carbonate
(b) sulphide
(c) sulphate
(d) sulphite

70. Reaction of $Zn(OH)_2$ with NaOH produces:
(a) Na_2ZnO_2
(b) ZnO
(c) Na_2O
(d) None of these

71. In group separation, before precipitating out group III metal ions as hydroxides, it is necessary to boil then solution of the salt mixture with a few drops of concentrated HNO_3 is treated. This is done to convert:
(a) Co^{2+} to Co^{3+}
(b) Fe^{2+} to Fe^{3+}
(c) Mn^{2+} to MnO_4^-
(d) Cr^{3+} to CrO_4^{2-}

72. A compound '*X*' on heating gives a colourless gas. The residue is dissolved in water to obtain '*Y*'. Excess CO_2 is passed through aqueous solution of '*Y*' when '*Z*' is formed. '*Z*' on gentle heating gives back '*X*'. The compound '*X*' is:

(a) $NaHCO_3$ (b) Na_2CO_3
(c) $Ca(HCO_3)_2$ (d) $CaCO_3$

73. An aqueous solution of a substance gives a white precipitate on treatment with dil. HCl which dissolves on heating, When H_2S is passed through the hot acidic solution, black precipitate is obtained. The substance is:

(a) Hg_2^{2+} salt (b) Hg^{2+} salt (c) Ag^+ salt (d) Pb^{2+} salt

74. A solid mixture of AgCl and $K_2Cr_2O_7$ is heated with conc. H_2SO_4 and produces:

(a) greenish yellow gas (b) colourless gas
(c) red coloured gas (d) no gas

75. Which of the following has the highest value of K_p ?

(a) $BeCO_3$ (b) $MgCO_3$ (c) $CaCO_3$ (d) $BaCO_3$

76. When copper sulphate solution is treated with potassium iodide a white precipitate is formed. The white ppt. is due to formation of:

(a) $Na_2S_4O_6$ (b) CuI_2 (c) CuI (d) NaI

77. The ferrous ion in a given sample is detected by the formation of a white precipitate on the addition of a potassium ferrocyanide solution to it. The precipitate has the constitutional formula.

(a) $K_2Fe^{II}[Fe^{II}(CN)_6]$ (b) $K_2Fe^{III}[Fe(CN)_6]$
(c) $KFe^{III}[Fe^{II}(CN)_6]$ (d) $KFe^{II}[Fe^{III}(CN)_6]$

78. Which one is correct group reagent for group cations?

(a) Mn^{2+} Co^{2+} Zn^{2+} Ni^{2+}; $HCl + H_2S$
(b) Mn^{2+} Co^{2+} Zn^{2+} Ni^{2+}; dil. HCl
(c) Mn^{2+} Co^{2+} Zn^{2+} Ni^{2+}; $NH_4Cl + NH_4OH$
(d) Mn^{2+} Co^{2+} Zn^{2+} Ni^{2+}; $NH_4Cl + NH_4OH + H_2S$

79. Cobalt salt + $KNO_2 + CH_3COOH \longrightarrow$ yellow ppt. The yellow precipitate is:

(a) Potassium cobaltonitrate (b) Potassium cobaltinitrite
(c) Cobalt nitrite (d) Cobalt nitrate

80. Sulphide ions react with $Na_2[Fe(NO)(CN)_5]$ to form a purple coloured compound $Na_4[Fe(CN)_5(NOS)]$. In the reaction, the oxidation state of iron:

(a) Changes from +2 to +3 (b) Changes from +3 to +2
(c) Changes from +2 to +4 (d) Does not change

81. White crystal (*A*) on treatment with $AgNO_3$ gives white crystalline precipitate. (*A*) discharge the colour of $KMnO_4$ solution but no gas is evolved. Probable radical present in (*A*) is:

(a) Cl^- (b) Br^- (c) NO_2^- (d) CO_3^{2-}

82. Iodate ions (IO_3^-) can be reduced to iodine by iodide ions. The half equation which represent the redox reaction are :

$$IO_3^-(aq.) + 6H^+(aq.) + 5e \longrightarrow \frac{1}{2}I_2(s) + 3H_2O(l) \quad \ldots(i)$$

$$I^-(aq.) \longrightarrow \frac{1}{2}I_2(s) + e^- \quad \ldots(ii)$$

How many moles of iodine are produced for every mole of iodate ions consumed in the reaction?

(a) 0.5 (b) 1 (c) 2.5 (d) 3

83. $Cl_2 + OH^- \longrightarrow Cl^- + ClO_3^-$. What is the coefficient for OH^- when this equation is balanced with the smallest integer coefficients?

(a) 2 (b) 3 (c) 4 (d) 6

84. A solution of metal hydroxide (MOH) with copper sulphate and mixed tartarate of metal M with another metal M_1 of the same group, is used in the detection of —CHO group. Metal M and M_1 are respectively:

(a) K, Na (b) K, Rb (c) Na, Li (d) Rb, Na

85. (i) $A + Na_2CO_3 \longrightarrow B + C$, (ii) $A \xrightarrow{CO_2}$ (Milky) C

The chemical formula of A and B are respectively:

(a) NaOH and $Ca(OH)_2$ (b) $Ca(OH)_2$ and NaOH

(c) NaOH and CaO (d) CaO and $Ca(OH)_2$

86. On passing H_2S gas into first group filtrate sometimes yellow turbidity appears even in the absence of II group radicals, this is because of :

(a) sulphur is present in the mixture as impurity

(b) (IV) group radicals are precipitated as sulphides

(c) the oxidation of H_2S gas by some acid radicals

(d) III group radicals are precipitated as hydroxides

87. Incorrect order of solubility product (K_{sp}) of given precipitated compound is :

(a) $AgCl < PbCl_2$ (b) $Al(OH)_3 < Zn(OH)_2$

(c) $BaCO_3 < MgCO_3$ (d) $MnS < Ag_2S$

88. On adding KI to a metal salt solution, no precipitate was observed but the salt solution gives yellow precipitate with K_2CrO_4 in the presence of CH_3COOH. Then the salt is :

(a) $Sr(NO_3)_2$ (b) $Pb(CH_3COO)_2$ (c) $AgNO_3$ (d) $BaCl_2$

89. Which of the following precipitate is soluble in excess of NH_3 solution ?

(a) $Pb(OH)_2$ (b) $Fe(OH)_2$ (c) $Ni(OH)_2$ (d) Ag_2S

90. When a black metal sulphide reacts with dil. HCl, a gas liberates, which of the following pair of cation can be separated by the liberated gas ?

(a) Zn^{2+}, Cd^{2+} (b) Hg^{2+}, Ag^+ (c) Cu^{2+}, Pb^{2+} (d) Mn^{2+}, Ni^{2+}

91. Which of the following mixtures can be separated by using excess NH_3 solution?

(a) $Bi^{3+}(aq.)$ and $Al^{3+}(aq.)$ (b) $Al^{3+}(aq.)$ and $Zn^{2+}(aq.)$

(c) $Hg^{2+}(aq.)$ and $Pb^{2+}(aq.)$ (d) $Cu^{2+}(aq.)$ and $Cd^{2+}(aq.)$

92. Which of the following salt on heating with concentrated H_2SO_4, coloured vapours do not evolve ?

(a) NaBr (b) $NaNO_3$ (c) CaF_2 (d) KI

Level 2

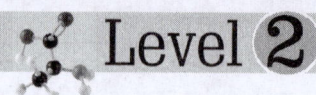

1. When a reagent (X) reacts with Fe^{3+} salt solution turns red due to the formation of a compound (Y). This reagent causes no change in colour with Fe^{2+} salt solution. Compound (X) and (Y) are respectively :

(a) NH_4SCN and $Fe(SCN)_3$ (b) $K_4[Fe(CN)_6]$ and $FeSO_4$

(c) Na_2HPO_4 and $FeSO_4$ (d) $K_3[Fe(CN)_6]$ and $K_2Fe[Fe(CN)_6]$

2. Which of the following mixtures can be separated by using excess NH_3 solution ?

(a) Bi^{3+} (aq.) and Al^{3+} (aq.) (b) Al^{3+} (aq.) and Zn^{2+} (aq.)

(c) Hg^{2+} (aq.) and Pb^{2+} (aq.) (d) Cu^{2+} (aq.) and Cd^{2+} (aq.)

3. Which of the following salt will not give positive brown ring test ?

(a) $Cu(NO_3)_2$ (b) $Pb(NO_3)_2$ (c) $Zn(NO_3)_2$ (d) $Mg(NO_3)_2$

4. Consider the following reactions

$P + Q \longrightarrow R + K_2SO_4$

$R \longrightarrow 2CuI + I_2$

$Ag^+ + Q \longrightarrow S + K^+$

Then according to given information the incorrect match is :

(a) $P = CuSO_4$ (b) $Q = KI$ (c) $R = CuI_2$ (d) $S = K[AgI_2]$

5. A very dilute acidic solution of Cd^{2+} and Ni^{2+} gives only yellow ppt. of CdS on passing H_2S, this is due to :

(a) Solubility product (K_{sp}) of CdS is more than that of NiS

(b) Solubility product (K_{sp}) of CdS is less than that of NiS

(c) Cd^{2+} belong to IIB group while Ni^{2+} belongs to IVth group

(d) CdS is insoluble in yellow ammonium sulphide (YAS)

6.

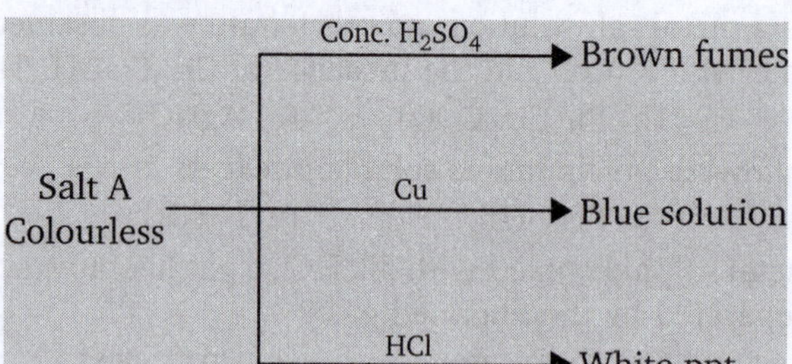

Identify salt (A) satisfying above chemical property:

(a) $Cu(NO_3)_2$ (b) $NaNO_3$ (c) $AgNO_3$ (d) $Pb(NO_3)_2$

7. Reddish brown (chocolate) precipitate is formed by mixing solutions containing:

(a) Cu^{2+} and $[Fe(CN)_6]^{3-}$ ions (b) Cu^{2+} and $Fe(CN)_6]^{4-}$ ions

(c) Pb^{2+} and SO_4^{2-} ions (d) Pb^{2+} and I^- ions

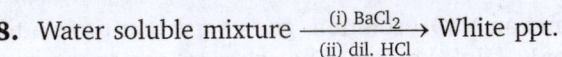

8. Water soluble mixture $\xrightarrow[\text{(ii) dil. HCl}]{\text{(i) BaCl}_2}$ White ppt.

Filtrate + (Hot and conc.) $HNO_3 + BaCl_2 \longrightarrow$ White ppt.

The mixture contains:

(a) SO_4^{2-} (b) SO_3^{2-} (c) both (a) and (b) (d) none of these

9. Which of the following compounds after mixing can produce blue colouration?

(I) $K_4[Fe(CN)_6]$ and $FeCl_3$ solution (II) Excess NH_4OH and $CuSO_4$ solution

(III) Adding anhydrous $CuSO_4$ to water (IV) Excess $NH_4OH + NiSO_4$ solution

Choose the correct code:

(a) I, II, III (b) II, III (c) I, III (d) I, II, III, IV

10. A bromide ion does not interfere with the chromyl chloride test because when a bromide is present:

(a) Br_2 is liberated, which leaves the NaOH solution colourless

(b) CrO_2Br_2 formed does not volatilise as CrO_2Cl_2 does

(c) CrO_2Br_2 does not react with NaOH

(d) no gaseous substance containing bromine is produced

11. A red solid is insoluble in water but soluble in the presence of KI. Heating the red solid in a test tube result in the formation of yellow sublimate in the part of the test tube. The red solid is:

(a) Pb_3O_4 (b) HgI_2 (c) HgO (d) $(NH_4)_2Cr_2O_7$

12. Which of the following reaction(s) is relevant to the microcosmic salt bead test?

(a) $Cr_2O_3 + 3B_2O_3 \rightarrow 2Cr(BO_2)_3$

(b) $CoO + ZnO \rightarrow CoZnO_2$

(c) $CoO + NaPO_3 \rightarrow NaCoPO_4$

(d) $Al_2(SO_4)_3 + 3Na_2CO_3 \rightarrow Al_2O_3 + 3Na_2SO_4 + 3CO_2$

13. Solid KCl, when heated with solid $K_2Cr_2O_7$ and concentrated H_2SO_4, gives red vapours (*a*) that turn NaOH solution yellow (*b*). The yellow solution, when acidified with acetic acid and treated with lead acetate, gives a yellow precipitate (*c*). Which of the following is true with respect to *a*, *b* and *c*?

(a) *a* and *b* contain CrO_4^{2-} (b) *a* and *c* contain CrO_4^{2-}

(c) *a*, *b* and *c* contain CrO_4^{2-} (d) *a*, *b* and *c* contain Cr(VI)

14. Choose the correct code by identifying (X), (Y) and (Z) in each case for the changes indicated:

(i) $CrO_2Cl_2 \xrightarrow{\text{KOH}} (X) \xrightarrow{\text{conc. } H_2SO_4} (Y) \xrightarrow{AgNO_3} (Z)$

(ii) $CrCl_3(aq) \xrightarrow[\text{NaOH}]{\text{excess}} (X) \xrightarrow[H_2O\text{, boil}]{Na_2O_2} (Y) \xrightarrow[\text{acetate}]{\text{lead}} (Z)$

(iii) $ZnSO_4(aq) \xrightarrow{Na_2CO_3} (X) \xrightarrow{\Delta} (Y) \xrightarrow[\text{nitrate, } \Delta]{\text{cobalt}} (Z)$

(iv) $CuCl_2(aq) \xrightarrow[H_2S]{NH_4OH} (X) \xrightarrow[\Delta]{HNO_3} (Y) \xrightarrow[\text{excess}]{\text{KCN}} (Z)$

(a) $X = K_2CrO_4$ $Y = K_2Cr_2O_7$ $Z = Ag_2CrO_4$

(b) $X = [Cr(OH)_4]^-$ $Y = Na_2CrO_4$ $Z = PbCrO_4$

(c) $X = ZnCO_3$ $Y = ZnO$ $Z = CoZnO_2$

(d) $X = CuS$ $Y = Cu(NO_3)_2$ $Z = K_3[Cu(CN)_4]$

15. A salt, when warmed with zinc powder and an NaOH solution, gives a gas that turns a filter paper soaked with an alkaline solution of $K_2[HgI_4]$ brown. The salt responds to the brown ring test when acetic acid is used in place of sulphuric acid. The anion present in the salt is:
(a) NO_3^- (b) NO_2^- (c) Br^- (d) None of these

16. A sulphate of a metal (*A*) on heating evolves two gases (*B*) and (*C*) and an oxide (*D*). Gas (*B*) turns $K_2Cr_2O_7$ paper green while gas (*C*) forms a trimer in which there is no S–S bond. Compound (*D*) with conc. HCl forms a Lewis acid (*E*) which exists in a dimer. Compounds (*A*), (*B*), (*C*), (*D*) and (*E*) are respectively:
(a) $FeSO_4, SO_2, SO_3, Fe_2O_3, FeCl_3$ (b) $Al_2(SO_4)_3, SO_2, SO_3, Al_2O_3, FeCl_3$
(c) $FeS, SO_2, SO_3, FeSO_4, FeCl_3$ (d) $FeS, SO_2, SO_3, Fe_2(PO_4)_3, FeCl_2$

17. $X + HNO_3 \longrightarrow Y + NO_2 + H_2O + S$, Y + Ammonium molybdate $\longrightarrow$ yellow ppt. Identify X :
(a) As_2S_5 (b) Sb_2S_5 (c) SnS_2 (d) CdS

18. (X) (Black) $\xrightarrow{\text{dil. } H_2SO_4}$ (Y) (gas) $\xrightarrow{\text{dil. } HNO_3}$ Colloidal sulphur; Identify (X):
(a) CuS (b) FeS (c) PbS (d) NiS

19. A mixture of Na_2CO_3 and Na_2SO_3 is treated with dilute H_2SO_4 in a setup such that the gaseous mixture emerging can pass first through a solution of $BaCl_2$ and then gases mixture passed through acidified $K_2Cr_2O_7$. Which of the following will you observe?
(a) The $BaCl_2$ solution remains unaffected and the acidified dichromate solution turns green
(b) The $BaCl_2$ solution gives a white precipitate and the acidified dichromate solution remains unaffected
(c) The $BaCl_2$ solution gives a white precipitate and the acidified dichromate solution turns green
(d) Both the solutions remain unaffected

20. An organic compound (*A*) on heating produces two gases (*B*) and (*C*) and neutral oxide (*D*) which turns cobalt chloride paper pink. Gas (*B*) turns lime water milky and produces an acidic solution with water. Gas (*C*) produces a poisonous gas (*E*) with chlorine gas, this gas with ammonia gives an organic compound (*F*) which on further reaction with (*D*) gives NH_3 gas. Then, compounds (*A*) and (*F*) can be found as:
(a) $H_2C_2O_4$ and NH_2CONH_2 (b) CH_3COOH and NH_2CONH_2
(c) $CHCl_3$ and CH_3CONH_2 (d) CH_3Cl and NH_2COONH_4

21. Which of the following compounds is/are partially soluble or insoluble in NH_4OH solution:
(1) $Fe(OH)_3$ (2) Ag_2CrO_4 (3) $Al(OH)_3$
(4) Ag_2CO_3 (5) $Ni(OH)_2$
(a) 1, 3, 5 (b) 2, 3, 4 (c) 1, 3 (d) 2, 3, 5

22. Which of the following will be precipitated when a solution containing calcium acetate, strontium acetate and barium acetate is treated with $(NH_4)_2SO_4$?
(a) $CaSO_4$ and $SrSO_4$ (b) $SrSO_4$ and $BaSO_4$
(c) $BaSO_4$ and $CaSO_4$ (d) $SrSO_4$ only

23. Give the correct order of initials **T** or **F** for following statements. Use **T** if statement is true and **F** if it is false.
(i) Cu^+ undergoes disproportionation to Cu and Cu^{2+} in aqueous solution
(ii) Hg_2Cl_2 does not impart chromyl chloride test
(iii) Sulphide ions react with sodium nitroprusside to form a purple coloured complex. In this reaction, oxidation state of iron changes.
(a) TFF (b) FTT (c) TFT (d) TTF

24. In this sequence *X, Y, Z* are respectively:

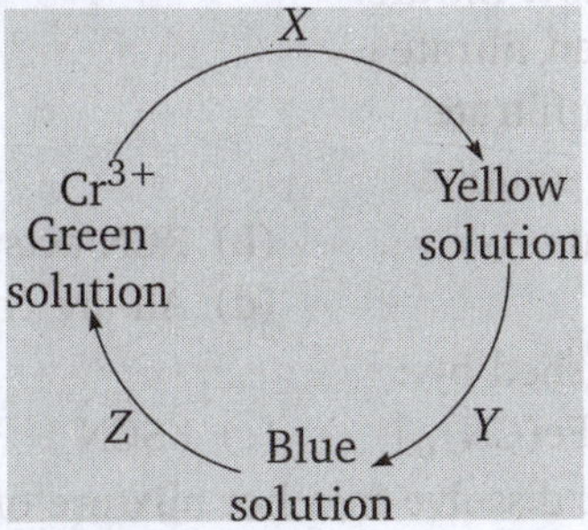

(a) Acidified H_2O_2; Alkaline H_2O_2; Acidified H_2O_2
(b) Alkaline H_2O_2; Acidified H_2O_2; Zn/HCl
(c) Acidified H_2O_2; Heat; Alkaline H_2O_2
(d) Alkaline H_2O_2; Acidified H_2O_2; On standing

25. What will be the colour of the solution when $Mn(OH)_2$ is treated with concentrated HNO_3 and sodium bismuthate (or red lead or lead dioxide)?
(a) Yellow (b) Purple (c) Green (d) Blue

26. A white powder "*A*" on heating gave a non-combustible gas and a white residue. The residue on heating turns yellow. The residue dissolves in dil. HCl and the solution gives a white ppt. with $K_4[Fe(CN)_6]$. "*A*" would be:
(a) $CaCO_3$ (b) $ZnCO_3$ (c) $CaSO_3$ (d) $CuCO_3$

27. An aqueous solution of $FeSO_4 \cdot Al_2(SO_4)_3$ and chromium alum is heated with excess of Na_2O_2 and filtered. The material obtained are:
(a) a colourless filtrate and green residue (b) a yellow filtrate and brown residue
(c) a yellow filtrate and a green residue (d) a green filtrate and a brown residue

28. When a solution of $Na_2Cr_2O_7$ is treated with amyl alcohol and acidified H_2O_2, the layer of amyl alcohol turns blue. What is the blue colouration ?
(a) Cr^{2+} (b) CrO_5 (c) CrO_4 (d) $Cr^{2+} + CrO_5$

29. Hg_2^{2+} when reacts with H_2S, black ppt. (*A*) formed which when reacts with Na_2S followed by filtration leaving behind black ppt. (*B*). The filtrate with H^+ gives black ppt. (*C*). *A*, *B* and *C* are:
(a) Hg_2S, Hg, HgS (b) $Hg + HgS, HgS, Hg$
(c) $Hg + HgS, Hg, HgS$ (d) Hg_2S, HgS, Hg

30. (*A*) light blue coloured compound on heating will convert into black (*B*) which reacts with glucose gives red compound (*C*) and (*A*) reacts with ammonium hydroxide in excess in presence of ammonium sulphate give blue compound (*D*). What is (*A*), (*B*), (*C*) and (*D*)?
(a) $[Cu(NH_3)_4]SO_4, CuO, Cu_2O, CuSO_4$ (b) $CuSO_4, CuO, Cu_2O, Cu(OH)_2$
(c) $Cu(OH)_2, Cu_2O, CuO, [Cu(NH_3)_4]SO_4$ (d) $Cu(OH)_2, CuO, Cu_2O, [Cu(NH_3)_4]SO_4$

31. A mixture of ferric alum, chrome alum and potash alum is dissolved in water and treated with an excess of NH_3 solution and warmed with a mixture of NaOH and H_2O_2 and filtered. We will get:

(a) a green residue and a yellow filtrate
(b) a brown residue and a yellow filtrate
(c) a brown residue and a green filtrate
(d) a blue residue and a green filtrate

32. When KCN is added to $CuSO_4$ solution:
(a) KCN acts an reducing agent
(b) KCN acts as an complexing agent
(c) $K_3[Cu(CN)_4]$ is formed
(d) All are correct

33. Fe^{2+} and Fe^{3+} can be distinguished by :
(a) $K_3[Fe(CN)_6]$ (b) $K_4[Fe(CN)_6]$ (c) KSCN (d) All are correct

34. Which of the following will not dissolve in a hot mixture of NaOH and H_2O_2?
(a) $Fe(OH)_3$ (b) $Al(OH)_3$ (c) $Cr(OH)_3$ (d) $Zn(OH)_2$

35. Match the following.

(I) HCO_2^- — (P) Obtained through Solvay's process
(II) K_2CO_3 — (Q) Green colouration due to $[Cr(H_2O)_6]^{3+}$ ion
(III) $S_2O_3^{2-} + FeCl_3$ solution — (R) Reduces $[Cu(C_4H_4O_6)_2]^{2-}$ to red ppt.
(IV) $SO_3^{2-} + K_2Cr_2O_7 / H^+$ — (S) Green colouration
(V) Na_2CO_3 — (T) Melts at 850°C

	(P)	(Q)	(R)	(S)	(T)
(a)	I	III	V	IV	II
(b)	I	III	II	IV	V
(c)	V	IV	I	III	II
(d)	V	IV	III	I	II

36. $(X) \xrightarrow{KOH} (Y)$ (gas turns red litmus blue) $+ (Z) \xrightarrow{Zn + KOH} (Y)$ (gas).
$(X) \xrightarrow{\Delta}$ gas (does not support combustion)
Identify (X) to (Z):
(a) $X = NH_4NO_2$ $Y = NH_3$ $Z = KNO_2$
(b) $X = (NH_4)_2Cr_2O_7$ $Y = NH_3$ $Z = Cr_2O_3$
(c) $X = (NH_4)_2SO_4$ $Y = NH_3$ $Z = K_2SO_4$
(d) $X = NH_4NO_3$ $Y = NH_3$ $Z = KNO_3$

37. $SO_3^{2-} + S^* \xrightarrow{boil} SS^*O_3^{2-}$, $SS^*O_3^{2-} + 2H^+ \longrightarrow H_2SO_3 + S^*$
The above reaction sequence proves:
(a) Two sulphur atoms of thiosulphate are not equivalent
(b) Both are equivalent
(c) Both of the above are correct
(d) None of these

38. $\text{(A)} \xrightarrow{X} \text{(B)} \xrightarrow{Y} \text{(A)} \xrightarrow{Z} \text{(C)}$

Pale yellow complex → Yellow complex → Regenerated → Deep blue solution

The sequential unknown reagents is/are:

(a) H_2O_2/neutral medium, H_2O_2/H^+, Cu^{2+} salt solution

(b) H_2O_2/H^+, H_2O_2/OH^-, Fe^{3+} salt solution

(c) H_2O_2/OH^-, H_2O_2/H^+, Co^{2+} salt solution

(d) H_2O_2/neutral medium, H_2O_2/OH^-, Fe^{2+} salt solution

39. (Clear solution) $D \xleftarrow{\text{dil. HCl}} A \xrightarrow[\text{(in acetic acid)}]{K_2CrO_4} B$ (Yellow ppt.)

$A \xrightarrow{\text{dil. } H_2SO_4} C$ (White ppt.)

Compound(s) A is/are:

(a) lead carbonate (b) red lead

(c) barium carbonate (d) calcium carbonate

40. Which of the following is precipitated when an arsenate reacts with a magnesia mixture?

(a) $MgHAsO_3$ (b) Mg_2AsO_3

(c) $MgNH_4AsO_4 \cdot 6H_2O$ (d) $Mg_2NH_4AsO_4 \cdot 6H_2O$

41. A coloured solution known to contain two metal ions, was treated with excess cold sodium hydroxide solution. When filtered a whitish solid, slowly changing to brown, was retained on the filter paper and a colourless solution collected as the filtrate. Dropwise addition of hydrochloric acid to the filtrate produced a white ppt. which dissolved in excess acid. Treatment of the residue on filter paper with a solution of strong oxidiser produced a reddish-violet solution. Indicate any pairs of ions:

(a) Zn^{2+} and Mn^{2+} ions (b) Mg^{2+} and Zn^{2+} ions

(c) Mn^{2+} and Mg^{2+} ions (d) Fe^{2+} and Zn^{2+} ions

42. Which of the following statement is incorrect?

(I) In $S_2O_3^{2-}$ both sulphur are different in nature

(II) Sodium acetate and lead acetate on heating giving same type of product, whereas Mn, Sn, Fe oxalate salt giving different type of products.

(III) Aqueous solution OCl^-, S^{2-} and CO_3^{2-} basic in nature

(IV) Acidified NO_2^- oxidises I^- whereas Br_2 and Cl_2 oxidises NO_2^-

(a) II only (b) II, III, IV (c) II, IV (d) I, II, IV

43. On strongly heating, a blue salt leaves a black residue. Which of the following cations can be present in the salt?

(a) Fe^{2+} (b) Fe^{3+} (c) Cu^{2+} (d) Zn^{2+}

44. Which of the following, when dissolved in yellow ammonium sulphide, forms a thiocomplex containing the metal in the oxidation state +IV?

(a) As_2S_3 (b) As_2S_5 (c) Sb_2S_3 (d) SnS

45. Thenard's blue is:
(a) $CoAl_2O_4$ (b) $Fe_4[Fe(CN)_6]_3$ (c) $K_2Fe[Fe(CN)_6]$ (d) $[Cu(NH_3)_4](OH)_2$

46. A salt imparts a yellow colour to a borax bead in an oxidising flame. What would be the colour of the bead in a reducing flame?
(a) Green (b) Blue (c) Red (d) Violet

47. $BiCl_3$ can be reduced to metallic bismuth by:
(a) H_2S (b) SO_2 (c) $FeSO_4$ (d) $Na_2[Sn(OH)_4]$

48. The blue colour in an oxidising flame of a microcosmic bead containing Cu^{2+} is due to:
(a) $NaCuPO_4$ (b) $Cu(PO_3)_2$ (c) $Cu_3(PO_4)_2$ (d) None of these

49. Which of the following reactions is/are relevant to the microcosmic bead test?
(a) $Na(NH_4)HPO_4 \cdot 4H_2O \rightarrow NaPO_3 + NH_3 + 5H_2O$
(b) $CoO + NaPO_3 \rightarrow NaCoPO_4$
(c) $CuO + NaPO_3 \rightarrow NaCuPO_4$
(d) All of these

50. Which of the following is formed in solution when $[Cu(NH_3)_4]^{2+}$ is treated with KCN till the colour of the complex is discharged?
(a) $Cu(CN)_2$ (b) $[Cu(CN)_4]^{2-}$ (c) $[Cu(CN)_4]^{3-}$ (d) $[Cu(CN)_6]^{4-}$

51. A white solid forms Rinmann's green in the charcoal cavity test in an oxidising flame. On treatment with dilute H_2SO_4, this solid produces a gas that turns an acidified dichromate paper green and lead acetate paper black. The white solid is:
(a) PbS (b) $ZnSO_3$ (c) ZnS (d) Na_2S

52. A white solid imparts a violet colour to a Bunsen flame. On being heated with concentrated H_2SO_4, the solid gives violet vapours that turns starch paper blue. The salt may be:
(a) NaI (b) KI (c) $CaBr_2$ (d) MgI_2

53. Which of the following is soluble in boiling water, but less soluble in cold water?
(a) $PbCl_2$ (b) $PbBr_2$ (c) PbI_2 (d) All of these

54. Which of the following pairs of cations cannot be separated by using dilute HCl?
(a) Hg_2^{2+}, Pb^{2+} (b) Hg^{2+}, Ag^+ (c) Ag^+, Cu^{2+} (d) Hg_2^{2+}, Bi^{3+}

55. If NH_4OH in presence of NH_4Cl is added to a solution containing $Al_2(SO_4)_3$ and $MgSO_4$, which of the following will precipitate?
(a) $Al(OH)_3$ only (b) $Mg(OH)_2$ only
(c) $Al(OH)_3$ and $Mg(OH)_2$ (d) None of these

56. Which of the following pairs of cations can be separated by adding NH_4Cl, NH_4OH and then $(NH_4)_2CO_3$ to the mixture?
(a) Ca^{2+}, Mg^{2+} (b) Ba^{2+}, Sr^{2+} (c) Sr^{2+}, Ca^{2+} (d) Ba^{2+}, Ca^{2+}

57. H_2S is passed through the solution in an acidic medium to precipitate the sulphides of group II cations, but in an alkaline medium to precipitate the sulphides of group IV cations because:
(a) the sulphides of group II cations are more soluble than those of group IV cations
(b) the sulphides of group II cations have lower solubility products than those of group IV cations
(c) the sulphides of group II cations are soluble in an acidic medium, but those of group IV cations are not
(d) the sulphides of group IV cations are soluble in an alkaline medium but those of group II cations are not

58. Which of the following pairs of cations can be separated by passing H_2S through the mixture in the presence of 0.2 *M* HCl?
(a) Pb^{2+}, Cu^{2+} (b) Ag^{+}, Cu^{2+} (c) Cd^{2+}, Bi^{3+} (d) Cu^{2+}, Zn^{2+}

59. Which of the following pairs of cations can be separated by using an NH_3 solution ?
(a) Cu^{2+}, Ag^{+} (b) Pb^{2+}, Ag^{+} (c) Ag^{+}, Zn^{2+} (d) Cu^{2+}, Cd^{2+}

60. Which of the following ions cannot be detected by the borax bead or microcosmic bead test?
(a) Cu^{2+} (b) Cr^{3+} (c) Fe^{3+} (d) Zn^{2+}

61. Which of the following pairs of cations will turn borax beads blue in an oxidising flame?
(a) Fe^{2+} and Co^{2+} (b) Co^{2+} and Cu^{2+} (c) Cu^{2+} and Mn^{2+} (d) Cu^{2+} and Cr^{3+}

62. A colourless crystalline salt, on being heated, gives a colourless gas with a pungent smell. On being passed through an $AgNO_3$ solution, this gas forms a white precipitate insoluble in HNO_3 but readily soluble in an NH_3 solution. Which of the following reaction can lead to the above observation ?
(a) $MgCl_2 \cdot 6H_2O \xrightarrow{\Delta} MgO + 2HCl + 5H_2O$
(b) $(NH_4)_2CO_3 \longrightarrow 2NH_3 + CO_2 + H_2O$
(c) $ZnSO_3 \longrightarrow ZnO + SO_2$
(d) $NaNH_4HPO_4 \longrightarrow NaPO_3 + NH_3 + H_2O$

63. When NH_4Cl is not used together with NH_4OH in group-III reagent which of the following cation will not be precipitated?
(a) Fe^{2+} (b) Cr^{3+} (c) Zn^{2+} (d) Ba^{2+}

64. $\underset{\text{imparts violet colour to flame}}{(T)} \xrightarrow{\text{compound } (U) + \text{conc. } H_2SO_4} \underset{\text{Red gas}}{(V)} \xrightarrow{NaOH + AgNO_3} \underset{\text{Red ppt.}}{(W)} \xrightarrow{NH_3 \text{ soln.}} (X)$

$(W) \xrightarrow{\text{dil. HCl}} (Y)$ white ppt.

$(U) \xrightarrow[\Delta]{NaOH} (Z)$ gas (gives white fumes with HCl)

Identify (*T*) to (*Z*).
(a) $T = KMnO_4, U = HCl, V = Cl_2, W = HgI_2, X = Hg(NH_2)NO_3, Y = Hg_2Cl_2, Z = N_2$
(b) $T = K_2Cr_2O_7,\ U = NH_4Cl,\ V = CrO_2Cl_2,\ W = Ag_2CrO_4,\ X = [Ag(NH_3)_2]^+,\ Y = AgCl,$
$Z = NH_3$
(c) $T = K_2CrO_4,\ U = KCl,\ V = CrO_2Cl_2, W = HgI_2, X = Na_2CrO_4, Y = BaCO_3, Z = NH_4Cl$
(d) $T = K_2MnO_4, U = NaCl, V = CrO_3, W = AgNO_2, X = (NH_4)_2CrO_4, Y = CaCO_3, Z = SO_2$

65. In the separation of Cu^{2+} and Cd^{2+} in II group qualitative analysis of cations tetrammine copper (II) sulphate and tetrammine cadmium (II) sulphate react with KCN to form the corresponding cyano complexes. Which one of the following pairs of the complexes and their relative stability enables the separation of Cu^{2+} and Cd^{2+}?
(a) $K_3[Cu(CN)_4]$ is perfect and $K_2[Cd(CN)_4]$ is inperfect complex
(b) $K_3[Cu(CN)_4]$ and $K_2[Cd(CN)_4]$ is perfect complex
(c) $K_2[Cu(CN)_4]$ inperfect and $K_2[Cd(CN)_4]$ perfect complex
(d) $K_3[Cu(CN)_4]$ inperfect and $K_2[Cd(CN)_4]$ is perfect complex

66. The only cations present in a slightly acidic solution are Fe^{3+}, Zn^{2+} and Cu^{2+}. The reagent that when added in excess to this solution would identify and separate Fe^{3+} in one step is:

(a) 2 *M* HCl (b) 6 *M* NH_3

(c) 6 *M* NaOH (d) H_2S gas

67. When conc. H_2SO_4 was treated with $K_4[Fe(CN)_6]$, CO gas was evolved. By mistake, somebody used dilute H_2SO_4 instead of conc. H_2SO_4, then the gas evolved was:

(a) CO (b) HCN

(c) N_2 (d) CO_2

68. Unknown salt '*A*' + solid $K_2Cr_2O_7$ + Conc. $H_2SO_4 \longrightarrow$ Reddish brown fumes. Which is the correct statement regarding the above observation?

(a) It confirms the presence of Cl^- ion

(b) It confirms the presence of Br^- ion

(c) It confirms the presence of both

(d) It neither confirms Cl^- nor Br^- unless it is passed through NaOH solution

69. An inorganic red coloured compound (*A*) on heating gives a compound (*B*) and a gas (*C*). (*A*) on treatment with dil. HNO_3 gives compound (*D*), brown colour substance (*E*) and a neutral oxide (*F*). Compound (*D*) on warming gives off again gas (*C*). Then, (*E*) will be:

(a) Mn_3O_4 (b) PbO_2

(c) Pb_3O_4 (d) Fe_2O_3

70. Select correct statement(s):

(I) When excess $FeCl_3$ solution is added to $K_4[Fe(CN)_6]$ solution, in addition to $Fe^{III}[Fe^{II}(CN)_6]^-$, $Fe^{II}[Fe^{III}(CN)_6]^-$ is also formed due to side redox reaction

(II) When $FeCl_2$ is added to $K_3[Fe(CN)_6]$ solution, in addition to $Fe^{II}[Fe^{III}(CN)_6]^-$, $Fe^{III}[Fe^{II}(CN)_6]^-$ is also formed due to side redox reaction

(III) $Fe^{III}[Fe^{II}(CN)_6]^-$ is paramagnetic while $Fe^{II}[Fe^{III}(CN)_6]^-$ is diamagnetic

(IV) $Fe^{III}[Fe^{II}(CN)_6]^-$ is diamagnetic while $Fe^{II}[Fe^{III}(CN)_6]^-$ is paramagnetic

(a) I, II (b) III, IV

(c) both (a) and (b) (d) None of these

71. Which of the following reagents are used for the detection of acetate and oxalate ions respectively?

(a) $BaCl_2$ and $CaCl_2$ (b) NaOH and $BaCl_2$

(c) $FeCl_3$ and $CaCl_2$ (d) $FeCl_3$ and NaOH

72. Which of the following mixtures of ions can be separated by using an excess of an NaOH solution?

(a) Pb^{2+} and Zn^{2+} (b) Al^{3+} and Zn^{2+}

(c) Fe^{3+} and Al^{3+} (d) Sn^{2+} and Pb^{2+}

73. A metal carbonate, on being heated strongly gives a solid that forms a green solid with CoO. In which analytical group will the cation be precipitate and what will be the colour of the precipitate?

(a) Group I, white (b) Group II, yellow

(c) Group III, white (d) Group IV, white

74. A solution of a metal ion, when treated with KI, gives a red precipitate which dissolves in an excess of KI to give a colourless solution. Moreover, the solution of the metal ion on treatment with a solution of cobalt (II) thiocyanate gives rise to a deep blue crystalline precipitate. The metal ions is:

(a) Pb^{2+} (b) Hg^{2+}

(c) Cu^{2+} (d) Co^{2+}

75. A white powder solid *A* forms a light green solution with water, which on treatment with potassium hexacyanoferrate(III) gives a blue precipitate. On being strongly heated, *A* leaves a brown residue and forms a mixture of two gaseous oxides, which turns a dichromate solution green and forms a white precipitate with a $BaCl_2$ solution containing concentrated HCl. *A* is:

(a) $CuSO_4$ (b) $Fe_2(SO_4)_3$

(c) $FeSO_4$ (d) $Cr_2(SO_4)_3$

76. Which of the following is the composition of the yellow precipitate obtained in the test for phosphates using ammonium molybdate?

(a) $(NH_4)_3[PMo_{12}O_{40}]$ (b) $(NH_4)_3[PMo_{12}O_{36}]$

(c) $(NH_4)_3PO_4 \cdot 10MoO_3$ (d) $(NH_4)_3PO_4 \cdot 14MoO_3$

77. Which of the following mixtures can be separated by using an NH_3 solution?

(a) Fe^{3+} and Al^{3+} (b) Al^{3+} and Zn^{2+}

(c) Sn^{2+} and Pb^{2+} (d) Cu^{2+} and Cd^{2+}

Level 3

Passage 1

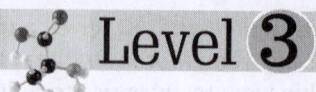

A pale yellow inorganic compound *K* is insoluble in hot and dil. HNO_3 but dissolves in concentrated ammonia solution and compound *L* is formed. On treatment with dil. HNO_3 compound *L* produces a metal cation which gives white precipitate *M* with Hypo solution. When an aqueous solution of (*M*) is boiled, a black precipitate of (*N*) is formed which dissolves in hot dil. HNO_3 and on adding HCl gives a white precipitate. When the compound (*K*) is heated with concentrated H_2SO_4 and MnO_2 brown fumes are observed.

1. The compound (*K*) is :
(a) AgI (b) AgBr (c) $AgNO_2$ (d) PbI_2

2. Compound (*M*) and black precipitate of (*N*) are respectively :
(a) PbI_2, PbS (b) PbS_2O_3, PbS (c) $Ag_2S_2O_3$, Ag_2S (d) $AgSO_3$, Ag

3. Compound (*K*) on heating with conc. H_2SO_4 and MnO_2 gives :
(a) I_3^- (b) Br_2 (c) HI (d) NO_2

Passage 2

A colourless inorganic compound (*A*) imparts a green colour to the flame. Its solution gives a white ppt. (*B*) with H_2SO_4. When heated with $K_2Cr_2O_7$ and conc. H_2SO_4, a brown red vapour/gas (*C*) is formed. The gas/vapour when passed through aqueous NaOH solution, it turns into a yellow solution (*D*) which forms yellow precipitate (*E*) with CH_3COOH and $(CH_3COO)_2Pb$. With reference to above information, answer the following questions.

1. The colourless inorganic compound (*A*) is :
(a) $Ba(NO_3)_2$ (b) $BaCl_2$ (c) $CuCl_2$ (d) $CrBr_3$

2. The liberated gas vapour (*C*) is :
(a) Br_2 (b) NO_2 (c) CrO_2Cl_2 (d) Cl_2

3. The yellow ppt. formed when (*D*) reacts with CH_3COOH and $(CH_2COO)_2Pb$ is :
(a) PbI_2 (b) $PbCrO_4$ (c) $BaCrO_4$ (d) AgBr

Passage 3

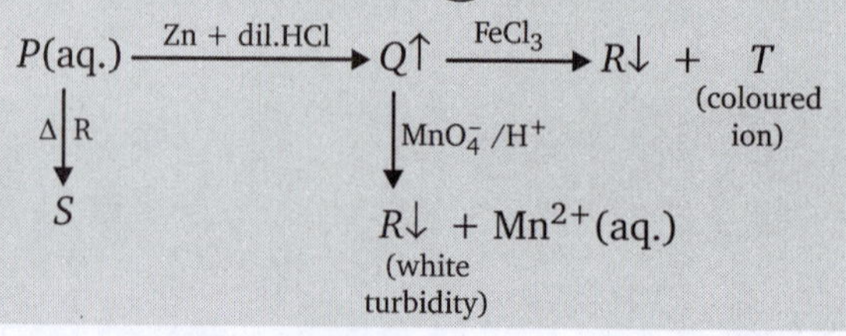

1. '*T*' can not be identified by :
(a) NH_3 solution (b) NH_4SCN (c) $(NH_4)_2S$ (d) excess KCN

2. Species *P* and *S* are respectively :
(a) SO_3^{2-}(aq.), S (b) SO_3^{2-}(aq.), $S_2O_3^{2-}$(aq.)
(c) $S_2O_3^{2-}$(aq.), SO_3^{2}(aq.) (d) None of these

Passage 4

[A] colourless salt $\xrightarrow[\Delta]{KOH}$ [B] gas (gives white fumes with HCl)

[A] $\xrightarrow{CaCl_2}$ [C] white ppt.

[C] white ppt. $\xrightarrow[\text{(purple)}]{KMnO_4}$ colourless solution

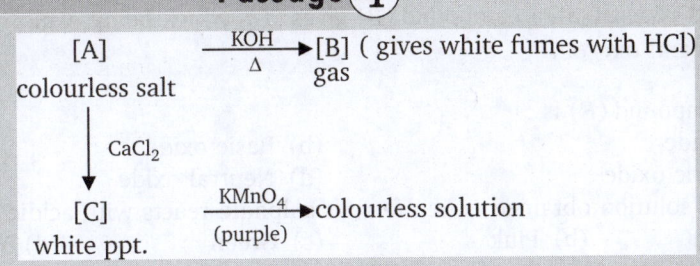

1. The salt [*A*] is:
(a) CaC_2O_4 (b) $K_2C_2O_4$ (c) $(NH_4)_2C_2O_4$ (d) BaC_2O_4

2. When gas [*B*] reacted with excess Cl_2 gives:
(a) NOCl (b) NCl_3 (c) NH_4Cl (d) $NOCl_3$

3. Which of the following metal chloride gives white ppt. and black ppt. respectively with aqueous solution of gas [*B*]?
(a) $HgCl_2, Hg_2Cl_2$ (b) $Hg_2Cl_2, HgCl_2$ (c) $Hg_2Cl_2, ZnCl_2$ (d) $HgCl_2, ZnCl_2$

Passage 5

A teacher gave a student two salts (*A*) and (*B*) told him to identify these salts. The student heated salt (*A*) strongly and observed two oxides of sulphur. He added NaOH solution to the aqueous solution of (*A*) and observed a green precipitate, which turned brown on exposure to air.

When he took salt (*B*) to flame test, green colour was observed. On heating salt (*B*) with a solid compound (*X*) and concentrated sulphuric acid, orange red vapours are evolved. When this gas is passed through an aqueous solution of a base, the solution turns yellow.

1. The salt (*A*) can be:
(a) $Fe_2(SO_4)_3$ (b) $FeSO_4$
(c) $FeSO_4 \cdot 7H_2O$ (d) both (b) and (c)

2. Salt (*B*) suggest that the cation and anion in it are respectively:
(a) Ba^{2+} and SO_4^{2-} (b) Ba^{2+} and Cl^-
(c) Ba^{2+} and S^{2-} (d) Ba^{2+} and CO_3^{2-}

3. Compound (*X*) is:
(a) $K_2Cr_2O_7$ (b) NH_4Cl
(c) CaF_2 (d) $Na_2B_4O_7 \cdot 10H_2O$

Passage 6

$$\text{Black solid} \xrightarrow[\Delta]{\text{KOH + Air}} \underset{\text{(green)}}{(A)} \xrightarrow{H_2SO_4} \underset{\text{(purple)}}{(B)} + (C)$$

(i) KI on reaction with alkaline solution of (*B*) changes into a compound (*D*).
(ii) The colour of the compound (*B*) disappears on treatement with the acidic solution of $FeSO_4$
(iii) With cold conc. H_2SO_4 compound (*B*) gives (*E*), which being explosive decomposes to yield (*F*) and oxygen.

1. Nature of compound (*E*) is :
(a) Acidic oxide (b) Basic oxide
(c) Amphoteric oxide (d) Neutral oxide

2. Colour of the solution obtained, when ferrous sulphate reacts with acidic solution of (*B*):
(a) Colourless (b) Pink (c) Green (d) Yellow

3. Which of the following options is correct?
(a) (*C*) and (*F*) are same compounds having same colour.
(b) (*C*) and (*F*) are different compounds having same colour.
(c) Compound (*B*) forms similar compound (*E*) with hot and conc. H_2SO_4.
(d) Compound (*A*) does not give same type of reaction in acidic and neutral medium.

4. Type of hybridization in compound (*D*):
(a) sp^2 (b) sp^3 (c) sp^3d (d) No hybridization

Passage 7

$(A) + NaCl \longrightarrow (B)$ (white ppt.),

$(B) + KI \longrightarrow (C)$ (green ppt.)

$(C) + \underset{\text{(excess)}}{KI} \longrightarrow (D) + (E)$ (colourless solution)

$(E) + NH_3 + KOH \longrightarrow (F)$

1. Compounds (*A*) and (*B*) are respectively:
(a) $AgNO_3$ and $AgCl$ (b) $Pb(NO_3)_2$ and $PbCl_2$
(c) $Hg_2(NO_3)_2$ and Hg_2Cl_2 (d) $Cu_2(NO_3)_2$ and Cu_2Cl_2

2. When compound (*A*) reacts with Na_2CrO_4 solution, the colour of the compound formed is :
(a) Black (b) Red
(c) Yellow (d) White

3. Type of hybridization in compound (*E*) is :
(a) d^2sp^3 (b) sp^3d^2
(c) sp^3 (d) dsp^2

4. Colour of the compound (*F*) is :
(a) Yellow (b) Blue
(c) White (d) Brown

Passage 8

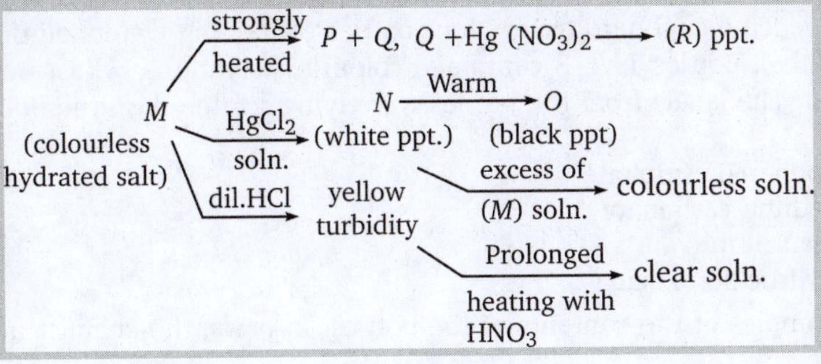

1. The colour of the compound R is:
(a) White
(b) Yellow
(c) Black
(d) Brown

2. The structure of compound P is:
(a) Linear
(b) Crown shaped
(c) Square pyramidal
(d) Zig-zag chain

3. Compound M is used
(I) in photography
(II) in analytical chemistry
(III) as a dehydrating agent
(IV) as an oxidizing as well as reducing agent
Choose the correct code:
(a) I, III
(b) I, II and III
(c) I, II
(d) I, II, III and IV

Passage 9

A white crystalline solid 'A' on boiling with caustic soda solution gives a gas 'B', which on passing through an alkaline solution of potassium tetraiodomercurate (II) solution gives a brown ppt. The substance 'A' on heating evolves a neutral gas 'C', which is inert at room temperature and reactive is presence of catalyst and does not give brown fumes with nitric oxide.

1. The gas 'B' is:
(a) H_2S
(b) NH_3
(c) HCl
(d) CO_2

2. The gas 'C' is:
(a) N_2O
(b) O_2
(c) NO
(d) N_2

3. The substance 'A' is:
(a) NH_4Cl
(b) NH_4NO_3
(c) NH_4NO_2
(d) $NaNO_3$

Passage 10

A chemist opened a cupboard to find four bottles containing water solutions, each of which has lost its label. Bottles 1, 2, 3 contained colourless solutions, whilst Bottle 4 contained a blue solution. The labels from the bottles were lying scattered on the floor of the cupboard. They were

copper(II) sulphate
sodium carbonate
lead nitrate
hydrochloric acid

By mixing samples of the contents of the bottles, in pairs, the chemist made the following observations:

(i)	Bottle 1 + Bottle 2	white precipitate
(ii)	Bottle 1 + Bottle 3	white precipitate
(iii)	Bottle 1 + Bottle 4	white precipitate
(iv)	Bottle 2 + bottle 3	colourless gas evolved
(v)	Bottle 2 + Bottle 4	no visible reaction
(vi)	bottle 3 + Bottle 4	blue precipitate

1. Chemical formula of white precipitate in observation (i) is :
(a) $CuCl_2$ (b) $PbCl_2$ (c) $PbCO_3$ (d) $CuSO_3$

2. Colourless solution present in Bottle-1 is:
(a) $CuSO_4$ (b) HCl (c) $Pb(NO_3)_2$ (d) Na_2CO_3

3. Nature of gas evolved in observation (iv) is :
(a) Acidic (b) Neutral
(c) Basic (d) Amphoteric

4. Chemical formula of white ppt. formed in observation (iii) is:
(a) $PbCl_2$ (b) $PbCO_3$ (c) $CuCO_3$ (d) $PbSO_4$

Passage 11

A coloured compound (*A*) reacts with dilute H_2SO_4 to produce a colourless gas (*B*) and colourless solution (*C*). The reaction between (*B*) and the acidified $K_2Cr_2O_7$ solution produces a green solution and a slightly yellowish precipitate (*D*). The substance (*D*) burns in air to produce a gas (*E*) which also can change the colour of $K_2Cr_2O_7$ solution.

1. "*A*" probably, is:
(a) $ZnSO_3$ (b) CoS (c) MnS (d) NiS

2. When "*B*" reacts with "*E*":
(a) a new gas *F* will be produced (b) it produces *D* and a colourless liquid
(c) there will be no reaction between them (d) it yields *B* and an acidic oxide

3. Which is not correct about *E*?
(a) It is colourless and highly water soluble (b) The molecule is linear
(c) Its aqueous solution is acidic (d) It turns starch iodate paper blue

4. When D is boiled with alkaline sulphite solution a compound F is formed. F can be used in

(I) Iodine titrations in volumetric analysis
(II) Bleaching industry to destroy excess Cl_2
(III) Photography for 'fixing' films
(IV) Iodometric titrations

Choose the correct codes:

(a) I and IV
(b) I, III and IV
(c) II and III
(d) I, II, III and IV

5. When colourless solution (C) reacts with Pb_3O_4/H^+, it acquires a violet red colour due to formation of:

(a) MnO_4^-
(b) PbO_2
(c) I_3^-
(d) $[Ni(en)_3]S_2O_3$

Passage 12

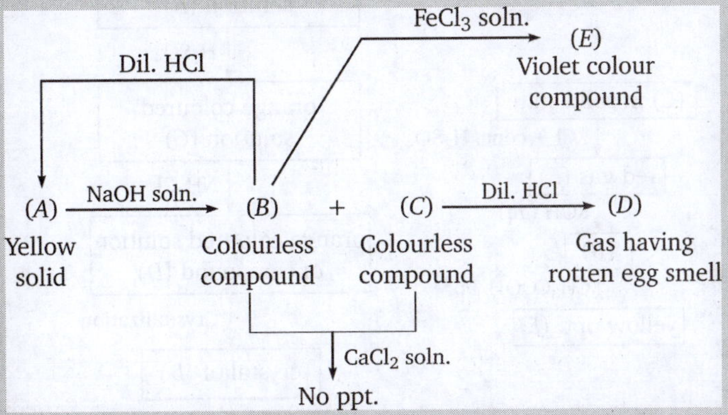

1. The structure of compound (A) is:

(a) Linear
(b) Crown shaped
(c) Square pyramidal
(d) Zig-zag chain

2. Compound (B) on strong heating produces compound(s) which has/have:

(a) Chain structure
(b) Tetrahedral structure
(c) Both (a) and (b)
(d) None of these

3. Which of the following statements is/are correct for the gas D?

(I) It has the state of hybridisation sp^3
(II) Gas can be identified by $CaCl_2$ solution
(III) Gas can be identified by $Pb(OAc)_2$ solution
(IV) Gas can be identified by passing through sodium nitroprusside solution

(a) I, IV
(b) I, III
(c) III only
(d) I, II, IV

4. Compound (B) on reaction with $[Ni(en)_3](NO_3)_2$ gives a coloured complex exhibiting

(a) Optical isomerism
(b) Geometrical isomerism
(c) Linkage isomerism
(d) No isomerism

Passage 13

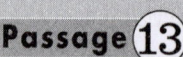

Read the following short write up and answer subsequent questions based on observations (A) to (J).

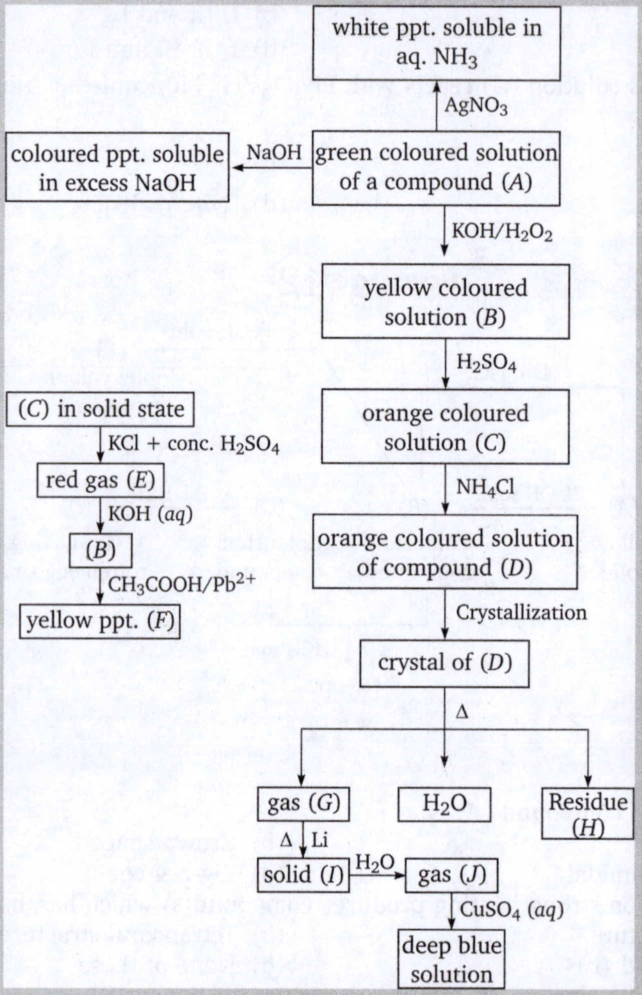

1. Compound A and B are respectively:

(a) $FeCl_2, FeCl_3$ (b) $CuCl_2{\cdot}2H_2O, [CuCl_4]^{-2}$

(c) $CrCl_3, K_2CrO_4$ (d) $NiCl_2, NiCl_3$

2. Gas (J) is also produced by:

(i) heating NH_4NO_3 (ii) heating NH_4NO_2

(iii) heating NH_4Cl (iv) reaction of NH_4Cl and $Ca(OH)_2$

(a) (i) and (iii) (b) (i) and (ii) (c) (i) and (iv) (d) (iii) and (iv)

3. Select the incorrect reaction:

(a) (C) in solid state + KBr + conc. $H_2SO_4 \longrightarrow$ Red gas

(b) (C) in solid state + KCl + conc. $H_2SO_4 \longrightarrow$ Red gas

(c) (*C*) in solid state + $FeCl_3$ + conc. H_2SO_4 $\longrightarrow$ Red gas

(d) (*C*) in solid state + $HgCl_2$ + conc. H_2SO_4 $\longrightarrow$ Red gas

Passage 14

An unknown mixture contains one or two of the following : $CaCO_3$, $BaCl_2$, $AgNO_3$, Na_2SO_4, $ZnSO_4$ and NaOH. The mixture is completely soluble in water and solution gives pink colour with phenolphthalein. When dilute hydrochloric acid is gradually added to the solution, a precipitate is formed which dissolves with further addition of the acid.

1. Which of the following combination of compounds is soluble in water?

(a) $BaCl_2$ and $AgNO_3$
(b) $AgNO_3$ and NaOH
(c) $BaCl_2$ and Na_2SO_4
(d) $ZnSO_4$ and excess NaOH

2. The aqueous solution of mixture gives white precipitate with dil. HCl which dissolves in excess of dil. HCl. It confirms:

(a) $BaCl_2 + NaOH$
(b) $Na_2SO_4 + NaOH$
(c) $ZnSO_4 + NaOH$
(d) $AgNO_3 + NaOH$

3. The white precipitate is:

(a) $ZnSO_4$
(b) Na_2ZnO_2
(c) $Zn(OH)_2$
(d) $ZnCl_2$

Passage 15

Aqueous solution of a salt '*A*', when mixed with NaOH solution and warmed, a black precipitate is formed. Black ppt. is filtred and dissolved in dil. H_2SO_4 solution. The resulting solution gives a chocolate coloured precipitate with potassium ferrocyanide solution. The filtrate obtained after filtering off the black precipitate, upon warming with Zn and NaOH evolves a pungent smelling gas. The resulting solution also responds to the ring test. The filtrate does not evolve any gas when it is boiled with urea in the presence of H_2SO_4.

1. Salt '*A*' consists of:

(a) Cu^{2+}
(b) Hg^{2+}
(c) Cu^{+}
(d) Pb^{2+}

2. The filtrate obtained after filtering off the black precipitate consists of:

(a) NO_2^-
(b) NO_3^-
(c) CO_3^{2-}
(d) Cl^-

3. The chocolate coloured precipitate is:

(a) $Fe_2[Fe(CN)_6]$
(b) $Cu_2[Fe(CN)_6]$
(c) $HgSO_4$
(d) $[Fe(H_2O)_5(NO)]SO_4$

Passage 16

Borax Bead Test is carried out when the original mixture is coloured. It is done with the help of a clean platinum wire on which a small loop is made at the end. When borax is heated on platinum wire loop a transparent glass like bead is obtained. The hot bead is brought in contact with salt till it reacts with fused borax and colour is imparted to the bead. Bead colour is noted.

Colour of the bead	Ion
1. Blue green	Cu^{2+}
2. Yellow	Fe^{3+}
3. Green	Cr^{3+}
4. Violet	Mn^{2+}
5. Dark blue	Co^{2+}
6. Brown	Ni^{2+}

1. Glassy bead is of:
(a) $B_2O_3 + NaBO_2$
(b) $NaBO_2 + Na_3BO_3$
(c) $Na_2B_4O_7 + B_2O_3$
(d) $SiO_2 + B_2O_3$

2. Blue bead can be of:
(a) $Cu(BO_2)_2$
(b) $Co(BO_2)_2$
(c) Both (a) and (b)
(d) None of these

3. The flame used in Borax Bead Test is:
(a) Reducing
(b) Oxidising
(c) Both (a) and (b)
(d) Neither (a) nor (b)

Passage 17

When a crystalline compound *X* is heated with $K_2Cr_2O_7$ and concentrated H_2SO_4, a reddish brown gas *A* is evolved. On passing *A* into caustic soda, a yellow solution of *B* is formed. A yellow precipitate of *C* is obtained when a solution of *B* is neutralised with acetic acid and then treated with a lead acetate solution. When *X* is heated with NaOH, a colourless gas is evolved which, when passed into a solution of $K_2[HgI_4]$, gives a reddish brown precipitate of *D*.

1. Compound (*X*) is:
(a) NH_4Br
(b) NH_4Cl
(c) NH_4NO_2
(d) NH_4NO_3

2. If the solution *B* is colourless, which of the following ions would not be present in the solid *X*?
(a) Cl^-
(b) Br^-
(c) NO_3^-
(d) NO_2^-

3. Which of the following is the composition of the brown precipitate (*D*) ?
(a) HgI_2
(b) $Hg(NH_2)I$
(c) HgO
(d) $HgO{\cdot}Hg(NH_2)I$

Passage 18

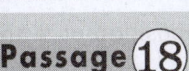

A white solid *A* reacts with dilute H_2SO_4 to produce a colourless gas *B* and a colourless solution *C*. The reaction between *B* and acidified dichromate yields a green solution and a slightly coloured precipitate *D*. The substance *D*, when burnt in air, gives a gas *E* which reacts with *B* to yield *D* and a colourless liquid. Anhydrous copper sulphate turns blue with this colourless liquid. The addition of aqueous NH_3 or NaOH to *C* produces a precipitate that dissolves in an excess of the reagent to form a clear solution.

1. Which of the following gases are *B* and *E* respectively?

(a) CO_2 and SO_2 (b) SO_2 and H_2S
(c) H_2S and SO_2 (d) CO_2 and H_2S

2. What would happen if the gas *E* were passed through an acidified $KMnO_4$ solution?

(a) Bleaching of the permangnate solution without any precipitation
(b) Bleaching of the permangnate solution which would show a yellowish white turbidity
(c) Bleaching of the permangnate solution and the formation of a brown precipitate
(d) No action

3. What would appear if the gas *B* were passed through an aqueous solution of $Pb(NO_3)_2$?

(a) A white precipitate soluble in hot dilute HNO_3
(b) A black precipitate soluble in hot dilute HNO_3
(c) A black precipitate insoluble in hot dilute HNO_3
(d) A yellow precipitate soluble in hot concentrated HNO_3

4. Which of the following reactions are relevant to the action of NH_3 or NaOH solution on *C*?

(a) $Zn(OH)_2 + 4NH_3 \longrightarrow [Zn(NH_3)_4]^{2+} + 2OH^-$
(b) $Zn(OH)_2 + 2OH^- \longrightarrow [Zn(OH)_4]^{2-}$
(c) $Pb(OH)_2 + 4NH_3 \longrightarrow [Pb(NH_3)_4]^{2+} + 2OH^-$
(d) $Pb(OH)_2 + 2OH^- \longrightarrow [Pb(OH)_4]^{2-}$

5. Suppose the solution obtained by the treatment of the solution *C* with an excess of NaOH is acidified with acetic acid and the gas *B* is passed through it. Which of the following will obtained?

(a) A colourless solution (b) A yellow precipitate
(c) A black precipitate (d) A white precipitate

Passage 19

(i) An aqueous solution of a compound *A* is acidic towards litmus and *A* sublimes at about 300°C.

(ii) A solution of *A*, on treatment with an excess of NH_4SCN, gives a red compound *B*, and on treatment with a solution of $K_4[Fe(CN)_6]$, gives a blue compound *C*.

(iii) The solid *A*, on being heated with an excess of $K_2Cr_2O_7$ in the presence of concentrated H_2SO_4, evolves deep red vapours of *D*.

(iv) On passing the vapours of *D* into a solution of NaOH and then adding the solutions of acetic acid and lead acetate, a yellow precipitate of a compound *E* is obtained.

1. Which of the following can be the composition of *B* and *C* respectively?

(a) $Ni(SCN)_2$ and $Ni_2[Fe(CN)_6]$ (b) $Co(SCN)_2$ and $Co_2[Fe(CN)_6]$

(c) $[Fe(SCN)_6]^{3-}$ and $Fe_3[Fe(CN)_6]_2$ (d) $Fe(SCN)_3$ and $Fe_4[Fe(CN)_6]_3$

2. Which is the oxidation state of the central atom in vapour *D* ?

(a) +VI (b) +V (c) +III (d) –II

3. Can the compound *A* be prepared in the anhydrous form by strongly heating its hydrated crystals?

(a) No, because the water molecules are very strongly bound in the hydrated crystals.

(b) No, because the salt gets hydrolysed in the process

(c) Yes, because the water molecules are loosely bound in the hydrated crystals

(d) Yes, because the salt sublimes at 300°C

Passage 20

(i) A yellow precipitate of the compound *A* is formed on passing H_2S through a neutral solution of the salt *B*.

(ii) The compound *A* is soluble in hot dilute HNO_3 but insoluble in yellow ammonium sulphide.

(iii) The solution of *B*, on treatment with a small quantity of NH_3, gives a white precipitate soluble in an excess of the reagent, forming a compound *C*.

(iv) The solution of *B* gives a white precipitate with a small concentration of KCN. The precipitate is soluble in an excess of the reagent, forming a compound *D*.

(v) The solution of *D*, on treatment with H_2S, gives *A*.

(vi) The solution of *B* in dilute HCl, on treatment with a solution of $BaCl_2$, gives a white precipitate of the compound *E*, which is almost insoluble in concentrated HNO_3.

1. Which of the following is the cation present in *B* ?

(a) As^{3+} (b) Sb^{3+}

(c) Zn^{2+} (d) Cd^{2+}

2. Which of the following anions is present in *B* ?

(a) SO_4^{2-} (b) CO_3^{2-}

(c) SO_3^{2-} (d) S^{2-}

3. Which of the following are the white precipitate and the soluble substance formed by the excess of the NaOH reagent, respectively ?

(a) AsOCl and AsO_3^{3-} (b) SbOCl and SbO_3^{3-}

(c) $Zn(OH)_2$ and $[Zn(NH_3)_4]^{2+}$ (d) $Cd(OH)_2$ and $[Cd(NH_3)_4]^{2+}$

4. Which of the following are the white precipitate and the soluble substance formed by the excess of the KCN reagent, respectively, in (iv)?

(a) $As(CN)_3$ and $[As(CN)_6]^{3-}$ (b) $Sb(CN)_3$ and $[Sb(CN)_6]^{3-}$

(c) $Zn(CN)_2$ and $[Zn(CN)_4]^{2-}$ (d) $Cd(CN)_2$ and $[Cd(CN)_4]^{2-}$

Passage 21

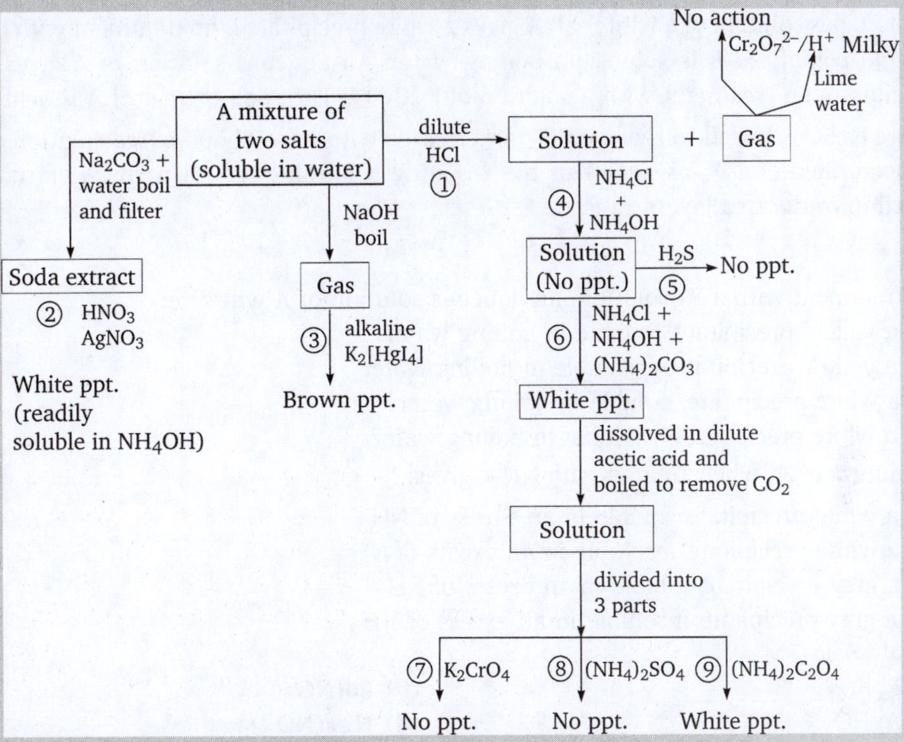

1. The white precipitate obtained in step (2) when filtered, washed with water and dissolved in NH_4OH, furnishes the ions:

(a) Ag^+, NH_4^+ and OH^- (b) $Ag^+ + NH_4^+ + Cl^-$

(c) $[Ag(NH_3)_2]^+, Cl^-$ (d) $[Ag(OH)_2]^-, NH_4^+, Cl^-$

2. The white precipitate obtained in step (6) is:

(a) $BaCO_3$ (b) $SrCO_3$

(c) $CaCO_3$ (d) $PbCO_3$

3. What will happen if the white precipitate obtained in step (9) is treated with a large volume of dilute H_2SO_4 and then with a few drops of a $KMnO_4$ solution?

(a) The precipitate will dissolve in dilute H_2SO_4 and the solution will decolorise the permangnate solution

(b) The precipitate will dissolve in dilute H_2SO_4 and the solution will give a brown precipitate with the $KMnO_4$ solution

(c) The precipitate will dissolve in dilute H_2SO_4 and the solution will not react with $KMnO_4$

(d) The precipitate will not dissolve in dilute H_2SO_4 and the mixture will not react with $KMnO_4$

Passage 22

An aqueous solution of a white salt *A* gives a white precipitate *B* on treatment with dilute HCl in cold condition. *B* is soluble in boiling water. An aqueous solution of *A* gives a yellow precipitate on treatment with a solution of K_2CrO_4. The soda extract of *A* is acidified with dilute H_2SO_4, boiled to remove CO_2 and treated with a freshly prepared solution of $FeSO_4$. Concentrated H_2SO_4 is added to the resulting solution . A brown ring is formed at the junction of the two layers.

1. On treatment with a KI solution, an aqueous solution of *A* will give:
(a) a yellow precipitate, soluble in boiling water
(b) a yellow precipitate, insoluble in boiling water
(c) a white precipitate, soluble in boiling water
(d) a white precipitate, insoluble in boiling water

2. A solution of *A*, when treated with NH_3, gives:
(a) a white precipitate soluble in an excess of NH_3
(b) a white precipitate insoluble in an excess of NH_3
(c) a grey precipitate soluble in an excess of NH_3
(d) a grey precipitate insoluble in an excess of NH_3

3. The salt *A* is:
(a) $PbBr_2$ (b) $Pb(NO_3)_2$
(c) $AgNO_3$ (d) $Hg_2(NO_3)_2$

Passage 23

Consider the following sequence of reactions.

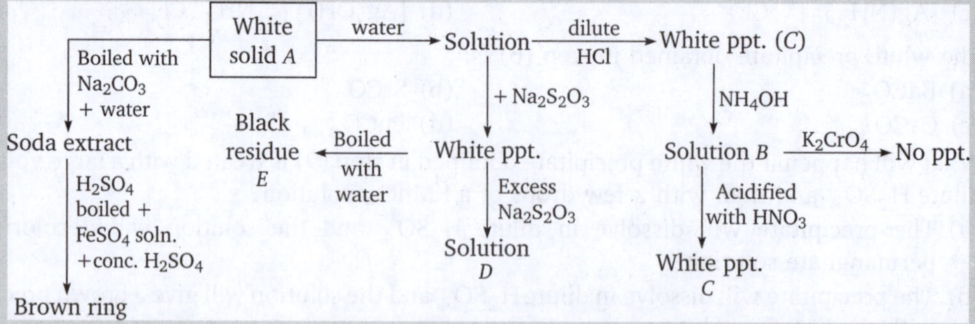

1. The white solid *A* is a:
(a) Chloride (b) Nitrate
(c) Nitrite (d) Bromide

2. The change from *B* to *C* involves the reaction:
(a) $[Hg(NH_3)_4]^{2+} + 2H^+ + Cl^- \rightarrow Hg(NH_2)Cl\downarrow + 3NH_4^+$
(b) $[Pb(NH_3)_4]^{2+} + 4H^+ + 2Cl^- \rightarrow PbCl_2\downarrow + 4NH_4^+$
(c) $[Pb(OH)_4]^{2-} + 4H^+ + 2Cl^- \rightarrow PbCl_2\downarrow + 4H_2O$
(d) $[Ag(NH_3)_2]^+ + 2H^+ + Cl^- \rightarrow AgCl\downarrow + 2NH_4^+$

3. The solution *D* and the residue *E* respectively contain:
(a) $Hg_2S_2O_3$ and Hg_2S
(b) PbS_2O_3 and Pb
(c) $[Ag(S_2O_3)_2]^{3-}$ and Ag_2S
(d) None of these

Passage 24

(i) When an aqueous solution of a colourless mixture of two salts is treated with a drop of chlorine water, the solution becomes brown. Some chloroform is added to the brown solution and the resulting mixture is shaken well. The chloroform layer becomes violet.

(ii) When chlorine water is again added dropwise to the above mixture, the chloroform layer becomes colourless.

(iii) On being heated with solid $K_2Cr_2O_7$ and concentrated H_2SO_4, the solid mixture gives vapours of a dark colour which form a yellow solution with aqueous NaOH. On acidification with acetic acid followed by treatment with lead acetate, the yellow solution gives a yellow precipitate.

(iv) When boiled with an NaOH solution, the mixture gives a gas that produces thick white fumes with HCl vapours and turns Nessler's reagent brown. The mixture does not respond to any other test for cations.

(v) The mixture, on being heated, gets completely sublimed.

1. The brown solution obtained in (i) is due to:
(a) Br_3^-
(b) I_3^-
(c) Cl_2
(d) NO_2

2. Which of the following reactions takes place in (ii)?
(a) $I_2 + 2Cl^- \longrightarrow 2I^- + Cl_2\uparrow$
(b) $Br_2 + 2Cl^- \longrightarrow 2Br^- + Cl_2\uparrow$
(c) $I_3^- + 8Cl_2 + 9H_2O \longrightarrow 3IO_3^- + 16Cl^- + 18H^+$
(d) $Br_3^- + 8Cl_2 + 9H_2O \longrightarrow 3BrO_3^- + 16Cl^- + 18H^+$

3. The vapours obtained in (iii) contain:
(a) CrO_2Cl_2 and I_2
(b) CrO_2Cl_2 only
(c) I_2 only
(d) CrO_2Br_2

4. What is the oxidation sate of the central atom in the anion constituting the yellow precipitate obtained in (iii)?
(a) 0
(b) +2
(c) +4
(d) +6

5. The original mixture contains:
(a) NH_4Cl and NH_4Br
(b) NH_4Br and NH_4I
(c) NH_4Cl and NH_4I
(d) NH_4Cl and NH_4NO_3

Passage 25

(i) A white solid mixture of two salts containing a common cation is insoluble in water. It dissolves in dilute HCl producing two gases (with effervescence) that turn an acidified dichromate solution green. After the gases are passed through the acidified dichromate solution, the emerging gas turns baryta water milky.

(ii) On treatment with dilute HNO_3, the white solid gives a solution which does not directly give a precipitate with a $BaCl_2$ solution but gives a white precipitate when warmed with H_2O_2 and then treated with a $BaCl_2$ solution.

(iii) The solution of the mixture in dilute HCl, when treated with NH_4Cl, NH_4OH and an Na_2HPO_4 solution, gives a white precipitate.

1. The gases evolved in (i) are:
(a) CO_2 and HCl (b) SO_2 and CO_2 (c) SO_2 and H_2S (d) NH_3 and CO_2

2. The white precipitate obtained in (ii) indicates the presence of a:
(a) carbonate (b) sulphide (c) sulphite (d) chloride

3. The white precipitate obtained in (iii) consists of:
(a) $Ba_3(PO_4)_2$ (b) $Sr_3(PO_4)_2$ (c) $Ca_3(PO_4)_2$ (d) $MgNH_4PO_4 \cdot 6H_2O$

ONE OR MORE ANSWERS IS/ARE CORRECT

1. Basic radical(s) which can not be identified by borax bead test :
(a) Mg^{2+} (b) Pb^{2+} (c) Fe^{3+} (d) Ag^{+}

2. 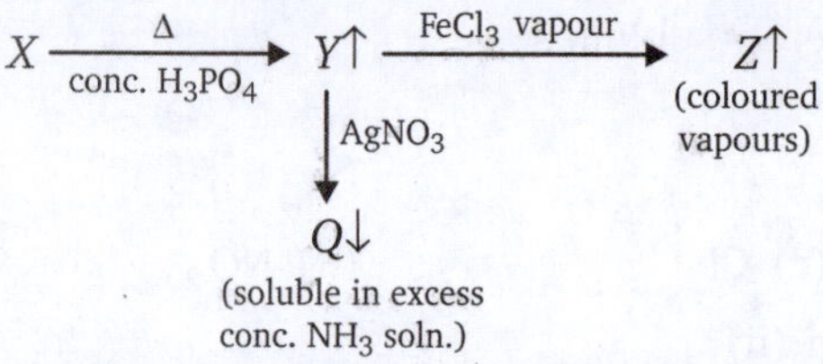

Which of the following anion cannot be in X ?
(a) F^- (b) Cl^- (c) Br^- (d) I^-

3. When ozone reacts with an excess of potassium iodide solution buffered with a borate buffer (pH 9.2) iodine is liberated which can be titrated against a standard solution of sodium thiosulphate, this is a quantitative method for estimating O_3 gas. When liberated I_2 and sodium thiosulphate will react, then product is/are :
(a) $S_4O_6^{2-}$ (b) SO_4^{2-} (c) $S_2O_4^{2-}$ (d) S

4. Which of the following pairs of cations cannot be separate by using an NaOH solution?
(a) Fe^{3+}, Al^{3+} (b) Cr^{3+}, Al^{3+}
(c) Sn^{2+}, Pb^{2+} (d) Cu^{2+}, Pb^{2+}

5. 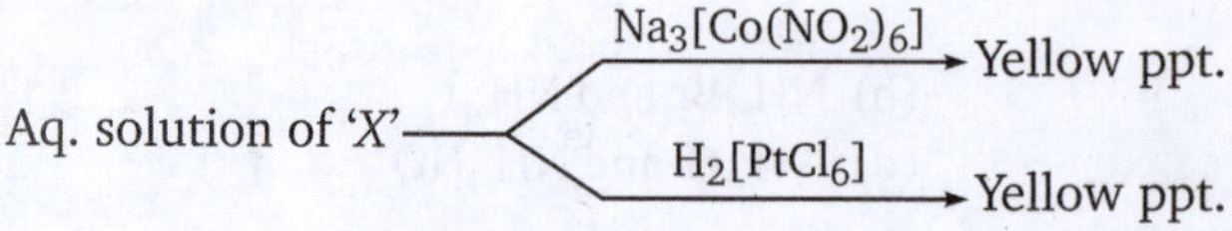

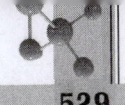

The cation(s) present in 'X' is/are:

(a) NH_4^+ (b) Na^+ (c) Mg^{2+} (d) K^+

6. Potassium chromate solution is added to aqueous solutions of metal nitrate. The yellow precipitate thus obtained are insoluble in acetic acid. These are subjected to flame test, flame colour of individual ppt. is/are:

(a) Lilac (b) Apple green
(c) Crimson red (d) Blue

7. A white sublimable solid, when boiled with an NaOH solution, gives a colourless gas that turns Nessler's reagent brown. The solid, on being heated with solid $K_2Cr_2O_7$ and concentrated H_2SO_4, gives red brown vapours. The white solid can be:

(a) NH_4I (b) NH_4Br (c) NH_4Cl (d) $(NH_4)_2SO_4$

8.
$KMnO_4$ + gas 'B'
H_2O_2 + gas 'B' ⟶ Aq. suspension $\xrightarrow[\text{Reagent}]{[P]}$ H_2SO_4
Br_2 water + gas 'B'

Which of the following option(s) is/are correct regarding 'P' among the following?

(a) O_3 (b) Excess Cl_2 water (c) conc. HNO_3 (d) HCl

9. In which of the following cases a violet colouration be observed?

(a) An alkaline solution of sodium nitroprusside is treated with a solution of Na_2S
(b) A solution of sodium cobaltinitrite is treated with one of KCl
(c) A solution of $Mn(NO_3)_2$ is treated with sodium bismuthate or red lead in the presence of concentrated HNO_3
(d) A solution of sodium nitroprusside in aqueous NaOH is treated with Na_2SO_3

10. Conc. H_2SO_3 is heated at 150°C in a closed container. The product obtained is treated with $BaCl_2$ solution. What is/are the observation(s)?

(a) No ppt. (b) Yellow turbidity
(c) Evolution of SO_2 (d) White ppt.

11. Which reaction is/are possible?

(a) $MgCl_2 + NaNO_3 \longrightarrow$ (b) $BaSO_4 + HCl \longrightarrow$
(c) $ZnSO_4 + BaS \longrightarrow$ (d) $BaCO_3 + CH_3COOH \longrightarrow$

12. Which of the following combinations in an aqueous medium will give a blue colour or precipitate?

(a) $Fe^{2+} + [Fe(CN)_6]^{3+}$ (b) $Fe^{3+} + [Fe(CN)_6]^{4-}$
(c) $Hg^{2+} + SCN^- + Co^{2+}$ (d) $Fe^{3+} + SCN^-$

13. Which statement is/are correct with reference to the ferrous and ferric ions?

(a) Fe^{2+} gives brown colour with potassium ferricyanide
(b) Fe^{2+} gives blue colour with potassium ferricyanide
(c) Fe^{3+} gives red colour with potassium thiocyanate
(d) Fe^{2+} gives brown colour with potassium thiocyanate

14. Which of the following combinations in an aqueous medium will give a red colour or precipitate?

(a) $Fe^{3+} + SCN^-$ (b) $Fe^{2+} + [Fe(CN)_6]^{3-}$
(c) Ni^{2+} + dimethylglyoxime + NH_3 solution (d) $Co^{2+} + SCN^-$

15. Which of the following sulphates are soluble in water?
(a) $CuSO_4$ (b) $PbSO_4$
(c) Ag_2SO_4 (d) $BaSO_4$

16. Which of the following pair(s) contain species, which react with each other on mixing their aqueous solutions to give yellow precipitate?
(a) NaI and NaCl (b) NaCl and I_2
(c) $AgNO_3$ and NaI (d) $Pb(NO_3)_2$ and NaI

17. Which of the following sulphides dissolve in dilute HCl?
(a) CoS (b) NiS (c) MnS (d) ZnS

18. Acidic $K_2Cr_2O_7$ reacts with H_2S to produce:
(a) Cr^{6+} ions (b) Cr^{3+} ions (c) SO_2 (d) S

19. Which of the following reagents can be used to distinguish between SO_2 and CO_2?
(a) Lime water (b) $BaCl_2$ solution
(c) $H_2O_2 + BaCl_2$ solution + dil. HCl (d) Acidified dichromate paper

20. Which of the following will dissolve in a mixture of NaOH and H_2O_2?
(a) $Fe(OH)_3$ (b) $Cr(OH)_3$ (c) $Al(OH)_3$ (d) $Zn(OH)_2$

21. Which of the following reagents will not be useful in separating a mixture of Zn^{2+} and Cu^{2+}?
(a) H_2S in an acid medium (b) H_2S in an alkaline medium
(c) Excess NaOH solution (d) NH_3 solution

22. Which of the following mixtures cannot be separated by passing H_2S through their solutions containing dilute HCl ?
(a) Cu^{2+} and Sb^{3+} (b) Pb^{2+} and Cd^{2+}
(c) Pb^{2+} and Al^{3+} (d) Zn^{2+} and Mn^{2+}

23. Which of the following substances on being heated will give a gas that turns limewater milky?
(a) Na_2CO_3 (b) $ZnCO_3$ (c) $ZnSO_3$ (d) $MgCO_3$

24. A white precipitate is obtained when:
(a) a solution of $BaCl_2$ is treated with Na_2SO_3
(b) a solution of $NaAlO_2$ is heated with NH_4Cl
(c) H_2S is passed through a solution of $ZnSO_4$
(d) a solution of $ZnSO_4$ is treated with Na_2CO_3

25. Which of the following cations will turn a borax bead green in an oxidising flame?
(a) Fe^{2+} (b) Mn^{2+} (c) Cr^{3+} (d) Cu^{2+}

26. Which of the following substances are blue?
(a) $Fe(BO_2)_2$ (b) $CoAl_2O_4$ (c) $Co(BO_2)_2$ (d) $NaCoPO_4$

27. On reaction with dilute H_2SO_4, which of the following salts will give out a gas that turns an acidified dichromate paper green ?
(a) Na_2CO_3 (b) Na_2S (c) $ZnSO_3$ (d) FeS

28. A yellow precipitate is obtained when:
(a) lead acetate solution is treated with K_2CrO_4
(b) $Pb(NO_3)_2$ solution is treated with K_2CrO_4
(c) $AgNO_3$ solution treated with KI
(d) H_2S is passed through a solution of $CdSO_4$

29. Which of the following ions can be separated by using NH_4Cl and NH_4OH?
(a) Fe^{3+} and Cr^{3+} (b) Cr^{3+} and Co^{2+} (c) Cr^{3+} and Al^{3+} (d) Al^{3+} and Ba^{2+}

30. Which of the following cations cannot be separated by passing H_2S through their solutions to which NH_4Cl and NH_4OH have been added?
(a) Ca^{2+} and Ni^{2+} (b) Mg^{2+} and Mn^{2+} (c) Ni^{2+} and Mn^{2+} (d) Co^{2+} and Zn^{2+}

31. Which of the following mixtures of ions in solution can be separated by using NH_3 solution?
(a) Hg_2^{2+} and Ag^+ (b) Bi^{3+} and Cu^{2+} (c) Ag^+ and Pb^{2+} (d) Cu^{2+} and Cd^{2+}

32. Which of the following compounds are coloured?
(a) $PbCl_2$ (b) PbI_2 (c) AgCl (d) AgI

33. Which of the following mixtures of ions in solution can be separated by using dilute H_2SO_4?
(a) Zn^{2+} and Pb^{2+} (b) Ba^{2+} and Pb^{2+} (c) Mn^{2+} and Sr^{2+} (d) Sr^{2+} and Ba^{2+}

34. Which of the following species will be decomposed on acidification?
(a) $[Ag(NH_3)_2]^+$ (b) $[Cu(NH_3)_4]^{2+}$
(c) $[Zn(OH)_4]^{2-}$ (d) $[Pb(OH)_4]^{2-}$

35. Which of the following mixtures of ions in solution can be separated by using NaOH solution?
(a) Fe^{3+} and Pb^{2+} (b) Pb^{2+} and Sn^{2+} (c) Zn^{2+} and Sn^{2+} (d) Al^{3+} and Cu^{2+}

36. Which of the following ions can be separated by using dilute HCl?
(a) Ag^+ and Cu^{2+} (b) Ag^+ and Hg_2^{2+} (c) Hg_2^{2+} and Cd^{2+} (d) Ag^+ and Al^{3+}

37. Which of the following substances will leave a black residue on strong heating ?
(a) $CuSO_4 \cdot 5H_2O$ (b) $ZnCO_3$ (c) $PbCO_3$ (d) $MnSO_4$

38. By which of the following reagents can a sublimate of $HgCl_2$ be distinguished from NH_4Cl ?
(a) H_2S (b) $BaCl_2$ (c) $NaNO_3$ (d) $FeCl_3$

39. An aqueous solution is prepared by dissolving a mixture containing $ZnCl_2$, $CdCl_2$ and $CuCl_2$. Now H_2S gas is passed through the aqueous solution of salt to form precipitate.
(a) CdS (b) CuS (c) ZnS (d) No ppt.

40. An aqueous solution containing S^{2-} ions will not give:
(a) Yellow precipitate with the suspension of $CdCO_3$ in water
(b) Black precipitate with lead acetate solution
(c) White precipitate with $BaCl_2$ solution
(d) Purple colour with sodium thiosulphate solution

41. Which of the following statement(s) is/are correct when a solid mixture of NaCl and $K_2Cr_2O_7$ is gently warmed with conc. H_2SO_4 ?
(a) A deep red vapour is evolved
(b) The vapour when passed into NaOH solution gives a yellow solution of Na_2CrO_4
(c) Chlorine gas is evolved
(d) Chromyl chloride is formed

42. Choose the correct reaction:
(a) $BaCl_2 + AcOH + K_2CrO_4 \longrightarrow$ yellow ppt.
(b) $BaCO_3(s) + K_2C_2O_4 + AcOH \longrightarrow$ white ppt.
(c) $BaCO_3(s) + K_2CrO_4 + AcOH \longrightarrow$ No ppt.
(d) $SrCO_3(s) + K_2CrO_4 + AcOH \longrightarrow$ No ppt.

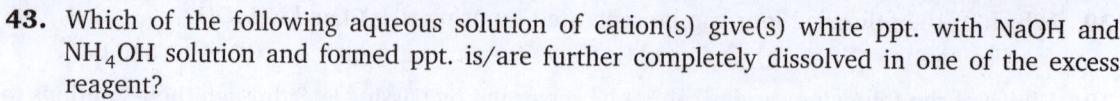

43. Which of the following aqueous solution of cation(s) give(s) white ppt. with NaOH and NH_4OH solution and formed ppt. is/are further completely dissolved in one of the excess reagent?

(a) Cd^{2+} (b) Cr^{3+} (c) Sn^{2+} (d) Bi^{3+}

44. $Al_2(SO_4)_3 + NH_4OH \longrightarrow X$

Select the correct statement(s) about compound X:

(a) X is a white coloured compound (b) X is insoluble in excess of NH_4OH

(c) X is soluble in NaOH (d) X can be used as an antacid

45. The evolution of a red-brown gas on heating a salt with $K_2Cr_2O_7$ and concentrated H_2SO_4 can arise from:

(a) chloride (b) bromide (c) nitrate (d) nitrite

MATCH THE COLUMN

Column-I and Column-II contains four entries each. Entries of column-I are to be matched with some entries of column-II. Each entry of column-I may have the matching with one or more than one entries of column-II.

1.

Column-I (Reaction with Salt/Radical)	Column-II (Salt/Radical)
(A) $Zn + dil.H_2SO_4$	(P) $Pb(NO_2)_2$
(B) dil. HCl	(Q) $(NH_4)_2S$
(C) NaOH (excess)	(R) $MnO_4^-(aq.)$
(D) KI	(S) $Hg_2^{2+}(aq.)$
	(T) $Bi^{3+}(aq.)$

2.

Column-I	Column-II
(A) Colourless gas evolved on addition of dil. H_2SO_4	(P) $S_2O_3^{2-}$
(B) White ppt. on addition of $AgNO_3$	(Q) S^{2-}
(C) Black ppt. obtained when $HgCl_2$ is added in little amount	(R) NO_2^-
(D) The ppt. obtained on addition of $AgNO_3$ followed by NH_3 solution	(S) $CH_3CO_2^-$

3.

Column-I	Column-II
(A) Precipitate with KCN, which is soluble in excess of reagent	(P) Fe^{2+}
(B) Precipitate with NaOH and NH_4OH, which is insoluble in both excess of reagent	(Q) Hg^{2+}
(C) Coloured ppt. with KI, which is soluble in excess of reagent	(R) Pb^{2+}
(D) Black ppt. with H_2S, which is soluble in hot and dil. HNO_3	(S) Ag^+

4.

Column-I	Column-II
(A) $ZnCl_2 + H_2S$	(P) Pale green colouration
(B) $CuSO_4 +$ Excess KI	(Q) Brown solution/ppt.
(C) $Pb_3O_4 +$ dil. HNO_3	(R) Yellow turbidity
(D) $FeCl_3 + H_2S$	(S) No change is observed

5.

Column-I (Radicals)	Column-II (Test reagent)
(A) Oxalate	(P) Sodium nitroprusside
(B) Acetate	(Q) Conc. H_2SO_4
(C) Sulphide	(R) Neutral $FeCl_3$
(D) Thiosulphate	(S) Dil. HCl

6.

Column-I	Column-II
(A) $(NH_4)_2Cr_2O_7$	(P) Gives N_2O on heating
(B) $FeSO_4$	(Q) Gives CO_2 on heating
(C) $Mg(HCO_3)_2$	(R) Gives SO_2 and SO_3 on heating
(D) NH_4NO_3	(S) Gives N_2 on heating

7.

Column-I	Column-II
(A) Gas evolved by the action of dilute H_2SO_4 on a sulphite	(P) Colour of acidified $KMnO_4$ is discharged
(B) Gas evolved by the action of dilute H_2SO_4 on a carbonate	(Q) Acidified dichromate solution is turned green
(C) Gas evolved by heating an ammonium salt with NaOH	(R) Nessler's reagent gives a brown precipitate
(D) Gas evolved by the action of dilute H_2SO_4 on a sulphide	(S) Baryta water turns milky
	(T) Alkaline nitroprusside truns violet

8.

Column-I	Column-II
(A) Red vapours	(P) $MnSO_4 + NaBiO_3$ + Conc. HNO_3
(B) NaOH solution is turned yellow by the vapours	(Q) KCl + Solid $K_2Cr_2O_7$ + conc.H_2SO_4
(C) Purple solution	(R) KBr heated with MnO_2 and conc. H_2SO_4
(D) A colourless solution results when the evolved gas is absorbed in NaOH solution	(S) $Na_2S + Na_2[Fe(CN)_5(NO)]$

9.

Column-I	Column-II
(A) Soluble in a concentrated NH_3 solution	(P) Ag_2S
(B) Soluble in excess KCN solution	(Q) $Cu(OH)_2$
(C) Soluble in excess hypo solution	(R) AgBr
(D) Insoluble in conc. HNO_3	(S) AgCl

ASSERTION-REASON TYPE QUESTIONS

These questions consist of two statements each, printed as assertion and reason, while answering these questions you are required to choose any one of the following responses

(A) If assertion is true but the reason is false

(B) If assertion is false but reason is true

(C) If both assertion and reason are true and reason is the correct explanation of assertion

(D) If both assertion and reason are true but reason is not the correct explanation of assertion

1. **Assertion** : $AgNO_3$ reacts with KCN to form white ppt. of AgCN. This white ppt. disappears when excess KCN is added.
   Reason : AgCN decomposes to form silver-carbide and evolve N_2 gas.
2. **Assertion** : $HgCl_2$ does not respond chromyl chloride test.
   Reason : $HgCl_2$ being covalent compound ionises upto 2%.
3. **Assertion** : $Zn + HNO_3(conc.) \longrightarrow Zn(NO_3)_2 + NO_2 + H_2O$
   Reason : Nitric acid plays a double role in action on Zn metal, it acts as an acid as well as an oxidising agent.
4. **Assertion** : If yellow precipitate is obtained on adding ammonium molybdate solution on boiling then phosphate radical is identified.
   Reason : Ammonium phosphomolybdate is a yellow compound.
5. **Assertion** : $HgCl_2$ and $SnCl_2$ cannot exist together in an aqueous solution.
   Reason : $SnCl_2$ is a strong reducing agent because Sn shows inert pair effect.
6. **Assertion** : Sometimes a white turbidity is obtained when a solution is prepared in water .
   Reason : Pb^{2+} cations are precipitated as $PbCl_2$ which is sparingly soluble in water.

7. Assertion : CdS and As_2S_3 are yellow coloured compounds.
Reason : CdS and As_2S_3 can be separated by ammonium sulphide.

8. Assertion : Green edge flame test tells presence of borate ion.
Reason : Green colour of the flame is due to burning of tri ethyl borate.

9. Assertion : A solution of AgCl in NH_4OH gives a white precipitate when acidified with HNO_3.
Reason : $[Ag(NH_3)_2]^+$ decomposes in the presence of HNO_3.

10. Assertion : When H_2S is passed through a solution of $CuSO_4$, no precipitate of CuS is obtained until the solution is acidified with HCl.
Reason : The solubility product constant of CuS is not so high as to require a high concentration of S^{2-} for the precipitation of CuS.

11. Assertion : When H_2S is passed through a solution containing $[Cu(CN)_4]^{3-}$ and $[Cd(CN)_4]^{2-}$ ions, only cadmium precipitates as CdS.
Reason : The oxidation state and co-ordination number of cadmium in $[Cd(CN)_4]^{2-}$ are II and 4 respectively.

12. Assertion : A concentrated solution of $BiCl_3$ can be hydrolysed with water.
Reason : $BiCl_3$ does not change in composition with dilution.

13. Assertion : The blue precipitate formed by the action of $K_4[Fe(CN)_6]$ on Fe^{3+} and by that of $K_3[Fe(CN)_6]$ on Fe^{2+} have the common formula.
Reason : $[Fe(CN)_6]^{3-}$ oxidises Fe^{2+} to Fe^{3+} and itself gets reduced to $[Fe(CN)_6]^{4-}$.

14. Assertion : $Zn(OH)_2$ dissolves in an excess of NaOH solution as well as NH_4OH solution.
Reason : $Zn(OH)_2$ forms the soluble zincate salts with these alkalies.

15. Assertion : When a solution of Na_2ZnO_2 is acidified with dilute HCl and treated with H_2S, a precipitate of ZnS is formed.
Reason : Na_2ZnO_2 is decomposed by HCl to give Zn^{2+} ions.

16. Assertion : Br^- ions do not interfere in the chromyl chloride test for chlorides.
Reason : A bromide, on oxidation with $K_2Cr_2O_7$/ concentrated H_2SO_4, liberates Br_2, which dissolves in NaOH to give a colourless solution.

17. Assertion : Basic radical of V group are precipitated as their carbonates in presence of $NH_4Cl + NH_4OH$.
Reason : NH_4OH maintains the pH of the solution basic.

18. Assertion : NO_3^- ion can not be detected by brown ring test in presence of NO_2^- ion.
Reason : Both NO_2^- and NO_3^- ions evolve brown NO_2 gas with conc. H_2SO_4 acid.

SUBJECTIVE PROBLEMS

1. Consider the following reaction

$$Na_2SO_4 + C \xrightarrow{\Delta} (A) \xrightarrow{Na_2[Fe(CN)_5NO]} (B) \text{ Purple complex}$$

$$(A) \xrightarrow{Cd(NO_3)_2} (C) \text{ yellow ppt.}$$

Then calculate value of $|X^2 - Y^2|$ (where X and Y are total number of electrons present in "t_{2g}" and "e_g" orbitals respectively in d-block metal ion of compound B).

2. Find number of basic radicals among the following cations, which can form soluble complex on adding excess of NH_3 solution :

Cd^{2+} (aq.), Pb^{2+} (aq.), Ni^{2+} (aq.), Mn^{2+} (aq.), Zn^{2+} (aq.), Ag^{+} (aq.), Hg^{2+} (aq.), Fe^{3+} (aq.), Mg^{2+} (aq.)

3. Consider the following reaction

$Na_3PO_4 + (NH_4)_2MoO_4 + HNO_3(\text{dil.}) \longrightarrow$ 'X' (canary yellow ppt.)

Then calculate total number of atoms of 15th group elements which are sp^3 hybridized in compound 'X'.

4. How many anions will give colourless acid vapour/ gas with conc. H_2SO_4 on reaction with following given anions ?

CH_3COO^-, Cl^-, Br^-, S^{2-}, SO_3^{2-}, BO_3^{3-}, NO_2^-, $C_2O_4^{2-}$, I^-

5. $\underset{\text{Black}}{X(s)} \xrightarrow{\text{dil HCl}} Y\uparrow \xrightarrow[\text{NaOH}]{Na_2[Fe(CN)_5(NO)]}$ Purple solution Gas Y has been allowed to react with following species in neutral/acidic medium :

(a) $FeCl_3$ (b) $CuSO_4$ (c) $BaCl_2$ (d) SO_2

(e) $Cr_2O_7^{2-}$ (f) CH_3COONa (g) Hg^{2+}

Then calculate value of $(P + Q - R)$

P : Number of species which undergoes redox reaction with gas Y.

Q : Number of species with which gas Y undergoes precipitation.

R : Number of species with which gas Y produce no observable change.

6. Consider the sulphide HgS, PbS, CuS, Sb_2S_3, As_2S_3 and CdS. Number of these sulphides soluble in 50% HNO_3 is ________ .

Answers

Level-1

1. (c)	**2.** (c)	**3.** (b)	**4.** (c)	**5.** (d)	**6.** (d)	**7.** (d)	**8.** (d)	**9.** (a)	**10.** (b)
11. (c)	**12.** (a)	**13.** (a)	**14.** (b)	**15.** (c)	**16.** (d)	**17.** (c)	**18.** (a,d)	**19.** (a)	**20.** (a)
21. (a)	**22.** (c)	**23.** (b)	**24.** (a)	**25.** (b)	**26.** (c)	**27.** (b,c)	**28.** (a)	**29.** (a)	**30.** (c)
31. (b)	**32.** (a)	**33.** (b,c)	**34.** (b)	**35.** (a)	**36.** (c)	**37.** (c)	**38.** (c)	**39.** (c)	**40.** (d)
41. (b)	**42.** (a)	**43.** (b,d)	**44.** (a)	**45.** (d)	**46.** (b)	**47.** (c)	**48.** (b)	**49.** (d)	**50.** (a)
51. (c)	**52.** (b)	**53.** (a)	**54.** (a)	**55.** (c)	**56.** (b)	**57.** (c)	**58.** (a)	**59.** (a)	**60.** (a)
61. (c)	**62.** (d)	**63.** (c)	**64.** (b)	**65.** (a)	**66.** (b)	**67.** (c)	**68.** (a)	**69.** (d)	**70.** (a)
71. (b)	**72.** (d)	**73.** (d)	**74.** (d)	**75.** (a)	**76.** (c)	**77.** (a)	**78.** (d)	**79.** (b)	**80.** (d)
81. (c)	**82.** (d)	**83.** (d)	**84.** (a)	**85.** (b)	**86.** (c)	**87.** (d)	**88.** (d)	**89.** (c)	**90.** (a)
91. (b)	**92.** (c)								

Level-2

1. (a)	**2.** (b)	**3.** (b)	**4.** (d)	**5.** (b)	**6.** (c)	**7.** (b)	**8.** (c)	**9.** (d)	**10.** (a)
11. (b)	**12.** (c)	**13.** (d)	**14.** (d)	**15.** (b)	**16.** (a)	**17.** (a)	**18.** (b)	**19.** (c)	**20.** (a)
21. (c)	**22.** (b)	**23.** (d)	**24.** (d)	**25.** (b)	**26.** (b)	**27.** (b)	**28.** (b)	**29.** (c)	**30.** (d)
31. (b)	**32.** (d)	**33.** (d)	**34.** (a)	**35.** (c)	**36.** (a)	**37.** (a)	**38.** (b)	**39.** (c)	**40.** (c)
41. (a)	**42.** (a)	**43.** (c)	**44.** (d)	**45.** (a)	**46.** (a)	**47.** (d)	**48.** (a)	**49.** (d)	**50.** (c)
51. (c)	**52.** (b)	**53.** (d)	**54.** (a)	**55.** (a)	**56.** (a)	**57.** (b)	**58.** (d)	**59.** (b)	**60.** (d)
61. (b)	**62.** (a)	**63.** (d)	**64.** (b)	**65.** (a)	**66.** (b)	**67.** (b)	**68.** (d)	**69.** (b)	**70.** (a)
71. (c)	**72.** (c)	**73.** (d)	**74.** (b)	**75.** (c)	**76.** (a)	**77.** (b)			

Level-3

Passage-1	1.	(b)	2.	(c)	3.	(b)				
Passage-2	1.	(b)	2.	(c)	3.	(b)				
Passage-3	1.	(b)	2.	(b)						
Passage-4	1.	(c)	2.	(b)	3.	(a)				
Passage-5	1.	(d)	2.	(b)	3.	(a)				
Passage-6	1.	(a)	2.	(d)	3.	(a)	4.	(b)		
Passage-7	1.	(c)	2.	(b)	3.	(c)	4.	(d)		
Passage-8	1.	(b)	2.	(d)	3.	(c)				
Passage-9	1.	(b)	2.	(d)	3.	(c)				
Passage-10	1.	(b)	2.	(c)	3.	(a)	4.	(d)		
Passage-11	1.	(c)	2.	(b)	3.	(b)	4.	(d)	5.	(a)
Passage-12	1.	(b)	2.	(c)	3.	(c)	4.	(a)		
Passage-13	1.	(c)	2.	(d)	3.	(d)				
Passage-14	1.	(d)	2.	(c)	3.	(c)				
Passage-15	1.	(a)	2.	(b)	3.	(b)				
Passage-16	1.	(a)	2.	(c)	3.	(c)				
Passage-17	1.	(b)	2.	(a)	3.	(d)				
Passage-18	1.	(c)	2.	(a)	3.	(b)	4.	(a,b)	5.	(d)
Passage-19	1.	(d)	2.	(a)	3.	(b)				
Passage-20	1.	(d)	2.	(a)	3.	(d)	4.	(d)		
Passage-21	1.	(c)	2.	(c)	3.	(a)				
Passage-22	1.	(a)	2.	(b)	3.	(b)				
Passage-23	1.	(b)	2.	(d)	3.	(c)				
Passage-24	1.	(b)	2.	(c)	3.	(a)	4.	(d)	5.	(c)
Passage-25	1.	(b)	2.	(c)	3.	(d)				

One or More Answers is/are Correct

1. (a, b, d) **2.** (a, d) **3.** (a) **4.** (b, c) **5.** (a, d) **6.** (b, d)
7. (b, c) **8.** (a, c, c) **9.** (a, c) **10.** (b, d) **11.** (c, d) **12.** (a, b, c)
13. (b, c) **14.** (a, c) **15.** (a, c) **16.** (c, d) **17.** (c, d) **18.** (b, d)
19. (c, d) **20.** (b, c, d) **21.** (b, d) **22.** (a, b, d) **23.** (b, c, d) **24.** (a, b, d)
25. (c) **26.** (b, c, d) **27.** (b, c, d) **28.** (a, b, c, d) **29.** (b, d) **30.** (c, d)
31. (a, b, c) **32.** (b, d) **33.** (a, c) **34.** (a, b, c, d) **35.** (a, d) **36.** (a, c, d)
37. (a, d) **38.** (a) **39.** (a, b) **40.** (c, d) **41.** (a, b, d) **42.** (a, d)
43. (a, c) **44.** (a, b, c, d) **45.** (a, b, c, d)

Match The Column

1. A → P, Q, R, S, T; B → P, Q, R, S; C → P, Q, R, S, T; D → P, R, S, T
2. A → P, Q, S; B → P, R, S; C → Q; D → Q
3. A → P, S; B → P, Q; C → Q, R; D → R, S
4. A → S; B → Q; C → Q; D → P, R
5. A → Q; B → Q, R, S; C → P, S; D → R, S
6. A → S; B → R; C → Q; D → P
7. A → P, Q, S; B → S; C → R; D → P, Q, T
8. A → Q,R B → Q; C → P, S; D → R
9. A → Q, R, S; B → P, Q, R, S; C → Q, R, S; D → P, R, S

Assertion-Reason Type Questions

1. (A) **2.** (C) **3.** (C) **4.** (B) **5.** (A) **6.** (D) **7.** (D) **8.** (C) **9.** (C) **10.** (B)
11. (D) **12.** (A) **13.** (C) **14.** (A) **15.** (B) **16.** (C) **17.** (D) **18.** (C)

Subjective Problems

1. 36
2. 4
3. 4
4. 6
5. 3
6. 5

Hints and Solutions

Level 1

1. (c) $\underset{\text{(Amphoteric)}}{Al(OH)_3} \xrightarrow[\text{Excess}]{\text{NaOH}} Na[Al(OH)_4] + H_2O$

2. (c) (i) $Al^{3+}_{(aq.)} + NaOH \longrightarrow \underset{\substack{\text{White ppt.}\\\text{(Amphoteric)}}}{Al(OH)_3\downarrow} \xrightarrow{\text{NaOH}} Na[Al(OH)_4]$

(ii) $Zn^{2+}_{(aq.)} + NaOH \longrightarrow \underset{\substack{\text{White ppt.}\\\text{(Amphoteric)}}}{Zn(OH)_2\downarrow} \xrightarrow{\text{NaOH}} Na_2[Zn(OH)_4]$

(iii) $Cu^{2+}_{(aq.)} + OH^- \longrightarrow \underset{\substack{\text{Blue ppt.}\\\text{(Basic)}}}{CuOH_2\downarrow} \xrightarrow{\text{NaOH}} \text{No reaction}$

3. (b) $Bi^{3+} + 3I^- \longrightarrow \underset{\text{(black)}}{BiI_3} \xrightarrow{I^-} \underset{\substack{\text{(orange)}\\\text{soluble}}}{[BiI_4]^-}$

23. (b) The value of K_{sp} of hydroxides of Fe^{3+}, Cr^{3+}, Al^{3+} are lower than that of Co^{2+}, Ni^{2+}, Mn^{2+} and Zn^{2+}. Therefore; in the presence of NH_4Cl, dissociation of NH_4OH is suppressed and conc. of OH^-, furnished from NH_4OH, is such that only third group basic radicals are precipitate.

24. (a)

$$Bi_2S_3 + \underset{\text{(dil.)}}{8HNO_3} \xrightarrow{\text{hot}} 2Bi(NO_3)_3 + 3S\downarrow + 2NO + 4H_2O$$

$$Bi(NO_3)_3 + 3NH_4OH \longrightarrow \underset{(C)}{Bi(OH)_3\downarrow} + 3NH_4NO_3$$

$$Bi(OH)_3\downarrow + 3HCl \longrightarrow \underset{(D)}{BiCl_3} + 3H_2O$$

$$\underset{(D)}{BiCl_3} + H_2O \rightleftharpoons \underset{\text{white turbidity}}{BiOCl} + 2HCl$$

29. (a) Cu^{2+} is second group radical, gets precipitated first due to having lower solubility product $[CuS\text{–}K_{sp} = 1 \times 10^{-44}]$

31. (b) $Ba(NO_3)_2 + Na_2SO_4 \longrightarrow \underset{\text{white ppt.}}{BaSO_4\downarrow} + 2NaNO_3$

32. (a)

$$NH_4Cl \xrightarrow{\Delta} \underset{Y}{NH_3} + \underset{Z}{HCl}$$

$$\underset{Y}{NH_3} + \underset{\text{Nessler's reagent}}{2K_2[HgI_4]} + 3KOH \longrightarrow \underset{\substack{\text{brown ppt.}\\\text{iodide of Millon's base}}}{H_2NHgO\cdot HgI} + 7KI + H_2O$$

33. (c) I_2 is reduced to HI thus decolorisation of the colour takes places.

$$SO_2 + I_2 + 2H_2O \longrightarrow H_2SO_4 + 2HI$$

34. (b)

$$Pb(NO_3)_2 + 2NH_4OH \longrightarrow \underset{\text{white ppt.}}{Pb(OH)_2} + 2NH_4NO_3$$

$$Pb(NO_3)_2 + 2NaCl \longrightarrow \underset{\text{white ppt.}}{PbCl_2} + 2NaNO_3$$

$$Pb(NO_3)_2 + H_2S \longrightarrow \underset{\text{black ppt.}}{PbS} + 2HNO_3$$

36. (c) $S_2O_3^{2-} + 2H^+ \xrightarrow{\Delta} \underset{\text{gas pungent odour}}{SO_2} + \underset{\text{pale yellow ppt.}}{S} + H_2O$

37. (c) $AgNO_3 \xrightarrow{\Delta} \underset{(W)}{Ag} + \underset{(X)}{NO_2} + \frac{1}{2}O_2$

$$\underset{(X)}{NO_2} + H_2O \longrightarrow HNO_2 + HNO_3$$

$$\underset{(W)}{3Ag} + 4HNO_3 \longrightarrow 3AgNO_3 + NO + 2H_2O$$

$$AgNO_3 + 2Na_2S_2O_3 \longrightarrow Na_3[Ag(S_2O_3)_2] + NaNO_3$$

72. (d) $CaCO_3 \xrightarrow{\text{heat}} CaO + \underset{\text{colourless gas}}{CO_2\uparrow}$

$$\underset{\text{residue}}{CaO} + H_2O \longrightarrow \underset{'Y'}{Ca(OH)_2}$$

$$\underset{'Y'}{Ca(OH)_2} + \underset{\text{excess}}{2CO_2} \longrightarrow Ca(HCO_3)_2$$

$$\underset{'Z'}{Ca(HCO_3)_2} \xrightarrow{\text{heat}} \underset{'X'}{CaCO_3} + CO_2 + H_2O$$

73. (d) $Pb^{2+}(aq) + 2HCl\ (\text{dil.}) \longrightarrow PbCl_2$ (white ppt.)
White ppt. of $PbCl_2$ is soluble in hot water. Pb^{2+} ions give black ppt. of PbS with H_2S.

82. (d) $I^-(aq) \longrightarrow \frac{1}{2}I_2(s) + e^-\} \times 5$

$$IO_3^-(aq) + 6H^+(aq) + 5e \longrightarrow \frac{1}{2}I_2(s) + 3H_2O\ (l)$$

$$5I^-(aq) + IO_3^-(aq) + 6H^+(aq) \longrightarrow 3I_2 + 3H_2O\ (l)$$

83. (d) $3Cl_2 + 6OH^- \longrightarrow 5Cl^- + ClO_3^- + 3H_2O$

84. (a) NaOH + $CuSO_4$ + Sodium (M) + Potassium (M_1) tartarate solution is known as Fehling's solution and is used in the detection of –CHO group.

85. (b) $\underset{(A)}{Ca(OH)_2} + Na_2CO_3 \longrightarrow \underset{(B)}{2NaOH} + \underset{(C)}{CaCO_3}$ $\underset{(A)}{Ca(OH)_2} \xrightarrow{CO_2} \underset{C\ \text{(milky)}}{CaCO_3}$

86. (c) On passing H_2S gas into first group filtrate sometimes yellow turbidity appears even in the absence of II group radicals, this is because of the oxidation of H_2S gas by some acid radicals and form collidal solution of sulphur.

$$Fe^{3+}_{(aq.)} \xrightarrow[\text{(Redox reaction)}]{H_2S/H^+} Fe^{2+}_{(aq.)} + S\downarrow$$

87. (d) Correct order of K_{sp} is $Ag_2S < MnS$ according to classification of basic radical.

88. (d) (i) $BaCl_2 + KI \longrightarrow$ No ppt.
(ii) $BaCl_{2(aq.)} + CrO_4^{2-} \longrightarrow \underset{\text{Yellow ppt.}}{BaCrO_4\downarrow}$ (insoluble in CH_3COOH acid)

89. (c) The green ppt. of $Ni(OH)_2$ is soluble in excess of NH_3 solution.

$$\underset{\text{Green ppt.}}{Ni(OH)_2\downarrow} + 6NH_3 \longrightarrow \underset{\text{Deep blue}}{[Ni(NH_3)_6]^{2+}} + 2OH^-$$

90. (a) Both Zn^{2+} and Cd^{2+} cations can be separated by passing H_2S gas in acidic as well as in neutral medium.
(i) $Zn^{2+} + H_2S \longrightarrow$ No ppt. (ii) $Cd^{2+} + H_2S \longrightarrow \underset{\text{Yellow ppt.}}{CdS\downarrow}$

91. (b) Al^{3+} and Zn^{2+} both form white ppt. with NH_3 solution but white ppt. of $Zn(OH)_2$ is soluble in excess of NH_3.

$$Al^{3+} + 3NH_3 + 3H_2O \longrightarrow Al(OH)_3\downarrow \xrightarrow{\text{Ex. } NH_3 \text{ solution}} \text{No reaction}$$

$$Zn^{2+} + 2NH_3 + 2H_2O \longrightarrow Zn(OH)_2\downarrow \xrightarrow{\text{Ex. } NH_3 \text{ solution}} [Zn(NH_3)_4]^{2+}$$

92. (c)

(a) $NaBr + H_2SO_4 \longrightarrow Na_2SO_4 + HBr\uparrow \xrightarrow[\text{(Remaining part)}]{\text{Conc. } H_2SO_4} \underset{\text{raddish brown}}{Br_2\uparrow}$

(b) $NaNO_3 + H_2SO_4 \longrightarrow \underset{\text{Raddish brown}}{NO_2\uparrow}$

(c) $CaF_2 + H_2SO_4 \longrightarrow CaSO_4 + \underset{\text{Colourless}}{HF\uparrow}$

(d) $KI + H_2SO_4 \longrightarrow K_2SO_4 + 2HI \xrightarrow[\text{(Remaining part)}]{\text{Conc. } H_2SO_4} \underset{\text{(Violet)}}{I_2\uparrow}$

Level 2

1. (a) $Fe^{3+} + \underset{(X)}{3NH_4SCN} \longrightarrow 3NH_4^+ + \underset{\text{(Blood red colour solution)}}{\underset{(Y)}{Fe(SCN)_3}}$

NH_4SCN has no change in colour with Fe^{2+}.

2. (b) $Bi^{3+}(aq) + Al^{3+}(aq)$

↓ NH_3 sol.

$\underset{\text{(white)}}{Bi(OH)_3\downarrow} + \underset{\text{(Gelatinous white)}}{Al(OH)_3\downarrow}$

↓ Excess of NH_3 sol.

both are not soluble

(b) $Al^{3+}(aq) + Zn^{2+}(aq)$

↓ NH_3 sol.

$\underset{\text{(Gelatinous white)}}{Al(OH)_3\downarrow} + \underset{\text{(Gelatinous white)}}{Zn(OH)_3\downarrow}$

↓ Excess NH_3 sol.

ppt. $Al(OH)_3$ | Filtrate $[Zn(NH_3)_4]$ colourless sol.

(c) $Hg^{2+}(aq) + Pb^{2+}(aq)$

↓ NH_3 sol.

$\underset{\text{white}}{HgO\cdot Hg(NH_2)(NO_3)\downarrow} + \underset{\text{white}}{Pb(OH)_2\downarrow}$

↓ Excess of NH_3 sol.

both are not soluble

(d) $Cu^{2+}(aq) + Cd^{2+}(aq)$

↓ NH_3 sol.

$\underset{\text{(Blue)}}{Cu^{2+}(OH)_2\downarrow} + \underset{(W)}{Cd(OH)_2\downarrow}$

↓ Excess of NH_3 sol.

$[Cu^{2+}(NH_3)_4]^{2+} + [Cd(NH_3)_4]^{2+}$

both are soluble

3. (b) During Brown ring test, ppt. of $PbSO_4$ will be formed, which hinder the formation of brown ring.

4. (d) $\underset{(P)}{CuSO_4} + \underset{(Q)}{2KI} \longrightarrow \underset{(R)}{CuI_2} + K_2SO_4$

(unstable)

$$2CuI_2 \longrightarrow 2CuI\downarrow + I_2\uparrow$$

$$Ag^+ + KI \longrightarrow AgI\downarrow + K^+$$

5. (b) Basic radicals are classified on the basis of increasing order of K_{sp} Cd^{2+} in II group while Ni^{2+} in IV group.

14. (d) (i) $CrO_2Cl_2 \xrightarrow{KOH} \underset{(X)}{K_2CrO_4} \xrightarrow[H_2SO_4]{conc.} \underset{(Y)}{K_2Cr_2O_7} \xrightarrow{AgNO_3} \underset{(Z)}{Ag_2Cr_2O_7}$

(ii) $CrCl_3(aq) \xrightarrow[NaOH]{excess} \underset{(X)}{Na[Cr(OH)_4]} \xrightarrow[H_2O,\ boil]{Na_2O_2} \underset{(Y)}{Na_2CrO_4} \xrightarrow[acetate]{lead}$ No ppt. in basic medium

(iii) $ZnSO_4(aq) \xrightarrow[H_2O]{Na_2CO_3} \underset{(X)}{ZnCO_3 \cdot 3Zn(OH)_2} \xrightarrow{\Delta} \underset{(Y)}{ZnO} \xrightarrow[nitrate,\ \Delta]{cobalt} \underset{(Z)}{CoZnO_2}$

(iv) $CuCl_2(aq) \xrightarrow[H_2S]{NH_4OH} \underset{(X)}{CuS} \xrightarrow[\Delta]{HNO_3} \underset{(Y)}{Cu(NO_3)_2} \xrightarrow[excess]{KCN} \underset{(Z)}{K_3[Cu(CN)_4]}$

16. (a)
$$\underset{(A)}{2FeSO_4} \longrightarrow \underset{(D)}{Fe_2O_3} + \underset{(B)}{SO_2} + \underset{(C)}{SO_3}$$
$$Fe_2O_3 + 6HCl \longrightarrow 2FeCl_3 + 3H_2O$$

17. (a) $As_2S_5 + HNO_3 \longrightarrow H_3AsO_4 + NO_2 + H_2O + S$ (ammonium molybdate)
$H_3AsO_4 + (NH_4)_2MoO_4 \longrightarrow$ yellow ppt. of $(NH_4)_3AsO_4 \cdot 12MoO_3$

18. (b) $\underset{Black}{FeS} \xrightarrow{dil.\ H_2SO_4} \underset{gas}{H_2S} \xrightarrow{dil.\ HNO_3} \underset{colloidal}{S} + NO_2 + 2H_2O$

20. (a)
$$\underset{(A)}{H_2C_2O_4} \xrightarrow{\Delta} \underset{(B)}{CO_2(g)} + \underset{(C)}{CO(g)} + \underset{(D)}{H_2O(g)}$$
$$\underset{(B)}{CO_2} + Ca(OH)_2 \longrightarrow \underset{(milky)}{CaCO_3} + H_2O$$
$$\underset{(B)}{CO_2} + H_2O \rightleftharpoons 2H^+ + CO_3^{2-}$$
$$\underset{(C)}{CO} + Cl_2 \longrightarrow \underset{(Phosgene)}{\underset{(E)}{COCl_2}} \xrightarrow[-\ 2HCl]{2NH_3} \underset{(Urea)}{\underset{(F)}{O=C(NH_2)_2}} \xrightarrow{H_2O\ (D)} CO_2\uparrow + NH_3$$

21. (c) Ppts. of Ag_2CrO_4, Ag_2CO_3 are soluble in NH_4OH due to formation of $[Ag(NH_3)_2]^+$
Green ppt. of $Ni(OH)_2$ is soluble in NH_4OH due to formation of $[Ni(NH_3)_6]^{2+}$
$$Ag_2CrO_4\uparrow + 4NH_4OH \longrightarrow 2[Ag(NH_3)_2]^+ + CrO_4^{2-} + 4H_2O$$
$$Ag_2CO_3\uparrow + 4NH_4OH \longrightarrow 2[Ag(NH_3)_2]^+ + CO_3^{2-} + 4H_2O$$
$$\underset{green\ ppt.}{Ni(OH)_2\uparrow} + 8NH_4OH \longrightarrow [Ni(NH_3)_6]^{2+} + 2OH^- + 6H_2O$$
$Fe(OH)_3$ is insoluble in NH_4OH.
$Al(OH)_3$ is insoluble in NH_4OH.

23. (d) (i) $2Cu^+(aq) \longrightarrow Cu^{2+}(aq) + Cu(s)$
(ii) Hg_2Cl_2 does not furnish Cl^-, for chromyl chloride test.
(iii) $[Fe(H_2O)_5NO]^{2+}$ is unstable, as iron is present in +1 oxidation state

24. (d) $X : \underset{green}{2Cr^{3+}} + 10OH^- + 3H_2O_2 \longrightarrow \underset{yellow}{2CrO_4^{2-}} + H_2O$

$Y : CrO_4^{2-} + 2H_2O_2 + 2H^+ \rightarrow$ 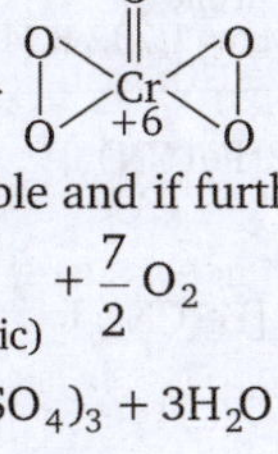 $+ 3H_2O$

In aq. solution CrO_5 is unstable and if further decomposes

$Z :\ 2CrO_5 \longrightarrow \underset{(Amphoteric)}{Cr_2O_3} + \frac{7}{2}O_2$

$Cr_2O_3 + 3H_2SO_4 \longrightarrow Cr_2(SO_4)_3 + 3H_2O$

26. (b)

$$\underset{(A)}{ZnCO_3(s)} \xrightarrow{\Delta} ZnO(s) + CO_2(g)$$

$$ZnO + 2HCl \longrightarrow ZnCl_2 + H_2O$$

$$3\,Zn^{2+} + 2K_4[Fe(CN)_6] \longrightarrow \underset{\text{white ppt.}}{K_2Zn_3[Fe(CN)_6]_2\downarrow} + 6K^+$$

or,

$$2\,Zn^{2+} + K_4[Fe(CN)_6] \longrightarrow \underset{\text{white ppt.}}{Zn_2[Fe(CN)_6]} + 4K^+$$

33. (d) $Fe^{2+} + [Fe(CN)_6]^{3-} \rightleftharpoons Fe^{3+} + [Fe(CN)_6]^{4-} \longrightarrow \underset{\text{(Prussian blue)}}{\underset{\text{Turnbull's blue}}{Fe_4[Fe(CN)_6]_3}}$

$$Fe^{3+} + [Fe(CN)_6]^{3-} \longrightarrow \underset{\text{solution}}{\underset{\text{Brown colour}}{Fe[Fe(CN)_6]}}$$

$$Fe^{2+} + K_4[Fe(CN)_6] \longrightarrow \underset{\text{white ppt.}}{K_2Fe[Fe(CN)_6]} + 2K^+$$

$$4\,Fe^{3+} + 3K_4[Fe(CN)_6] \longrightarrow \underset{\text{Prussian blue}}{Fe_4[Fe(CN)_6]_3} + 12K^+$$

$$Fe^{2+} + KSCN \longrightarrow \text{No coloured solution}$$

$$Fe^{3+} + 3KSCN \longrightarrow \underset{\text{solution}}{\underset{\text{blood red}}{Fe(SCN)_3}} + 3K^+$$

35. (c) (I) Fehling's solution : $CuSO_4 + NaKC_4H_4O_6$ (Rochell's salt) + NaOH

(II) K_2CO_3 (m.pt.) = 850° C

(III) $FeCl_3 + 2S_2O_3^{2-} \longrightarrow \underset{\text{Violet sol.}}{[Fe(S_2O_3)_2]^-} + 3Cl^-$

$$[Fe(S_2O_3)_2]^- + Fe^{3+} \longrightarrow \underset{\text{(green)}}{2Fe^{2+}} + S_4O_6^{2-}$$

(IV) $\underset{\text{(Orange)}}{Cr_2O_7^{2-}} + 8\,H^+ + 3\,SO_3^{2-} \longrightarrow \underset{\text{(green)}}{2\,Cr^{3+}} + 3\,SO_4^{2-} + 4H_2O$

(V) Na_2CO_3 : Solvay process

36. (a)

$$\underset{(X)}{NH_4NO_2} + KOH \longrightarrow \underset{(Y)}{NH_3\uparrow} + \underset{(Z)}{KNO_2} + H_2O$$

$$\underset{(Z)}{NO_2^-} + 3Zn + 5OH^- + 5H_2O \longrightarrow \underset{\text{soluble}}{3[Zn(OH)_4]^{2-}} + \underset{(Y)}{NH_3\uparrow}$$

$$\underset{(X)}{NH_4NO_2} \xrightarrow{\Delta} \underset{\text{(does not support combustion)}}{N_2\uparrow} + 2H_2O$$

37. (a) 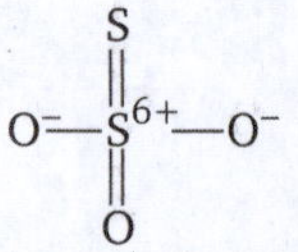

38. (b)

$$\underset{(A)}{\underset{\text{M.M.} = 0}{\underset{\text{Pale yellow}}{2[Fe(CN)_6]^{4-}}}} + \underbrace{H_2O_2 + 2H^+}_{X} \longrightarrow \underset{(B)}{\underset{\text{M.M.} = 1.732 \text{ B.M.}}{\underset{\text{Yellow}}{2[Fe(CN)_6]^{3-}}}} + 2H_2O$$

$$\underset{(B)}{2[Fe(CN)_6]^{3-}} + \underbrace{2OH^- + H_2O_2}_{Y} \longrightarrow \underset{(A)}{2[Fe(CN)_6]^{4-}} + 2H_2O + O_2$$

$$3[Fe(CN)_6]^{4-} + 4Fe^{3+} \longrightarrow \overset{\text{III}}{Fe_4}[\overset{\text{II}}{Fe}(CN)_6]_3\downarrow$$

39. (c)

$$\underset{(A)}{BaCO_3} + K_2CrO_4 \xrightarrow{H^+} \underset{(B)\ \text{yellow}}{BaCrO_4} + 2K^+ + CO_3^{2-}$$

$$BaCO_3 + H_2SO_4 \longrightarrow \underset{(C)\ \text{white}}{BaSO_4 \downarrow} + CO_2\uparrow + H_2O$$

$$BaCO_3 + 2HCl \longrightarrow \underset{\substack{\text{Clear sol.}\\(D)}}{BaCl_2} + CO_2\uparrow + H_2O$$

63. (d) In the absence of NH_4^+ ions or NH_4Cl, dissociation of NH_4OH is large *i.e.*, concentration of OH^- is considerable to increase ionic products of hydroxides of Fe^{2+}, Cr^{3+} and Zn^{2+} from their respective K_{sp} values, hence they will precipitate in IIIrd group. However, $Ba(OH)_2$ is soluble due to high K_{sp} value.

64. (b)

$$\underset{(T)}{Cr_2O_7^{2-}} + 6H^+ + \underset{(U)}{4NH_4Cl} \longrightarrow \underset{(V)}{2CrO_2Cl_2} + 4\overset{+}{N}H_4 + 3H_2O$$

$$CrO_2Cl_2 + 2NaOH \longrightarrow Na_2CrO_4 + 2HCl$$

$$Na_2CrO_4 + 2AgNO_3 \longrightarrow \underset{(W)}{Ag_2CrO_4} + 2NaNO_3$$

$$\underset{(W)}{Ag_2CrO_4} + 4NH_3 \longrightarrow \underset{(X)}{2[Ag(NH_3)_2]^+} + CrO_4^{2-}$$

$$Ag_2CrO_4 + 2HCl \longrightarrow \underset{(Y)}{2AgCl\downarrow} + 2H^+ + CrO_4^{2-}$$

$$\underset{(U)}{NH_4Cl} + NaOH \longrightarrow \underset{(Z)}{NH_3\uparrow} + NaCl + H_2O$$

67. (b)

$$K_4[Fe(CN)_6] + \underset{\text{(conc.)}}{6H_2SO_4} + 6H_2O \longrightarrow 2K_2SO_4 + FeSO_4 + 3(NH_4)_2SO_4 + 6CO\uparrow$$

$$K_4[Fe(CN)_6] + \underset{\text{(dil.)}}{3H_2SO_4} \longrightarrow 2K_2SO_4 + FeSO_4 + 6HCN\uparrow$$

68. (d) When Cl^- salt is heated with $K_2Cr_2O_7$ + Conc. H_2SO_4 red vapours of CrO_2Cl_2 are evolved which on passing into NaOH solution gives yellow solution of CrO_4^{2-} ions. Latter further gives yellow ppt. of $PbCrO_4$ with $Pb(CH_3CO)_2$ and acetic acid.

$$4Cl^- + Cr_2O_7^{2-} + 6H^+ \longrightarrow \underset{\text{reddish brown vapours}}{2CrO_2Cl_2\uparrow} + 3H_2O$$

$$CrO_2Cl_2 + 4OH^- \longrightarrow \underset{\text{Yellow soln.}}{CrO_4^{2-}} + 2Cl^- + 2H_2O$$

While on heating a bromide salt with conc. H_2SO_4 and $K_2Cr_2O_7$, instead of CrO_2Br_2, reddish brown fumes of Br_2 are formed due to reducing character of HBr formed during the reaction. Br_2 dissolves in NaOH and no colour is produced.

$$6Br^- + Cr_2O_7^{2-} + H^+ \longrightarrow \underset{\substack{\text{Reddish}\\\text{brown vapours}}}{3Br_2\uparrow} + Cr^{3+} + 7H_2O$$

$$2NaOH + Br_2 \longrightarrow \underset{\text{colourless}}{NaBr} + NaOBr + H_2O$$

69. (b)

$$\underset{\substack{(A)\\\text{(Red lead)}}}{2Pb_3O_4} \xrightarrow{\Delta} \underset{(B)}{6PbO} + \underset{(C)}{O_2(g)}$$

$$\underset{(A)}{Pb_3O_4} + \underset{\text{(conc.)}}{4HNO_3} \longrightarrow \underset{(D)}{2Pb(NO_3)_2} + \underset{\substack{(E)\\\text{(Brown)}}}{PbO_2} + \underset{(F)}{2H_2O}$$

$$\underset{(D)}{2Pb(NO_3)_2} \xrightarrow{\Delta} 2PbO + 4NO_2(g) + \underset{(C)}{O_2(g)}$$

72. (c) NaOH or KOH solution cannot be used to separate a mixture of two cations, of which both oxides/ hydroxides are amphoteric because amphoteric oxides/ hydroxides dissolve in an excess of the alkali to form salts.

Fe^{3+} and Al^{3+} can be separated as the precipitate of $Fe(OH)_3$ formed does not dissolve in an excess of the alkali whereas that of $Al(OH)_3$ does.

$$Fe^{3+} + 3OH^- \longrightarrow Fe(OH)_3\downarrow \xrightarrow{OH^-} \text{no action}$$

$$Al^{3+} + 3OH^- \longrightarrow Al(OH)_3\downarrow \xrightarrow{OH^-} AlO_2^- + 2H_2O$$

73. (d) The formation of a green solid with CoO indicates Zn^{2+} (charcoal cavity test)

$$ZnCO_3 \xrightarrow{\text{heat}} ZnO \xrightarrow[\text{heat}]{CoO} \underset{\text{Rinmann's green}}{CoZnO_2}$$

74. (b) Hg^{2+} ions react with KI to give a red precipitate of HgI_2, which dissolves in an excess of the reagent.

$$Hg^{2+} + 2I^- \longrightarrow \underset{\text{(red)}}{HgI_2\downarrow} \xrightarrow{2I^-} \underset{\text{(colourless)}}{[HgI_4]^{2-}}$$

Hg^{2+} ions react with cobalt(II) thiocyanate to give a blue precipitate of $Hg[Co(SCN)_4]$, also formulated as $Co[Hg(SCN)_4]$.

$$Hg^{2+} + Co^{2+} + 4SCN^- \longrightarrow \underset{\text{(blue)}}{Hg[Co(SCN)_4]\downarrow}$$

77. (b) NH_3 solution (NH_4OH) furnishes OH^- ions as well as NH_3. It can separate one cation from another provided both the cations precipitate as hydroxides but one of the hydroxides forms a soluble complex with NH_3 whereas the other does not.

Of the $Al(OH)_3$ and $Zn(OH)_2$ formed first, the latter dissolves in excess of the NH_3 solution whereas the former does not.

$$Zn(OH)_2 + 4NH_3 \longrightarrow [Zn(NH_3)_4]^{2+} + 2OH^-$$

Level 3

Passage-1

3. (b)

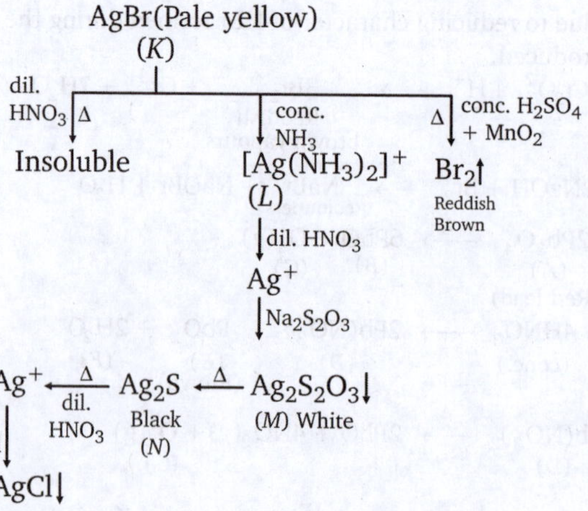

Passage-2

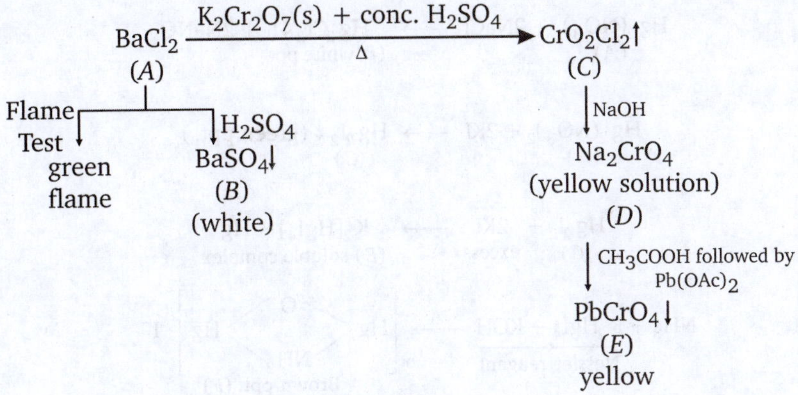

Passage-3

2. (b)

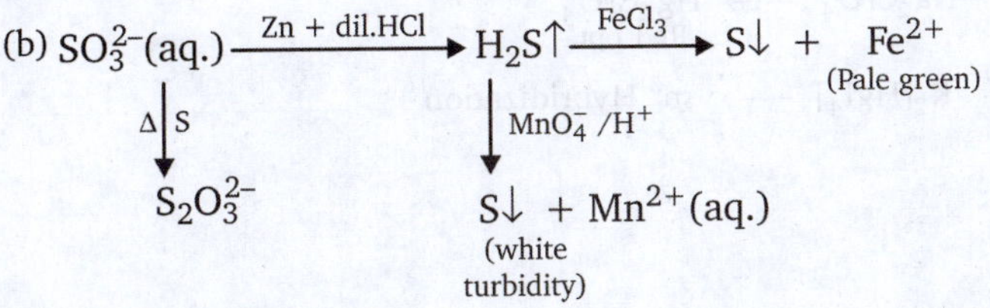

* $Fe^{2+} + NH_4SCN \rightarrow$ no reaction
* $Fe^{3+} + NH_4SCN \rightarrow Fe(SCN)_3$ blood red.

Passage-6

$$\underset{\text{Black solid}}{2MnO_2} + 4KOH + O_2 \longrightarrow \underset{\substack{\text{green}\\(A)}}{2K_2MnO_4} + 2H_2O$$

$$3MnO_4^{2-} + 4H^+ \longrightarrow \underset{\substack{(B)\\ \text{purple}}}{2MnO_4^-} + \underset{(C)}{MnO_2} + 2H_2O$$

(i) $2KMnO_4 + H_2O + KI \longrightarrow 2KOH + 2MnO_2 + \underset{(D)}{KIO_3}$

(ii) $2KMnO_4 + 8H_2SO_4 + 10FeSO_4 \longrightarrow 2MnSO_4 + 5Fe_2(SO_4)_3 + K_2SO_4 + 8H_2O$

(iii) $2KMnO_4 + H_2SO_4 \xrightarrow{\text{cold}} \underset{(E)}{Mn_2O_7} + K_2SO_4 + H_2O$

$$\underset{(E)}{Mn_2O_7} \longrightarrow \underset{(F)}{2MnO_2} + \frac{3}{2}O_2$$

$$6KMnO_4 + 10FeC_2O_4 + 24H_2SO_4 \longrightarrow 6MnSO_4 + \underset{\text{(yellow)}}{5Fe_2(SO_4)_3} + 20CO_2 + 3K_2SO_4 + 24H_2O$$

$$3NaSCN + FeCl_3 \longrightarrow \underset{\substack{\text{Blood red}\\ \text{colouration}}}{Fe(SCN)_3\downarrow} + 3NaCl$$

Passage-7

$$\underset{(A)}{Hg_2(NO_3)_2} + 2NaCl \longrightarrow \underset{(B)\text{white ppt.}}{Hg_2Cl_2\downarrow} + 2NaNO_3$$

$$\underset{(A)}{Hg_2(NO_3)_2} + 2KI \longrightarrow \underset{(C)}{Hg_2I_2\downarrow}\text{(green ppt.)}$$

$$\underset{(C)}{Hg_2I_2} + \underset{\text{excess}}{2KI} \longrightarrow \underset{(E)\text{ soluble complex}}{K_2[HgI_4] + Hg}$$

$$NH_3 + \underbrace{K_2HgI_4 + KOH}_{\text{Nessler reagent}} \longrightarrow$$

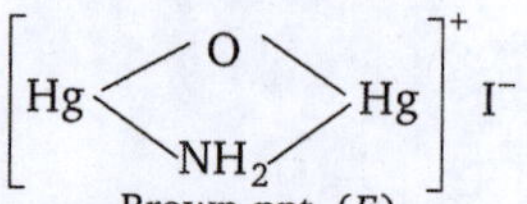

Brown ppt. (*F*)
Iodide of million's base

$$\underset{(A)}{Hg_2(NO_3)_2} + Na_2CrO_4 \longrightarrow \underset{\text{Red ppt.}}{Hg_2CrO_4}$$

$$K_2[HgI_4] \longrightarrow sp^3 \text{ Hybridization}$$

Passage-8

2. (d)

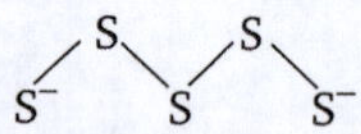

S_5^{2-} (Chain structure)

3. (c)

$$\underset{(M)}{4Na_2S_2O_3\cdot 5H_2O} \xrightarrow[-20H_2O]{>220°C} \underset{(P)}{Na_2S_5} + \underset{(Q)}{3Na_2SO_4}$$

$$\underset{(Q)}{Na_2SO_4} + Hg(NO_3)_2 \longrightarrow \underset{\substack{(R)\\ \text{yellow}}}{HgO\cdot HgSO_4\downarrow} + 2Na^+ + 2NO_3^-$$

$$\underset{(M)}{Na_2S_2O_3} + HgCl_2 \longrightarrow \underset{\substack{(N)\\ \text{White}}}{HgS_2O_3\downarrow} + 2NaCl$$

$$\underset{(N)}{HgS_2O_3\downarrow} + H_2O \longrightarrow \underset{\substack{(O)\\ \text{black}}}{HgS\downarrow} + 2H^+ + SO_4^{2-}$$

$$\underset{(N)}{HgS_2O_3\downarrow} + \underset{(M)}{Na_2S_2O_3} \longrightarrow 2Na^+ + \underset{\text{soluble}}{[Hg(S_2O_3)_2]^{2-}}$$

$$Na_2S_2O_3 + 2HCl \longrightarrow 2NaCl + SO_2 + \underset{\substack{\text{white/yellow}\\ \text{Turbidity}}}{S\downarrow} + H_2O$$

$$S\downarrow + 2HNO_3 \longrightarrow \underset{\text{clear sol.}}{H_2SO_4} + 2NO\uparrow$$

Passage-9

$$\underset{(A)}{NH_4NO_2} + NaOH \longrightarrow \underset{(B)}{NH_3\uparrow} + NaNO_2 + H_2O$$

$$NH_3 + 2K_2[HgI_4] + 3KOH \longrightarrow \underset{\text{Brown ppt.}}{[HgO\cdot Hg(NH_2)_2]I\downarrow} + 3H_2O + 7KI$$

$$NH_4NO_2 \longrightarrow \underset{(C)}{N_2(g)} + 2H_2O$$

Passage-10

1. (b) $Pb(NO_3)_2 + 2HCl \longrightarrow \underset{\text{white}}{PbCl_2\downarrow} + 2HNO_3$

2. (c) $Pb(NO_3)_2 \longrightarrow$ Completely soluble in water.

3. (a) $Na_2CO_3 + 2HCl \longrightarrow 2NaCl + \underset{\substack{\text{Acidic}\\\text{character}}}{CO_2\uparrow} + H_2O$

4. (d) $Pb(NO_3)_2 + CuSO_4 \longrightarrow Cu(NO_3)_2 + \underset{\text{white ppt.}}{PbSO_4\downarrow}$

Passage-11

$$\underset{\substack{(A)\\\text{Pink/Buff}}}{MnS} + \underset{\substack{\text{(dil.)}\\\text{colour}}}{H_2SO_4} \longrightarrow \underset{\substack{(B)\\\text{colourless}}}{H_2S(g)} + \underset{\substack{(C)\\\text{colourless}}}{MnSO_4}$$

$$K_2Cr_2O_7 + 4H_2SO_4 + 3H_2S \longrightarrow K_2SO_4 + \underset{\text{(green)}}{Cr_2(SO_4)_3} + \underset{\text{(yellow) }(D)}{3S\downarrow}$$

$$S + O_2 \longrightarrow \underset{(E)}{SO_2}$$

$$K_2Cr_2O_7 + H_2SO_4 + 3SO_2 \longrightarrow K_2SO_4 + \underset{\text{(green)}}{Cr_2(SO_4)_3} + H_2O$$

$$\underset{(B)}{2H_2S} + \underset{(E)}{SO_2} \longrightarrow \underset{(D)}{3S\downarrow} + 2H_2O$$

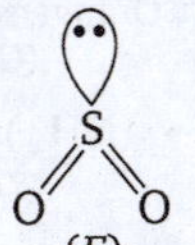

(E)

$$Na_2SO_3 + S \longrightarrow Na_2S_2O_3$$

Hypo solution is used as an antichlor to remove excess of Cl_2 from bleached articles.

$$Na_2S_2O_3 + Cl_2 + H_2O \longrightarrow Na_2SO_4 + S + 2HCl$$

$$2Mn^{2+} + 5PbO_2 + 4H^+ \longrightarrow \underset{\text{violet red}}{2MnO_4^-} + 5Pb^{2+} + 2H_2O$$

Passage-12

$$\underset{(A)}{S_8} + 12NaOH \longrightarrow \underset{(B)}{2Na_2S_2O_3} + \underset{(C)}{4Na_2S} + 6H_2O$$

$$Na_2S_2O_3 + FeCl_3 \longrightarrow \underset{\text{Violet sol. }(E)}{[Fe(S_2O_3)_2]^-} + 3\,Cl^- + 4Na^+$$

$$Na_2S_2O_3 + 2HCl \longrightarrow 2NaCl + SO_2\downarrow + \underset{(A)}{S\uparrow} + H_2O$$

$$Na_2S_2O_3 + CaCl_2 \longrightarrow \text{No ppt. as } CaS_2O_3 \text{ is soluble}$$

$$Na_2S_2O_3 \xrightarrow[\text{above 220°C}]{\Delta} Na_2S_5 + Na_2SO_4$$

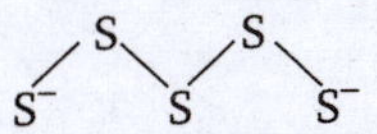

S_5^{2-} (Chain structure)

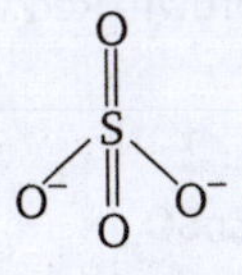

SO_4^{2-} (Tetrahedral)

H_2S reacts with sodium nitroprusside only in alkali medium

$$\underset{}{Na_2[Fe(CN)_5(NO)]} + 2NaOH + H_2S\uparrow \longrightarrow \underset{\text{purple}}{Na_4[Fe(CN)_5(NOS)]} + 2H_2O$$

$$Na_2S_2O_3 + [Ni(en)_3](NO_3)_2 \longrightarrow \underset{\substack{\text{Violet}\\\text{(optically active)}}}{[Ni(en)_3]S_2O_3\downarrow} + 2Na^+ + 2NO_3^-$$

Passage-13

$$\underset{(A)}{CrCl_3} + 3AgNO_3 \longrightarrow \underset{\text{white}}{3AgCl\downarrow} + Cr^{3+} + 3NO_3^-$$

$$AgCl + 2NH_3 \rightleftharpoons \underset{\text{soluble}}{[Ag(NH_3)_2]^+} + Cl^-$$

$$\underset{(A)}{CrCl_3} + 3NaOH \longrightarrow \underset{\text{green}}{Cr(OH)_3\downarrow} + 3Na^+ + 3Cl^-$$

$$Cr(OH)_3\downarrow + \underset{\text{excess}}{OH^-} \rightleftharpoons \underset{\text{soluble}}{[Cr(OH)_4]^-}$$

$$\underset{(A)}{2Cr^{3+}} + 3H_2O_2 + 10OH^- \longrightarrow \underset{\substack{(B)\\\text{yellow solution}}}{2CrO_4^{2-}} + 8H_2O$$

$$2CrO_4^{2-} + 2H^+ \longrightarrow \underset{\substack{\text{Orange solution}\\(C)}}{Cr_2O_7^{2-}} + H_2O$$

$$Cr_2O_7^{2-} + 2NH_4Cl \longrightarrow \underset{(D)}{(NH_4)_2Cr_2O_7} + 2Cl^-$$

$$\underset{(D)}{(NH_4)_2Cr_2O_7} \xrightarrow{\Delta} \underset{\substack{(H)\\\text{Residue}}}{Cr_2O_3} + N_2(g) + 4H_2O(g)$$

$$\underset{(G)}{N_2} + 6Li \longrightarrow \underset{(I)}{2Li_3N} \xrightarrow{H_2O} \underset{(J)}{NH_3} + 6LiOH$$

$$NH_3 \xrightarrow{CuSO_4(aq)} \underset{\text{deep blue sol.}}{[Cu(NH_3)_4]^{2+}} + SO_4^{2-}$$

$$4KCl + \underset{\text{solid}}{K_2Cr_2O_7} + \underset{\text{conc.}}{6H_2SO_4} \longrightarrow \underset{\substack{(E)\\\text{red vapours}}}{2CrO_2Cl_2\uparrow} + 6KHSO_4 + 3H_2O$$

$$CrO_2Cl_2\uparrow + 2OH^- \longrightarrow \underset{(B)}{CrO_4^{2-}} + 2HCl$$

$$CrO_4^{2-} + Pb^{2+} \xrightarrow{AcOH} \underset{\text{yellow }(F)}{PbCrO_4\downarrow}$$

— $HgCl_2$ does not give chromyl chloride test.

— In case of Br^-, Reddish brown/Red vapours of Br_2 are evolved on heating it with $K_2Cr_2O_7$ and conc. H_2SO_4.

Passage-14

Mixture contains NaOH + $ZnSO_4$

$$NaOH + ZnSO_4 \longrightarrow \underset{\text{soluble}}{Na_2ZnO_2} + Na_2SO_4 + 2H_2O$$

$$Na_2ZnO_2 + 2HCl \longrightarrow 2NaCl + Zn(OH)_2\downarrow$$

$$Zn(OH)_2 + 2HCl \longrightarrow \underset{\text{soluble}}{ZnCl_2} + 2H_2O$$

Passage-15

1. (a) $Cu(NO_3)_2 + 2NaOH \longrightarrow Cu(OH)_2\downarrow + 2NaNO_3$

$$Cu(OH)_2 \xrightarrow{\Delta} \underset{\text{black ppt.}}{CuO\downarrow} + H_2O$$

2. (b) $4Zn + NaNO_3 + 7NaOH \longrightarrow 4Na_2ZnO_2 + 2H_2O + \underset{\text{pungent smell}}{NH_3\uparrow}$

3. (b) $CuO + H_2SO_4 \longrightarrow CuSO_4 + H_2S$

$$2CuSO_4 + K_4[Fe(CN)_6] \longrightarrow \underset{\text{chocolate ppt.}}{Cu_2[Fe(CN)_6]\downarrow} + 2K_2SO_4$$

Passage-17

The formation of *D* indicates NH_4^+.

Heating *X* with $K_2Cr_2O_7$ and concentrated H_2SO_4, resulting in the formation of *A*, which in subsequent reactions gives *B* and *C* are the different steps of the chromyl chloride test. Thus, *X* is NH_4Cl.

$$\underset{X}{NH_4Cl} + H_2SO_4 \longrightarrow NH_4HSO_4 + HCl$$

$$K_2Cr_2O_7 + 2H_2SO_4 \longrightarrow 2KHSO_4 + 2CrO_3 + H_2O$$

$$CrO_2 + 2HCl \longrightarrow \underset{\text{chromyl chloride}}{CrO_2Cl_2} + H_2O$$

$$CrO_2Cl_2 + \underset{(NaOH)}{4OH^-} \longrightarrow \underset{\substack{\text{chromate ion}\\ \text{(yellow) } B}}{CrO_4^{2-}} + 2H_2O + 2Cl^-$$

$$CrO_4^{2-} + \underset{[Pb(CH_3COO)_2]}{Pb^{2+}} \longrightarrow \underset{\substack{\text{lead chromate}\\ \text{(yellow) } C}}{PbCrO_4\downarrow}$$

$$NH_4^+ + OH^- \xrightarrow{\text{heat}} NH_3\uparrow + H_2$$

$$NH_3 + 2[HgI_4]^{2-} + 3OH^- \longrightarrow \underset{\text{(brown) } D}{\left[O\begin{smallmatrix}Hg\\ \\ Hg\end{smallmatrix}NH_2\right]I\downarrow} + 7I^- + 2H_2O$$

2. (a) Cl^- would have given rise to CrO_2Cl_2 which would turn an NaOH solution yellow. Br^- would have given rise to formation of colourless compounds (a mixture of NaBr and $NaBrO/NaBrO_3$). NO_3^- and NO_2^- would have given rise to NO_2 which reacts with an NaOH solution to produce a mixture of colourless compounds $NaNO_3$ and $NaNO_2$.

$$2NO_2 + 2NaOH \longrightarrow NaNO_3 + NaNO_2 + H_2O$$

Passage-18

One of the three colourless gases—CO_2, SO_2 and H_2S—is generally produced by the action of dilute H_2SO_4 on a salt. As the gas turns acidified dichromate solution green along with the formation of a slightly coloured precipitate (may be S), the gas seems to be H_2S and so the substance *A* seems to be a sulphide. Again, the action of NH_3 or an NaOH solution on the solution of the substance in dilute

H_2SO_4 suggests that the substance is a zinc salt. Thus, *A* is most likely ZnS. Let us go through the reactions now.

$$\underset{\substack{\text{(white)}\\ A}}{ZnS} + 2H^+ \longrightarrow \underset{\substack{\text{(colourless)}\\ C}}{Zn^{2+}} + \underset{\substack{\text{(colourless)}\\ B}}{H_2S\uparrow}$$

$$Cr_2O_7^{2-} + 14H^+ + \underset{\substack{(H_2S)\\ B}}{3S^{2-}} \longrightarrow \underset{\text{(green)}}{2Cr^{3+}} + 7H_2O + \underset{\substack{\text{(yellowish white)}\\ D}}{3S}$$

$$\underset{D}{S} + O_2 \longrightarrow \underset{E}{SO_2\uparrow}$$

$$2H_2S + SO_2 \longrightarrow \underset{D}{3S} + \underset{\text{(colourless liquid)}}{2H_2O} \xrightarrow[\text{CuSO}_4\text{ (white)}]{\text{anhydrous}} \underset{\substack{\text{hydrated copper(II)}\\ \text{sulphate (blue)}}}{CuSO_4 \cdot xH_2O}$$

$$\xrightarrow[\substack{\text{excess}\\ \text{NaOH}}]{2OH^-} [Zn(OH)_4]^{2-} \text{ or } ZnO_2^{2-} + 2H_2O$$

$$\underset{C}{Zn^{2+}} + \underset{\substack{(NH_4OH\\ \text{or NaOH})}}{2\,OH^-} \longrightarrow \underset{\text{(White)}}{Zn(OH)_2} \xrightarrow[\substack{\text{excess}\\ NH_4OH}]{4NH_3} \underset{\substack{\text{tetrammine}\\ \text{zinc(II) ion}\\ \text{(soluble)}}}{[Zn(OH_3)_4]^{2+}} + 2\,OH^-$$

Passage-19

The reactions at step (ii) suggest the presence of Fe^{3+}.

$$[Fe(H_2O)_6]^{3+} + xSCN^- \longrightarrow \underset{\text{(red) }B}{[Fe(SCN)_x(H_2O)_{6-x}]^{+3-x}} + xH_2O$$

or

$$Fe^{3+} + 3SCN^- \longrightarrow \underset{\text{(red) }B}{Fe(SCN)_3}$$

$$4Fe^{3+} + 3\,[Fe(CN)_6]^{4-} \longrightarrow \underset{\text{(Prussian blue) }C}{Fe_4[Fe(CN)_6]_3}$$

The reactions in steps (iii) and (iv) indicate the presence of Cl^- (chromyl chloride test).

$$Cl^- + H_2SO_4 \longrightarrow HCl + HSO_4^-$$

$$K_2Cr_2O_7 + 2H_2SO_4 \longrightarrow 2KHSO_4 + 2CrO_3 + H_2O$$

$$CrO_3 + 2HCl \longrightarrow \underset{\substack{\text{chromyl}\\ \text{chloride}\\ \text{(red) }D}}{CrO_2Cl_2} \longrightarrow CrO_2Cl_2\uparrow + H_2O$$

$$CrO_2Cl_2 + 4OH^- \longrightarrow \underset{\substack{\text{chromate ion}\\ \text{(yellow)}}}{CrO_4^{2-}} + 2Cl^- + 2H_2O$$

$$CrO_4^{2-} + Pb^{2+} \longrightarrow \underset{\text{(yellow) }E}{PbCrO_4\downarrow}$$

Thus, *A* is $FeCl_3$, *B* is $[Fe(SCN)_x(H_2O)_{6-x}]^{+3-x}$ or $Fe(SCN)_3$, *C* is $Fe_4[Fe(CN)_6]_3$, *D* is CrO_2Cl_2 and *E* is $PbCrO_4$.

Anhydrous $FeCl_3$ is a covalent compound, subliming at about 300°C, but the hydrated salt ($FeCl_3 \cdot 6H_2O$) or an aqueous solution of it contains Fe^{3+} and Cl^- ions.

An aqueous solution of $FeCl_3$ is acidic to litmus because of the hydrolysis of the salt.

Passage-20

The yellow precipitate of a sulphite could be CdS (group IIA) or $As_2S_3/As_2S_3/SnS_2$ (group IIB), but as it is insoluble in yellow ammonium polysulphide, it should be CdS. Thus, the cation appears to be Cd^{2+} which is confirmed by reactions (ii) to (v). Reaction (vi) indicates SO_4^{2-}. Hence, the compound *B* is $CdSO_4$.

(i) $\underset{\substack{(CdSO_4)\\ B}}{Cd^{2+}} + \underset{(H_2S)}{S^{2-}} \longrightarrow \underset{\substack{\text{(yellow)}\\ A}}{CdS\downarrow}$

(ii) $CdS\downarrow + \underset{(HNO_3)}{2H^2} \longrightarrow Cd^{2+} + H_2S\uparrow \quad \underset{A}{CdS} \xrightarrow{(NH_4)_2S_x}$ No action

(iii) $\underset{\substack{(CdSO_4)\\ B}}{Cd^{2+}} + \underset{(NH_4OH)}{2OH^-} \longrightarrow \underset{\text{(white)}}{Cd(OH)_2\downarrow} \xrightarrow[\text{excess}]{4NH_3} \underset{\substack{\text{tetramminecadmium(II) ion}\\ \text{(soluble) } C}}{[Cd(NH_3)_4]^{2+}} + 2OH^-$

(iv) $\underset{\substack{(CdSO_4)\\ B}}{Cd^{2+}} + \underset{(KCN)}{2CN^-} \longrightarrow \underset{\text{(white)}}{Cd(CN)_2\downarrow} \xrightarrow[(KCN)]{2CN^-} \underset{\substack{\text{tetracyanocadmiate(II) ion}\\ \text{(soluble) } D}}{[Cd(CN)_4]^{2-}}$

(v) The tetracyanocadmiate(II) ion, formed in (iv), has a low stability constant value and, therefore, furnishes Cd^{2+} ions in sufficient concentration to give a precipitate of CdS(*A*).

$$[Cd(CN)_4]^{2-} \rightleftharpoons Cd^{2+} + 4CN^-$$
$$Cd^{2+} \xrightarrow[(H_2S)]{S^{2-}} \underset{A}{CdS\downarrow}$$

(vi) $\underset{(BaCl_2)}{Ba^{2+}} + \underset{(CdSO_4)}{SO_4^{2-}} \longrightarrow \underset{\substack{\text{(white)}\\ \text{insoluble in HCl}\\ \text{or } HNO_3}}{BaSO_4\downarrow}$

Thus, *A* is CdS, *B* is $CdSO_4$, *C* is $[Cd(NH_3)_4]^{2+}$, *D* is $[Cd(CN)_4]^{2-}$.

Passage-21

The fact that the mixture is insoluble in water but soluble in dilute HCl and that the solution does not give a precipitate with H_2S suggest that groups I and II are absent. The evolution of a gas (during the dissolution of the mixture of dilute HCl) turning lime water milky but not acting on an acidified dichromate solution suggests the presence of CO_3^{2-} in the mixture. The formation of a white precipitate by the action of $AgNO_3$ on the soda extract, acidified with HNO_3, suggests the presence of Cl^-.
The formation of a brown precipitate when an alkaline solution of $K_2[HgI_4]$, *i.e.*, Nessler's reagent, is treated with the gas formed by boiling the mixture with an NaOH solution indicates the presence of NH_4^+. Step (4) suggests the absence of group IIIA cations and step (5) that of group IIB cations. Step (6) suggests the presence of group IV cation(s). Steps (7) and (8) suggest the absence of Ba^{2+} and Sr^{2+} respectively, and (9) suggests the presence of Ca^{2+}.

$$(Ca^{2+} + C_2O_4^{2-} \longrightarrow \underset{\text{(white)}}{CaC_2O_4\downarrow})$$

Thus, the mixture contains the cations NH_4^+ and Ca^{2+} and the anions Cl^- and CO_3^{2-}.

1. (c) $\underset{(AgNO_3)}{Ag^+} + \underset{\text{(soda extract)}}{Cl^-} \longrightarrow \underset{\text{(white)}}{AgCl\downarrow} \xrightarrow{2NH_4OH} [Ag(NH_3)_2]^{2+} + Cl^- + 2H_2O$

As there is an excess of NH_4OH, some NH_4^+ and OH^- ions will also be present.

3. (a) The precipitate is CaC_2O_4, which dissolves in minerals acids to set oxalic acid free, which decolorises a solution of $KMnO_4$.

$$\underset{\text{(calcium acetate)}}{Ca^{2+}} + \underset{\text{(ammonium oxalate)}}{C_2O_4^{2-}} \longrightarrow CaC_2O_4\downarrow \xrightarrow{H_2SO_4} Ca^{2+} + SO_4^{2-} + \underset{\text{oxalic acid}}{H_2C_2O_4}$$

$$[MnO_4^- + 8H^+ + 5e \longrightarrow Mn^{2+} + 4H_2O] \times 2$$
$$[H_2C_2O_4 \longrightarrow 2CO_2 + 2H^+ + 2e] \times 5$$
$$2MnO_4^- + 6H^+ + 5H_2C_2O_4 \longrightarrow 2Mn^{2+} + 8H_2O + 10CO_2$$

(Oxalic acid is a weak acid, and is therefore represented as $H_2C_2O_4$. It could also be represented as $C_2O_4^{2-}$ along with $2H^+$).

ONE OR MORE ANSWERS IS/ARE CORRECT

1. (a, b, d)

Only metal cations having unpaired electron(s) produce colour beads of metaborates.

2. (a, d)

AgCl and AgBr dissolve in excess of conc. ammonia solution.
AgI does not dissolve in excess conc. NH_3 solution.

3. (a) $I_2 + 2S_2O_3^{2-} \longrightarrow 2I^- + S_4O_6^{2-}$

5. (a, d)

$$3K^+ + Na_3[Co(NO_2)_6] \longrightarrow \underset{\text{Yellow}}{K_3[Co(NO_2)_6]\downarrow} + 3Na^+]$$

Na^+ and Mg^{2+} do not give test.

6. (b, d)

Pb^{2+} and Ba^{2+} both form yellow ppt. with CrO_4^{2-} ion which is not soluble in CH_3COOH.
Flame test Ba^{2+} —— Apple green
Pb^{2+} —— Blue

8. (a, b, c)

O_3, Cl_2 water and conc. HNO_3 being strong oxidants will oxidise sulphur into H_2SO_4.

10. (b, d)

$$SO_2\uparrow + H_2O \longrightarrow H_2SO_3$$
$$3H_2SO_3 \xrightarrow[\text{closed vessle}]{150°C} S + 2H_2SO_4 + H_2O$$
$$H_2SO_4 \xrightarrow{BaCl_2} BaSO_4\downarrow \text{ (white ppt.)}$$

11. (c, d)

$MgCl_2 + 2NaNO_3 \longrightarrow 2Na^+ + Mg^{2+} + 2Cl^- + 2NO_3^-$ (No reaction)
$BaSO_4 + HCl \longrightarrow$ No reaction (remains insoluble)
$$ZnSO_4 + BaS \longrightarrow \underset{\text{(white)}}{ZnS\downarrow} + \underset{\text{(white)}}{BaSO_4\downarrow}$$
$$\underset{\text{(white)}}{BaCO_3\downarrow} + 2CH_3COOH \longrightarrow Ba^{2+} + 2CH_3COO^- + CO_2\uparrow + H_2O$$

19. (c, d)

SO_2/CO_2 + Lime Water $\longrightarrow$ milky soln.
$$SO_2/CO_2 + BaCl_2 \longrightarrow \underset{\text{white ppt.}}{BaSO_3/BaCO_3\downarrow} \text{ (soluble in dil. HCl)}$$

H_2O_2 oxidises SO_2 to H_2SO_4, which reacts with a $BaCl_2$ solution to give a white precipitate of $BaSO_4$, insoluble in HCl. CO_2 does not react with H_2O_2, but reacts with a $BaCl_2$ solution forming a white precipitate of $BaCO_3$ soluble in HCl.
Acidified dichromate turns green with SO_2 but not with CO_2.

21. (b, d)

NH_3 solution cannot be used because both of these cations form soluble complexes with NH_3.

22. (a, b, d)

(i) Cations of the same group cannot be separated by the group reagent, and

(ii) A cation, not treated with its own group reagent, is generally precipitated by the reagent of a later group.

H_2S in an acid medium is the reagent for group II. So the cations mentioned in (a) and (b) cannot be separated as they all belong to group II. Those mentioned in (c) can be separated because Pb^{2+} (group II) is precipitated as PbS and Al^{3+} (group III) is not. The cations mentioned in (d) Remain unaffected by the reagent.

38. (a)

$HgCl_2$ reacts with H_2S, in the presence of moisture, to leave a black residue of HgS, whereas NH_4Cl does not. Other reagents do not react with $HgCl_2$ and NH_4Cl.

41. (a, b, d)

When a solid mixture of NaCl, $K_2Cr_2O_7$ and conc. H_2SO_4 is heated, the products obtained are :

$$4KCl + K_2Cr_2O_7 + 6H_2SO_4 \longrightarrow \underset{\text{red vapours}}{2CrO_2Cl_2} + 6KHSO_4 + 3H_2O$$

$$CrO_2Cl_2 + 4NaOH \longrightarrow \underset{\text{yellow solution}}{Na_2CrO_4} + 2NaCl + 2H_2O$$

42. (a, d)

Ba^{2+} ions produce yellow ppt. with CrO_4^{2-}, which is not soluble in CH_3COOH

$BaCO_3$ dissolves in CH_3COOH and produces Ba^{2+} ion which gives yellow ppt. with CrO_4^{2-} which is insoluble in CH_3COOH

$SrCO_3$ is soluble in CH_3COOH and produces Sr^{2+} ion which does not give yellow ppt. of $SrCrO_4$ in CH_3COOH.

43. (a, c)

(a) $Cd^{2+} + 2NaOH \rightarrow \underset{\text{white ppt.}}{Cd(OH)_2} \downarrow$
- $\xrightarrow{\text{Excess NaOH}}$ Not soluble
- $\xrightarrow{\text{Excess } NH_4OH}$ $[Cd(NH_3)_4]^{2+}$ soluble

(b) $Cr^{3+} + 3NaOH \rightarrow \underset{\text{green ppt.}}{Cr(OH)_3}$
- $\xrightarrow{\text{Excess NaOH}}$ $Na[Cr(OH)_4]$ soluble
- $\xrightarrow{\text{Excess } NH_4OH}$ $[Cr(NH_3)_6]^{3+}$ soluble

$\because$ $Cr(OH)_3$ soluble in both NaOH (excess) and NH_4OH (excess)

(c) $Sn^{2+} + 2NaOH \rightarrow \underset{\text{white ppt.}}{Sn(OH)_2}$
- $\xrightarrow{\text{Excess NaOH}}$ $Na_2[Sn(OH)_4]$ soluble
- $\xrightarrow{\text{Excess } NH_4OH}$ Insoluble

(d) $Bi^{3+} + 3NaOH \rightarrow \underset{\text{white ppt.}}{Bi(OH)_3} \downarrow$
- $\xrightarrow{\text{Excess NaOH}}$ Insoluble
- $\xrightarrow{\text{Excess } NH_4OH}$ Insoluble

44. (a, b, c, d)

$$Al_2(SO_4)_3 + 6NH_4OH \longrightarrow \underset{\text{white gelatinous ppt.}}{2Al(OH)_3\downarrow} + 3(NH_4)_2SO_4$$

$\Rightarrow$ ppt. of $Al(OH)_3$ is insoluble in NH_3 sol. but soluble in NaOH

$$Al(OH)_3\downarrow + OH \rightleftharpoons [Al(OH)_4]^-$$

$\Rightarrow$ $Al(OH)_3$ can be used as antacid.

45. (a, b, c, d)

A chloride will give CrO_2Cl_2, bromide will give Br_2, and nitrate and nitrite will give NO_2. All these gases are red-brown.

MATCH THE COLUMN

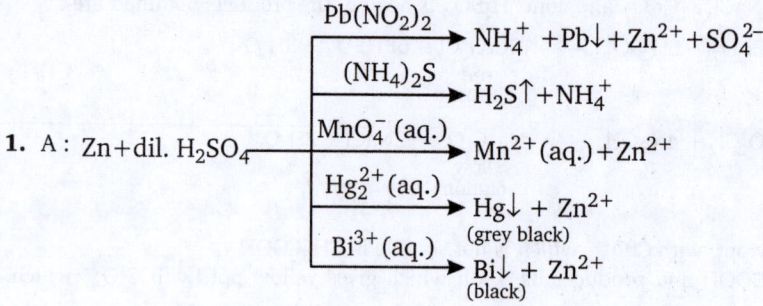

1. A : $Zn + \text{dil. } H_2SO_4$

- $\xrightarrow{Pb(NO_2)_2} NH_4^+ + Pb\downarrow + Zn^{2+} + SO_4^{2-}$
- $\xrightarrow{(NH_4)_2S} H_2S\uparrow + NH_4^+$
- $\xrightarrow{MnO_4^-\,(aq.)} Mn^{2+}(aq.) + Zn^{2+}$
- $\xrightarrow{Hg_2^{2+}\,(aq.)} \underset{\text{(grey black)}}{Hg\downarrow} + Zn^{2+}$
- $\xrightarrow{Bi^{3+}\,(aq.)} \underset{\text{(black)}}{Bi\downarrow} + Zn^{2+}$

B : dil. HCl

- $\xrightarrow{Pb(NO_2)_2} \underset{\text{(white)}}{PbCl_2\downarrow} + HNO_3 + NO\uparrow$
- $\xrightarrow{(NH_4)_2S} H_2S\uparrow + NH_4^+ + Cl^-$
- $\xrightarrow{MnO_4^-\,(aq)} Mn^{2+}(aq) + Cl_2\uparrow$
- $\xrightarrow{Hg_2^{2+}\,(aq)} \underset{\text{(white)}}{Hg_2Cl_2\downarrow}$
- $\xrightarrow{Bi^{3+}\,(aq)} BiCl_3 \rightleftharpoons Bi^{3+} + 3Cl^-$

  i.e., No Reaction

C : NaOH(excess)

- $\xrightarrow{Pb(NO_2)_2} (Pb(OH)_4]_2^- + NO_2^-$
- $\xrightarrow{(NH_4)_2S} NH_3\uparrow + 2Na^+ + S^{2-}$
- $\xrightarrow{MnO_4^-\,(aq.)} \underset{\text{(green)}}{MnO_4^{2-}} + O_2\uparrow$
- $\xrightarrow{Hg_2^{2+}\,(aq.)} \underset{\text{(Black)}}{Hg + HgO}$
- $\xrightarrow{Bi^{3+}\,(aq.)} \underset{\text{(white)}}{Bi(OH)_3\downarrow}$

D : KI

- $KI \xrightarrow{Pb(NO_2)_2} PbI_2\downarrow + NO_2^-$
- $KI \xrightarrow{(NH_4)_2S}$ No Reaction
- $KI \xrightarrow{MnO_4^-\ (aq.)} Mn^{2+} + I_2\uparrow$
- $KI \xrightarrow{Hg_2^{2+}(aq.)} \underset{(green)}{Hg_2I_2\downarrow} \xrightarrow{Warm} Hg\downarrow + \underset{Scarlet}{HgI_2\downarrow}$
- $KI \xrightarrow{Bi^{3+}(aq.)} \underset{(Black)}{BiI_3\downarrow} \xrightarrow{excess} \underset{(Orange\ solution)}{[BiI_4]^-}$

2. (A) H_2SO_4

- $H_2SO_4 \xrightarrow{S_2O_3^{2-}} SO_2\uparrow + S\downarrow$
- $H_2SO_4 \xrightarrow{S^{2-}} H_2S\uparrow$
- $H_2SO_4 \xrightarrow{NO_2^-} NO_2\uparrow$
- $H_2SO_4 \xrightarrow{CH_3COO^-} CH_3COOH\uparrow$

⇒ SO_2, H_2S, CH_3COOH: Colourless
⇒ NO_2: Brown

(B) $AgNO_3$

- $AgNO_3 \xrightarrow{S_2O_3^{2-}} Ag_2S_2O_3\downarrow$ (white)
- $AgNO_3 \xrightarrow{S^{2-}} Ag_2S\downarrow$ (black)
- $AgNO_3 \xrightarrow{NO_2^-} AgNO_2\downarrow$ (white)
- $AgNO_3 \xrightarrow{CH_3COO^-} CH_3COOAg\downarrow$ (white)

(C) $HgCl_2$

- $HgCl_2 \xrightarrow{S_2O_3^{2-}} Ag\ S_2O_3\downarrow$ (white)
- $HgCl_2 \xrightarrow{S^{2-}} HgS$ (black)
- $HgCl_2 \xrightarrow{NO_2^-}$ No ppt.
- $HgCl_2 \xrightarrow{CH_3COO^-}$ No ppt.

(D) Ag_2S is insoluble in NH_3 soluble.

3. (A) (P) $Fe^{2+} + 2KCN \longrightarrow \underset{brown\ ppt.}{Fe(CN)_2\downarrow} \xrightarrow[excess]{4KCN} \underset{pale\ yellow\ colouration}{K_4[Fe(CN)_6]}$

(S) $Ag^+ + KCN \longrightarrow \underset{white\ ppt.}{AgCN\downarrow} \xrightarrow{KCN} \underset{soluble\ complex}{K[Ag(CN)_2]}$

(B) (P) $Fe(OH)_2$ is not soluble in both excess NaOH and excess NH_4OH solution

(Q) HgO not soluble in excess NaOH and excess NH_4OH solution

(C) (Q) $Hg^{2+} + 2KI \longrightarrow HgI_2\downarrow$ (scarlet red)

$\underset{scarlet\ red\ ppt}{HgI_2} \xrightarrow{2KI} \underset{soluble}{K_2[HgI_4]}$

(R) $Pb^{2+} + 2KI \longrightarrow PbI_2\downarrow + 2K^+$

$\underset{Yellow\ ppt.}{PbI_2\downarrow} + \underset{excess}{2KI} \longrightarrow \underset{soluble}{K_2[PbI_4]}$

(D) (R) $Pb^{2+} + H_2S \longrightarrow \underset{\text{black ppt.}}{PbS\downarrow} + 2H^+$

$3PbS + 8HNO_3 \longrightarrow 3Pb(NO_3)_2 + 2NO + 3S + 4H_2O$

(S) $2Ag^+ + H_2S \longrightarrow \underset{\text{black ppt.}}{Ag_2S\downarrow} + 2H^+$

$\underset{\text{Black ppt.}}{3Ag_2S\downarrow} + 8HNO_3 \longrightarrow AgNO_3 + 2NO + 3S + 4H_2O$

4. (A) Due to high K_{sp} of ZnS, it is precipitated in alkaline medium.

(B) $2Cu^{2+} + 5I^- \longrightarrow \underbrace{\underset{\text{white ppt.}}{Cu_2I_2\downarrow} + \underset{\text{Brown}}{I_3^-}}_{\text{brown ppt.}}$

(C) $Pb_3O_4 + HNO_3 \longrightarrow 2Pb(NO_3)_2 + \underset{\text{Brown}}{PbO_2\downarrow} + 2H_2O$

(D) $2FeCl_3 + H_2S \longrightarrow \underset{\text{pale green solution}}{2Fe^{2+}} + \underset{\text{white turbidity}}{S\downarrow} + 2H^+ + 6Cl^-$

5. Oxalate—on heating with conc. H_2SO_4 gives a mixture of CO and CO_2 gases

Acetate—on heating with conc. H_2SO_4, a vinegar smell of acetic acid is produced and with $FeCl_3$ (neutral), gives a red ppt.

Sulphide—with dil. H_2SO_4 producing SO_2 gas which turns lead acetate paper black and sodium nitroprusside produces violet colour of $Na_4[Fe(CN)_5(NOS)]$.

Thiosulphate—with dil. H_2SO_4 producing SO_2 gas and colloidal sulphur.

ASSERTION-REASON TYPE QUESTIONS

3. (C) HNO_3 oxidises Zn metal into ZnO which is further neutralized by HNO_3 and salt of $Zn(NO_3)_2$ is formed with liberation of water.

4. (B) On mild heating (temp. should not be greater than 40°C) ammonium molybdate with phosphate radical in presence of conc. HNO_3, yellow ppt. is obtained.

$$(NH_4)_3PO_4 \cdot 12MoO_3 \text{ (yellow ppt.)}$$

5. (A) $2HgCl_2 + SnCl_2 \longrightarrow \underset{\text{white}}{Hg_2Cl_2\downarrow} + SnCl_4$

$$Hg_2Cl_2 + SnCl_2 \longrightarrow \underset{\text{grey}}{2Hg\downarrow} + SnCl_4$$

6. (D) The white ppt. is due to the formation of the BiOCl or SbOCl

$$BiCl_3 + H_2O \rightleftharpoons BiOCl + 2HCl$$

$$SbCl_3 + H_2O \rightleftharpoons SbOCl + 2HCl$$

$$Pb^{2+} + 2Cl^- \longrightarrow PbCl_2\downarrow$$

17. (D) Group reagent for V group is $(NH_4)_2CO_3$ in presence of NH_4Cl and because of NH_4OH, pH of solution is maintained.

SUBJECTIVE PROBLEMS

1. $B = Na_4[\overset{II}{Fe}(CN)_6(NOS)]$

$Fe^{2+}(d^6) \Rightarrow t_{2g}^6 e_g^\circ$

$|6^2 - 0^2| \Rightarrow$ "36"

2. Soluble in excess NH_3 soln.

$Cd^{2+}(aq.)$, $Ni^{2+}(aq.)$, $Zn^{2+}(aq.)$, $Ag^+(aq.)$

3. $X \Rightarrow (NH_4)_3PO_4 \cdot 12MoO_3$

15th group and sp^3 hybridized atoms in $X = 4$, (3, N-atoms +1 P-atom)

5. $\Rightarrow \underset{(X)}{FeS(s)} \xrightarrow{\text{dil .HCl}} \underset{(Y)}{H_2S\uparrow} \xrightarrow[\text{NaOH}]{Na_2[Fe(CN)_5(NO)]} \underset{\text{Purple solution}}{Na_4[Fe(CN_5)(NO)]}$

(a) $2FeCl_3 + 2H_2S\uparrow \xrightarrow[\text{Neutral}]{\text{Acidic/}} 2Fe^{2+} + S\downarrow + 4H^+ + 6Cl^-$

(b) $CuSO_4 + H_2S\uparrow \xrightarrow[\text{Neutral}]{\text{Acidic/}} \underset{\text{Black}}{CuS\downarrow} + 2H^+ + SO_4^{2-}$

(c) $BaCl_2 + H_2S\uparrow \xrightarrow[\text{Neutral}]{\text{Acidic}} \underset{\text{No observable change}}{Ba^{2+} + 2Cl^- + 2H^+ + S^{2-}}$

(d) $SO_2\uparrow + 2H_2S\uparrow \longrightarrow 2S\downarrow + H_2O$ or $SO_2\uparrow + H_2O \longrightarrow H_2SO_3 \xrightarrow{H_2S} S\downarrow + H_2O$

(e) $Cr_2O_7^{2-} + 8H^+ + 3H_2S\uparrow \xrightarrow[\text{Neutral}]{\text{Acidic/}} 2Cr^{3+} + S\downarrow + 7H_2O$

(f) $2CH_3COONa + H_2S\uparrow \xrightarrow[\text{Neutral}]{\text{Acidic/}} \underset{\text{No observable change}}{2CH_3COOH + 2Na^+ + S^{2-}}$

(g) $Hg^{2+} + H_2S \xrightarrow[\text{Neutral}]{\text{Acidic/}} HgS\downarrow + 2H^+$

$\therefore$ $P = 3$; $Q = 2$; $R = 2$

Hence value of $(P + Q - R) = 3 + 2 - 2 =$ **3**

11

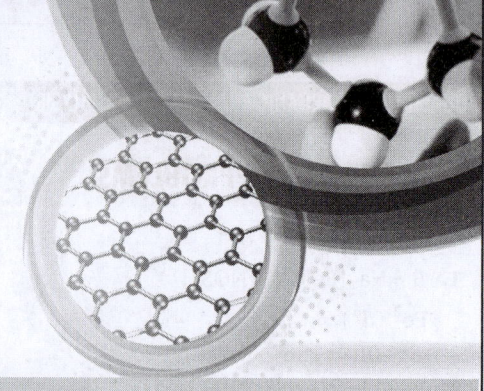

ENVIRONMENTAL CHEMISTRY

Level 1

1. The term biosphere is used for the zone of the earth where life exists:
   (a) On the lithosphere
   (b) In the hydrosphere
   (c) In the lithosphere and hydrosphere
   (d) In the lithosphere, hydrosphere and atmosphere
2. Biosphere is:
   (a) In which individual interact to each other
   (b) By which life originated
   (c) The name of a bird
   (d) Organic compound by which life diminishes
3. Which is not a renewable source?
   (a) Forest (b) Coal (c) Water (d) Forest organism
4. Noosphere is synonyms of:
   (a) Environment (b) Atmosphere
   (c) Hydrosphere (d) Stratosphere
5. The living organisms on or around the earth constitute:
   (a) Biome (b) Biosphere
   (c) Community (d) Biocoenosis
6. Biosphere refers to:
   (a) Plants of the world (b) Special plants
   (c) Area occupied by living beings (d) Plants of a particular area
7. What is the correct sequence of atmospheric layers starting from earth?
   (a) Stratosphere troposphere, mesosphere, thermosphere
   (b) Troposphere, stratosphere, mesosphere, thermosphere
   (c) Mesosphere, troposphere, stratosphere, thermosphere
   (d) Thermosphere, mesosphere, stratosphere, troposphere

8. On earth all living organisms constitute:
(a) Community (b) Biome
(c) Association (d) Biosphere

9. A biosphere is composed of:
(a) Living organisms
(b) Living organisms + lithosphere
(c) Living organisms + lithosphere + lithosphere
(d) Living organisms + lithosphere + atmosphere hydrosphere

10. Pollution can be controlled by:
(a) Sewage treatment
(b) Checking atomic blasts
(c) Manufacturing electrically operated vehicles
(d) All the above

11. If water pollution continues at its present rate, if will eventually:
(a) Stop water cycle
(b) Prevent precipitation
(c) Make oxygen molecules unavailable to water plants
(d) Make nitrate molecules unavailable to water plants

12. Recent reports of acid rains industrial cities are due to the effect of atmospheric pollution by:
(a) Excessive release of NO_2 and SO_2 by burning of fossil fuels
(b) Excessive release of CO_2 by burning of fuel like wood and charcoal, cutting of forests and increased animal population
(c) Excessive release of NH_3 by industrial plants and coal gas
(d) Excessive release of CO in atmosphere by incomplete combustion of cock, charcoal and other carbonaceous fuels in pancity of oxygen

13. Pollution is a change in physical, chemical or biological characters of our land and water that may be:
(a) Desirable and harmful to human (b) Desirable and useful to human
(c) Undesirable and harmful to human (d) Undesirable and useful to human

14. Which is the greatest air pollution these days?
(a) Factories (b) Moto vehicles
(c) Domestic appliances (d) Animals

15. Removal of the soil by the action of wind and water is known as:
(a) Erosion (b) Fossilization
(c) Leaching (d) Calcification

16. Acid rain occur due to atmospheric pollution of:
(a) SO_2 (b) NH_3 (c) CO_2 (d) N_2O

17. An increase in CO_2 concentration in the atmosphere will result in:
(a) Adverse effects of natural vegetation
(b) Global warming
(c) Temperature decrease in global atmosphere
(d) Genetic disorders in plants and animals

18. Planting more and more trees helps to:
(a) reduce CO_2 in the air (b) increase CO_2 in the air
(c) reduce O_2 in the air (d) reduce CO_2 and increase O_2 in the air

19. The basic component of smog is:
(a) PAN (b) PBN (c) NO_2 (d) All of these

20. Which of the following protects life on earth from harmful effects of UV radiations from sun?
(a) N_2 (b) CO_2 (c) O_2 (d) O_3

21. The ozone layer forms natural by:
(a) the interaction of CFC with oxygen
(b) the interaction of UV radiation with oxygen
(c) the interaction of IR radiation with oxygen
(d) the interaction of oxygen and water vapour

22. Fish die in water bodies polluted by sewage due to:
(a) pathogens (b) reduction in oxygen
(c) foul smell (d) none of these

23. Main pollutant from automobile exhaust is:
(a) CO (b) CO_2 (c) NO (d) hydrocarbons

24. Ultraviolet radiation is absorbed by:
(a) exosphere (b) ionosphere
(c) mesosphere (d) stratosphere

25. Global warming may result in:
(a) flood (b) cyclone
(c) decrease in forest productivity (d) all of the above

26. BHC and DDT act as:
(a) carcinogens (b) allergens
(c) asthmatic agents (d) all of these

27. Which of the following statement is wrong?
(a) Polar stratospheric clouds (PSCs) are clouds formed over Antarctica
(b) Acid rain dissolves heavy metals such as Cu, Pb, Hg and Al from soil, rocks and sediments.
(c) H_2SO_4 is major contributor to acid rain, HNO_3 ranks second and HCl third in this respect
(d) Fishes grow as well in warm as in cold water

28. Ozone depletion in the stratosphere is mainly caused by:
(a) SO_2 (b) NO_2
(c) NO (d) chlorofluorocarbons

29. Persons working in cement plants and lime stone quarries are more prone to disease like:
(a) asthma (b) cancer (c) silicosis (d) pneumoconiosis

Level 2

1. Which of the following gases is not a green house gas?
(a) CO (b) O_3 (c) CH_4 (d) H_2O vapour

2. Photochemical smog occurs in warm, dry and sunny climate. One of the following is not amongst the components of photochemical smog, identify it.
(a) NO_2 (b) O_3
(c) SO_2 (d) Unsaturated hydrocarbon

3. Which of the following statements is not true about classical smog?
(a) Its main components are produced by the action of sunlight on emissions of automobiles and factories
(b) Produced in cold and humid climate
(c) It contains compounds of reducing nature
(d) It contains smoke, fog and sulphur dioxide

4. Biochemical Oxygen Demand, (BOD) is a measure of organic material present in water. BOD value less than 5 ppm indicates a water sample to be..... .
(a) rich in dissolved oxygen (b) poor in dissolved oxygen
(c) highly polluted (d) not suitable for aquatic life

5. Which of the following statements is wrong?
(a) Ozone is produced in upper stratosphere by the action of UV rays on oxygen
(b) Ozone can oxidise sulphur dioxide present in the atmosphere to sulphur trioxide
(c) Ozone hole is thinning of ozone layer present in stratosphere
(d) None of these

6. Sewage containing organic waste should not be disposed in water bodies because it causes major water pollution. Fishes in such a polluted water die because of:
(a) Large number of mosquitoes
(b) Increase in the amount of dissolved oxygen
(c) Decrease in the amount of dissolved oxygen in water
(d) Clogging of gills by mud

7. Which of the following statements about photochemical smog is wrong?
(a) It has high concentration of oxidising agents
(b) It has low concentration of oxidising agent
(c) It can be controlled by controlling the release of NO_2, hydrocarbons, ozone etc.
(d) Plantation of some plants like pinus helps in controlling photochemical smog

8. The gaseous envelope around the earth is known as atmosphere. The lowest layer of this is extended upto 10 km from sea level, this layer is ....
(a) Stratosphere (b) Troposphere (c) Mesosphere (d) Hydrosphere

9. Dinitrogen and dioxygen are main constituents of air but these do not react with each other to form oxides of nitrogen because...................... .
(a) the reaction is endothermic and requires very high temperature
(b) the reaction can be initiated only in presence of a catalyst
(c) oxides of nitrogen are unstable
(d) N_2 and O_2 are unreactive

10. The pollutants which come directly in the air from sources are called primary pollutants. Primary pollutants are sometimes converted into secondary pollutants. Which of the following belongs to secondary air pollutants?

(a) CO (b) Hydrocarbon
(c) Peroxyacetyl nitrate (d) NO

11. Which of the following statements is correct?
(a) Ozone hole is a hole formed in stratosphere from which ozone oozes out.
(b) Ozone holes is a hole formed in the troposphere from which ozone oozes out
(c) Ozone hole is thinning of ozone layer of stratosphere at some places
(d) Ozone hole means vanishing of ozone layer around the earth completely

12. Which of the following practices will not come under green chemistry?
(a) If possible, making use of soap made of vegetable oils instead of using synthetic detergents
(b) Using H_2O_2 for bleaching purpose instead of using chlorine based bleaching agents
(c) Using bicycle for travelling small distances instead of using petrol/diesel based vehicles
(d) Using plastic cans for neatly storing substances

13. Which of the following acts as rocket propellants?
(a) Liq. H_2 + Liq. O_2 (b) Liq. N_2 + Liq. O_2
(c) Liq. H_2 + Liq. N_2 (d) Liq. O_2 + Liq. Argon

14. When rain is accompanied by a thunderstorm, the collected rain water will have pH?
(a) slightly lower than that of rain water without thunderstorm
(b) slightly higher than that of rain water without thunderstorm
(c) uninfluenced by occurrence of thunderstorm
(d) which depends on amount of dust in air

15. The smog is essentially caused by the presence of:
(a) O_3 and N_2 (b) O_2 and N_2
(c) Oxides of sulphur and N_2 (d) O_2 and O_3

16. Ozone in stratosphere is depleted by:
(a) CF_2Cl_2 (b) C_7F_{16} (c) $C_6H_6Cl_6$ (d) C_6F_6

17. Which of the following is responsible for depletion of ozone layer in upper strata of the atmosphere?
(a) Polyhalogens (b) Ferrocene (c) Fullerenes (d) Freons

18. Identify the wrong statements in the following:
(a) Chlorofluorocarbons are responsible for ozone layer depletion
(b) Green house effect is responsible for global warming
(c) Ozone layer does not permit infrared radiation from the sun to reach the earth
(d) Acid rain is mostly because of oxides of nitrogen and sulphur

19. Identify the incorrect statement from the following.
(a) Oxides of nitrogen in the atmosphere can cause the depletion of ozone layer
(b) Ozone absorbs the intense ultraviolet radiation of the sun
(c) Depletion of ozone layer is because of its chemical reactions with chlorofluoro alkanes
(d) Ozone absorbs infra red radiations

20. What is DDT among the following?
(a) Green house gas (b) A fertilizer
(c) Biodegradable pollutant (d) Non-biodegradable pollutant

21. The gas leaked from a storage tank of the Union Carbide plant in Bhopal gas tragedy was:
(a) Phosgene (b) Methyl isocyanate
(c) Methyl amine (d) Ammonia

Level 3

Passage 1

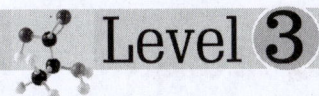

When healthy, earth's stratosphere contains a low concentration of ozone (O_3) that absorbs potentially harmful ultraviolet (UV) radiations by the cycle shown below:

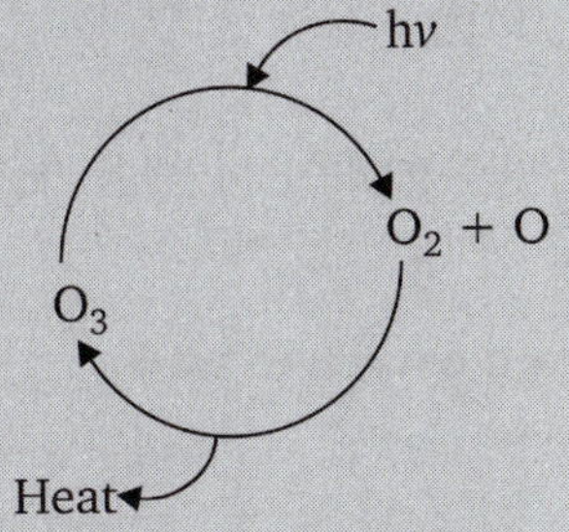

chlorofluoro carbon refrigerants, such as freon 12 (CF_2Cl_2), are stable in lower atmosphere, but in the stratosphere, they absorb high energy UV radiation to generate chlorine radicals.

$$CF_2Cl_2 \xrightarrow{h\nu} \dot{C}F_2Cl + Cl^{\bullet}$$

The presence of small number of chlorine radicals appears to lower ozone concentrations dramatically. The following reactions are all known to be exothermic (except the one requiring light) and to have high rate constant.

A : $Cl-O-O-Cl \xrightarrow{h\nu} O_2 + 2Cl^{\bullet}$

B : $Cl-O^{\bullet} + O \longrightarrow O_2 + Cl^{\bullet}$

C : $Cl^{\bullet} + O_3 \longrightarrow Cl-O^{\bullet} + O_2$

D : $2Cl-O^{\bullet} \longrightarrow Cl-O-O-Cl$

1. Ozone has the ability to absorb:
(a) UV radiations
(b) electromagnetic radiations
(c) CFC
(d) green house gases

2. Increased UV radiations due to hole in ozone layer:
(a) will cause increase in cases of skin diseases
(b) will cause more ice to melt
(c) will cause summer to be more warmer
(d) will cause more rain

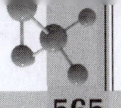

ONE OR MORE ANSWERS IS/ARE CORRECT

1. Which of the following conditions shows the polluted environment?
(a) pH of rain water is 5.6
(b) amount of carbondioxide in the atmosphere is 0.03%
(c) biochemical oxygen demand 10 ppm.
(d) eutrophication

2. Phosphate containing fertilisers cause water pollution. Addition of such compounds in water bodies causes ....
(a) enhanced growth of algae
(b) decrease in amount of dissolved oxygen in water
(c) deposition of calcium phosphate
(d) increase in fish population

3. The acids present in acid rain are ....
(a) Peroxyacetylnitrate
(b) H_2CO_3
(c) HNO_3
(d) H_2SO_4

4. The consequences of global warming may be ....
(a) increase in average temperature of the earth
(b) melting of Himalayan Glaciers
(c) increased biochemical oxygen demand
(d) eutrophication

MATCH THE COLUMN

Column-I and **Column-II** contains four entries each. Entries of column-I are to be matched with some entries of column-II. Each entry of column-I may have the matching with one or more than one entries of column-II.

1.

Column-I	Column-II
(A) Acid rain	(P) $CHCl_2 - CHF_2$
(B) Photochemical smog	(Q) CO
(C) Combination with haemoglobin	(R) CO_2
(D) Depletion of ozone layer	(S) SO_2
	(T) Unsaturated hydrocarbons

2.

Column-I	Column-II
(A) Oxides of sulphur	(P) Global warming
(B) Nitrogen dioxide	(Q) Damage to kidney
(C) Carbon dioxide	(R) 'Blue baby' syndrome
(D) Nitrate in drinking water	(S) Respiratory diseases
(E) Lead	(T) Red haze in traffic and congested areas

3.

Column-I (Activity)	Column-II (Effect)
(A) Releasing gases to the atmosphere after burning waste material containing sulphur	(P) Water pollution
(B) Using carbamates as pesticides	(Q) Photochemical smog, damage to plant life, corrosion to building material, induce breathing problems, water pollution
(C) Using synthetic detergents for washing clothes	(R) Damaging ozone layer
(D) Releasing gases produced by automobiles and factories in the atmosphere	(S) May cause nerve diseases in human
(E) Using chlorofluorocarbon compounds for cleaning computer parts	(T) Classical smog, acid rain, water pollution, induce breathing problems, damage to buildings, corrosion of metals

4.

Column-I	Column-II
(A) Phosphate fertilizers in water	(P) BOD level of water increases
(B) Methane in air	(Q) Acid ran
(C) Synthetic detergents in water	(R) Global warming
(D) Nitrogen oxides in air	(S) Eutrophication

ASSERTION-REASON TYPE QUESTIONS

The questions given below consist of "Assertion" and their "Reason". Use the following key to choose the appropriate answer.

(A) If both assertion and reason are CORRECT, and reason is the CORRECT explanation of the assertion.

(B) If both assertion and reason are CORRECT, but reason is NOT the CORRECT explanation of the assertion.

(C) If assertion is CORRECT but reason is INCORRECT.

(D) If assertion is INCORRECT but reason is CORRECT.

1. **Assertion** : Green house effect was observed in houses used to grow plants and these are made of green glass.
   Reason : Green house name has been given because glass houses are made of green glass.
2. **Assertion** : The pH of acid rain is less than 5.6.
   Reason : Carbon dioxide present in the atmosphere dissolves in rain water and forms carbonic acid.
3. **Assertion** : Photochemical smog is oxidising in nature.
   Reason : Photochemical smog contains NO_2 and O_3, which are formed during the sequence of reactions.
4. **Assertion** : Carbon dioxide is one of the important green house gases.
   Reason : It is largely produced by respiratory function of animals and plants.
5. **Assertion** : Ozone is destroyed by solar radiation in upper stratosphere.
   Reason : Thinning of the ozone layer allows excessive UV radiations to reach the surface of earth.
6. **Assertion** : Excessive use of chlorinated synthetic pesticides causes soil and water pollution.
   Reason : Such pesticides are non-biodegradable.
7. **Assertion** : If BOD level of water in a reservoir is more than 5 ppm it is highly polluted.
   Reason : High biological oxygen demand means low activity of bacteria in water.

Answers

Level-1

1. (d)	**2.** (a)	**3.** (b)	**4.** (a)	**5.** (b)	**6.** (c)	**7.** (b)	**8.** (d)	**9.** (d)	**10.** (d)
11. (c)	**12.** (a)	**13.** (c)	**14.** (b)	**15.** (a)	**16.** (a)	**17.** (b)	**18.** (d)	**19.** (c)	**20.** (d)
21. (b)	**22.** (b)	**23.** (b)	**24.** (d)	**25.** (d)	**26.** (a)	**27.** (d)	**28.** (d)	**29.** (c)	

Level-2

1. (a)	**2.** (c)	**3.** (a)	**4.** (a)	**5.** (d)	**6.** (c)	**7.** (b)	**8.** (b)	**9.** (a)	**10.** (c)
11. (c)	**12.** (d)	**13.** (a)	**14.** (a)	**15.** (c)	**16.** (a)	**17.** (d)	**18.** (c)	**19.** (d)	**20.** (d)
21. (b)									

Level-3

Passage–1	**1.** (a)	**2.** (a)

One or More Answers is/are correct

1. (c,d) **2.** (a,b) **3.** (b,c,d) **4.** (a,b)

Match the Column

1. A → R, S;	B → T, S;	C → Q;	D → P
2. A → S;	B → T;	C → P;	D → R; E → Q
3. A → T;	B → S;	C → P;	D → Q; E → R
4. A → P, S;	B → R;	C → P;	D → Q

Assertion-Reason Type Questions

1. (C) **2.** (B) **3.** (A) **4.** (B) **5.** (D) **6.** (A) **7.** (C)

12

TYPES OF REACTIONS

Level 1

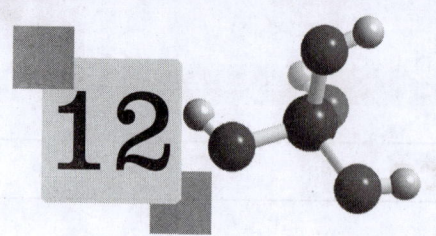

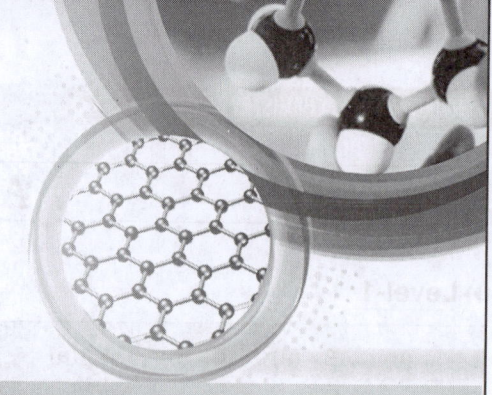

Assign A, B, C, D from given type of reactions.

A for precipitate formation reaction.

B for precipitate dissolution reaction.

C for precipitate exchange reaction.

D for no reaction.

1. $Pb(NO_3)_2 + 2NaOH \longrightarrow Pb(OH)_2 + 2NaNO_3$
2. $Zn(OH)_2 + 2NaOH \longrightarrow Na_2ZnO_2 + 2H_2O$
3. $2Na[Al(OH)_4] + CO_2 \longrightarrow 2Al(OH)_3 + Na_2CO_3$
4. $CuSO_4 + 2NaOH(excess) \longrightarrow Cu(OH)_2 + Na_2SO_4$
5. $Fe(OH)_3 + NaOH(excess) \longrightarrow$ No reaction
6. $Mg(OH)_2 + 2HCl \longrightarrow MgCl_2 + 2H_2O$
7. $Mn(NO_3)_2 + 2NaOH \longrightarrow Mn(OH)_2 + 2NaNO_3$
8. $CH_3COOAg + HNO_3 \longrightarrow AgNO_3 + CH_3COOH$
9. $Hg(NO_3)_2 + NH_3(soln.) \longrightarrow HgO \cdot HgNH_2NO_3$
10. $Cu(OH)_2 + 4NH_3(soln.) \longrightarrow [Cu(NH_3)_4]^{2+} + 2OH^-$
11. $CaC_2O_4 + CH_3COOH \longrightarrow$ No reaction
12. $BaC_2O_4 + 2AcOH \longrightarrow Ba(AcO)_2 + H_2C_2O_4$
13. $Fe(CN)_2 + 4KCN \longrightarrow K_4[Fe(CN)_6]$
14. $SrC_2O_4 + 2HCl \longrightarrow SrCl_2 + H_2C_2O_4$
15. $Fe(CN)_3 + KCN \longrightarrow K_3Fe(CN)_6$
16. $CaSO_3 + SO_2 + H_2O \longrightarrow Ca(HSO_3)_2$
17. $K_4[Fe(CN)_6] + ZnSO_4 \longrightarrow Zn_2[Fe(CN)_6]$

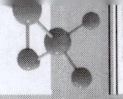

18. $3PbS + 8HNO_3(dil.) \longrightarrow 3Pb(NO_3)_2 + 3S + 2NO$
19. $K_4[Fe(CN)_6] + 2CuSO_4 \longrightarrow Cu_2[Fe(CN)_6]$
20. $MnS + 2HCl \longrightarrow MnCl_2 + H_2S$
21. $AgCl + 2KCN \longrightarrow K[Ag(CN)_2] + KCl$
22. $HgS + Na_2S \rightleftharpoons Na_2[HgS_2]$
23. $CuSO_4 + 2KCN \longrightarrow CuCN + (CN)_2 + K_2SO_4$
24. $FeS + 2HCl \longrightarrow FeCl_2 + H_2S$
25. $Cd(CN)_2 + 2KCN \longrightarrow K_2[Cd(CN)_4]$
26. $2AgF + MgCl_2 \longrightarrow MgF_2 + 2AgCl$
27. $Pb(NO_3)_2 + 2\,KI \longrightarrow PbI_2 + 2KNO_3$
28. $PbCl_2 + \text{Hot water} \longrightarrow Pb^2(aq.) + 2Cl^-(aq.)$
29. $HgI_2 + KI \rightleftharpoons K_2[HgI_4]$
30. $AgI + 2Na_2S_2O_3 \longrightarrow Na_3[Ag(S_2O_3)_2] + NaI$
31. $CuSO_4 + 2KI \longrightarrow CuI + \frac{1}{2}I_2 + K_2SO_4$
32. $KNO_2 + AgF \longrightarrow AgNO_2 + KF$
33. $BaSO_4 + Na_2CO_3 \longrightarrow \text{No reaction}$
34. $FeCl_3 + Na_3PO_4 \longrightarrow FePO_4 + 3NaCl$
35. $BaSO_4 + \text{dil.HCl (Excess)} \longrightarrow \text{No reaction}$
36. $2AgNO_3 + Na_2C_2O_4 \longrightarrow Ag_2C_2O_4 + 2NaNO_3$
37. $2BaCrO_4 + 4HCl \longrightarrow 2BaCl_2 + H_2Cr_2O_7 + H_2O$
38. $PbCrO_4 + 4NaOH(\text{Excess}) \longrightarrow Na_2[Pb(OH)_4]$
39. $BaCrO_4 + CH_3COOH\ (\text{Excess}) \longrightarrow \text{No reaction}$
40. $PbCl_2 + H_2SO_4 \rightleftharpoons PbSO_4 + 2HCl$
41. $Ba(NO_3)_2 + Na_2SO_4 \longrightarrow BaSO_4 + 2NaNO_3$
42. $Pb(NO_3)_2 + H_2SO_4 \longrightarrow PbSO_4 + 2HNO_3$
43. $SrCrO_4 + 2AcOH\ (\text{Excess}) \longrightarrow Sr(AcO)_2 + H_2Cr_2O_7$
44. $MCrO_4\ (M^{2+} = Ba^{2+} Pb^{2+}) + AcOH \longrightarrow \text{No dissolution}$
45. $CaCl_2 + Na_2C_2O_4 \longrightarrow CaC_2O_4 + 2NaCl$
46. $CaSO_4 + Pb(NO_3)_2 \longrightarrow PbSO_4 + Ca(NO_3)_2$
47. $Hg_2(NO_3)_2 + NH_3(\text{solution}) \longrightarrow Hg + HgO \cdot HgNH_2NO_3$
48. $BaCO_3 + 2HCl \longrightarrow BaCl_2 + CO_2 + H_2O$
49. $AlCl_3 + 3NaOH \longrightarrow Al(OH)_3 + 3NaCl$
50. $BaCO_3 + CO_2 + H_2O \longrightarrow Ba(HCO_3)_2$
51. $ZnS + 2HCl \longrightarrow ZnCl_2 + H_2S$
52. $NiCl_2 + 2dmg \xrightarrow{NH_4OH} Ni(dmg)_2$
53. $CaCl_2 + Na_2SO_4 \longrightarrow \text{No reaction}$
54. $BaCO_3 + 2AcOH \longrightarrow Ba(AcO)_2 + CO_2 + H_2O$
55. $Na_2S_2O_3 + BaCl_2 \longrightarrow BaS_2O_3 + 2NaCl$
56. $Ba(AcO)_2 + K_2CrO_4 \longrightarrow BaCrO_4 + 2AcOK$

57. $3AgNO_3 + Na_3PO_4 \longrightarrow Ag_3PO_4 + 3NaNO_3$
58. $Ag_2CO_3 + 2HCl \longrightarrow AgCl + CO_2 + H_2O$
59. $BaSO_3 + H_2SO_4 \longrightarrow BaSO_4 + SO_2 + H_2O$
60. $HgS + HNO_3$ (Conc.) $\longrightarrow$ No dissolution
61. $Sr(AcO)_2 + Ag_2SO_4 \longrightarrow 2AcOAg + SrSO_4$
62. $Ca(OH)_2$ (lime water) $+ 2HF \longrightarrow CaF_2 + 2H_2O$
63. $Ca(OH)_2$ (lime water) $+ CO_2 \longrightarrow CaCO_3 + H_2O$
64. $CaSO_3 + H_2SO_4 \longrightarrow CaSO_4 + SO_2 + H_2O$
65. $Ca(OH)_2$ (lime water) $+ SO_2 \longrightarrow CaSO_3 + H_2O$
66. $Na_2SO_3 + BaCl_2 \longrightarrow BaSO_3 + 2NaCl$
67. $Pb(AcO)_2 + H_2S \longrightarrow PbS + 2AcOH$
68. $NaCl + AgNO_3 \longrightarrow AgCl + NaO_3$
69. $HgI_2 + 2KI \longrightarrow K_2[HgI_4]$
70. $PbO_2 + HNO_3$(dil.) $\longrightarrow$ No dissolution
71. $PbO_2 + HNO_3$(Conc.) $\longrightarrow Pb(NO_3)_2 + H_2O + [O]$
72. $K_2[Cd(CN)_4] + H_2S \longrightarrow CdS + 2KCN + 2HCN$
73. $Pb(AcO)_2 + Na_2CrO_4 \longrightarrow PbCrO_4 + 2AcONa$
74. $NaBr + AgNO_3 \longrightarrow AgBr + NaNO_3$

In the following reactions assign for underlined atom for product of complete hydrolysis at R.T.

A. If products are oxy acid with –ic suffix.
B. If product is oxy acid with –ous suffix.
C. If product are two oxy acids one with –ic suffix and otherone with –ous suffix.
D. If product is not oxy acid, neither with –ic suffix nor with –ous suffix.

75. $\underline{B}_2O_3 + H_2O \longrightarrow H_3BO_3 + H_2O \rightleftharpoons H[B(OH)_4] + H^+$
76. $\underline{S}O_2 + H_2O \longrightarrow H_2SO_3$
77. $\underline{B}F_3 + H_2O \longrightarrow H_3BO_3 + H[BF_4]$
78. $\underline{Te}F_6 + H_2O \longrightarrow TeO_3 \cdot 3H_2O$ (solid) $+ HF$
79. $H_4\underline{P}_2O_5 + H_2O \longrightarrow H_3PO_3$
80. $\underline{C}O + H_2O \longrightarrow$ No reaction
81. $\underline{S}O_3 + H_2O \longrightarrow H_2SO_4$
82. $H_4\underline{P}_2O_6 + H_2O \longrightarrow H_3PO_3 + H_3PO_4$
83. $\underline{B}Cl_3 + H_2O \longrightarrow H_3BO_3 + HCl$
84. $\underline{I}F_7 + H_2O \longrightarrow HIO_4 + HF$
85. $\underline{C}O_2 + H_2O \longrightarrow H_2CO_3$
86. $\underline{Cl}_2O + H_2O \longrightarrow HClO$
87. $H_4\underline{P}_2O_7 + H_2O \longrightarrow 2H_3PO_4$
88. $\underline{C}Cl_4 + H_2O \longrightarrow$ No reaction

89. $ClF_5 + H_2O \longrightarrow HClO_3 + HF$
90. $N_2O + H_2O \longrightarrow$ No reaction
91. $ClO_2 + H_2O \longrightarrow HClO_2 + HClO_3$
92. $H_4P_2O_8 + H_2O \longrightarrow H_3PO_4 + H_2O_2$
93. $NF_3 + H_2O \longrightarrow$ No reaction
94. $BrF_5 + H_2O \longrightarrow HBrO_3 + HF$
95. $NO + H_2O \longrightarrow$ No reaction
96. $ClO_3 + H_2O \longrightarrow HClO_3 + HClO_4$
97. $HNO_4 + H_2O \longrightarrow HNO_3 + H_2O_2$
98. $NCl_3 + H_2O \longrightarrow HOCl + NH_3$
99. $IF_5 + H_2O \longrightarrow HIO_3 + HF$
100. $N_2O_3 + H_2O \longrightarrow HNO_2$
101. $Cl_2O_7 + H_2O \longrightarrow HClO_4$
102. $H_3PO_5 + H_2O \longrightarrow H_3PO_4 + H_2O_2$
103. $SiF_4 + H_2O \rightleftharpoons H_4SiO_4 + H_2[SiF_6]$
104. $ICl_3 + H_2O \longrightarrow HIO_2 + HCl$
105. $N_2O_4 + H_2O \longrightarrow HNO_3 + HNO_2$
106. $I_2O_5 + H_2O \longrightarrow HIO_3$
107. $H_2SO_5 + H_2O \longrightarrow H_2SO_4 + H_2O_2$
108. $SiCl_4 + H_2O \longrightarrow H_4SiO_4 + HCl$
109. $CrO_2Cl_2 + 2H_2O \longrightarrow H_2CrO_4 + 2HCl$
110. $N_2O_5 + H_2O \longrightarrow HNO_3$
111. $PCl_3 + H_2O \longrightarrow H_3PO_3 + HCl$
112. $ClF_3 + H_2O \longrightarrow HClO_2 + HF$
113. $SiO_2 + H_2O \longrightarrow$ No reaction
114. $H_4B_2O_5 + H_2O \longrightarrow H_3BO_3$
115. $H_2S_2O_6 + H_2O \longrightarrow H_2SO_3 + H_2SO_4$
116. $PCl_5 + H_2O \longrightarrow H_3PO_4 + HCl$
117. $ClF + H_2O \longrightarrow HOCl + HF$
118. $P_4O_6 + H_2O \longrightarrow H_3PO_3$
119. $H_4B_2O_6 + H_2O \longrightarrow H_3BO_3 + H_2O_2$
120. $H_6Si_2O_7 + H_2O \longrightarrow H_4SiO_4$
121. $SF_4 + H_2O \longrightarrow H_2SO_3 + HF$
122. $BrF + H_2O \longrightarrow HBrO + HF$
123. $H_2S_2O_7 + H_2O \longrightarrow H_2SO_4$
124. $H_2S_2O_8 + H_2O \longrightarrow H_2SO_4 + H_2O_2$
125. $SF_6 + H_2O \longrightarrow$ No reaction
126. $ICl + H_2O \longrightarrow HIO + HCl$
127. $P_4O_8 + H_2O \longrightarrow H_3PO_3 + H_3PO_4$
128. $P_4O_{10} + H_2O \longrightarrow H_3PO_4$
129. $POCl_3 + H_2O \longrightarrow H_3PO_4 + HCl$

130. $\underline{I}OF_5 + H_2O \longrightarrow HIO_4 + HF$

131. $\underline{P}_4 + H_2O \longrightarrow$ No reaction

132. $Na\underline{H} + H_2O \longrightarrow NaOH + H_2$

133. $\underline{B}_2H_6 + H_2O \longrightarrow H_3BO_3 + H_2$

134. $\underline{Cl}_2 + H_2O \longrightarrow HOCl + HCl$

135. $\underline{S}_8 + H_2O \longrightarrow$ No reaction

136. $\underline{S}OCl_2 + H_2O \longrightarrow H_2SO_3 + HCl$

137. $\underline{S}O_2Cl_2 + H_2O \longrightarrow H_2SO_4 + HCl$

138. $\underline{Si}H_4 + H_2O \longrightarrow H_4SiO_4 + H_2$

139. $\underline{I}_2 + H_2O \longrightarrow$ No reaction

140. $\underline{S}OF_4 + H_2O \longrightarrow H_2SO_4 + HF$

141. $\underline{F}_2 + H_2O \longrightarrow HF + O_2$ (Ozonide Oxygen)

Assign A, B, C, D from given type of reactions.

A for disproportionation reaction.

B for comproportionation reaction.

C for either intermolecular redox reaction or displacement reaction.

D for either thermal combination redox reaction or thermal decomposition redox reaction.

142. $C(s) + O_2(g) \xrightarrow{\Delta} CO_2$

143. $3Mg(s) + N_2(g) \longrightarrow Mg_3N_2$

144. $NaH(s) + H_2O \longrightarrow NaOH + H_2$

145. $CuSO_4(aq.) + Zn(s) \longrightarrow ZnSO_4 + Cu$

146. $Na(s) + H_2O(l) \xrightarrow{\text{R.T.}} NaOH + H_2$

147. $Ca(s) + H_2O(l) \xrightarrow{\text{R.T.}} Ca(OH)_2 + H_2$

148. $Mg(s) + H_2O(l) \xrightarrow{\text{Warm}} Mg(OH)_2 + H_2$

149. $Fe(s) + H_2O(l) \xrightarrow{\text{Boil}} Fe_3O_4 + H_2$

150. $Zn(s) + 2HCl \longrightarrow ZnCl_2 + H_2$

151. $Mg(s) + 2HCl \longrightarrow MgCl_2 + H_2$

152. $Fe(s) + 2HCl \longrightarrow FeCl_2 + H_2$

153. $Cl_2(g) + KI(aq.) \longrightarrow KCl + I_2$

154. $H_2O_2 \xrightarrow{\text{R.T.}} H_2O + \frac{1}{2}O_2$

155. $P_4 + NaOH \longrightarrow PH_3 + NaH_2PO_2$

156. $S_8 + NaOH \longrightarrow Na_2S + Na_2S_2O_3$

157. $Cl_2 + NaOH \longrightarrow NaCl + NaOCl$

158. $I_2 + NaOH \longrightarrow NaI + NaOI$

159. $Pb_3O_4 + HCl(conc.) \xrightarrow{Warm} PbCl_2 + Cl_2 + H_2O$

160. $Pb_3O_4 + HNO_3(dil.) \xrightarrow{R.T.} Pb(NO_3)_2 + PbO_2$

161. $PbO_2 + HCl(dil.) \xrightarrow{Warm} PbCl_2 + Cl_2 + H_2O$

162. $Cr_2O_7^{2-} + H^+ + SO_3^{2-} \longrightarrow Cr^{3+}(aq.) + SO_4^{2-}$

163. $MnO_4^- + H^+ + Br^- \longrightarrow Mn^{2+}(aq.) + Br_2$

164. $Fe^{2+}(aq.) + Cr_2O_7^{2-} + H^+ \longrightarrow Fe^{3+}(aq.) + Cr^{3+}$

165. $I_2 + S_2O_3^{2-} \longrightarrow I^- + S_4O_6^{2-}$

166. $Cu^{2+}(aq.) + 2I^- \longrightarrow CuI + \frac{1}{2}I_2$

167. $CuO + 2H \longrightarrow Cu + H_2O$

168. $H_3PO_2 + AgNO_3 \longrightarrow Ag + H_3PO_4 + NO$

169. $H_3PO_2 + CuSO_4 \longrightarrow Cu + H_3PO_4 + H_2SO_4$

170. $NaNO_3 \xrightarrow{\Delta} NaNO_2 + O_2$

171. $N_2O_3 \xrightarrow{R.T.} NO + NO_2$

172. $Ca(OH)_2 + Cl_2 \longrightarrow CaOCl_2$ or $Ca(OCl)Cl$

173. $XeF_4 + H_2O \longrightarrow Xe + XeO_3 + HF + O_2$

174. $CO + I_2O_5(s) \longrightarrow CO_2 + I_2$

175. $FeCr_2O_4 + Na_2CO_3 + O_2 \longrightarrow Fe_2O_3 + Na_2CrO_4 + 8CO_2\uparrow$

176. $MnO_2 + 2KOH + \frac{1}{2}O_2 \longrightarrow K_2MnO_4 + H_2O$

177. $K_2MnO_4 + H^+ \longrightarrow KMnO_4 + MnO_2$

178. $KMnO_4 \xrightarrow{\Delta} K_2MnO_4 + MnO_2 + O_2$

179. $K_2Cr_2O_7 \xrightarrow{\Delta} K_2CrO_4 + Cr_2O_3 + O_2$

180. $(NH_4)_2Cr_2O_7 \xrightarrow{\Delta} N_2 + Cr_2O_3 + H_2O$

181. $NH_4Cl + NaNO_2 \xrightarrow{\Delta} N_2 + NaCl + H_2O$

182. $Ba(N_3)_2 \xrightarrow{\Delta} Ba + N_2$

183. $N_2 + O_2 \xrightarrow{\text{High temp.}} NO - \text{Heat}$

184. $N_2 + 3H_2 \longrightarrow NH_3$

185. $NH_4NO_3 \xrightarrow{\Delta} N_2O + H_2O$

186. $NaNO_2 + FeSO_4 + H_2SO_4 \longrightarrow \underset{\text{(Ring complex)}}{[Fe(H_2O)_5NO]SO_4}$

187. $NO + NO_2 \xrightarrow{-11^\circ C} N_2O_3$

188. $Pb(NO_3)_2 \xrightarrow{\Delta} PbO + NO_2 + O_2$

189. $P_4 + 6Cl_2 \xrightarrow{\Delta} PCl_3$

190. $P_4 + 10Cl_2 \xrightarrow{\Delta} PCl_5$

191. $Ag + PCl_5 \xrightarrow{\Delta} AgCl + PCl_3$

192. $Sn + PCl_5 \xrightarrow{\Delta} SnCl_4 + PCl_3$

193. $PCl_5 \xrightarrow{\Delta} PCl_3 + Cl_2$

194. $\text{Red P} + \text{Alkali} \longrightarrow Na_4P_2O_6 + P_2H_4$

195. $H_3PO_3 \xrightarrow{\Delta} H_3PO_4 + PH_3$

196. $Se_2Cl_2 \xrightarrow{\Delta} SeCl_4 + Se$

197. $Na_2S + H_2SO_4(\text{Conc.}) \longrightarrow S + SO_2 + Na_2SO_4$

198. $MnO_2 + NaCl + H_2SO_4(\text{Conc.}) \longrightarrow MnSO_4 + Cl_2$

199. $NaBr + MnO_2 + H_2SO_4(\text{Conc.}) \longrightarrow MnSO_4 + Br_2$

200. $NaI + H_2SO_4(\text{Conc.}) \longrightarrow Na_2SO_4 + I_2 + SO_2$

201. $NaI + MnO_2 + H_2SO_4(\text{Conc.}) \longrightarrow MnSO_4 + I_2$

202. $NaNO_3 + H_2SO_4(\text{Conc.}) \xrightarrow{\text{Hot}} Na_2SO_4 + NO_2 + O_2$

203. $Na_2C_2O_4 + H_2SO_4(\text{Conc.}) \longrightarrow Na_2SO_4 + CO + CO_2$

204. $3PbS + 8HNO_3(\text{Dil.}) \longrightarrow 3Pb(NO_3)_2 + 3S + 2NO + 4H_2O$

205. $S + HNO_3(\text{conc.}) \longrightarrow H_2SO_4 + NO$

206. $CuSO_4 + Zn(s) \longrightarrow ZnSO_4 + Cu$

Assign A, B, C, D from given type of reactions.

A for coloured ppt./Black ppt. formation reaction.

B for coloured solution formation reaction.

C for clear/colourless solution formation reaction.

D for white ppt. formation reaction.

207. $2NaOH + Zn(OH)_2 \longrightarrow Na_2ZnO_2 + 2H_2O$

208. $Mn(OH)_2 + H_2SO_4 \longrightarrow MnSO_4 + 2H_2O$

209. $2AgNO_3 + 2NaOH \longrightarrow Ag_2O + 2NaNO_3 + H_2O$

210. $Cr(OH)_3 + NH_3(\text{Excess}) \longrightarrow [Cr(NH_3)_6]^{3+}$

211. $CuSO_4 + NH_3(\text{Excess}) \longrightarrow [Cu(NH_3)_4]^{2+}$

212. $NiCl_2 + NH_3(\text{Excess}) \longrightarrow [Ni(NH_3)_6]^{2+}$

213. $FeCl_3 + NH_3(\text{Excess}) \longrightarrow Fe(OH)_3$

214. $Na_2[Zn(OH)_4] + 4HCl \longrightarrow ZnCl_2 + NaCl + H_2O$

215. $[Cr(NH_3)_6]^{3+} + 6HCl \longrightarrow Cr^{3+}(aq.) + 6NH_4Cl$

216. $2KCN + Pb(NO_3)_2 \longrightarrow Pb(CN)_2 + 2KNO_3$
217. $4KCN + Fe(CN)_2 \longrightarrow K_4[Fe(CN)_6]$
218. $3KCN + Fe(CN)_3 \longrightarrow K_3[Fe(CN)_6]$
219. $CuSO_4 + KCN(Excess) \longrightarrow K_3[Cu(CN)_4] + \frac{1}{2}(CN)_2$
220. $K_3[Fe(CN)_6] + FeCl_3 \longrightarrow Fe[Fe(CN)_6]$
221. $K_3[Fe(CN)_6] + FeCl_2 \longrightarrow Fe_3[Fe(CN)_6]_2$
222. $KI + BiI_3 \longrightarrow K[BiI_4]$
223. $2KI + HgI_2 \longrightarrow K_2[HgI_4]$
224. $KI + AgNO_3 \longrightarrow AgI$
225. $2KI + FeCl_2 \longrightarrow$ No reaction
226. $2KI + CuSO_4 \longrightarrow CuI + \frac{1}{2}I_2 + K_2SO_4$
227. $BaCO_3 + CO_2 + H_2O \longrightarrow Ba(HCO_3)_2$
228. $Ba(OH)_2 + CO_2 \longrightarrow BaCO_3 + H_2O$
229. $BaSO_3 + SO_2 + H_2O \longrightarrow Ba(HSO_3)_2$
230. $Ba(OH)_2 + SO_2 \longrightarrow BaSO_3 + H_2O$
231. $Na_2CO_3 + PbSO_4 \longrightarrow$ No reaction
232. $Na_2CO_3 + Pb(NO_3)_2 \longrightarrow PbCO_3 + NaNO_3$
233. $Na_2CO_3 + KNO_3 \longrightarrow$ No reaction
234. $Na_2CO_3 + AgNO_3 \longrightarrow Ag_2CO_3 + NaNO_3$
235. $Na_3PO_4 + Fe_2(SO_4)_3 \longrightarrow FePO_4 + Na_2SO_4$
236. $NiCl_2$(Solution) + $NaNO_3$(Solution) $\longrightarrow$ No reaction
237. $CuSO_4$(Solution) + $ZnCl_2$(Solution) $\longrightarrow$ No reaction
238. $FeSO_4 + Na_2S \longrightarrow FeS$
239. $FeCl_3 + KI$ (acidified) $\longrightarrow Fe^{2+}(aq.) + KI_3$
240. $AlCl_3 + Na_3PO_4 \longrightarrow AlPO_4$
241. $CrCl_3$(Solution) + $ZnSO_4$(Solution) $\longrightarrow$ No reaction
242. $Na_2CrO_4 + HCl \longrightarrow H_2Cr_2O_7 + Na_2SO_4$
243. $K_2Cr_2O_7 + NaOH \longrightarrow CrO_4^{2-}$
244. $Na_2CrO_4 + AgF \longrightarrow Ag_2CrO_4 + NaF$
245. $KMnO_4 + NaNO_3 \longrightarrow$ No reaction
246. $MnSO_4 + Sr(NO_3)_2 \longrightarrow SrSO_4$
247. $ZnSO_4$(Solution) + $MgCl_2$(Solution) $\longrightarrow$ No reaction
248. $AgNO_3$(Solution) + NaF(Solution) $\longrightarrow$ No reaction
249. $(NH_4)_2SO_4 + Ba(OH)_2 \longrightarrow BaSO_4 + 2NH_3$
250. $(PH_4)_2SO_4 + Sr(OH)_2 \longrightarrow SrSO_4 + 2PH_3$

Level 2

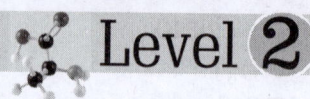

1. Which of the following metal nitrate produces gaseous product when reacts with KCN solution?
(a) $Cu(NO_3)_2$ (b) $AgNO_3$ (c) $Cd(NO_3)_2$ (d) $Pb(NO_3)_2$

2. Which of these reaction is correct ?
(a) $Cl^- + Br_2 \longrightarrow Br^- + Cl_2$
(b) Mohr's salt $\xrightarrow{\text{NaOH solution}} NH_3 \uparrow (g)$
(c) $K_2Cr_2O_7$ solution $\xrightarrow{SO_3}$ Green colour solution
(d) $FeCl_2 \xrightarrow{\text{NaOH}}$ (ppt. coloured) $\xrightarrow{\text{Excess NaOH}}$ Soluble complex

3. Compound which on heating produces paramagnetic acidic gas?
(a) $Mg(NO_3)_2$ (b) $Fe_2(SO_4)_3$ (c) $FeCO_3$ (d) HgC_2O_4

4. Which compound on heating produces coloured metal oxide finally?
(a) $Al_2(SO_4)_3$ (b) $HgCO_3 3Hg(OH)_2$
(c) $Cu(NO_3)_2$ (d) $Ba(OH)_2$

5. $\underset{\text{(Coloured solution)}}{P} + BaCl_2 \longrightarrow \underset{\text{(White)}}{Q\downarrow} + \underset{\text{(Coloured solution)}}{R}$

Then salt '*P*' in above reaction is :
(a) Na_2CrO_4 (b) $ZnSO_4$ (c) $CuSO_4$ (d) $AgNO_3$

6. Oxygen gas is not produced from the following decomposition reaction :
(a) $K_2Cr_2O_7 \xrightarrow{\Delta}$ (b) $Ag_2C_2O_4 \xrightarrow{\Delta}$
(c) $Pb(NO_3)_2 \xrightarrow{\Delta}$ (d) $Ag_2CO_3 \xrightarrow{\Delta}$

7. Consider the following reaction and select incorrect statement about gas (*P*) :

$$Zn + HNO_3(\text{Dilute}) \longrightarrow Zn(NO_3)_2 + P\uparrow$$

(a) Gives neutral solution in water (b) Contains more O_2 than Air
(c) Forms Brown ring with $FeSO_4$ solution (d) None of these

8. Which of the following ionic/molecular species does not disproportionate in water at room temperature?
(a) NO_2 (b) Cu^+ (c) MnO_4^{2-} (d) $Ca(OCl)Cl$

9. Which halogen oxidizes water at room temperature but does not undergo disproportionation into it?
(a) F_2 (b) Cl_2 (c) Br_2 (d) I_2

10. Which of the following combination doesn't evolve Cl_2 gas ?
(a) $HCl(aq.) + KMnO_4$ (b) $HCl + MnO_2$
(c) $HCl + I_2$ (d) $HCl + F_2$

11. Which of the following combination does not liberate NH_3 gas ?
(a) Heating of NH_4ClO_4 (b) Heating of NH_4Cl
(c) $(NH_4)_2CO_3 + NaOH$ (d) $Li_3N + H_2O$

12. Which of the following compound on heating does not produce metal oxide?
(a) $MgCl_2 \cdot 6H_2O$ (b) $K_2Cr_2O_7$ (c) K_2CO_3 (d) $Cu(NO_3)_2$

13. Select the compound in which HCl is not the product of Hydrolysis :
(a) NCl_3 (b) PCl_3 (c) $AsCl_3$ (d) $BiCl_3$

14. How many moles of H_2O are liberatd when one mole hydrated $MgCl_2$ is heated?
(a) 6 (b) 5 (c) 4 (d) 3

15. Consider the following sequence of reactions :

$$M^{2+}(aq.) \xrightarrow{NH_4Cl(s)+(NH_4)_2CO_3\text{ sol.}} Q\downarrow \xrightarrow[\text{Followed by addition of }(NH_4)_2C_2O_4]{CH_3COOH} R\downarrow$$

Which of the following cation can form ppt. *Q* but does not form ppt. '*R*' ?
(a) $Mg^{2+}(aq.)$ (b) $Ca^{2+}(aq.)$ (c) $Sr^{2+}(aq.)$ (d) $Ba^{2+}(aq.)$

16. Which of the following compound does not liberate oxygen gas on warming with conc. H_2SO_4 ?
(a) SO_3 (b) PbO_2 (c) MnO_2 (d) CrO_5

17. One of the hydrolysed product of the following compound does not react with silica of glass vessel :
(a) BF_3 (b) ClF_5 (c) XeF_2 (d) SF_4

18. $M(\text{Salt}) + \text{Dil. HCl} \xrightarrow{\text{Warm}} N\uparrow + P\downarrow$

gas '*N*' changes colour of $FeSO_4$ solution into yellow solution then salt *M* in above reaction is :
(a) BaS_2O_3 (b) Ag_2SO_3 (c) $AgNO_2$ (d) $Pb(NO_3)_2$

19. $Pb + \text{Dil.}HNO_3 \xrightarrow{\text{Warm}} P + Q\uparrow + H_2O$

Incorrect statement for *Q* is :
(a) Paramagnetic colourless gas
(b) It is oxidized to paramagnetic coloured gas by air
(c) It combines with $Fe_2(SO_4)_3$
(d) It can be also obtained by disproportionation of HNO_2

20. In which of the following redox reaction precipitate is not formed ?
(a) $Cr^{3+}(aq.) + Na_2O_2(\text{Solution}) \longrightarrow$
(b) $Fe^{3+}(aq.) + (NH_4)_2S \longrightarrow$
(c) $Mn^{2+}(aq.) + H_2O_2 + NH_3(\text{Solution}) \longrightarrow$
(d) $Fe^{2+}(aq.) + Na_2O_2(\text{Solution}) \longrightarrow$

21. Which metal sulphide is soluble in excess NH_3 solution ?
(a) ZnS (b) MnS (c) FeS (d) None

22. $I^-(aq.) + MnO_4^-(aq.) \xrightarrow{H^+} X + Mn^{2+}(aq.)$

$I^-(aq.) + MnO_4^-(aq.) \xrightarrow[\text{weakly }OH^-]{\text{Neutral or}} Y + MnO_2$

$MnO_4^-(aq.) + Mn^{2+}(aq.) \xrightarrow{ZnSO_4} Z + 4H^+$

Products *X*, *Y* and *Z* are respectively :
(a) I_2, IO_3^-, MnO_2 (b) IO_3^-, I_2, MnO_2 (c) I_2, IO_3^-, MnO_4^{2-} (d) IO_3^-, I_2, MnO_4^{2-}

23. $Br_2 + NaOH \xrightarrow{\text{R.T.}} Y + Z$

If Y gives precipitate with $AgNO_3$, then Z does not undergo reaction with :

(a) $Cr^{3+}(aq.)$ (b) $Fe^{2+}(aq.)$ (c) $Al^{3+}(aq.)$ (d) $Sn^{2+}(aq.)$

24. $(P) \xrightarrow{\Delta} (Q)$ metallic solid $+ (R)\uparrow + (S)\uparrow$

$(X) \xrightarrow{\Delta} (Y)$ amphoteric $+ (R)\uparrow + (S)\uparrow$

P & X are respectively :

(a) $AgNO_3$, $LiNO_3$ (b) $AgNO_3$, $Pb(NO_3)_2$

(c) $Hg_2(NO_3)_2$, $Ca(NO_3)_2$ (d) $NaNO_3$, $Zn(NO_3)_2$

25. Iodine is not oxidized to Iodic acid by :

(a) conc. HNO_3 (b) Hot & conc. H_2SO_4

(c) Excess Cl_2 water (d) conc. H_3PO_4

26. Colourless gas that has oxidising as well as reducing properties :

(a) CO_2 (b) SO_2 (c) NO_2 (d) SO_3

27. $Pb + \text{dil. } HNO_3 \xrightarrow{\text{Warm}} P + Q\uparrow + H_2O$

incorrect statement for Q is :

(a) Paramagnetic colourless gas

(b) It is oxidized to paramagnetic coloured gas by air

(c) It combines with $Fe_2(SO_4)_3$

(d) It is also obtained by disproportionation of HNO_2

28. Which reaction has positive value of $\Delta G°$?

(a) $F_2 + H_2O \xrightarrow{\text{R.T.}} 2HF + \frac{1}{2}O_2\uparrow$

(b) $Cl_2 + H_2O \xrightarrow{\text{R.T.}} HCl + HOCl$

(c) $Br_2 + H_2O \xrightarrow{\text{R.T.}} HBr + HOBr$

(d) $I_2 + H_2O \xrightarrow{\text{R.T.}} HI + HOI$

29. Which does not undergo comproportionation reaction ?

(a) $H_2S + SO_2 \longrightarrow$ (b) $I^-(aq.) + IO_3^-(aq.) + H^+(aq.) \longrightarrow$

(c) $K_2MnO_4 + H^+(aq.) \longrightarrow$ (d) $MnO_4^- + Mn^{2+}(aq.) \longrightarrow$

30. Select the incorrect match :

(a) $Fe^{3+} + [Fe(CN)_6]^{4-} \longrightarrow$ Blue colour ppt.

(b) $Fe^{3+} + [Fe(CN)_6]^{3-} \longrightarrow$ Red brown colouration

(c) $Fe^{2+} + [Fe(CN)_6]^{3-} \longrightarrow$ Blue colour ppt.

(d) $Fe^{2+} + [Fe(CN)_6]^{4-} \longrightarrow$ Red brown colouration

31. $Cu^{2+}(aq.) + X^-(aq.) \xrightleftharpoons{\text{R.T.}} CuX\downarrow + X_2$; 'X' cannot be :

(a) $Cl^-(aq.)$ (b) $I^-(aq.)$ (c) $CN^-(aq.)$ (d) $SCN^-(aq.)$

32. In which of the following reaction SO_2 gas is not produced ?

(a) $S_8 + \text{conc. } H_2SO_4 \xrightarrow{\text{Warm}}$

(b) $S_8 + \text{conc. } HNO_3 \xrightarrow{\text{Warm}}$

(c) $PbS + O_2 \xrightarrow{\Delta}$

(d) $FeS_2 + O_2 \xrightarrow{\Delta}$

33. Which metal gives NH_4NO_3, when react with dilute HNO_3 acid?
(a) Zn (b) Pb (c) Cu (d) Au

34. Select the salt whose aqueous solution is not green :
(a) $FeSO_4$ (b) $CrCl_3$ (c) $NiCl_2$ (d) $MnCl_2$

35. Select the ion exchange reaction, which proceeds to forward direction in aqueous medium :

(a) $2AgCl + CaF_2 \xrightarrow{\text{Aqueous}} 2AgF + CaCl_2$

(b) $BaSO_4 + 2NaOH \xrightarrow{\text{Aqueous}} Ba(OH)_2 + Na_2SO_4$

(c) $Pb(NO_3)_2 + 2CH_3COONa \xrightarrow{\text{Aqueous}} Pb(OAc)_2 + 2NaNO_3$

(d) $Na_2CrO_4 + BaCl_2 \xrightarrow{\text{Aqueous}} BaCrO_4 + 2NaCl$

36. Which of the following metal hydroxide is not soluble in excess of NH_3 solution ?
(a) $Fe(OH)_2$ (b) $Ni(OH)_2$ (c) $Cd(OH)_2$ (d) $Cu(OH)_2$

37. Which of the following combination of reagents does not undergo redox reaction in aqueous medium?
(a) $SnCl_2 + HgCl_2$ (b) $CuSO_4 + KCN$
(c) $Pb(CH_3COO)_2 + KI$ (d) $Ag_2O + SO_2$

38. $K_4[Fe(CN)_6] + M^{x+}(aq.) \longrightarrow \underset{\text{Coloured precipitate}}{M_4[Fe(CN)_6]_x \downarrow}$

Which of the following cation does not respond to the above reaction ?
(a) $Cu^{2+}(aq.)$ (b) $Fe^{3+}(aq.)$ (c) $Zn^{2+}(aq.)$ (d) None of these

39. Sodium salt solution + $AgNO_3$ soln. $\longrightarrow$ Coloured precipitate.
If coloured precipitate is soluble in both dil. HNO_3 and excess conc. NH_3 solution then which of the following anion is present in the salt solution ?
(a) $S^{2-}(aq.)$ (b) $I^-(aq.)$ (c) $PO_4^{3-}(aq.)$ (d) $Br^-(aq.)$

40. Chlorine gas is not produced by heating :
(a) $SOCl_2$ (b) $PbCl_4$ (c) $FeCl_3$ (d) Hg_2Cl_2

41. Which of the following anion does not produce precipitate with $BaCl_2$ solution however gives precipitate with $AgNO_3$?
(a) $CO_3^{2-}(aq.)$ (b) $C_2O_4^{2-}(aq.)$ (c) $MnO_4^-(aq.)$ (d) $S^{2-}(aq.)$

42. Which of the following compound is completely water soluble ?
(a) $BaSO_4$ (b) $Ba(OH)_2$ (c) $Al(OH)_3$ (d) CaF_2

43. Which chemical reaction contains incorrect products ?

(a) $SnSO_4 \xrightarrow{\Delta} SnO_2 + SO_3\uparrow + SO_2\uparrow$

(b) $Ag_2C_2O_4 \xrightarrow{\Delta} Ag + CO_2 \uparrow$

(c) $P_4O_{10}(s) + CaO(s) \xrightarrow{\Delta} Ca_3(PO_4)_2$

(d) $PbCl_4 \xrightarrow{\Delta} PbCl_2 + Cl_2 \uparrow$

44. Which of the following compound undergoes disproportionation in presence of SO_3 gas ?
(a) K_2MnO_4 (b) K_2CrO_4 (c) I_2 (d) $Hg(NO_3)_2$

45. Consider the following reactions :

$X(aq.) \xrightarrow{K_4[Fe(CN)_6]}$ Chocolate brown ppt.

$X(aq.) \xrightarrow{AgNO_3}$ White ppt. (insoluble in dil. HNO_3)

Then 'X' will be :
(a) $ZnSO_4$ (b) $CuCl_2$ (c) $FeSO_4$ (d) $FeCl_3$

46. Which of the following reagent does not oxidize HCl ?
(a) PbO_2 (b) conc. H_2SO_4 (c) MnO_2 (d) $K_2Cr_2O_7$ / H^+

47. Select correct match :

Anions	Separated by reagent
(a) CO_3^{2-}, SO_3^{2-}	$BaCl_2$
(b) CO_3^{2-}, HCO_3^-	$CaCl_2$
(c) SO_3^{2-}, SO_4^{2-}	$(CH_3COO)_2Pb$
(d) Cl^-, Br^-	$AgNO_3$

48. Which of the following compound does not produce green coloured product on thermal decomposition?
(a) $K_2Cr_2O_7$ (b) $KMnO_4$ (c) $(NH_4)_2Cr_2O_7$ (d) NH_4NO_3

49. Aqueous solution of $FeSO_4$ does not produce precipitate with :
(a) NaOH (b) NH_3 solution
(c) Na_2CO_3 (d) None of these

50. Comproportionation occurs between :
(a) $Cl^-(aq.) + ClO^-(aq.) + OH^-(aq.)$ (b) $PH_3(g) + H_3PO_4$ acid
(c) $Na_2S(aq.) + Na_2SO_3(aq.)$ (d) $MNO_4^-(aq.) + Mn^{2+}(aq.) + ZnSO_4(aq.)$

51. Colour of $CrO_4^{2-}(aq.)$ is not changed by :
(a) dil. HCl (b) NH_3 solution
(c) CH_3COOH (d) NO_2 gas

52. $Mg_3N_2(s) + H_2O \xrightarrow{R.T.} P \downarrow + Q \uparrow$

Excess 'Q' gas does not form coloured complex with :
(a) $Ni^{2+}(aq.)$ (b) $Zn^{2+}(aq.)$ (c) $Cr^{3+}(aq.)$ (d) $CO^{2+}(aq.)$

53. Which of the following pair of cations can be separated by excess NaOH solution ?
(a) $Fe^{3+}(aq.)$, $Zn^{2+}(aq.)$ (b) $Mn^{2+}(aq.)$, $Cd^{2+}(aq.)$
(c) $Mg^{2+}(aq.)$, $Hg^{2+}(aq.)$ (d) $Al^{3+}(aq.)$, $Cr^{3+}(aq.)$

54. Consider following reaction :

$$Cl_2(g) + H_2O \xrightarrow{R.T.} P + Q$$

If molecular weight of P is less than Q then incorrect statement is :
(a) On warming 'P' can form deep red coloured vapours with CrO_3
(b) 'Q' exhibits bleaching property
(c) MnO_2 can change 'P' into Cl_2 gas on warming
(d) 'P' reacts with H_2S gas while 'Q' does not

55. Which of the following reagent can dissolves precipitate of $HgS\downarrow$?
(a) NH_3 solution (b) conc. HCl
(c) conc. HNO_3 (d) Na_2S solution

56. Which of the following reaction is incorrect ?
(a) $PCl_3 + 3H_2O \longrightarrow H_3PO_3 + 3HCl$
(b) $NCl_3 + 3H_2O \longrightarrow NH_3 + 3HOCl$
(c) $SbCl_3 + 3H_2O \longrightarrow H_2SbO_3 + 3HCl$
(d) $BiCl_3 + H_2O \longrightarrow BiOCl + 2HCl$

57. Concentrated sodium hydroxide can seperate a mixture of :
(a) Al^{3+} and Cr^{3+} (b) Cr^{3+} and Fe^{3+}
(c) Al^{3+} and Zn^{2+} (d) Zn^{2+} and Pb^{2+}

58. Select correct set of species which can't react with water but react with NaOH :
(i) NO_2 (ii) P_4 (iii) Al (iv) I_2
(a) Only (iv) (b) (iii) and (iv)
(c) (ii), (iii) and (iv) (d) All (i), (ii), (iii) and (iv)

59. Fe(Finely powdered) + HCl(dil.) $\longrightarrow P + Q\uparrow$
compound 'P' does not precipitate with :
(a) $AgNO_3$ (b) $K_3[Fe(CN)_6]$ (c) $(NH_4)_2S$ (d) $NH_4Cl + NH_4OH$

60. Which combination gives maximum number of products ?
(a) $P_4 + SOCl_2$ (b) $P_4 + SO_2Cl_2$
(c) $XeF_4 + H_2O$ (d) $NH_4NO_3 + Zn + \text{Excess NaOH}$

61. Cu^{2+} (*aq.*) does not undergo redox reaction with solution of :
(a) $(NH_4)_2S$ (b) $Na_2S_2O_3$ (c) KI (d) NH_4SCN

62. Hydrolysis of which of the following compound liberates acidic gas ?
(a) Li_2NH (b) Al_2S_3 (c) CaC_2 (d) CaNCN

63. The non-metal which does not react with water but reacts with alkali ?
(a) Boron (b) Bromine (c) P_4 (d) Fluorine

64. A very dilute acidic solution of Cd^{2+} & Ni^{2+} gives only yellow ppt. of CdS on passing H_2S, this is due to :
(a) Solubility product (K_{sp}) of CdS is more than that of NiS.
(b) Solubility product (K_{sp}) of CdS is less than that of NiS.
(c) Cd^{2+} belong to II B group while Ni^{2+} belongs to IVth group.
(d) CdS is insoluble in yellow ammonium sulphide (YAS).

65. Thermal decomposition of which of the salt listed below yield a basic and acidic oxides simultaneouly?
(a) NH_4ClO_4 (b) $CaCO_3$
(c) $NaNO_3$ (d) NH_4NO_2

66. What are formed products, when aqueous solution of $CuCl_2$ and $(NH_4)_2S$ are mixed?
(a) $CuS(aq.)$ and $NH_4Cl(s)$ (b) $CuS(s)$ and $NH_4Cl(aq.)$
(c) $CuS(aq.)$ and $NH_4Cl(g)$ (d) $CuS(s)$ and $NH_4Cl(s)$

67. Which of the following compound does not react with cold and dil. HNO_3?
(a) PbO (b) PbO_2 (c) $FeSO_4$ (d) $PbCl_2$

68. The incorrect order of solubility in water is :
(a) $Ca(OH)_2 < Sr(OH)_2 < Ba(OH)_2$ (b) $Li_2CO_3 < Na_2CO_3 < K_2CO_3$
(c) $CsNO_3 < RbNO_3 < KNO_3$ (d) $BeS_2O_3 < MgS_2O_3 < CaS_2O_3$

69. The correct order of increasing solubility in water is :
(a) KF < NaF < LiF (b) $NaHCO_3 < KHCO_3 < RbHCO_3$
(c) $K_2CO_3 < Na_2CO_3 < Li_2CO_3$ (d) $LiNO_3 < NaNO_3 < KNO_3$

70. Bromine is commercially prepared from sea water by displacement reaction

$$Cl_2 + 2Br^-(aq.) \longrightarrow 2Cl^-(aq.) + Br_2$$

Br_2 gas thus formed is dissolved into solution of Na_2CO_3 and then pure Br_2 is obtained by treatment of the solution with :
(a) $Ca(OH)_2$ (b) NaOH (c) H_2SO_4 (d) HI

71. Which of the following metal on burning in moist air does not give smell of ammonia?
(a) Mg (b) Ca (c) K (d) Li

72. Gas that cannot be collected over water is :
(a) N_2 (b) O_2 (c) SO_2 (d) PH_3

73. Compound having lowest thermal stability is :
(a) $NaHCO_3$ (b) $KHCO_3$ (c) $RbHCO_3$ (d) $CsHCO_3$

74. Which of the following statement is incorrect regarding Fe^{2+} and Fe^{3+} cations?
(a) Fe^{3+} gives brown colour solution with potassium ferricyanide
(b) Fe^{2+} gives blue precipitate with potassium ferricyanide
(c) Fe^{3+} gives red colour solution with potassium thiocyanate
(d) Fe^{2+} gives brown colour with ammonium thiocyanate

75. $(NH_4)_2Cr_2O_7$ on heating liberates a gas. The same gas will be obtained by :
(a) Heating NH_4NO_2 (b) Heating NH_4NO_3
(c) Heating $(NH_4)_2SO_4$ (d) Treating Mg_3N_2 with H_2O

76. Which of the following compound liberates acidic gas during its hydrolysis?
(a) Ca_3P_2 (b) AlN (c) Al_2S_3 (d) CaH_2

77. Which of the following combination does not evolve Cl_2 gas?
(a) $HCl(aq.) + KMnO_4$ (b) $HCl + MnO_2$
(c) $HCl + Br_2$ (d) $HCl + F_2$

78. NH_3 gas does not liberate by which of the following combination?
(a) Heating of NH_4ClO_4 (b) Heating of NH_4Cl
(c) $(NH_4)_2CO_3 + NaOH$ (d) $Li_3N + H_2O$

79. If salt Q undergoes redox reaction with H_2S in acidic medium then which of the following species can not be possible product?
(a) $MnO_4^{2-}(aq.)$ (b) S (c) MnO_2 (d) Both (a) and (c)

80. Metal sulphate $(A) \xrightarrow{\text{Heat}}$ Oxide (B) + Gas (C) + Gas $(D) \xrightarrow{Cr_2O_7^{2-}/H^+}$ Green solution $\xrightarrow[\text{Excess}]{Na_2O_2}$ E (Yellow solution)

Compund A, B, C, D and E are respectively :
(a) $FeSO_4$, Fe_2O_3, SO_3, SO_2, Na_2CrO_4
(b) $Al_2(SO_4)_3$, Al_2O_3, SO_3, SO_2, Na_2CrO_4
(c) $CuSO_4$, CuO, SO_3, SO_2, Na_2CrO_4
(d) $ZnSO_4$, ZnO, SO_3, SO_2, Na_2CrO_4

81. Which of the following radical does not liberate gas with (Zn + dil. HCl) on warming?
(a) S^{2-} (b) SO_3^{2-} (c) NO_3^- (d) CH_3COO^-

82. Which of the following cation does not give precipitate with H_2S in neutral medium?
(a) Fe^{3+} (b) Cu^{2+} (c) Bi^{3+} (d) Ag^+

83. NaCl(solid) + $K_2Cr_2O_7$(solid) + conc. $H_2SO_4 \xrightarrow{\text{Warm}}$ Reddish brown fumes of 'X'.
The oxidation state of central atom in compound 'X' is :
(a) +6 (b) +3 (c) +2 (d) Zero

84. Diamagnetic gas neutral towards water is :
(a) N_2O (b) NO_2 (c) NO (d) N_2O_3

85. Which of the following reagent can be used to separate AgCl and AgI ?
(a) dil. HNO_3 (b) NH_4OH solution
(c) KCN solution (d) $Na_2S_2O_3$ solution

86. When PbO_2 reacts with conc. HNO_3 then evolved gas is :
(a) NO_2 (b) O_2 (c) N_2 (d) N_2O

87. In a closed container there is a mixture of SO_2, CO_2 and O_2 gas. Which sequence of reagent can be helpful to separate them?
(I) Limewater
(II) Acidified potassium dichromate
(III) Alkaline pyragallol.
(a) (I), (II) and (III) (b) (II), (I), (III)
(c) (III), (II), (I) (d) (III), (I), (II)

88. Which salt is colourless?
(a) $KMnO_4$ (b) $BaSO_4$ (c) Na_2CrO_4 (d) $CoCl_2$

89. Which of the following Xenon compound does not produce explosive XeO_3 on its complete hydrolysis?
(a) XeO_2F_2 (b) XeF_2 (c) XeF_4 (d) XeF_6

90. $FeSO_4 \cdot 7H_2O$ (Green Vitriol) salt on thermal decomposition does not produce :
(a) SO_2 (b) O_2 (c) SO_3 (d) H_2O vapour

91. $X(aq.) + Na_2O_2 \longrightarrow Y(aq.) \xrightarrow{BaCl_2} \underset{\text{Insoluble in dil. HCl}}{Z\downarrow}$

X and Y are different sodium salts, then anion present in the salt (X) is :

(a) $Cr_2O_7^{2-}$ (b) $C_2O_4^{2-}$ (c) SO_3^{2-} (d) SO_4^{2-}

92. Which of the following chloride does not react with PCl_5 on heating?

(a) Hg_2Cl_2 (b) $FeCl_2$ (c) S_2Cl_2 (d) BCl_3

93. $\underset{\text{Coloured}}{P(\text{soln.})} \xrightarrow{\text{Air}} \underset{\text{(Coloured)}}{Q(\text{soln.})} \xrightarrow{\text{KOH}} \underset{\substack{\text{(ppt.)} \\ \text{(Insoluble in both excess} \\ \text{NaOH and excess } NH_3 \text{ solution)}}}{R\downarrow}$

Then P contains :

(a) $Cu^{2+}(aq.)$ (b) $Fe^{2+}(aq.)$

(c) $Cr^{2+}(aq.)$ (d) $Ni^{2+}(aq.)$

94. $X_2S_n + \text{water} \longrightarrow X(OH)_n\downarrow + \underset{\text{(Gas)}}{Y\uparrow} \xrightarrow{Pb(CH_3COO)_2} \underset{\text{(Black ppt.)}}{Z\downarrow}$

Then (X) cation can not be :

(a) Fe^{3+} (b) Al^{3+} (c) Cr^{3+} (d) Mg^{2+}

95. $X(\text{salt}) + AgNO_3(aq.) \longrightarrow \underset{\text{(Yellow ppt.)}}{Y\downarrow}$ (soluble in excess of NH_3 solution)

Salt X, does not contain :

(a) PO_4^{3-} (b) Br^- (c) I^- (d) AsO_3^{3-}

96. $M^{n+}(aq.) + KI \longrightarrow \underset{\text{ppt.}}{X\downarrow} \xrightarrow[\text{KI}]{\text{Excess}}$ ppt. remains insoluble in excess KI solution.

then cation $M^{n+}(aq.)$ can be :

(a) $Pb^{2+}(aq.)$ (b) $Cu^{2+}(aq.)$

(c) $Bi^{3+}(aq.)$ (d) $Hg^{2+}(aq.)$

97. Aqueous solution of which of the following cation gives precipitate with potash alum?

(a) $Cu^{2+}(aq.)$ (b) $Zn^{2+}(aq.)$

(c) $Ba^{2+}(aq.)$ (d) $Ni^{2+}(aq.)$

98. Colour of acidified $K_2Cr_2O_7$ is not changed by :

(a) H_2O_2 (b) $Sn^{2+}(aq.)$

(c) HF (d) HBr

Level 3

Passage 1

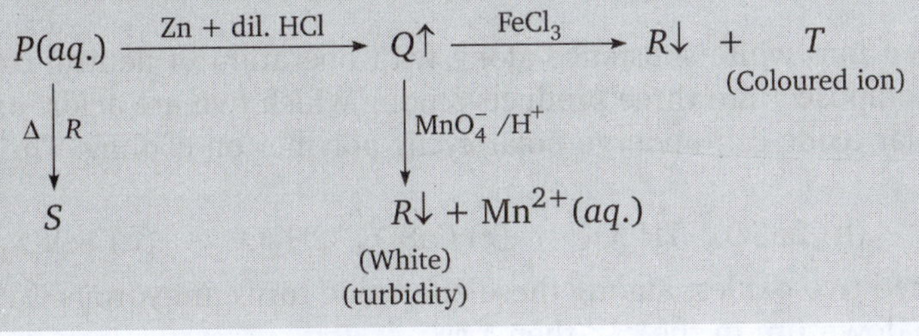

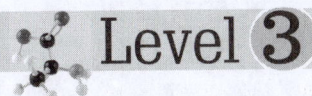

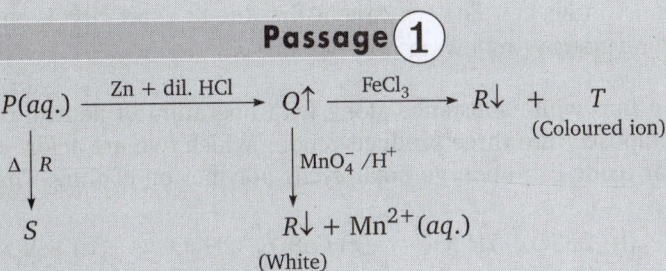

1. Species P and S are respectively :

(a) $SO_3^{2-}(aq.)$, S
(b) $SO_3^{2-}(aq.)$, $S_2O_3^{2-}(aq.)$
(c) $S_2O_3^{2-}(aq.)$, $SO_3^{2-}(aq.)$
(d) None of these

2. 'T' cannot be identified by :

(a) NH_3 solution
(b) NH_4SCN
(c) $(NH_4)_2S$
(d) Excess KCN

Passage 2

Consider three P, Q, R salts among them P and Q salts have different cations and also have different coloured polyatomic anion due to charge transfer phenomenon while P and R salts have same cation but have different anions. Salt R decomposes into an acidic gas and a basic gas.

1. Salt R can not be :

(a) NH_4NO_3
(b) $(NH_4)_2CO_3$
(c) $(NH_4)_2S$
(d) NH_4Cl

2. Salt P decomposes on heating into a coloured solid, neutral gas and neutral vapour, then which of the following can not be the product of salt P after decomposition ?

(a) N_2
(b) Cr_2O_3
(c) I_2
(d) H_2O

3. If salt Q undergoes redox reaction with H_2S in acidic medium then which of the following species can not be possible product ?

(a) $MnO_4^{2-}(aq.)$
(b) S
(c) MnO_2
(d) Both (a) and (c)

Passage 3

Three compounds *X*, *Y* and *Z* were taken into three different laboratory vessels and they were carried out by a chemist in his car. The car caught fire due to short circuit and the chemist came out of the car and noticed following observations :

1. Compound *X* changed into white substance along with liberation of neutral oxide and then white substance decomposed into three products among which two are acidic oxides. Among these oxides non-polar oxide can undergo polar cyclic polymer on cooling. The compound *X* will be :

(a) $MgSO_4 \cdot 7H_2O$ (b) $ZnSO_4 \cdot 7H_2O$ (c) $CaSO_4 \cdot 2H_2O$ (d) $FeSO_4 \cdot 7H_2O$

2. Compound *Y* produced two oxides, among these one oxide turns anhydrous $CuSO_4$ into blue and other gas slows down fire in the car, then *Y* is :

(a) NH_4NO_2 (b) $NaHCO_3$ (c) MgC_2O_4 (d) NH_4NO_3

3. Which of the following compound does not react with cold and dil. HNO_3 ?

(a) PbO (b) PbO_2 (c) $FeSO_4$ (d) $PbCl_2$

Passage 4

In salts of polyatomic anion, as polarising power of cation increases, thermal stability of the salt decreases, and decomposed species may further undergo redox reaction.

1. Which of the following species undergoes non-redox thermal decomposition reaction on heating?

(a) $FeSO_4$ (b) $SnSO_4$ (c) $H_2C_2O_4$ (d) Na_2HPO_4

2. Water soluble salt (*x*) was heated into three products *A*, *B* and *C* and *B* and *C* are two different paramagnetic gases. *A* is yellow in hot condition, then salt (*x*) is :

(a) $Hg(NO_3)_2$ (b) FeC_2O_4 (c) $ZnSO_4$ (d) $Pb(NO_3)_2$

Passage 5

Dioxygen directly reacts with nearly all metals and non-metals except some metals (*e.g.*, Au, Pt) and some noble gases and form oxide(s). Oxides can be simple (*e.g.*, MgO, Al_2O_3) or mixed (Pb_3O_4, Fe_3O_4). Simple oxides can be classified on the basis of their acidic, basic or amphoteric character. An oxide that combines with water to give an acid is termed acidic oxide (*e.g.*, $SO_2, Cl_2O_7, CO_2, N_2O_5$). For example, SO_2 combines with water to give H_2SO_3, an acid.

$$\text{Gaseous non-metal } (A) \xrightarrow[\text{approp. temp.}]{O_2} P\uparrow \xrightarrow[\text{room temp.}]{O_2} Q\uparrow \xrightarrow{H_2O} R \text{ (oxy acid)} + P\uparrow$$

$$\text{Solid non-metal } (B) \xrightarrow[\text{approp. temp.}]{O_2} X\uparrow \xrightarrow[\text{approp. catalyst \& temp.}]{O_2} Y\uparrow \xrightarrow{H_2O} Z \text{ (oxy acid)} + \text{Heat}$$

1. If, R (dil.) $\xrightarrow{Zn} N_2O\uparrow$; R (dil.) $\xrightarrow{Cu} P\uparrow$ R (conc.) $\xrightarrow{Zn} Q\uparrow$; R (conc.) $\xrightarrow{Cu} Q\uparrow$

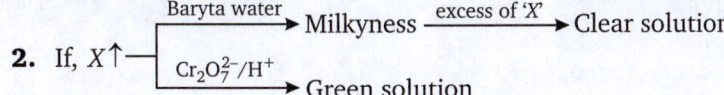

Then select correct statement with respect to gas 'Q' :

(a) Paramagnetic gas (b) Neutral oxide

(c) Colourless gas (d) Diatomic gas

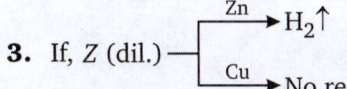

2. If, $X\uparrow \xrightarrow{\text{Baryta water}}$ Milkyness $\xrightarrow{\text{excess of 'X'}}$ Clear solution ; $X\uparrow \xrightarrow{Cr_2O_7^{2-}/H^+}$ Green solution

then 'X' is :

(a) NO (b) CO_2

(c) SO_2 (d) SO_3

3. If, Z (dil.) $\xrightarrow{Zn} H_2\uparrow$; Z (dil.) $\xrightarrow{Cu}$ No reaction Z (conc.) $\xrightarrow{Zn} X\uparrow$; Z (conc.) $\xrightarrow{Cu} X\uparrow$

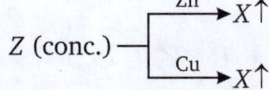

Then select incorrect statement with respect to gas 'X' :

(a) Burning sulphur smell (b) Reacts with Cl_2

(c) Residue of sulphur with H_2S (d) Does not react with Ca(OCl)Cl

Passage 6

Consider the following reactions and answer the following questions.

M (Double salt) + $NH_4Cl(s)$ + $NH_4OH \longrightarrow$ No ppt.

M (Double salt) + NaOH solution $\longrightarrow N\uparrow + P\downarrow$ (coloured ppt.)

1. Which of the following pair of cations are present in salt M ?

(a) PH_4^+, Mg^{2+} (b) NH_4^+, Fe^{3+}

(c) PH_4^+, Zn^{2+} (d) NH_4^+, Fe^{2+}

2. $P\downarrow$ + conc. HCl $\longrightarrow Q$ (coloured solution)

Incorrect statement about Q is :

(a) It can exist in dimeric form

(b) Its aqueous solution is acidic

(c) It is used in methylene blue test for H_2S

(d) On passing Cl_2 gas colour of aqueous solution of Q changes

3. Reaction does not occur with salt M and gas N :

(a) $NaNO_2$ + dil. H_2SO_4 + M (salt solution) $\longrightarrow$

(b) $HgI_2 + N\uparrow \longrightarrow$

(c) M (salt solution) + $H_2S \longrightarrow$

(d) M (salt solution) + $Br_2 \longrightarrow$

Passage 7

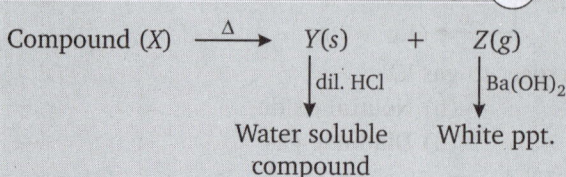

Compound (X) $\xrightarrow{\Delta}$ $Y(s)$ + $Z(g)$

$Y(s)$ $\xrightarrow{\text{dil. HCl}}$ Water soluble compound

$Z(g)$ $\xrightarrow{Ba(OH)_2}$ White ppt.

1. Compound 'X' is :

(a) $NaNO_3$ (b) $Ag_2C_2O_4$ (c) $PbSO_4$ (d) $ZnCO_3$

2. Incorrect statement for 'Y' and 'Z' is :

(a) Colour of 'Y' changes on heating (b) 'Z' is anhydride of H_2CO_3

(c) 'Y' can react with NaOH (d) 'Z' does not act as Lewis acid

Passage 8

The unique behaviour of Cu, having a positive $E°$ (Reduction potential) accounts for its inability to liberate H_2 from acids. Only oxidising acids (nitric acid and hot concentrated sulphuric acid) react with Cu. The high energy to transform Cu(s) to Cu^{2+} ($aq.$) is not balanced by its hydration enthalpy.

On the other hand, all Cu (II) halides are known except iodide. In this case, Cu^{2+} oxidises I^- to I_2 :

$$2Cu^{2+} + 4I^- \longrightarrow 2CuI(s) + I_2$$

However, copper (I) compounds are unstable in aqueous solution and undergo disproportionation.

$$2Cu^+(aq.) \longrightarrow Cu^{2+}(aq.) + Cu$$

The stability of Cu^{2+} ($aq.$) rather than Cu^+ ($aq.$) is due to the much more negative ΔH_{Hyd} of Cu^{2+} ($aq.$) than Cu^+ ($aq.$).

1. Consider the following transformation :

$$CuSO_4(aq.) + KI \text{ (Excess)} \longrightarrow \text{Product}$$

Select the correct statement :

(a) Product contains $[Cu(H_2O)_4]^{2+}$ ion.

(b) Presence of brown colouration in product is due to I_3^- ion

(c) Oxidation state of sulphur in reactant and product is different

(d) White ppt. of CuI_2 is observed in product

2. Select the correct chemical change :

(a) $Cu + \text{dil.} H_2SO_4 \longrightarrow CuSO_4 + H_2(g)$

(b) $Cu + \text{dil.} HNO_3 \longrightarrow Cu(NO_3)_2 + N_2O(g)$

(c) $CuSO_4(aq.) + KCN \text{ (excess)} \longrightarrow K_2[Cu(CN)_4]$

(d) $CuSO_4(aq.) + NH_4OH \longrightarrow Cu(OH)_2 \downarrow$

Passage 9

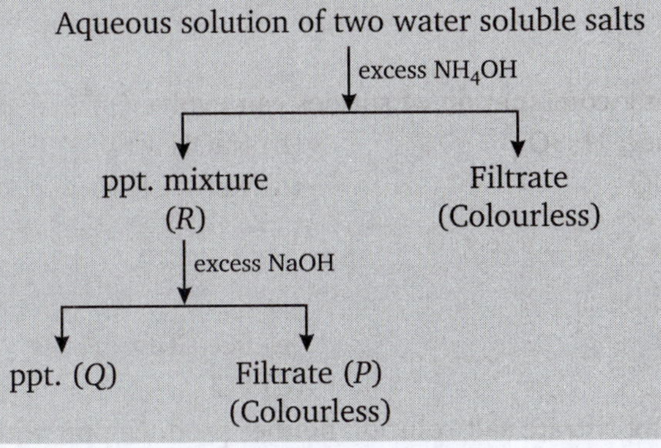

1. When H_2S gas was passed into filtrate (*P*), a coloured precipitate was obtained, then cation present in the filtrate is :

(a) Zn^{2+} (*aq.*) (b) Cr^{3+} (*aq.*)

(c) Al^{3+} (*aq.*) (d) Pb^{2+} (*aq.*)

2. Precipitate (*Q*) was treated with dil. HCl and coloured solution was obtained. On passing H_2S gas into this solution no precipitate was obtained but colour of the solution changes, then cation present in the precipitate (*Q*) can be identified by :

(a) $Na_2S_2O_3$ solution (b) KI + Starch

(c) $K_4[Fe(CN)_6]$ (d) All

ONE OR MORE ANSWERS IS/ARE CORRECT

1. Which of the following combination of species can evolve O_2 ?

(a) PbO_2 + warm conc. H_2SO_4 (b) $NaOH + F_2$

(c) PbO_2 + conc. HNO_3 (d) $XeF_2 + H_2O$

2. $SO_2(g) + Cl_2(g) \longrightarrow X \xrightarrow{P_4} Y + Z$

Then X, Y and Z can be :

(a) $SOCl_2$ (b) SO_2Cl_2

(c) SO_2 (d) PCl_5

3. Which of the following Nitrate salt solution neither produce ppt. with excess NaOH nor with excess NH_4OH solution ?

(a) $Al(NO_3)_3$ (b) $Zn(NO_3)_2$

(c) $Cr(NO_3)_3$ (d) $Pb(NO_3)_2$

4. Which of the following compound(s) give two acids on dissolution in H_2O ?

(a) P_4O_8 (b) $POCl_3$

(c) NO_2 (d) C_3O_2

5. $Xe + F_2 \xrightarrow{1:20} X \xrightarrow{H_2O} Y \xrightarrow{H_2O} Z \xrightarrow{H_2O} XeO_3$

Select correct option(s) for X, Y, Z and given chemical change :

(a) X, Y and Z are in same oxidation state

(b) All have equal number of lone pair on central atom

(c) All are non-planar

(d) All have equal number of covalent bonds

6. Which of the following sulphide(s) does/do not liberate H_2S on warming with dil. HCl ?

(a) HgS (b) ZnS

(c) FeS (d) CuS

7. $I_2 + Na_2CO_3$ soln. $\xrightarrow{\text{Hot}} X + Y$

If 'X' gives coloured ppt. with $Pb(CH_3COO)_2$ solution, then 'Y' will respond to which of the following?

(a) $Y + H^+(aq.) + H_2S$ (b) $Y + Cr_2O_7^{2-}(aq.) + OH^-(aq.)$

(c) $Y + H^+(aq.) + SO_2$ (d) $Y + H^+(aq.) + I^-(aq.)$

8. $SO_2\uparrow \xrightarrow{\text{Excess } Na_2CO_3 \text{ soln.}} P(aq.) \xrightarrow[\text{Boil}]{Q} R$

$SO_2\uparrow \xrightarrow{H_2S\uparrow} Q\downarrow$

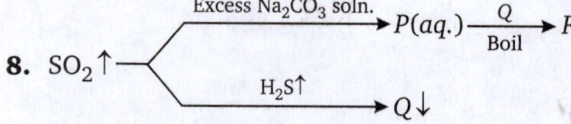

Incorrect statement about 'R' is :

(a) Antichlor agent (b) Fixing agent in photography

(c) Forms ppt. with $CaCl_2$ solution (d) Reduces $Cu^{2+}(aq.)$ cation

9. NO_2 gas evolves on thermal decomposition of which of the following compound(s)?

(a) $Hg(NO_3)_2$ (b) KNO_3 (c) N_2O_4 (d) N_2O_3

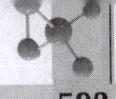

10. Which of the following precipitate(s) is/are dissolved to colourless solution on adding sufficient amount of dilute HCl?
(a) $CaCO_3$ (b) $BaCrO_4$
(c) MgC_2O_4 (d) $BaSO_4$

11. Which of the following combination of reagent(s) produce observable change in aqueous medium?
(a) $Ba(OH)_2$ solution + $SO_2(g)$ (b) AgF solution + $NaNO_3$ solution
(c) $Pb(OAc)_2$ solution + Na_2CO_3 solution (d) $CuCl_2$ solution + NH_3 (excess)

12. Which of the following species is/are not liberating oxygen gas on reaction with water at 25°C?
(a) Na_2O_2 (b) Cl_2 (c) P_4 (d) KO_2

13. Hydrogen gas is not evolved by :
(a) $Mg + NH_3$ (liq.) (b) $B_2H_6 + H_2O$
(c) $NaNH_2 + H_2O$ (d) $Be + H_2O$

14. Which of the following metal sulphide does not undergo hydrolysis?
(a) Cr_2S_3 (b) Al_2S_3 (c) MgS (d) FeS

15. Which of the following gas is not dried by conc. H_2SO_4 ?
(a) HCl (b) HBr (c) H_2S (d) SO_2

16. 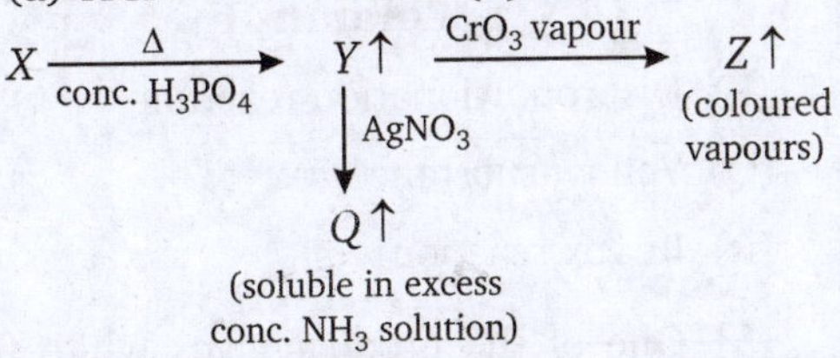

Which of the following anion cannot be in *X* ?
(a) F^- (b) Cl^- (c) Br^- (d) I^-

17. When ozone reacts with an excess of potassium iodide solution buffered with a borate buffer (pH 9.2) iodine is liberated which can be titrated against a standard solution of sodium thiosulphate, this is a quantitative method for estimating O_3 gas. When liberated I_2 and sodium thiosulphate will react, then product is/are :
(a) $S_4O_6^{2-}$ (b) SO_4^{2-} (c) $S_2O_4^{2-}$ (d) S^0

18. In which of the following reactions NH_3 gas evolution occurs?
(a) $NO_3^- + Zn + \text{dil.} H_2SO_4 \xrightarrow{\text{warm}}$ (b) NH_4^+ salt + NaOH $\xrightarrow{\Delta}$
(c) AlN + steam $\longrightarrow$ (d) $CH_3COONH_4 \xrightarrow{\Delta}$

19. Which of the following compound(s) during heating undergo redox decomposition reaction?
(a) $HgCO_3(s)$ (b) $Ag_2C_2O_4(s)$ (c) $FeCl_3 \cdot 6H_2O(s)$ (d) $K_2Cr_2O_7(s)$

20. Which of the following combination of species undergo(es) comproportionation?
(a) $MnO_4^-(aq.) + Mn^{2+}(aq.) \xrightarrow{ZnO/ZnSO_4}$ (b) $S + \text{conc.} \underset{\text{(excess)}}{H_2SO_4} \xrightarrow{\text{warm}}$
(c) $PH_3 + H_3PO_4 \longrightarrow$ (d) $NO(g) + NO_2(g) \xrightarrow{\text{Cool}}$

MATCH THE COLUMN

Entries of Column-I are to be matched with entries of Column-II. Each entry of Column-I may have the matching with one or more than one entries of Column-II.

1.

Column-I (Ionic Compounds)	Column-II (Possible observations on thermal decomposition)
(A) $HgCO_3$	(P) Acidic gas evolves
(B) $FeSO_4$	(Q) Metallic residue is obtained as final product
(C) BeC_2O_4	(R) Metal cation of salt undergoes redox reaction
(D) $AgNO_3$	(S) Metallic oxide can be obtained
	(T) Neutral gas is evolved

2.

Column-I	Column-II
(A) $Na_2S_2O_3 + \text{dil. HCl}$	(P) Disproportionation reaction
(B) $ICl_3 + H_2O$	(Q) Yellow substance
(C) $FeCl_3 + H_2S/H^+$	(R) Redox reaction
(D) $H_2SO_3 \xrightarrow{\Delta}$	(S) One of the product gives white fumes with NH_3

3.

Column-I (Halide compound)	Column-II (Characteristics)
(A) PCl_3	(P) Act as π-acid ligand
(B) NF_3	(Q) Final hydrolysed product is a proton donor oxyacid
(C) $SbCl_3$	(R) Act as classical/normal ligand
(D) BF_3	(S) Undergoes partial hydrolysis
	(T) Final hydrolysed product has ($p\pi$-$p\pi$) bond

4.

Column-I (Anions)	Column-II [Reaction of anion(s) with dil. HCl/conc. H_2SO_4]
(A) SO_3^{2-}	(P) Colourless volatile product is formed
(B) CO_3^{2-}	(Q) Coloured volatile product is formed
(C) Cl^-	(R) Volatile product forms precipitate with $Ba(OH)_2$ solution
(D) NO_2^-	(S) Volatile product forms precipitate with $AgNO_3$ solution
	(T) Formed volatile product decolourizes MnO_4^-/H^+ solution

5.

Column-I (Reactions)	Column-II (Characteristics of any one product)
(A) $(NH_4)_2Cr_2O_7 \xrightarrow{\Delta}$	(P) Amphoteric species
(B) $FeSO_4 \xrightarrow{\Delta}$	(Q) Basic species
(C) $Pb(NO_3)_2 \xrightarrow{\Delta}$	(R) Non-polar gas
(D) $P_4 \xrightarrow[\Delta]{NaOH}$	(S) Polar acidic gas
	(T) Coloured residue

6.

Column-I (Complete hydrolysis)	Column-II (Characteristics of any hydrolysed product/hydrolysis)
(A) $NCl_3 \xrightarrow{H_2O}$	(P) Dibasic acid
(B) $NO_2 \xrightarrow{H_2O}$	(Q) Can act as flexidentate ligand
(C) $H_2S_2O_8 \xrightarrow{H_2O}$	(R) Can act as both oxidising and reducing agent
(D) $SF_4 \xrightarrow{H_2O}$	(S) Can act as monodentate ligand
	(T) Non-redox hydrolysis

7.

Column-I (Reaction with Salt/Radical)	Column-II (Salt/Radical)
(A) $Zn + dil. H_2SO_4$	(P) $Pb(NO_2)_2$
(B) dil. HCl	(Q) $(NH_4)_2S$
(C) NaOH (excess)	(R) $MnO_4^-(aq.)$
(D) KI	(S) $Hg_2^{2+}(aq.)$
	(T) $Bi^{3+}(aq.)$

8.

Column-I	Column-II
(A) Disproportionation in alkaline medium	(P) Cl_2
(B) Oxidizing agent	(Q) NO_2
(C) Reacts with water	(R) XeF_6
(D) Basic gas evolves on heating	(S) NaH_2PO_3
	(T) $(NH_4)_2S$

9.

Column-I	Column-II
(A) NO_2	(P) Hydrolysis occurs through redox reaction
(B) SOF_2	(Q) Hydrolysed product can undergo tautomeric change
(C) XeF_4	(R) All hydrolysed products are acids
(D) ClF_5	(S) Hybridization of central atom remains same in final hydrolysed product
	(T) One of the hydrolysed product reacts with glass

10.

Column-I (Acidic Radicals)	Column-II (Observations)
(A) $S^{2-}(aq.)$	(P) Redox reaction with alkaline Br_2
(B) $SO_3^{2-}(aq.)$	(Q) Evolution of diamagnetic gas with dil. HCl on warming
(C) $NO_2^-(aq.)$	(R) White ppt. with $Pb(CH_3COO)_2$ and ppt. remains white even after boiling
(D) $S_2O_3^{2-}(aq.)$	(S) Evolution of gas with (Al + NaOH solution).
	(T) Evolution of same gas with dil. HCl as well as with conc. H_2SO_4 on warming

11.

Column-I	Column-II
(A) Undergoes hydrolysis *via.* SN_2 mechanism	(P) BCl_3
(B) Undergoes hydrolysis *via.* SN_{AE} mechanism	(Q) NCl_3
(C) Hybridisation of central atom in transition state changes during hydrolysis	(R) SOF_2
(D) Proton donor oxy acid is formed as final hydrolysed product	(S) $POCl_3$
	(T) ClF_3

SUBJECTIVE PROBLEMS

1. Find total number of reagents which can produce I_2 from KI solution.

Conc. H_2SO_4, $Hg(NO_3)_2$ solution, $CuSO_4$ solution, Conc. H_3PO_4, $K_2Cr_2O_7/H^+$, Cl_2 water, $Pb(CH_3COO)_2$ solution, $Ca(OCl)Cl/H^+$, $NaNO_2$ + dil. HCl

2. Find total number of metal cations which are ppted as metal sulphide on passing H_2S gas through metal salt solution.

$Pb^{2+}(aq.)$, $Mn^{2+}(aq.)$, $Sn^{2+}(aq.)$, $Cr^{3+}(aq.)$, $Mg^{2+}(aq.)$, $Hg^{2+}(aq.)$, $Cu^{2+}(aq.)$, $Ag^{+}(aq.)$, $Al^{3+}(aq.)$, $Ni^{2+}(aq.)$

3. Consider the following reaction $P_4 + KOH \longrightarrow PH_3 + X$

How many P—H bonds are present in species X?

4. Which of the following species/reagent can reduce $Fe^{3+}(aq.)$ into $Fe^{2+}(aq.)$ at normal conditions?

$(NH_4)_2S$, HI, $Sn^{2+}(aq.)$, $CN^-(aq.)$, $NaNO_2$, SO_2, $Na_2S_2O_3$, $SCN^-(aq.)$, Acidified $NaIO_3$

5. Find out number ionic compound(s) which is/are water insoluble at room temperature.

$BaSO_4$, $AgNO_3$, $PbCO_3$, $CaCl_2$, $Mg(OH)_2$, $KMnO_4$, CH_3COOAg, $Ca_3(PO_4)_2$, $(NH_4)_2S$

6. Find the value of expression $|x - y|$ for following compounds.

where,

x = Total number of water insoluble salts.

y = Total number of salts, which can liberate non-polar acidic gas during their complete thermal decomposition.

$BaCO_3$, $PbSO_4$, $AgNO_3$, CaC_2O_4, $CsHCO_3$, Na_3PO_4, CH_3COOAg, $Mg(OH)_2$, $Pb(NO_3)_2$

7. Find out total number of coloured compound(s) from following :

$BaCO_3$, HgO, $PbSO_4$, Ag_2S, HgI_2, PbO, CdS, $AgNO_2$, $PbCrO_4$

8. Find out total number of cation(s) that produce precipitate with aqueous solution of Na_2CO_3.
Cu^{2+} (*aq.*), Mg^{2+} (*aq.*), Fe^{3+} (*aq.*), Pb^{2+} (*aq.*), Al^{3+} (*aq.*), Hg^{2+} (*aq.*), Zn^{2+} (*aq.*), NH_4^+ (*aq.*), Cs^+ (*aq.*)

9. $P_4 + SOCl_2 \xrightarrow{\Delta}$ Products

Find out total number of non-planar and polar molecules of products in balanced equation for one mole of P_4.

10. What is average oxidation state of sulphur in product formed in given reaction?

$$Na_2SO_3 + Na_2S + I_2 \longrightarrow \text{.........} + NaI$$

11. Find out total number of coloured/black water insoluble compound(s) from following substances :

$Ag_2O, HgI_2, FeS, Ag_3PO_4, Ba(MnO_4)_2, Na_2CrO_4, PbI_2, AgNO_2, Ag_2C_2O_4$

12. Find out toal number of compounds which on heating undergo redox reactions.

$PbCl_4, Mg(NO_3)_2, HgC_2O_4, Ag_2CO_3, Pb(CN)_4, Al(OH)_3, Cu(CN)_2$

13. How many following Ammonium salts will evolve N_2 gas on heating ?

$(NH_4)_2CO_3, (NH_4)_2Cr_2O_7, NH_4NO_2, NH_4ClO_4, NH_4Cl, (NH_4)_2S, (NH_4)_2C_2O_4$

14. How many following metals evolve NO (Nitric oxide) gas with dil. HNO_3 (20%) ?

Hg, Cu, Pb, Zn, Fe, Al, Ag, Au, Mn

15. Find number of basic radicals among the following cations, which can form soluble complex on adding excess of NH_3 solution :
Cd^{2+} (*aq.*), Pb^{2+} (*aq.*), Ni^{2+} (*aq.*), Mn^{2+} (*aq.*), Zn^{2+} (*aq.*), Ag^+ (*aq.*), Hg^{2+} (*aq.*), Fe^{3+} (*aq.*), Mg^{2+} (*aq.*)

16. Calculate difference between oxidation state of chromium (Cr) in blue and green coloured chromium species formed during the following given transformation.

17. If hydrolysis of interhalogen compound can be represented by following general reaction :

$$XY_{n_1} \xrightarrow{\text{water}} n_1 HY + HXO_{n_2}$$

If given interhalogen compound is polar and non-planar, then calculate value of $n_1 + n_2$.

18. Total number of species that can be oxidized by acidic permanganate ion (MnO_4^-/H^+).

$I^-, Fe^{2+}, CO_2, C_2O_4^{2-}, S^{2-}, SO_3^{2-}, NO_2^-, PO_4^{3-}, SO_4^{2-}$

19. How many following metals evolve N_2O gas with dil. HNO_3 (20%)?

Cr, Cu, Pb, Zn, Fe, Al, Ag, Au, Mn

20. How many following Ammonium salts will evolve NH_3 gas on heating ?
$(NH_4)_2CO_3, (NH_4)_2Cr_2O_7, CH_3COONH_4, NH_4ClO_4, NH_4Cl, (NH_4)_2S, (NH_4)_2C_2O_4, (NH_4)_2SO_4, NH_4NO_3$

21. Find out the number of cation(s) which form(s) black ppt. (soluble in hot and dilute HNO_3) on passing H_2S gas into their salt solution?
Mg^{2+} (*aq.*), Cu^{2+} (*aq.*), Ba^{2+} (*aq.*), Fe^{3+} (*aq.*), Ag^+ (*aq.*), Al^{3+} (*aq.*), Hg^{2+} (*aq.*), Pb^{2+} (*aq.*), Mn^{2+} (*aq.*)

Answers

Level-1

1.	(A)	2.	(B)	3.	(A)	4.	(A)	5.	(D)	6.	(B)	7.	(A)	8.	(B)	9.	(A)	10.	(B)
11.	(D)	12.	(B)	13.	(B)	14.	(B)	15.	(B)	16.	(B)	17.	(A)	18.	(B)	19.	(A)	20.	(B)
21.	(B)	22.	(B)	23.	(A)	24.	(B)	25.	(B)	26.	(A)	27.	(A)	28.	(B)	29.	(B)	30.	(B)
31.	(A)	32.	(A)	33.	(C)	34.	(A)	35.	(D)	36.	(A)	37.	(B)	38.	(B)	39.	(D)	40.	(C)
41.	(A)	42.	(A)	43.	(B)	44.	(D)	45.	(A)	46.	(A)	47.	(A)	48.	(B)	49.	(A)	50.	(B)
51.	(B)	52.	(A)	53.	(D)	54.	(B)	55.	(A)	56.	(A)	57.	(A)	58.	(C)	59.	(C)	60.	(D)
61.	(A)	62.	(A)	63.	(A)	64.	(B)	65.	(A)	66.	(A)	67.	(A)	68.	(A)	69.	(B)	70.	(D)
71.	(B)	72.	(A)	73.	(A)	74.	(A)	75.	(A)	76.	(B)	77.	(A)	78.	(A)	79.	(B)	80.	(D)
81.	(A)	82.	(C)	83.	(A)	84.	(A)	85.	(A)	86.	(B)	87.	(A)	88.	(D)	89.	(A)	90.	(D)
91.	(C)	92.	(A)	93.	(D)	94.	(A)	95.	(D)	96.	(A)	97.	(A)	98.	(D)	99.	(A)	100.	(B)
101.	(A)	102.	(A)	103.	(A)	104.	(B)	105.	(C)	106.	(A)	107.	(A)	108.	(A)	109.	(A)	110.	(A)
111.	(B)	112.	(B)	113.	(D)	114.	(A)	115.	(C)	116.	(A)	117.	(B)	118.	(B)	119.	(A)	120.	(A)
121.	(B)	122.	(B)	123.	(A)	124.	(A)	125.	(D)	126.	(B)	127.	(C)	128.	(A)	129.	(A)	130.	(A)
131.	(D)	132.	(D)	133.	(A)	134.	(B)	135.	(D)	136.	(B)	137.	(A)	138.	(A)	139.	(D)	140.	(A)
141.	(D)	142.	(D)	143.	(D)	144.	(B,C)	145.	(C)	146.	(C)	147.	(C)	148.	(C)	149.	(C)	150.	(C)
151.	(C)	152.	(C)	153.	(C)	154.	(A)	155.	(A)	156.	(A)	157.	(A)	158.	(A)	159.	(C)	160.	(C)
161.	(C)	162.	(C)	163.	(C)	164.	(C)	165.	(C)	166.	(C)	167.	(C)	168.	(C)	169.	(C)	170.	(D)
171.	(A)	172.	(A)	173.	(A)	174.	(C)	175.	(C)	176.	(C)	177.	(A)	178.	(D)	179.	(D)	180.	(D)
181.	(B)	182.	(D)	183.	(C,D)	184.	(D)	185.	(B,D)	186.	(C)	187.	(B)	188.	(D)	189.	(C,D)	190.	(C,D)
191.	(C)	192.	(C)	193.	(D)	194.	(A)	195.	(A,D)	196.	(A,D)	197.	(C)	198.	(C)	199.	(C)	200.	(C)
201.	(C)	202.	(D)	203.	(A)	204.	(C)	205.	(C)	206.	(C)	207.	(C)	208.	(B)	209.	(A)	210.	(B)
211.	(B)	212.	(B)	213.	(A)	214.	(C)	215.	(B)	216.	(D)	217.	(B)	218.	(B)	219.	(C)	220.	(B)
221.	(A)	222.	(B)	223.	(C)	224.	(A)	225.	(B)	226.	(D)	227.	(C)	228.	(D)	229.	(C)	230.	(D)
231.	(D)	232.	(D)	233.	(C)	234.	(D)	235.	(A)	236.	(B)	237.	(B)	238.	(A)	239.	(B)	240.	(D)
241.	(B)	242.	(B)	243.	(B)	244.	(A)	245.	(B)	246.	(D)	247.	(C)	248.	(C)	249.	(D)	250.	(D)

Level-2

1.	(a)	2.	(b)	3.	(a)	4.	(c)	5.	(c)	6.	(b)	7.	(c)	8.	(d)	9.	(a)	10.	(c)
11.	(a)	12.	(c)	13.	(a)	14.	(b)	15.	(d)	16.	(a)	17.	(a)	18.	(c)	19.	(c)	20.	(a)
21.	(d)	22.	(a)	23.	(c)	24.	(b)	25.	(d)	26.	(b)	27.	(c)	28.	(d)	29.	(c)	30.	(d)
31.	(a)	32.	(b)	33.	(a)	34.	(d)	35.	(d)	36.	(a)	37.	(c)	38.	(c)	39.	(c)	40.	(d)
41.	(d)	42.	(b)	43.	(a)	44.	(a)	45.	(b)	46.	(b)	47.	(b)	48.	(d)	49.	(d)	50.	(d)
51.	(b)	52.	(b)	53.	(a)	54.	(d)	55.	(d)	56.	(c)	57.	(b)	58.	(c)	59.	(d)	60.	(c)
61.	(a)	62.	(b)	63.	(c)	64.	(b)	65.	(b)	66.	(b)	67.	(b)	68.	(d)	69.	(b)	70.	(c)
71.	(c)	72.	(c)	73.	(a)	74.	(d)	75.	(a)	76.	(c)	77.	(c)	78.	(a)	79.	(d)	80.	(a)
81.	(c)	82.	(a)	83.	(a)	84.	(a)	85.	(b)	86.	(b)	87.	(b)	88.	(b)	89.	(b)	90.	(b)
91.	(c)	92.	(d)	93.	(b)	94.	(a)	95.	(c)	96.	(b)	97.	(c)	98.	(c)				

Level-3

Passage-1	1.	(b)	2.	(b)		
Passage-2	1.	(a)	2.	(c)	3.	(d)
Passage-3	1.	(d)	2.	(b)	3.	(b)
Passage-4	1.	(d)	2.	(d)		
Passage-5	1.	(a)	2.	(c)	3.	(d)
Passage-6	1.	(d)	2.	(c)	3.	(c)
Passage-7	1.	(d)	2.	(d)		
Passage-8	1.	(b)	2.	(d)		
Passage-9	1.	(d)	2.	(d)		

One or More Answers is/are correct

1. (a, b, c, d) 2. (b, c, d) 3. (b) 4. (a, b, c) 5. (a, b, c, d) 6. (a, d)
7. (a, c, d) 8. (c) 9. (a, c, d) 10. (a, c) 11. (a, c, d) 12. (b, c)
13. (a, c, d) 14. (d) 15. (b, c) 16. (a, d) 17. (a) 18. (b, c, d)
19. (a, b, d) 20. (a, d)

Match the Column

1. A→ P, Q, R, S, T; B→ P, R, S; C→ P, S, T; D→ P, Q, R, S, T
2. A→ Q, R; B→ S; C→ Q, R; D→ P, Q, R
3. A→ P, Q; B→ R, T; C→ S, T; D→ S, T
4. A→ P, R, S, T; B→ P, R, S; C→ P, S, T; D→ Q, S, T
5. A→ P, R, T; B→ Q, R, S, T; C→ P, R, S, T; D→ Q
6. A→ R, S, T; B→ Q, R, S; C→ P, Q, R, S, T; D→ P, Q, R, S, T
7. A→ P, Q, R, S, T; B→ P, Q, R, S; C→ P, Q, R, S, T; D→ P, R, S, T
8. A→ P, Q, R; B→ P, Q, R; C→ P, Q, R, S, T; D→ S, T
9. A→ P, Q, R, S; B→ Q, R, S, T; C→ P, T; D→ Q, R, T
10. A→ P, Q, S; B→ P, Q, R, T; C→ P, S, T; D→ P, Q, T
11. A→ P, Q, T; B→ R, S; C→ P, R, S, T; D→ Q, R, S, T

Subjective Problems

1. (6) 2. (5) 3. (2) 4. (5) 5. (5) 6. (0) 7. (6) 8. (7) 9. (6) 10. (2)
11. (5) 12. (6) 13. (3) 14. (4) 15. (4) 16. (3) 17. (8) 18. (6) 19. (5) 20. (6)
21. (3)

Hints and Solutions

Level 2

1. (a)

(a) $2Cu(NO_3)_2 + 4KCN \longrightarrow KNO_3 + \underset{(Redox)}{2CuCN} + (CN)_2\uparrow$

(b) $AgNO_3 + KCN \longrightarrow KNO_3 + AgCN\downarrow$ (ppt. formation)

(c) $Cd(NO_3)_2 + 2KCN \longrightarrow 2KNO_3 + Cd(CN)_2\downarrow$ (ppt. formation)

(d) $Pb(NO_3)_2 + 2KCN \longrightarrow 2KNO_3 + Pb(CN)_2\downarrow$ (ppt. formation)

2. (b) Any NH_4^+ salt when react with base gives NH_3 as product

$$NH_4^+ + OH^- \longrightarrow NH_3\uparrow + H_2O$$

3. (a)

(a) $Mg(NO_3)_2 \xrightarrow{\Delta} MgO + \underset{(Paramagnetic)}{NO_2\uparrow} + O_2\uparrow$

(b) $Fe_2(SO_4)_3 \xrightarrow{\Delta} Fe_2O_3 + SO_3\uparrow$

(c) $FeCO_3 \xrightarrow{\Delta} FeO + CO_2\uparrow$

(d) $HgC_2O_4 \xrightarrow{\Delta} Hg + CO\uparrow + CO_2\uparrow + \frac{1}{2}O_2\uparrow$

4. (c)

(a) $Al_2(SO_4)_3 \xrightarrow{\Delta} Al_2O_3 + SO_3\uparrow$

(b) $HgCO_3 \cdot 3Hg(OH)_2 \xrightarrow{\Delta} Hg + O_2\uparrow + CO_2\uparrow + H_2O$

(c) $Cu(NO_3)_2 \xrightarrow{\Delta} \underset{(Brown)}{CuO} + 2NO_2\uparrow + \frac{1}{2}O_2\uparrow$

(d) $Ba(OH)_2 \xrightarrow{\Delta} BaO + H_2O\uparrow$

5. (c)

(a) $\underset{\text{yellow solution}}{Na_2CrO_4} + BaCl_2 \longrightarrow \underset{\text{yellow ppt}}{BaCrO_4\downarrow} + \underset{\text{clear solution}}{2NaCl}$

(b) $\underset{\text{clear solution}}{ZnSO_4} + BaCl_2 \longrightarrow \underset{\text{white ppt}}{BaSO_4\downarrow} + \underset{\text{clear solution}}{ZnCl_2}$

(c) $\underset{\text{blue solution}}{CuSO_4} + BaCl_2 \longrightarrow \underset{\text{white ppt}}{BaSO_4\downarrow} + \underset{\text{blue solution}}{CuCl_2}$

(d) $\underset{\text{clear solution}}{2AgNO_3} + BaCl_2 \longrightarrow \underset{\text{white ppt}}{2AgCl\downarrow} + \underset{\text{clear solution}}{Ba(NO_3)_2}$

6. (b) $2K_2Cr_2O_7 \xrightarrow{\Delta} 2K_2CrO_4 + Cr_2O_3 + \frac{3}{2}O_2$

$Ag_2C_2O_4 \xrightarrow{\Delta} 2Ag + 2CO_2$

$Pb(NO_3)_2 \xrightarrow{\Delta} PbO + 2NO_2 + \frac{1}{2}O_2$

$Ag_2CO_3 \xrightarrow{\Delta} 2Ag + CO_2 + \frac{1}{2}O_2$

7. (c) $Zn + HNO_3(dil.) \longrightarrow Zn(NO_3)_2 + N_2O$

N_2O is neutral, contain 33.3% oxygen which is more than air.

NO gas forms brown ring complex with $FeSO_4$ solution, whereas N_2O gas does not.

8. (d) $2NO_2 + H_2O \longrightarrow HNO_3 + HNO_2 \xrightarrow[\text{dispn. Rn.}]{\text{R.T.}} HNO_3 + NO$

$2Cu^+(aq.) \xrightarrow{\text{R.T.}} Cu + Cu^{2+}(aq.)$

$3\overset{+6}{Mn}O_4^{2-}(aq.) \xrightarrow[\text{dispn. Rn.}]{\text{R.T.}} 2\overset{+7}{Mn}O_4^-(aq.) + \overset{+4}{Mn}O_2 + 4OH^-$

$Ca(OCl)Cl \xrightarrow{\text{Water}} Ca^{2+}(aq.) + Cl^-(aq.) + OCl^-(aq.)$

9. (a) $F_2 + H_2O \longrightarrow 2HF + \frac{1}{2}O_2$

$Cl_2 + H_2O \longrightarrow HCl + HOCl$

$Br_2 + H_2O \longrightarrow HBr + HOBr$

$I_2 + H_2O \longrightarrow$ No reaction $[\Delta G > 0$ at R. T.$]$

10. (c) $8HCl + KMnO_4 \longrightarrow MnCl_2 + \frac{5}{2}Cl_2\uparrow + KCl + 4H_2O$

$4HCl + MnO_2 \longrightarrow MnCl_2 + Cl_2\uparrow + 2H_2O$

$HCl + I_2 \longrightarrow$ No reaction

$HCl + F_2 \longrightarrow HF + Cl_2\uparrow$

11. (a) $2NH_4ClO_4 \xrightarrow{\Delta} N_2\uparrow + Cl_2\uparrow + 2O_2\uparrow + 4H_2O$

$NH_4Cl \xrightarrow{\Delta} NH_3\uparrow + HCl\uparrow$

$(NH_4)_2CO_3 + 2NaOH \longrightarrow 2NH_3 + Na_2CO_3 + H_2O$

$Li_3N + 3H_2O \longrightarrow 3LiOH + NH_3\uparrow$

12. (c) $MgCl_2 \cdot 6H_2O \xrightarrow{\Delta} MgO + 2HCl + 5H_2O$

$2K_2Cr_2O_7 \xrightarrow{\Delta} 2K_2CrO_4 + Cr_2O_3 + \frac{3}{2}O_2\uparrow$

$K_2CO_3 \xrightarrow{\Delta}$ does not decompose but melts

$Cu(NO_3)_2 \xrightarrow{\Delta} CuO + 2NO_2\uparrow + \frac{1}{2}O_2\uparrow$

13. (a) $NCl_3 + 3H_2O \longrightarrow NH_3 + 3HOCl$

$PCl_3 + 3H_2O \longrightarrow H_3PO_3 + 3HCl$

$AsCl_3 + 3H_2O \longrightarrow H_3AsO_3 + 3HCl$

$BiCl_3 + H_2O \rightleftharpoons \underset{\text{turbidity}}{BiOCl} + 2HCl$

14. (b) $MgCl_2 \cdot 6H_2O \xrightarrow{\Delta} MgO + 2HCl + 5H_2O$

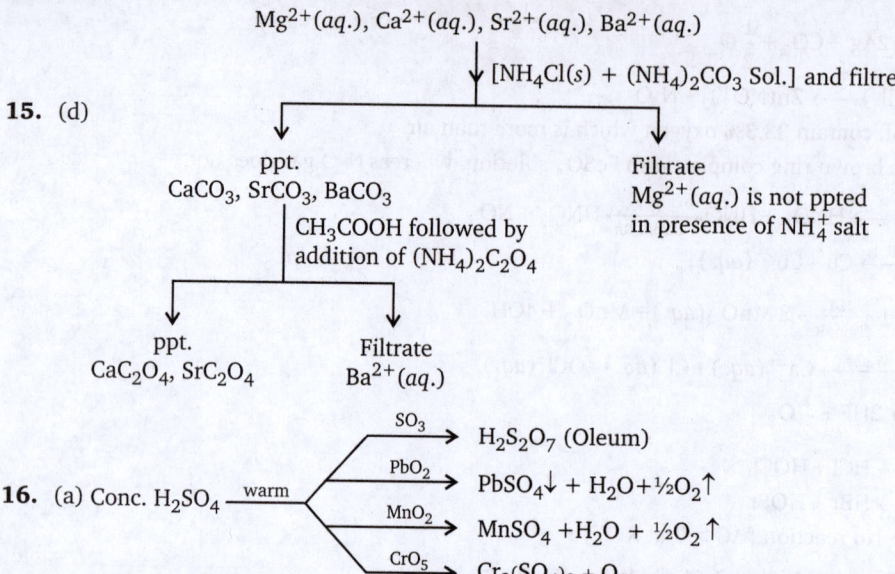

15. (d)

$Mg^{2+}(aq.)$, $Ca^{2+}(aq.)$, $Sr^{2+}(aq.)$, $Ba^{2+}(aq.)$

↓ [$NH_4Cl(s)$ + $(NH_4)_2CO_3$ Sol.] and filtre

- ppt. $CaCO_3$, $SrCO_3$, $BaCO_3$
  - CH_3COOH followed by addition of $(NH_4)_2C_2O_4$
    - ppt. CaC_2O_4, SrC_2O_4
    - Filtrate $Ba^{2+}(aq.)$
- Filtrate $Mg^{2+}(aq.)$ is not ppted in presence of NH_4^+ salt

16. (a) Conc. H_2SO_4 $\xrightarrow{\text{warm}}$

$$\xrightarrow{SO_3} H_2S_2O_7 \text{ (Oleum)}$$
$$\xrightarrow{PbO_2} PbSO_4\downarrow + H_2O + \tfrac{1}{2}O_2\uparrow$$
$$\xrightarrow{MnO_2} MnSO_4 + H_2O + \tfrac{1}{2}O_2\uparrow$$
$$\xrightarrow{CrO_5} Cr_2(SO_4)_3 + O_2$$

17. (a) HF is formed as one of the hydrolysed product of ClF_5, XeF_2, SF_4 and HF react with silica of glass vessel. While in case of hydrolysis of BF_3

$$4BF_3 + 3H_2O \xrightarrow{\text{R.T.}} H_3BO_3 + \underbrace{3H[BF_4]}_{\text{does not react with silica }(SiO_2)}$$

18. (c) $BaS_2O_3 + HCl \xrightarrow{\text{Warm}} BaCl_2 + SO_2\uparrow \xrightarrow{FeSO_4 \text{ sol.}}$ No reaction hence solution remains green.

$Ag_2SO_3 + HCl \xrightarrow{\text{Warm}} AgCl\downarrow + SO_2\uparrow \xrightarrow{FeSO_4 \text{ sol.}}$ No reaction hence solution remains green.

$AgNO_2 + HCl \xrightarrow{\text{Warm}} AgCl\downarrow + NO_2\uparrow \xrightarrow[\text{air}]{FeSO_4 \text{ sol.}} Fe^{3+}(aq.)$ (yellow sol.)

⇒ $Pb(NO_3)_2$ salt is not decompose by dose HCl acid.

20. (a) $Cr^{3+}(aq.) + Na_2O_2 \text{ sol.} \longrightarrow CrO_4^{2-}(aq.)$

$Fe^{3+}(aq.) + (NH_4)_2S \longrightarrow FeS\downarrow$

$Mn^{2+}(aq.) + H_2O_2 + NH_3 \longrightarrow MnO(OH)_2\downarrow$ or $MnO_2\downarrow\cdot 2H_2O$

$Fe^{2+}(aq.) + Na_2O_2 \text{ sol.} \longrightarrow Fe(OH)_3\downarrow$

21. (d) ZnS, MnS, FeS do not dissolve in excess NH_3 solution due to their low K_{sp} values.

$$Cr_2S_3 + 6NH_3 \rightleftharpoons [Cr(NH_3)_6]^{3+} + S^{2-}(aq.)$$

22. (a) MnO_4^- in basic medium is better oxidant than acidic medium, hence oxidises $I^-(aq.)$ ion upto $IO_3^-(aq.)$ ion.

23. (c) $Br_2 + NaOH \longrightarrow NaBr(Y) + NaBrO(Z)$

NaBrO is an oxidising agent which can oxidize

$Cr^{3+} \longrightarrow Cr^{6+}$, $Fe^{2+} \longrightarrow Fe^{3+}$, $Sn^{2+} \longrightarrow Sn^{4+}$

but oxidation of Al^{3+} is not possible.

24. (b) $AgNO_3 \xrightarrow{\Delta} Ag + NO_2\uparrow + \frac{1}{2}O_2\uparrow$

$$Pb(NO_3)_2 \xrightarrow{\Delta} \underset{\text{Amphoteric}}{PbO} + 2NO_2 + \frac{1}{2}O_2\uparrow$$

25. (d)

$$I_2 \xrightarrow[\text{warm}]{\text{conc. } H_2SO_4} HIO_3 + SO_2\uparrow$$

$$I_2 \xrightarrow[\text{warm}]{\text{conc. } HNO_3} HIO_3 + NO_2$$

$$I_2 \xrightarrow[\text{R.T.}]{Cl_2 \text{ water}} HIO_3 + Cl^-$$

$$I_2 \xrightarrow[\text{warm}]{H_3PO_4} \text{No reaction}$$

26. (b) $S\downarrow \xleftarrow{\text{Reducing agent}} SO_2\uparrow \xrightarrow{\text{Oxidising agent}} SO_4^{2-}(aq.)$

SO_2 is colourless gas.

27. (c) $Pb + \text{dil. } HNO_3 \longrightarrow Pb(NO_3)_2 + NO\uparrow + H_2O$

$NO\ (15\ e^-)$ paramagnetic, colourless gas

$NO\uparrow \xrightarrow[\text{R.T.}]{O_2} NO_2\uparrow$ paramagnetic, coloured gas

$HNO_2 \longrightarrow HNO_3 + NO\uparrow + H_2O$

28. (d) $I_2 + H_2O \xrightarrow{\text{R.T.}} 2HI + 1/2\,O_2$, ΔG of this reaction is positive, hence oxidation of $I^-(aq.)$ into I_2 is feasible.

29. (c) $H_2S\uparrow + SO_2\uparrow \xrightarrow{\text{Comprop.}} S\downarrow + H_2O$

$I^-(aq.) + IO_3^-(aq.) + H^+(aq.) \xrightarrow{\text{Comprop.}} I_2 + H_2O$

$K_2MnO_4 + H^+(aq.) \xrightarrow{\text{disprop.}} KMnO_4 + MnO_2\downarrow$

$MnO_4^-(aq.) + Mn^{2+}(aq.) \xrightarrow{\text{Comprop.}} MnO_2\downarrow$

30. (d) $Fe^{2+} + [Fe(CN)_6]^{4-} \longrightarrow$ White colour ppt.

31. (a) $Cu^{2+}(aq.)$ has oxidizing property it oxidizes $I^-(aq.)\,CN^-(aq.)\,SCN^-(aq.)$ into I_2, $(CN)_2$, $(SCN)_2$ respectively but does not oxidize $Cl^-(aq.)$ as it is weaker reductant.

32. (b) $\frac{1}{8}S_8 + \text{conc. } 2H_2SO_4 \xrightarrow{\text{Warm}} 3SO_2 + 2H_2O$

$\frac{1}{8}S_8 + \text{conc. } 6HNO_3 \xrightarrow{\text{Warm}} 6NO_2 + H_2SO_4 + 2H_2O$

$PbS + \frac{3}{2}O_2 \xrightarrow{\Delta} PbO + SO_2\uparrow$

$2FeS_2 + \frac{11}{2}O_2 \xrightarrow{\Delta} Fe_2O_3 + 4SO_2\uparrow$

33. (a) Zn reacts with very dil. HNO_3 while Pb, Cu, Au metals do not react with very dil. HNO_3.

34. (d) Aq. solution of $MnCl_2$ is light pink or colourless.

35. (d)

(a) $\underset{\text{(Insoluble)}}{2AgCl\downarrow} + \underset{\text{(Soluble)}}{CaF_2(aq.)} \xrightarrow{\text{Aqueous}} \text{No reaction}$

(b) $\underset{\text{(Insoluble)}}{BaSO_4\downarrow} + \underset{\text{(Soluble)}}{2NaOH} \xrightarrow{\text{Aqueous}} \underset{\text{(Soluble)}}{Ba(OH)_2} + \underset{\text{(Soluble)}}{Na_2SO_4}$

(c) $\underset{\text{(Soluble)}}{Pb(NO_3)_2} + \underset{\text{(Soluble)}}{2CH_3COONa} \xrightarrow{\text{Aqueous}} \underset{\text{(Soluble)}}{Pb(OAc)_2} + \underset{\text{(Soluble)}}{2NaNO_3}$

(d) $\underset{\text{(Soluble)}}{Na_2CrO_7} + \underset{\text{(Soluble)}}{BaCl_2} \xrightarrow{\text{Aqueous}} \underset{\text{(Insoluble)}}{BaCrO_4\downarrow} + \underset{\text{(Soluble)}}{2NaCl}$

36. (a) $Fe(OH)_2$ is insoluble in NH_3 solution.

37. (c)

(a) $SnCl_2 + HgCl_2 \xrightarrow{\text{Redox}} Hg\downarrow + SnCl_4$

(b) $CuSO_4 + KCN \longrightarrow K_2SO_4 + Cu(CN)_2\downarrow \xrightarrow[\text{Intramolecular redox}]{\text{Spontaneous (R.T.)}} Cu(CN)\downarrow + (CN)_2\uparrow$

(c) $Pb(CH_3COO)_2 + KI \xrightarrow[\text{Non-redox reaction}]{\text{Ion Exchange reaction}} PbI_2\downarrow + CH_3COOK$

(d) $Ag_2O + SO_2 \xrightarrow{\text{Redox}} Ag + SO_3\uparrow$

38. (c) $K_4[Fe(CN)_6] + Zn^{2+}(aq.) \longrightarrow \underset{\text{(White ppt.)}}{Zn_2[Fe(CN)_6]\downarrow}$

39. (c) $Na_2S + AgNO_3 \longrightarrow \underset{\text{(Black ppt.)}}{Ag_2S\downarrow} + NaNO_3$

$NaI + AgNO_3 \longrightarrow \underset{\text{(Yellow ppt.)}}{AgI\downarrow} + NaNO_3$

$Na_3PO_4 + AgNO_3 \longrightarrow \underset{\text{(Yellow ppt.)}}{Ag_3PO_4\downarrow} + NaNO_3$

$NaBr + AgNO_3 \longrightarrow \underset{\text{(Pale Yellow ppt.)}}{AgBr\downarrow} + NaNO_3$

* Ag_2S is insoluble in NH_3 solution.
* AgBr is insoluble in dil. HNO_3 and soluble in conc. NH_3.
* AgI is insoluble in dil. HNO_3 and conc. NH_3.
* Ag_3PO_4 is soluble in both dil. HNO_3 and conc. NH_3.

40. (d) Hg_2Cl_2 do not produce chlorine gas.

41. (d)

(a) $CO_3^{2-}(aq.)$ — $\xrightarrow{BaCl_2} BaCO_3\downarrow$; $\xrightarrow{AgNO_3} Ag_2CO_3\downarrow$

(b) $C_2O_4^{2-}(aq.)$ — $\xrightarrow{BaCl_2} BaC_2O_4\downarrow$; $\xrightarrow{AgNO_3} Ag_2C_2O_4\downarrow$

(c) $MnO_4^-(aq.)$ — $\xrightarrow{BaCl_2}$ No reaction [$Ba(MnO_4)_2\downarrow$ is water soluble.] ; $\xrightarrow{AgNO_3}$ No reaction [$AgMnO_4$ is water soluble.]

(d) $S^{2-}(aq.)$ — $\xrightarrow{BaCl_2}$ No reaction [BaS is water soluble.] ; $\xrightarrow{AgNO_3} Ag_2S\downarrow$

42. (b) $Ba(OH)_2$ is water soluble.

43. (a) $SnSO_4 \xrightarrow{\Delta} SnO_2 + SO_2\uparrow$ (SO_3 is not formed.)

44. (a) The green solution of $MnO_4^{2-}(aq.)$ is stable only in strong basic medium, in neutral (or) acidic (or) less basic medium it disproportionates into MnO_2 and MnO_4^-.

$$K_2MnO_4\text{(Green)} \xrightarrow[SO_3/\text{acidic medium}]{\text{In presence of}} KMnO_4\text{(Purple)} + MnO_2 \text{ (Dark brown)}$$

45. (b) $2CuCl_2(aq.) \xrightarrow{K_4[Fe(CN)_6]} Cu_2[Fe(CN)_6]\downarrow$(Chocolate brown ppt.) + $4KCl(aq.)$

$CuCl_2(aq.) \xrightarrow{2AgNO_3} 2AgCl$(white ppt.)$\downarrow + Cu(NO_3)_2(aq.)$

46. (b) Cl^- being weak reducing nature it can only be oxidize by strong oxidizing agent.

(a) $2HCl + PbO_2 \longrightarrow PbO + Cl_2\uparrow + H_2O$

(b) $HCl + \text{conc.} H_2SO_4 \longrightarrow$ No reaction

(c) $4HCl + MnO_2 \longrightarrow MnCl_2 + 2Cl_2\uparrow + 2H_2O$

(d) $2HCl + K_2Cr_2O_7 + 12H^+ \longrightarrow 2Cr^{3+}(aq.) + 2K^+(aq.) + Cl_2\uparrow + 7H_2O$

47. (b) $CO_3^{2-}, HCO_3^- \xrightarrow{CaCl_2 \text{ sol.}} CaCO_3\downarrow$(ppt.) + HCO_3^-(Soluble) $\xrightarrow{\text{Filtrate}} HCO_3^-$

48. (d)

(a) $2K_2Cr_2O_7$(Orange) $\xrightarrow{\Delta} 2K_2CrO_4$(Yellow) + Cr_2O_3(Green) + $\frac{3}{2}O_2\uparrow$

(b) $2KMnO_4$(Purple) $\xrightarrow{\Delta} K_2MnO_4$(Green) + MnO_2(Black) + $O_2\uparrow$

(c) $(NH_4)_2Cr_2O_7 \xrightarrow{\Delta} Cr_2O_3$(Green) + $N_2\uparrow$ + $4H_2O$

(d) $NH_4NO_3 \xrightarrow{\Delta} N_2O(g)$(Colourless) + $2H_2O$

49. (d)

(a) $Fe^{2+}(aq.) \xrightarrow{\text{NaOH soln.}} Fe(OH)_2\downarrow$(Dirty green ppt.)

(b) $Fe^{2+}(aq.) \xrightarrow{NH_3 \text{ soln.}} Fe(OH)_2\downarrow$(Dirty green ppt.)

(c) $Fe^{2+}(aq.) \xrightarrow{Na_2CO_3} FeCO_3\downarrow$(Brown ppt.)

50. (d) $MnO_4^-(aq.) + Mn^{2+}(aq.) \xrightarrow[\text{Comproportionation Reaction}]{Zn^{2+}(aq.)} MnO_2$

51. (b) $\underset{\text{(yellow)}}{CrO_4^{2-}(aq.)} \underset{\substack{pH>7 \\ \text{(Basic)}}}{\overset{\substack{\text{(Acidic)} \\ pH<7}}{\rightleftharpoons}} \underset{\text{(orange)}}{Cr_2O_7^{2-}(aq.)}$

NH_3 being basic in solution, does not change yellow colour of $CrO_4^{2-}(aq.)$.

52. (b) $Mg_3N_2(s) + H_2O \xrightarrow{\text{R.T.}} \underset{P}{Mg(OH)_2\downarrow} + \underset{Q}{NH_3\uparrow}$

$\underset{(3d^{10}4s^0)}{\overset{+II}{Zn}}(aq.) + 4NH_3 \rightleftharpoons \underset{\text{(colourless complex ion)}}{[Zn(NH_3)_4]^{2+}}$

53. (a)

$Fe^{3+}(aq.), Zn^{2+}(aq.)$

↓ NaOH (excess)

ppt.	Filtrate
$Fe(OH)_3$	$[Zn(OH)_4]^{2-}$

54. (d) $Cl_2(g) + H_2O \xrightarrow{\text{R.T.}} \underset{(P)}{HCl} + \underset{(Q)}{HClO}$

$H_2S(g) + HCl \longrightarrow$ No reaction

$H_2S(g) + HClO \longrightarrow HCl + S\downarrow + H_2O$

55. (d) $HgS + Na_2S(aq.) \rightleftharpoons \underset{\text{Soluble}}{Na_2[HgS_2]}$

56. (c) $SbCl_3 + H_2O \Rightarrow SbOCl + 2HCl$

57. (b) NaOH separates when one of the metal cation form amphoteric oxide and other form basic oxide $Al^{3+}, Cr^{3+}, Zn^{2+}, Pb^{2+}$ amphoteric; Fe^{3+} basic.

58. (c) $NO_2 + H_2O \longrightarrow HNO_2 + HNO_3$ $\quad NO_2 + NaOH \longrightarrow NaNO_2 + NaNO_3$

$P_4 + H_2O \longrightarrow$ No reaction $\quad P_4 + NaOH \longrightarrow NaH_2PO_2 + PH_3$

$Al + H_2O \longrightarrow$ No reaction $\quad Al + NaOH \longrightarrow NaAlO_2 + H_2\uparrow$

$I_2 + H_2O \longrightarrow$ No reaction $\quad I_2 + NaOH \longrightarrow NaI + NaOI$

59. (d) $S_8 + \text{con.} H_2SO_4 \longrightarrow SO_2\uparrow$

$SO_2 + H_2O \rightleftharpoons H_2SO_3$

$S_8 + \text{con.} HNO_3 \longrightarrow H_2SO_4 + NO_2\uparrow$

$B + \text{con.} H_2SO_4 \longrightarrow B_2O_3$

$B_2O_3 + H_2O \longrightarrow H_3BO_3 \xrightleftharpoons{Ka<<1} H^+[B(OH)_4]^-$

$B + \text{con.} HNO_3 \longrightarrow H_3BO_3 + NO_2\uparrow$

$Si + \text{con.} H_2SO_4 \longrightarrow SiO_2$

$SiO_2 + H_2O \longrightarrow$ No reaction

$Si + \text{con.} HNO_3 \longrightarrow H_4SiO_4 + NO_2\uparrow$

60. (c)

(a) $P_4 + SOCl_2 \longrightarrow PCl_3 + SO_2 + S_2Cl_2$

(b) $P_4 + SO_2Cl_2 \longrightarrow PCl_5 + SO_2$

(c) $XeF_4 + H_2O \longrightarrow Xe + XeO_3 + HF + O_2$

(d) $NH_4NO_3 + Zn + \text{excess } NaOH \longrightarrow NH_3\uparrow + Na_2ZnO_2 + H_2O$

61. (a) $Cu^{2+}(aq.)$ do not undergo redox reaction with $(NH_4)_2S$.

62. (b) Al_2S_3 on hydrolysis gives H_2S gas which is acidic.

63. (c) $Ce^{4+}(aq.)$ act as oxidising agent.

Thus it accepts electrons from reducing agents and get reduced to $Ce^{3+}(aq.)$.

$$Ce^{4+}(aq.) + e^- \longrightarrow Ce^{3+}(aq.)$$

64. (b) Basic radicals are classified on the basis of increasing order of K_{sp}. Cd^{2+} in II group while Ni^{2+} in IV group.

65. (b) $2NH_4ClO_4 \xrightarrow{\Delta} N_2\uparrow + Cl_2\uparrow + 2O_2\uparrow + 4H_2O$

$CaCO_3 \xrightarrow{\Delta} \underset{\text{Basic}}{CaO} + \underset{\text{Acidic}}{CO_2}\uparrow$

$NH_4NO_2 \xrightarrow{\Delta} N_2\uparrow + 2H_2O$

$NaNO_3 \xrightarrow[500°C]{\text{below}} NaNO_2 + \frac{1}{2}O_2\uparrow$

$2NaNO_3 \xrightarrow{800°C} Na_2O + N_2\uparrow + \frac{5}{2}O_2\uparrow$

66. (b) $\underset{\text{soluble}}{CuCl_2} + \underset{\text{soluble}}{(NH_4)_2S} \longrightarrow \underset{\text{ppt.}}{CuS\downarrow} + \underset{\text{soluble}}{2NH_4Cl}$

67. (b) PbO_2 does not react with cold dil. HNO_3 due to its more acidic nature.

69. (b) Order of solubility in water

→ $LiF < NaF < KF$

→ $LiNO_3 > NaNO_3 > KNO_3$

→ $Li_2CO_3 < Na_2CO_3 < K_2CO_3$

70. (c) $3Br_2 + 3Na_2CO_3 \longrightarrow 5NaBr + NaBrO_3 + 3CO_2\uparrow$
(Impure) (Hot Aq. Sol.)

$\Delta \downarrow H_2SO_4$

$3Br_2\uparrow + Na_2SO_4$
(Pure)

71. (c) In I group only Li form nitride and all II group metal form nitride.

$Mg + N_2 \longrightarrow Mg_3N_2 \xrightarrow{H_2O\ (moist)} Mg(OH)_2 + NH_3$

$Ca + N_2 \longrightarrow Ca_3N_2 \xrightarrow{H_2O\ (moist)} Ca(OH)_2 + NH_3$

$Li + N_2 \longrightarrow Li_3N \xrightarrow{H_2O\ (moist)} LiOH + NH_3$

$K + N_2 \longrightarrow$ No reaction

72. (c) SO_2 soluble in water. So cannot be collected over water.

73. (a) $\because \phi$ of metal cation $\propto \dfrac{1}{\text{T.S. of ionic compound poly atomic anion}}$

$NaHCO_3 < KHCO_3 < RbHCO_3 < CsHCO_3$

74. (d)

(a) $Fe^{3+} + K_3[Fe(CN)_6] \longrightarrow Fe[Fe(CN)_6]$
Brown Colour

(b) $Fe^{2+} + K_3[Fe(CN)_6] \longrightarrow Fe_3[Fe(CN)_6]_2$
Turn Bull's blue

(c) $Fe^{3+} +$ KSCN (Pot. thioyanate) $\longrightarrow Fe(SCN)_3$ (Blood red colour)

(d) $Fe^{2+} +$ KSCN $\longrightarrow$ No reaction

75. (a) $(NH_4)_2Cr_2O_7 \longrightarrow N_2 + Cr_2O_3 + 4H_2O$

(a) $NH_4NO_2 \longrightarrow N_2 + H_2O$

76. (c)

(a) $Ca_3P_2 + 6H_2O \longrightarrow 3Ca(OH)_2 + 2PH_3\uparrow$
Basic   Basic gas

(b) $AlN + 3H_2O \longrightarrow Al(OH)_3 + NH_3\uparrow$
Basic gas

(c) $Al_2S_3 + 6H_2O \longrightarrow 2Al(OH)_3 + 3H_2S\uparrow$
Basic gas

(d) $CaH_2 + 2H_2O \longrightarrow Ca(OH)_2 + 2H_2\uparrow$
Neutral gas

77. (c)

(a) $HCl + KMnO_4 \longrightarrow Mn^{2+} + Cl_2\uparrow$

(b) $HCl + MnO_2 \longrightarrow Mn^{2+} + Cl_2\uparrow$

(c) $HCl + Br_2 \longrightarrow$ No reaction ($\Delta G = +$ve, because Br_2 is weaker oxidant than Cl_2)

(d) $HCl + F_2 \longrightarrow HF + Cl_2\uparrow$ ($\Delta G = -$ve, because F_2 is stronger oxidant than Cl_2)

78. (a)

(a) $2NH_4ClO_4 \xrightarrow{\Delta} N_2\uparrow + Cl_2\uparrow + 2O_2\uparrow + 4H_2O$

(b) $NH_4Cl \xrightarrow{\Delta} NH_3\uparrow + HCl\uparrow$

(c) $(NH_4)_2CO_3 \xrightarrow{+2NaOH} NH_3 + 2H_2O + Na_2CO_3$ (NH_4^+ Salt decomposition reaction)

(d) $Li_3N \xrightarrow{+3H_2O} 3LiOH + NH_3$

79. (d) $\underset{(\text{O.A. } MnO_4^-)}{\text{'Q' salt}} + \underset{(\text{R.A.})}{H_2S} \xrightarrow{H^+} S + Mn^{2+}(aq.)$

80. (a) $\underset{(A)}{FeSO_4(s)} \xrightarrow{\Delta} \underset{(B)}{Fe_2O_3(s)} + \underset{(C)}{SO_3(g)} + \underset{(D)}{SO_2(g)}$

$SO_2 \xrightarrow{Cr_2O_7^{2-}/H^+} \underset{(\text{Green solution})}{Cr^{3+}(aq.)} \xrightarrow[\text{excess}]{Na_2O_2} \underset{(\text{Yellow solution})}{Na_2CrO_4}$

81. (c)

(a) $S^{2-} + \underbrace{Zn + \text{dil. } HCl}_{\text{St. Reducing agent}} \xrightarrow{[H]} H_2S\uparrow$

(b) $SO_3^{2-} + \underbrace{Zn + \text{dil. } HCl}_{\text{St. Reducing agent}} \xrightarrow{[H]} H_2S\uparrow$

(c) $NO_3^- + \underbrace{Zn + \text{dil. } HCl}_{\text{St. Reducing agent}} \xrightarrow{[H]} NH_3 \xrightarrow{\text{dil. HCl}} NH_4Cl(s)$

(d) $CH_3COO^- + \underbrace{Zn + \text{dil. } HCl}_{\text{St. Reducing agent}} \xrightarrow{[H]} C_2H_6$

82. (a) $Fe^{3+}(aq.) + H_2S \xrightarrow{\text{Redox}} S\downarrow + Fe^{2+}(aq.) \xrightarrow{\text{Neutral } H_2S} \text{No ppt.}$

83. (a) $NaCl(s) + K_2Cr_2O_7(s) + \underset{(\text{Few Drops})}{\text{Conc. } H_2SO_4} \xrightarrow{\text{Non-Redox reaction}} \underset{(\text{Chromyl chloride})}{\overset{+6}{Cr}O_2Cl_2}$ (Reddish brown fumes)

84. (a)

(a) $N_2O \longrightarrow$ Diamagnetic, Neutral

(b) $NO_2 \longrightarrow$ Paramagnetic, Acidic

(c) $NO \longrightarrow$ Paramagnetic, Neutral

(d) $N_2O_3 \longrightarrow$ Diamagnetic, Acidic

85. (b) AgCl and AgI both are insoluble in dil. HNO_3, and both are soluble in complexing agents (CN^- solution and Hypo solution), but AgCl is soluble in dil. NH_3 solution whereas AgI is insoluble even in highly conc. NH_3 solution.

86. (b) $PbO_2 + \underset{\text{conc.}}{2HNO_3} \longrightarrow Pb(NO_3)_2 + H_2O + \frac{1}{2}O_2\uparrow$

87. (b) $\underset{\text{Mixture of gases}}{\boxed{SO_2, CO_2, O_2}} \xrightarrow[\text{Absorbs Only } SO_2 \text{ (Redox reaction)}]{K_2Cr_2O_7/H^+} \boxed{CO_2, O_2} \xrightarrow[\text{Absorbs Only } CO_2 \text{ (Acid base reaction)}]{Ca(OH)_2} \boxed{O_2}$

O_2 → Absorbed by alkaline pyragallol

88. (b)

(a) $KMnO_4$: Pink/Purple

(b) $BaSO_4$: Colourless

(c) Na_2CrO_4 : Yellow

(d) $CoCl_2$: Blue compound

89. (b)

(a) $XeO_2F_2 + H_2O \longrightarrow XeO_3 + 2HF$

(b) $2XeF_2 + 2H_2O \longrightarrow 2Xe + 4HF + O_2$

(c) $6XeF_4 + 12H_2O \longrightarrow 4Xe + 2XeO_3 + 24HF + 3O_2$

(d) $XeF_6 + 3H_2O \longrightarrow XeO_3 + 6HF$

90. (b) $2FeSO_4 \cdot 7H_2O \xrightarrow[-14H_2O]{300°C} 2FeSO_4 \xrightarrow{\Delta} Fe_2O_3(s) + SO_2\uparrow + SO_3\uparrow$

Level 3

Passage-1

1. (b) $SO_3^{2-}(aq.) \xrightarrow{Zn + dil.\ HCl} H_2S\uparrow \xrightarrow{FeCl_3} S°\downarrow + \underset{\text{(pale green)}}{Fe^{2+}}$

$SO_3^{2-} \xrightarrow{\Delta,\ S°} S_2O_3^{2-}$

$H_2S \xrightarrow{MnO_4^-/H^+} \underset{\text{(white turbidity)}}{S°\downarrow} + Mn^{2+}(aq.)$

2. (b) * $Fe^{2+} + NH_4SCN \longrightarrow$ No reaction.

* $Fe^{3+} + NH_4SCN \longrightarrow Fe(SCN)_3$ blood red.

Passage-2

1. (a) For salt '*R*'

(a) $NH_4NO_3 \xrightarrow{\Delta} \underset{\text{(Neutral)}}{N_2O} + \underset{\text{(Neutral)}}{H_2O}$

(b) $(NH_4)_2CO_3 \xrightarrow{\Delta} \underset{\text{(Basic)}}{NH_3\uparrow} + \underset{\text{(Acidic)}}{CO_2\uparrow} + H_2O$

(c) $(NH_4)_2S \xrightarrow{\Delta} \underset{\text{(Basic)}}{NH_3\uparrow} + \underset{\text{(Acidic)}}{H_2S\uparrow}$

(d) $NH_4Cl \xrightarrow{\Delta} \underset{\text{(Basic)}}{NH_3\uparrow} + \underset{\text{(Acidic)}}{HCl\uparrow}$

2. (c) Salt '*P*' can be $(NH_4)_2CrO_4$:

$\underset{\text{(Orange)}}{(NH_4)_2Cr_2O_7} \xrightarrow{\Delta} \underset{\text{(Neutral gas)}}{N_2} + \underset{\text{(Coloured solid)}}{Cr_2O_3} + \underset{\text{(Neutral vapours)}}{H_2O}$

3. (d) $\underset{(O.A.\ MnO_4^-)}{\text{'}Q\text{' salt}} + \underset{(R.A.)}{H_2S} \xrightarrow{H^+} S + Mn^{2+}(aq.)$

Passage-3

1. (d) $\underset{\text{(Green)}}{FeSO_4 \cdot 7H_2O} \xrightarrow[-7H_2O]{\Delta} \underset{\text{(White from 2 moles)}}{FeSO_4} \xrightarrow{300°C} \underset{\text{(Brown)}}{Fe_2O_3} + \underset{(\mu_D \neq 0)}{SO_2\uparrow} + \underset{(\mu_D = 0)}{SO_3\uparrow}$

$3SO_3(g) \xrightarrow{cool} \underset{(\mu_D \neq 0)}{S_3O_9}$

2. (b) $2NaHCO_3 \xrightarrow{\Delta} Na_2CO_3 + \underset{\text{(Extinguishes fire)}}{CO_2\uparrow} + H_2O\uparrow$

$H_2O \xrightarrow{CuSO_4\text{(White)}} \underset{\text{(Blue)}}{CuSO_4 \cdot 5H_2O}$

$$NH_4NO_2 \xrightarrow{\Delta} \underbrace{N_2}_{\text{(has no fire extinguishing property)}} + 2H_2O$$

$$2H_2O \xrightarrow{CuSO_4(\text{White})} \underset{\text{(Blue)}}{CuSO_4 \cdot 5H_2O}$$

3. (b) PbO_2 does not react with cold dil. HNO_3 due to its more acidic nature.

Passage-4

1. (d) $\Rightarrow$ $2FeSO_4 \xrightarrow{\Delta} Fe_2O_3 + SO_2\uparrow + SO_3\uparrow$

$\Rightarrow$ $SnSO_4 \xrightarrow{\Delta} SnO_2 + SO_2\uparrow$

$\Rightarrow$ $H_2C_2O_4 \xrightarrow{\Delta} CO\uparrow + CO_2\uparrow + H_2O$

$\Rightarrow$ $2Na_2HPO_4 \xrightarrow{\Delta} Na_4P_2O_7 + H_2O$

2. (d) $\Rightarrow$ $Pb(NO_3)_2 \xrightarrow{\Delta} \underset{\substack{\text{Red in hot} \\ \text{(Litharge)}}}{PbO} + \underbrace{2NO_2\uparrow + \frac{1}{2}O_2}_{\substack{\text{Two different} \\ \text{paramagnetic gases}}}$

$\Rightarrow$ $Hg(NO_3)_2 \xrightarrow{\Delta} Hg + 2NO_2\uparrow + O_2\uparrow$

$\Rightarrow$ $FeC_2O_4 \xrightarrow{\Delta} FeO + CO\uparrow + CO_2\uparrow$

$\Rightarrow$ $ZnSO_4 \xrightarrow{>800°C} ZnO + SO_2\uparrow + \frac{1}{2}O_2\uparrow$

Passage-5

1. (a) $\Rightarrow$ $\underset{(A)}{N_2(g)} \xrightarrow[3000°C]{O_2} \underset{(P)}{NO\uparrow} \xrightarrow{O_2} \underset{(Q)}{NO_2\uparrow} \xrightarrow{H_2O} \underset{(R)}{HNO_3 + NO\uparrow}$

$\underset{(R)}{\text{dil. } HNO_3} \xrightarrow{Zn} N_2O\uparrow$; $\underset{(R)}{\text{dil. } HNO_3} \xrightarrow{Cu} \underset{(P)}{NO\uparrow}$

$\underset{(R)}{\text{conc. } HNO_3} \xrightarrow{Zn} \underset{(Q)}{NO_2\uparrow}$; $\underset{(R)}{\text{conc. } HNO_3} \xrightarrow{Cu} \underset{(Q)}{NO_2\uparrow}$

NO_2 is an acidic oxide, brown colour triatomic paramagnetic gas.

2. (c) $\Rightarrow$ $S_8(B) \xrightarrow{O_2} \underset{(x)}{SO_2\uparrow} \xrightarrow[\text{Approp. catalyst and temp.}]{O_2} \underset{(y)}{SO_3\uparrow} \xrightarrow{H_2O} \underset{(z)}{H_2SO_4} + \text{Heat}$

$SO_2 + \underset{\text{(Baryta water)}}{Ba(OH)_2} \longrightarrow \underset{\text{(White turbidity)}}{BaSO_3\downarrow}$

$BaSO_3\downarrow + \underset{\text{(Excess)}}{SO_2\uparrow} + H_2O \longrightarrow \underset{\text{(Clear solution)}}{Ba(HSO_3)_2}$

$Cr_2O_7^{2-}(aq.) + 3SO_2\uparrow + H^+(aq.) \longrightarrow \underset{\text{(Green sol.)}}{2Cr^{3+}(aq.)} + 3SO_4^{2-}(aq.) + H_2O$

$SO_2\uparrow + H_2S\uparrow \longrightarrow S\downarrow$

$SO_2\uparrow + Cl_2\uparrow \longrightarrow SO_2Cl_2$

3. (d) $Ca(OCl)Cl + SO_2\uparrow \longrightarrow CaSO_4 + 2Cl^-$

Passage-6

1. (d) $FeSO_4 \cdot (NH_4)_2SO_4 \cdot 6H_2O + NH_4Cl(s) + NH_4OH \longrightarrow$ No ppt.

$$\underbrace{Fe^{2+}(aq.) + NH_4^+(aq.)}_{\text{From double salt }(M)} + NaOH(soln.) \longrightarrow \underset{(N)}{NH_3\uparrow} + \underset{\substack{(P)\\(Green)}}{Fe(OH)_2\downarrow}$$

2. (c) $\Rightarrow$ $\underset{\text{(Green ppt.)}}{Fe(OH)_2\downarrow} + \text{conc. } HCl \longrightarrow \underset{\text{(Green soln.)}}{FeCl_2} \xrightarrow{Cl_2(g)} \underset{\text{(Yellow soln.)}}{FeCl_3(aq.)}$

$\Rightarrow$ 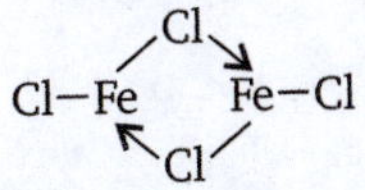

$\Rightarrow$ In methylene blue test for H_2S gas $FeCl_3$ is used.

3. (c) $NaNO_2 + \text{dil.} H_2SO_4 + Fe^{2+}(aq.) \longrightarrow \underset{\text{(Brown ring complex)}}{[Fe(H_2O)_5(NO)]^{2+}}$

$$HgI_2 + NH_3\uparrow + H_2O \longrightarrow \underset{\text{(Brown ppt)}}{HgO \cdot Hg(NH_2)I\downarrow}$$

$$Fe^{2+}(aq.) + NH_4^+(aq.) + H_2S\uparrow \longrightarrow \text{No reaction}$$

$$\underset{\text{(Green)}}{Fe^{2+}(aq.)} + Br_2 \longrightarrow \underset{\text{(Yellow)}}{Fe^{3+}(aq.)} + Br^-(aq.)$$

Passage-7

1. (d) $\underset{(X)}{ZnCO_3} \xrightarrow{\Delta} \underset{(Y)}{ZnO} + \underset{(Z)}{CO_2\uparrow}$

$ZnO \xrightarrow{\text{dil. HCl}} \underset{\text{(Water soluble)}}{ZnCl_2}$; $CO_2 \xrightarrow{Ba(OH)_2} \underset{\text{(White ppt.)}}{BaCO_3\downarrow}$

2. (d)

(a) ZnO is yellow when hot and white when cold.

(b) CO_2 is the acid anhydride of H_2CO_3.

(c) $ZnO + NaOH \xrightarrow{aq.} Na_2[Zn(OH)_4]$ or $Na_2ZnO_2 + 2H_2O$

(d) CO_2 is a lewis acid.

Passage-8

1. (b) $CuSO_4(aq.) + \underset{\text{Excess}}{3I^-(aq.)} \longrightarrow \underset{\text{White}}{CuI\downarrow} + \underset{\text{Brown Colour}}{I_3^-(aq.)} + SO_4^{2-}(aq.)$

2. (d) $Cu^{2+}(aq.) + 2CN^-(aq.) \longrightarrow \underset{\text{Unstable}}{Cu(CN)_2} \xrightarrow{\text{I.M.R.}} CuCN\downarrow + (CN)_2\uparrow$

$$CuCN\downarrow + \underset{\text{Excess}}{3KCN} \rightleftharpoons \underset{\text{Colourless soln.}}{K_3[Cu(CN)_4]}$$

Passage-9

1. (d) PbS (Black ppt.)

2. (d) $Fe(OH)_3$ (*Q*) undergo redox reaction with $Na_2S_2O_3$ solution, KI + Starch, $K_4[Fe(CN)_6]$ showing change in colour.

ONE OR MORE ANSWERS IS/ARE CORRECT

1. (a, b, c, d)

(a) $PbO_2 + \text{warm conc.}H_2SO_4 \longrightarrow PbSO_4\downarrow + O_2\uparrow$

(b) $2NaOH + F_2 \longrightarrow 2NaF + \frac{1}{2}O_2 + H_2O$

(c) $2PbO_2 + \text{conc.}2HNO_3 \longrightarrow 2PbNO_3 + \frac{5}{2}O_2 + H_2O$

(d) $XeF_2 + H_2O \longrightarrow Xe + \frac{1}{2}O_2 + 2HF$

2. (b, c, d)

$$SO_2(g) + Cl_2(g) \longrightarrow SO_2Cl_2 \xrightarrow{P_4} PCl_5 + SO_2$$

3. (b, c)

Al^{3+} (*s*-block):
$$Al^{3+} \xrightarrow{NaOH} Al(OH)_3\downarrow \xrightarrow{NaOH} Na[Al(OH)_4] \text{ soluble}$$
$$Al^{3+} \xrightarrow{NH_3} Al(OH)_3\downarrow \xrightarrow{NH_3} \text{insoluble}$$

Zn^{2+} (*d*-block):
$$Zn^{2+} \xrightarrow{NaOH} Zn(OH)_2\downarrow \xrightarrow{NaOH} Na_2[Zn(OH)_4] \text{ soluble}$$
$$Zn^{2+} \xrightarrow{NH_3} Zn(OH)_2\downarrow \xrightarrow{NH_3} [Zn(NH_3)_4]^{2+} \text{ soluble}$$

Cr^{3+} (*d*-block):
$$Cr^{3+} \xrightarrow{NaOH} Cr(OH)_3\downarrow \xrightarrow{NaOH} Na[Cr(OH)_4] \text{ soluble}$$
$$Cr^{3+} \xrightarrow{NH_3} Cr(OH)_3\downarrow \xrightarrow{NH_3} [Cr(NH_3)_6]^{3+} \text{ soluble}$$

Pb^{2+} (*p*-block):
$$Pb^{2+} \xrightarrow{NaOH} Pb(OH)_2\downarrow \xrightarrow{NaOH} Na[Pb(OH)_4] \text{ soluble}$$
$$Pb^{2+} \xrightarrow{NH_3} Pb(OH)_2\downarrow \longrightarrow \text{insoluble}$$

4. (a, b, c)

$P_4O_3 + H_2O \longrightarrow H_3PO_3 + H_3PO_4$

$POCl_3 + H_2O \longrightarrow H_3PO_4 + HCl$

$NO_2 + H_2O \longrightarrow HNO_2 + HNO_3$

5. (a, b, c, d)

$$Xe + F_2 \xrightarrow{1:20} \underset{(X)}{XeF_6} \xrightarrow{H_2O} \underset{(Y)}{XeOF_4} \xrightarrow{H_2O} \underset{(Z)}{XeO_2F_2} \xrightarrow{H_2O} XeO_3$$

	Geometry	Oxidation state of Xe	Lone pair on Xe	No. of Covalent bonds
XeF_6	distorted octahedral	+6	1	6
$XeOF_4$	square pyramidal	+6	1	6
XeO_2F_2	see-saw	+6	1	6

6. (a, d)

Black colour sulphide (HgS, CuS) do not react with non-oxidizing acids dil. HCl except FeS

$$ZnS + 2HCl \longrightarrow ZnCl_2 + H_2S\uparrow$$

7. (a, c, d)

$$3I_2 + \underset{\text{(hot aq. sol. of } Na_2CO_3)}{6OH^-} \longrightarrow 5I^-(aq.) + IO_3^-(aq.) + 3H_2O$$

$$2NaI + Pb(CH_3COO)_2 \longrightarrow CH_3COONa + \underset{\text{(Yellow ppt.)}}{PbI_2\downarrow}$$

$$IO_3^- + H^+ + H_2S\uparrow \longrightarrow S\downarrow + I_3^-$$
$$IO_3^- + H^+ + SO_2\uparrow \longrightarrow SO_4^- + I_3^-$$
$$IO_3^- + H^+ + I^- \xrightarrow{\text{comprop.}} I_2$$

$Cr_2O_7^{2-}$ does not exhibit oxidising property in alkaline medium.

8. (c) $SO_2 \xrightarrow{Na_2CO_3} \underset{(P)}{Na_2SO_3\downarrow} \xrightarrow[\text{Boil}]{S} \underset{(R)}{Na_2S_2O_3}$

$SO_2 \xrightarrow{H_2S} \underset{(Q)}{S\downarrow}$

CaS_2O_3 is water soluble.

9. (a, c, d)

$$Hg(NO_3)_2 \longrightarrow HgO + NO_2 + O_2$$
$$HgO \longrightarrow Hg + O_2$$

$$KNO_3 \longrightarrow KNO_2 + O_2$$
$$N_2O_4 \longrightarrow 2NO_2$$
$$N_2O_3 \longrightarrow NO + NO_2$$

10. (a, c)

(a) $CaCO_3\downarrow + \text{dil. } HCl \longrightarrow CaCl_2(aq.) + H_2CO_3$

(b) $BaCrO_4\downarrow + \text{dil. } HCl \longrightarrow BaCl_2(aq.) + \underset{\text{(Organe solution)}}{H_2Cr_2O_7}$

(c) $MgC_2O_4\downarrow + \text{dil. } HCl \longrightarrow MgCl_2(aq.) + H_2C_2O_4$

(d) $BaSO_4 + \text{dil. } HCl \longrightarrow \text{(No reaction)}$

11. (a, c, d)

(a) $Ba(OH)_2(aq.) + SO_2(g) \longrightarrow BaSO_3\downarrow$

(b) $AgF(aq.) + NaNO_3(aq.) \longrightarrow$ No reaction

(c) $Pb(OAc)_2(aq.) + Na_2CO_3(aq.) \longrightarrow PbCO_3\downarrow + CH_3COONa\,(aq.)$

(d) $CuCl_2(aq.) + NH_3(\text{Excess}) \longrightarrow \underset{\text{(Deep blue solution)}}{[Cu(NH_3)_4]Cl_2}$

12. (b, c)

(a) $Na_2O_2 + H_2O \xrightarrow{25°C} NaOH + O_2\uparrow$

(b) $Cl_2 + H_2O \xrightarrow{25°C} HCl + HOCl$

(c) $P_4 + H_2O \xrightarrow{25°C}$ No reaction

(d) $KO_2 + H_2O \xrightarrow{25°C} KOH + O_2\uparrow$

13. (a, c, d)

(a) $Mg + NH_3(l) \longrightarrow$ No Interaction

(b) $B_2H_6 + H_2O \longrightarrow H_3BO_3 + H_2\uparrow$

(c) $NaNH_2 + H_2O \longrightarrow NaOH + NH_3\uparrow$

(d) $Be + H_2O \longrightarrow$ No reaction

14. (d) HgI_2, HgS, $HgCO_3$ are insoluble. Thus addition of KI, H_2S and Na_2CO_3 can shift reaction in backward direction.

15. (b, c)

Conc. H_2SO_4 oxidizes both HBr and H_2S.

16. (a, d)

AgCl and AgBr dissolve in excess of conc. ammonia solution.

AgI does not dissolve in excess conc. NH_3 solution.

17. (a) $I_2 + 2S_2O_3^{2-} \longrightarrow 2I^- + S_4O_6^{2-}$

18. (b, c, d)

(a) $NO_3^- + Zn + \text{dil. } H_2SO_4 \xrightarrow{\Delta}$ Formed NH_3 is neutralized to NH_4^+ by H_2SO_4 and NH_3 is not liberated.

(b) $NH_4Cl + NaOH \xrightarrow{\Delta} NH_3\uparrow + NaCl + H_2O$

(c) $2AlN + \underset{\text{(Steam)}}{3H_2O} \xrightarrow{\Delta} Al_2O_3 + 2NH_3\uparrow$

(d) $CH_3COONH_4 \xrightarrow{\Delta} CH_3COOH + NH_3\uparrow$

19. (a, b, d)

(a) $\overset{(+2)}{Hg}CO_3 \xrightarrow[\text{(Redox)}]{\Delta} \overset{(0)}{Hg} + CO_2(g) + \frac{1}{2}O_2(g)$

(b) $\overset{(+1)}{Ag_2}C_2O_4 \xrightarrow[\text{(Redox)}]{\Delta} 2\overset{(0)}{Ag} + 2CO_2(g)$

(c) $2\overset{(+3)}{Fe}Cl_3 \cdot 6H_2O \xrightarrow[\text{(Non-Redox)}]{\Delta} \overset{(+3)}{Fe_2}O_3(s) + 6HCl + 9H_2O$

(d) $2K_2Cr_2O_7 \xrightarrow[\text{(Redox)}]{\Delta} 2K_2CrO_4(s) + Cr_2O_3(s) + \frac{3}{2}O_2(g)$

MATCH THE COLUMN

1. (A) $HgCO_3 \xrightarrow{\Delta} HgO + CO_2$

$HgO \xrightarrow{\Delta} Hg + O_2$

(B) $FeSO_4 \xrightarrow{\Delta} Fe_2O_3 + SO_2 + SO_3$

$SO_3 \xrightarrow{\Delta} SO_2 + O_2$

(C) $BeC_2O_4 \xrightarrow{\Delta} BeO + CO_2 + CO$

(D) $AgNO_3 \xrightarrow{\Delta} Ag_2O + NO_2 + O_2$

$Ag_2O \xrightarrow{\Delta} Ag + O_2$

2. $Na_2S_2O_3 + 2HCl \xrightarrow{\text{R.T.}} 2NaCl + H_2S_2O_3$

$H_2S_2O_3 \xrightarrow{\text{I.M.R.}} H_2O + \underset{\text{(Yellow)}}{S\downarrow} + SO_2\uparrow$

$ICl_3 + 2H_2O \xrightarrow{\text{R.T.}} HIO_2 + 3HCl$

$2FeCl_3 + H_2S(aq.) \xrightarrow{\text{R.T.}} 2Fe^{2+}(aq.) + S\downarrow + 2HCl + 4Cl^-(aq.)$

$H_2\overset{+IV}{S}O_3 \xrightarrow{\Delta} S + H_2\overset{+VI}{S}O_4$

3. $\ddot{P}Cl_3$: due to presence of vacant *d*-orbital it can act as π-acid ligand it does not act as classical ligand.

$\Rightarrow PCl_3 + 3H_2O \xrightarrow{R.T.} H_3PO_3 + 3HCl$: undergoes only complete hydrolysis

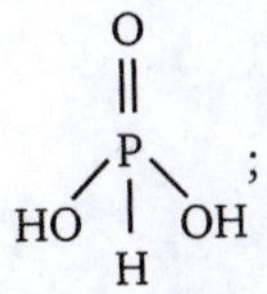

; No. of pπ - dπ bonds = 1

$\ddot{N}F_3$: No vacant *d*-orbital or π* M.O, and N-atom has lone pair; hence does not act as π-acid ligand but act as classical ligand.

⇒ Undergoes complete hydrolysis under drastic conditions

$2NF_3 + 3H_2O \xrightarrow{300°C} Na_2O_3 + 6HF$

↓

$NO + NO_2 + 6HF$

$\ddot{S}bCl_3$: Sb has vacant *d*-orbital, hence it can act as π-acid ligand and does not act as classical ligand.

⇒ Undergoes only partial hydrolysis

$SbCl_3 + H_2O \underset{}{\overset{R.T.}{\rightleftharpoons}} SbOCl + 2HCl$ (SbOCl: White turbidity)

BF_3 ⇒ Boron has no lone pair hence it does not act as ligand.

⇒ Undergoes only partial hydrolysis

$4BF_3 + 3H_2O \xrightarrow{R.T.} H_3BO_3 + 3HBF_4$

4. (A) $SO_3^{2-} + 2HCl \xrightarrow{\Delta} SO_2\uparrow + 2Cl^- + H_2O$

SO_2 (Colourless)

- $Ba(OH)_2$ → $BaSO_3\downarrow$ White
- $AgNO_3$ → $Ag_2SO_3\downarrow$ White
- MnO_4^-/H^+ → $Mn^{2+} + SO_4^{2-}$ Colourless or light pink

(B) $CO_3^{2-} + 2HCl \xrightarrow{R.T.} CO_2\uparrow + 2Cl^- + H_2O$

CO_2 (Colourless)

- $Ba(OH)_2$ → $BaCO_3\downarrow$ White
- $AgNO_3$ → $Ag_2CO_3\downarrow$ Yellowish-white
- MnO_4^-/H^+ → $CO_2\uparrow$ No Decolourization

(C) $Cl^-(s) + H_2SO_4 \xrightarrow{\Delta} HCl\uparrow + HSO_4^-$

HCl (Colourless)

- $Ba(OH)_2$ → $BaCl_2$ Soluble *i.e.*, No ppt.
- $AgNO_3$ → $AgCl\downarrow$ White
- MnO_4^-/H^+ → $Mn^{2+} + Cl_2\uparrow$ Colourless or Light pink

(D) $NO_2^- + HCl \longrightarrow HNO_2$

$3HNO_2 \xrightarrow{\Delta} HNO_3 + 2NO\uparrow + H_2O$

$\downarrow$ atm air

$NO_2\uparrow$
Reddish-Brown

$Ba(OH)_2$	$AgNO_3$	MnO_4^-/H^+
$Ba(NO_2)_2$	$AgNO_2\downarrow$	$Mn^{2+} + NO_3^-$
Soluble or $Ba(NO_3)_2$ soluble	White	Colourless or light pink

5. A : $(NH_4)_2Cr_2O_7(s) \xrightarrow{\Delta} \underset{\text{Non-polar}}{N_2\uparrow} + \underset{\text{Green amphoteric}}{Cr_2O_3(s)} + 4H_2O$

B : $2FeSO_4(s) \xrightarrow{\Delta} \underset{\text{Brown (Basic)}}{Fe_2O_3(s)} + \underset{\text{Polar acidic}}{SO_2\uparrow} + \underset{\text{Non-polar}}{SO_3\uparrow}$

C : $Pb(NO_3)_2(s) \xrightarrow{\Delta} \underset{\text{Red (Amphoteric)}}{PbO(s)} + \underset{\text{Polar acidic}}{2NO_2\uparrow} + \underset{\text{Non-polar}}{\frac{1}{2}O_2\uparrow}$

D : $P_4 + 3NaOH + 3H_2O \xrightarrow{\Delta} \underset{\text{Basic}}{PH_3\uparrow} + NaH_2PO_2$

6. (A) $NCl_3 + 3H_2O \xrightarrow{R.T.} \overset{-III}{N}H_3 + 3HO\overset{+I}{Cl}$

→ Non-redox hydrolysis

→ HOCl can act as both oxidizing and reducing agent.

→ NH_3 : Monodentate ligand.

(B) $NO_2 + H_2O \xrightarrow{R.T.} \overset{+III}{HNO_2} + \overset{+V}{HNO_3}$

→ NO_2^-, NO_3^- can act as flexidentate ligand.

→ HNO_2 can act as both oxidizing and rducing agent.

→ NO_2^-, NO_3^- can act as monodentate ligand.

(C) $H_2S_2O_8 + 2H_2O \xrightarrow{R.T.} 2H_2\overset{-VI}{S}O_4 + H_2\overset{-I}{O}_2$

→ H_2SO_4 : Dibasic acid

→ SO_4^{2-} can act as flexidentate ligand.

→ H_2O_2 can act as both oxidizing and rducing agent.

→ SO_4^{2-}, can act as monodentate ligand.

→ Non-redox reaction.

(D) $SF_4 + 3H_2O \xrightarrow{R.T.} H_2SO_3 + 4HF$

H_2SO_3 : Dibasic acid

SO_3^{2-} : Can act as flexidentate ligand.

H_2SO_3 : Can act as both oxidising and reducing agent.

SO_3^{2-} : Can act as monodentate ligand.

T : Non-redox hydrolysis.

7. (A) Zn + dil. H_2SO_4 —

- $\xrightarrow{Pb(NO_2)_2} NH_4^+ + Pb\downarrow + Zn^{2+} + SO_4^{2-}$
- $\xrightarrow{(NH_4)_2S} H_2S\uparrow + NH_4^+$
- $\xrightarrow{MnO_4^-(aq.)} Mn^{2+}(aq.) + Zn^{2+}$
- $\xrightarrow{Hg_2^{2+}(aq.)} Hg\downarrow + Zn^{2+}$ (Grey black)
- $\xrightarrow{Bi^{3+}(aq.)} Bi\downarrow + Zn^{2+}$ (Black)

(B) dil. HCl —

- $\xrightarrow{Pb(NO_2)_2} PbCl_2\downarrow + HNO_3 + NO\uparrow$ (White)
- $\xrightarrow{(NH_4)_2S} H_2S\uparrow + NH_4^+ + Cl^-$
- $\xrightarrow{MnO_4^-(aq.)} Mn^{2+}(aq.) + Cl_2\uparrow$
- $\xrightarrow{Hg_2^{2+}(aq.)} Hg_2Cl_2\downarrow$ (White)
- $\xrightarrow{Bi^{3+}(aq.)} BiCl_3 \rightleftharpoons Bi^{3+} + 3Cl^-$ *i.e.*, No reaction

(C) NaOH (excess) —

- $\xrightarrow{Pb(NO_2)_2} [Pb(OH)_4]_2^- + NO_2^-$
- $\xrightarrow{(NH_4)_2S} NH_3\uparrow + 2Na^+ + S^{2-}$
- $\xrightarrow{MnO_4^-(aq.)} MnO_4^{2-} + O_2\uparrow$ (Green)
- $\xrightarrow{Hg_2^{2+}(aq.)} Hg + HgO$ (Black)
- $\xrightarrow{Bi^{3+}(aq.)} Bi(OH)_3\downarrow$ (White)

(D) KI —

- $\xrightarrow{Pb(NO_2)_2} PbI_2\downarrow + NO_2^-$
- $\xrightarrow{(NH_4)_2S}$ No Reaction
- $\xrightarrow{MnO_4^-(aq.)} Mn^{2+} + I_2\uparrow$
- $\xrightarrow{Hg_2^{2+}(aq.)} Hg_2I_2\downarrow$ (Green) $\xrightarrow{Warm} Hg\downarrow + HgI_2\downarrow$ (Scarlet)
- $\xrightarrow{Bi^{3+}(aq.)} BiI_3\downarrow$ (Black) $\xrightarrow{excess} [BiI_4]^-$ Orange solution

9. (A) $\overset{+4}{NO_2} + H_2O \xrightarrow{Redox} \overset{+5}{HNO_3} + \overset{+3}{HNO_2}$
$\quad (sp^2) \qquad\qquad (sp^2) \qquad (sp^2)$

Redox reaction (Disproportionation)

HNO_2 can show tautomerism.

$$H-O-N=O \rightleftharpoons H-N(=O)\rightarrow O$$

Hybridisation remain same.

Ans. [P, Q, R, S]

(B) $\underset{\substack{F \\ F}}{S} + 2H_2O \xrightarrow{\text{Hydrolysis}} 2HF + \underset{\substack{HO \\ HO}}{S} \underset{O}{\overset{\text{Equilibrium}}{\underset{\text{Backward}}{\overset{\longrightarrow}{\longleftarrow}}}} \underset{\text{Remains}}{} H-\overset{O}{\underset{OH}{S}}=O$ 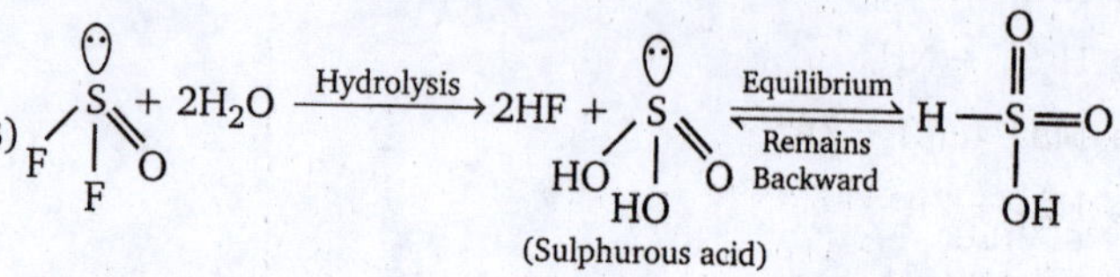

$\qquad\qquad\qquad\qquad\qquad\qquad\qquad$ (Sulphurous acid)

Non-redox reaction

Sulphurous acid undergoes tautomerism

All have same hybridisation (sp^3)

HF (Hydrolysed Product) can react with SiO_2 (Glass)

$SiO_2 + 4HF \longrightarrow SIF_4 + 2H_2O$

Ans. [Q, R, S, T]

(C) $XeF_4 + H_2O \longrightarrow Xe + O_2 + XeO_3 + HF$

Redox reaction

HF reacts SiO_2 (Glass)

Ans. [P, T]

(D) $\overset{+5}{ClF}_5 + 3H_2O \xrightarrow{\text{Non-Redox}} \overset{+5}{HClO}_3 + 5HF$

All hydrolysis product are acids.

HF reacts with glass (SiO_2).

$HClO_3$ can undergo tautomerism.

10. (A) $S^{2-}(aq.)$

$\xrightarrow{Br_2} S\downarrow + Br^-$ (White/yellow)

$\xrightarrow[\Delta]{\text{dil. HCl}} H_2S\uparrow$ (Diamagnetic)

$\xrightarrow{Pb(OAc)_2} PbS\downarrow$ (Black)

$\xrightarrow{(Al+NaOH)} Na_2S(aq.)$

$\xrightarrow[\Delta]{\text{Conc. } H_2SO_4} SO_2\uparrow$

(B) $SO_3^{2-}(aq.)$

$\xrightarrow{Br_2} SO_4^{2-} + Br^\ominus$

$\xrightarrow[\Delta]{\text{dil. HCl}} SO_2$ (Diamagnetic)

$\xrightarrow{Pb(OAc)_2} PbSO_3\downarrow \xrightarrow{\text{Boil}}$ Remain same (White)

$\xrightarrow{(Al+NaOH)} Na_2S(aq.)$

$\xrightarrow[\Delta]{\text{Conc. } H_2SO_4} SO_2\uparrow$

(C) $NO_2^-(aq.)$

$\xrightarrow{Br_2} NO_3^-$

$\xrightarrow[\Delta]{\text{dil. HCl}} HNO_2 \xrightarrow[\text{Warm}]{\text{Disproportionation}} HNO_3 + NO\uparrow \xrightarrow{O_2 \text{ (Air)}} NO_2\uparrow$ (Paramagnetic) (Paramagnetic)

$\xrightarrow{Pb(OAc)_2}$ No ppt.

$\xrightarrow{(Al+NaOH)} NH_3\uparrow$

$\xrightarrow[\Delta]{\text{Conc. } H_2SO_4} HNO_2 \xrightarrow[\text{Warm}]{\text{Disproportionation}} HNO_3 + NO\uparrow \xrightarrow{O_2 \text{ (Air)}} NO_2\uparrow$

(D) $S_2O_3^{2-}(aq.)$

- $\xrightarrow[\text{(Redox)}]{Br_2}$ $SO_4^{2-} + Br^-$
- $\xrightarrow[\Delta]{\text{dil. HCl}}$ $SO_2\uparrow + S\downarrow$ (Diamagnetic)
- $\xrightarrow{Pb(OAc)_2}$ $PbS_2O_3\downarrow$ (White) $\xrightarrow{\text{Boil}}$ $PbS\downarrow$ (Black)
- $\xrightarrow{(Al+NaOH)}$ $Na_2S(aq.)$
- $\xrightarrow[\Delta]{\text{Conc. } H_2SO_4}$ $SO_2\uparrow$

11. (P) BCl_3 (sp^2) $+ H_2O \xrightarrow{SN_2}$

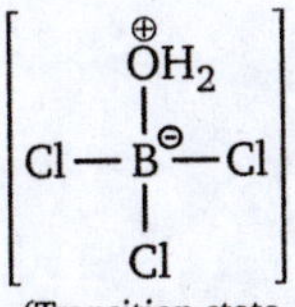

(Transition state hybridization : sp^3)

$\longrightarrow BCl_2(OH) \xrightarrow{+2H_2O} B(OH)_3 + 3HCl$

(Q)

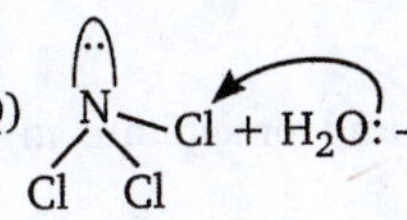

$+ H_2O: \longrightarrow$

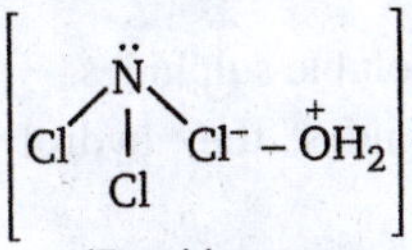

(Transition state hybridization : sp^3)

$\longrightarrow NHCl_2 + HOCl \xrightarrow{+2H_2O} NH_3 + 2HOCl$

(R) $\ddot{S}OF_2$ (sp^3) $+ H_2O \xrightarrow{SN_{AE}}$

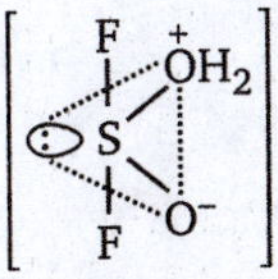

Transition state Hyb. (sp^3d)

$\xrightarrow{-HF} SO(OH)F \xrightarrow{H_2O} H_2SO_3 + 2HF$

(S) $POCl_3$ (sp^3) $+ H_2O \xrightarrow{SN_{AE}}$

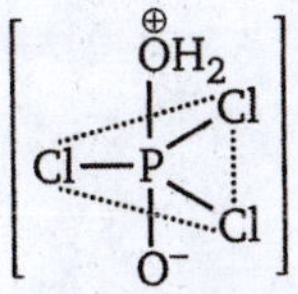

Transition state Hyb. (sp^3d)

$\xrightarrow{-HCl} POCl_2(OH) \xrightarrow{2H_2O} H_3PO_4 + 3HCl$

(T) $\ddot{C}lF_3$ (sp^3d) $+ H_2O \xrightarrow{SN_2}$

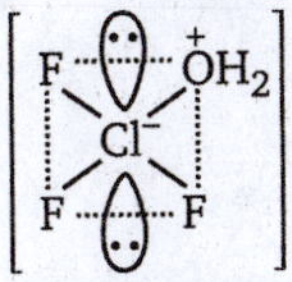

Transition state Hyb. sp^3d^3

$\xrightarrow{-HF} ClF_2(OH) \xrightarrow{2H_2O} HClO_2 + 3HF$

SUBJECTIVE PROBLEMS

1. Conc. $H_2SO_4 + 2KI \longrightarrow K_2SO_4 + HI + \frac{1}{2}I_2\uparrow$

$Hg(NO_3)_2 + 2KI \longrightarrow HgI_2\downarrow + 2KNO_3$

$CuSO_4 + KI \longrightarrow Cu_2I_2\downarrow + K_2SO_4 + I_2$

Conc. $H_3PO_4 + KI \longrightarrow$ No obs.

$Cr_2O_7^{2-}/H^+ + KI \longrightarrow Cr^{3+} + I_2$

$Pb(CH_3OO)_2 + KI \longrightarrow PbI_2\downarrow + CH_3COOK$

$Ca(OCl)Cl + KI \longrightarrow CaCl_2 + I_2$

$NaNO_2 +$ dil. $HCl + KI \longrightarrow KCl + NaCl + NO + I_2$

2. ⇒ H_2S/H^+ gives ppt. with 1st and 2nd group radicals.

⇒ H_2S gives ppt. with 1st, 2nd group radicals.

⇒ H_2S/OH^- gives ppt. will all cations with form insoluble sulphides.

⇒ $Al^{3+}, Mg^{2+}, Cr^{3+}, Fe^{3+}$ do not form stable sulphides, they hydrolysed and precipitate in form of hydroxide.

3. $P_4 + KOH \longrightarrow PH_3 + KH_2PO_2$

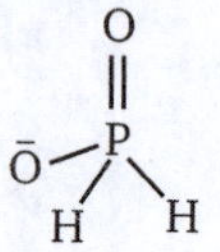

(two P—H bonds)

4. $(NH_4)_2S + Fe^{3+} \longrightarrow FeS + S\downarrow + NH_4^+$

$HI + Fe^{3+} \longrightarrow FeI_2 + I_2$

$Sn^{2+} + Fe^{3+} \longrightarrow Fe^{2+} + Sn^{4+}$

$CN^- + Fe^{3+} \longrightarrow \underset{\text{Yellow brown ppt.}}{Fe(CN)_3\downarrow} \xrightarrow[\text{KCN}]{\text{Excess}} [Fe(CN)_6]^{3-}$

$NaNO_2 + Fe^{3+} \longrightarrow$ No reaction

$SO_2 + Fe^{3+} \longrightarrow Fe^{+2} + SO_4^{2-}$

$S_2O_3^{2-} + Fe^{3+} \longrightarrow Fe^{+2} + S_4O_6^{2-}$

$SCN^- + Fe^{3+} \longrightarrow \underset{\text{Blood red colour}}{Fe(SCN)_3}$ or $[Fe(SCN)(H_2O)_5]^{2+}$

$NaIO_3/H^+ + Fe^{3+} \longrightarrow$ No reaction.

5. $BaSO_4$, $PbCO_3$, $Mg(OH)_2$, CH_3COOAg, $Ca_3(PO_4)_2$

6. $x = 5(BaCO_3, PbSO_4, CaC_2O_4, CH_3COOAg, Mg(OH)_2)$

$y = 5(BaCO_3, PbSO_4, CaC_2O_4, CsHCO_3, CH_3COOAg)$

8. All carbonates are water insoluble except $(NH_4)_2CO_3$ and alkali metal carbonates. Thus $(NH_4)_2CO_3$ and Cs_2CO_3 are only water soluble while others are insoluble.

9. $P_4 + 8SOCl_2 \longrightarrow \underset{\text{(Non-planar polar)}}{4PCl_3} + \underset{\text{(Planar polar)}}{4SO_2} + \underset{\text{(Non-planar polar)}}{2S_2Cl_2}$

$\therefore\ 4 + 2 = 6$

10. $Na_2SO_3 + Na_2S + I_2 \longrightarrow Na_2S_2O_3 + 2NaI$

Average oxidation state of S in $S_2O_3^{2-} = 2$

11. Ag_2O, HgI_2, FeS, Ag_3PO_4, PbI_2

12. $PbCl_4$, $Mg(NO_3)_2$, HgC_2O_4, Ag_2CO_3, $Pb(CN)_4$, $Cu(CN)_2$

13. ⇒ Ammonium salts having anions NO_2^-, NO_3^-, ClO_4^- and $Cr_2O_7^{2-}$ produce N_2 on heating/strong heating.

14. ⇒ Pb, Cu, Ag * Hg evolve NO gas on their reaction with 20% HNO_3.

15. Soluble in excess NH_3 solution.

$Cd^{2+}(aq.)$, $Ni^{2+}(aq.)$, $Zn^{2+}(aq.)$, $Ag^+(aq.)$

16. $CrO_4^{2-}(aq.)+2H_2O_2+2H^+(aq.) \xrightarrow{\text{Non-Redox}} \underset{\text{(Blue Solution)}}{CrO_5} + 3H_2O$

$$\underset{\text{Unstable}}{2CrO_5} \xrightarrow{\text{Aq. Solution}} \underset{\text{Amphotic}}{Cr_2O_3} + \frac{7}{2}O_2$$

$$Cr_2O_3 + 6H^+(aq.) \xrightarrow{\text{Acid-base reaction}} 2Cr^{3+}(aq.) + 3H_2O$$

Net reaction : $CrO_4^{2-}(aq.) \xrightarrow{H_2O_2/H^+ \text{ Green}} \underset{\text{(Blue)}}{[CrO_5]} \xrightarrow[\text{On standing}]{\text{Aq. solution}} \underset{\text{(Green)}}{Cr^{3+}}(aq.)$

17. $XY_{n_1} \xrightarrow{\text{water}} n_1HY + HXO_{n_2}$

Among all interhalogen compounds, only (XY_5) type compound is polar and non-polar.

$XY_5 \xrightarrow{\text{water}} 5HY + HXO_3$ $[n_2 = 3]$

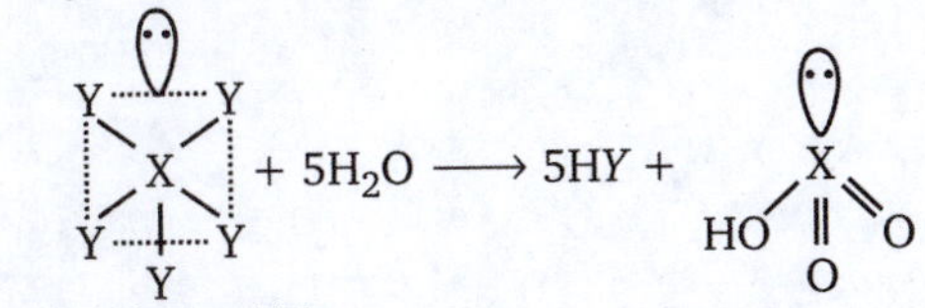

Trigonal pyramidal

Ans. $n_1 + n_2 = 8$

18. All the species which are not in their highest oxidation state can be oxidised by MnO_4^-/H^+.

I^-, Fe^{2+}, $C_2O_4^{2-}$, S^{2-}, SO_3^{2-}, NO_2^-, [Six].

19. All those metals which are more electropositive than hydrogen in electrochemical series gives N_2O gas with dil. HNO_3(20%) except Pb and Sn.

→ Cr, Zn, Fe, Al, Mn

20. All those ammonium salts which have anions having nonoxidizing or weak oxidizing character, on heating product NH_3 gas.

$(NH_4)CO_3$, CH_3COONH_4, NH_4Cl, $(NH_4)_2S$, $(NH_4)_2C_2O_4$, $(NH_4)_2SO_4$

[Total = 6]